PEARSON ALWAYS LEARNING

Allen R. Angel • Christine D. Abbott • Dennis C. Runde

A Survey of Mathematics with Applications
Topics in Mathematics MGF 1106

Third Custom Edition for Santa Fe College

Taken from:
A Survey of Mathematics with Applications, Ninth Edition
by Allen R. Angel, Christine D. Abbott, and Dennis C. Runde

Cover Art: Illustration by Kristen Kiley

Taken from:

A Survey of Mathematics with Applications, Ninth Edition
by Allen R. Angel, Christine D. Abbott, and Dennis C. Runde
Copyright © 2013, 2009, 2005, 2001 by Pearson Education, Inc.
Published by Pearson
Upper Saddle River, New Jersey 07458

This special edition published in cooperation with Pearson Learning Solutions.

All trademarks, service marks, registered trademarks, and registered service marks are the property of their respective owners and are used herein for identification purposes only.

Pearson Learning Solutions, 501 Boylston Street, Suite 900, Boston, MA 02116
A Pearson Education Company
www.pearsoned.com

Printed in the United States of America

3 4 5 6 7 8 9 10 V0CR 17 16 15 14

000200010271626008

SE

ISBN 10: 1-256-69816-4
ISBN 13: 978-1-256-69816-6

To my wife, Kathy Angel (photo on page 56)
A. R. A.

To the memory of my parents, Ed and June Dunn
C. D. A.

To my parents, Bud and Tina Runde
D. C. R.

Contents

To the Student

Mathematics is an exciting, living study. Its applications shape the world around you and influence your everyday life. We hope that as you read this book you will realize just how important mathematics is and gain an appreciation of both its usefulness and its beauty. We also hope to teach you some practical mathematics that you can use every day and that will prepare you for further mathematics courses.

The primary purpose of this text is to provide material that you can read, understand, and enjoy. To this end, we have used straightforward language and tried to relate the mathematical concepts to everyday experiences. We have also provided many detailed examples for you to follow.

The concepts, definitions, and formulas that deserve special attention are in boxes or are set in boldface, italics, or color type. In the exercise sets, within each category, the exercises are graded, with more difficult problems appearing at the end. At the end of most exercise sets are Challenge Problems/Group Activities Exercises that contain challenging or exploratory exercises. At the end of each chapter are Group Projects that reinforce the material learned or provide related material.

Be sure to read the chapter summary, work the review exercises, and take the chapter test at the end of each chapter. The answers to the odd-numbered exercises, all review exercises, and all chapter test exercises appear in the answer section in the back of the text. You should, however, use the answers only to check your work. The answers to all Recreational Mathematics exercises are provided in either the Recreational Mathematics boxes themselves, or in the back of the book.

It is difficult to learn mathematics without becoming involved. To be successful, we suggest that you read the text carefully *and work each exercise in each assignment in detail*. Check with your instructor to determine which supplements are available for your use.

We welcome your suggestions and your comments. You may contact us at the following address:

Allen Angel
c/o Marketing
Mathematics and Statistics
Pearson
75 Arlington St., Suite 300
Boston, MA 02116

or by email at:

math@pearson.com

Subject: for Allen Angel

Good luck with your adventure in mathematics!

Allen R. Angel
Christine D. Abbott
Dennis C. Runde

We present *A Survey of Mathematics with Applications*, Ninth Edition, with the vision in mind that we use mathematics every day. In this edition, we stress how mathematics is used in our daily lives and why it is important. Our primary goal is to give students a text they can read, understand, and enjoy while learning how mathematics affects the world around them. Numerous real-life applications are used to motivate topics. A variety of interesting and useful exercises demonstrate the real-life nature of mathematics and its importance in students' lives.

The text is intended for students who require a broad-based general overview of mathematics, especially those majoring in the liberal arts, elementary education, the social sciences, business, nursing, and allied health fields. It is particularly suitable for those courses that satisfy the minimum competency requirement in mathematics for graduation or transfer.

New to This Edition

- Why This Is Important is a new concept woven throughout the book to help students make the connection between their lives and the mathematics they're learning. Why This Is Important notes can be found in all chapter and section openers as well as the Mathematics Today features.
- Many chapter and section openers contain new, interesting, and motivational information and applications to introduce the section and illustrate the real-world nature of the material in that section. For example, Section 2.3 introduces Venn diagrams and set operations with the experience of purchasing a laptop computer. The Chapter 3 opener indicates how logic has become important in electronic devices such as cell phones and digital cameras.
- Recreational Mathematics boxes added throughout the book show various ways that math can be fun!
- Approximately 40% of the examples and exercises in the book are changed. We updated many examples and exercises to reflect current data and topics of interest to students.
- Exercise sets now begin with fill-in-the-blank Warm Up Exercises.
- We revised and greatly expanded the chapter summaries into a chart format for easier studying.
- All chapter tests have been reorganized to include exactly 20 questions for consistency in length while thoroughly covering the content presented in the chapter.

Content Revision

In this edition, we have revised and expanded certain topics to introduce new material and to increase understanding.

Chapter 1 "Critical Thinking Skills," includes exciting and current examples and exercises.

Chapter 2 "Sets," includes many new applications of sets pertaining to a greater variety of topics, such as the sales of iPods and other electronic devices.

Chapter 3 "Logic," contains new exercises, as well as a greater variety of exercises. We include several puzzles, sudoku and kakuro, as Recreational Mathematics exercises. Also, we now show an alternative method to work truth tables.

Chapter 4 "Systems of Numeration," contains information on the bases 2, 8, and 16, which have many applications in modern devices such as smart phones, cameras, and high-definition televisions.

Chapter 5 "Number Theory and the Real Number System," has updated information regarding the largest prime number found and the most calculated digits of pi. We updated exercise sets to reflect current economic numbers involving the national debt, the gross domestic product, population growth and so on.

Chapter 6 "Algebra, Graphs, and Functions," has updated examples and exercises dealing with real-life situations. We moved material on exponential equations from Section 6.3 to Section 6.10 and updated it to include examples and exercises on population growth.

Chapter 7 "Systems of Linear Equations and Inequalities," contains many updated examples and exercises.

Chapter 8 "The Metric System," has many new up-to-date examples, exercises, and photographs of real-life metric use throughout the world.

Chapter 9 "Geometry," includes many updated examples and exercises, and we rewrote several topics for greater clarity.

Chapter 10 "Mathematical Systems," has many new examples, exercises, and real-life applications to modern technology.

Chapter 11 "Consumer Mathematics," contains updated interest rates involving a variety of loans and investments. We rewrote much of the material clearly and concisely. We now calculate monthly payments on installment loans and principal and interest for a mortgage payment, using a formula in addition to a table.

Chapter 12 "Probability," has updated examples and exercises that deal with real-life applications, including video games, smart phones, and Facebook.

Chapter 13 In "Statistics," the authors combined Sections 13.3 and 13.4 to emphasize the relationship between frequency distributions and statistical graphs. We rewrote material in Section 13.7, The Normal Curve, for greater clarity, and we updated many examples and exercises with real-life applications.

Chapter 14 "Graph Theory," involves many new applications of graphs to a variety of topics, including maps, social networks (such as Facebook), and other real-world applications.

Chapter 15 "Voting and Apportionment," includes many updated examples and exercises about voting and apportionment. We rewrote some of this material for greater clarity.

Continuing and Revised Features

- **Chapter Openers** Interesting and motivational applications introduce each chapter, which includes the Why This Is Important section, and illustrate the real-world nature of the chapter topics.

- **Problem Solving** Beginning in Chapter 1, students are introduced to problem solving and critical thinking. We continue the theme of problem solving throughout the text and present special problem-solving exercises in the exercise sets.
- **Critical Thinking Skills** In addition to a focus on problem solving, this book also features sections on inductive and deductive reasoning, estimation, and dimensional analysis.
- **Profiles in Mathematics** Brief historical sketches and vignettes present stories of people who have advanced the discipline of mathematics.
- **Did You Know?** The colorful, engaging, and lively Did You Know? boxes highlight the connections of mathematics to history, the arts and sciences, technology, and a broad variety of disciplines.
- **Mathematics Today** These boxes discuss current real-life uses of the mathematical concepts in the chapter. Each box ends with Why This Is Important.
- **Technology Tips** The material in these boxes explains how students can use calculators, Excel, or other technologies to work certain types of application problems.
- **Timely Tips** These easy-to-identify boxes offer helpful information to make the material under discussion more understandable.
- **Boxed Material** Important definitions, formulas, and procedures are boxed, making key information easy to identify for students.
- **Group Projects** At the end of each chapter are suggested group projects that instructors can use to encourage students to work together. Instructors can also assign these projects to individual students.
- **Chapter Summaries, Review Exercises, and Chapter Tests** The end-of-chapter Summaries, now in chart format, provide an easier study experience by directing students to the location in the text where specific concepts are discussed. Review Exercises and Chapter Tests also help students review material and prepare for exams.

Online Homework Systems

MyMathLab® Online Course (access code required)

MyMathLab delivers **proven results** in helping individual students succeed. It provides **engaging experiences** that personalize, stimulate, and measure learning for each student. And it comes from a **trusted partner** with educational expertise and an eye on the future.

To learn more about how MyMathLab combines proven learning applications with powerful assessment, visit **www.mymathlab.com** or contact your Pearson representative.

MyMathLab® Ready to Go Course (access code required)

These new Ready to Go courses provide students with all the same great MyMathLab features that you're used to, but make it easier for instructors to get started. Each course includes pre-assigned homeworks and quizzes to make creating your course even simpler. Ask your Pearson representative about the details for this particular course or to see a copy of this course.

MathXL® Online Course (access code required)

Math XL® is the homework and assessment engine that runs MyMathLab. (MyMathLab is MathXL plus a learning management system.) With MathXL, instructors can:

- Create, edit, and assign online homework and tests using algorithmically generated exercises correlated at the objective level to the textbook.
- Create and assign their own online exercises and import TestGen tests for added flexibility.
- Maintain records of all student work tracked in MathXL's online gradebook.

With MathXL, students can:

- Take chapter tests in MathXL and receive personalized study plans and/or personalized homework assignments based on their test results.
- Use the study plan and/or the homework to link directly to tutorial exercises for the objectives they need to study.
- Access supplemental animations and video clips directly from selected exercises.

MathXL is available to qualified adopters. For more information, visit our website at www.mathxl.com, or contact your Pearson representative.

Student's Solutions Manual

ISBN 13: 978-0-321-63931-8; ISBN 10: 0-321-63931-6

by Tamsen Herrick of Butte College

This for-sale manual contains solutions to all odd-numbered exercises and to all Review and Chapter Test exercises.

Video Resources

These digitized videos review chapter content for student use at home or on the go. They are ideal for distance learning and supplemental instruction.

Annotated Instructor's Edition

ISBN 13: 978-0-321-63928-8; ISBN 10: 0-321-63928-6

This special edition of the text includes answers next to the exercises, for quick reference. Answers that do not fit next to the exercise are placed in a separate section in the back of the book. Answers to all text exercises are included.

Online Supplements

Online supplements are available for download only at **www.pearsonhighered.com/irc.**

Instructor's Solutions Manual

by Tamsen Herrick of Butte College

This manual contains solutions to all exercises in the text and answers to Group Projects.

Instructor's Testing Manual

This manual includes three alternate tests per chapter.

Insider's Guide

This manual includes resources and helpful section-specific teaching tips designed to assist both new and adjunct faculty with course preparation.

PowerPoint Lecture Presentation

These fully editable lecture slides include definitions, key concepts, and examples for use in a lecture setting and are available for each section of the text.

TestGen®

TestGen enables instructors to build, edit, print, and administer tests using a computerized bank of questions developed to cover all the objectives of the text. TestGen is algorithmically based, allowing instructors to create multiple but equivalent versions of the same question or test with the click of a button. Instructors can also modify test bank questions or add new questions. Tests can be printed or administered online. The software and testbank are available for download from Pearson Education's online catalog.

Acknowledgments

We thank our spouses, Kathy Angel, Jason Abbott, and Kris Runde, for their support and encouragement throughout the project. They helped us in a great many ways, including proofreading, typing, and offering valuable suggestions. We are grateful for their wonderful support and understanding while we worked on the book.

We also thank our children: Robert and Steven Angel; Matthew and Jake Abbott; and Alex, Nick, and Max Runde. They also gave us support and encouragement and were very understanding when we could not spend as much time with them as we wished because of book deadlines. Without the support and understanding of our families, this book would not be a reality.

We thank Patricia Nelson of the University of Wisconsin–LaCrosse and James Lapp for their conscientious job of checking the text and answers for accuracy. We also thank Sherry Tornwall of the University of Florida for continually making valuable suggestions for improving the book. And thanks to Becky Troutman for preparing the Index of Applications.

Many people at Pearson deserve thanks, including all those listed on the copyright page. In particular, we thank Anne Kelly, Editor in Chief; Marnie Greenhut, Acquisitions Editor; Chere Bemelmans, Senior Content Editor; Elle Driska, Assistant Editor; Peggy McMahon, Senior Production Project Manager; Roxanne McCarley, Executive Marketing Manager; Caitlin Crain, Marketing Assistant; Tracy Menoza, Media Producer; and Beth Paquin, Senior Designer. We also thank Judith Bucci of Nesbitt Graphics, Inc., for her assistance as Project Manager for this edition.

Tamsen Herrick of Butte College also deserves our thanks for the excellent work she did on the *Student's* and *Instructor's Solutions Manuals*.

Finally, we thank the reviewers from all editions of the book and all the students who have offered suggestions for improving it. A list of reviewers for all editions of this book follows. Thanks to you all for helping make *A Survey of Mathematics with Applications* the most successful liberal arts mathematics textbook in the country.

Allen R. Angel

Christine D. Abbott

Dennis C. Runde

Reviewers for This and Previous Editions

*Marilyn Ahrens, Missouri Valley College

*David Allen, Iona College

Mary Anne Anthony-Smith, Santa Ana College

Frank Asta, College of DuPage

Robin L. Ayers, Western Kentucky University

Hughette Bach, California State University–Sacramento

Madeline Bates, Bronx Community College

Rebecca Baum, Lincoln Land Community College

Vivian Baxter, Fort Hays State University

Una Bray, Skidmore College

David H. Buckley, Polk State College

Robert C. Bueker, Western Kentucky University

Carl Carlson, Moorhead State University

Kent Carlson, St. Cloud State University

Donald Catheart, Salisbury State College

Yungchen Cheng, Southwest Missouri State University

Joseph Cleary, Massasoit Community College

Donald Cohen, SUNY College of Agriculture & Technology at Cobleskill

David Dean, Santa Fe College

*John Diamantopoulos, Northeastern State University

*Greg Dietrich, Florida State College at Jacksonville

Charles Downey, University of Nebraska

*Jeffrey Downs, Western Nevada College

Annie Droullard, Polk State College

Ruth Ediden, Morgan State University

Lee Erker, Tri-County Community College

*Nancy Eschen, Florida State College at Jacksonville

Karen Estes, St. Petersburg College

Teklay Fessanaye, Santa Fe College

Kurtis Fink, Northwest Missouri State University

Raymond Flagg, McPherson College

Penelope Fowler, Tennessee Wesleyan College

Gilberto Garza, El Paso Community College

Judith L. Gersting, Indiana University–Purdue University at Indianapolis

*Patricia Granfield, George Mason University

Lucille Groenke, Mesa Community College

*Kaylinda Holton, Tallahassee Community College

John Hornsby, University of New Orleans

*Judith Ink, Regent University

Nancy Johnson, Broward College

*Phyllis H. Jore, Valencia College

*Heidi Kiley, Suffolk County Community College

Daniel Kimborowicz, Massasoit Community College

Mary Lois King, Tallahassee Community College

*Harriet H. Kiser, Georgia Highlands College

*Julia Ledet, Louisiana State University

David Lehmann, Southwest Missouri State University

Peter Lindstrom, North Lake College

James Magliano, Union College

Yash Manchanda, East Los Angeles College & Fullerton College

*Richard Marchand, Slippery Rock University

Don Marsian, Hillsborough Community College

Marilyn Mays, North Lake College

*Susan McCourt, Bristol Community College

Robert McGuigan, Westfield State College

Wallace H. Memmer, Brookdale Community College

Maurice Monahan, South Dakota State University

Julie Monte, Daytona State College

Karen Mosely, Alabama Southern Community College

*Kathleen Offenholley, Brookdale Community College

Edwin Owens, Pennsylvania College of Technology

Wing Park, College of Lake County

Bettye Parnham, Daytona State College

Joanne Peeples, El Paso Community College

*Traci M. Reed, St. John's River Community College

Nelson Rich, Nazareth College

Kenneth Ross, University of Oregon

Ronald Ruemmler, Middlesex County College

Rosa Rusinek, Queensborough Community College

Len Ruth, Sinclair Community College

John Samoylo, Delaware County Community College

Sandra Savage, Orange Coast College

Gerald Schultz, Southern Connecticut State University

Richard Schwartz, College of Staten Island

Kara Shavo, Mercer County Community College

Minnie Shuler, Chipola College

Paula R. Stickles, University of Southern Indiana

Kristin Stoley, Blinn College–Bryan

Steve Sworder, Saddleback College

Shirley Thompson, Moorhead College

Alvin D. Tinsley, Central Missouri State University

*Sherry Tornwall, University of Florida

William Trotter, University of South Carolina

Zia Uddin, Lock Haven University of Pennsylvania

*Michael Vislocky, University of Cincinnati

Sandra Welch, Stephen F. Austin State University

Joyce Wellington, Southeastern Community College

Sue Welsch, Sierra Nevada College

Robert F. Wheeler, Northern Illinois University

Susan Wirth, Indian River State College

James Wooland, Florida State University

*Judith B. Wood, Central Florida Community College

Jean Woody, Tulsa Community College

Michael A. Zwick, Monroe Community College

*Denotes reviewers for ninth edition.

1

Critical Thinking Skills

What You Will Learn

- Inductive and deductive reasoning processes
- Estimation
- Problem-solving techniques

Why This is Important

Life constantly presents new problems. The more sophisticated our society becomes, the more complex the problems. We as individuals are constantly solving problems. For example, when we consider ways to reduce our expenses or when we plan a trip, we make problem-solving decisions. We also have to make problem-solving decisions when we figure out how to divide our time between studying, friends, family, work, and recreational activities. Additionally, businesses are constantly trying to solve problems that involve making a profit for the company and keeping customers satisfied.

The goal of this chapter is to help you master the skills of reasoning, estimating, and problem solving. These skills will aid you in solving problems in the remainder of this book as well as those you will encounter in everyday life.

◄ Planning a trip uses critical thinking skills to stay within a budget while visiting exciting new places.

SECTION 1.1   Inductive Reasoning

▲ *A device like this can be used to gain access to your computer.*

Thus far, no two people have been found to have the same fingerprints or DNA. So fingerprints and DNA have become forms of identification. As technology improves, so do identification techniques. Computerized fingerprint scanners are now showing up in police stations, in high-tech security buildings, and with personal computers. You can purchase a personal USB fingerprint scanner that requires your distinctive fingerprint to gain access to your computer. The belief that no two people have the same finger size, shape, and density is based on a type of reasoning we will discuss in this section.

Why *This is Important* As you will see in this section, we use a type of reasoning, called *inductive reasoning*, every day when we make decisions based on past experiences.

Inductive Reasoning

Before looking at some examples of inductive reasoning and problem solving, let us first review a few facts about certain numbers. The *natural numbers* or *counting numbers* are the numbers 1, 2, 3, 4, 5, 6, 7, 8, ... The three dots, called an *ellipsis*, mean that 8 is not the last number but that the numbers continue in the same manner. A word that we sometimes use when discussing the counting numbers is "divisible." If $a \div b$ has a remainder of zero, then *a is divisible by b*. The counting numbers that are divisible by 2 are 2, 4, 6, 8,.... These numbers are called the *even counting numbers*. The counting numbers that are not divisible by 2 are 1, 3, 5, 7, 9,.... These numbers are the *odd counting numbers*. When we refer to *odd numbers* or *even numbers*, we mean odd or even counting numbers.

Recognizing patterns is sometimes helpful in solving problems, as Examples 1 and 2 illustrate.

Example 1 *The Product of Two Even Numbers*

If two even numbers are multiplied together, will the product always be an even number?

Solution To answer this question, we will examine the products of several pairs of even numbers to see if there is a pattern.

$2 \times 2 = 4$	$4 \times 6 = 24$	$6 \times 8 = 48$
$2 \times 4 = 8$	$4 \times 8 = 32$	$6 \times 10 = 60$
$2 \times 6 = 12$	$4 \times 10 = 40$	$6 \times 12 = 72$
$2 \times 8 = 16$	$4 \times 12 = 48$	$6 \times 14 = 84$

All the products are even numbers. Thus, we might predict from these examples that the product of any two even numbers is an even number. ■

Example 2 *The Sum of an Odd Number and an Even Number*

If an odd number and an even number are added, will the sum be an odd number or an even number?

Solution Let's look at a few examples in which one number is odd and the other number is even.

3 + 4 = 7	9 + 6 = 15	23 + 18 = 41
5 + 12 = 17	5 + 14 = 19	81 + 32 = 113

All these sums are odd numbers. Therefore, we might predict that the sum of an odd number and an even number is an odd number. ∎

In Examples 1 and 2, we cannot conclude that the results are true for all counting numbers. From the patterns developed, however, we can make predictions. This type of reasoning process, arriving at a general conclusion from specific observations or examples, is called *inductive reasoning*, or *induction*.

Definition: Inductive Reasoning

Inductive reasoning is the process of reasoning to a general conclusion through observations of specific cases.

Induction often involves observing a pattern and from that pattern predicting a conclusion. Imagine an endless row of dominoes. You knock down the first, which knocks down the second, which knocks down the third, and so on. Assuming the pattern will continue uninterrupted, you conclude that any one domino that you select in the row will eventually fall, even though you may not witness the event.

Inductive reasoning is often used by mathematicians and scientists to predict answers to complicated problems. For this reason, inductive reasoning is part of the *scientific method*. When a scientist or mathematician makes a prediction based on specific observations, it is called a *hypothesis* or *conjecture*. After looking at the products in Example 1, we might conjecture that the product of two even numbers will be an even number. After looking at the sums in Example 2, we might conjecture that the sum of an odd number and an even number is an odd number.

Examples 3 and 4 illustrate how we arrive at a conclusion using inductive reasoning.

Example 3 *Fingerprints and DNA*

What reasoning process has led to the conclusion that no two people have the same fingerprints or DNA? This conclusion has resulted in the use of fingerprints and DNA in courts of law as evidence to convict persons of crimes.

Solution In millions of tests, no two people have been found to have the same fingerprints or DNA. By induction, then, we believe that fingerprints and DNA provide a unique identification and can therefore be used in a court of law as evidence. Is it possible that sometime in the future two people will be found who do have exactly the same fingerprints or DNA? ∎

Example 4 *Divisibility by 3*

Consider the following conjecture: "If the sum of the digits of a number is divisible by 3, then the number itself is divisible by 3." We will test several numbers to see if the conjecture appears to be true or false.

Solution Let's look at some numbers whose sum of the digits is divisible by 3.

Number	Sum of the Digits	Is the Sum of the Digits Divisible by 3?	Is the Number Divisible by 3?
243	2 + 4 + 3 = 9	Yes; 9 ÷ 3 = 3	Yes; 243 ÷ 3 = 81
2088	2 + 0 + 8 + 8 = 18	Yes; 18 ÷ 3 = 6	Yes; 2088 ÷ 3 = 696
6783	6 + 7 + 8 + 3 = 24	Yes; 24 ÷ 3 = 8	Yes; 6783 ÷ 3 = 2261
49,116	4 + 9 + 1 + 1 + 6 = 21	Yes; 21 ÷ 3 = 7	Yes; 49,116 ÷ 3 = 16,372

In each case, we find that if the sum of the digits of a number is divisible by 3, then the number itself is divisible by 3. From these examples, we might be tempted to generalize that the conjecture "If the sum of the digits of a number is divisible by 3, then the number itself is divisible by 3"* is true.   ■

Example 5 *Pick a Number, Any Number*

Pick any number, multiply the number by 4, add 2 to the product, divide the sum by 2, and subtract 1 from the quotient. Repeat this procedure for several different numbers and then make a conjecture about the relationship between the original number and the final number.

Solution Let's go through this one together.

Pick a number:	say, 5
Multiply the number by 4:	$4 \times 5 = 20$
Add 2 to the product:	$20 + 2 = 22$
Divide the sum by 2:	$22 \div 2 = 11$
Subtract 1 from the quotient:	$11 - 1 = 10$

Note that we started with the number 5 and finished with the number 10. If you start with the number 2, you will end with the number 4. Starting with 3 would result in a final number of 6, 4 would result in 8, and so on. On the basis of these few examples, we may conjecture that when you follow the given procedure, the number you end with will always be twice the original number.   ■

The result reached by inductive reasoning is often correct for the specific cases studied but not correct for all cases. History has shown that not all conclusions arrived at by inductive reasoning are correct. For example, Aristotle (384–322 B.C.) reasoned inductively that heavy objects fall at a faster rate than light objects. About 2000 years later, Galileo (1564–1642) dropped two pieces of metal—one 10 times heavier than the other—from the Leaning Tower of Pisa in Italy. He found that both hit the ground at exactly the same moment, so they must have traveled at the same rate.

When forming a general conclusion using inductive reasoning, you should test it with several special cases to see whether the conclusion appears correct. If a special case is found that satisfies the conditions of the conjecture but produces a different result, such a case is called a *counterexample*. A counterexample proves that the conjecture is false because only one exception is needed to show that a conjecture is not valid. Galileo's counterexample disproved Aristotle's conjecture. If a counterexample cannot be found, the conjecture is neither proven nor disproven.

Deductive Reasoning

A second type of reasoning process is called *deductive reasoning*, or *deduction*. Mathematicians use deductive reasoning to *prove* conjectures true or false.

Definition: **Deductive Reasoning**
Deductive reasoning is the process of reasoning to a specific conclusion from a general statement.

Example 6 *Pick a Number, n*

Prove, using deductive reasoning, that the procedure in Example 5 will always result in twice the original number selected.

---

*This statement is in fact true, as is discussed in Section 5.1.

Solution To use deductive reasoning, we begin with the *general* case rather than specific examples. In Example 5, specific cases were used. Let's select the letter n to represent *any number*.

Pick any number: n

Multiply the number by 4: $4n$ 4n means 4 times n

Add 2 to the product: $4n + 2$

Divide the sum by 2: $\dfrac{4n + 2}{2} = \dfrac{\overset{2}{4n}}{\underset{1}{2}} + \dfrac{\overset{1}{2}}{\underset{1}{2}} = 2n + 1$

Subtract 1 from the quotient: $2n + 1 - 1 = 2n$

Note that for any number n selected, the result is $2n$, or twice the original number selected. ■

In Example 5, you may have *conjectured*, using specific examples and inductive reasoning, that the result would be twice the original number selected. In Example 6, we *proved*, using deductive reasoning, that the result will always be twice the original number selected.

SECTION 1.1   *Exercises*

Warm Up Exercises

In Exercises 1–8, fill in the blank with an appropriate word, phrase, or symbol(s).

1. Another name for the natural numbers is the _____ numbers.

2. If $a \div b$ has a remainder of 0, then a is _____ by b.

3. A belief based on specific observations that has not been proven or disproven is called a conjecture or _____.

4. A specific case that satisfies the conditions of a conjecture but shows the conjecture is false is called a _____.

5. The process of reasoning to a general conclusion through observation of specific cases is called _____ reasoning.

6. The process of reasoning to a specific conclusion from a general statement is called _____ reasoning.

7. The type of reasoning used to prove a conjecture is called _____ reasoning.

8. The type of reasoning generally used to arrive at a conjecture is called _____ reasoning.

9. While logging on to your computer, you type in your username followed by what you believe is your password. The computer indicates that a mistake has been made and asks you to try again. You retype your username and the same password. Again, the computer indicates a mistake has been made. You decide not to try again, reasoning you will get the same error message from the computer. What type of reasoning did you use? Explain.

10. You have purchased one lottery ticket each week for many months and have not won more than $5.00. You decide, based on your past experience, that you are not going to win the grand prize and so you stop playing the lottery. What type of reasoning did you use? Explain.

Practice the Skills

In Exercises 11–14, use inductive reasoning to predict the next line in the pattern.

11. $1 \times 5 = 5$
$2 \times 5 = 10$
$3 \times 5 = 15$
$4 \times 5 = 20$

12. $12 \times 10 = 120$
$12 \times 11 = 132$
$12 \times 12 = 144$
$12 \times 13 = 156$

13.
$$1$$
$$1 \quad 1$$
$$1 \quad 2 \quad 1$$
$$1 \quad 3 \quad 3 \quad 1$$
$$1 \quad 4 \quad 6 \quad 4 \quad 1$$

14. $10 = 10^1$
$100 = 10^2$
$1000 = 10^3$
$10{,}000 = 10^4$

In Exercises 15–18, draw the next figure in the pattern (or sequence).

15.

16.

17.

18.

In Exercises 19–28, use inductive reasoning to predict the next three numbers in the pattern (or sequence).

19. 2, 4, 6, 8, …

20. 3, 7, 11, 15, …

21. 3, −3, 3, −3, …

22. 5, 3, 1, −1, …

23. 1, $\frac{1}{2}$, $\frac{1}{3}$, $\frac{1}{4}$, …

24. 4, −20, 100, −500, …

25. 1, 4, 9, 16, 25, …

26. 0, 1, 3, 6, 10, 15, …

27. 1, 1, 2, 3, 5, 8, 13, 21, …

28. 3, $-\frac{9}{4}$, $\frac{27}{16}$, $-\frac{81}{64}$, …

Problem Solving

29. Find the letter that is the 118th entry in the following sequence. Explain how you determined your answer.

    Y, R, R, Y, R, R, Y, R, R, Y, R, R, Y, R, R, …

30. a) Select a variety of one- and two-digit numbers between 1 and 99 and multiply each by 9. Record your results.

    b) Find the sum of the digits in each of your products in part (a). If the sum is not a one-digit number, find the sum of the digits again until you obtain a one-digit number.

    c) Make a conjecture about the sum of the digits when a one- or two-digit number is multiplied by 9.

31. *A Square Pattern* The ancient Greeks labeled certain numbers as **square numbers**. The numbers 1, 4, 9, 16, 25, and so on are square numbers.

1   4   9   16   25

a) Determine the next three square numbers.

b) Describe a procedure to determine the next five square numbers without drawing the figures.

c) Is 72 a square number? Explain how you determined your answer.

32. *A Triangular Pattern* The ancient Greeks labeled certain numbers as *triangular numbers*. The numbers 1, 3, 6, 10, 15, 21, and so on are triangular numbers.

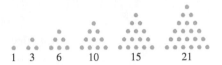

1   3   6   10   15   21

a) Can you determine the next two triangular numbers?

b) Describe a procedure to determine the next five triangular numbers without drawing the figures.

c) Is 72 a square number? Explain how you determined your answer.

33. *Quilt Design* The pattern shown is taken from a quilt design known as a triple Irish chain. Complete the color pattern by indicating the color assigned to each square.

34. *Triangles in a Triangle* Four rows of a triangular figure are shown.

a) If you added six additional rows to the bottom of this triangle, using the same pattern displayed, how many triangles would appear in the 10th row?

b) If the triangles in all 10 rows were added, how many triangles would appear in the entire figure?

35. *Airline Revenues* The graph at the top of page 7 shows the annual operating revenues, in millions of dollars, for U.S. passenger and cargo airlines from 2002 through 2008.

a) Assuming this trend continues, use the graph to predict the annual operating revenue, in millions of dollars, for U.S. passenger and cargo airlines in 2009.

b) Explain how you are using inductive reasoning to determine your answer.

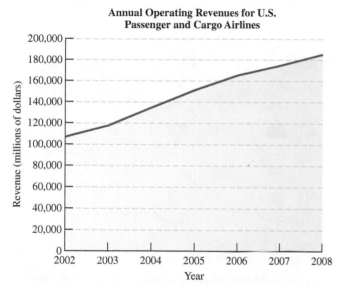

Annual Operating Revenues for U.S. Passenger and Cargo Airlines

Source: Air Transport Association of America

36. *Government Spending* The graph shows the amount of money spent, in trillions of dollars, by the U.S. government each year from 2000 through 2008.

a) Assuming this trend continues, use the graph to predict the amount of money the U.S. government will spend in 2014.

b) Explain how you are using inductive reasoning to determine your answer.

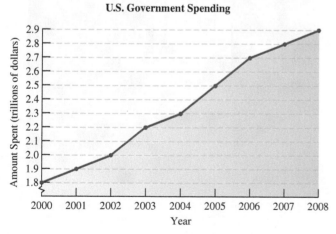

U.S. Government Spending

Source: U.S. Department of Treasury

In Exercises 37 and 38, draw the next diagram in the pattern (or sequence).

37.   **38.**

39. Pick any number, multiply the number by 4, add 12 to the product, divide the sum by 4, and subtract 3 from the quotient. See Example 5.

a) What is the relationship between the number you started with and the final number?

b) Arbitrarily select some different numbers and repeat the process, recording the original number and the result.

c) Can you make a conjecture about the relationship between the original number and the final number?

d) Try to prove, using deductive reasoning, the conjecture you made in part (c). See Example 6.

40. Pick any number and multiply the number by 4. Add 6 to the product. Divide the sum by 2 and subtract 3 from the quotient.

a) What is the relationship between the number you started with and the final answer?

b) Arbitrarily select some different numbers and repeat the process, recording the original number and the results.

c) Can you make a conjecture about the relationship between the original number and the final number?

d) Try to prove, using deductive reasoning, the conjecture you made in part (c).

41. Pick any number and add 1 to it. Find the sum of the new number and the original number. Add 9 to the sum. Divide the sum by 2 and subtract the original number from the quotient.

a) What is the final number?

b) Arbitrarily select some different numbers and repeat the process. Record the results.

c) Can you make a conjecture about the final number?

d) Try to prove, using deductive reasoning, the conjecture you made in part (c).

42. Pick any number and add 10 to the number. Divide the sum by 5. Multiply the quotient by 5. Subtract 10 from the product. Then subtract your original number.

a) What is the result?

b) Arbitrarily select some different numbers and repeat the process, recording the original number and the result.

c) Can you make a conjecture regarding the result when this process is followed?

d) Try to prove, using deductive reasoning, the conjecture you made in part (c).

In Exercises 43–48, find a counterexample to show that each statement is incorrect.

43. The difference between two odd numbers is an odd number.

44. The quotient of any two counting numbers is a counting number.

45. When a counting number is added to 3 and the sum is divided by 2, the quotient will be an even number.

46. The product of any two three-digit numbers is a five-digit number.

47. The difference of any two counting numbers will be a counting number.

48. The sum of any two odd numbers is divisible by 4.

49. *Interior Angles of a Triangle*
   a) Construct a triangle and measure the three interior angles with a protractor. What is the sum of the measures?

   b) Construct three other triangles, measure the angles, and record the sums. Are your answers the same?

   c) Make a conjecture about the sum of the measures of the three interior angles of a triangle.

50. *Interior Angles of a Quadrilateral*
   a) Construct a quadrilateral (a four-sided figure) and measure the four interior angles with a protractor. What is the sum of the measures?

   b) Construct three other quadrilaterals, measure the angles, and record the sums. Are your answers the same?

   c) Make a conjecture about the sum of the measures of the four interior angles of a quadrilateral.

Challenge Problems/Group Activities

51. Complete the following square of numbers. Explain how you determined your answer.

1	2	3	4
2	5	10	17
3	10	25	52
4	17	52	?

52. Find the next three numbers in the sequence.

1, 8, 11, 88, 101, 111, 181, 808, 818, 888, 1001, 1111, ...

Recreational Mathematics

53.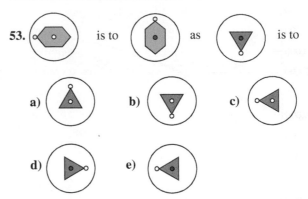

Internet/Research Activities

54. a) Using newspapers, the Internet, magazines, and other sources, find examples of conclusions arrived at by inductive reasoning.

   b) Explain how inductive reasoning was used in arriving at the conclusion.

55. When a jury decides whether or not a defendant is guilty, do the jurors collectively use primarily inductive reasoning, deductive reasoning, or an equal amount of each? Write a brief report supporting your answer.

SECTION 1.2 | Estimation

▲ *Estimate the sales tax on a $10,000 motorcycle if the sales tax rate is 8%.*

What is the approximate sales tax on a $10,000 motorcycle if the sales tax rate is 8%? What is the approximate cost to purchase 52 forty-four-cent stamps? In this section, we will introduce a technique for arriving at an approximate answer to a question.

Why **This is Important** Estimation is a technique we use every day for determining whether an answer is reasonable.

An important step in solving mathematical problems—or, in fact, *any* problem—is to make sure that the answer you've arrived at makes sense. One technique for determining whether an answer is reasonable is to estimate. *Estimation* is the process of arriving at an approximate answer to a question. This section demonstrates several estimation methods.

To estimate, or approximate, an answer, we often round numbers, as illustrated in the following examples. The symbol ≈ means *is approximately equal to*.

Example 1 *Estimating the Cost of Bagels*

Sandy Mendez decides to purchase bagels for her colleagues. Estimate her cost if she purchases 29 bagels at $1.99 each.

Solution We may round the amounts as follows to obtain an estimate.

Number	Number Rounded
29	30
× $1.99	× $2.00
	$60.00

Thus, the 29 bagels would cost approximately $60.00, written ≈ $60.00

In Example 1, the true cost is $1.99 × 29, or $57.71. *Estimates are not meant to give exact values for answers but are a means of determining whether your answer is reasonable.* If you calculated an answer of $57.71 and then did a quick estimate to check it, you would know that the answer is reasonable because it is close to your estimated answer.

Example 2 *Two Ways to Estimate*

At a local office supply store, Karen Bowlby purchased pens for $15.89, a calendar for $7.19, a ruler for $1.94, index cards for $1.49, legal pads for $8.29, scissors for $10.79, and paper clips for $0.82. The cashier said the total bill was $55.41. Use estimation to determine whether this amount is reasonable.

Solution The most expensive item is $15.89, and the least expensive is $0.82. How should we estimate? We will estimate two different ways. First, we will round the cost of each item to the nearest 10 cents. For the second method, we will round the cost of each item to the nearest dollar. Rounding to the nearest 10 cents is more accurate. To determine whether the total bill is reasonable, however, we may need to round only to the nearest dollar.

	Round to the Nearest 10 Cents		Round to the Nearest Dollar	
Pens	$15.89 →	$15.90	$15.89 →	$16.00
Calendar	7.19 →	7.20	7.19 →	7.00
Ruler	1.94 →	1.90	1.94 →	2.00
Index cards	1.49 →	1.50	1.49 →	1.00
Legal pads	8.29 →	8.30	8.29 →	8.00
Scissors	10.79 →	10.80	10.79 →	11.00
Paper clips	0.82 →	0.80	0.82 →	1.00
		$46.40		$46.00

Using either estimate, we find that the bill of $55.41 is quite high. Therefore, Karen should check the bill carefully before paying it. Adding the prices of all seven items gives the true cost of $46.41. ■

Example 3   *Select the Best Estimate*

The number of bushels of grapes produced at a vineyard are 71,309 Cabernet Sauvignon, 123,879 French Colombard, 106,490 Chenin Blanc, 5960 Charbono, and 12,104 Chardonnay. Select the best estimate of the total number of bushels produced by the vineyard.

a) 500,000   b) 30,000   c) 300,000   d) 5,000,000

Solution   Following are suggested roundings. On the left, the numbers are rounded to thousands. For a less accurate estimate, round to ten thousands, as illustrated on the right.

Round to the Nearest Thousand		Round to the Nearest Ten Thousand	
71,309 →	71,000	71,309 →	70,000
123,879 →	124,000	123,879 →	120,000
106,490 →	106,000	106,490 →	110,000
5,960 →	6,000	5,960 →	10,000
12,104 →	12,000	12,104 →	10,000
	319,000		320,000

Either rounding procedure indicates that the best estimate is (c), or 300,000. ■

Example 4   *Using Estimation in Calculations*

The Martellos traveled 1276 miles from their home in Springfield, Missouri, to Yellowstone National Park.

a) If their trip took 19.9 hours of driving time, estimate the average speed in miles per hour, that their car traveled.
b) If their car used 52 gallons of gasoline, estimate the average gas mileage of their car, in miles per gallon.
c) If the cost of gasoline averaged $3.51 per gallon, estimate the total cost of the gasoline used.

Solution

a) To estimate the average miles per hour, divide the number of miles by the number of hours.

$$\frac{1276}{19.9}$$

Round these numbers to obtain an estimate.

$$\frac{1300}{20} = 65$$

Therefore, the car averaged about 65 miles per hour.

b) To estimate the average gas mileage, divide the number of miles by the number of gallons.

$$\frac{1276}{52}$$

Round these numbers to obtain an estimate.

$$\frac{1300}{50} = 26$$

Therefore, the car averaged about 26 miles per gallon.

c) To estimate the total cost of gasoline, multiply the price per gallon by the number of gallons. Round the number of gallons of gasoline to 50 gallons and the price of the gasoline to $3.50 per gallon. The cost of the gasoline is about 50 × $3.50, or $175. ∎

Now let's look at some different types of estimation problems.

Example 5 *Estimating Distances on Trails to the West*

In the mid-1800s, thousands of settlers followed trails to the West to gain cheap, fertile land and a chance to make a fortune. One of the main trails to the West was the Oregon Trail, which ran from Independence, Missouri, to the Oregon Territory. Another trail, the California Trail, ran from Fort Hall on the Oregon Trail to Sacramento, California. A map of the Oregon Trail and the California Trail is shown below.

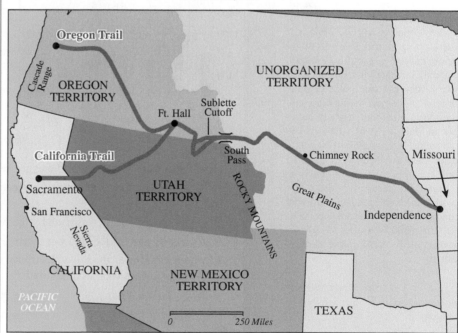

Trails West, 1850

a) Using the Oregon Trail, estimate the distance from Independence, Missouri, to Fort Hall in the Oregon Territory.

b) Using the California Trail, estimate the distance from Fort Hall in the Oregon Territory to Sacramento, California.

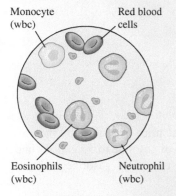
Solution

a) Using a ruler and the scale given on the map, we can determine that approximately $\frac{3}{4}$-inch represents 250 miles (mi). One way to determine the distance from Independence, Missouri, to Fort Hall in the Oregon Territory is to mark off $\frac{3}{4}$-inch intervals along the Oregon Trail. If you do so, you should obtain approximately 4 intervals. Thus, the distance is about 4 × 250 mi, or about 1000 mi.

　Sometimes on a map like this one, it may be difficult to get an accurate estimate because of the curves on the map. To get a more accurate estimate, you may want to use a piece of string. Place the beginning of the string at Independence, Missouri, and, using tape or pins, align the string with the road. Indicate on the string the point represented by Fort Hall. Then remove the string and make $\frac{3}{4}$-inch interval markings on the string (or measure the length of string you marked off). If, for example, your string from Independence, Missouri, to Fort. Hall measures $3\frac{1}{4}$ inch, then the distance is about 1083 mi.

b) Using the procedure discussed in part (a), we estimate that the distance from Fort Hall in the Oregon Territory to Sacramento, California, is about $1\frac{5}{8}$ inch, or about 2.2 three-quarter-inch intervals. Thus, the distance from Fort Hall in the Oregon Territory to Sacramento, California, is about 2.2 × 250 mi, or about 550 mi. ■

Example 6 *Estimated Energy Use*

Some utility bills contain graphs illustrating the amount of electricity and natural gas used. The following graphs show gas and electric use at a specific residence for a period of 13 months, starting in November 2010 and going through November 2011 (the month of the current bill). Also shown, in red, is the bill for the average residential customer for November 2011. Using these graphs, answer the following questions.

a) How often were actual gas and electric readings made?

b) Estimate the number of therms of gas used by the average residential customer in November 2011.

c) Estimate the amount of gas used by the resident in November 2011.

d) If the cost of gas is $1.12295 per therm, estimate the gas bill in March 2011.

e) In which month was the most electricity used? How many kilowatt-hours (kWh) of electricity were used in this month?

f) If the cost of electricity is 8.1716 cents per kWh, estimate the cost of the electricity in January 2011.

Solution

a) Actual readings were made every other month, in November 2010, January 2011, March 2011, May 2011, July 2011, September 2011, and November 2011. Thus, actual readings were made 7 times.

b) In November 2011, approximately 75 therms were used by the average residential customer, as shown by the height of the red bar.

c) In November 2011, approximately 60 therms were used by the resident.

d) In March 2011, about 180 therms were used. The rate is $1.12295 per therm. To get a rough approximation, round the rate to $1.12 per therm.

$$1.12 \times 180 = \$201.60$$

Thus, the cost of gas used was about $201.60.

e) The most electricity was used in July 2011. Approximately 2400 kWh of electricity were used.

f) In January 2011, about 1200 kWh were used. Write 8.1716 cents as $0.081716. Rounding the rate to $0.08 per kWh and multiplying by 1200 yields an estimate of $96.

$$0.08 \times 1200 = \$96$$

Thus, the cost of electricity in January 2011 was about $96. ∎

Example 7 *Estimating the Number of Corn Kernels in a Photo*

Estimate the number of corn kernels in the top layer in the accompanying photograph.

Solution To estimate the number of kernels, we can divide the photograph into rectangles with equal areas and then select one area that appears to be representative of all the areas. Estimate (or count) the number of kernels in this single area and then multiply this number by the number of equal areas.

Let's divide the photo into 20 approximately equal areas. We will select the left region in the top row as the representative region. We enlarge this region and count the kernels in it. If half a kernel is in the region, we count it (see enlargement on page 14). There are about 18 kernels in this region. Multiplying by 20 gives $18 \times 20 = 360$. Thus, there are about 360 kernels in the photo.

In problems similar to that in Example 7, the number of regions or areas into which you choose to divide the total area is arbitrary. Generally, the more regions, the better the approximation, as long as the region selected is representative of the other regions in the map, diagram, or photo.

When you estimate an answer, the amount that your approximation differs from the actual answer will depend on how you round the numbers. For example, in estimating the product of $196,000 \times 0.02520$, using the rounded values $195,000 \times 0.025$ would yield an estimate much closer to the true answer than using the rounded values $200,000 \times 0.03$. Without a calculator, however, the product of $195,000 \times 0.025$ might be more difficult to find than $200,000 \times 0.03$. When estimating, you need to determine the accuracy desired in your estimate and round the numbers accordingly.

SECTION 1.2   *Exercises*

Warm Up Exercises

In Exercises 1–2, fill in the blank with an appropriate word, phrase, or symbol(s).

1. The process of arriving at an approximate answer to a question is called _____.

2. The symbol $\approx$ means is approximately _____ to.

Practice the Skills

In Exercises 3–57, your answers may vary from the answers given in the back of the text, depending on how you round your answers.

In Exercises 3–12, estimate the answer. There is no one correct estimate. Your answer, however, should be something near the answer given.

3. $261 + 127.4 + 273.9 + 16.2 + 81.5$

4. $2.57 + 212.6 + 176.2 + 83$

5. $198,600 \times 3.072$

6. 1854×0.0096

7. $\dfrac{405}{0.049}$

8. 0.63×1523

9. $51,608 \times 6981$

10. 11% of 8221

11. 18% of 1576

12. $296.3 \div 0.0096$

Problem Solving

In Exercises 13–22, estimate the answer.

13. The cost of one pen if a box of 5 pens costs $10.49

14. The cost of a dozen clams if 20 dozen clams cost $37.80

15. The amount of money Rick spends on gasoline in a year if the average amount he spends per month is $120.80.

16. An 8% sales tax on a car that costs $11,250

17. One third of an annual profit of $8795

18. The cost of 5 items purchased at a hardware store if the items cost $1.29, $6.86, $12.43, $25.62, and $8.99

19. The total weight of three people on an elevator if their weights are 95 lb, 127 lb, and 210 lb.

20. The weight of one pork chop in a package of six pork chops if the weight of the package is 3.25 lb

21. A 15% tip on a meal that costs $26.32

22. The number of months needed to save $400 if you save $23 each month

23. **Utility Bill** Joe Kuby pays $114.99 per month for the Verizon Fios Triple Play Offer. This package includes unlimited local and long-distance telephone, cable TV, and Internet service. His previous monthly costs for these services were $65.99, $49.99, and $49.95, respectively. Estimate the amount of money Joe saves per month with the Triple Play Offer.

24. **Estimating Weights** In a tug of war, the weight of the members of the two three-person teams is given below. Estimate the difference in the weights of the teams.

Team A	Team B
189	183
172	229
191	167

25. **Picking Strawberries** Chuck Chase hires 11 people to pick strawberries from his field. He agrees to pay them $1.50 for each quart they pick. Estimate the total amount of money he will have to pay if each person picks 8 quarts.

26. **Estimating Time** Donna Burke is a long-distance runner whose average time per mile in marathons is 6 minutes, 25 seconds. Estimate the time it will take her to complete a 26-mile, 385-yard (or ≈ 26.2-mile) marathon.

27. **Currency** Estimate the difference in the value of 50 U.S. dollars and 100 Mexican pesos. Assume that one Mexican peso is about 0.083 U.S. dollar.

28. **The Cost of a Vacation** The Kleins are planning a vacation in the Great Smoky Mountains National Park. Their round-trip airfare from Houston, Texas, to Knoxville, Tennessee, totals $973. Car rental is $61 per day and lodging is a total of $97 per day, and they estimate a total of $200 per day for food, gas, and other miscellaneous items. If they are planning to stay six full days and nights, estimate their total expenses.

29. **The Pacific Coast Highway** Above and to the right is a map of California's scenic Pacific Coast Highway. Using the scale on the map, estimate the distance between Pfeiffer Big Sur State Park and Hearst Castle.

▲ Hearst Castle

30. **The Olympic Peninsula** Below is a map of the Olympic Peninsula in the state of Washington. Using the scale on the map, estimate the distance of the route shown in red, starting at Port Angeles and ending at Forks, passing through Sappho.

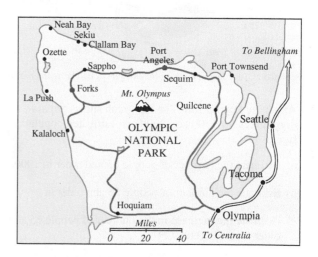

31. *Health Club Membership* The circle graph below shows the percent of health club memberships, by age, in the United States in 2011. *Fit for Life* health club had 700 members in 2011. Assuming this graph applies to the *Fit for Life* membership,

a) estimate the number of *Fit for Life* health club members who were between the ages of 18 and 34.

b) estimate the number of *Fit for Life* health club members who were age 17 and younger.

c) estimate the number of *Fit for Life* health club members who were age 55 or older.

Health Club Membership by Age in 2011

32. *Dream Jobs* The circle graph below shows the kind of job parents of children ages 5 to 17 hope their children will grow up to have. The survey involved 504 parents.

a) Estimate the number of parents who hope their child will become a doctor.

b) Estimate the number of parents who hope their child will become a professional athlete.

c) Estimate the number of parents who hope their child will start a successful new business.

Jobs That Parents Hope Their Children Will Have

Source: Office Depot Back-to-School survey by Harris Interactive

33. *An Aging Population* The bar graph shows population figures for 1900 and 2000 and estimated population figures for 2050.

a) Estimate the number of people 65 and older in 1900.

b) Estimate the number of people 65 and older in 2050.

c) Estimate the increase in the number of people 65 and older from 2000 to 2050.

d) Estimate the total U.S. population in 2000 by adding the five categories.

Population by Age

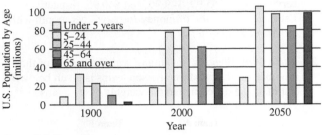

Source: U.S. Census Bureau

34. *Gaining Weight* The graph shows that as a society we tend to get heavier as we grow older. Also, with age, the amount of muscle tends to drop, and fat accounts for a greater percentage of weight.

a) Estimate the average percent of body fat for a woman, age 18 to 25.

b) Estimate the average percent of body fat for a man, age 56+.

c) Greg, an average 40-year-old man, weighs 179 lb. Estimate the number of pounds of body fat he has.

Getting Older Usually Means Getting Fatter

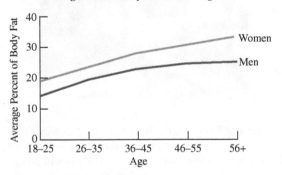

35. *Land Ownership by the Federal Government* The federal government owns a great deal of land in the United States. The graph at the top of page 17 shows the percent of land owned by the federal government in the 12 states in which the federal government owns the greatest percentage of a state's land.

a) Estimate the percent of land owned by the federal government in Nevada.

b) Estimate the difference between Alaska and Oregon in the percent of land owned by the federal government.

c) Nevada has a total area of 70,264,320 acres. Estimate the number of acres owned by the federal government in Nevada.

d) By just looking at the graph, is it possible to determine whether the federal government owns more land in Nevada or Utah? Explain.

Percent of Land Owned by the Federal Government

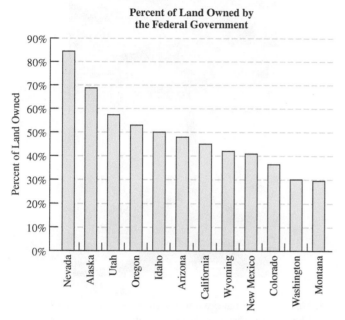

Source: Office of Governmentwide Policy, General Services Administration

36. Calories and Exercise The chart shows the calories burned per hour for an average person who weighs 150 lb.

a) Estimate the number of calories Phyllis Nye, who weighs 150 lb, burns in a week if she stair-climbs for 2 hours each week and jogs at 5 miles per hour for 4 hours each week.

b) Estimate the difference in the calories Phyllis will burn each week if she runs for 4 hours at 8 miles per hour rather than does casual bike riding for 4 hours.

c) Assume Phyllis jogs at 5 miles per hour for 3 hours and bicycles at 13 miles per hour for 3 hours each week. Estimate the number of calories she will burn in a year from these exercises.

Activity	Calories* per Hour
Running, 8 mph	920
Bicycling, 13 mph	545
Jogging, 5 mph	545
Air-walking	480
Stair-climbing	410
Weight-lifting	410
Walking, 4 mph	330
Casual bike riding	300

*For a 150-lb person.

In Exercises 37 and 38, estimate the maximum number of smaller figures (at left) that can be placed in the larger figure (at right) without the small figures overlapping.

37.

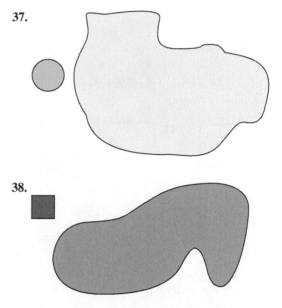

38.

39. Estimate the number of bananas shown in the photo.

40. Estimate the number of berries shown in the photo.

In Exercises 41 and 42, estimate, in degrees, the measure of the angles depicted. For comparison purposes a right angle, *, measures 90°.*

41.

42.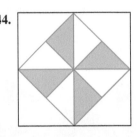

In Exercises 43 and 44, estimate the percent of area that is shaded in the following figures.

43.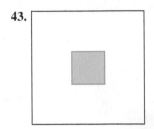

44.

In Exercises 45 and 46, if each square represents one square unit, estimate the area of the shaded figure in square units.

45.

46.

47. *Statue of Liberty* The length of the torch of the Statue of Liberty, from the tip of the flame to the bottom of the torch's baton, is 29 feet. Estimate the height of the Statue of Liberty from the top of the base to the top of the torch (the statue itself).

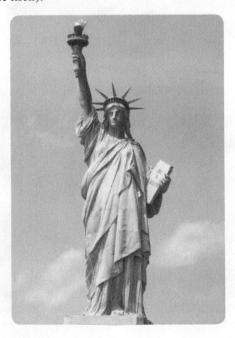

48. *Estimating Heights* If the height of the woman in the photo is 62 in. tall, estimate the height of the tree.

49. *Distance* Estimate, without a ruler, a distance of 12 in. Measure the distance. How good was your estimate?

50. *Weight* In a bag, place objects that you believe have a total weight of 10 lb. Weigh the bag to determine the accuracy of your estimate.

51. *Phone Call* Estimate the number of times the phone will ring in 1 minute if unanswered. Have a classmate phone you so that you can count the rings and thus test your estimate.

52. *Temperature* Fill a glass with water and estimate the water's temperature. Then use a thermometer to measure the temperature and check your estimate.

53. *Pennies* Estimate the number of pennies that will fill a 3-ounce (oz) paper cup. Then actually fill a 3-oz paper cup with pennies, counting them to determine the accuracy of your estimate.

54. *Height* Estimate the ratio of your height to your waist size. Then have a friend measure your height and waist size. Determine the stated ratio and check the accuracy of your estimate.

55. *Walking Speed* Estimate how fast you can walk 60 ft. Then mark off a distance of 60 ft and use a watch with a second hand to time yourself walking it. Determine the accuracy of your estimate.

Challenge Problems/Group Activities

56. *Shopping* Make a shopping list of 20 items you use regularly that can be purchased at a supermarket. Beside each item write down what you estimate to be its price. Add these price guesses to estimate the total cost of the

20 items. Next, make a trip to your local supermarket and record the actual price of each item. Add these prices to determine the actual total cost. How close was your estimate? (Don't forget to add tax on the taxable items.)

57. *A Ski Vacation* Two friends, Tiffany Connolly and Ana Pott, are planning a skiing vacation in the Rockies. They plan to purchase round-trip airline tickets from Atlanta, Georgia, to Denver, Colorado. They will fly into Denver on a Friday morning, rent a midsize car, and drive to Aspen that same day. They will stay at the Holiday Inn in Aspen. They will begin skiing at the Buttermilk Ski Area on Saturday, ski up to and including Wednesday, drive back to Denver on Thursday, and fly out of Denver Thursday evening.

a) Estimate the total cost of the vacation for the two friends. Do not forget items such as food, tips, gas, and other incidentals.

b) Using informational sources, including the Internet, determine the airfare cost, hotel cost, cost of ski tickets, cost of a car rental, and so forth. You will need to make an estimate for food and other incidentals.

c) How close was your estimate in part (a) to the amount you found in part (b)? Was your estimate in part (a) lower or higher than the amount obtained in part (b)?

Recreational Mathematics

58. *A Dime* Look at a dime. Around the edge of a dime are many lines. Estimate the number of lines there are around the edge of a dime.

59. *A Million Dollars*

a) Estimate the time it would take, in days, to spend $1 million if you spent $1 a second until the $1 million is used up.

b) Calculate the actual time it would take, in days, to spend $1 million if you spent $1 a second. How close was your estimate?

Internet/Research Activities

60. *Water Usage*

a) About how much water does your household use per day? Use the following data to estimate your household's daily water usage.

Activity	Typical Use
Running clothes washer	40 gal
Bath	35 gal
5-minute shower	25 gal
Doing dishes in sink, water running	20 gal
Running dishwasher	11 gal
Flushing toilet	4 gal
Brushing teeth, water running	2 gal

Source: U.S. Environmental Protection Agency

b) Determine from your water department (or company) your household's average daily usage by obtaining the total number of gallons used per year and dividing that amount by 365. How close was your estimate in part (a)?

c) Current records indicate that the average household uses about 300 gal of water per day (the average daily usage is 110 gal per person). Based on the number of people in your household, do you believe your household uses more or less than the average amount of water? Explain your answer.

61. Develop a monthly budget by estimating your monthly income and your monthly expenditures. Your monthly income should equal your monthly expenditures.

62. Identify three ways that you use estimation in your daily life. Discuss each of them briefly and give examples.

SECTION 1.3   Problem Solving

To maximize their profits, businesses try to keep their expenses down. We, as individuals, also try to do the same, and we often look for "bargains" or the "best deal." For example, suppose we need to purchase several pizzas and have only $75 to spend. How can we determine the maximum number of slices that we can purchase if large pizzas with 12 slices sell for $12 and medium pizzas with 8 slices sell for $9. We'll answer this question in Example 1.

Why *This is Important* Problem-solving skills can help you find solutions to problems you may encounter in everyday life.

▲ *Getting the most for your money while purchasing pizza involves problem solving.*

Solving mathematical puzzles and real-life mathematical problems can be enjoyable. You should work as many exercises in this section as possible. By doing so, you will sample a variety of problem-solving techniques.

You can approach any problem by using a general procedure developed by George Polya. Before learning Polya's problem-solving procedure, let's consider an example that illustrates the procedure.

Example 1   *Saving Money When Purchasing Pizza*

Karen Morris plans to purchase pizza for a party she is hosting. Pizza Corner sells medium pizzas (14" diameter) for $9 and large pizzas (17" diameter) for $12. A medium pizza has 8 slices and a large pizza has 12 slices. Only entire pizzas are sold. Assume the pizza slices are all about the same size.

a) Determine the maximum number of slices of pizza that Karen can purchase for $75 or less.

b) If the maximum number of slices determined in part (a) is purchased in the most economical way, how much will the pizzas cost?

Solution

a) The first thing to do is read the problem carefully. Read it at least twice. Be sure you understand the facts given and what you are being asked to find. Next, make a list of the given facts and determine which facts are relevant to answering the question or questions asked.

GIVEN INFORMATION

> Party host: Karen Morris
>
> Pizza shop: Pizza Corner
>
> A medium pizza costs $9.
>
> A medium pizza has a 14" diameter.
>
> A medium pizza contains 8 slices.
>
> A large pizza costs $12.
>
> A large pizza has a 17" diameter.
>
> A large pizza contains 12 slices.
>
> Only entire pizzas can be purchased.

We need to determine the maximum number of slices Karen can purchase for $75 or less. To determine this number, we need to know the number of slices in each pizza and the cost of each pizza. We also need to know that only entire pizzas can be purchased.

Ostriches

How many ostriches must replace the question mark to balance the fourth scale? Assume that all animals of the same kind have the same weight. That is, all giraffes weigh the same, and so forth.

Answer: 3 ostriches

RELEVANT INFORMATION

A medium pizza costs $9.

A medium pizza contains 8 slices.

A large pizza costs $12.

A large pizza contains 12 slices.

Only entire pizzas can be purchased.

The next step is to determine the answer to the question. That is, we need to determine the maximum number of slices that can be purchased for $75 or less.

We now need a plan for solving the problem. One method is to set up a table or chart to compare costs of different combinations of pizzas. Start by using the maximum number of large pizzas that can be purchased. Then reduce the number of large pizzas and add more medium pizzas. In each case, we need to keep the cost at $75 or less.

Because one large pizza costs $12, we can determine the number of large pizzas that can be purchased by dividing 75 by 12. Because the quotient is 6.25 and only entire pizzas can be purchased, only 6 large pizzas can be purchased. Six large pizzas would cost $12 \times 6 = $72. Because medium pizzas cost $9, there would not be enough money left to purchase any medium pizzas. Since large pizzas have 12 slices, 6 large pizzas provide $12 \times 6 = 72$ slices. Thus, for $75 or less, one option is 6 large pizzas, which gives 72 slices. This option is illustrated in the first row of the table below. Also given in the table is the cost of this option, which is $72. We complete the other rows of the table in a similar manner.

Large Pizzas and Medium Pizzas	Number of Slices	Cost
6 large and 0 medium	$(6 \times 12) + (0 \times 8) = 72$	$72
5 large and 1 medium	$(5 \times 12) + (1 \times 8) = 68$	$69
4 large and 3 medium	$(4 \times 12) + (3 \times 8) = 72$	$75
3 large and 4 medium	$(3 \times 12) + (4 \times 8) = 68$	$72
2 large and 5 medium	$(2 \times 12) + (5 \times 8) = 64$	$69
1 large and 7 medium	$(1 \times 12) + (7 \times 8) = 68$	$75
0 large and 8 medium	$(0 \times 12) + (8 \times 8) = 64$	$72

The question asks us to find the maximum number of slices of pizza that can be purchased for $75 or less. From the second column of the table, we see that the answer is 72 slices of pizza. This result can be obtained in two different ways: either 6 large pizzas and 0 medium pizzas or 4 large pizzas and 3 medium pizzas.

b) When comparing the two possibilities for purchasing the 72 slices of pizza discussed in part (a), we see that the most economical way to purchase the slices is to purchase 6 large pizzas and 0 medium pizzas. The cost is $72. ∎

Following is a general procedure for problem solving as given by George Polya. Note that Example 1 demonstrates many of these guidelines.

Profile in Mathematics

George Polya

Ｇeorge Polya (1887–1985) was educated in Europe and taught at Stanford University. In his book *How to Solve It*, Polya outlines four steps in problem solving. We will use Polya's four steps as guidelines for problem solving.

PROCEDURE

GUIDELINES FOR PROBLEM SOLVING

1. *Understand the problem.*
   - Read the problem *carefully* at least twice. In the first reading, get a general overview of the problem. In the second reading, determine (a) exactly what you are being asked to find and (b) what information the problem provides.
   - Try to make a sketch to illustrate the problem. Label the information given.
   - Make a list of the given facts that are pertinent to the problem.
   - Determine if the information you are given is sufficient to solve the problem.
2. *Devise a plan to solve the problem.*
   - Have you seen the problem or a similar problem before? Are the procedures you used to solve the similar problem applicable to the new problem?
   - Can you express the problem in terms of an algebraic equation? (We explain how to write algebraic equations in Chapter 6.)
   - Look for patterns or relationships in the problem that may help in solving it.
   - Can you express the problem more simply?
   - Can you substitute smaller or simpler numbers to make the problem more understandable?
   - Will listing the information in a table help in solving the problem?
   - Can you make an educated guess at the solution? Sometimes if you know an approximate solution, you can work backward and eventually determine the correct procedure to solve the problem.
3. *Carry out the plan.*
   - Use the plan you devised in Step 2 to solve the problem.
4. *Check the results.*
   - Ask yourself, "Does the answer make sense?" and "Is the answer reasonable?" If the answer is not reasonable, recheck your method for solving the problem and your calculations.
   - Can you check the solution using the original statement?
   - Is there an alternative method to arrive at the same conclusion?
   - Can the results of this problem be used to solve other problems?

The following examples show how to apply the guidelines for problem solving.

▲ *San Antonio, Texas*

Example 2   *Shuttle Revenue*

Airport Express shuttle service provides service from San Antonio International Airport to downtown hotels, approximately 10 miles away. One particular shuttle makes 16 round trips per day, carrying 5 passengers per trip. The fare each way is $18. What are the receipts from one day's operation for this particular shuttle?

Solution   We need to find the total receipts from one day's operation. Let's make a list of all the information given and mark with an asterisk (*) the information that is pertinent to solving the problem.

     Distance from airport to downtown hotels $\approx$ 10 miles
   * Number of round trips per day $= 16$
   * Number of passengers per trip $= 5$
   * Fare each way $= \$18$

All the information is needed to solve the problem except the distance between the airport and the downtown hotels. To determine the total receipts for the day, we need to know the number of round trips per day, the number of passengers per trip, and the round trip cost per passenger. The product of these three numbers will yield the total daily receipts. For a round trip, the cost per passenger is $\$18 \times 2 = \$36$.

     Thus the total receipts for one day's operation $= 16 \times 5 \times \$36 = \$2880$.   ■

In Example 2, we could have used 32 one-way trips at a fare of $18 per person to obtain the answer. Why?

Archimedes Treatise, On Floating Bodies

Scientists are using problem-solving techniques and modern technology to unlock ancient secrets. In May 2005, scientists at the Stanford Linear Accelerator Center used x-rays to decipher pages of the only known copy of a 2300-year-old Greek text by the mathematician Archimedes. Scholars believe that the 174-page treatise, *On Floating Bodies*, was copied by a scribe in the 10th century from Archimedes' original Greek scrolls, written in the 3rd century B.C. The treatise was erased 200 years later by a monk who reused the parchment for a prayer book, creating a twice-used parchment.

To reveal much of the hidden text, the scientists used digital cameras and processing techniques as well as ultraviolet and infrared filters developed for medicine and space research. Through the use of x-rays, scientists were able to read the remaining pages of the treatise. The text and diagrams contain the roots of modern calculus and gravitational theory.

Example 3 *Retirement*

It is never too early to start planning for retirement. U.S. Census Bureau data indicate that at age 65 the average woman will live another 20 years and the average man will live another 17.2 years. The data also indicate that about 33% of the average person's retirement income will come from Social Security.

When discussing retirement planning, many investment firms and financial planners use the graph in Fig. 1.1,* which shows how long a typical retiree's assets (or "nest egg") will last based on the percentage of the assets withdrawn each year.

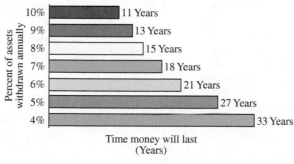

How Much You Withdraw Annually Affects How Long Your Money Will Last

Source: Ned Davis research

Figure 1.1

a) If a typical retiree has retirement assets of $500,000, how much can he or she withdraw annually if he or she wishes the assets to last 21 years?

b) How much should a retiree have in assets if he or she wishes to withdraw $25,000 annually and wishes his or her assets to last 18 years?

Solution

a) Quite a bit of information is provided in the example. We will first need to determine what information is needed to answer the question. To answer the question, we only need to use the information provided in the graph. From the graph, we can see that for assets to last 21 years, about 6% of the assets can be withdrawn annually. The amount that can be withdrawn annually is found as follows.

$$\text{Amount} = 6\% \text{ of assets}$$
$$\text{Amount} = 0.06\,(500{,}000) = 30{,}000$$

Thus, about $30,000 can be withdrawn annually.

b) Again, to solve this part of the example, we only need the information provided in the graph. From the graph, we can determine that if a retiree wishes for his or her assets to last 18 years, then 7% of the assets can be withdrawn annually. We need to determine the total assets such that 7% of the total assets is $25,000.

$$7\% \text{ of assets} = \$25{,}000 \quad \text{or} \quad 0.07 \times \text{assets} = \$25{,}000$$

Because 0.07 is multiplied by the assets to obtain $25,000, we can determine the assets by dividing the $25,000 by 0.07 as follows.

$$\text{Assets} = \frac{25{,}000}{0.07} = 357{,}142.86$$

Therefore, if the retiree has assets of about $357,142.86, he or she will be able to withdraw $25,000 annually and the assets will last 18 years.

*The information in this graph is based on past performance of the stock market, with 50% invested in large company stocks and 50% invested in intermediate-term bonds. Past performance is not indicative of future results.

Example 4   *Determining a Tip*

The cost of Freddie Rojo's meal before tax is $28.00.

a) If a $6\frac{1}{2}\%$ sales tax is added to his bill, determine the total cost of the meal including tax.

b) If Freddie wants to leave a 10% tip on the *pretax* cost of the meal, how much should he leave?

c) If he wants to leave a 15% tip on the *pretax* cost of the meal, how much should he leave?

Solution

a) The sales tax is $6\frac{1}{2}\%$ of $28.00. To determine the sales tax, first change the $6\frac{1}{2}\%$ to a decimal number. $6\frac{1}{2}\%$ when written as a decimal number is 0.065 (if you have forgotten how to change a percent to a decimal number, read Section 11.1). Next, multiply the decimal number, 0.065, by the amount, $28.00.

$$\text{Sales tax} = 6\tfrac{1}{2}\% \text{ of } 28.00$$
$$= 0.065(28.00) = 1.82$$

The sales tax is $1.82. The total bill is the cost of the meal + the sales tax.

$$\text{Total bill} = \text{cost of meal} + \text{sales tax}$$
$$= 28.00 + 1.82 = 29.82$$

Thus, the bill, including sales tax, is $29.82.

b) To find 10% of any number, we can multiply the number by 0.10.

$$10\% \text{ of pretax cost} = 0.10(28.00)$$
$$= 2.80$$

A simple way to find 10% of any number is to simply move the decimal point in the number one place to the left. Moving the decimal point in $28.00 one place to the left gives $2.80, the same answer we obtained by our calculations.

c) To find 15% of $28.00, multiply as follows.

$$15\% \text{ of } 28.00 = 0.15(28.00) = 4.20$$

Thus, 15% of $28.00 is $4.20. A second method to find a 15% tip is to find 10% of the cost, as in part (b), then add to it half that amount. Following this procedure, we get

$$\$2.80 + \frac{\$2.80}{2} = \$2.80 + \$1.40 = \$4.20$$

In most cases, tips are rounded. If the service is excellent, some people leave a 20% tip. Can you give two methods to determine a 20% tip on $28.00? Determine the 20% tip now.

Example 5   *A Recipe for 6*

The chart at the top of page 25 shows the amount of each ingredient recommended to make 2, 4, and 8 servings of Potato Buds. Determine the amount of each ingredient necessary to make 6 servings of Potato Buds by using the following procedures.

a) Multiply the amount for 2 servings by 3.*

b) Add the amounts for 2 servings to the amounts for 4 servings.

c) Find the average of the amounts for 4 servings and for 8 servings.

---

*Addition, subtraction, multiplication, and division of fractions are discussed in detail in Section 5.3.

d) Subtract the amounts for 2 servings from the amounts for 8 servings.

e) Compare the answers for parts (a) through (d). Are they the same? If not, explain why not.

f) Which is the correct procedure for obtaining 6 servings?

Servings	2	4	8
Water	$\frac{2}{3}$ cup	$1\frac{1}{3}$ cups	$2\frac{2}{3}$ cups
Milk	2 tbsp	$\frac{1}{3}$ cup	$\frac{2}{3}$ cup
Butter or margarine	1 tbsp	2 tbsp	4 tbsp
Salt*	$\frac{1}{4}$ tsp	$\frac{1}{2}$ tsp	1 tsp
Potato Buds	$\frac{2}{3}$ cup	$1\frac{1}{3}$ cups	$2\frac{2}{3}$ cups

*Less salt can be used if desired.

Solution

a) We multiply the amounts for 2 servings by 3.

Water: $3\left(\frac{2}{3}\right) = 2$ cups

Milk: $3(2) = 6$ tablespoons (tbsp)

Butter or margarine: $3(1) = 3$ tbsp

Salt: $3\left(\frac{1}{4}\right) = \frac{3}{4}$ teaspoon (tsp)

Potato Buds: $3\left(\frac{2}{3}\right) = 2$ cups

b) We find the amount of each ingredient by adding the amount for 2 and 4 servings.

Water: $\frac{2}{3}$ cup $+ 1\frac{1}{3}$ cups $= 2$ cups

Milk: 2 tbsp $+ \frac{1}{3}$ cup

To add these two amounts, we must convert one of them so that both ingredients have the same units. By looking in a cookbook or a book of conversion factors, we see that 16 tbsp = 1 cup. The milk in part (a) was given in tablespoons, so we convert $\frac{1}{3}$ cup to tablespoons to compare answers. One-third cup equals $\frac{1}{3}(16) = \frac{16}{3}$ or $5\frac{1}{3}$ tbsp. Therefore,

Milk: 2 tbsp $+ 5\frac{1}{3}$ tbsp $= 7\frac{1}{3}$ tbsp

Let's continue with the rest of the ingredients:

Butter: 1 tbsp $+$ 2 tbsp $=$ 3 tbsp

Salt: $\frac{1}{4}$ tsp $+ \frac{1}{2}$ tsp $= \frac{3}{4}$ tsp

Potato Buds: $\frac{2}{3}$ cup $+ 1\frac{1}{3}$ cups $= 2$ cups

c) We compute the amounts of the ingredients by finding the average of the amounts for 4 and 8 servings. We do so by adding the amounts for each ingredient and dividing the sum by 2.

Water: $\dfrac{1\frac{1}{3} \text{ cups} + 2\frac{2}{3} \text{ cups}}{2} = \dfrac{4 \text{ cups}}{2} = 2$ cups

Milk: $\dfrac{\frac{1}{3} \text{ cup} + \frac{2}{3} \text{ cup}}{2} = \dfrac{1 \text{ cup}}{2} = \frac{1}{2}$ cup (or 8 tbsp)

Butter: $\dfrac{2 \text{ tbsp} + 4 \text{ tbsp}}{2} = \dfrac{6 \text{ tbsp}}{2} = 3$ tbsp

Salt: $\dfrac{\frac{1}{2} \text{ tsp} + 1 \text{ tsp}}{2} = \dfrac{\frac{3}{2} \text{ tsp}}{2} = \frac{3}{4}$ tsp

$$\text{Potato Buds:} \quad \frac{1\frac{1}{3}\text{ cups} + 2\frac{2}{3}\text{ cups}}{2} = \frac{4\text{ cups}}{2} = 2\text{ cups}$$

d) We obtain the amounts of ingredients by subtracting the amounts for 2 servings from the amounts for 8 servings.

Water: $2\frac{2}{3}$ cups $- \frac{2}{3}$ cup $= 2$ cups

Milk: $\frac{2}{3}$ cup $- 2$ tbsp $= \frac{2}{3}(16)$ tbsp $- 2$ tbsp

$\qquad\qquad\qquad = \frac{32}{3}$ tbsp $- \frac{6}{3}$ tbsp

$\qquad\qquad\qquad = \frac{26}{3}$ tbsp, or $8\frac{2}{3}$ tbsp

Butter: 4 tbsp $- 1$ tbsp $= 3$ tbsp

Salt: 1 tsp $- \frac{1}{4}$ tsp $= \frac{3}{4}$ tsp

Potato Buds: $2\frac{2}{3}$ cups $- \frac{2}{3}$ cup $= 2$ cups

e) Comparing the answers in parts (a) through (d), we find that the amounts of all ingredients, except milk, are the same. For milk, we get the following results.

Part (a): Milk $= 6$ tbsp   Part (c): Milk $= 8$ tbsp

Part (b): Milk $= 7\frac{1}{3}$ tbsp   Part (d): Milk $= 8\frac{2}{3}$ tbsp

Why are all these answers different? After rechecking, we find that all our calculations are correct, so we must look deeper. Note that milk is the only ingredient that has different units for 2 servings and 4 servings. Let's check the relationship between 2 tbsp and $\frac{1}{3}$ cup. In going from 2 servings to 4 servings, we would expect that $\frac{1}{3}$ cup should be twice 2 tbsp. We know that 1 cup $= 16$ tbsp, so

$$\tfrac{1}{3}\text{ cup} = \tfrac{1}{3}(16) = \tfrac{16}{3} = 5\tfrac{1}{3}\text{ tbsp}$$

Therefore, instead of the 4 tbsp of milk we expected for 4 servings, we get $5\frac{1}{3}$ tbsp. This change causes all our calculations for milk to be different.

f) Which is the correct answer? Because all our calculations for milk are correct, there is no single correct answer. All our answers are correct. Using $8\frac{2}{3}$ tbsp instead of 6 tbsp might make the Potato Buds a little thinner. When we cook, we generally do not add the *exact* amount recommended. We rely on experience to alter the recommended amounts according to individual taste. ∎

Many real-life problems, such as the one in Example 6, can be solved by using proportions. A proportion is a statement of equality between two ratios (or fractions.)*

Example 6 *Spraying Weed Killer*

The instructions on the Ortho Weed-B-Gon lawn weed killer indicate that to cover 1000 square feet (ft²) of lawn, 20 teaspoons (tsp) of the weed killer should be mixed in 5 gallons (gal) of water. Ron Haines wishes to spray his lawn with the weed killer using his pressurized sprayer.

a) How much weed killer should be mixed with 8 gal of water to get a solution of the proper strength?

b) How much weed killer is needed to cover an area of 2820 ft² of lawn?

Solution

a) Use the information that 20 teaspoons of weed killer is to be mixed with 5 gal of water.

*Proportions are discussed in greater detail in Section 6.2.

Given ratio $\begin{cases} \dfrac{20 \text{ tsp}}{5 \text{ gal water}} = \dfrac{? \text{ tsp}}{8 \text{ gal}} \end{cases}$ ← Item to be found
← Other information given

Notice in the proportion that teaspoons and gallons are placed in the same relative positions. Often, the unknown quantity is replaced with an x. The proportion may be written as follows and solved using cross-multiplication.

$$\frac{20}{5} = \frac{x}{8}$$

$20(8) = 5x$ Cross multiplication

$160 = 5x$

$\dfrac{160}{5} = \dfrac{\cancel{5}x}{\cancel{5}}$ Divide both sides of the equation by 5 to solve for x.

$32 = x$

Thus, Ron must mix 32 tsp [or $10\frac{2}{3}$ tablespoons (tbsp) or $\frac{2}{3}$ cup] of the weed killer with 8 gal of water. This answer seems reasonable because we would expect to get an answer greater than 20 tsp.

b) To answer this question, we use the same procedure discussed in part (a). This time, we will use the information that 1000 ft^2 requires 20 tsp of weed killer. The areas may be placed either on the top or the bottom of the fraction, as long as they are placed in the same relative position.

Given ratio $\begin{cases} \dfrac{1000 \text{ sq ft}}{20 \text{ tsp}} = \dfrac{2820 \text{ sq ft}}{? \text{ tsp}} \end{cases}$ ← Other information given
← Item to be found

Now replace the question mark with an x and solve the proportion.

$$\frac{1000}{20} = \frac{2820}{x}$$

$1000(x) = 20(2820)$ Cross multiplication

$1000x = 56,400$

$\dfrac{\cancel{1000}x}{\cancel{1000}} = \dfrac{56,400}{1000}$ Divide both sides of the equation by 1000 to solve for x.

$x = 56.4$

Thus, about 56.4 tsp are needed. This answer is reasonable because we would expect the answer to be more than twice the 20 tsp required for 1000 ft^2. ■

Most of the problems solved so far have been practical ones. Many people, however, enjoy solving brainteasers. One example of such a puzzle follows.

Example 7   *Magic Squares*

A magic square is a square array of numbers such that the numbers in all rows, columns, and diagonals have the same sum. Use the digits 1, 2, 3, 4, 5, 6, 7, 8, and 9 to construct a magic square.

Solution The first step is to create a figure with nine cells, as in Fig.1.2(a) on page 28. We must place the nine numbers in the cells so that the same sum is obtained in each row, column, and diagonal. Common sense tells us that 7, 8, and 9 cannot be in the same row, column, or diagonal. We need some small and large numbers in the same row, column, and diagonal. To see a relationship, we list the numbers in order:

$$1, 2, 3, 4, 5, 6, 7, 8, 9$$

Note that the middle number is 5 and the smallest and largest numbers are 1 and 9, respectively. The sum of 1, 5, and 9 is 15. If the sum of 2 and 8 is added to 5, the sum is 15. Likewise 3, 5, 7, and 4, 5, 6 have sums of 15. We see that in each group of three numbers the sum is 15 and 5 is a member of the group.

(a)   (b)   (c)   (d)

Figure 1.2

Because 5 is the middle number in the list of numbers, place 5 in the center square. Place 9 and 1 to the left and right of 5, as in Fig. 1.2(a). Now we place the 2 and the 8. The 8 cannot be placed next to 9 because $8 + 9 = 17$, which is greater than 15. Place the smaller number 2 next to the larger number 9. We elected to place the 2 in the lower left-hand cell and the 8 in the upper right-hand cell, as in Fig. 1.2(b). The sum of 8 and 1 is 9. To arrive at a sum of 15, we place 6 in the lower right-hand cell, as in Fig. 1.2(c). The sum of 9 and 2 is 11. To arrive at a sum of 15, we place 4 in the upper left-hand cell as in Fig. 1.2(c). Now the diagonals 2, 5, 8, and 4, 5, 6 have sums of 15. The numbers that remain to be placed in the empty cells are 3 and 7. Using arithmetic, we can see that 3 goes in the top middle cell and 7 goes in the bottom middle cell, as in Fig. 1.2(d). A check shows that the sum in all the rows, columns, and diagonals is 15. ■

The solution to Example 7 is not unique. Other arrangements of the nine numbers in the cells will produce a magic square. Also, other techniques of arriving at a solution for a magic square may be used. In fact, the process described will not work if the number of squares is even, for example, 16 instead of 9. Magic squares are not limited to the operation of addition or to the set of counting numbers.

SECTION 1.3   *Exercises*

Practice the Skills/Problem Solving

1. *Reading a Map* The scale on a map is 1 inch = 12 miles. How long a distance is a route on the map if it measures 5.75 in.?

2. *Blueprints* Tony Schmidt, an architect, is designing a new enclosure for the elephants at a zoo. The scale of his plan is 1 in. = 2.5 yd. He draws a 20.1-in. line on the blueprint to represent the northern boundary of the enclosure. What actual distance does this boundary line represent?

3. *Height of a Tree* At a given time of day, the ratio of the height of an object to the length of its shadow is the same for all objects. If a 3-ft stick in the ground casts a shadow of 1.2 ft, find the height of a tree that casts a shadow that is 19.36 ft.

4. *Grass Seed* A bag of Turf Builder Sun and Shade Mix grass seed covers an area of 4000 ft². How many bags are needed to cover an area of 35,000 ft²?

5. *College Tuition Cost* According to the College Board, the average tuition at a public four-year college increased by 6.4% from 2009 to 2010. The average tuition at a public four-year college in 2009 was $7605. Determine the average tuition at a public four-year college in 2010. Round your answer to the nearest dollar.

6. *Hotel Room Rate* The average price of a hotel room in Las Vegas decreased by 30% from 2008 to 2009. The average price of a hotel room in Las Vegas in 2008 was $117. Determine the average price of a hotel room in Las Vegas in 2009.

7. *How Americans Spend Their Money* The circle graph at the top of page 29 shows the percent of Americans' net monthly income spent on housing, entertainment/miscellaneous, transportation, food, insurance/retirement, and healthcare. Patricia Peck has a net monthly income of $1750. Assuming this graph applies to Patricia's spending,

   a) how much more money per month does Patricia spend on entertainment/miscellaneous than on food?

   b) how much more money per month does Patricia spend on housing than on transportation?

**How Americans Spend
Their Money**

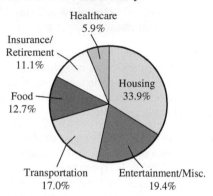

Healthcare
5.9%

Insurance/
Retirement
11.1%

Housing
33.9%

Food
12.7%

Transportation
17.0%

Entertainment/Misc.
19.4%

Source: U.S. Bureau of Labor Statistics

8. *Experience Level of U.S Teachers* The circle graph below shows the percent of U.S. teachers with 0–3, 4–10,
11–20, and more than 21 years of teaching experience. In
2009, there were 6.2 million elementary and secondary
teachers in the United States.

a) How many more teachers had 11–20 years of teaching
experience than 0–3 years?

b) How many more teachers had 4–10 years of teaching
experience than 11–20 years?

**Years of Experience
of U.S. Teachers**

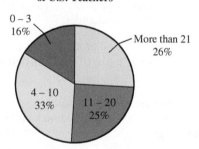

0–3
16%

More than 21
26%

4–10
33%

11–20
25%

Source: Scholastic

9. *Housing Market* The following tables show where the
average U.S. house prices have increased the most and
decreased the most during 2004–2009. The tables also
show the percent change from 2008–2009 for those areas.

Where House Prices Have Increased the Most

	% Change 2004–2009	% Change 2008–2009
Wenatchee, WA	66.86	−2.25
Coeur-d'Alene, ID	61.40	−1.92
Virginia Beach, VA	55.24	−1.25
Spokane, WA	55.14	−1.46
Honolulu, HI	54.46	−1.06
Flagstaff, AZ	53.26	−1.85
Bellingham, WA	52.39	−1.04

Where House Prices Have Decreased the Most

	% Change 2004–2009	% Change 2008–2009
Merced, CA	−29.13	8.33
Stockton, CA	−21.78	3.21
Detroit, MI	−19.80	2.90
Modesto, CA	−18.83	3.30
Vallejo, CA	−16.64	−0.23

Source: Federal Housing Finance Agency

a) If a house in Honolulu, HI, cost $200,000 in 2004, how
much did a similar house cost in 2009?

b) If a house in Detroit, MI, cost $180,000 in 2008, how
much did a similar house cost in 2009?

c) From 2008 to 2009, how much more did a $200,000
house in Flagstaff, AZ, decrease in price than a
$200,000 house in Bellingham, WA?

10. *Subway Cost* Chandler Heisinger buys a monthly
MetroCard, which entitles him to unlimited subway
travel in New York City, for $81 per month. Without the
Metrocard, each subway ride costs $2.00. How many rides
per month would Chandler have to take so that the cost of
the rides with the MetroCard is less than the cost of the
rides without the MetroCard?

11. *Buying a Computer* Emily Putnam wants to purchase a
computer that sells for $1250. She can either pay the total
amount at the time of purchase or she can agree to pay the
store $120 down and $80 a month for 15 months. How
much money can she save by paying the total amount at
the time of purchase?

12. *Flu Shots* The price of a flu shot at Maxim Health
Systems increased by 20% from 2006 to 2009. In 2006,
Maxim Health Systems charged $25 for a flu shot. If
Maxim Health sold flu shots to 2 million people in
2006 and to 2 million people in 2009, how much more
money did they earn from selling flu shots in 2009 than
in 2006?

13. *Buying a House* The Browns want to purchase a
house that costs $140,000. They plan to take out a
$100,000 mortgage on the house and put $40,000 as
a down payment. The bank informs them that with a
15-year mortgage their monthly payment would be
$777.83 and with a 30-year mortgage their monthly
payment would be $521.65. Determine the amount
they would save on the cost of the house if they
selected the 15-year mortgage rather than the 30-year
mortgage.

14. *Getting an 80 Average* On four exams, Wallace Memmer's grades were 79, 93, 91, and 68. What grade must he obtain on his fifth exam to have an 80 average?

15. *Playing a Lottery* In one state lottery game, you must select four-digits (digits may be repeated). If your number matches exactly the four-digits selected by the lottery commission, you win.

    a) How many different numbers may be chosen?

    b) If you purchase one lottery ticket, what is your chance of winning?

16. *Energy Value and Energy Consumption* The table gives the approximate energy values of some foods, in kilojoules (kJ), and the energy requirements of some activities.

    a) How soon would you use up the energy from a fried egg by swimming?

    b) How soon would you use up the energy from a hamburger by walking?

    c) How soon would you use up the energy from a piece of strawberry shortcake by cycling?

    d) How soon would you use up the energy from a hamburger and a chocolate milkshake by running?

Food	Energy Value (kJ)	Activity	Energy Consumption (kJ/min)
Chocolate milkshake	2200	Walking	25
Fried egg	460	Cycling	35
Hamburger	1550	Swimming	50
Strawberry shortcake	1400	Running	80
Glass of skim milk	350		

17. *Gas Mileage* Wendy Weisner fills her gas tank completely and makes a note that the odometer reads 38,451.4 miles. The next time she put gas in her car, filling the tank took 12.6 gal and the odometer read 38,687.0 miles. Determine the number of miles per gallon that Wendy's car got on this tank of gas.

18. *Saving for a Stereo* Fernando Diez works 40 hours per week and makes $8.50 per hour.

    a) How much money can he expect to earn in 1 year (52 weeks)?

    b) If he saves all the money he earns, how long will he have to work to save for a stereo receiver that costs $1275?

19. *Mail-Order Purchase* Mary Liotta purchased 4 tires by mail order. She paid $52.80 per tire plus $5.60 per tire for shipping and handling. There is no sales tax on this purchase because the tires were purchased out of state. She also had to pay $8.56, including tax, per tire for mounting and balancing. At a local tire store, her total for the 4 tires with mounting and balancing would be $324 plus an 8% sales tax. How much did Mary save by purchasing the tires through the mail?

20. *Computer Technician* Dave Maliwauki, a computer technician, charges a $25 flat rate plus $30 per hour to repair computers. During one month, his total income from repairing 15 computers was $885. How many hours did he spend repairing computers?

21. *Rain or Snow* A plane is flying at an altitude of 15,000 ft, where the temperature is −6°F. The nearby airport, at an altitude of 3000 ft, is reporting precipitation. If the temperature increases 2.4°F for every 1000-ft decrease in altitude, will the precipitation at the airport be rain or snow? Assume that rain changes to snow at 32°F.

22. *Profit Margins* The following chart shows retail stores' average percent profit margin on certain items.

Product Category	Average Profit Margin (%)
Video equipment	12
Audio components	14
Stereo speakers	20–25
Extended warranties	50–60

Source: *Consumer Reports*

    a) Determine the average profit of a store that has the list price of $620 on a camcorder.

    b) Determine the average profit of a store that has a list price of $1200 on a pair of speakers (use a 22% profit margin).

    c) If you negotiate and get the salesperson to sell the speakers for $1000, find the store's profit (use a 22% profit margin).

23. *Income Taxes* The federal income tax rate schedule for a joint return in 2010 is illustrated in the table. If Steve and Maureen Tomlin paid $13,365 in federal taxes, find the family's adjusted gross income.

Adjusted Gross Income	Taxes
$0–$16,750	10% of income
$16,750–$68,000	$1675 + 15% of amount over $16,750
$68,000–$137,300	$9362.50 + 25% of amount over $68,000
$137,300–$209,250	$26,687.50 + 28% of amount over $137,300
$209,250–$373,650	$46,833.50 + 33% of amount over $209,250
$373,650 and above	$101,085.50 + 35% of amount over $373,650

24. *Leaking Faucet* A faucet is leaking at a rate of one drop of water per second. Assume that the volume of one drop of water is 0.1 cubic centimeter (0.1 cm^3).

a) Determine the volume of water in cubic centimeters lost in 1 year.

b) How many days would it take to fill a rectangular basin 30 cm by 20 cm by 20 cm?

25. *Wasted Water* A faucet leaks 1 oz of water per minute.

a) How many gallons of water are wasted in a year? (A gallon contains 128 oz.)

b) If water costs $11.20 per 1000 gal, how much additional money is being spent on the water bill?

26. *Airport Parking* The chart shows parking rates at John F. Kennedy (JFK) Airport in New York, New York, as of August 1, 2011.

JFK Airport Parking Rates			
Short-term Rates			
First half hour	$\frac{1}{2}$ hour–1 hour	Each Additional Half Hour After the First Hour	Daily Maximum
$3	$6	$3	$33

Long-term Rates Daily	Additional Day 0–8 Hours
$18	$6

a) Jeff Grace is going out of town for 5 full days. How much will he save by parking in the long-term lot rather than the short-term lot?

b) What is the cost of parking in the short-term lot for 4 hours?

c) If Jeff plans to park at the airport for 5 hours, is it cheaper to park in short-term or long-term parking? How much is the difference?

27. *Tire Pressure* When a car's tire pressure is 30 pounds per square inch (psi), it averages 20.8 mpg of gasoline. If the tire pressure is increased to 35 psi, the car averages 21.6 mpg of gasoline.

a) If Mr. Levy drives an average of 20,000 mi per year, how many gallons of gasoline will he save in a year by increasing his tire pressure from 30 to 35 psi?

b) If gasoline costs $3.00 per gallon, how much will he save in a year?

c) If we assume that there are about 140 million cars in the United States and that these changes are typical of each car, how many gallons of gasoline would be saved if all drivers increased their cars' tire pressure?

28. *Toys and Games* The table illustrates the 10 countries that spent the most money, per person, on toys and games in 2008. The table also shows the total amount of money spent on toys and games for each country.

Country	Amount Spent per person ($)	Total Amount Spent (in millions $)
United Kingdom	184.90	11,237.53
Australia	177.89	3633.20
United States	151.40	45,592.59
France	147.30	9385.96
Netherlands	130.70	2165.70
Sweden	120.60	1089.02
Belgium	113.70	1181.34
Canada	105.80	3532.66
Spain	93.40	3778.03
Italy	85.70	4983.46

Source: Euromonitor International

a) By looking at the data provided, is it possible to determine the population of each country? If so, explain how to do so.

b) Using the procedure you gave in part (a), determine the population of the United States.

c) Using the procedure you gave in part (a), determine the population of the United Kingdom.

29. *Adjusting for Inflation* Assume that the rate of inflation is 6% per year for the next 2 years. What will the price of a dishwasher be 2 years from now if the dishwasher costs $799 today?

30. *Investing* You place $1000 in a mutual fund. The first year, the value of the fund increases by 10%. The second year, the value of the fund decreases by 10%. Determine the value of the fund at the end of the second year. Is it greater than, less than, or equal to your initial investment?

31. *X-rays* With a certain medical insurance policy, the customer must first pay an annual $100 deductible, and then the policy covers 80% of the cost of x-rays. The first insurance claims for a specific year submitted by Yungchen Cheng are for two x-rays. The first x-ray cost $640, and the second x-ray cost $920. How much, in total, will Yungchen need to pay for these x-rays?

32. *Buying a Yacht* Four partners decide to share the cost of a yacht equally. By bringing in an additional partner, they can reduce the cost to each of the five partners by $3000. What is the total cost of the yacht?

33. *Making Cream of Wheat* The following amounts of ingredients are recommended to make various servings of Nabisco Instant Cream of Wheat. *Note:* 16 tbsp = 1 cup.

Ingredient	1 Serving	2 Servings	4 Servings
Mix water or milk	1 cup	2 cups	$3\frac{3}{4}$ cups
With salt (optional)	$\frac{1}{8}$ tsp	$\frac{1}{4}$ tsp	$\frac{1}{2}$ tsp
Add Cream of Wheat	3 tbsp	$\frac{1}{2}$ cup	$\frac{3}{4}$ cups

Determine the amount of each ingredient needed to make 3 servings using the following procedures.

a) Multiply the amounts for 1 serving by 3.

b) Find the average of the amounts for 2 and 4 servings.

c) Subtract the amounts for 1 serving from the amounts for 4 servings.

d) Compare the answers obtained in parts (a) through (c) and explain any differences.

34. *Making Rice* Following are the amounts of ingredients recommended to make various servings of Uncle Ben's Original Converted Rice. *Note:* 1 tbsp = 3 tsp.

Ingredient	2 Servings	4 Servings	6 Servings	12 Servings
Rice (cups)	$\frac{1}{2}$	1	$1\frac{1}{2}$	3
Water (cups)	$1\frac{1}{3}$	$2\frac{1}{4}$	$3\frac{1}{3}$	6
Salt (teaspoons)	$\frac{1}{4}$	$\frac{1}{2}$	$\frac{3}{4}$	$1\frac{1}{2}$
Butter	1 tsp	2 tsp	1 tbsp	2 tbsp

Determine the amount of each ingredient needed to make 8 servings using the following procedures.

a) Multiply the amount for 2 servings by 4.

b) Multiply the amount for 4 servings by 2.

c) Add the amounts for 2 and 6 servings.

d) Subtract the amount for 4 servings from the amount for 12 servings.

e) Compare the answers obtained in parts (a) through (d) and explain any differences.

35. *Purchasing DVDs* The manager of the video department at Target plans to purchase a large number of DVDs of the movie *Toy Story* 3. One supplier is selling boxes of 20 DVD movies for $240, and a second supplier is selling boxes of 12 DVD movies for $180. Only complete boxes of DVD movies can be purchased.

a) If the manager can purchase boxes of DVD movies from either or both suppliers, determine the maximum number of DVD movies that can be purchased for $425. Indicate how many boxes of 20 and how many boxes of 12 will be purchased.

b) How much will the DVD movies cost?

36. *Who Will Win?* Steve Kilner and Mark Ernsthausen ran a 100-yard race. Mark won by 5 yards, which means Steve had run only 95 yards when Mark crossed the finish line. They decided to race again, with Mark starting 5 yards behind the starting line. Assuming both runners run the second race at the same pace as the first race, who will win?

37. *One Square Foot* How many square inches, 1 in. by 1 in., fit in an area of 1 square foot, 1 ft by 1 ft?

38. *Cubic Inches* How many cubic inches fit in 1 cubic foot?

39. *Rectangle* If the length and width of a rectangle each double, what happens to the area of the rectangle?

40. *A Square Partition* A 20 ft by 20 ft carpet is partitioned into 5 ft by 5 ft squares. How many squares will there be?

41. *Cube* If the length, width, and height of a cube all double, what happens to the volume of the cube?

42. *Pole in a Lake* A pole is in the middle of a small lake. One half of the pole is in the ground. One third of the pole is covered by water. Eleven feet, or one sixth, of the pole are out of water. What is the length of the pole?

43. *Buying Candy* How much do 10 pieces of candy cost if 1000 pieces cost $10?

44. *A Balance* On the balance below, where should the one missing block ▪ be placed so that the balance would balance on the triangle (the fulcrum). Assume that each block has the same weight.

45. *Ties, Ties, Ties* I have at least three ties. All my ties are red except two. All my ties are blue except two. All my ties are brown except two. How many ties do I have?

46. *Palindromes* A *palindrome* is a number (or word) that reads the same forward and backward. The numbers 1991 and 43234 are examples of palindromes. How many palindromes are there between the numbers 2000 and 3000? List them.

47. *Supermarket Display* The figure shows grapefruits in a supermarket display stacked in a *square pyramid* (the base is a square).

a) How many grapefruits are in the pyramid shown if the base has 4 grapefruits by 4 grapefruits?

b) How many grapefruits would be in a square pyramid if the base has 7 grapefruits by 7 grapefruits?

48. *Balancing a Scale* If you have a balance scale and only the four weights 1 gram (g), 3 g, 9 g, and 27 g, explain how you could show that an object had the following weights. (*Hint:* Weights must be added to both sides of the balance scale.)

a) 5 g   **b)** 16 g

49. *Numbers in Circles* Place the numbers 1 through 6 in the circles below so that the sum along each of the three straight lines is the same. Each number must be used exactly once. (*Note:* There is more than one correct answer.)

50. *Cuts in Cheese* If you make the three complete cuts in the cheese as shown, how many pieces of cheese will you have?

51. *Magic Square* Create a magic square by using the numbers 2, 4, 6, 8, 10, 12, 14, 16, and 18. The sum of the numbers in every column, row, and diagonal must be 30.

52. *Magic Square* Create a magic square by using the numbers 3, 4, 5, 6, 7, 8, 9, 10, and 11. The sum of the numbers in every column, row, and diagonal must be 21.

In Exercises 53–55, use the three magic squares illustrated to obtain the answers.

8	1	6
3	5	7
4	9	2

3	2	7
8	4	0
1	6	5

10	9	14
15	11	7
8	13	12

53. *Magic Square* Examine the 3 by 3 magic squares and find the sum of the four corner entries of each magic square. How can you determine the sum by using a key number in the magic square?

54. *Magic Square* For a 3 by 3 magic square, how can you determine the sum of the numbers in any particular row, column, or diagonal by using a key value in the magic square?

55. *Magic Square* For a 3 by 3 magic square, how can you determine the sum of all the numbers in the square by using a key value in the magic square?

56. *Stack of Cubes* Identical cubes are stacked in the corner of a room as shown. How many of the cubes are not visible?

57. *Dominos* Consider a domino with six dots as shown. Two ways of connecting the three dots on the left with the three dots on the right are illustrated. Using three lines, in how many ways can the three dots on the left be connected with the three dots on the right?

58. *Handshakes All Around* Five salespeople gather for a sales meeting. How many handshakes will each person make if each must shake hands with each of the four others?

59. *Consecutive Digits* Place the digits 1 through 8 in the eight boxes so that each digit is used exactly once and no two consecutive digits touch horizontally, vertically, or diagonally.

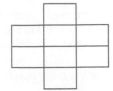

60. *A Digital Clock* Digital clocks display numerals by lighting all or some of the seven parts of the pattern shown. If each digit 0 through 9 is displayed once, which of the seven parts is used least often? Which part is used most often?

61. *A Grid* Place five 1's, five 2's, five 3's, five 4's, and five 5's in a 5 × 5 grid so that each digit—that is, 1, 2, 3, 4, 5—appears exactly once in each row and exactly once in each column.

Challenge Problems/Group Activities

62. *Insurance Policies* Ray Kelley owns two cars (a Ford Mustang and a Ford Focus), a house, and a rental apartment. He has auto insurance for both cars, a homeowner's policy, and a policy for the rental property. The costs of the policies are
Mustang: $1648 per year
Focus: $1530 per year
Homeowner's: $640 per year
Rental property: $750 per year

Ray is considering taking out a $1 million personal umbrella liability policy. The annual cost of the umbrella policy would be $450. If he has the umbrella policy, he can lower the limits on parts of his auto policies and still have equal or better protection. If Ray purchases the umbrella policy, he can reduce his premium on the Mustang by $90 per year and his premium on the Focus by 12%. If he purchases the umbrella policy and reduces the amount he pays for auto insurance, what is the net amount he is actually paying for the umbrella policy?

63. *A Sports Puzzle* Peter, Paul, and Mary are three sports professionals. One is a tennis player, one is a golfer, and one is a skier. They live in three adjacent houses on City View Drive. From the following information, determine which is the professional skier. (*Hint:* A table may be helpful.)
Mary does not play tennis.
Peter skis and plays tennis, but does not golf.
The golfer and the skier live next to each other.
Three years ago, Paul broke his leg skiing and has not tried it since.

Mary lives in the last house.
The golfer and the tennis player share a common backyard swimming pool.

64. *Counting Triangles* How many triangles are in the figure?

65. *Finding the Area* Rectangle ABCD is made up entirely of squares. The black square has a side of 1 unit. Find the area of rectangle ABCD.

66. *Spending Money* Samantha Smith went into a store and spent half her money and then spent $20 more. Samantha then went into a second store and spent half her remaining money and then spent $20 more. After spending money in the second store, Samantha had no money left. How much money did she have when she went into the first store?

67. *Boxes of Fruit* There are three boxes on a table, each with a label. Thomas Abernathy knows that one box contains grapes, one box contains cherries, and the third box contains both grapes and cherries. He also knows that the three labels used—grapes, cherries, and grapes and cherries—were mixed up and that none of the boxes received the correct label. He opens just one box and, without looking into the box, takes out one piece of fruit. He looks at the fruit and immediately labels all the boxes correctly. Which box did Thomas open? How did he know how to correctly label the boxes?

Internet/Research Activities

68. *Puzzles* Many fun and interesting puzzle books and magazines are available. Using this chapter and puzzle books as a guide, construct five of your own puzzles and present them to your instructor.

CHAPTER 1 — *Summary*

Important Facts and Concepts	Examples and Discussion
Section 1.1	
The **natural numbers** or **counting numbers** are 1, 2, 3, 4,. . . .	Examples 1, 2, 4, 5, pages 2–4
A **conjecture** is a prediction based on specific observations.	Example 4, page 3
A **counterexample** is a special case that satisfies all the conditions of a conjecture, but proves the conjecture false.	Discussion page 4
Inductive reasoning is the process of reasoning to a general conclusion through observations of specific cases.	Examples 1 and 2, pages 2–3
Deductive reasoning is the process of reasoning to a specific conclusion from a general statement.	Example 6, pages 4–5
Section 1.2	
Estimation is the process of arriving at an approximate answer to a question.	Examples 1–7, pages 9–13
Section 1.3	
Guidelines for Problem Solving	Discussion page 22
1. Understand the problem.	Examples 1–7, pages 20–28
2. Devise a plan to solve the problem.	
3. Carry out the plan.	
4. Check the results.	

CHAPTER 1 — *Review Exercises*

1.1 †

In Exercises 1–8, use inductive reasoning to predict the next three numbers or figures in the pattern.

1. 7, 12, 17, 22, . . .

2. 2, 5, 10, 17, . . .

3. −3, 6, −12, 24, . . .

4. 5, 7, 10, 14, 19, . . .

5. 25, 24, 22, 19, 15, . . .

6. 6, 3, $\frac{3}{2}$, $\frac{3}{4}$, . . .

7. , . . .

8. , . . .

9. *Pattern* Examine the grid above and to the right for a pattern and then select the answer which completes the pattern. (*Hint:* Think about rotating groups of four squares at a time.)

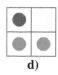

a) b) c) d)

10. Pick any number and multiply the number by 10. Add 5 to the product. Divide the sum by 5. Subtract 1 from the quotient.

a) What is the relationship between the number you started with and the final number?

b) Arbitrarily select some different numbers and repeat the process. Record the original number and the results.

c) Make a conjecture about the original number and the final number.

d) Prove, using deductive reasoning, the conjecture you made in part (c).

---

†The number in color indicates the section in which the material is covered.

11. Pick any number between 1 and 20. Add 5 to the number. Multiply the sum by 6. Subtract 12 from the product. Divide the difference by 2. Divide the quotient by 3. Subtract the number you started with from the quotient. What is your answer? Try this process with a different number. Make a conjecture as to what your final answer will always be.

12. *Counterexample* Find a counterexample to the statement "The sum of two squares is an even number."

1.2

In Exercises 13–25, estimate the answer. Your answers may vary from those given in the back of the book, depending on how you round to arrive at the answer, but your answers should be something near the answers given.

13. $210,302 \times 2002$

14. $215.9 + 128.752 + 3.6 + 861 + 792$

15. 19% of 1025

16. *Distance* Estimate the distance from your wrist to your elbow and estimate the length of your foot. Which do you think is greater? With the help of a friend, measure both lengths to determine which is longer.

17. *Cost* Estimate the cost of 52 shovels if the cost is $99.97 per shovel.

18. *Sales Tax* Estimate the amount of a 7% sales tax on an Oriental rug that costs $1999.

19. *Walking Speed* Estimate your average walking speed in miles per hour if you walked 1.1 mi in 22 min.

20. *Groceries* Estimate the total cost of six grocery items that cost $2.49, $0.79, $1.89, $0.10, $2.19, and $6.75.

21. *A Walking Path* The scale of the map is $\frac{1}{4}$ in. = 0.1 mi. Estimate the distance of the walking path indicated in red.

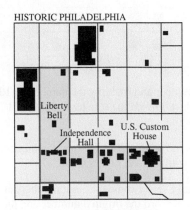

In Exercises 22 and 23, refer to the following graph, which illustrates the number of registered nurses (RNs) needed (demand) and the number of RNs available (supply) from 2000 to 2010. The graph also illustrates the projected number of RNs needed and the projected number of RNs available from 2011 to 2020.

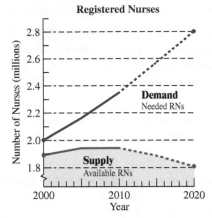

Source: U.S. Bureau of Health Professions

22. Estimate the difference in the number of RNs needed and the number of RNs available in 2010.

23. Estimate the difference in the projected number of RNs needed and the projected number of RNs available in 2020.

24. *Estimating an Area* If each square represents one square unit, estimate the size of the shaded area.

25. *Railroad Car Estimation* The scale of a model railroad is 1 in. = 12.5 ft. Estimate the size of an actual box car if this drawing is the same size as the model box car.

1.3

Solve the following problems.

26. *Buying a Copy Machine* David Stewart can buy a copier from Staples for $500 that prints, copies, and scans. He can either pay the total amount at the time of purchase, or he can agree to pay the store $50 down and $40 a month for 12 months. How much money can he save by paying the total amount at the time of purchase?

27. *Buying in Quantity* A six-pack of cola costs $2.69. A carton of 4 six-packs costs $9.60. How much will be saved by purchasing the carton rather than 4 individual six-packs?

28. *Renting a Post Hole Digger* The cost to rent a gas-powered post hole digger from Taylor Rental is $45 for 8 hours, and the cost from Admar Rental is $8 per hour. If Justin Calhoun plans to rent a post hole digger for 6 hours, which is the better deal, and by how much?

29. *Fishing Charter* Sam Stevens and four other friends want to schedule a 6-hour fishing trip on Lake Ontario with Reel Easy Sport Fishing. The cost for five people is $445. The cost for six people is $510. How much money per person will Sam and each of his friends save if they can find one more friend to go on their fishing trip? Assume that they will split the total cost equally.

30. *Applying Fertilizer* Ron Williams needs to apply fertilizer to his lawn on his farm. A 30-pound bag of fertilizer will cover an area of 2500 square feet.

   a) How many pounds are needed to cover an area of 24,000 square feet?

   b) If Ron has only 150 pounds of fertilizer, how many square feet can he fertilize?

31. *Auto Insurance* Most insurance companies reduce premiums by 10% until age 25 for people who successfully pass a driver's education course. A particular driver's education course costs $60. Patrick Flanigan, who just turned 18, has auto insurance that costs $1030 per year. By taking

the driver's education course, how much would he save in auto insurance, including the cost of the course, from the age of 18 until the age of 25?

32. *Pediatric Dosage* If 1.5 milligrams of a medicine is to be given for 10 lb of body weight, how many milligrams should be given to a child who weighs 47 lb?

33. *Qualifying for a Mortgage* Banks will usually grant an applicant a mortgage if the monthly payments are not greater than 28% of the person's take-home pay. What is the maximum monthly mortgage payment you can make if your gross salary is $5000 a month and your payroll deductions are 30% of your gross salary?

34. *Flying West* New York City is on eastern standard time, St. Louis is on central standard time (1 hr earlier than eastern standard time), and Las Vegas is on Pacific standard time (3 hr earlier than eastern standard time). A flight leaves New York City at 9 A.M. eastern standard time, stops for 50 min in St. Louis, and arrives in Las Vegas at 1:35 P.M. Pacific time. How long is the plane actually flying?

35. *Crossing Time Zones* The international date line is an imaginary line of longitude (from the North Pole to the South Pole) on Earth's surface between Japan and Hawaii in the Pacific Ocean. Crossing the line east to west adds a day to the present date. Crossing the line west to east subtracts a day. At 3:00 P.M. on July 25 in Hawaii, what is the time and date in Tokyo, Japan, which is four time zones to the west?

36. **a)** If one mile = 5280 feet, what is 1 mile per hour equal to in feet per second?

   b) What is 55 miles per hour equal to in feet per second?

37. *Dot Pattern* If the following pattern is continued, how many dots will be in the hundredth figure?

38. *Magic Square* The following magic square uses each number from 6 to 21 exactly once. Complete the magic square by using the unused numbers from 6 through 21 exactly once.

21	7		18
10		15	
14	12	11	17
9	19		

39. *Magic Square* Create a magic square by using the numbers 13, 15, 17, 19, 21, 23, 25, 27, and 29. The sum of the numbers in every row, column, and diagonal must be 63.

40. *Microbes in a Jar* A colony of microbes doubles in number every second. A single microbe is placed in a jar, and in an hour the jar is full. When was the jar half full?

41. *Brothers and Sisters* Jim Carraway has four more brothers than sisters. How many more brothers than sisters does his sister Mary have?

42. *A Missing Dollar* Three friends check into a single room in a motel and pay $10 apiece. The room costs $25 instead of $30, so a clerk is sent to the room to give $5 back. The friends each take back $1, and the clerk is given $2 for his trouble. Now each of the friends paid $9, a total of $27, and the clerk received $2. What happened to the missing dollar?

43. *The Average Weight* Four women in a room have an average weight of 130 lb. A fifth woman who weighs 180 lb enters the room. Find the average weight of all five women.

44. *Change for a Dollar* Could a person have $1.15 worth of change in his pocket and still not be able to give someone change for a dollar bill? If so, what coins might he have?

45. *Volume of a Cube* Here is a flat pattern for a cube to be formed by folding. The sides of each square are 6 cm. Find the volume of the cube.

46. *The Heavier Coin* You have 13 coins, which all look alike. Twelve coins weigh exactly the same, but the other one is heavier. You have a pan balance. Tell how to find the heavier coin in just three weighings.

47. *The Sum of Numbers* Find the sum of the first 500 counting numbers. (*Hint:* Group in pairs.)

48. *Balancing a Scale* On a balance scale, three green balls balance six blue balls, two yellow balls balance five blue balls, and six blue balls balance four white balls. How many blue balls are needed to balance four green, two yellow, and two white balls?

49. *Palindromes* How many three-digit numbers greater than 100 are palindromes?

50. *Figures* Describe the fifth figure.

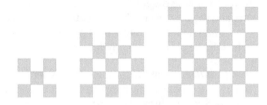

51. *Patterns* How many orange tiles will be required to build the sixth figure in this pattern?

52. *Sum of Numbers* Place the numbers 1 through 12 in the 12 circles so that the sum of the numbers in each of the six rows is 26. Use each number from 1 through 12 exactly once.

53. *People in a Line* People stand in a line at movies, the grocery store, and many other places.

a) In how many ways can two people stand in a line?

b) In how many ways can three people stand in a line?

c) In how many ways can four people stand in a line?

d) In how many ways can five people stand in a line?

e) Using the results from parts (a) through (d), make a conjecture about the number of ways in which n people can stand in a line.

CHAPTER 1 Test

In Exercises 1 and 2, use inductive reasoning to determine the next three numbers in the pattern.

1. 3, 9, 15, 21, …

2. $1, \frac{1}{2}, \frac{1}{4}, \frac{1}{8}$, …

3. Pick any number, multiply the number by 5, and add 10 to the number. Divide the sum by 5. Subtract 1 from the quotient.

a) What is the relationship between the number you started with and the final answer?

b) Arbitrarily select some different numbers and repeat the process. Record the original number and the results.

c) Make a conjecture about the relationship between the original number and the final answer.

d) Prove, using deductive reasoning, the conjecture made in part (c).

In Exercises 4 and 5, estimate the answers.

4. $0.21 \times 82{,}000$

5. $\dfrac{175{,}000}{0.09}$

6. *Estimating Area* If each square represents one square unit, estimate the area of the shaded figure.

7. *Body Mass Index* The federal government gives a procedure to determine if a child is overweight. To make this decision, first determine the child's body mass index (BMI). Then compare the BMI with one of the two charts, one for boys and one for girls, provided by the government. Below, we give the chart for boys up to age 20. To determine a child's BMI:

1) Divide the child's weight (in pounds) by the child's height (in inches).

2) Divide the results from part 1 by the child's height again.

3) Multiply the result from part 2 by 703.

Richard is a 14-year-old boy who weighs 130 lb and is 63 in. tall.

a) Determine his BMI.

b) Does he appear to be at risk for being overweight, or is he overweight? Explain.

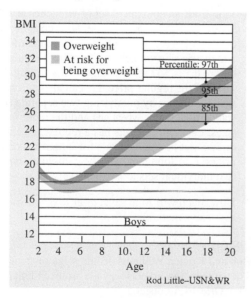

8. *Holding Multiple Jobs* The following graph shows the number of American men and women who held multiple jobs, as of July 2009.

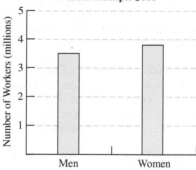

Source: U.S. Bureau of Labor Statistics

a) Estimate the number of American men who held multiple jobs.

b) Estimate the difference between the number of American women and American men who held multiple jobs.

9. *Cell Phone Cost* Verizon Wireless charges $59.99 for its Basic Plan for cell phones, which includes 900 minutes of call time. The company charges $0.40 for each additional minute. If the Smiths' cell phone bill for December was $85.99, how many additional minutes did they use during that month?

10. *Cans of Soda* At a local store a six-pack of soda costs $2.59 and individual cans cost $0.80. What is the maximum number of cans of soda that can be purchased for $15?

11. *Cutting Wood* How much time does it take Carla Knab, a carpenter, to cut a 10-ft length of wood into four equal pieces, if each cut takes $2\frac{1}{2}$ min?

12. *Determining Size* In this photo of *Sunflowers*, an 1889 painting by Vincent van Gogh, 1 in. equals 15.8 in. on the actual painting. Find the dimensions of the actual painting.

▲ Sunflowers *by Vincent van Gogh*

13. *Payment Shortfall* Monica Wilson gets $12.75 per hour with time and a half for any time over 40 hours per week. If she works a 50-hr week and gets paid $652.25, by how much was she underpaid?

14. *Magic Square* Create a magic square by using the numbers 5, 10, 15, 20, 25, 30, 35, 40, and 45. The sum of the numbers in every row, column, and diagonal must be 75.

15. *A Drive to the Beach* Mary Chin drove from her home to the beach that is 30 mi from her house. The first 15 mi she drove at 60 mph, and the next 15 mi she drove at 30 mph. Would the trip take more, less, or the same time if she traveled the entire 30 mi at a steady 45 mph?

16. *Chili Recipe* Three teaspoons equal one tablespoon. A recipe for chili calls for $\frac{1}{2}$ teaspoon of salt for 2 pounds of ground beef. How many tablespoons of salt are needed for 6 pounds of ground beef?

17. *Area of a Concrete Walkway* A 10 meter by 12 meter rectangular lawn has a concrete walkway 1 meter wide around the outside of the lawn. What is the area of the walkway?

18. *Jelly Bean Guess* One guess is off by 9, another guess is off by 17, and yet another guess is off by 31. How many jelly beans are in the jar above and to the right?

19. *Buying Plants* David Mackin wants to purchase nine herb plants. Countryside Nursery has herbs that are on sale at three for $3.99. David has a coupon for 25% off an unlimited number of herb plants at the original price of $1.75 per plant.

   a) Determine the cost of purchasing nine plants at the sale price.

   b) Determine the cost of purchasing nine plants if the coupon is used.

   c) Which is the least expensive way to purchase the nine plants, and by how much?

20. *Arranging Letters* In how many different ways can four letters, A, B, C, D, be arranged?

GROUP PROJECTS

Holiday Shopping

1. It is December 1 and John needs to begin his holiday shopping. He intends to purchase gifts for three people: his girlfriend, Melissa; his mother, Ruth; and his father, Don. He doesn't want to spend more than a total of $325, including the 7% sales tax.

   a) If John were to spend the $325 equally among the three people, approximate the amount that would be spent on each person.

   b) If John were to spend the $325 equally among the three people, determine the maximum amount, *before tax*, that he could spend on each person and not exceed the maximum of $325, including tax.

   c) John decides to get a new set of wrenches for his father. He sees the specific set he wants on sale at Sears. He calls four Sears stores to see if they have the set of wrenches in stock. They all reply that the set is out of stock. He decides that calling additional Sears stores is useless because he believes that they will also tell him that the set of wrenches is out of

stock. What type of reasoning did John use in arriving at his conclusion? Explain.

   d) John finds an equivalent set of wrenches at a True Value hardware store. The set he is considering is a combination set that contains both standard U.S. size and metric size wrenches. The store's regular price before tax is $62 for the set, but it is selling them for 10% off the regular price. He can also purchase the same wrenches by purchasing two separate sets, one for standard U.S. size wrenches and the other for metric sizes. Each of these sets has a regular price, before tax, of $36, but both are on sale for 20% off their regular prices. Can John purchase the combination set or the two individual sets less expensively?

   e) How much will John save, *after tax*, by using the less expensive method?

Going on Vacation

2. Bob and Kristen Williams decide to go on a vacation. They live in San Francisco, California, and plan to drive to New Orleans, Louisiana.

a) Obtain a map that shows routes that they may take from San Francisco to New Orleans. Write directions for them from San Francisco to New Orleans via the shortest distance. Use major highways whenever possible.

b) Use the scale on the map to estimate the one-way distance to New Orleans.

c) If the Williams estimate that they will average 50 mph (including comfort stops), estimate the travel time, in hours, to New Orleans.

d) If the Williams want to travel about 400 miles per day, locate a town in the vicinity of where they will stop each evening.

e) If they begin each segment of the trip each day at 9 A.M., at about what time will they look for a hotel each evening?

f) Use the information provided in parts (a) through (e) to estimate the time of day they will arrive in New Orleans.

g) Estimate the mileage of a typical midsized car and the cost per gallon of a gallon of regular unleaded gasoline. Then estimate the cost of gasoline for the Williams' trip.

h) Estimate the cost of a typical breakfast, a typical lunch, and a typical dinner for two adults, and the cost of a typical motel room. Then estimate the total cost, including meals, gas, and lodging, for the Williams' trip from San Francisco to New Orleans (one way).

Problem Solving

3. Four acrobats who bill themselves as the "Tumbling Tumbleweeds" finish up their act with the amazing "Human Pillar," in which the acrobats form a tower, each one standing on the shoulders of the one below. Each acrobat (Ernie, Jed, Tex, and Zeke Tumbleweed) wears a different distinctive item of western garb (chaps, holster, Stetson hat, or leather vest) in the act. Can you identify the members of the "Human Pillar," from top to bottom, by name and apparel?

a) Jed Tumbleweed is not on top, but he is somewhere above the man in the Stetson.

b) Zeke Tumbleweed does not wear the holster.

c) The man in the vest is not on top.

d) The man in the chaps is somewhere above Tex but somewhere below Zeke.

ORDER	NAME	APPAREL
_____	_____	_____
_____	_____	_____
_____	_____	_____
_____	_____	_____

2
Sets

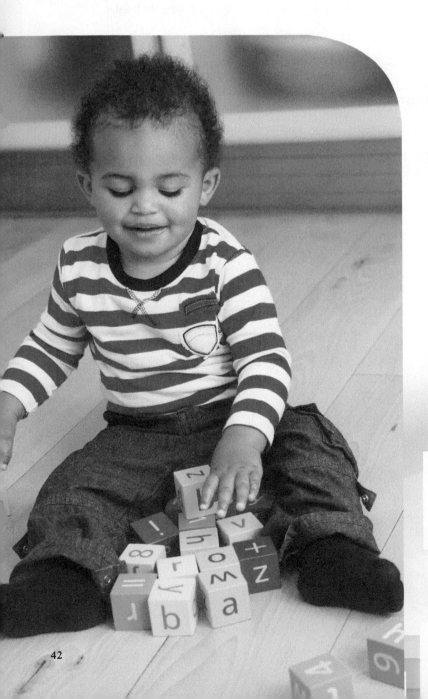

What You Will Learn

- Methods to indicate sets, equal sets, and equivalent sets
- Subsets and proper subsets
- Venn diagrams
- Set operations such as complement, intersection, union, difference, and Cartesian product
- Equality of sets
- Applications of sets
- Infinite sets

Why This is Important

A basic human impulse is to sort or classify things. As you will see in this chapter, putting elements into sets helps you order and arrange your world. It allows you to deal with large quantities of information. Set building is a learning tool that helps answer the question, What are the characteristics of this group? For example, when students read a college catalog to determine which courses fulfill their degree requirements, they are looking for courses that are in a particular set. Studying sets is also important because sets underlie other mathematical topics such as logic and abstract algebra.

◄ Children learn how to classify sets, such as shapes and colors, at a very early age.

▲ *Many different restaurant categories include McDonald's*

Can you think of a few different categories or groups to which the restaurant McDonald's belongs? One way you could categorize McDonald's is as a fast food restaurant. Another way is as a restaurant selling hamburgers. A third way is as a restaurant selling breakfast. In this section, we will discuss ways to sort or classify objects. We will also discuss different methods that can be used to indicate collections of objects.

Why *This is Important* Set classifications are important in a range of applications from placing students in courses to classifying stars in the universe.

Profile in Mathematics

Georg Cantor

Georg Cantor (1845–1918), born in St. Petersburg, Russia, is recognized as the founder of set theory. Cantor's creative work in mathematics was nearly lost when his father insisted that he become an engineer rather than a mathematician. His two major books on set theory, *Foundations of General Theory of Aggregates* and *Contributions to the Founding of the Theory of Transfinite Numbers,* were published in 1883 and 1895, respectively. See the Profile in Mathematics on page 85 for more information on Cantor and Leopold Kronecker.

We encounter sets in many different ways every day of our lives. A *set* is a collection of objects, which are called *elements* or *members* of the set. For example, the United States is a collection, or set, of 50 states plus the District of Columbia. The 50 individual states plus the District of Columbia are the members or elements of the set that is called the United States.

A set is *well defined* if its contents can be clearly determined. The set of U.S. presidents is a well-defined set because its contents, the presidents, can be named. The set of the three best movies is not a well-defined set because the word *best* is interpreted differently by different people. In this text, we use only well-defined sets.

Three methods are commonly used to indicate a set: (1) description, (2) roster form, and (3) set-builder notation.

The method of indicating a set by *description* is illustrated in Example 1.

Example 1 *Description of Sets*

Write a description of the set containing the elements Monday, Tuesday, Wednesday, Thursday, Friday, Saturday, Sunday.

Solution The set is the days of the week. ∎

Listing the elements of a set inside a pair of *braces*, { }, is called *roster form.* The braces are an essential part of the notation because they identify the contents as a set. For example, $\{1, 2, 3\}$ is notation for the set whose elements are 1, 2, and 3, but $(1, 2, 3)$ and $[1, 2, 3]$ are not sets because parentheses and brackets do not indicate a set. For a set written in roster form, commas separate the elements of the set. The order in which the elements are listed is not important.

Sets are generally named with capital letters. For example, the name commonly selected for the set of *natural numbers* or *counting numbers* is N.

Definition: **Natural Numbers**
$$N = \{1, 2, 3, 4, 5, \ldots\}$$

The three dots after the 5, called an *ellipsis,* indicate that the elements in the set continue in the same manner. An ellipsis followed by a last element indicates that the elements continue in the same manner up to and including the last element. This notation is illustrated in Example 2(b).

▲ *The planets of Earth's solar system.*

┌─ Example **2**   *Roster Form of Sets*

Express the following in roster form.

a) Set A is the set of natural numbers less than 6.

b) Set B is the set of natural numbers less than or equal to 80.

c) Set P is the set of planets in Earth's solar system.

Solution

a) The natural numbers less than 6 are 1, 2, 3, 4, and 5. Thus, set A in roster form is
$A = \{1, 2, 3, 4, 5\}$.

b) $B = \{1, 2, 3, 4, \ldots, 80\}$. The 80 after the ellipsis indicates that the elements continue in the same manner up to and including the number 80.

c) $P = \{$Mercury, Venus, Earth, Mars, Jupiter, Saturn, Uranus, Neptune$\}$* ∎

┌─ Example **3**   *The Word* **Inclusive**

Express the following in roster form.

a) The set of natural numbers between 7 and 12.

b) The set of natural numbers between 7 and 12, inclusive.

Solution

a) $A = \{8, 9, 10, 11\}$

b) $B = \{7, 8, 9, 10, 11, 12\}$. Note that the word *inclusive* indicates that the values of 7 and 12 are included in the set. ∎

The symbol $\in$, read, "is an element of," is used to indicate membership in a set. In Example 3, because 8 is an element of set A, we write $8 \in A$. This may also be written $8 \in \{8, 9, 10, 11\}$. We may also write $6 \notin A$, meaning that 6 is not an element of set A.

Set-builder notation (sometimes called *set-generator notation*) may be used to symbolize a set. Set-builder notation is frequently used in algebra. The following example illustrates its form.

Consider $E = \{x \mid x \in N \text{ and } x > 10\}$. The statement is read: "Set E is the set of all the elements x such that x is a natural number and x is greater than 10." The conditions that x must meet to be a member of the set are $x \in N$, which means that x must be a natural number, and $x > 10$, which means that x must be greater than 10. The numbers that meet both conditions are the set of natural numbers greater than 10. Set E in roster form is

$$E = \{11, 12, 13, 14, \ldots\}$$

┌─ Example **4**   *Using Set-Builder Notation*

a) Write set $B = \{1, 2, 3, 4, 5\}$ in set-builder notation.

b) Write, in words, how you would read set B in set-builder notation.

────────────

*In August 2006, Pluto was reclassified as a dwarf planet.

Solution

a) Because set B consists of the natural numbers less than 6, we write

$$B = \{x \mid x \in N \text{ and } x < 6\}$$

Another acceptable answer is $B = \{x \mid x \in N \text{ and } x \leq 5\}$.

b) Set B is the set of all elements x such that x is a natural number and x is less than 6.

Example 5 *Roster Form to Set-Builder Notation*

a) Write set $C = \{$North America, South America, Europe, Asia, Australia, Africa, Antarctica$\}$ in set-builder notation.
b) Write in words how you would read set C in set-builder notation.

Solution

a) $C = \{x \mid x \text{ is a continent}\}$.
b) Set C is the set of all elements x such that x is a continent.

Example 6 *Set-Builder Notation to Roster Form*

Write set $A = \{x \mid x \in N \text{ and } 2 \leq x < 8\}$ in roster form.

Solution $A = \{2, 3, 4, 5, 6, 7\}$

Example 7 *Oldest Colleges in the United States*

The table shows the 10 oldest colleges in the United States. Let set C be the set of colleges that are located in Virginia that are among the 10 oldest colleges in the United States. Write set C in roster form.

▲ *Harvard University*

Ten Oldest Colleges in the United States	State	Year Chartered
Harvard University	Massachusetts	1636
College of William and Mary	Virginia	1692
Yale University	Connecticut	1701
University of Pennsylvania	Pennsylvania	1740
Moravian College	Pennsylvania	1742
Princeton University	New Jersey	1746
Washington and Lee University	Virginia	1749
Columbia University	New York	1754
Brown University	Rhode Island	1764
Rutgers	New Jersey	1766

Source: National Center for Education Statistics

Solution By examining the table, we find that two colleges located in Virginia appear in the table. They are College of William and Mary and Washington and Lee University. Thus, set $C = \{$College of William and Mary, Washington and Lee University$\}$. ∎

A set is said to be *finite* if it either contains no elements or the number of elements in the set is a natural number. The set $B = \{2, 4, 6, 8, 10\}$ is a finite set because the number of elements in the set is 5, and 5 is a natural number. A set that is not finite is said to be *infinite*. The set of counting numbers is one example of an infinite set. Infinite sets are discussed in more detail in Section 2.6.

Another important concept is equality of sets.

Definition: Equal Sets

Set A is **equal** to set B, symbolized by $A = B$, if and only if set A and set B contain exactly the same elements.

For example, if set $A = \{1, 2, 3\}$ and set $B = \{3, 1, 2\}$, then $A = B$ because they contain exactly the same elements. The order of the elements in the set is not important. If two sets are equal, both must contain the same number of elements. The number of elements in a set is called its *cardinal number*.

Definition: Cardinal Number

The **cardinal number** of set A, symbolized by $n(A)$, is the number of elements in set A.

Both set $A = \{1, 2, 3\}$ and set $B = \{$England, Brazil, Japan$\}$ have a cardinal number of 3; that is, $n(A) = 3$, and $n(B) = 3$. We can say that set A and set B both have a cardinality of 3.

Two sets are said to be *equivalent* if they contain the same number of elements.

Definition: Equivalent Sets

Set A is **equivalent** to set B if and only if $n(A) = n(B)$.

Any sets that are equal must also be equivalent. Not all sets that are equivalent are equal, however. The sets $D = \{$a, b, c$\}$ and $E = \{$apple, orange, pear$\}$ are equivalent because both have the same cardinal number, 3. Because the elements differ, however, the sets are not equal.

Two sets that are equivalent or have the same cardinality can be placed in *one-to-one correspondence*. Set A and set B can be placed in one-to-one correspondence if every element of set A can be matched with exactly one element of set B and every element of set B can be matched with exactly one element of set A. For example, there is a one-to-one correspondence between the student names on a class list and the student identification numbers because we can match each student with a student identification number.

Consider set S, states, and set C, state capitals.

$$S = \{\text{North Carolina, Georgia, South Carolina, Florida}\}$$

$$C = \{\text{Columbia, Raleigh, Tallahassee, Atlanta}\}$$

Two different one-to-one correspondences for sets S and C follow.

$$S = \{\text{North Carolina, Georgia, South Carolina, Florida}\}$$

$$C = \{\text{Columbia, Raleigh, Tallahassee, Atlanta}\}$$

$$S = \{\text{North Carolina, Georgia, South Carolina, Florida}\}$$

$$C = \{\text{Columbia, Raleigh, Tallahassee, Atlanta}\}$$

Other one-to-one correspondences between sets S and C are possible. Do you know which capital goes with which state?

Null or Empty Set

Some sets do not contain any elements, such as the set of zebras that live in your house.

Definition: Empty Set

The set that contains no elements is called the **empty set** or **null set** and is symbolized by $\{\ \}$ or $\varnothing$.

Note that $\{\varnothing\}$ is not the empty set. This set contains the element $\varnothing$ and has a cardinality of 1. The set $\{0\}$ is also not the empty set because it contains the element 0. It also has a cardinality of 1.

┌ Example **8** *Natural Number Solutions*

Indicate the set of natural numbers that satisfies the equation $x + 2 = 0$.

Solution The values that satisfy the equation are those natural numbers that make the equation a true statement. Only the number -2 satisfies this equation. Because -2 is not a natural number, the solution set of this equation is $\{\ \}$ or $\varnothing$.   ∎

Universal Set

Another important set is a *universal set*.

Definition: Universal Set

A **universal set**, symbolized by U, is a set that contains all the elements for any specific discussion.

When a universal set is given, only the elements in the universal set may be considered when working the problem. If, for example, the universal set for a particular problem is defined as $U = \{1, 2, 3, 4, \ldots, 10\}$, then only the natural numbers 1 through 10 may be used in that problem.

SECTION 2.1   *Exercises*

Warm Up Exercises

In Exercises 1–12, fill in the blank with an appropriate word, phrase, or symbol(s).

1. A collection of objects is called a(n) _____.

2. Three dots placed in a set to show that the set continues in the same manner is called a(n) _____.

3. The three ways a set can be written are _____, _____, and _____.

4. A set that contain no elements or the number of elements in the set is a natural number is called a(n) _____ set.

5. A a set that is not finite is called a(n) _____. set.

6. Two sets that contain the same elements are called _____ sets.

7. Two sets that contain the same number of elements are called _____ sets.

8. The number of elements in a set is called the _____ number.

9. The set that contains no elements is called the _____ set.

10. The two ways to indicate an empty set are _____ and _____.

11. A set that contains all the elements for any specific discussion is called a(n) _____ set.

12. Two sets that have the same cardinal number can be placed in a(n) _____ correspondence.

Practice the Skills

In Exercises 13–18, determine whether each set is well defined or not well defined.

13. The set of the best colleges

14. The set of the most interesting courses at your school

15. The set of states that have a common border with Kansas

16. The set of the four states in the United States having the largest population on January 1, 2010

17. The set of astronauts who walked on the moon

▲ *Eugene A. Cernan on the moon*

18. The set of the most interesting teachers at your school

In Exercises 19–24, determine whether each set is finite or infinite.

19. $\{1, 3, 5, 7, \ldots\}$

20. The set of multiples of 4 between 0 and 50

21. The set of odd numbers greater than 25

22. The set of fractions between 1 and 2

23. The set of odd numbers greater than 15

24. The set of apple trees in Gro-More Farms Orchards

In Exercises 25–34, express each set in roster form. You may need to use the Internet or some other reference source.

25. The set of states in the United States whose names begin with the letter M

26. The set of countries in Europe whose names begin with S

27. The set of natural numbers between 10 and 178

28. $C = \{x \mid x + 6 = 10\}$

29. $B = \{x \mid x \in N \text{ and } x \text{ is even}\}$

30. The set of states west of the Mississippi River that have a common border with the state of Florida

31. The set of football players over the age of 70 who are still playing in the National Football League

32. The set of states in the United States that have a common border with the state of Washington

33. $E = \{x \mid x \in N \text{ and } 14 \leq x < 85\}$

34. The set of states in the United States that are not in the contiguous 48 states

In Exercises 35–38, use the following table, which shows the attendance, in millions, at the 10 most visited museums in the world in 2008. Let the 10 museums in the list represent the universal set.

Museum	Attendance (in millions)	Location
1. Louvre Museum	8.50	Paris, France
2. British Museum	5.93	London, UK
3. National Gallery of Art	4.96	Washington, DC
4. Tate Modern	4.95	London, UK
5. Metropolitan Museum of Art	4.82	New York, NY
6. Vatican Museums	4.44	Vatican City
7. National Gallery	4.38	London, UK
8. Musee d'Orsay	3.03	Paris, France
9. Musee d'Art Moderne Prado	2.98	Paris, France
10. Museum of Modern Art	2.90	New York, NY

Source: The *Art Newspaper*

Use the list to determine each set in roster form.

35. The set of museums in which the attendance was more than 4.5 million

36. The set of museums in which the attendance was less than 3 million

37. The set of museums in which the attendance was between 2 million and 4 million

38. The set of museums in which the attendance was between 3.5 million and 5.5 million

In Exercises 39–42, use the graph on page 49, which shows iPod sales, in millions, for the years 2003–2008.

Use the graph to determine each set in roster form.

39. The set of years in which iPod sales were more than 52 million

40. The set of years in which iPod sales were less than 8 million

41. The set of years in which iPod sales were between 8 million and 60 million

42. The set of years in which iPod sales were more than 65 million

iPod Sales

In Exercises 43–50, express each set in set-builder notation.

43. $B = \{7, 8, 9, 10, 11, 12, 13, 14\}$

44. $A = \{1, 2, 3, 4, 5, 6, 7, 8, 9\}$

45. $C = \{3, 6, 9, 12, \ldots\}$

46. $D = \{5, 10, 15, 20, \ldots\}$

47. E is the set of odd natural numbers.

48. A is the set of national holidays in the United States in July.

49. C is the set of months that contain less than 30 days.

50. $F = \{15, 16, 17, \ldots, 100\}$

In Exercises 51–58, write a description of each set.

51. $A = \{1, 2, 3, 4, 5, 6, 7\}$

52. $D = \{3, 6, 9, 12, 15, 18, \ldots\}$

53. $V = \{a, e, i, o, u\}$

54. $S = \{$Bashful, Doc, Dopey, Grumpy, Happy, Sleepy, Sneezy$\}$

▲ Snow White and the Seven Dwarfs

55. $T = \{$oak, maple, elm, pine, $\ldots\}$

56. $E = \{x \mid x \in N \text{ and } 4 \le x < 11\}$

57. $S = \{$spring, summer, fall, winter$\}$

58. $B = \{$John Lennon, Ringo Starr, Paul McCartney, George Harrison$\}$

▲ The Beatles

In Exercises 59–62, use the following list, which shows the 10 countries with the most cellular subscribers, in millions, as of 2008. Let the 10 countries in the list represent the universal set.

Country	Number of Subscribers
1. China	649.70
2. India	376.12
3. United States	260.00
4. Russia	172.00
5. Brazil	151.90
6. Indonesia	115.60
7. Japan	102.98
8. Germany	101.50
9. Pakistan	91.40
10. United Kingdom	70.00

Source: CIA

Use the list to determine each set in roster form.

59. $\{x \mid x$ is a country with at least 250 million cellular subscribers$\}$

60. $\{x \mid x$ is a country with fewer than 100 million cellular subscribers$\}$

61. $\{x \mid x$ is a country with between 100 million and 200 million cellular subscribers$\}$

62. $\{x \mid x$ is a country with between 250 million and 500 million cellular subscribers$\}$

In Exercises 63–66, use the following graph, which shows the cost of a 30-second commercial during the Super Bowl from 1996 to 2011. Let the 16 years represent the universal set.

Use the graph to represent each set in roster form.

63. The set of years in which the cost of a Super Bowl commercial was more than $2.5 million

64. The set of years in which the cost of a Super Bowl commercial was less than $2.0 million

65. The set of years in which the cost of a Super Bowl commercial was between $2.0 million and $2.5 million

66. The set of years in which the cost of a Super Bowl commercial was more than $2.5 million and less then $3 million

Cost of a 30-Second Commercial During the Super Bowl

Source: www.industry.bnet.com

In Exercises 67–74, state whether each statement is true or false. If false, give the reason.

67. $\{e\} \in \{a, e, i, o, u\}$

68. $b \in \{a, b, c, d, e, f\}$

69. $h \in \{a, b, c, d, e, f\}$

70. Mickey Mouse $\in$ {characters created by Walt Disney}

71. $3 \notin \{x \mid x \in N \text{ and } x \text{ is odd}\}$

72. Amazon $\in$ {rivers in the United States}

73. *Titanic* $\in$ {top 10 motion pictures with the greatest revenues}

74. $2 \in \{x \mid x \text{ is an odd natural number}\}$

In Exercises 75–78, for the sets $A = \{2, 4, 6, 8\}$, $B = \{1, 3, 7, 9, 13, 21\}$, $C = \{\ \}$, *and* $D = \{\#, \&, \%, \square, *\}$.

75. Determine $n(A)$.

76. Determine $n(B)$.

77. Determine $n(C)$.

78. Determine $n(D)$.

In Exercises 79–84, determine whether the pairs of sets are equal, equivalent, both, or neither.

79. $A = \{$algebra, geometry, trigonometry$\}$,
$B = \{$geometry, trigonometry, algebra$\}$

80. $A = \{7, 9, 10\}, B = \{a, b, c\}$

81. $A = \{$grapes, apples, oranges$\}$,
$B = \{$grapes, peaches, apples, oranges$\}$

82. A is the set of Siamese cats.
B is the set of cats.

83. A is the set of letters in the word *bank*.
B is the set of letters in the word *post*.

84. A is the set of states.
B is the set of state capitals.

Problem Solving

85. Set-builder notation is often more versatile and efficient than listing a set in roster form. This versatility is illustrated with the following two sets.

$$A = \{x \mid x \in N \text{ and } x > 2\}$$
$$B = \{x \mid x > 2\}$$

a) Write a description of set A and set B.

b) Explain the difference between set A and set B. (*Hint:* Is $4\frac{1}{2} \in A$? Is $4\frac{1}{2} \in B$?)

c) Write set A in roster form.

d) Can set B be written in roster form? Explain your answer.

86. Consider sets A and B below
$$A = \{x \mid 2 < x \leq 5 \text{ and } x \in N\}$$
and
$$B = \{x \mid 2 < x \leq 5\}$$

a) Write a description of set A and set B.

b) Explain the difference between set A and set B.

c) Write set A in roster form.

d) Can set B be written in roster form? Explain your answer.

*A cardinal number answers the question "How many?" An **ordinal number** describes the relative position that an element occupies. For example, Molly's desk is the third desk from the aisle.*

In Exercises 87–90, determine whether the number used is a cardinal number or an ordinal number.

87. J. K. Rowling has written 7 Harry Potter books.

▲ *J. K. Rowling*

88. Study the chart on page 25 in the book.

89. Lincoln was the sixteenth president of the United States.

90. Emily paid $35 for her new blouse.

91. Describe three sets of which you are a member.

92. Describe three sets that have no members.

93. Write a short paragraph explaining why the universal set and the empty set are necessary in the study of sets.

Challenge Problem/Group Activity

94. a) In a given exercise, a universal set is not specified, but we know that actor Orlando Bloom is a member of the universal set. Describe five different possible universal sets of which Orlando Bloom is a member.

   b) Write a description of one set that includes all the universal sets in part (a).

Internet/Research Activity

95. Georg Cantor is recognized as the founder and a leader in the development of set theory. Do research and write a paper on his life and his contributions to set theory and to the field of mathematics. References include history of mathematics books, encyclopedias, and the Internet.

SECTION 2.2 Subsets

▲ *The set of intercollegiate sports includes basketball.*

Consider the following sets. Set $A = \{$baseball, basketball, hockey$\}$. Set $B = \{$baseball, football, basketball, hockey, softball$\}$. Note that each element of set A is also an element of set B. In this section, we will discuss how to illustrate the relationship between two sets, A and B, when each element of set A is also an element of set B.

Why *This is Important* The relationship between sets is important throughout life. For example, to gain a promotion at work, you may need to fulfill different sets of criteria.

In our complex world, we often break larger sets into smaller, more manageable sets, called *subsets*. For example, consider the set of people in your class. Suppose we categorize the set of people in your class according to the first letter of their last name (the A's, B's, C's, etc.). When we do so, each of these sets may be considered a subset of the original set. Each of these subsets can be separated further. For example, the set of people whose last name begins with the letter A can be categorized as either male or female or by their age. Each of these collections of people is also a subset. A given set may have many different subsets.

Definition: Subset
Set A is a **subset** of set B, symbolized by $A \subseteq B$, if and only if all the elements of set A are also elements of set B.

The symbol $A \subseteq B$ indicates that "set A is a subset of set B." The symbol $\not\subseteq$ is used to indicate "is not a subset." Thus, $A \not\subseteq B$ indicates that set A is not a subset of set B. To show that set A is not a subset of set B, we must find at least one element of set A that is not an element of set B.

Example 1 A Subset?

Determine whether set A is a subset of set B.

a) $A = \{$rain, snow, sleet$\}$
   $B = \{$rain, snow, sleet, hail$\}$

b) $A = \{q, r, s, t\}$
   $B = \{q, r\}$

c) $A = \{x \mid x$ is a yellow fruit$\}$
   $B = \{x \mid x$ is a red fruit$\}$

d) $A = \{$vanilla, chocolate, rocky road$\}$
   $B = \{$chocolate, vanilla, rocky road$\}$

Solution

a) All the elements of set A are contained in set B, so $A \subseteq B$.

b) The elements s and t are in set A but not in set B, so $A \nsubseteq B$ (A is not a subset of B). In this example, however, all the elements of set B are contained in set A; therefore, $B \subseteq A$.

c) There are fruits, such as bananas, that are in set A that are not in set B, so $A \nsubseteq B$.

d) All the elements of set A are contained in set B, so $A \subseteq B$. Note also that $B \subseteq A$. In fact, set $A =$ set B.

Proper Subsets

Definition: Proper Subset

Set A is a **proper subset** of set B, symbolized by $A \subset B$, if and only if all the elements of set A are elements of set B and set $A \neq$ set B (that is, set B must contain at least one element not in set A).

Consider the sets $A = \{$red, blue, yellow$\}$ and $B = \{$red, orange, yellow, green, blue, violet$\}$. Set A is a *subset* of set B, $A \subseteq B$, because every element of set A is also an element of set B. Set A is also a *proper subset* of set B, $A \subset B$, because set A and set B are not equal. Now consider $C = \{$car, bus, train$\}$ and $D = \{$train, car, bus$\}$. Set C is a subset of set D, $C \subseteq D$, because every element of set C is also an element of set D. Set C, however, is not a proper subset of set D, $C \not\subset D$, because set C and set D are equal sets.

Example 2 A Proper Subset?

Determine whether set A is a proper subset of set B.

a) $A = \{$jazz, pop, hip hop$\}$
   $B = \{$classical, jazz, pop, rap, hip hop$\}$

b) $A = \{a, b, c, d\}$ $B = \{a, c, b, d\}$

Solution

a) All the elements of set A are contained in set B, and sets A and B are not equal; thus, $A \subset B$.

b) Set $A =$ set B, so $A \not\subset B$. (However, $A \subseteq B$.)

Every set is a subset of itself, but no set is a proper subset of itself. For all sets A, $A \subseteq A$, but $A \not\subset A$. For example, if $A = \{1, 2, 3\}$, then $A \subseteq A$ because every element of set A is contained in set A, but $A \not\subset A$ because set $A =$ set A.

Let $A = \{\ \}$ and $B = \{1, 2, 3, 4\}$. Is $A \subseteq B$? To show $A \nsubseteq B$, you must find at least one element of set A that is not an element of set B. Because this cannot be done, $A \subseteq B$ must be true. Using the same reasoning, we can show that *the empty set is a subset of every set, including itself.*

Example 3 *Element or Subset?*

Determine whether the following are true or false.
a) $3 \in \{3, 4, 5\}$
b) $\{3\} \in \{3, 4, 5\}$
c) $\{3\} \in \{\{3\}, \{4\}, \{5\}\}$
d) $\{3\} \subseteq \{3, 4, 5\}$
e) $3 \subseteq \{3, 4, 5\}$
f) $\{\ \} \subseteq \{3, 4, 5\}$

Solution

a) $3 \in \{3, 4, 5\}$ is a true statement because 3 is an element of the set $\{3, 4, 5\}$.
b) $\{3\} \in \{3, 4, 5\}$ is a false statement because $\{3\}$ is a set, and the set $\{3\}$ is not an element of the set $\{3, 4, 5\}$.
c) $\{3\} \in \{\{3\}, \{4\}, \{5\}\}$ is a true statement because $\{3\}$ is an element in the set. The elements of the set $\{\{3\}, \{4\}, \{5\}\}$ are themselves sets.
d) $\{3\} \subseteq \{3, 4, 5\}$ is a true statement because every element of the first set is an element of the second set.
e) $3 \subseteq \{3, 4, 5\}$ is a false statement because the 3 is not in braces, so it is not a set and thus cannot be a subset. The 3 is an element of the set as indicated in part (a).
f) $\{\ \} \subseteq \{3, 4, 5\}$ is a true statement because the empty set is a subset of every set.

Number of Subsets

How many distinct subsets can be made from a given set? The empty set has no elements and has exactly one subset, the empty set. A set with one element has two subsets. A set with two elements has four subsets. A set with three elements has eight subsets. This information is illustrated in Table 2.1.

Table 2.1 Number of Subsets

Set	Subsets	Number of Subsets
$\{\ \}$	$\{\ \}$	$1 = 2^0$
$\{a\}$	$\{a\}$	
	$\{\ \}$	$2 = 2^1$
$\{a, b\}$	$\{a, b\}$	
	$\{a\}, \{b\}$	
	$\{\ \}$	$4 = 2 \times 2 = 2^2$
$\{a, b, c\}$	$\{a, b, c\}$	
	$\{a, b\}, \{a, c\}, \{b, c\}$	
	$\{a\}, \{b\}, \{c\}$	
	$\{\ \}$	$8 = 2 \times 2 \times 2 = 2^3$

SECTION 2.2 *Exercises*

Warm Up Exercises

In Exercises 1–4, fill in the blank with an appropriate word, phrase, or symbol(s).

1. If all the elements of set *A* are also elements of set *B*, then set *A* is a (n) _____ of set *B*.

2. If all the elements of set *A* are also elements of set *B*, and set *A* $\neq$ set *B*, then set *A* is a (n) _____ subset of set *B*.

3. The expression for determining the number of distinct subsets for a set with *n* distinct elements is _____ .

4. The expression for determining the number of distinct proper subsets for a set with *n* distinct elements is _____ .

Practice the Skills

In Exercises 5–26, answer true or false. If false, give the reason.

5. $\{\text{book}\} \subseteq \{\text{magazine, newspaper, book}\}$

6. $\{\text{Italy}\} \subseteq \{\text{Italy, Spain, France, Switzerland, Austria}\}$

7. $\{\text{McIntosh, Red Delicious}\} \subseteq \{\text{Empire, Gala, Cortland, Red Delicious}\}$

8. $\{\text{pepper, salt}\} \subseteq \{\text{salt, butter, mayonnaise}\}$

9. $\{\text{motorboat, kayak}\} \subset \{\text{kayak, fishing boat, motorboat, sailboat}\}$

10. $\{\text{polar bear, tiger, lion}\} \subset \{\text{tiger, lion, polar bear, penguin}\}$

11. $\{4, 2, 7\} \subset \{4, 7, 2\}$

12. $\{c, a, r, t\} \subset \{t, r, a, c\}$

13. Xbox 360 $\in \{\text{PSIII, Wii, Xbox 360}\}$

14. LaGuardia $\in \{\text{JFK, LaGuardia, Newark}\}$

15. $\{\text{swimming}\} \in \{\text{sailing, water skiing, swimming}\}$

16. $\{\ \} \in \{1, 3, 5, 7\}$

17. $5 \notin \{2, 4, 6\}$

18. $\{\ \} \subseteq \{\text{table, chair, sofa}\}$

19. $\{\text{red}\} \subset \{\text{red, blue, green}\}$

20. $\{3, 5, 9\} \not\subset \{3, 9, 5\}$

21. $\{\ \} = \{\varnothing\}$

22. $\varnothing = \{\ \}$

23. $\{0\} = \varnothing$

24. $\{\ \} \subseteq \{\ \}$

25. $0 = \{\ \}$

26. $\{1\} \in \{\{1\}, \{2\}, \{3\}\}$

In Exercises 27–34, determine whether $A = B, A \subseteq B$, $B \subseteq A, A \subset B, B \subset A$, or if none of these applies. (There may be more than one answer.)

27. $A = \{\text{penny, nickel, dime, quarter}\}$
    $B = \{\text{penny, quarter}\}$

28. $A = \{x \mid x \in N \text{ and } x < 6\}$
    $B = \{x \mid x \in N \text{ and } 1 \leq x \leq 5\}$

29. Set *A* is the set of states that border the Atlantic Ocean. Set *B* is the set of states east of the Mississippi River.

30. $A = \{1, 3, 5, 7, 9\}$
    $B = \{3, 9, 5, 7, 6\}$

31. $A = \{x \mid x \text{ is a brand of soft drink}\}$
    $B = \{\text{A \& W, Coca-Cola, Dr Pepper, Mountain Dew}\}$

32. $A = \{x \mid x \text{ is a sport that uses a ball}\}$
    $B = \{\text{basketball, soccer, tennis}\}$

33. Set *A* is the set of natural numbers between 2 and 7. Set *B* is the set of natural numbers greater than 2 and less than 7.

34. Set *A* is the set of all cars manufactured by General Motors. Set *B* is the set of sports cars manufactured by General Motors.

In Exercises 35–38, list all the subsets of the sets given.

35. $D = \varnothing$

36. $A = \{\circ\}$

37. $B = \{\text{cow, horse}\}$

38. $C = \{\text{steak, pork, chicken}\}$

Problem Solving

39. For set $A = \{a, b, c, d\}$,

   a) list all the subsets of set A.

   b) state which of the subsets in part (a) are not proper subsets of set A.

40. A set contains nine elements.

   a) How many subsets does it have?

   b) How many proper subsets does it have?

In Exercises 41–52, if the statement is true for all sets A and B, write "true." If it is not true for all sets A and B, write "false." Assume that $A \neq \emptyset$, $U \neq \emptyset$, and $A \subset U$.

41. If $A \subseteq B$, then $A \subset B$.   **42.** If $A \subset B$, then $A \subseteq B$.

43. $A \subseteq A$ **44.** $A \subset A$

45. $\emptyset \subset A$ **46.** $\emptyset \subseteq A$

47. $A \subseteq U$ **48.** $\emptyset \subset \emptyset$

49. $\emptyset \subset U$ **50.** $U \subseteq \emptyset$

51. $\emptyset \subseteq \emptyset$ **52.** $U \subset \emptyset$

53. *Ordering a Pizza* Jasmine Sullivan is ordering a pizza at Domino's Pizza. She can add any of the following toppings: cheese, pepperoni, sausage, onions, green peppers, mushrooms, anchovies, and ham. How many different variations of the pizza and toppings can be made?

54. *Building a House* The Jacobsens are planning to build a house in a new development. They can either build the base model offered by the builder or add any of the following options: deck, hot tub, security system, hardwood flooring. How many different variations of the house are possible?

55. *Salad Toppings* Donald Wheeler is ordering a salad at a Ruby Tuesday restaurant. He can purchase a salad consisting of just lettuce, or he can add any of the following items: cucumber, onion, tomato, carrot, green pepper, olive, mushroom. How many different variations of a salad are possible?

56. *Telephone Features* A customer with Verizon can order telephone service with some, all, or none of the following features: call waiting, call forwarding, caller identification, three-way calling, voice mail, fax line. How many different variations of the set of features are possible?

57. If $E \subseteq F$ and $F \subseteq E$, what other relationship exists between E and F?

58. How can you determine whether the set of boys is equivalent to the set of girls at a roller-skating rink?

59. For the set $D = \{a, b, c\}$

   a) is a an element of set D?

   b) is c a subset of set D?

   c) is $\{a, b\}$ a subset of set D?

Challenge Problem/Group Activity

60. *Hospital Expansion* A hospital has four members on the board of directors: Arnold, Benitez, Cathy, and Dominique.

   a) When the members vote on whether to add a wing to the hospital, how many different ways can they vote (abstentions are not allowed)? For example, Arnold—yes, Benitez—no, Cathy—no, and Dominique—yes is one of the many possibilities.

   b) Make a listing of all the possible outcomes of the vote. For example, the vote described in part (a) could be represented as (YNNY).

   c) How many of the outcomes given in part (b) would result in a majority supporting the addition of a wing to the hospital? That is, how many of the outcomes have three or more Y's?

Recreational Mathematics

61. How many elements must a set have if the number of proper subsets of the set is $\frac{1}{2}$ of the total number of subsets of the set?

62. If $A \subset B$ and $B \subset C$, must $A \subset C$?

63. If $A \subset B$ and $B \subseteq C$, must $A \subset C$?

64. If $A \subseteq B$ and $B \subseteq C$, must $A \subset C$?

Internet/Research Activity

65. On page 53, we discussed the ladder of life. Do research and indicate all the different classifications in the Linnaean system, from most general to the most specific, in which a koala belongs.

Suppose you go to a store to purchase a new laptop and tell a computer sales-person that you wish to purchase a laptop with a 14-inch display *and* 4 GB of memory. The salesperson was a bit distracted and thought you said you wanted to purchase a laptop with a 14-inch display *or* 4 GB of memory. Which laptops are in the set of laptops with a 14-inch display *and* 4 GB of memory? Which lap-tops are in the set of laptops with a 14-inch display *or* 4 GB of memory? These two questions are quite different. The first involves laptops joined by the word *and*. The second involves laptops joined by the word *or*. In this section, you will learn how to illustrate these and other set relationships.

▲ *Some Laptops have A 14-inch display, some laptops have 4 GB of memory, and some laptops have a 14-inch display and 4 GB of memory.*

Why *This is Important* Words such as *and* and *or* have important meaning in a variety of everyday applications, such as ordering from a menu or understanding the meaning of a legal document.

A useful technique for illustrating set relationships is the Venn diagram, named for English mathematician John Venn (1834–1923). Venn invented the diagrams and used them to illustrate ideas in his text on symbolic logic, published in 1881.

In a Venn diagram, a rectangle usually represents the universal set, *U*. The items inside the rectangle may be divided into subsets of the universal set. The subsets are usually represented by circles. In Fig. 2.1, the circle labeled *A* represents set *A*, which is a subset of the universal set.

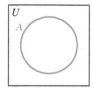

Figure 2.1

Two sets may be represented in a Venn diagram in any of four different ways, as shown in Fig. 2.2. Two sets *A* and *B* are *disjoint* when they have no elements in common. Two disjoint sets *A* and *B* are illustrated in Fig. 2.2(a). If set *A* is a proper subset of set *B*, $A \subset B$, the two sets may be illustrated as in Fig. 2.2(b). If set *A* contains exactly the same elements as set *B*, that is, $A = B$, the two sets may be illustrated as in Fig. 2.2(c). Two sets *A* and *B* with some elements in common are shown in Fig. 2.2(d), which is regarded as the most general form of a Venn diagram.

If we label the regions of the diagram in Fig. 2.2(d) using I, II, III, and IV, we can illustrate the four possible cases with this one diagram, Fig. 2.3.

(a)   (b)

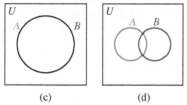

(c)   (d)

Figure 2.2

CASE 1: DISJOINT SETS When sets *A* and *B* are disjoint, they have no elements in common. Therefore, region II of Fig. 2.3 is empty.

CASE 2: SUBSETS When $A \subseteq B$, every element of set *A* is also an element of set *B*. Thus, there can be no elements in region I of Fig. 2.3. If $B \subseteq A$, however, then region III of Fig. 2.3 is empty.

CASE 3: EQUAL SETS When set $A =$ set *B*, all the elements of set *A* are elements of set *B* and all the elements of set *B* are elements of set *A*. Thus, regions I and III of Fig. 2.3 are empty.

CASE 4: OVERLAPPING SETS When sets *A* and *B* have elements in common, those elements are in region II of Fig. 2.3. The elements that belong to set *A* but not to set *B* are in region I. The elements that belong to set *B* but not to set *A* are in region III.

In each of the four cases, any element belonging to the universal set but not be-longing to set *A* or set *B* is placed in region IV.

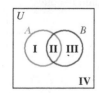

Figure 2.3

Next we introduce set operations. Venn diagrams will be helpful in understand-ing set operations. The basic operations of arithmetic are $+$, $-$, $\times$, and $\div$. When we see these symbols, we know what procedure to follow to determine the answer. Some of the operations in set theory are $'$, $\cap$, $\cup$, $-$, and $\times$. They represent complement, intersection, union, difference, and Cartesian product, respectively.

Complement

Figure 2.4

Definition: Complement

The **complement** of set A, symbolized by A', is the set of all the elements in the universal set that are not in set A.

In Fig. 2.4, the shaded region outside set A within the universal set represents the complement of set A, or A'.

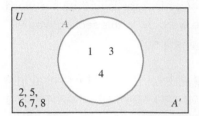

Figure 2.5

┌ Example **1** *A Set and Its Complement*

Given
$$U = \{1, 2, 3, 4, 5, 6, 7, 8\} \text{ and } A = \{1, 3, 4\}$$
find A' and illustrate the relationship among sets U, A, and A' in a Venn diagram.

 Solution The elements in U that are not in set A are 2, 5, 6, 7, 8. Thus, $A' = \{2, 5, 6, 7, 8\}$. The Venn diagram is illustrated in Fig. 2.5. ∎

Intersection

The word *intersection* brings to mind the area common to two crossing streets. The red car in the figure is in the intersection of the two streets. The set operation intersection is defined as follows.

Definition: Intersection

The **intersection** of sets A and B, symbolized by $A \cap B$, is the set containing all the elements that are common to both set A and set B.

The shaded region, region II, in Fig. 2.6 represents the intersection of sets A and B.

Figure 2.6

┌ Example **2** *Sets with Overlapping Regions*

Let the universal set, U, represent the 50 states in the United States. Let set A represent the set of states with a population of more than 10 million people as of 2009. Let set B represent the set of states that have at least one city with a population of more than 1 million people, as of 2009 (see the table). Draw a Venn diagram illustrating the relationship between set A and set B.

States with a Population of More Than 10 Million People	States with at Least One City with a Population of More Than 1 Million People
California	California
Texas	Texas
New York	New York
Florida	Illinois
Illinois	Pennsylvania
Pennsylvania	Arizona
Ohio	

Source: Bureau of the U.S. Census

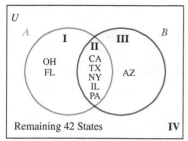

Figure 2.7

Solution First determine the intersection of sets A and B. The states common to both sets are California, Texas, New York, Illinois, and Pennsylvania. Therefore,

$$A \cap B = \{\text{California, Texas, New York, Illinois, Pennsylvania}\}$$

Place these elements in region II of Fig. 2.7. Complete region I by determining the elements in set A that have not been placed in region II. Therefore, Ohio and Florida are placed in region I. Complete region III by determining the elements in set B that have not been placed in region II. Thus, Arizona is placed in region III. Finally, place those elements in U that are not in either set within the rectangle but are outside both circles. This group includes the remaining 42 states, which are placed in region IV. ∎

─Example **3** *The Intersection of Sets*

Given

$$U = \{1, 2, 3, 4, 5, 6, 7, 8, 9, 10\}$$
$$A = \{1, 2, 3, 8\}$$
$$B = \{1, 3, 6, 7, 8\}$$
$$C = \{\ \}$$

find

a) $A \cap B$.   b) $A \cap C$.   c) $A' \cap B$.   d) $(A \cap B)'$.

Solution

a) $A \cap B = \{1, 2, 3, 8\} \cap \{1, 3, 6, 7, 8\} = \{1, 3, 8\}$. The elements common to both set A and set B are 1, 3, and 8.

b) $A \cap C = \{1, 2, 3, 8\} \cap \{\ \} = \{\ \}$. There are no elements common to both set A and set C.

c) To determine $A' \cap B$, we must first determine A'.
$$A' = \{4, 5, 6, 7, 9, 10\}$$
$$A' \cap B = \{4, 5, 6, 7, 9, 10\} \cap \{1, 3, 6, 7, 8\}$$
$$= \{6, 7\}$$

d) To find $(A \cap B)'$, first determine $A \cap B$.
$$A \cap B = \{1, 3, 8\} \text{ from part (a)}$$
$$(A \cap B)' = \{1, 3, 8\}' = \{2, 4, 5, 6, 7, 9, 10\}$$
∎

Union

The word *union* means to unite or join together, as in marriage, and that is exactly what is done when we perform the operation of union.

· Definition: **Union**
The **union** of set A and set B, symbolized by $A \cup B$, is the set containing all the elements that are members of set A or of set B (or of both sets).

Figure 2.8

The three shaded regions of Fig. 2.8, regions I, II, and III, together represent the union of sets A and B. If an element is common to both sets, it is listed only once in the union of the sets.

─Example **4** *Determining Sets from a Venn Diagram*

Use the Venn diagram in Fig. 2.9 to determine the following sets.

a) U b) A c) B' d) $A \cap B$
e) $A \cup B$ f) $(A \cup B)'$ g) $n(A \cup B)$

Figure 2.9

Solution

a) The universal set consists of all the elements within the rectangle, that is, the elements in regions I, II, III, and IV. Thus, $U = \{9, \triangle, \square, \bigcirc, 3, 7, ?, \#, 8\}$.

b) Set A consists of the elements in regions I and II. Thus, $A = \{9, \triangle, \square, \bigcirc\}$.

c) B' consists of the elements outside set B, or the elements in regions I and IV. Thus, $B' = \{9, \triangle, \#, 8\}$.

d) $A \cap B$ consists of the elements that belong to both set A and set B (region II). Thus, $A \cap B = \{\square, \bigcirc\}$.

e) $A \cup B$ consists of the elements that belong to set A or set B (regions I, II, or III). Thus, $A \cup B = \{9, \triangle, \square, \bigcirc, 3, 7, ?\}$.

f) $(A \cup B)'$ consists of the elements in U that are not in $A \cup B$. Thus, $(A \cup B)' = \{\#, 8\}$.

g) $n(A \cup B)$ represents the *number of elements* in the union of sets A and B. Thus, $n(A \cup B) = 7$, as there are seven elements in the union of sets A and B. ∎

Example 5 *The Union of Sets*

Given

$$U = \{1, 2, 3, 4, 5, 6, 7, 8, 9, 10\}$$
$$A = \{1, 2, 4, 6\}$$
$$B = \{1, 3, 6, 7, 9\}$$
$$C = \{\ \}$$

determine each of the following.

a) $A \cup B$ b) $A \cup C$ c) $A' \cup B$ d) $(A \cup B)'$

Solution

a) $A \cup B = \{1, 2, 4, 6\} \cup \{1, 3, 6, 7, 9\} = \{1, 2, 3, 4, 6, 7, 9\}$

b) $A \cup C = \{1, 2, 4, 6\} \cup \{\ \} = \{1, 2, 4, 6\}$. Note that $A \cup C = A$.

c) To determine $A' \cup B$, we must determine A'.

$$A' = \{3, 5, 7, 8, 9, 10\}$$
$$A' \cup B = \{3, 5, 7, 8, 9, 10\} \cup \{1, 3, 6, 7, 9\}$$
$$= \{1, 3, 5, 6, 7, 8, 9, 10\}$$

d) Determine $(A \cup B)'$ by first determining $A \cup B$, and then find the complement of $A \cup B$.

$$A \cup B = \{1, 2, 3, 4, 6, 7, 9\} \text{ from part (a)}$$
$$(A \cup B)' = \{1, 2, 3, 4, 6, 7, 9\}' = \{5, 8, 10\}$$

∎

Example 6 *Union and Intersection*

Given

$$U = \{a, b, c, d, e, f, g\}$$
$$A = \{a, b, e, g\}$$
$$B = \{a, c, d, e\}$$
$$C = \{b, e, f\}$$

determine each of the following.

a) $(A \cup B) \cap (A \cup C)$ b) $(A \cup B) \cap C'$ c) $A' \cap B'$

a) $(A \cup B) \cap (A \cup C) = \{a, b, c, d, e, g\} \cap \{a, b, e, f, g\}$
$= \{a, b, e, g\}$

b) $(A \cup B) \cap C' = \{a, b, c, d, e, g\} \cap \{a, c, d, g\}$
$= \{a, c, d, g\}$

c) $A' \cap B' = \{c, d, f\} \cap \{b, f, g\}$
$= \{f\}$

The Meaning of *and* and *or*

The words *and* and *or* are very important in many areas of mathematics. We use these words in several chapters in this book, including Ch.12, Probability. The word *and* is generally interpreted to mean *intersection*, whereas *or* is generally interpreted to mean *union*. Suppose $A = \{1, 2, 3, 5, 6, 8\}$ and $B = \{1, 3, 4, 7, 9, 10\}$. The elements that belong to set A *and* set B are 1 and 3. These are the elements in the intersection of the sets. The elements that belong to set A *or* set B are 1, 2, 3, 4, 5, 6, 7, 8, 9, and 10. These are the elements in the union of the sets.

The Relationship Between $n(A \cup B)$, $n(A)$, $n(B)$, and $n(A \cap B)$

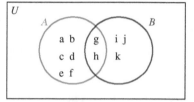

Figure 2.10

Having looked at unions and intersections, we can now determine a relationship between $n(A \cup B), n(A), n(B)$, and $n(A \cap B)$. Suppose set A has eight elements, set B has five elements, and $A \cap B$ has two elements. How many elements are in $A \cup B$? Let's make up some arbitrary sets that meet the criteria specified and draw a Venn diagram. If we let set $A = \{a, b, c, d, e, f, g, h\}$, then set B must contain five elements, two of which are also in set A. Let set $B = \{g, h, i, j, k\}$. We construct a Venn diagram by filling in the intersection first, as shown in Fig. 2.10. The number of elements in $A \cup B$ is 11. The elements g and h are in both sets, and if we add $n(A) + n(B)$, we are counting these elements twice.

To find the number of elements in the union of sets A and B, we can add the number of elements in sets A and B and then subtract the number of elements common to both sets.

The Number of Elements in $A \cup B$

For any finite sets A and B,
$$n(A \cup B) = n(A) + n(B) - n(A \cap B)$$

Example 7   *How Many Visitors Speak Spanish or French?*

The results of a survey of visitors at the Grand Canyon showed that 25 speak Spanish, 14 speak French, and 4 speak both Spanish and French. How many speak Spanish or French?

If we let set A be the set of visitors who speak Spanish and let set B be the set of visitors who speak French, then we need to determine $n(A \cup B)$. We can use the above formula to find $n(A \cup B)$.

$$n(A \cup B) = n(A) + n(B) - n(A \cap B)$$
$$n(A \cup B) = 25 + 14 - 4$$
$$= 35$$

Thus, 35 of the visitors surveyed speak either Spanish or French.

┌─ Example **8**   *The Number of Elements in Set A*

Of the homes listed for sale with RE/MAX, 39 have either a three-car garage or a fireplace, 31 have a fireplace, and 18 have both a three-car garage and a fireplace. How many of these homes have a three-car garage?

Solution   If we let set A be the set of homes with a three-car garage and set B be the set of homes with a fireplace, we need to determine $n(A)$. We are given the number of homes with either a three-car garage or a fireplace, which is $n(A \cup B)$. We are also given the number of homes with a fireplace, $n(B)$, and the number of homes that have both a three-car garage and a fireplace, $n(A \cap B)$. We can use the formula $n(A \cup B) = n(A) + n(B) - n(A \cap B)$ to solve for $n(A)$.

$$n(A \cup B) = n(A) + n(B) - n(A \cap B)$$
$$39 = n(A) + 31 - 18$$
$$39 = n(A) + 13$$
$$39 - 13 = n(A) + 13 - 13$$
$$26 = n(A)$$

Thus, the number of homes listed for sale that have a three-car garage is 26.   ■

Two other set operations are the difference of two sets and the Cartesian product. We will first discuss the difference of two sets.

Difference of Two Sets

Definition: **Difference of Two Sets**
The **difference of two sets** A and B, symbolized $A - B$, is the set of elements that belong to set A but not to set B.

Using set-builder notation, the difference of two sets A and B is indicated by $A - B = \{x \mid x \in A \text{ and } x \notin B\}$. The shaded region, region I, in Fig. 2.11 represents the difference of two sets A and B, or $A - B$.

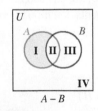

$A - B$

Figure 2.11

┌─ Example **9**   *The Difference of Two Sets*

Given

$$U = \{a, b, c, d, e, f, g, h, i, j, k\}$$
$$A = \{b, d, e, f, g, h\}$$
$$B = \{a, b, d, h, i\}$$
$$C = \{b, e, g\}$$

determine

a) $A - B$ b) $A - C$ c) $A' - B$ d) $A - C'$

Solution

a) $A - B$ is the set of elements that are in set A but not set B. The elements that are in set A but not set B are $e, f,$ and g. Therefore, $A - B = \{e, f, g\}$.

b) $A - C$ is the set of elements that are in set A but not set C. The elements that are in set A but not set C are $d, f,$ and h. Therefore, $A - C = \{d, f, h\}$.

c) To determine $A' - B$, we must first determine A'.

$$A' = \{a, c, i, j, k\}$$

$A' - B$ is the set of elements that are in set A' but not set B. The elements that are in set A' but not set B are $c, j,$ and k. Therefore, $A' - B = \{c, j, k\}$.

d) To determine $A - C'$, we must first determine C'.
$$C' = \{a, c, d, f, h, i, j, k\}$$
$A - C'$ is the set of elements that are in set A but not set C'. The elements that are in set A but not set C' are b, e, and g. Therefore, $A - C' = \{b, e, g\}$. ■

Next we discuss the Cartesian product.

Cartesian Product

Definition: Cartesian Product

The **Cartesian product** of set A and set B, symbolized by $A \times B$ and read "A cross B," is the set of all possible *ordered pairs* of the form (a, b), where $a \in A$ and $b \in B$.

To determine the ordered pairs in a Cartesian product, select the first element of set A and form an ordered pair with each element of set B. Then select the second element of set A and form an ordered pair with each element of set B. Continue in this manner until you have used each element of set A.

Example 10 *The Cartesian Product of Two Sets*

Given $A = \{$orange, banana, apple$\}$ and $B = \{1, 2\}$, determine the following.
a) $A \times B$ b) $B \times A$ c) $A \times A$ d) $B \times B$

Solution

a) $A \times B = \{$(orange, 1), (orange, 2) (banana, 1), (banana, 2), (apple, 1), (apple, 2)$\}$
b) $B \times A = \{$(1, orange), (1, banana), (1, apple), (2, orange), (2, banana), (2, apple)$\}$
c) $A \times A = \{$(orange, orange), (orange, banana), (orange, apple), (banana, orange), (banana, banana), (banana, apple), (apple, orange), (apple, banana), (apple, apple)$\}$
d) $B \times B = \{$(1, 1), (1, 2), (2, 1), (2, 2)$\}$ ■

We can see from Example 10 that, in general, $A \times B \neq B \times A$. The ordered pairs in $A \times B$ are not the same as the ordered pairs in $B \times A$ because (orange, 1) $\neq$ (1, orange).

In general, if a set A has m elements and a set B has n elements, then the number of ordered pairs in $A \times B$ will be $m \times n$. In Example 10, set A contains 3 elements and set B contains 2 elements. Notice that $A \times B$ contains 3×2 or 6 ordered pairs.

SECTION 2.3   *Exercises*

Warm Up Exercises

In exercises 1–8, fill in the blank with an appropriate word, phrase, or symbol(s).

1. The set of all the elements in the universal set that are not in set A is called the _____ of set A.

2. The set containing all the elements that are members of set A or of set B or of both sets is called the _____ of set A and set B.

3. The set containing all the elements that are common to both set A and set B is called the _____ of set A and set B.

4. The set of elements that belong to set A, but not to set B, is called the _____ of two sets A and B.

5. The set of all possible ordered pairs of the form (a, b), where $a \in A$ and $b \in B$, is called the _____ product of set A and set B.

6. If set *A* has *m* elements and set *B* has *n* elements, the Cartesian product $A \times B$ has _____ elements.

7. Two sets with no elements in common are called _____ sets.

8. In a Venn diagram with two overlapping sets there are _____ regions.

Practice the Skills

In Exercises 9–13, use Fig. 2.2 as a guide to draw a Venn diagram that illustrates the situation described.

9. Set *A* and set *B* are disjoint sets.

10. $A \subset B$

11. $B \subset A$

12. $A = B$

13. Set *A* and set *B* are overlapping sets.

14. Which set operation is the word *or* generally interpreted to mean?

15. Which set operation is the word *and* generally interpreted to mean?

16. Give the relationship between $n(A \cup B), n(A), n(B),$ and $n(A \cap B)$.

Problem Solving

17. *Cellular Telephones* For the sets *U, A,* and *B,* construct a Venn diagram and place the elements in the proper regions.

$U = \{$iPhone, Blackberry, LG, DROID, Samsung, Nokia, Motorola, Sony$\}$

$A = \{$iPhone, Blackberry, LG, Motorola, DROID$\}$

$B = \{$LG, DROID, Nokia, Motorola$\}$

18. *National Parks* For the sets *U, A,* and *B,* construct a Venn diagram and place the elements in the proper regions.

$U = \{$Badlands, Death Valley, Glacier, Grand Teton, Mammoth Cave, Mount Rainier, North Cascades, Shenandoah, Yellowstone, Yosemite$\}$

$A = \{$Badlands, Glacier, Grand Teton, Mount Rainier, Yellowstone$\}$

$B = \{$Death Valley, Glacier, Mammoth Cave, Mount Rainier, Yosemite$\}$

▲ *Yellowstone National Park*

19. *Occupations* The following table shows the fastest-growing occupations for college graduates, based on employment in 2008 and the estimated employment in 2016. Let the occupations in the table represent the universal set.

Fastest-Growing Occupations for College Graduates, 2008–2016		
	Employment (in thousands of jobs)	
Occupation	2008	2016
Biomedical engineers (BE)	16	28
Network systems analysts (NSA)	292	448
Financial examiners (FE)	27	38
Medical scientists (MS)	109	154
Physicians assistants (PA)	75	104
Biochemists (B)	23	32
Athletic trainers (AT)	16	22
Dental hygienists (DH)	174	237
Veterinary technicians (VT)	80	108
Computer software engineers (CSE)	515	690

Source: U.S. Bureau of Labor Statistics

Let *A* = the set of fastest-growing occupations for college graduates whose 2008 employment was at least 80,000.

Let *B* = the set of fastest-growing occupations for college graduates whose estimated employment in 2016 is at least 200,000.

Using the abbreviations listed in the table for each occupation, construct a Venn diagram illustrating the sets.

20. *Racing Standings* The following table shows the 2009 NASCAR Sprint Cup Series Final Standings, with the 10 drivers having the highest point total and the number of races won. Let the drivers in the table represent the universal set.

2009 NASCAR Sprint Cup Series Final Standings		
Driver	**Points**	**Wins**
Jimmie Johnson	6652	7
Mark Martin	6511	5
Jeff Gordon	6473	1
Kurt Busch	6446	2
Denny Hamlin	6335	4
Tony Stewart	6309	4
Greg Biffle	6292	0
Juan Montoya	6252	0
Ryan Newman	6175	0
Kasey Kahne	6128	2

Source: NASCAR

Let A = the set of drivers with more than 6400 points

Let B = the set of drivers with more than 1 win

Construct a Venn diagram illustrating the sets. Use the driver's initials in the Venn diagram.

21. Let U represent the set of animals in U.S. zoos. Let A represent the set of animals in the San Diego zoo. Describe A'.

▲ *San Diego Zoo*

22. Let U represent the set of U.S. colleges and universities. Let A represent the set of U.S. colleges and universities in the state of Mississippi. Describe A'.

In Exercises 23–28,

    U is the set of farms in the United States.

    A is the set of farms that produce corn.

    B is the set of farms that produce tomatoes.

Describe each of the following sets in words.

23. A'

24. B'

25. $A \cup B$

26. $A \cap B$

27. $A \cap B'$

28. $A \cup B'$

In Exercises 29–34,

    U is the set of furniture stores.

    A is the set of furniture stores that sell mattresses.

    B is the set of furniture stores that sell outdoor furniture.

    C is the set of furniture stores that sell leather furniture.

Describe the following sets.

29. $A \cup C$

30. $A \cap B$

31. $B' \cap C$

32. $A \cap B \cap C$

33. $A \cup B \cup C$

34. $A' \cup C'$

In Exercises 35–42, use the Venn diagram in Fig. 2.12 to list the set of elements in roster form.

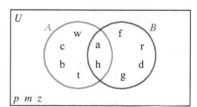

Figure 2.12

35. A **36.** B

37. $A \cap B$ **38.** U

39. $A \cup B$

40. $(A \cup B)'$

41. $A' \cap B'$

42. $(A \cap B)'$

In Exercises 43–50, use the Venn diagram in Fig. 2.13 to list the set of elements in roster form.

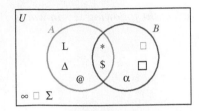

Figure 2.13

43. A

44. B

45. U

46. $A \cap B$

47. $A' \cup B$

48. $A \cup B'$

49. $A' \cap B$

50. $(A \cup B)'$

In Exercises 51–60, let

$$U = \{1, 2, 3, 4, 5, 6, 7, 8\}$$
$$A = \{1, 2, 4, 5, 7\}$$
$$B = \{2, 3, 5, 6\}$$

Determine the following.

51. $A \cup B$

52. $A \cap B$

53. B'

54. $A \cup B'$

55. $(A \cup B)'$

56. $A' \cap B'$

57. $(A \cup B)' \cap B$

58. $(A \cup B) \cap (A \cup B)'$

59. $(B \cup A)' \cap (B' \cup A')$ **60.** $A' \cup (A \cap B)$

In Exercises 61–70, let

$$U = \{a, b, c, d, e, f, g, h, i, j, k\}$$
$$A = \{a, c, d, f, g, i\}$$
$$B = \{b, c, d, f, g\}$$
$$C = \{a, b, f, i, j\}$$

Determine the following.

61. B'

62. $B \cup C$

63. $A \cap C$

64. $A' \cup B'$

65. $(A \cap C)'$

66. $(A \cap B) \cup C$

67. $A \cup (C \cap B)'$

68. $A \cup (C' \cup B')$

69. $(A' \cup C) \cup (A \cap B)$ **70.** $(C \cap B) \cap (A' \cap B)$

In Exercises 71–78, let

$$U = \{1, 2, 3, 4, 5, 6, 7, 8, 9, 10\}$$
$$A = \{1, 2, 4, 6, 9\}$$
$$B = \{1, 3, 4, 5, 8\}$$
$$C = \{4, 5, 9\}$$

Determine the following.

71. $A - B$

72. $A - C$

73. $A - B'$

74. $A' - C$

75. $(A - B)'$

76. $(A - B)' - C$

77. $C - A'$

78. $(C - A)' - B$

In Exercises 79–84, let

$$A = \{a, b, c\}$$
$$B = \{1, 2\}$$

79. Determine $A \times B$.

80. Determine $B \times A$.

81. Does $A \times B = B \times A$?

82. Determine $n(A \times B)$.

83. Determine $n(B \times A)$.

84. Does $n(A \times B) = n(B \times A)$?

Problem Solving

In Exercises 85–98, let

$$U = \{x \mid x \in N \text{ and } x < 10\}$$
$$A = \{x \mid x \in N \text{ and } x \text{ is odd and } x < 10\}$$
$$B = \{x \mid x \in N \text{ and } x \text{ is even and } x < 10\}$$
$$C = \{x \mid x \in N \text{ and } x < 6\}$$

Determine the following.

85. $A \cap B$

86. $A \cup B$

87. $A' \cup B$

88. $(B \cup C)'$

89. $A \cap C'$

90. $A \cap B'$

91. $(B \cap C)'$

92. $(A \cup C) \cap B$

93. $(C' \cup A) \cap B$

94. $(C \cap B) \cup A$

95. $(A \cap B)' \cup C$

96. $(A' \cup C) \cap B$

97. $(A' \cup B') \cap C$

98. $(A' \cap C) \cup (A \cap B)$

99. When will a set and its complement be disjoint? Explain and give an example.

100. When will $n(A \cap B) = 0$? Explain and give an example.

101. *Pet Ownership* The results of a survey of customers at PetSmart showed that 27 owned dogs, 38 owned cats, and 16 owned both dogs and cats. How many people owned either a dog or a cat?

102. *Student Council and Intramurals* At Madison High School, 46 students participated in student council or intramurals, 30 participated in student council, and 4 participated in student council and intramurals. How many students participated in intramurals?

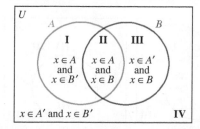

103. Consider the formula

$$n(A \cup B) = n(A) + n(B) - n(A \cap B)$$

a) Show that this relation holds for $A = \{a, b, c, d\}$ and $B = \{b, d, e, f, g, h\}$.

b) Make up your own sets A and B, each consisting of at least six elements. Using these sets, show that the relation holds.

c) Use a Venn diagram and explain why the relation holds for any two sets A and B.

104. The Venn diagram in Fig. 2.14 shows a technique of labeling the regions to indicate membership of elements in a particular region. Define each of the four regions with a set statement. (*Hint:* $A \cap B'$ defines region I.)

Figure 2.14

In Exercises 105–114, let $U = \{0, 1, 2, 3, 4, 5, \ldots\}$, $A = \{1, 2, 3, 4, \ldots\}$, $B = \{4, 8, 12, 16, \ldots\}$, *and* $C = \{2, 4, 6, 8, \ldots\}$. *Determine the following.*

105. $A \cup B$

106. $A \cap B$

107. $B \cup C$

108. $B \cap C$

109. $A \cap C$

110. $A' \cap C$

111. $B' \cap C$

112. $(B \cup C)' \cup C$

113. $(A \cap C) \cap B'$

114. $U' \cap (A \cup B)$

Challenge Problems/Group Activities

In Exercises 115–122, determine whether the answer is $\varnothing$, A, *or* U. *(Assume* $A \neq \varnothing, A \neq U$.)

115. $A \cap A'$

116. $A \cup A'$

117. $A \cup \varnothing$

118. $A \cap \varnothing$

119. $A' \cup U$

120. $A \cap U$

121. $A \cup U$

122. $A \cap A$

In Exercises 123–128, determine the relationship between set A and set B if

123. $A \cap B = B$.

124. $A \cup B = B$.

125. $A \cap B = \varnothing$.

126. $A \cup B = A$.

127. $A \cap B = A$.

128. $A \cup B = \varnothing$.

SECTION 2.4
Venn Diagrams with Three Sets and Verification of Equality of Sets

Suppose a college offers intramurals in basketball, flag football, and softball. Is there a way the director of intramurals can determine which students participate in all three activities or which students participate in exactly two of these activities? The answer is yes by using a *Venn Diagram*. A Venn diagram that can be used to convey important information quickly and efficiently.

Why *This is Important*   Classifying sets using diagrams often helps us understand the relationship among various sets.

▲ *Venn diagrams can be used to answer questions regarding the number of people participating in an intramural activity at a college.*

In Section 2.3, we learned how to use Venn diagrams to illustrate two sets. Venn diagrams can also be used to illustrate three sets.

For three sets, *A*, *B*, and *C*, the diagram is drawn so the three sets overlap (Fig. 2.15), creating eight regions. The diagrams in Fig. 2.16 emphasize selected regions of three intersecting sets. *When constructing Venn diagrams with three sets, we generally start with region V and work outward,* as explained in the procedure given on page 69.

Figure 2.15

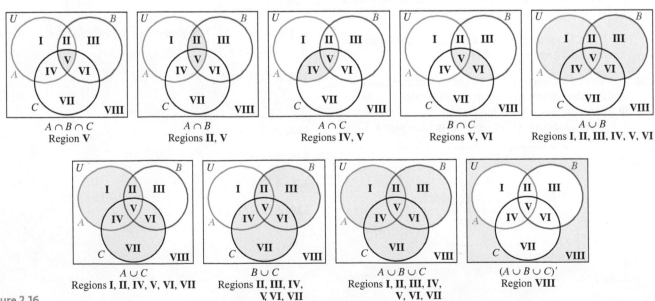

Figure 2.16

> **PROCEDURE**   GENERAL PROCEDURE FOR CONSTRUCTING VENN
> DIAGRAMS WITH THREE SETS, *A*, *B*, AND *C*
>
> 1. Determine the elements to be placed in region V by finding the elements that are
>   common to all three sets, $A \cap B \cap C$.
> 2. Determine the elements to be placed in region II. Find the elements in $A \cap B$.
>   The elements in this set belong in regions II and V. Place the elements in the set
> $A \cap B$ that are not listed in region V in region II. The elements in regions IV
>   and VI are found in a similar manner.
> 3. Determine the elements to be placed in region I by determining the elements in
>   set *A* that are not in regions II, IV, and V. The elements in regions III and VII
>   are found in a similar manner.
> 4. Determine the elements to be placed in region VIII by finding the elements in
>   the universal set that are not in regions I through VII.

Example 1 illustrates the general procedure.

┌Example 1   *Constructing a Venn Diagram for Three Sets*

Construct a Venn diagram illustrating the following sets.

$$U = \{1, 2, 3, 4, 5, 6, 7, 8, 9, 10, 11, 12, 13, 14, 15\}$$
$$A = \{1, 4, 8, 9, 10, 12\}$$
$$B = \{2, 4, 5, 9, 10, 13\}$$
$$C = \{1, 3, 4, 8, 9, 11\}$$

Solution   First find the intersection of all three sets. Because the elements 4 and 9
are in all three sets, $A \cap B \cap C = \{4, 9\}$. The elements 4 and 9 are placed in
region V in Fig.2.17. Next complete region II by determining the intersection of
sets *A* and *B*.

$$A \cap B = \{4, 9, 10\}$$

$A \cap B$ consists of regions II and V. The elements 4 and 9 have already been placed
in region V, so 10 must be placed in region II.

  Now determine what numbers go in region IV.

$$A \cap C = \{1, 4, 8, 9\}$$

Since 4 and 9 have already been placed in region V, place the 1 and 8 in region IV.
Now determine the numbers to go in region VI.

$$B \cap C = \{4, 9\}$$

Since both the 4 and 9 have been placed in region V, there are no numbers to be placed
in region VI. Now complete set *A*. The only element of set *A* that has not previously
been placed in regions II, IV, or V is 12. Therefore, place the element 12 in region I.
The element 12 that is placed in region I is only in set *A* and not in set *B* or set *C*. Using set *B*, complete region III using the same general procedure used to determine the
numbers in region I. Using set *C*, complete region VII by using the same procedure
used to complete regions I and III. To determine the elements in region VIII, find the
elements in *U* that have not been placed in regions I–VII. The elements 6, 7, 14, and
15 have not been placed in regions I–VII, so place them in region VIII.   ∎

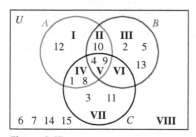

Figure 2.17

Venn diagrams can be used to illustrate and analyze many everyday problems.
One example follows.

┌ Example **2** *Blood Types*

Human blood is classified (typed) according to the presence or absence of the specific antigens A, B, and Rh in the red blood cells. Antigens are highly specified proteins and carbohydrates that will trigger the production of antibodies in the blood to fight infection. Blood containing the Rh antigen is labeled positive, +, while blood lacking the Rh antigen is labeled negative, −. Blood lacking both A and B antigens is called type O. Sketch a Venn diagram with three sets A, B, and Rh and place each type of blood listed in the proper region. A person has only one type of blood.

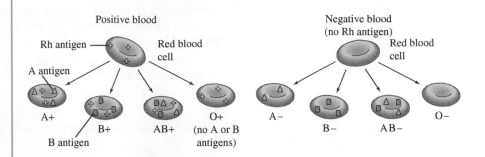

Solution

As illustrated in Chapter 1, the first thing to do is to read the question carefully and make sure you understand what is given and what you are asked to find. There are three antigens A, B, and Rh. Therefore, begin by naming the three circles in a Venn diagram with the three antigens; see Fig. 2.18.

Any blood containing the Rh antigen is positive, and any blood not containing the Rh antigen is negative. Therefore, all blood in the Rh circle is positive, and all blood outside the Rh circle is negative. The intersection of all three sets, region V, is AB+. Region II contains only antigens A and B and is therefore AB−. Region I is A− because it contains only antigen A. Region III is B−, region IV is A+, and region VI is B+. Region VII is O+, containing only the Rh antigen. Region VIII, which lacks all three antigens, is O−.   ■

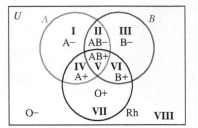

Figure 2.18

Verification of Equality of Sets

In this chapter, for clarity we may refer to operations on sets, such as $A \cup B'$ or $A \cap B \cap C$, as *statements involving sets* or simply as *statements*. Now we discuss how to determine if two statements involving sets are equal.

Consider the question: Is $A' \cup B = A' \cap B$ *for all sets A and B?* For the specific sets $U = \{1, 2, 3, 4, 5\}$, $A = \{1, 3\}$, and $B = \{2, 4, 5\}$, is $A' \cup B = A' \cap B$? To answer the question, we do the following.

Find $A' \cup B$	Find $A' \cap B$
$A' = \{2, 4, 5\}$	$A' = \{2, 4, 5\}$
$B = \{2, 4, 5\}$	$B = \{2, 4, 5\}$
$A' \cup B = \{2, 4, 5\}$	$A' \cap B = \{2, 4, 5\}$

For these sets, $A' \cup B = A' \cap B$, because both set statements are equal to $\{2, 4, 5\}$. At this point you may believe that $A' \cup B = A' \cap B$ for all sets A and B. If we select the sets $U = \{1, 2, 3, 4, 5\}$, $A = \{1, 3, 5\}$, and $B = \{2, 3\}$, we see that $A' \cup B = \{2, 3, 4\}$ and $A' \cap B = \{2\}$. For this case, $A' \cup B \neq A' \cap B$.

Thus, we have proved that $A' \cup B \neq A' \cap B$ for all sets A and B by using a *counterexample*. A counterexample, as explained in Chapter 1, is an example that shows a statement is not true.

In Chapter 1, we explained that proofs involve the use of *deductive reasoning*. Recall that deductive reasoning begins with a general statement and works to a specific conclusion. To verify, or determine whether set statements are equal for any two sets selected, we use deductive reasoning with Venn diagrams. Venn diagrams are used because they can illustrate general cases. To determine if statements that contain sets, such as $(A \cup B)'$ and $A' \cap B'$, are equal for all sets A and B, we use the regions of Venn diagrams. If both statements represent the same regions of the Venn diagram, then the statements are equal for all sets A and B. See Example 3.

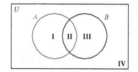

Figure 2.19

Example 3 *Equality of Sets*

Determine whether $(A \cup B)' = A' \cap B'$ for all sets A and B.

Solution Draw a Venn diagram with two sets A and B, as in Fig. 2.19. Label the regions as indicated.

Find $(A \cup B)'$

Set	Corresponding Regions
A	I, II
B	II, III
$A \cup B$	I, II, III
$(A \cup B)'$	IV

Find $A' \cap B'$

Set	Corresponding Regions
A'	III, IV
B'	I, IV
$A' \cap B'$	IV

Both statements are represented by the same region, IV, of the Venn diagram. Thus, $(A \cup B)' = A' \cap B'$ for all sets A and B. ∎

In Example 3, when we proved that $(A \cup B)' = A' \cap B'$, we started with two general sets and worked to the specific conclusion that both statements represented the same regions of the Venn diagram. We showed that $(A \cup B)' = A' \cap B'$ *for all sets A and B*. No matter what sets we choose for A and B, this statement will be true. For example, let $U = \{1, 2, 3, 4, 5, 6, 7, 8, 9, 10\}$, $A = \{3, 4, 6, 10\}$, and $B = \{1, 2, 4, 5, 6, 8\}$.

$$(A \cup B)' = A' \cap B'$$
$$\{1, 2, 3, 4, 5, 6, 8, 10\}' = \{3, 4, 6, 10\}' \cap \{1, 2, 4, 5, 6, 8\}'$$
$$\{7, 9\} = \{1, 2, 5, 7, 8, 9\} \cap \{3, 7, 9, 10\}$$
$$\{7, 9\} = \{7, 9\}$$

We can also use Venn diagrams to prove statements involving three sets.

Example 4 *Equality of Sets*

Determine whether $A \cup (B \cap C) = (A \cup B) \cap (A \cup C)$ for all sets, A, B, and C.

Solution Because the statements include three sets, A, B, and C, three circles must be used. The Venn diagram illustrating the eight regions is shown in Fig. 2.20.

First we will find the regions that correspond to $A \cup (B \cap C)$, and then we will find the regions that correspond to $(A \cup B) \cap (A \cup C)$. If both answers are the same, the statements are equal.

Figure 2.20

Using Venn Diagrams

Financial Planning Services

Investment   Retirement

College
Planning

A financial planning company uses the Venn diagram above to illustrate the financial planning services it offers. From the diagram, we can see that this company offers advice in an "intersection" of the areas investment, retirement, and college planning, the intersection of all three sets.

We categorize items on a daily basis. Children are taught how to categorize items at an early age when they learn how to classify items according to color, shape, and size. Biologists categorize items when they classify organisms according to shared characteristics.

Why **This is Important** A Venn diagram is a very useful tool to help order and arrange items and to picture the relationship between sets.

Find $A \cup (B \cap C)$

Set	Corresponding Regions
A	I, II, IV, V
$B \cap C$	V, VI
$A \cup (B \cap C)$	I, II, IV, V, VI

Find $(A \cup B) \cap (A \cup C)$

Set	Corresponding Regions
$A \cup B$	I, II, III, IV, V, VI
$A \cup C$	I, II, IV, V, VI, VII
$(A \cup B) \cap (A \cup C)$	I, II, IV, V, VI

The regions that correspond to $A \cup (B \cap C)$ are I, II, IV, V, and VI, and the regions that correspond to $(A \cup B) \cap (A \cup C)$ are also I, II, IV, V, and VI. The results show that both statements are represented by the same regions, namely, I, II, IV, V, and VI, and therefore $A \cup (B \cap C) = (A \cup B) \cap (A \cup C)$ for all sets A, B, and C. ∎

In Example 4, we proved that $A \cup (B \cap C) = (A \cup B) \cap (A \cup C)$ for all sets A, B, and C. Show that this statement is true for the specific sets $U = \{1, 2, 3, 4, 5, 6, 7, 8, 9, 10\}$, $A = \{1, 2, 3, 7\}$, $B = \{2, 3, 4, 5, 7, 9\}$, and $C = \{1, 4, 7, 8, 10\}$.

De Morgan's Laws

In set theory, logic, and other branches of mathematics, a pair of related theorems known as De Morgan's laws make it possible to transform statements and formulas into alternative and often more convenient forms. In set theory, *De Morgan's laws* are symbolized as follows.

De Morgan's Laws

1. $(A \cap B)' = A' \cup B'$
2. $(A \cup B)' = A' \cap B'$

Law 2 was verified in Example 3. We suggest that you verify law 1 at this time. The laws were expressed verbally by William of Ockham in the fourteenth century. In the nineteenth century, Augustus De Morgan expressed them mathematically. De Morgan's laws will be discussed more thoroughly in Chapter 3, Logic.

SECTION 2.4 *Exercises*

Warm Up Exercises

In Exercises 1–4, fill in the blank with an appropriate word, phrase, or symbol(s).

1. The number of regions created when constructing a Venn diagram with three overlapping sets is _____ .

2. a) When constructing a Venn diagram with three overlapping sets, region _____ is generally completed first.

   b) When constructing a Venn diagram with three overlapping sets, after completing region V, the next regions generally completed are II, IV, and _____ .

3. Complete DeMorgan's laws:

   a) $(A \cup B)' =$ _____

   b) $(A \cap B)' =$ _____

4. When using Venn diagrams to verify or determine whether set statements are equal we use _____ reasoning.

Practice the Skills/Problem Solving

5. A Venn diagram contains three sets, A, B, and C, as in Fig. 2.15 on page 68. If region V contains 4 elements and there are 12 elements in $B \cap C$, how many elements belong in region VI? Explain.

6. A Venn diagram contains three sets, *A*, *B*, and *C*, as in Fig. 2.15 on page 68. If region V contains 4 elements and there are 9 elements in $A \cap B$, how many elements belong in region II? Explain.

7. a) For $U = \{1, 2, 3, 4, 5\}$, $A = \{1, 4, 5\}$, and $B = \{1, 4, 5\}$, does $A \cup B = A \cap B$?

   b) By observing the answer to part (a), can we conclude that $A \cup B = A \cap B$ for all sets *A* and *B*? Explain.

   c) Using a Venn diagram, determine if $A \cup B = A \cap B$ for all sets *A* and *B*.

8. Construct a Venn diagram illustrating the following sets.
$$U = \{a, b, c, d, e, f, g, h, i, j\}$$
$$A = \{c, d, e, g, h, i\}$$
$$B = \{a, c, d, g\}$$
$$C = \{c, f, i, j\}$$

9. Construct a Venn diagram illustrating the following sets.
$U = \{$*Cinderella, Pinochio, Ratatouille, Fantasia, Dumbo, Bambi, Pocahontas, Hercules, Mulan, Tarzan, Cars*$\}$

$A = \{$*Bambi, Hercules, Pocahontas, Tarzan*$\}$

$B = \{$*Ratatouille, Bambi, Mulan, Hercules*$\}$

$C = \{$*Pocahontas, Cinderella, Bambi, Ratatouille, Fantasia*$\}$

▲ *Bambi*

10. Construct a Venn diagram illustrating the following sets.
$U = \{$microwave oven, freezer, dishwasher, refrigerator, washer, dryer, toaster, blender, food processor, iron$\}$

$A = \{$toaster, blender, iron, dishwasher, washer, dryer$\}$

$B = \{$dishwasher, iron, freezer$\}$

$C = \{$washer, dryer, iron, freezer, microwave oven$\}$

11. Construct a Venn diagram illustrating the following sets.
$U = \{$American Eagle, Best Buy, Wal-Mart, Kmart, Target, Sears, JCPenney, Costco, Kohl's, Gap, Gap Kids, Foot Locker, Old Navy, Macy's$\}$

$A = \{$American Eagle, Wal-Mart, Target, JCPenney, Old Navy$\}$

$B = \{$Best Buy, Target, Costco, Old Navy, Macy's$\}$

$C = \{$Target, Sears, Kohl's, Gap, JCPenney$\}$

12. Construct a Venn diagram illustrating the following sets.
$U = \{$Louis Armstrong, Glenn Miller, Stan Kenton, Charlie Parker, Duke Ellington, Benny Goodman, Count Basie, John Coltrane, Dizzy Gillespie, Miles Davis, Thelonius Monk$\}$

$A = \{$Stan Kenton, Count Basie, Dizzy Gillespie, Duke Ellington, Thelonius Monk$\}$

$B = \{$Louis Armstrong, Glenn Miller, Count Basie, Duke Ellington, Miles Davis$\}$

$C = \{$Count Basie, Miles Davis, Stan Kenton, Charlie Parker, Duke Ellington$\}$

13. *Olympic Medals* Consider the following table, which shows countries that won at least 25 medals in the 2008 Summer Olympics. Let the countries in the table represent the universal set.

Country	Gold Medals	Silver Medals	Bronze Medals	Total Medals
United States	36	38	36	110
China	51	21	28	100
Russia	23	21	28	72
Great Britain	19	13	15	47
Australia	14	15	17	46
Germany	16	10	15	41
France	7	16	17	40
South Korea	13	10	8	31
Italy	8	10	10	28
Ukraine	7	5	15	27
Japan	9	6	10	25

Source: United States Olympic Committee.

Let $A =$ set of countries that won at least 30 gold medals.
Let $B =$ set of countries that won at least 15 silver medals.
Let $C =$ set of countries that won at least 10 bronze medals.

Construct a Venn diagram that illustrates the sets *A, B,* and *C*.

14. *Popular TV Shows* Construct a Venn diagram illustrating the following sets.

$U = \{$*American Idol (AI), CSI, Dancing with the Stars (DWS), Family Guy (FG), Gossip Girl (GG), Monday Night Football (MNF), NCIS, Sunday Night Football (SNF), Survivor (S)*$\}$.

$A = \{$*AI, CSI, DWS, SNF, NCIS*$\}$

$B = \{$*AI, DWS, SNF, NCIS, MNF*$\}$

$C = \{$*AI, CSI, SNF, NCIS, MNF, S*$\}$

Rankings of Fruit-Producing Countries For Exercises 15–20, use the following table, which shows the top 10 countries for production of apples, oranges, and nuts, The universal set is the set of countries listed in the table.

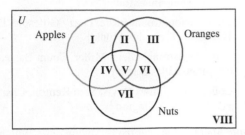

Figure 2.21

Ranking of Fruit-Producing countries		
Apples	**Oranges**	**Nuts**
1. China	1. Brazil	1. United States
2. United States	2. United States	2. Indonesia
3. Iran	3. Mexico	3. Mexico
4. Turkey	4. India	4. Ethiopia
5. Russia	5. China	5. China
6. Italy	6. Spain	6. Australia
7. India	7. Indonesia	7. Guatemala
8. France	8. Iran	8. Portugal
9. Chile	9. Italy	9. Thailand
10. Argentina	10. Egypt	10. Philippines

Source: Food and Agriculture of the United Nations

Indicate in which region, I–VIII in Fig. 2.21, each of the following countries belongs.

15. Italy   **16.** United States

17. Canada   **18.** Portugal

19. Spain   **20.** Mexico

Figures In Exercises 21–32, indicate in Fig. 2.22 the region in which each of the figures would be placed.

Figure 2.22

21.   **22.**   **23.** ▲

24. ⬤   **25.** ⬢   **26.** ◼

27. ●   **28.** ▫   **29.** ▲

30.   **31.** ⬤   **32.** ○

Senate Bills During a session of the U.S. Senate, three bills were voted on. The votes of six senators are shown below the figure. Determine in which region of Fig. 2.23 each senator would be placed. The set labeled Bill 1 represents the set of senators who voted yes on Bill 1, and so on.

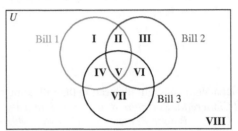

Figure 2.23

SENATOR	BILL 1	BILL 2	BILL 3
33. Hutchinson	yes	no	no
34. Kerry	no	no	yes
35. McCain	no	no	no
36. Mikulski	yes	yes	yes
37. Rand	no	yes	yes
38. Reid	no	yes	no

In Exercises 39–52, use the Venn diagram in Fig. 2.24 to list the sets in roster form.

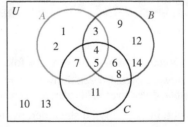

Figure 2.24

39. A **40.** U

41. B **42.** C

43. $A \cap B$ **44.** $A \cap C$

45. $(B \cap C)'$ **46.** $A \cap B \cap C$

47. $A \cup B$ **48.** $B \cup C$

49. $(A \cup C)'$ **50.** $A \cap (B \cup C)$

51. A' **52.** $(A \cup B \cup C)'$

In Exercises 53–60, use Venn diagrams to determine whether the following statements are equal for all sets A and B.

53. $(A \cap B)'$, $A' \cup B'$

54. $(A \cap B)'$, $A' \cup B$

55. $A' \cup B'$, $A \cap B$

56. $(A \cup B)'$, $(A \cap B)'$

57. $A' \cup B'$, $(A \cup B)'$

58. $A' \cap B'$, $A \cup B'$

59. $(A' \cap B)'$, $A \cup B'$

60. $A' \cap B'$, $(A' \cap B')'$

In Exercises 61–70, use Venn diagrams to determine whether the following statements are equal for all sets A, B, and C.

61. $A \cap (B \cup C)$, $(A \cap B) \cup C$

62. $A \cup (B \cap C)$, $(B \cap C) \cup A$

63. $A \cap (B \cup C)$, $(B \cup C) \cap A$

64. $A \cup (B \cap C)'$, $A' \cap (B' \cup C)$

65. $A \cap (B \cup C)$, $(A \cap B) \cup (A \cap C)$

66. $A \cup (B \cap C)$, $(A \cup B) \cap (A \cup C)$

67. $A \cup (B \cup C)'$, $A \cup (B' \cap C')$

68. $(A \cup B) \cap (B \cup C)$, $B \cup (A \cap C)$

69. $(A \cup B)' \cap C$, $(A' \cup C') \cap (B' \cup C)$

70. $(C \cap B)' \cup (A \cap B)'$, $A \cap (B \cap C)$

In Exercises 71–74, use set statements to write a description of the shaded area. Use union, intersection and complement as necessary. More than one answer may be possible.

71.

72.

73.

74.

75. Let

$$U = \{1, 2, 3, 4, 5, 6, 7, 8, 9, 10\}$$
$$A = \{1, 2, 3, 4\}$$
$$B = \{3, 6, 7\}$$
$$C = \{6, 7, 9\}$$

a) Show that $(A \cup B) \cap C = (A \cap C) \cup (B \cap C)$ for these sets.

b) Make up your own sets A, B, and C. Verify that $(A \cup B) \cap C = (A \cap C) \cup (B \cap C)$ for your sets A, B, and C.

c) Use Venn diagrams to verify that $(A \cup B) \cap C = (A \cap C) \cup (B \cap C)$ for all sets A, B, and C.

76. Let

$$U = \{a, b, c, d, e, f, g, h, i\}$$
$$A = \{a, c, d, e, f\}$$
$$B = \{c, d\}$$
$$C = \{a, b, c, d, e\}$$

a) Determine whether $(A \cup C)' \cap B = (A \cap C)' \cap B$ for these sets.

b) Make up your own sets, A, B, and C. Determine whether $(A \cup C)' \cap B = (A \cap C)' \cap B$ for your sets.

c) Determine whether $(A \cup C)' \cap B = (A \cap C)' \cap B$ for all sets A, B, and C.

77. *Blood Types* A hematology text gives the following information on percentages of the different types of blood worldwide.

Type	Positive Blood, %	Negative Blood, %
A	37	6
O	32	6.5
B	11	2
AB	5	0.5

Construct a Venn diagram similar to the one in Example 2 and place the correct percentage in each of the eight regions.

78. Define each of the eight regions in Fig. 2.25 using sets A, B, and C and a set operation. (*Hint:* $A \cap B' \cap C'$ defines region I.)

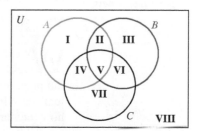

Figure 2.25

79. *Categorizing Contracts* J & C Mechanical Contractors wants to classify its projects. The contractors categorize set *A* as construction projects, set *B* as plumbing projects, and set *C* as projects with a budget greater than $300,000.

   a) Draw a Venn diagram that can be used to categorize the company projects according to the listed criteria.

   b) Determine the region of the diagram that contains construction projects and plumbing projects with a budget greater than $300,000. Describe the region using sets *A*, *B*, and *C* with set operations. Use union, intersection, and complement as necessary.

   c) Determine the region of the diagram that contains plumbing projects with a budget greater than $300,000 that are not construction projects. Describe the region using sets *A*, *B* and *C* with set operations. Use union, intersection, and complement as necessary.

   d) Determine the region of the diagram that contains construction projects and nonplumbing projects whose budget is less than or equal to $300,000. Describe the region using sets *A*, *B*, and *C* with set operations. Use union, intersection, and complement as necessary.

Challenge Problem/Group Activity

80. We were able to determine the number of elements in the union of two sets with the formula

$$n(A \cup B) = n(A) + n(B) - n(A \cap B).$$

Can you determine a formula for finding the number of elements in the union of three sets? In other words, write a formula to determine $n(A \cup B \cup C)$. [*Hint*: The formula

will contain each of the following: $n(A)$, $n(B)$, $n(C)$, $n(A \cap B \cap C')$, $n(A \cap B' \cap C)$, $n(A' \cap B \cap C)$, and $2n(A \cap B \cap C)$.

Recreational Mathematics

81. a) Construct a Venn diagram illustrating four sets, *A*, *B*, *C*, and *D*. (*Hint*: Four circles cannot be used, and you should end up with 16 *distinct* regions.) Have fun!

   b) Label each region with a set statement (see Exercise 78). Check all 16 regions to make sure that *each is distinct*.

Internet/Research Activity

82. The two Venn diagrams below illustrate what happens when colors are added or subtracted. Do research in an art text, an encyclopedia, the Internet, or another source and write a report explaining the creation of the colors in the Venn diagrams, using such terms as union of colors and subtraction (or difference) of colors.

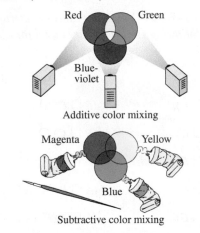

Additive color mixing

Subtractive color mixing

Applications of Sets

▲ *We can use a Venn diagram to determine how many members of a health club took a particular fitness class.*

The members of a health club were surveyed about taking fitness classes at the club. Suppose the results of the survey show how many members took a yoga class, how many members took a spinning class, and how many members took a class in yoga and a class in spinning. How can the manager of the club use this information to determine how many members took only a yoga class? In this section, we will learn how to use Venn diagrams to answer this type of question.

Why *This is Important* As you read through this section, you will see many real-life applications of set theory.

W e can solve practical problems involving sets by using the problem-solving process discussed in Chapter 1: Understand the problem, devise a plan, carry out the plan, and then examine and check the results. First determine: What is the problem? or What am I looking for? To devise the plan, list all the facts that are given and how they are related. *Look for key words or phrases* such as "only set *A*," "set *A* and set *B*," "set *A* or set *B*," "set *A* and set *B* and not set *C*." Remember that *and* means intersection, *or* means union, and *not* means complement. The problems we solve in this section contain two or three sets of elements, which can be represented in a Venn diagram. Our plan will generally include drawing a Venn diagram, labeling the diagram, and filling in the regions of the diagram.

Whenever possible, follow the procedure in Section 2.4 for completing the Venn diagram and then answer the questions. *Remember: When drawing Venn diagrams, we generally start with the intersection of the sets and work outward.*

Example 1 *Yogurt Taste Test*

A yogurt company wishes to introduce a new yogurt flavor. The company is considering two flavors: raspberry cheesecake (R) and orange creme (O). In a survey of 250 people it was found that

180 people liked raspberry cheesecake.

139 people liked orange creme.

82 people liked both flavors.

Of those surveyed, how many people

a) did not like either raspberry cheesecake or orange creme?

b) liked raspberry cheesecake, but not orange creme?

c) liked orange creme, but not raspberry cheesecake?

d) liked either raspberry cheesecake or orange creme?

Solution The problem provides the following information.

The number of people surveyed is 250: $n(U) = 250$.

The number of people surveyed who liked raspberry cheesecake is 180: $n(R) = 180$.

The number of people surveyed who liked orange creme is 139: $n(O) = 139$.

The number of people surveyed who liked both raspberry cheesecake and orange creme is 82: $n(R \cap O) = 82$.

We illustrate this information on the Venn diagram shown in Fig. 2.26. We already know that $R \cap O$ corresponds to region II. Because $n(R \cap O) = 82$, we write 82 in region II. Set R consists of regions I and II. We know that set R, the number of people who liked raspberry cheesecake, contains 180 people. Therefore, region I contains $180 - 82 = 98$ people. We write the number 98 in region I. Set O consists of regions II and III. Because $n(O) = 139$, the total in these two regions must be 139. Region II contains 82, leaving $139 - 82$, or 57, for region III. We write 57 in region III.

The total number of people surveyed who liked raspberry cheesecake or orange creme is found by adding the numbers in regions I, II, and III. Therefore $n(R \cup O) = 98 + 82 + 57 = 237$. The number in region IV is the difference between $n(U)$ and $n(R \cup O)$. There are $250 - 237$, or 13, members in region IV.

a) The people surveyed who did not like either raspberry cheesecake or orange creme are those people in the universal set who are not contained in set R or set O. The 13 people in region IV did not like raspberry cheesecake or orange creme.

b) The 98 people in region I are those people surveyed who liked raspberry cheesecake, but not orange creme.

c) The 57 people in region III are those people surveyed who liked orange creme, but not raspberry cheesecake.

d) The people in regions I, II, or III are those people surveyed who liked either raspberry cheesecake or orange creme. Thus, $98 + 82 + 57$, or 237, people surveyed liked either raspberry cheesecake or orange creme. Notice that the 82 people in region II who like both flavors are included in those people surveyed who liked either raspberry cheesecake or orange creme.

Figure 2.26

Similar problems involving three sets can be solved, as illustrated in Example 2.

Example 2 *Software Purchases*

CompUSA has recorded recent sales for three types of computer software: games, educational software, and utility programs. The following information regarding software purchases was obtained from a survey of 893 customers.

545 purchased games.

497 purchased educational software.

290 purchased utility programs.

297 purchased games and educational software.

196 purchased educational software and utility programs.

205 purchased games and utility programs.

157 purchased all three types of software.

Use a Venn diagram to answer the following questions. How many customers purchased

a) none of these types of software?

b) only games?

c) at least one of these types of software?

d) exactly two of these types of software?

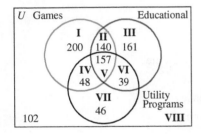

Figure 2.27

Solution   Begin by constructing a Venn diagram with three overlapping circles. One circle represents games, another educational software, and the third utilities. See Fig 2.27. Label the eight regions.

Whenever possible, work from the center of the diagram outward. First fill in region V. Since 157 customers purchased all three types of software, we place 157 in region V. Next determine the number to be placed in region II. Regions II and V together represent the customers who purchased both games and educational software. Since 297 customers purchased both of these types of software, the sum of the numbers in these regions must be 297. Since 157 have already been placed in region V, 297 − 157 = 140 must be placed in region II. Now we determine the number to be placed in region IV. Since 205 customers purchased both games and utility programs, the sum of the numbers in regions IV and V must be 205. Since 157 have already been placed in region V, 205 − 157 = 48 must be placed in region IV. Now determine the number to be placed in region VI. A total of 196 customers purchased educational software and utility programs. The numbers in regions V and VI must total 196. Since 157 have already been placed in region V, the number to be placed in region VI is 196 − 157 = 39.

Now that we have determined the numbers for regions V, II, IV, and VI, we can determine the numbers to be placed in regions I, III, and VII. We are given that 545 customers purchased games. The sum of the numbers in regions I, II, IV, and V must be 545. To determine the number to be placed in region I, subtract the amounts in regions II, IV, and V from 545. There must be 545 − 140 − 48 − 157 = 200 in region I. Determine the numbers to be placed in regions III and VII in a similar manner.

Region III = 497 − 140 − 157 − 39 = 161
Region VII = 290 − 48 − 157 − 39 = 46

Now that we have determined the numbers in regions I through VII, we can determine the number to be placed in region VIII. Adding the numbers in regions I through VII yields a sum of 791. The difference between the total number of customers surveyed, 893, and the sum of the numbers in regions I through VII must be placed in region VIII.

Region VIII = 893 − 791 = 102

Now that we have completed the Venn diagram, we can answer the questions.

a) One hundred two customers did not purchase any of these types of software. These customers are indicated in region VIII.

b) Region I represents those customers who purchased only games. Thus, 200 customers purchased only games.

c) The words *at least one* mean "one or more." All those in regions I through VII purchased at least one of the types of software. The sum of the numbers in regions I through VII is 791, so 791 customers purchased at least one of the types of software.

d) The customers in regions II, IV, and VI purchased exactly two of the types of software. Summing the numbers in these regions $140 + 48 + 39$ we find that 227 customers purchased exactly two of these types of software. Notice that we did not include the customers in region V. Those customers purchased all three types of software.

The procedure to work problems like those given in Example 2 is generally the same. Start by completing region V. Next complete regions II, IV, and VI. Then complete regions I, III, and VII. Finally, complete region VIII. When you are constructing Venn diagrams, be sure to check your work carefully.

Example 3 *Travel Packages*

Liberty Travel surveyed 125 potential customers. The following information was obtained.

    68 wished to travel to Hawaii.

    53 wished to travel to Las Vegas.

    47 wished to travel to Disney World.

    34 wished to travel to Hawaii and Las Vegas.

    26 wished to travel to Las Vegas and Disney World.

    23 wished to travel to Hawaii and Disney World.

    18 wished to travel to all three destinations.

Use a Venn diagram to answer the following questions. How many of those surveyed

a) did not wish to travel to any of these destinations?

b) wished to travel only to Hawaii?

c) wished to travel to Disney World *and* Las Vegas, but not to Hawaii?

d) wished to travel to Disney World *or* Las Vegas, but not to Hawaii?

e) wished to travel to exactly one of these destinations?

▲ Hawaii

Solution The Venn diagram is constructed using the procedures we outlined in Example 2. The diagram is illustrated in Fig. 2.28. We suggest you construct the diagram by yourself now and check your diagram with Fig. 2.28.

a) Twenty-two potential customers did not wish to travel to any of these destinations (see region VIII).

b) Twenty-nine potential customers wished to travel only to Hawaii (see region I).

c) Those potential customers in region VI wished to travel to Disney World *and* Las Vegas, but not to Hawaii. Therefore, eight customers satisfied the criteria.

d) The word *or* in this type of problem means one or the other or both. All the potential customers in regions II, III, IV, V, VI, and VII wished to travel to Disney World or Las Vegas. Those in regions II, IV, and V also wished to travel to Hawaii. The potential customers that wished to travel to Disney World or Las Vegas, but not to Hawaii, are found by adding the numbers in regions III, VI, and VII. There are $16 + 8 + 11 = 35$ potential customers who satisfy the criteria.

e) Those potential customers in regions I, III, and VII wished to travel to exactly one of the destinations. Therefore, $29 + 16 + 11 = 56$ customers wished to travel to exactly one of these destinations.

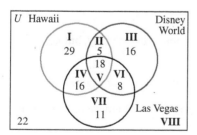
Figure 2.28

SECTION 2.5   *Exercises*

Practice The Skills/Problem Solving

In Exercises 1–15, draw a Venn diagram to obtain the answers.

1. *Market Purchases* During the fall festival at Wambach's Farmer's market, 200 customers made the following purchases.

    109 purchased pumpkins.
    98 purchased pies.
    61 purchased both pumpkins and pies.

    Of those surveyed,

    a) how many purchased only pumpkins?

    b) how many purchased only pies?

    c) how many did not purchase either of these items?

2. *Landscape Purchases* Agway Lawn and Garden collected the following information regarding purchases from 130 of its customers.

    74 purchased shrubs.
    70 purchased trees.
    41 purchased both shrubs and trees.

    Of those surveyed,

    a) how many purchased only shrubs?

    b) how many purchased only trees?

    c) how many did not purchase either of these items?

3. *Real Estate* The Maiellos are moving to Wilmington, Delaware. Their real estate agent located 83 houses listed for sale, in the Wilmington area, in their price range. Of these houses listed for sale,

    47 had a family room.
    42 had a deck.
    30 had a family room and a deck.

    How many had

    a) a family room but not a deck?

    b) a deck but not a family room?

    c) either a family room or a deck?

4. *Racing* Fleet Foot Racing interviewed 150 long-distance runners to determine the type of races in which they participated. The following information was determined.

    102 participated in a marathon.
    93 participated in a triathlon.
    55 participated in both a marathon and a triathlon.

How many

a) participated in only a marathon?

b) participated in only a triathlon?

c) participated in either a marathon or a triathlon?

d) had not participated in either a marathon or a triathlon?

5. *Cultural Activities* Thirty-three U.S. cities were researched to determine whether they had a professional sports team, a symphony, or a children's museum. The following information was determined.

    16 had a professional sports team.
    17 had a symphony.
    15 had a children's museum.
    11 had a professional sports team and a symphony.
    7 had a professional sports team and a children's museum.
    9 had a symphony and children's museum.
    5 had all three activities.

How many of the cities surveyed had

a) only a professional sports team?

b) a professional sports team and a symphony, but not a children's museum?

c) a professional sports team or a symphony?

d) a professional sports team or a symphony, but not a children's museum?

e) exactly two of the activities?

6. *Amusement Parks* In a survey of 85 amusement parks, it was found that

    24 had a hotel on site.
    55 had water slides.
    38 had a wave pool.
    13 had a hotel on site and water slides.
    10 had a hotel on site and a wave pool.
    19 had water slides and a wave pool.
    7 had all three features.

How many of the amusement parks surveyed had

a) only water slides?

b) exactly one of these features?

c) at least one of these features?

d) exactly two of these features?

e) none of these features?

7. ***Book Purchases*** A survey of 85 customers was taken at Barnes & Noble regarding the types of books purchased. The survey found that

    44 purchased mysteries.

    33 purchased science fiction.

    29 purchased romance novels.

    13 purchased mysteries and science fiction.

    5 purchased science fiction and romance novels.

    11 purchased mysteries and romance novels.

    2 purchased all three types of books.

How many of the customers surveyed purchased

a) only mysteries?

b) mysteries and science fiction, but not romance novels?

c) mysteries or science fiction?

d) mysteries or science fiction, but not romance novels?

e) exactly two types?

8. ***Movies*** A survey of 350 customers was taken at Regal Cinemas in Austin, Texas, regarding the type of movies customers liked. The following information was determined.

    196 liked dramas.

    153 liked comedies.

    88 liked science fiction.

    59 liked dramas and comedies.

    37 liked dramas and science fiction.

    32 liked comedies and science fiction.

    21 liked all three types of movies.

Of the customers surveyed, how many liked

a) none of these types of movies?

b) only dramas?

c) exactly one of these types of movies?

d) exactly two of these types of movies?

e) dramas or comedies?

9. ***Jobs at a Restaurant*** Panera Bread compiled the following information regarding 30 of its employees. The following was determined.

    8 cooked food.

    9 washed dishes.

    18 operated the cash register.

    4 cooked food and washed dishes.

    5 washed dishes and operated the cash register.

    3 cooked food and operated the cash register.

    2 did all three jobs.

How many of the employees

a) only cooked food ?

b) only operated the cash register?

c) washed dishes and operated the cash register but did not cook food?

d) washed dishes or operated the cash register but did not cook food?

e) did at least two of these jobs?

10. ***Electronic Devices*** In a survey of college students, it was found that

    356 owned an iPod.

    293 owned a laptop.

    285 owned a gaming system.

    193 owned an iPod and a laptop.

    200 owned an iPod and a gaming system.

    139 owned a laptop and a gaming system.

    68 owned an iPod, a laptop, and a gaming system.

    26 owned none of these devices.

a) How many college students were surveyed?

Of the college students surveyed, how many owned

b) an iPod and a gaming system, but not a laptop?

c) a laptop, but neither an iPod nor a gaming system?

d) exactly two of these devices?

e) at least one of these devices?

11. ***Homeowners' Insurance Policies*** A committee of the Florida legislature decided to analyze 350 homeowners' insurance policies to determine if the consumers' homes

were covered for damage due to sinkholes, mold, and floods. The following results were determined.

170 homes were covered for damage due to sinkholes.

172 homes were covered for damage due to mold.

234 homes were covered for damage due to floods.

105 homes were covered for damage due to sinkholes and mold.

115 homes were covered for damage due to mold and floods.

109 homes were covered for damage due to sinkholes and floods.

78 homes were covered for damage due to all three conditions.

How many of the homes

a) were covered for damage due to mold but were not covered for damage due to sinkholes?

b) were covered for damage due to sinkholes or mold?

c) were covered for damage due to mold and floods but were not covered for damage due to sinkholes?

d) were not covered for damage due to any of the three conditions?

12. *Appetizers Survey* Da Tulio's Restaurant hired Dennis Goldstein to determine what kind of appetizers customers liked. He surveyed 100 people, with the following results: 78 liked shrimp cocktail, 56 liked mozzarella sticks, and 35 liked both shrimp cocktail and mozzarella sticks. Every person interviewed liked one or the other or both kinds of appetizers. Does this result seem correct? Explain your answer.

13. *Discovering an Error* An immigration agent sampled cars going from the United States into Canada. In his report, he indicated that of the 85 cars sampled,

35 cars were driven by women.

53 cars were driven by U.S. citizens.

43 cars had two or more passengers.

27 cars were driven by women who are U.S. citizens.

25 cars were driven by women and had two or more passengers.

20 cars were driven by U.S. citizens and had two or more passengers.

15 cars were driven by women who are U.S. citizens and had two or more passengers.

After his supervisor reads the report, she explains to the agent that he made a mistake. Explain how his supervisor knew that the agent's report contained an error.

Challenge Problems/Group Activities

14. *Parks* A survey of 300 parks showed the following.

15 had only camping.

20 had only hiking trails.

35 had only picnicking.

185 had camping.

140 had camping and hiking trails.

125 had camping and picnicking.

210 had hiking trails.

Determine the number of parks that

a) had at least one of these features.

b) had all three features.

c) did not have any of these features.

d) had exactly two of these features.

15. *Surveying Farmers* A survey of 500 farmers in a midwestern state showed the following.

125 grew only wheat.

110 grew only corn.

90 grew only oats.

200 grew wheat.

60 grew wheat and corn.

50 grew wheat and oats.

180 grew corn.

Determine the number of farmers who

a) grew at least one of the three.

b) grew all three.

c) did not grow any of the three.

d) grew exactly two of the three.

16. *Family Reunion* When the Montesano family members discussed where their annual reunion should take place, they found that of all the family members,

   8 would not go to a park.

   7 would not go to a beach.

   11 would not go to the family cottage.

   3 would go to neither a park nor a beach.

   4 would go to neither a beach nor the family cottage.

   6 would go to neither a park nor the family cottage.

   2 would not go to a park or a beach or to the family cottage.

   1 would go to all three places.

   What is the total number of family members?

Recreational Mathematics

17. *Number of Elements* A universal set U consists of 12 elements. If sets A, B, and C are proper subsets of U and $n(U) = 12$, $n(A \cap B) = n(A \cap C) = n(B \cap C) = 6$, $n(A \cap B \cap C) = 4$, and $n(A \cup B \cup C) = 10$, determine

a) $n(A \cup B)$

b) $n(A' \cup C)$

c) $n(A \cap B)'$

SECTION 2.6   Infinite Sets

▲ *Georg Cantor, founder of set theory*

Which set is larger, the set of integers or the set of even integers? One might argue that because the set of even integers is a subset of the set of integers, the set of integers must be larger than the set of even integers. Yet both sets are infinite sets, so how can we determine which set is larger? This question puzzled mathematicians for centuries until 1874, when Georg Cantor developed a method of determining the cardinal number of an infinite set. In this section, we will discuss infinite sets and how to determine the number of elements in an infinite set.

Why *This is Important* The concept of infinity and which sets contain more elements has led to the expansion and understanding of many mathematical and scientific concepts.

On page 45, we state that a finite set is a set in which the number of elements is zero or the number of elements can be expressed as a natural number. On page 46, we define a one-to-one correspondence. To determine the number of elements in a finite set, we can place the set in a one-to-one correspondence with a subset of the set of counting numbers. For example, the set $A = \{\#, ?, \$\}$ can be placed in one-to-one correspondence with set $B = \{1, 2, 3\}$, a subset of the set of counting numbers.

$$A = \{\#, \, ?, \, \$\}$$
$$\downarrow \; \downarrow \; \downarrow$$
$$B = \{1, \, 2, \, 3\}$$

Because the cardinal number of set B is 3, the cardinal number of set A is also 3. Any two sets, such as set A and set B, that can be placed in a one-to-one correspondence must have the same number of elements (therefore the same cardinality) and must be equivalent sets. Note that $n(A)$ and $n(B)$ both equal 3.

German mathematician Georg Cantor (1845–1918), known as the father of set theory, thought about sets that were not bounded. He called an unbounded set an *infinite set* and provided the following definition.

Definition: **Infinite Set**

An **infinite set** is a set that can be placed in a one-to-one correspondence with a proper subset of itself.

In Example 1, we use Cantor's definition of an infinite set to show that the set of counting numbers is infinite.

Example 1 *The Set of Natural Numbers*

Show that $N = \{1, 2, 3, 4, 5, \ldots, n, \ldots\}$ is an infinite set.

Solution To show that the set N is infinite, we establish a one-to-one correspondence between the counting numbers and a proper subset of itself. By removing the first element from the set of counting numbers, we get the set $\{2, 3, 4, 5, 6, \ldots\}$, which is a proper subset of the set of counting numbers. Now we establish the one-to-one correspondence.

$$\text{Counting numbers} = \{1, 2, 3, 4, 5, \ldots, \quad n, \ldots\}$$
$$\downarrow \downarrow \downarrow \downarrow \downarrow \qquad \downarrow$$
$$\text{Proper subset} \quad = \{2, 3, 4, 5, 6, \ldots, n+1, \ldots\}$$

Note that for any number, n, in the set of counting numbers, its corresponding number in the proper subset is one greater, or $n+1$. We have now shown the desired one-to-one correspondence, and thus the set of counting numbers is infinite. ∎

Note in Example 1 that we showed the pairing of the general terms $n \rightarrow (n+1)$. Showing a one-to-one correspondence of infinite sets requires showing the pairing of the general terms in the two infinite sets.

In the set of counting numbers, n represents the general term. For any other set of numbers, the general term will be different. The general term in any set should be written in terms of n such that when 1 is substituted for n in the general term, we get the first number in the set; when 2 is substituted for n in the general term, we get the second number in the set; when 6 is substituted for n in the general term, we get the sixth number in the set; and so on.

Consider the set $\{4, 9, 14, 19, \ldots\}$. Suppose we want to write the general term for this set (or sequence) of numbers. What would the general term be? The numbers differ by 5, so the general term will be of the form $5n$ plus or minus some number. Substituting 1 for n yields $5(1)$, or 5. Because the first number in the set is 4, we need to subtract 1 from the 5. Thus, the general term is $5n - 1$. Note that when $n = 1$, the value is $5(1) - 1$ or 4; when $n = 2$, the value is $5(2) - 1$ or 9; when $n = 3$, the value is $5(3) - 1$ or 14; and so on. Therefore, we write the set of numbers with the general term as

$$\{4, 9, 14, 19, \ldots, 5n - 1, \ldots\}$$

Now that you are aware of how to determine the general term of a set of numbers, we can do some more problems involving sets.

Example 2 *The Set of Even Numbers*

Show that the set of even counting numbers $\{2, 4, 6, 8, \ldots, 2n, \ldots\}$ is an infinite set.

Solution   First create a proper subset of the set of even counting numbers by removing the first number from the set. Then establish a one-to-one correspondence.

Even counting numbers: $\{2, 4, 6, 8, \ldots, \quad 2n, \ldots\}$
$$\downarrow \downarrow \downarrow \downarrow \qquad \downarrow$$
Proper subset: $\{4, 6, 8, 10, \ldots, 2n + 2, \ldots\}$

A one-to-one correspondence exists between the two sets, so the set of even counting numbers is infinite.

Example 3   *The Set of Multiples of Five*

Show that the set $\{5, 10, 15, 20, \ldots, 5n, \ldots\}$ is an infinite set.

Solution

Given set: $\{5, 10, 15, 20, 25, \ldots, \quad 5n, \ldots\}$
$$\downarrow \downarrow \downarrow \downarrow \downarrow \qquad \downarrow$$
Proper subset: $\{10, 15, 20, 25, 30, \ldots, 5n + 5, \ldots\}$

Therefore, the given set is an infinite set.

Countable Sets

In his work with infinite sets, Cantor developed ideas on how to determine the cardinal number of an infinite set. He called the cardinal number of infinite sets "transfinite cardinal numbers" or "transfinite powers." He defined a set as *countable* if it is finite or if it can be placed in a one-to-one correspondence with the set of counting numbers. All infinite sets that can be placed in a one-to-one correspondence with the set of counting numbers have cardinal number *aleph-null*, symbolized $\aleph_0$ (the first Hebrew letter, aleph, with a zero subscript, read "null").

Example 4   *The Cardinal Number of the Set of Even Numbers*

Show that the set of even counting numbers has cardinal number $\aleph_0$.

Solution   In Example 2, we showed that the set of even counting numbers is infinite by setting up a one-to-one correspondence between the set and a proper subset of itself.

Now we will show that it is countable and has cardinality $\aleph_0$ by setting up a one-to-one correspondence between the set of counting numbers and the set of even counting numbers.

Counting numbers: $N = \{1, 2, 3, 4, \ldots, \quad n, \ldots\}$
$$\downarrow \downarrow \downarrow \downarrow \qquad \downarrow$$
Even counting numbers: $E = \{2, 4, 6, 8, \ldots, 2n, \ldots\}$

For each number n in the set of counting numbers, its corresponding number is $2n$. Since we found a one-to-one correspondence between the set of counting numbers and the set of even counting numbers, the set of even counting numbers is countable. Thus, the cardinal number of the set of even counting numbers is $\aleph_0$; that is, $n(E) = \aleph_0$. As we mentioned earlier, the set of even counting numbers is an infinite set, since it can be placed in a one-to-one correspondence with a proper subset of itself. Therefore, the set of even counting numbers is both infinite and countable.

Definition: Cardinal Number of Infinite Sets

Any set that can be placed in a one-to-one correspondence with the set of counting numbers has **cardinal number** (or cardinality) $\aleph_0$ and is infinite and is countable.

Example **5** *The Cardinal Number of the Set of Odd Numbers*

Show that the set of odd counting numbers has cardinality $\aleph_0$.

Solution To show that the set of odd counting numbers has cardinality $\aleph_0$, we need to show a one-to-one correspondence between the set of counting numbers and the set of odd counting numbers.

$$\text{Counting numbers:} \quad N = \{1, 2, 3, 4, 5, \ldots, \quad n \ , \ldots\}$$
$$\downarrow \downarrow \downarrow \downarrow \downarrow \qquad\qquad \downarrow$$
$$\text{Odd counting numbers:} \quad O = \{1, 3, 5, 7, 9, \ldots, 2n - 1, \ldots\}$$

Since there is a one-to-one correspondence, the odd counting numbers have cardinality $\aleph_0$; that is, $n(O) = \aleph_0$. ∎

We have shown that both the odd and the even counting numbers have cardinality $\aleph_0$. Merging the odd counting numbers with the even counting numbers gives the set of counting numbers, and we may reason that

$$\aleph_0 + \aleph_0 = \aleph_0$$

This result may seem strange, but it is true. What could such a statement mean? Well, consider a hotel with infinitely many rooms. If all the rooms are occupied, the hotel is, of course, full. If more guests appear, wanting accommodations, will they be turned away? The answer is *no,* for if the room clerk were to reassign each guest to a new room with a room number twice that of the present room, all the odd-numbered rooms would become unoccupied and there would be space for infinitely many more guests!

Cantor showed that there are different orders of infinity. Sets that are countable and have cardinal number $\aleph_0$ are the lowest order of infinity. Cantor showed that the set of integers and the set of rational numbers (fractions of the form p/q, where $q \neq 0$) are infinite sets with cardinality $\aleph_0$. He also showed that the set of real numbers (discussed in Chapter 5) could not be placed in a one-to-one correspondence with the set of counting numbers and that they have a higher order of infinity.

▲ *. . . where there's always room for one more. . .*

SECTION 2.6   *Exercises*

Warm Up Exercises

In exercises 1–2, fill in the blank with an appropriate word, phrase, or symbol(s).

1. A set that can be placed in a one-to-one correspondence with a proper subset of itself is called a(n) _____ set.

2. A set that is finite or can be placed in a one-to-one correspondence with the set of counting numbers is called a(n)_____ set.

Practice the Skills

In Exercises 3–12, show that the set is infinite by placing it in a one-to-one correspondence with a proper subset of itself. Be sure to show the pairing of the general terms in the sets.

3. $\{3, 4, 5, 6, 7, \ldots\}$

4. $\{30, 31, 32, 33, 34, \ldots\}$

5. $\{3, 5, 7, 9, 11, \ldots\}$

6. $\{20, 22, 24, 26, 28, \ldots\}$

7. $\{5, 9, 13, 17, 21, \ldots\}$

8. $\{6, 11, 16, 21, 26, \ldots\}$

9. $\{\frac{1}{2}, \frac{1}{4}, \frac{1}{6}, \frac{1}{8}, \frac{1}{10}, \ldots\}$

10. $\{1, \frac{1}{2}, \frac{1}{3}, \frac{1}{4}, \frac{1}{5}, \ldots\}$

11. $\{\frac{4}{11}, \frac{5}{11}, \frac{6}{11}, \frac{7}{11}, \frac{8}{11}, \ldots\}$

12. $\{\frac{6}{13}, \frac{7}{13}, \frac{8}{13}, \frac{9}{13}, \frac{10}{13}, \ldots\}$

In Exercises 13–22, show that the set has cardinal number $\aleph_0$ by establishing a one-to-one correspondence between the set of counting numbers and the given set. Be sure to show the pairing of the general terms in the sets.

13. $\{3, 6, 9, 12, 15, \dots\}$ **14.** $\{40, 41, 42, 43, 44, \dots\}$

15. $\{4, 6, 8, 10, 12, \dots\}$ **16.** $\{0, 2, 4, 6, 8, \dots\}$

17. $\{2, 5, 8, 11, 14, \dots\}$ **18.** $\{7, 11, 15, 19, 23, \dots\}$

19. $\{\frac{1}{3}, \frac{1}{6}, \frac{1}{9}, \frac{1}{12}, \frac{1}{15}, \dots\}$ **20.** $\{\frac{1}{2}, \frac{1}{4}, \frac{1}{6}, \frac{1}{8}, \dots\}$

21. $\{\frac{1}{3}, \frac{1}{4}, \frac{1}{5}, \frac{1}{6}, \frac{1}{7}, \dots\}$ **22.** $\{\frac{1}{2}, \frac{2}{3}, \frac{3}{4}, \frac{4}{5}, \frac{5}{6}, \dots\}$

Challenge Problems/Group Activities

In Exercises 23–26, show that the set has cardinality $\aleph_0$ by establishing a one-to-one correspondence between the set of counting numbers and the given set.

23. $\{1, 4, 9, 16, 25, \dots\}$ **24.** $\{2, 4, 8, 16, 32, \dots\}$

25. $\{3, 9, 27, 81, 243, \dots\}$ **26.** $\{\frac{1}{3}, \frac{1}{6}, \frac{1}{12}, \frac{1}{24}, \frac{1}{48}, \dots\}$

Recreational Mathematics

In Exercises 27–31, insert the symbol $<$, $>$, or $=$ in the shaded area to make a true statement.

27. $\aleph_0$ $\aleph_0 + \aleph_0$ **28.** $2\aleph_0$ $\aleph_0 + \aleph_0$

29. $2\aleph_0$ $\aleph_0$ **30.** $\aleph_0 + 5$ $\aleph_0 + 3$

31. $n(N)$ $\aleph_0$

32. There are a number of paradoxes (a statement that appears to be true and false at the same time) associated with infinite sets and the concept of infinity. One of these, called *Zeno's Paradox,* is named after the mathematician Zeno, born about 496 B.C. in Italy. According to Zeno's paradox, suppose Achelles starts out 1 meter behind a tortoise. Also, suppose Achelles walks 10 times as fast as the tortoise crawls. When Achelles reaches the point where the tortoise started, the tortoise is 1/10 of a meter ahead of Achelles; when Achelles reaches the point where the tortoise was 1/10 of a meter ahead, the tortoise is now 1/100 of a meter ahead; and so on. According to Zeno's Paradox, Achelles gets closer and closer to the tortoise but never catches up to the tortoise.

a) Do you believe the reasoning process is sound? If not, explain why not.

b) In actuality, if this situation were real, would Achelles ever pass the tortoise?

Internet/Research Activities

33. Do research to explain how Cantor proved that the set of rational numbers has cardinal number $\aleph_0$.

34. Do research to explain how it can be shown that the real numbers do not have cardinal number $\aleph_0$.

CHAPTER 2 | *Summary*

Important Facts and Concepts

Examples and Discussion

Section 2.1	
Methods Used to Indicate a Set	
Description	Example 1, page 43
Roster Form	Examples 2–3, 5–7 pages 44, 45
Set-Builder Notation	Examples 4–6, pages 44–45

Symbol	Meaning	
$\in$	is an element of	Examples 4–6, pages 44–45
$\notin$	is not an element of	
$n(A)$	number of elements in set A	
$\varnothing$ or $\{\ \}$	the empty set	
U	the universal set	

Section 2.2

Symbol	Meaning	
$\subseteq$	is a subset of	Examples 1 and 3, pages 52–53
$\not\subseteq$	is not a subset of	
$\subset$	is a proper subset of	
$\not\subset$	is not a proper subset of	

Number of distinct subsets of a finite set with n elements is 2^n.   Examples 4 and 5, pages 54

Section 2.3

Symbol	Meaning	
$'$	complement	Examples 1, 3–6, pages 57, 58–61
$\cap$	intersection	Examples 2, 3, 6, pages 58–61
$\cup$	union	Examples 4–6, pages 57–61
$-$	difference of two sets	Example 9, page 62
$\times$	cartesian product	Example 10, page 63

And is generally interpreted to mean *intersection*.   Examples 7 and 8, pages 61–62

Or is generally interpreted to mean *union*.   Examples 7 and 8, pages 61–62

For any sets A and B,   Examples 7 and 8, pages 61–62
$$n(A \cup B) = n(A) + n(B) - n(A \cap B)$$

Section 2.4

De Morgan's Laws

$$(A \cap B)' = A' \cup B'$$
$$(A \cup B)' = A' \cap B'$$

Example 3, page 71

Section 2.6

An **infinite set** is a set that can be placed in a one-to-one correspondence with a proper subset of itself.   Examples 1–5, pages 84–86, Discussion pages 83–84

$\aleph_0$ aleph-null   Examples 4–5, pages 85–86

Countable sets   Examples 4–5, pages 85–86

CHAPTER 2) Review Exercises

2.1, 2.2, 2.3, 2.4, 2.6

In Exercises 1–14, state whether each statement is true or false. If false, give a reason.

1. The set of cities located in the state of Indiana is a well-defined set.

2. The set of the three best movies is a well-defined set.

3. maple $\in$ {oak, elm, maple, sycamore}

4. { } $\subset \varnothing$

5. {3, 6, 9, 12, ... } and {2, 4, 6, 8, ... } are disjoint sets.

6. {$a, b, c,$ 1, 2} is an example of a set in roster form.

7. {purple, green, yellow} = {green, pink, yellow}

8. {apple, orange, banana, pear} is equivalent to {tomato, corn, spinach, radish}.

9. If A = {a, e, i, o, u}, then $n(A) = 5$.

10. A = {1, 3, 5, 7, ... } is a countable set.

11. A = {1, 4, 7, 10, ..., 31} is a finite set.

12. {2, 5, 7} $\subseteq$ {2, 5, 7, 10}.

13. {$x \mid x \in N$ and $3 < x \leq 9$} is a set in set-builder notation.

14. {$x \mid x \in N$ and $2 < x \leq 12$} $\subseteq$ {1, 2, 3, 4, 5, ..., 20}

In Exercises 15–18, express each set in roster form.

15. Set A is the set of odd natural numbers between 5 and 16.

16. Set B is the set of states that border Kansas.

17. $C = \{x \,|\, x \in N \text{ and } x < 162\}$

18. $D = \{x \,|\, x \in N \text{ and } 8 < x \leq 80\}$

In Exercises 19–22, express each set in set-builder notation.

19. Set A is the set of natural numbers between 50 and 150.

20. Set B is the set of natural numbers greater than 42.

21. Set C is the set of natural numbers less than 7.

22. Set D is the set of natural numbers between 27 and 51, inclusive.

In Exercises 23–26, express each set with a written description.

23. $A = \{x \,|\, x \text{ is a capital letter of the English alphabet from E through M inclusive}\}$

24. $B = \{\text{penny, nickel, dime, quarter, half-dollar}\}$

25. $C = \{a, b, c\}$

26. $D = \{x \,|\, 3 \leq x < 9\}$

In Exercises 27–36, let

$$U = \{1, 2, 3, 4, \dots, 10\}$$
$$A = \{1, 3, 5, 7\}$$
$$B = \{3, 7, 9, 10\}$$
$$C = \{1, 7, 10\}$$

Determine the following.

27. $A \cap B$

28. $A \cup B'$

29. $A' \cap B$

30. $(A \cup B)' \cup C$

31. $A - B$

32. $A - C'$

33. $A \times C$

34. $B \times A$

35. The number of subsets of set B

36. The number of proper subsets of set A

37. For the following sets, construct a Venn diagram and place the elements in the proper region.

$U = \{\text{lion, tiger, leopard, cheetah, puma, lynx, panther, jaguar}\}$

$A = \{\text{tiger, puma, lynx}\}$

$B = \{\text{lion, tiger, jaguar, panther}\}$

$C = \{\text{tiger, lynx, cheetah, panther}\}$

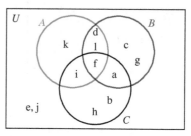

In Exercises 38–43, use Fig. 2.29 to determine the sets.

Figure 2.29

38. $A \cup B$ **39.** $A \cap B'$

40. $A \cup B \cup C$

41. $A \cap B \cap C$ **42.** $(A \cup B) \cap C$

43. $(A \cap B) \cup C$

Construct a Venn diagram to determine whether the following statements are true for all sets A, B, and C.

44. $(A' \cup B')' = A \cap B$

45. $(A \cup B') \cup (A \cup C') = A \cup (B \cap C)'$

In Exercises 46–51, use the following table, which shows the amount of sugar, in grams (g) and caffeine, in milligrams (mg), in an 8-oz serving of selected beverages. Let the beverages listed represent the universal set.

Beverage	Sugar (grams, g)	Caffeine (milligrams, mg)
Mountain Dew	31	37
Coca-Cola	27	23
Pepsi	27	25
Sprite	26	0
Brewed coffee	0	108
Brewed tea	0	47
Orange juice	24	0
Grape juice	40	0
Gatorade	14	0
Red Bull	26	76
Vitamin Water	13	17
Water	0	0

Source: International Food Information Council

Let A be the set of beverages that contain at least 20 g of sugar.

Let B be the set of beverages that contain at least 20 mg of caffeine.

Indicate in Fig 2.30 in which region, I–IV, each of the following beverages belongs.

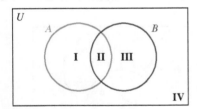

Figure 2.30

46. Pepsi   **47.** Brewed coffee

48. Orange juice   **49.** Vitamin Water

50. Gatorade   **51.** Mountain Dew

52. Red Bull

2.5

53. *Pizza Survey* A pizza chain was willing to pay $1 to each person interviewed about his or her likes and dislikes of types of pizza crust. Of the people interviewed, 200 liked thin crust, 270 liked thick crust, 70 liked both, and 50 did not like pizza at all. What was the total cost of the survey?

54. *Shopping Preferences* Visitors to a shopping mall in Atlanta, Georgia, were surveyed to determine their preference for shopping in wholesale warehouse stores. The following information was determined.

58 shopped in BJ's Wholesale Club.
49 shopped in Sam's Club.
45 shopped in Costco.
15 shopped in BJ's Wholesale Club and Sam's Club.
16 shopped in BJ's Wholesale Club and Costco.
12 shopped in Sam's Club and Costco.
 5 shopped in all three stores.
17 did not shop in any of the three stores.

Construct a Venn diagram and then determine how many people

a) completed the survey.

b) shopped only in BJ's Wholesale Club.

c) shopped in BJ's Wholesale Club and Sam's Club, but not Costco.

d) shopped in BJ's Wholesale Club or Costco, but not Sam's Club.

55. *TV Choices* TV Guide surveyed 510 subscribers asking which of the following three crime investigation shows they watched on a regular basis: *CSI:Crime Scene Investigation, CSI:Miami,* and *CSI:NY.* The results of the 510 questionnaires that were returned showed that

175 watched *CSI:NY.*
227 watched *CSI:Miami.*
285 watched *CSI:Crime Scene Investigation.*
100 watched *CSI:NY* and *CSI:Miami.*
 96 watched *CSI:NY* and *CSI:Crime Scene Investigation.*
 87 watched *CSI:Miami* and *CSI:Crime Scene Investigation.*
 59 watched all three shows.

Construct a Venn diagram and determine how many people

a) watched only *CSI:NY.*

b) watched exactly one of these shows.

c) watched *CSI:Miami* and *CSI:Crime Scene Investigation,* but not *CSI:NY.*

d) watched *CSI:NY* or *CSI:Crime Scene Investigation,* but not *CSI:Miami.*

e) watched exactly two of these shows.

▲ *Actors from CSI:NY*

2.6

In Exercises 56 and 57, show that the sets are infinite by placing each set in a one-to-one correspondence with a proper subset of itself.

56. $\{2, 4, 6, 8, 10, \dots\}$

57. $\{3, 5, 7, 9, 11, \dots\}$

In Exercises 58 and 59, show that each set has cardinal number $\aleph_0$ by setting up a one-to-one correspondence between the set of counting numbers and the given set.

58. $\{5, 8, 11, 14, 17, \dots\}$

59. $\{4, 9, 14, 19, 24, \dots\}$

CHAPTER 2 *Test*

In Exercises 1–8, state whether each is true or false. If the statement is false, explain why.

1. $\{2, y, \triangle, \$\}$ is equivalent to $\{p, \#, 4, \square\}$.

2. $\{3, 5, 9, h\} = \{9, 5, 3, j\}$

3. $\{\text{star, moon, sun}\} \subset \{\text{star, moon, sun, planet}\}$

4. $\{7\} \subseteq \{x \mid x \in N \text{ and } x < 7\}$

5. $\{p, q, r, s\}$ has 15 subsets.

6. If $A \cap B = \{\ \}$, then A and B are disjoint sets.

7. For any set A, $A \cup A' = \{\ \}$.

8. For any set A, $A \cap U = A$.

In Exercises 9 and 10, use set

$$A = \{x \mid x \in N \text{ and } x < 10\}$$

9. Write set A in roster form.

10. Write a description of set A.

In Exercises 11–16, use the following information.

$$U = \{3, 5, 7, 9, 11, 13, 15\}$$
$$A = \{3, 5, 7, 9\}$$
$$B = \{7, 9, 11, 13\}$$
$$C = \{3, 11, 15\}$$

Determine the following.

11. $A \cap B$
12. $A \cup C'$
13. $A \cap (B \cap C')$
14. $n(A \cap B')$
15. $A - B$
16. $A \times C$

17. Using the sets provided for Exercises 11–16, draw a Venn diagram illustrating the relationship among the sets.

18. Use a Venn diagram to determine whether

$$A \cap (B \cup C') = (A \cap B) \cup (A \cap C')$$

for all sets A, B, and C. Show your work.

19. *Water Activities* A survey of 155 residents of Lake Placid were asked what kind of water activities they participated in on a daily basis during the summer months. The following information was determined.

107 swam.

90 sailed.

76 water skied.

57 swam and sailed.

54 swam and water skied.

52 sailed and water skied.

35 swam, sailed, and water skied.

Construct a Venn diagram and then determine the number of residents who participated in

a) exactly one of these activities.

b) none of these activities.

c) at least two of these activities.

d) swimming and sailing, but not water skiing.

e) swimming or sailing, but not water skiing.

f) only water skiing.

20. Show that the following set is infinite by setting up a one-to-one correspondence between the set and a proper subset of itself.

$$\{7, 8, 9, 10, \dots\}$$

GROUP PROJECTS

Selecting a Family Pet

1. The Wilcox family is considering buying a dog. They have established several criteria for the family dog: It must be one of the breeds listed in the table, must not shed, must be less than 16 in. tall, and must be good with children.

    a) Using the information in the table,* construct a Venn diagram in which the universal set is the dogs listed. Indicate the set of dogs to be placed in each region of the Venn diagram.

    b) From the Venn diagram constructed in part (a), determine which dogs will meet the criteria set by the Wilcox family. Explain.

Breed	Sheds	Less than 16 in.	Good with children
Airedale	no	no	no
Basset hound	yes	yes	yes
Beagle	yes	yes	yes
Border terrier	no	yes	yes
Cairn terrier	no	yes	no
Cocker spaniel	yes	yes	yes
Collie	yes	no	yes
Dachshund	yes	yes	no
Poodle, miniature	no	yes	no
Schnauzer, miniature	no	yes	no
Scottish terrier	no	yes	no
Wirehaired fox terrier	no	yes	no

Classification of the Domestic Cat

2. Read the Mathematics Today feature on page 53. Do research and indicate the name of the following groupings to which the domestic cat belongs.

    a) Kingdom

    b) Phylum

    c) Class

    d) Order

    e) Family

    f) Genus

    g) Species

Who Lives Where

3. On Diplomat Row, an area of Washington, DC, there are five houses. Each owner is a different nationality, each has a different pet, each has a different favorite food, each has a different favorite drink, and each house is painted a different color.

    The green house is directly to the right of the ivory house.
    The Senegalese has the red house.
    The dog belongs to the Spaniard.
    The Afghanistani drinks tea.
    The person who eats cheese lives next door to the fox.
    The Japanese eats fish.
    Milk is drunk in the middle house.
    Apples are eaten in the house next to the horse.
    Ale is drunk in the green house.
    The Norwegian lives in the first house.
    The peach eater drinks whiskey.
    Apples are eaten in the yellow house.
    The banana eater owns a snail.
    The Norwegian lives next door to the blue house.

For each house find

    a) the color.

    b) the nationality of the occupant.

    c) the owner's favorite food.

    d) the owner's favorite drink.

    e) the owner's pet.

    f) Finally, the crucial question is: Does the zebra's owner drink vodka or ale?

*The information is a collection of the opinions of an animal psychologist, Dr. Daniel Tortora, and a group of veterinarians.

3

Logic

Why This is Important

The study of logic enables us to communicate effectively, make more convincing arguments, and develop patterns of reasoning for decision making. Logic is also used in the programming of modern electronic devices such as cell phones and digital cameras.

◄ *Logic is used in the programming of cell phones and digital cameras.*

▲ *"Melts in your mouth, not in your hands." Logic symbols can be used to help us analyze statements made by advertisers.*

Advertisements often rely on spoken or written statements that are used to favorably portray the advertised product and form a convincing argument that will persuade us to purchase the product. Some familiar advertising statements are: *Don't leave home without it; It takes a licking and keeps on ticking; Sometimes you feel like a nut, sometimes you don't; When it rains it pours*; and *Melts in your mouth, not in your hands*. In this section, we will learn how to represent statements using logic symbols that may help us better understand the nature of the statement. We will use these symbols throughout the chapter to analyze more complicated statements.

Why *This is Important* Statements appear in everyday life—for example, in legal documents, product instructions, and game rules in addition to advertising.

History

The ancient Greeks were the first people to systematically analyze the way humans think and arrive at conclusions. Aristotle (384–322 B.C.) organized the study of logic for the first time in a work called *Organon*. As a result of his work, Aristotle is called the father of logic. The logic from this period, called *Aristotelian logic*, has been taught and studied for more than 2000 years.

Since Aristotle's time, the study of logic has been continued by other great philosophers and mathematicians. Gottfried Wilhelm Leibniz (1646–1716) had a deep conviction that all mathematical and scientific concepts could be derived from logic. As a result, he became the first serious student of *symbolic logic*. One difference between symbolic logic and Aristotelian logic is that in symbolic logic, as its name implies, symbols (usually letters) represent written statements. A self-educated English mathematician, George Boole (1815–1864), is considered to be the founder of symbolic logic because of his impressive work in this area. Among Boole's publications are *The Mathematical Analysis of Logic* (1847) and *An Investigation of the Law of Thought* (1854). Mathematician Charles Dodgson, better known as Lewis Carroll, incorporated many interesting ideas from logic into his books *Alice's Adventures in Wonderland* and *Through the Looking Glass* and his other children's stories.

Logic has been studied through the ages to exercise the mind's ability to reason. Understanding logic will enable you to think clearly, communicate effectively, make more convincing arguments, and develop patterns of reasoning that will help you in making decisions. It will also help you to detect the fallacies in the reasoning or arguments of others such as advertisers and politicians. Studying logic has other practical applications, such as helping you to understand wills, contracts, and other legal documents.

The study of logic is also good preparation for other areas of mathematics. If you preview Chapter 12, on probability, you will see formulas for the probability of *A* or *B* and the probability of *A* and *B*, symbolized as *P*(*A* or *B*) and *P*(*A* and *B*), respectively. Special meanings of common words such as *or* and *and* apply to all areas of mathematics. The meaning of these and other special words is discussed in this chapter.

Logic and the English Language

In reading, writing, and speaking, we use many words such as *and, or,* and *if . . . then . . .* to connect thoughts. In logic we call these words *connectives*. How are these words interpreted in daily communication? A judge announces to a convicted offender, "I hereby sentence you to five months of community service *and* a fine of $100." In this case, we normally interpret the word *and* to indicate that *both* events will take place. That is, the person must perform community service and must also pay a fine.

Now suppose a judge states, "I sentence you to six months in prison *or* 10 months of community service." In this case, we interpret the connective *or* as meaning the convicted person must either spend the time in jail or perform community service, but not both. The word *or* in this case is the *exclusive or*. When the exclusive *or* is used, one or the other of the events can take place, but *not both*.

In a restaurant, a waiter asks, "May I interest you in a cup of soup or a sandwich?" This question offers three possibilities: You may order soup, you may order a sandwich, or you may order both soup and a sandwich. The *or* in this case is the *inclusive or*. When the inclusive *or* is used, one or the other, *or both* events can take place. *In this chapter, when we use the word* or *in a logic statement, it will mean the inclusive* or *unless stated otherwise.*

If–then statements are often used to relate two ideas, as in the bank policy statement "If the average daily balance is greater than $500, then there will be no service charge." If–then statements are also used to emphasize a point or add humor, as in the statement "If the Cubs win, then I will be a monkey's uncle."

Now let's look at logic from a mathematical point of view.

Statements and Logical Connectives

A sentence that can be judged either true or false is called a *statement*. Labeling a statement true or false is called *assigning a truth value* to the statement. Here are some examples of statements.

1. The Brooklyn Bridge goes over San Francisco Bay.
2. Disney World is in Idaho.
3. The Mississippi River is the longest river in the United States.

In each case, we can say that the sentence is either true or false. Statement 1 is false because the Brooklyn Bridge does not go over San Francisco Bay. Statement 2 is false because Disney World is in Florida. By looking at a map or reading an almanac, we can determine that the Mississippi River is the longest river in the United States; therefore, statement 3 is true.

The three sentences discussed above are examples of *simple statements* because they convey one idea. Sentences combining two or more ideas that can be assigned a truth value are called *compound statements*. Compound statements are discussed shortly.

Quantifiers

Sometimes it is necessary to change a statement to its opposite meaning. To do so, we use the *negation* of a statement. For example, the negation of the statement "Emily is at home" is "Emily is not at home." The negation of a true statement is always a false statement, and the negation of a false statement is always a true statement. We must use special caution when negating statements containing the words *all*, *none* (or *no*), and *some*. These words are referred to as *quantifiers*.

Consider the statement "All lakes contain fresh water." We know this statement is false because the Great Salt Lake in Utah contains salt water. Its negation must therefore be true. We may be tempted to write its negation as "No lake contains fresh water," but this statement is also false because Lake Superior contains fresh water. Therefore, "No lakes contain fresh water" is not the negation of "All lakes contain fresh water." The correct negation of "All lakes contain fresh water" is "Not all lakes contain fresh water" or "At least one lake does not contain fresh water" or "Some lakes do not contain fresh water." These statements all imply that at least one lake does not contain fresh water, which is a true statement.

▲ *The Brooklyn Bridge in New York City*

Now consider the statement "No birds can swim." This statement is false because at least one bird, the penguin, can swim. Therefore, the negation of this statement must be true. We may be tempted to write the negation as "All birds can swim," but because this statement is also false it cannot be the negation. The correct negation of the statement is "Some birds can swim" or "At least one bird can swim," each of which is a true statement.

Now let's consider statements involving the quantifier *some*, as in "Some students have a driver's license." This statement is true, meaning that at least one student has a driver's license. The negation of this statement must therefore be false. The negation is "No student has a driver's license," which is a false statement.

Consider the statement "Some students do not ride motorcycles." This statement is true because it means "At least one student does not ride a motorcycle." The negation of this statement must therefore be false. The negation is "All students ride motorcycles," which is a false statement.

The negation of quantified statements is summarized as follows:

Form of statement	Form of negation
All are.	Some are not.
None are.	Some are.
Some are.	None are.
Some are not.	All are.

The following diagram might help you to remember the statements and their negations:

The quantifiers diagonally opposite each other are the negations of each other.

Example 1   *Write Negations*

Write the negation of each statement.

a) Some telephones can take photographs.

b) All houses have two stories.

Solution

a) Since *some* means "at least one," the statement "Some telephones can take photographs" is the same as "At least one telephone can take photographs." Because it is a true statement, its negation must be false. The negation is "No telephones can take photographs," which is a false statement.

b) The statement "All houses have two stories" is a false statement, since some houses have one story, some have three stories, and some may have more than three stories. Its negation must therefore be true. The negation may be written as "Some houses do not have two stories" or "Not all houses have two stories" or "At least one house does not have two stories." Each of these statements is true. ∎

Compound Statements

Statements consisting of two or more simple statements are called **compound statements**. The connectives often used to join two simple statements are

and,   or,   if, … then …,   if and only if

In addition, we consider a simple statement that has been negated to be a compound statement. The word *not* is generally used to negate a statement.

To reduce the amount of writing in logic, it is common to represent each simple statement with a lowercase letter. For example, suppose we are discussing the simple statement "Leland is a farmer." Instead of writing "Leland is a farmer" over and over again, we can let p represent the statement "Leland is a farmer." Thereafter we can simply refer to the statement with the letter p. It is customary to use the letters p, q, r, and s to represent simple statements, but other letters may be used instead. Let's now look at the connectives used to make compound statements.

Not Statements

The negation is symbolized by $\sim$ and read "not." For example, the negation of the statement "Steve is a college student" is "Steve is not a college student." If p represents the simple statement "Steve is a college student," then $\sim p$ represents the compound statement "Steve is not a college student." For any statement p, $\sim(\sim p) = p$. For example, the negation of the statement "Steve is not a college student" is "Steve is a college student."

Consider the statement "Inga is not at home." This statement contains the word *not*, which indicates that it is a negation. To write this statement symbolically, we let p represent "Inga *is* at home." Then $\sim p$ would be "Inga is not at home." *We will use this convention of letting letters such as p, q, or r represent statements that are not negated. We will represent negated statements with the negation symbol, $\sim$.*

And Statements

The *conjunction* is symbolized by $\wedge$ and read "and." The $\wedge$ looks like an A (for And) with the bar missing. Let p and q represent the simple statements.

p: You will perform 5 months of community service.

q: You will pay a $100 fine.

Then the following is the conjunction written in symbolic form.

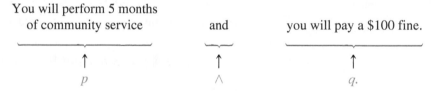

The conjunction is generally expressed as *and*. Other words sometimes used to express a conjunction are *but, however,* and *nevertheless.*

Example 2 *Write a Conjunction*

Write the following conjunction in symbolic form.

Green Day is not on tour, but Green Day is recording a new CD.

Solution Let t and r represent the simple statements.

t: Green Day is on tour.

r: Green Day is recording a new CD.

In symbolic form, the compound statement is $\sim t \wedge r$.

In Example 2, the compound statement is "Green Day is not on tour, but Green Day is recording a new CD." This statement could also be represented as "Green Day is not on tour, but *they* are recording a new CD." In this problem, it should be clear the word *they* means *Green Day.* Therefore, the statement "Green Day is not on tour, but they are recording a new CD" would also be symbolized as $\sim t \wedge r$.

Or Statements

The *disjunction* is symbolized by ∨ and read "or." The *or* we use in this book (except where indicated in the exercise sets) is the *inclusive or* described on page 95.

Example 3 *Write a Disjunction*

Let

  p: Maria will go to the circus.

  q: Maria will go to the zoo.

Write the following statements in symbolic form.

a) Maria will go to the circus or Maria will go to the zoo.

b) Maria will go to the zoo or Maria will not go to the circus.

c) Maria will not go to the circus or Maria will not go to the zoo.

Solution

a) $p \vee q$ b) $q \vee \sim p$ c) $\sim p \vee \sim q$ ■

Because *or* represents the *inclusive or*, the statement "Maria will go to the circus or Maria will go to the zoo" in Example 3(a) may mean that Maria will go to the circus, or that Maria will go to the zoo, or that Maria will go to both the circus *and* the zoo. The statement in Example 3(a) could also be written as "Maria will go to the circus or the zoo."

When a compound statement contains more than one connective, a comma can be used to indicate which simple statements are to be grouped together. When we write the compound statement symbolically, *the simple statements on the same side of the comma are to be grouped together within parentheses.*

For example, "Pink is a singer (*p*) or Jennifer Aniston is an actress (*j*), and Dallas is in Texas (*d*)" is written $(p \vee j) \wedge d$. Note that the *p* and *j* are both on the same side of the comma in the written statement. They are therefore grouped together within parentheses. The statement "Pink is a singer, or Jennifer Aniston is an actress and Dallas is in Texas" is written $p \vee (j \wedge d)$. In this case, *j* and *d* are on the same side of the comma and are therefore grouped together within parentheses.

Example 4 *Understand How Commas Are Used to Group Statements*

Let

  p: Dinner includes soup.

  q: Dinner includes salad.

  r: Dinner includes the vegetable of the day.

Write the following statements in symbolic form.

a) Dinner includes soup, and salad or the vegetable of the day.

b) Dinner includes soup and salad, or the vegetable of the day.

Solution

a) The comma tells us to group the statement "Dinner includes salad" with the statement "Dinner includes the vegetable of the day." Note that both statements are on the same side of the comma. The statement in symbolic form is $p \wedge (q \vee r)$.

  In mathematics, we always evaluate the information within the parentheses first. Since the conjunction, ∧, is outside the parentheses and is evaluated *last*, this statement is considered a *conjunction*.

b) The comma tells us to group the statement "Dinner includes soup" with the statement "Dinner includes salad." Note that both statements are on the same side of the comma. The statement in symbolic form is $(p \wedge q) \vee r$. Since the disjunction, $\vee$, is outside the parentheses and is evaluated *last,* this statement is considered a *disjunction.* ∎

The information provided in Example 4 is summarized below.

Statement	Symbolic representation	Type of statement
Dinner includes soup, and salad or the vegetable of the day.	$p \wedge (q \vee r)$	conjunction
Dinner includes soup and salad, or the vegetable of the day.	$(p \wedge q) \vee r$	disjunction

A negation symbol has the effect of negating only the statement that directly follows it. To negate a compound statement, we must use parentheses. When a negation symbol is placed in front of a statement in parentheses, it negates the entire statement in parentheses. The negation symbol in this case is read, "It is not true that … " or "It is false that … "

Example 5 *Change Symbolic Statements into Words*

Let

p: The house is for sale.

q: We can afford to buy the house.

Write the following symbolic statements in words.

a) $p \wedge {\sim}q$ b) ${\sim}p \vee {\sim}q$ c) ${\sim}(p \wedge q)$

Solution

a) The house is for sale and we cannot afford to buy the house.

b) The house is not for sale or we cannot afford to buy the house.

c) It is false that the house is for sale and we can afford to buy the house. ∎

Recall that the word *but* may also be used in a conjunction. Therefore, Example 5(a) could also be written "The house is for sale, *but* we cannot afford to buy the house."

Part (b) of Example 5 is a disjunction, since it can be written $({\sim}p) \vee ({\sim}q)$. Part (c), which is ${\sim}(p \wedge q)$, is a negation since the negation symbol negates the entire statement within parentheses. The similarity of these two statements is discussed in Section 3.4.

Occasionally, we come across a *neither–nor* statement, such as "John is neither handsome nor rich." This statement means that John is not handsome *and* John is not rich. If p represents "John is handsome" and q represents "John is rich," this statement is symbolized by ${\sim}p \wedge {\sim}q$.

If–Then Statements

The *conditional* is symbolized by $\rightarrow$ and is read "if–then." The statement $p \rightarrow q$ is read "If p, then q."[*] The conditional statement consists of two parts: the part that precedes the arrow is the *antecedent,* and the part that follows the arrow is the *consequent.*[†] In the conditional statement $p \rightarrow q$, the p is the antecedent and the q is the consequent.

---

[*]Some books indicate that $p \rightarrow q$ may also be read "p implies q." Many higher-level mathematics books, however, indicate that $p \rightarrow q$ may be read "p implies q" only under certain conditions. Implications are discussed in Section 3.3.

[†]Some books refer to the antecedent as the hypothesis or premise and the consequent as the conclusion.

In the conditional statement $\sim(p \lor q) \to (p \land q)$, the antecedent is $\sim(p \lor q)$ and the consequent is $(p \land q)$. An example of a conditional statement is "If you drink your milk, then you will grow up to be healthy." A conditional symbol may be placed between any two statements even if the statements are not related.

Sometimes the word *then* in a conditional statement is not explicitly stated. For example, the statement "If you get an A, I will buy you a car" is a conditional statement because it actually means "If you get an A, then I will buy you a car."

▲ *Zoe* by Beth Anderson

Example 6 *Write Conditional Statements*

Let

p: The portrait is a pastel.

q: The portrait is by Beth Anderson.

Write the following statements symbolically.

a) If the portrait is a pastel, then the portrait is by Beth Anderson.

b) If the portrait is by Beth Anderson, then the portrait is not a pastel.

c) It is false that if the portrait is by Beth Anderson then the portrait is a pastel.

Solution

a) $p \to q$ b) $q \to \sim p$ c) $\sim(q \to p)$

Example 7 *Use Commas When Writing a Symbolic Statement in Words*

Let

p: Jorge is enrolled in calculus.

q: Jorge's major is criminal justice.

r: Jorge's major is engineering.

Write the following symbolic statements in words and indicate whether the statement is a negation, conjunction, disjunction, or conditional.

a) $(q \to \sim p) \lor r$ b) $q \to (\sim p \lor r)$

Solution The parentheses indicate where to place the commas in the sentences.

a) "If Jorge's major is criminal justice then Jorge is not enrolled in calculus, or Jorge's major is engineering." This statement is a disjunction because $\lor$ is outside the parentheses.

b) "If Jorge's major is criminal justice, then Jorge is not enrolled in calculus or Jorge's major is engineering." This statement is a conditional because $\to$ is outside the parentheses.

If and Only if Statements

The *biconditional* is symbolized by $\leftrightarrow$ and is read "if and only if." The phrase *if and only if* is sometimes abbreviated as "iff." The statement $p \leftrightarrow q$ is read "p if and only if q."

Example 8 *Write Statements Using the Biconditional*

Let

p: Alex plays goalie on the lacrosse team.

q: The Titans win the Champion's Cup.

Write the following symbolic statements in words.

a) $p \leftrightarrow q$ c) $q \leftrightarrow \sim p$ b) $\sim(p \leftrightarrow \sim q)$

Solution

a) Alex plays goalie on the lacrosse team if and only if the Titans win the Champion's Cup.

b) The Titans win the Champion's Cup if and only if Alex does not play goalie on the lacrosse team.

c) It is false that Alex plays goalie on the lacrosse team if and only if the Titans do not win the Champion's Cup.

You will learn later that $p \leftrightarrow q$ means the same as $(p \rightarrow q) \wedge (q \rightarrow p)$. Therefore, the statement "I will go to college if and only if I can pay the tuition" has the same logical meaning as "If I go to college then I can pay the tuition, and if I can pay the tuition then I will go to college."

A summary of the connectives discussed in this section is given in Table 3.1.

Table 3.1 Logical Connectives

Formal Name	Symbol	Read	Symbolic Form
Negation	$\sim$	"Not"	$\sim p$
Conjunction	$\wedge$	"And"	$p \wedge q$
Disjunction	$\vee$	"Or"	$p \vee q$
Conditional	$\rightarrow$	"If-then"	$p \rightarrow q$
Biconditional	$\leftrightarrow$	"If and only if"	$p \leftrightarrow q$

SECTION 3.1   *Exercises*

Warm Up Exercises

In exercises 1–8, fill in the blanks with an appropriate word, phrase, or symbol(s).

1. A sentence that can be judged either true or false is called a _____.

2. A statement that conveys only one idea is called a _____ statement.

3. A statement that consists of two or more simple statements is called a _____ statement.

4. Words such as *all, none* (or *no*), and *some* are examples of _____.

5. a) The negation is symbolized by $\sim$ and is read "_____."

   b) The conjunction is symbolized by $\wedge$ and is read "_____."

   c) The disjunction is symbolized by $\vee$ and is read "_____."

d) The conditional is symbolized by $\rightarrow$ and is read "_____."

e) The biconditional is symbolized by $\leftrightarrow$ and is read "_____."

6. The negation of the statement *Some cars are hybrids* is: _____ cars are hybrids.

7. The negation of the statement *All golf courses are green* is: _____ golf courses are not green.

8. The negation of the statement *Some drivers are not safe* is: _____ drivers are safe.

Practice the Skills/Problem Solving

In Exercises 9–18, indicate whether the statement is a simple statement or a compound statement. If it is a compound statement, indicate whether it is a negation, conjunction, disjunction, conditional, or biconditional by using both the word and its appropriate symbol (for example, "a negation," ~).

9. John Waters is scuba diving.

10. If you have a cold, then you should eat some chicken soup.

11. Time will go backwards if and only if you travel faster than the speed of light.

12. Louis Armstrong did not play the drums.

13. Bobby Glewen joined the Army and he got married.

14. The book was neither a novel nor an autobiography.

15. If Cathy Smith walks 4 miles today, then she will be sore tomorrow.

16. Inhibor Melendez will be admitted to law school if and only if he earns his bachelor's degree.

17. It is false that Jeffery Hilt is a high school teacher and a grade school teacher.

18. The hurricane did $400,000 worth of damage to DeSoto County.

In Exercises 19–28, write the negation of the statement.

19. All butterflies are insects.

20. All houses are wired using parallel circuits.

21. Some turtles do not have claws.

22. No teachers made the roster.

23. No bicycles have three wheels.

24. All horses have manes.

25. Some pedestrians are in the crosswalk.

26. Some dogs with long hair do not get cold.

27. No Holsteins are Guernseys.

28. Some vitamins contain sugar.

In Exercises 29–34, write the statement in symbolic form.

Let

   p: A panther has a long tail.
   q: A bobcat can purr.

29. A panther does not have a long tail.

30. A panther has a long tail and a bobcat can purr.

31. A bobcat cannot purr or a panther does not have a long tail.

32. A bobcat cannot purr if and only if a panther does not have a long tail.

33. If a panther does not have a long tail, then a bobcat cannot purr.

34. A bobcat cannot purr, but a panther has a long tail.

In Exercises 35–40, write the statement in symbolic form.

Let

    p: The chili is spicy.
    q: The sour cream is cold.

35. The chili is not spicy, but the sour cream is cold.

36. Neither is the chili spicy nor is the sour cream cold.

37. The sour cream is not cold if and only if the chili is spicy.

38. If the chili is spicy, then the sour cream is not cold.

39. It is false that the chili is spicy or the sour cream is cold.

40. It is false that if the sour cream is not cold then the chili is spicy.

In Exercises 41–50, write the compound statement in words.

Let

    p: Joe has an iPad.
    q: Brie has a MacBook.

41. $\sim q$ **42.** $\sim p$

43. $p \wedge q$ **44.** $q \vee p$

45. $\sim p \rightarrow q$ **46.** $\sim p \leftrightarrow \sim q$

47. $\sim p \vee \sim q$ **48.** $\sim(q \vee p)$

49. $\sim(p \wedge q)$ **50.** $\sim p \wedge \sim q$

In Exercises 51–60, write the statements in symbolic form.

Let

    p: The temperature is 90°.
    q: The air conditioner is working.
    r: The apartment is hot.

51. The temperature is 90° and the air conditioner is not working, and the apartment is hot.

52. The temperature is not 90° and the air conditioner is working, but the apartment is hot.

53. The temperature is 90° and the air conditioner is working, or the apartment is hot.

54. If the apartment is hot and the air conditioner is working, then the temperature is 90°.

55. If the temperature is 90°, then the air conditioner is working or the apartment is not hot.

56. The temperature is not 90° if and only if the air conditioner is not working, or the apartment is not hot.

57. The apartment is hot if and only if the air conditioner is working, and the temperature is 90°.

58. It is false that if the apartment is hot then the air conditioner is not working.

59. If the air conditioner is working, then the temperature is 90° if and only if the apartment is hot.

60. The apartment is hot or the air conditioner is not working, if and only if the temperature is 90°.

In Exercises 61–70, write each symbolic statement in words.

Let

    p: The water is 70°.
    q: The sun is shining.
    r: We go swimming.

61. $(p \vee q) \wedge \sim r$ **62.** $(p \wedge q) \vee r$

63. $\sim p \wedge (q \vee r)$ **64.** $(q \rightarrow p) \vee r$

65. $\sim r \rightarrow (q \wedge p)$ **66.** $(q \wedge r) \rightarrow p$

67. $(q \rightarrow r) \wedge p$ **68.** $\sim p \rightarrow (q \vee r)$

69. $(q \leftrightarrow p) \wedge r$ **70.** $q \rightarrow (p \leftrightarrow r)$

Dinner Menu *In Exercises 71–74 on page 104, use the following information to arrive at your answers. Many restaurant dinner menus include statements such as the following. All dinners are served with a choice of: Soup or Salad, and Potatoes or Pasta, and Carrots or Peas. Which of the following selections are permissible? If a selection is not permissible, explain why. See the discussion of the exclusive* or *on page 95.*

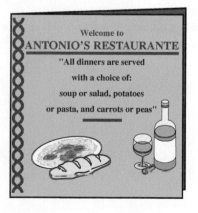

71. Soup, salad, and peas

72. Salad, pasta, and carrots

73. Soup, potatoes, pasta, and peas

74. Soup, pasta, and potatoes

In Exercises 75–83, (a) select letters to represent the simple statements and write each statement symbolically by using parentheses and (b) indicate whether the statement is a negation, conjunction, disjunction, conditional, or biconditional.

75. I bought the watch in Tijuana and I did not pay $100.

76. If the conference is in Las Vegas, then we can see Blue Man Group or we can play poker.

▲ *Blue Man Group*

77. It is false that if your speed is below the speed limit then you will not get pulled over.

78. If dinner is ready then we can eat, or we cannot go to the restaurant.

79. If the food has fiber or the food has vitamins, then you will be healthy.

80. If Corliss is teaching then Faye is in the math lab, if and only if it is not a weekend.

81. You may take this course, if and only if you did not fail the previous course or you passed the placement test.

82. If the car has gas and the battery is charged, then the car will start.

83. The classroom is empty if and only if it is the weekend, or it is 7 A.M.

Challenge Problems/Group Activities

84. *An Ancient Question* If Zeus could do anything, could he build a wall that he could not jump over? Explain your answer.

85. a) Make up three simple statements and label them p, q, and r. Then write compound statements to represent $(p \vee q) \wedge r$ and $p \vee (q \wedge r)$.

b) Do you think that the statements for $(p \vee q) \wedge r$ and $p \vee (q \wedge r)$ mean the same thing? Explain.

Recreational Mathematics

86. *Sudoku* Refer to the *Recreational Mathematics* on page 96. Complete the following Sudoku puzzle.

	8			3				
9			6	1				4
5	1	9				8	6	3
	6					4	8	
5								1
	2	4				5		
4	3	5			8	1	9	
2			5	1			7	
			2			6		

Internet/Research Activities

87. *Legal Documents* Obtain a legal document such as a will or rental agreement and copy one page of the document. Circle every connective used. Then list the number of times each connective appeared. Be sure to include conditional statements from which the word *then* was omitted from the sentence. Give the page and your listing to your instructor.

88. Write a report on the life and accomplishments of George Boole, who was an important contributor to the development of logic. In your report, indicate how his work eventually led to the development of the computer. References include encyclopedias, history of mathematics books, and the Internet.

Truth Tables for Negation, Conjunction, and Disjunction

▲ *Under what conditions is the statement Subway sells the most sandwiches or Taco Bell sells the most burritos true?*

Consider the following statement: Subway sells the most sandwiches or Taco Bell sells the most burritos. Under what conditions can the statement be considered true? Under what conditions can the statement be considered false? In this section, we will introduce a tool used to help us analyze such statements.

Why *This is Important*   Understanding when logical statements are true is essential to many different applications in everyday life.

A *truth table* is a device used to determine when a compound statement is true or false. Five basic truth tables are used in constructing other truth tables. Three are discussed in this section (Tables 3.2, 3.4, and 3.7), and two are discussed in the next section. Section 3.5 uses truth tables in determining whether a logical argument is valid or invalid.

Negation

The first truth table is for *negation*. If p is a true statement, then the negation of p, "not p," is a false statement. If p is a false statement, then "not p" is a true statement. For example, if the statement "The shirt is blue" is true, then the statement "The shirt is not blue" is false. These relationships are summarized in Table 3.2. For a simple statement, there are exactly two true–false cases, as shown.

If a compound statement consists of two simple statements p and q, there are four possible cases, as illustrated in Table 3.3. Consider the statement "The test is today and the test covers Chapter 5." The simple statement "The test is today" has two possible truth values, true or false. The simple statement "The test covers Chapter 5" also has two truth values, true or false. Thus, for these two simple statements there are four distinct possible true–false arrangements. Whenever we construct a truth table for a compound statement that consists of two simple statements, we begin by listing the four true–false cases shown in Table 3.3.

Conjunction

To illustrate the conjunction, consider the following situation. You have recently purchased a new house. To decorate it, you ordered a new carpet and new furniture from the same store. You explain to the salesperson that the carpet must be delivered before the furniture. He promises that the carpet will be delivered on Thursday and that the furniture will be delivered on Friday.

To help determine whether the salesperson kept his promise, we assign letters to each simple statement. Let p be "The carpet will be delivered on Thursday" and q be "The furniture will be delivered on Friday." The salesperson's statement written in symbolic form is $p \land q$. There are four possible true–false situations to be considered (Table 3.4).

CASE 1: p is true and q is true. The carpet is delivered on Thursday and the furniture is delivered on Friday. The salesperson has kept his promise and the compound statement is true. Thus, we put a T in the $p \land q$ column.

CASE 2: p is true and q is false. The carpet is delivered on Thursday but the furniture is not delivered on Friday. Since the furniture was not delivered as promised, the compound statement is false. Thus, we put an F in the $p \land q$ column.

Table 3.2 Negation

	p	$\sim p$
Case 1	T	F
Case 2	F	T

Table 3.3

	p	q
Case 1	T	T
Case 2	T	F
Case 3	F	T
Case 4	F	F

Table 3.4 Conjunction

	p	q	$p \land q$
Case 1	T	T	T
Case 2	T	F	F
Case 3	F	T	F
Case 4	F	F	F

CASE 3: *p* is false and *q* is true. The carpet is not delivered on Thursday but the furniture is delivered on Friday. Since the carpet was not delivered on Thursday as promised, the compound statement is false. Thus, we put an F in the $p \wedge q$ column.

CASE 4: *p* is false and *q* is false. The carpet is not delivered on Thursday and the furniture is not delivered on Friday. Since the carpet and furniture were not delivered as promised, the compound statement is false. Thus, we put an F in the $p \wedge q$ column.

Examining the four cases, we see that in only one case did the salesperson keep his promise: in case 1. Therefore, case 1 (T, T) is true. In cases 2, 3, and 4, the salesperson did not keep his promise and the compound statement is false. The results are summarized in Table 3.4, the truth table for the conjunction.

The **conjunction** $p \wedge q$ is true only when both *p* and *q* are true.

Disjunction

Consider the job description in the margin that describes several job requirements. Who qualifies for the job? To help analyze the statement, translate it into symbolic form. Let *p* be "A requirement for the job is a two-year college degree in civil technology" and *q* be "A requirement for the job is five years of related experience." The statement in symbolic form is $p \vee q$. For the two simple statements, there are four distinct cases (see Table 3.5).

CASE 1: *p* is true and *q* is true. A candidate has a two-year college degree in civil technology and five years of related experience. The candidate has both requirements and qualifies for the job. Consider qualifying for the job as a true statement and not qualifying as a false statement. Since the candidate qualifies for the job, we put a T in the $p \vee q$ column.

CASE 2: *p* is true and *q* is false. A candidate has a two-year college degree in civil technology but does not have five years of related experience. The candidate still qualifies for the job with the two-year college degree. Thus, we put a T in the $p \vee q$ column.

CASE 3: *p* is false and *q* is true. The candidate does not have a two-year college degree in civil technology but does have five years of related experience. The candidate still qualifies for the job with the five years of related experience. Thus, we put a T in the $p \vee q$ column.

CASE 4: *p* is false and *q* is false. The candidate does not have a two-year college degree in civil technology and does not have five years of related experience. The candidate does not meet either of the two requirements and therefore does not qualify for the job. Thus, we put an F in the $p \vee q$ column.

In examining the four cases, we see that there is only one case in which the candidate does not qualify for the job: case 4. As this example indicates, an *or* statement will be true in every case, except when both simple statements are false. The results are summarized in Table 3.5, the truth table for the disjunction.

The **disjunction** $p \vee q$ is true when either *p* is true, *q* is true, or both *p* and *q* are true.

The disjunction $p \vee q$ is false only when *p* and *q* are both false.

Civil Technician

Municipal program for redevelopment seeks on-site technician. **The applicant must have a two-year college degree in civil technology or five years of related experience**. Interested candidates please call 555-1234.

Table 3.5 Disjunction

p	*q*	$p \vee q$
T	T	T
T	F	T
F	T	T
F	F	F

Constructing Truth Tables

We will now construct additional truth tables for statements involving the negation, conjunction, and disjunction. We summarize these compound statements on page 107.

Negation, Conjunction, and Disjunction

- **Negation** $\sim p$ is read "not p." If p is true, then $\sim p$ is false; if p is false, then $\sim p$ is true. In other words, $\sim p$ will always have the *opposite* truth value of p.
- **Conjunction** $p \wedge q$ is read *"p and q."* $p \wedge q$ is true only when both p and q are true.
- **Disjunction** $p \vee q$ is read *"p or q."* $p \vee q$ is true when either p is true, q is true, or both p and q are true. In other words, $p \vee q$ is false only when both p and q are false.

We will discuss two methods for constructing truth tables. Although the two methods produce tables that will look different, the answer columns will be the same regardless of which method you use.

Example **1** *Construct a Truth Table*

Construct a truth table for $p \wedge \sim q$.

Solution Because there are two statements, p and q, construct a truth table with four cases; see Table 3.6(a). Then write the truth values under the p in the compound statement and label this column 1, as in Table 3.6(b). Copy these truth values directly from the p column on the left. Write the corresponding truth values under the q in the compound statement and call this column 2, as in Table 3.6(c). Copy the truth values for column 2 directly from the q column on the left. Now find the truth values of $\sim q$ by negating the truth values in column 2 and call this column 3, as in

Table 3.6

(a)

	p	q	$p \wedge \sim q$
Case 1	T	T	
Case 2	T	F	
Case 3	F	T	
Case 4	F	F	

(b)

p	q	$p \wedge \sim q$
T	T	T
T	F	T
F	T	F
F	F	F
		1

(c)

p	q	p	$\wedge$	$\sim$	q
T	T	T			T
T	F	T			F
F	T	F			T
F	F	F			F
		1			2

(d)

p	q	p	$\wedge$	$\sim$	q
T	T	T		F	T
T	F	T		T	F
F	T	F		F	T
F	F	F		T	F
		1		3	2

(e)

p	q	p	$\wedge$	$\sim$	q
T	T	T	F	F	T
T	F	T	T	T	F
F	T	F	F	F	T
F	F	F	F	T	F
		1	4	3	2

Table 3.6(d). Use the conjunction table, Table 3.4, and the entries in the columns labeled 1 and 3 to complete the column labeled 4, as in Table 3.6(e). The results in column 4 are obtained as follows:

Row 1: T $\wedge$ F is F.   Row 2: T $\wedge$ T is T.
Row 3: F $\wedge$ F is F.   Row 4: F $\wedge$ T is F.

The answer is always the last column completed. The columns labeled 1, 2, and 3 are only aids in arriving at the answer labeled column 4.

The statement $p \wedge \sim q$ in Example 1 actually means $p \wedge (\sim q)$. In the future, instead of listing a column for q and a separate column for its negation, we will make one column for $\sim q$, which will have the opposite values of those in the q column on the left. Similarly, when we evaluate $\sim p$, we will use the opposite values of those in the p column on the left. This procedure is illustrated in Example 2.

In Example 1, we spoke about *cases* and also *columns*. Consider Table 3.6(e) on page 107. This table has four cases indicated by the four different rows of the two left-hand (unnumbered) columns. The four *cases* are TT, TF, FT, and FF. In every truth table with two letters, we list the four cases (the first two columns) first. Then we complete the remaining columns in the truth table. In Table 3.6(e), after completing the two left-hand columns, we complete the remaining columns in the order indicated by the numbers below the columns. We will continue to place numbers below the columns to show the order in which the columns are completed.

In discussion of the truth table in Example 2, and all following truth tables, if we say column 1, it means the column labeled 1. Column 2 will mean the column labeled 2, and so on.

Example 2   *Construct and Interpret a Truth Table*

a) Construct a truth table for the following statement: Jo is not an artist and Jo is not a musician.

b) Under which conditions will the compound statement be true?

c) Suppose "Jo is an artist" is a false statement and "Jo is a musician" is a true statement. Is the compound statement given in part (a) true or false?

Solution

a) First write the simple statements in symbolic form by using simple nonnegated statements.

Let

$$p: \quad \text{Jo is an artist.}$$
$$q: \quad \text{Jo is a musician.}$$

Therefore, the compound statement may be written $\sim p \wedge \sim q$. Now construct a truth table with four cases, as shown in Table 3.7.

Fill in the column labeled 1 by negating the truth values under p on the far left. Fill in the column labeled 2 by negating the values under q in the second column from the left. Fill in the column labeled 3 by using the columns labeled 1 and 2 and the definition of conjunction.

In the first row, to determine the entry for column 3, we use false for $\sim p$ and false for $\sim q$. Since false $\wedge$ false is false (see case 4 of Table 3.4 on page 105), we place an F in column 3, row 1. In the second row, we use false for $\sim p$ and true for $\sim q$. Since false $\wedge$ true is false (see case 3 of Table 3.4), we place an F in column 3, row 2. In the third row, we use true for $\sim p$ and false for $\sim q$. Since true $\wedge$ false is false (see case 2 of Table 3.4), we place an F in column 3, row 3. In the fourth row, we use true for $\sim p$ and true for $\sim q$. Since true $\wedge$ true is true (see case 1 of Table 3.4), we place a T in column 3, row 4.

b) The compound statement in part (a) will be true only in case 4 (circled in blue) when both simple statements, p and q, are false, that is, when Jo is not an artist and Jo is not a musician.

c) We are told that p, "Jo is an artist," is a false statement and that q, "Jo is a musician," is a true statement. From the truth table (Table 3.7), we can determine that when p is false and q is true, the compound statement, case 3 (circled in red), is false.

Table 3.7

p	q	$\sim p$	$\wedge$	$\sim q$
T	T	F	F	F
T	F	F	F	T
F	T	T	(F)	F
F	F	T	(T)	T
		1	3	2

Table 3.8

p	q	$\sim$	$(\sim q$	$\vee$	$p)$
T	T	F	F	T	T
T	F	F	T	T	T
F	T	T	F	F	F
F	F	F	T	T	F
		4	1	3	2

Example 3 *Truth Table with a Negation*

Construct a truth table for $\sim(\sim q \vee p)$.

Solution First construct the standard truth table listing the four cases. Then work within parentheses. The order to be followed is indicated by the numbers below the columns (see Table 3.8). Under $\sim q$, column 1, write the negation of the q column. Then, in column 2, copy the values from the p column. Next, complete the *or* column, column 3, using columns 1 and 2 and the truth table for the disjunction (see Table 3.5 on page 106). The *or* column is false only when both statements are false, as in case 3. Finally, negate the values in the *or* column, column 3, and place these negated values in column 4. By examining the truth table you can see that the compound statement $\sim(\sim q \vee p)$ is true only in case 3, that is, when p is false and q is true. ∎

PROCEDURE **CONSTRUCTING TRUTH TABLES**

1. Study the compound statement and determine whether it is a negation, conjunction, disjunction, conditional, or biconditional statement, as was done in Section 3.1. The answer to the truth table will appear under $\sim$ if the statement is a negation, under $\wedge$ if the statement is a conjunction, under $\vee$ if the statement is a disjunction, under $\rightarrow$ if the statement is a conditional, and under $\leftrightarrow$ if the statement is a biconditional.

2. Complete the columns under the simple statements, p, q, r, and their negations, $\sim p$, $\sim q$, $\sim r$, within parentheses, if present. If there are nested parentheses (one pair of parentheses within another pair), work with the innermost pair first.

3. Complete the column under the connective within the parentheses, if present. You will use the truth values of the connective in determining the final answer in step 5.

4. Complete the column under any remaining statements and their negations.

5. Complete the column under any remaining connectives. Recall that the answer will appear under the column determined in step 1. If the statement is a conjunction, disjunction, conditional, or biconditional, you will obtain the truth values for the connective by using the last column completed on the left side and on the right side of the connective. If the statement is a negation, you will obtain the truth values by negating the truth values of the last column completed within the grouping symbols on the right side of the negation. Be sure to circle or highlight your answer column or number the columns in the order they were completed.

Table 3.9

p	q	$(\sim p$	$\vee$	$q)$	$\wedge$	$\sim p$
T	T	F	T	T	F	F
T	F	F	F	F	F	F
F	T	T	T	T	T	T
F	F	T	T	F	T	T
		1	3	2	5	4

Example 4 *Use the General Procedure to Construct a Truth Table*

Construct a truth table for the statement $(\sim p \vee q) \wedge \sim p$.

Solution We will follow the general procedure outlined in the box. This statement is a conjunction, so the answer will be under the conjunction symbol. Complete columns under $\sim p$ and q within the parentheses and call these columns 1 and 2, respectively (see Table 3.9). Complete the column under the disjunction, $\vee$, using the truth values in columns 1 and 2, and call this column 3. Next complete the column under $\sim p$, and call this column 4. The answer, column 5, is determined from the definition of the conjunction and the truth values in column 3, the last column completed on the left side of the conjunction, and column 4. ∎

So far, all the truth tables we have constructed have contained at most two simple statements. Now we will explain how to construct a truth table that consists of three simple statements, such as $(p \wedge q) \wedge r$. When a compound statement consists of three simple statements, there are eight different true–false possibilities,

Table 3.10

	p	*q*	*r*
Case 1	T	T	T
Case 2	T	T	F
Case 3	T	F	T
Case 4	T	F	F
Case 5	F	T	T
Case 6	F	T	F
Case 7	F	F	T
Case 8	F	F	F

as illustrated in Table 3.10. To begin such a truth table, write four Ts and four Fs in the column under *p*. Under the second statement, *q*, pairs of Ts alternate with pairs of Fs. Under the third statement, *r*, T alternates with F. This technique is not the only way of listing the cases, but it ensures that each case is unique and that no cases are omitted.

Example 5 *Construct a Truth Table with Eight Cases*

a) Construct a truth table for the statement "Santana is home and he is not at his desk, or he is sleeping."

b) Suppose that "Santana is home" is a false statement, that "Santana is at his desk" is a true statement, and that "Santana is sleeping" is a true statement. Is the compound statement in part (a) true or false?

Solution

a) First we will translate the statement into symbolic form.

Let

p: Santana is home.

q: Santana is at his desk.

r: Santana is sleeping.

In symbolic form, the statement is $(p \land \sim q) \lor r$.

Since the statement is composed of three simple statements, there are eight cases. Begin by listing the eight cases in the three left-hand columns; see Table 3.11. By examining the statement, you can see that it is a disjunction. Therefore, the answer will be in the $\lor$ column. Fill out the truth table by working in parentheses first. Place values under *p*, column 1, and $\sim q$, column 2. Then find the conjunctions of columns 1 and 2 to obtain column 3. Place the values of *r* in column 4. To obtain the answer, column 5, use columns 3 and 4 and the information for the disjunction contained in Table 3.5 on page 106.

Table 3.11

p	*q*	*r*	(*p*	$\land$	$\sim q$)	$\lor$	*r*
T	T	T	T	F	F	T	T
T	T	F	T	F	F	F	F
T	F	T	T	T	T	T	T
T	F	F	T	T	T	T	F
F	T	T	F	F	F	(T)	T
F	T	F	F	F	F	F	F
F	F	T	F	F	T	T	T
F	F	F	F	F	T	F	F
			1	3	2	5	4

b) We are given the following:

p: Santana is home—false.

q: Santana is at his desk—true.

r: Santana is sleeping—true.

We need to find the truth value of the following case: false, true, true. In case 5 of the truth table, *p*, *q*, and *r* are F, T, and T, respectively. Therefore, under these conditions, the original compound statement is true (as circled in the table).   ∎

We have learned that a truth table with one simple statement has two cases, a truth table with two simple statements has four cases, and a truth table with three simple statements has eight cases. In general, *the number of distinct cases in a truth table with n distinct simple statements is* 2^n. The compound statement $(p \lor q) \lor (r \land \sim s)$ has four simple statements, p, q, r, s. Thus, a truth table for this compound statement would have 2^4, or 16, distinct cases.

When we construct a truth table, we determine the truth values of a compound statement for every possible case. If we want to find the truth value of the compound statement for any specific case when we know the truth values of the simple statements, we do not have to develop the entire table. For example, to determine the truth value for the statement

$$2 + 3 = 5 \qquad \text{and} \qquad 1 + 1 = 3$$

we let p be $2 + 3 = 5$ and q be $1 + 1 = 3$. Now we can write the compound statement as $p \land q$. We know that p is a true statement and q is a false statement. Thus, we can substitute T for p and F for q and evaluate the statement:

$$p \land q$$
$$T \land F$$
$$F$$

Therefore, the compound statement $2 + 3 = 5$ and $1 + 1 = 3$ is a false statement.

Alternate Method for Constructing Truth Tables

We now present an alternate method for constructing truth tables. We will use the alternate method to construct truth tables for the same statements we analyzed in Examples 1, 2, and 3.

Example **6** *Use the Alternate Method to Construct a Truth Table*

Construct a truth table for $p \land \sim q$.

Solution We begin by constructing the first two columns of a truth table with four cases, as shown in Table 3.12 (a). We will add additional columns to Table 3.12(a) to develop our answer column. Since we wish to find the truth table for the compound statement $p \land \sim q$, we need to be able to compare the truth values for p with the truth values for $\sim q$. Table 3.12(a) already has a column showing the truth values for p. We next add a column showing the truth values for $\sim q$, as shown in Table 3.12(b). Recall that the values of $\sim q$ are the opposite of those for q.

Finally, we add the answer column for the compound statement $p \land \sim q$, as shown as shown in Table 3.12(c). To determine the truth values for the $p \land \sim q$ column, use the p column and the $\sim q$ column, and the conjunction table, Table 3.4,

Table 3.12

(a)

	p	q
Case 1	T	T
Case 2	T	F
Case 3	F	T
Case 4	F	F

(b)

p	q	$\sim q$
T	T	F
T	F	T
F	T	F
F	F	T

(c)

p	q	$\sim q$	$p \land \sim q$
T	T	F	F
T	F	T	T
F	T	F	F
F	F	T	F

Use these columns to determine the answer column

on page 105. Note that the answer column of Table 3.12(c) is the same as the answer column of Table 3.6(e) on page 107. ∎

Example 7 Use the Alternate Method to Construct a Truth Table

Construct a truth table for $\sim p \wedge \sim q$.

Solution Begin by constructing a truth table with four cases, as shown in Table 3.13(a). Since we wish to find the truth table for the compound statement $\sim p \wedge \sim q$, we will add a column for $\sim p$ and a column for $\sim q$, as shown in Table 3.13(b).

Table 3.13

(a)

p	q
T	T
T	F
F	T
F	F

(b)

p	q	$\sim p$	$\sim q$
T	T	F	F
T	F	F	T
F	T	T	F
F	F	T	T

(c)

p	q	$\sim p$	$\sim q$	$\sim p \wedge \sim q$
T	T	F	F	F
T	F	F	T	F
F	T	T	F	F
F	F	T	T	T

Use these columns to determine the answer column

Finally, we add our answer column for the compound statement $\sim p \wedge \sim q$. To determine the truth values for the $\sim p \wedge \sim q$ column, use the $\sim p$ column and the $\sim q$ column, and the conjunction table, Table 3.4, on page 105. Note that the answer column of Table 3.13(c) is the same as the answer column of Table 3.7 on page 108. ∎

Example 8 Use the Alternate Method to Construct a Truth Table

Construct a truth table for $\sim(\sim q \vee p)$.

Solution Begin by constructing a truth table with four cases, as shown in Table 3.14(a). To complete the truth table, we will work within parentheses first. Thus, we next add a column for $\sim q$, as shown in Table 3.14(b). We then will construct a column for the expression within parentheses $\sim q \vee p$ by using the $\sim q$ column and the p column, and the disjunction table, Table 3.5, on page 106.

Table 3.14

(a)

p	q
T	T
T	F
F	T
F	F

(b)

p	q	$\sim q$
T	T	F
T	F	T
F	T	F
F	F	T

(c)

p	q	$\sim q$	$\sim q \vee p$
T	T	F	T
T	F	T	T
F	T	F	F
T	F	T	T

Use these columns to determine the $\sim q \vee p$ column

Table 3.15

p	q	$\sim q$	$\sim q \vee p$	$\sim(\sim q \vee p)$
T	T	F	T	F
T	F	T	T	F
F	T	F	F	T
F	F	T	T	F

Take the opposite of this column to get the answer column

Finally, we add the answer column for the compound statement, $\sim(\sim q \vee p)$, as shown in Table 3.15. To determine the truth values for the $\sim(\sim q \vee p)$ column, take the opposite values of those shown in the $\sim q \vee p$ column. Note that the answer column of Table 3.15 is the same as the answer column of Table 3.8 on page 109. ∎

We have demonstrated two methods for constructing truth tables. Unless your instructor indicates otherwise, you may use either method. Although both methods will always lead to the correct answer, the alternate method gets more cumbersome and takes up more space as we construct truth tables with more statements. *In the remainder of this chapter, we will demonstrate the construction of truth tables using only the first method.*

Determine Truth Values Without Constructing a Truth Table

In the remaining examples in this section, we will determine the truth values of compound statements without constructing a truth table.

Example 9 *Determine the Truth Value of a Compound Statement*

Determine the truth value for each simple statement. Then, using these truth values, determine the truth value of the compound statement.

a) 15 is less than or equal to 9.

b) George Washington was the first U.S. president or Abraham Lincoln was the second U.S. president, but there has not been a U.S. president born in Antarctica.

Solution

a) Let

p: 15 is less than 9.

q: 15 is equal to 9.

The statement "15 is less than or equal to 9" means that 15 is less than 9 or 15 is equal to 9. The compound statement can be expressed as $p \lor q$. We know that both p and q are false statements, since 15 is greater than 9, so we substitute F for p and F for q and evaluate the statement:

$$p \lor q$$
$$F \lor F$$
$$F$$

Therefore, the compound statement "15 is less than or equal to 9" is a false statement.

b) Let

p: George Washington was the first U.S. president.

q: Abraham Lincoln was the second U.S. president.

r: There has been a U.S. president who was born in Antarctica.

The compound statement can be written in symbolic form as $(p \lor q) \land \sim r$. Recall that *but* is used to express a conjunction. We know that p is a true statement and that q is a false statement. We also know that r is a false statement since all U.S. presidents must be born in the United States. Thus, since r is a false statement, the negation, $\sim r$, is a true statement. So we will substitute T for p, F for q, and T for $\sim r$ and then evaluate the statement:

$$(p \lor q) \land \sim r$$
$$(T \lor F) \land T$$
$$T \land T$$
$$T$$

Therefore, the original compound statement is a true statement.

Example 10   *Pet Ownership in the United States*

The number of pets owned in the United States in 2009 is shown in Figure 3.1. Use this graph to determine the truth value of the following statement: There are more dogs owned than cats and there are fewer reptiles owned than birds, or the most numerous pets owned are not fish.

Pets Owned in the United States (millions)

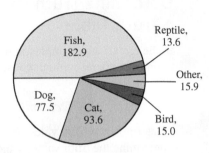

Source: American Pet Products Manufacturing Association

Figure 3.1

Solution   Let

    p: There are more dogs owned than cats.
    q: There are fewer reptiles owned than birds.
    r: The most numerous pets owned are fish.

The given compound statement can be written in symbolic form as $(p \wedge q) \vee {\sim} r$. From Fig. 3.1, we see that statement *p* is false: There are actually more cats owned than dogs. We also see that statement *q* is true: There are fewer reptiles owned than birds. We also see that statement *r* is true: The most numerous pets owned are fish. Since *r* is true, its negation, ${\sim} r$, is false. Therefore, we substitute F for *p*, T for *q*, and F for ${\sim} r$, which gives

$$(p \wedge q) \vee {\sim} r$$
$$(\text{F} \wedge \text{T}) \vee \text{F}$$
$$\text{F} \vee \text{F}$$
$$\text{F}$$

Thus, the original compound statement is a false statement.   ■

SECTION 3.2   *Exercises*

Warm Up Exercises

In Exercises 1–4, fill in the blanks with an appropriate word, phrase, or symbol(s).

1. The negation ${\sim} p$ will always have the _____ truth value of *p*.

2. The conjunction $p \wedge q$ is true only when both *p* and *q* are _____.

3. The disjunction $p \vee q$ is false only when both *p* and *q* are _____.

4. A truth table for a compound statement with

   a) one distinct simple statement will have _____ cases.

   b) two distinct simple statements will have _____ cases.

   c) three distinct simple statements will have _____ cases.

Practice the Skills/Problem Solving

In Exercises 5–18, construct a truth table for the statement.

5. $p \wedge \sim p$

6. $p \vee \sim p$

7. $q \vee \sim p$

8. $p \wedge \sim q$

9. $\sim p \vee \sim q$

10. $\sim (p \vee \sim q)$

11. $\sim (p \wedge \sim q)$

12. $\sim (\sim p \wedge \sim q)$

13. $\sim q \vee (p \wedge r)$

14. $(p \vee \sim q) \wedge r$

15. $r \vee (p \wedge \sim q)$

16. $(r \wedge q) \wedge \sim p$

17. $(r \vee \sim p) \wedge \sim q$

18. $\sim p \wedge (q \vee r)$

In Exercises 19–26, write the statement in symbolic form and construct a truth table.

19. Train recorded *Hey, Soul Sister* and The Black Eyed Peas recorded *Where Is the Love?*

▲ *The Black Eyed Peas*

20. We can eat at McDonald's, but we cannot eat breakfast.

21. I have worked all week, but I have not been paid.

22. It is false that Robert A. Farinelli is the president or that Pauline Chow is the treasurer.

23. It is false that Jasper Adams is a tutor and Mark Russo is a secretary.

24. Mike made pizza and Dennis made a chef salad, but Gil burned the lemon squares.

25. The copier is out of toner, or the lens is dirty or the corona wires are broken.

26. I am hungry, and I want to eat a healthy lunch and I want to eat in a hurry.

In Exercises 27–36, determine the truth value of the statement if

  a) *p* is true, *q* is false, and *r* is true.

  b) *p* is false, *q* is true, and *r* is true.

27. $(p \vee q) \wedge \sim r$

28. $p \vee (q \wedge \sim r)$

29. $(\sim p \wedge \sim q) \vee \sim r$

30. $\sim p \wedge (\sim q \vee \sim r)$

31. $(p \vee \sim q) \wedge \sim (p \wedge \sim r)$

32. $(p \wedge \sim q) \vee r$

33. $(\sim r \wedge p) \vee q$

34. $\sim q \vee (r \wedge p)$

35. $(\sim p \vee \sim q) \vee (\sim r \vee q)$

36. $(\sim r \wedge \sim q) \wedge (\sim r \vee \sim p)$

In Exercises 37–44, determine the truth value for each simple statement. Then use these truth values to determine the truth value of the compound statement. (You may have to use a reference source such as the Internet or an encyclopedia.)

37. $8 + 7 = 20 - 5$ and $63 \div 7 = 3 \cdot 3$

38. $0 < -3$ or $5 \geq 10$

39. Florida is in Canada or Texas borders Mexico.

40. Washington, DC is west of the Mississippi River and Virginia is an island in the Pacific Ocean.

41. Quentin Tarantino is a movie director and Zac Efron is an actor, but Scarlett Johansson is not an actress.

▲ *Scarlett Johansson*

42. Quebec is in Texas or Toronto is in California, and Cedar Rapids is in Iowa.

43. Iraq is in Africa or Iran is in South America, and Syria is in the Middle East.

44. Holstein is a breed of cattle and collie is a breed of dogs, or beagle is not a breed of cats.

Number of Movies Produced *In Exercises 45–48, use the table to determine the truth value of each simple statement. Then determine the value of the compound statement.*

Countries with the Highest Number of Feature Films Produced in 2008	
Country	**Number of Films**
India	1325
United States	520
Japan	418
China	406
France	240

Source: Screen Digest Magazine

45. India produced more feature films than the United States and China produced more feature films than Japan.

46. India produced more than twice as many feature films as the United States and India produced more feature films than Japan, China, and France combined.

47. The United States produced more feature films than Japan, but Japan produced more feature films than China.

48. The United States produced more than twice as many feature films as France or Japan produced more feature films than India.

Sleep Time *In Exercises 49–52, use the graph, which shows the number of hours Americans sleep, to determine the truth value of each simple statement. Then determine the truth value of the compound statement.*

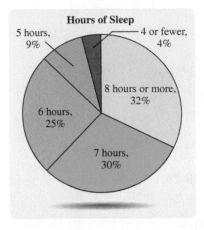

Hours of Sleep

5 hours, 9%
4 or fewer, 4%
8 hours or more, 32%
6 hours, 25%
7 hours, 30%

49. It is false that 30% of Americans get 6 hours of sleep each night and 9% get 5 hours of sleep each night.

50. Twenty-five percent of Americans get 6 hours of sleep each night, and 30% get 7 hours of sleep each night or 9% do not get 5 hours of sleep each night.

51. Thirteen percent of Americans get 5 or fewer hours of sleep each night or 32% get 6 or more hours of sleep each night, and 30% get 8 or more hours of sleep each night.

52. Over one-half of all Americans get 7 or fewer hours of sleep each night, and over one-quarter get 6 or fewer hours of sleep each night.

In Exercises 53–56, let

    p: Tanisha owns a convertible.
    q: Joan owns a Volvo.

Translate each statement into symbols. Then construct a truth table for each compound statement and indicate under what conditions the compound statement is true.

53. Tanisha owns a convertible and Joan does not own a Volvo.

54. Tanisha does not own a convertible, but Joan owns a Volvo.

55. Tanisha owns a convertible or Joan does not own a Volvo.

56. Tanisha does not own a convertible or Joan does not own a Volvo.

In Exercises 57–60 on page 117, let
    p: The house is owned by an engineer.
    q: The heat is solar generated.
    r: The car is run by electric power.

Translate each statement into symbols. Then construct a truth table for each and indicate under what conditions the compound statement is true.

57. The car is run by electric power or the heat is solar generated, but the house is owned by an engineer.

58. The house is owned by an engineer and the heat is solar generated, or the car is run by electric power.

59. The heat is solar generated, or the house is owned by an engineer and the car is not run by electric power.

60. The house is not owned by an engineer, and the car is not run by electric power and the heat is solar generated.

Obtaining a Loan In Exercises 61 and 62, read the requirements and each applicant's qualifications for obtaining a loan.

   a) Identify which of the applicants would qualify for the loan.

   b) For the applicants who do not qualify for the loan, explain why.

61. To qualify for a loan of $40,000, an applicant must have a gross income of $28,000 if single, $46,000 combined income if married, and assets of at least $6,000.

    Mrs. Rusinek, married with three children, earns $42,000. Mr. Rusinek does not have an income. The Rusineks have assets of $42,000.

    Mr. Duncan is not married, works in sales, and earns $31,000. He has assets of $9000.

    Mrs. Tuttle and her husband have total assets of $43,000. One earns $35,000, and the other earns $23,500.

62. To qualify for a loan of $45,000, an applicant must have a gross income of $30,000 if single, $50,000 combined income if married, and assets of at least $10,000.

    Mr. Argento, married with two children, earns $37,000. Mrs. Argento earns $15,000 at a part-time job. The Argentos have assets of $25,000.

    Ms. McVey, single, has assets of $19,000. She works in a store and earns $25,000.

    Mr. Siewert earns $24,000 and Ms. Fox, his wife, earns $28,000. Their assets total $8000.

63. *Airline Special Fares* An airline advertisement states, "To get the special fare you must purchase your tickets between January 1 and February 15 and fly round trip between March 1 and April 1. You must depart on a Monday, Tuesday, or Wednesday, and return on a Tuesday, Wednesday, or Thursday, and stay over at least one Saturday."

   a) Determine which of the following individuals will qualify for the special fare.

   b) If the person does not qualify for the special fare, explain why.

    Wing Park plans to purchase his ticket on January 15, depart on Monday, March 3, and return on Tuesday, March 18.

    Gina Vela plans to purchase her ticket on February 1, depart on Wednesday, March 12, and return on Thursday, April 3.

    Kara Shavo plans to purchase her ticket on February 14, depart on Tuesday, March 4, and return on Monday, March 19.

    Christos Supernaw plans to purchase his ticket on January 4, depart on Monday, March 10, and return on Thursday, March 13.

    Alex Chang plans to purchase his ticket on January 1, depart on Monday, March 3, and return on Monday, March 10.

▲ *See Exercise 63*

Problem Solving/Group Activities

In Exercises 64 and 65, construct a truth table for the symbolic statement.

64. $\sim[(\sim(p \vee q)) \vee (q \wedge r)]$

65. $[(q \wedge \sim r) \wedge (\sim p \vee \sim q)] \vee (p \vee \sim r)$

66. On page 111, we indicated that a compound statement consisting of *n* simple statements had 2^n distinct true–false cases.

   a) How many distinct true–false cases does a truth table containing simple statements *p*, *q*, *r*, and *s* have?

   b) List all possible true–false cases for a truth table containing the simple statements *p*, *q*, *r*, and *s*.

   c) Use the list in part (b) to construct a truth table for $(q \wedge p) \vee (\sim r \wedge s)$.

   d) Construct a truth table for $(\sim r \wedge \sim s) \wedge (\sim p \vee q)$.

67. Must $(p \wedge \sim q) \vee r$ and $(q \wedge \sim r) \vee p$ have the same number of trues in their answer columns? Explain.

Internet/Research Activities

68. Do research and write a report on each of the following.

   a) The relationship between *negation* in logic and *complement* in set theory.

   b) The relationship between *conjunction* in logic and *intersection* in set theory.

   c) The relationship between *disjunction* in logic and *union* in set theory.

Truth Tables for the Conditional and Biconditional

Suppose I said to you, "If you get an A, then I will buy you a car." As we discussed in Section 3.1, this statement is called a *conditional* statement. In this section, we will discuss under what conditions a conditional statement is true and under what conditions a conditional statement is false.

Why **This is Important** Understanding when conditional statements are true is essential to understanding logic and real-life documents such as wills, trusts, and contracts.

Conditional

In Section 3.1, we mentioned that the statement preceding the conditional symbol is called the *antecedent* and that the statement following the conditional symbol is called the *consequent*. For example, consider $(p \lor q) \to [\sim(q \land r)]$. In this statement, $(p \lor q)$ is the antecedent and $[\sim(q \land r)]$ is the consequent.

To develop a truth table for the conditional statement, consider the statement "If you get an A, then I will buy you a car." Assume this statement is true except when I have actually broken my promise to you.

Let
p: You get an A.
q: I buy you a car.

Translated into symbolic form, the statement becomes $p \to q$. Let's examine the four cases shown in Table 3.16.

CASE 1: (T, T) You get an A, and I buy a car for you. I have met my commitment, and the statement is true.

CASE 2: (T, F) You get an A, and I do not buy a car for you. I have broken my promise, and the statement is false.

What happens if you don't get an A? If you don't get an A, I no longer have a commitment to you, and therefore I cannot break my promise.

CASE 3: (F, T) You do not get an A, and I buy you a car. I have not broken my promise, and therefore the statement is true.

CASE 4: (F, F) You do not get an A, and I don't buy you a car. I have not broken my promise, and therefore the statement is true.

The conditional statement is false when the antecedent is true and the consequent is false. In every other case the conditional statement is true.

> The **conditional statement** $p \to q$ is true in every case except when p is a true statement and q is a false statement.

▲ *Under what conditions is the statement* If you get an A, then I will buy you a car *true?*

Table 3.16 Conditional

p	q	$p \to q$
T	T	T
T	F	F
F	T	T
F	F	T

Example 1 A Truth Table with a Conditional

Construct a truth table for the statement $\sim p \to \sim q$.

Solution Because this statement is a conditional, the answer will lie under the $\to$. Fill out the truth table by placing the appropriate truth values under $\sim p$, column 1,

Table 3.17

p	q	~p	→	~q
T	T	F	T	F
T	F	F	T	T
F	T	T	F	F
F	F	T	T	T
		1	3	2

Table 3.18

p	q	r	p	→	(~q	∧	r)
T	T	T	T	F	F	F	T
T	T	F	T	F	F	F	F
T	F	T	T	T	T	T	T
T	F	F	T	F	T	F	F
F	T	T	F	T	F	F	T
F	T	F	F	T	F	F	F
F	F	T	F	T	T	T	T
F	F	F	F	T	T	F	F
			4	5	1	3	2

and under $\sim q$, column 2 (see Table 3.17). Then, using the information given in the truth table for the conditional (Table 3.16 on page 118) and the truth values in columns 1 and 2, determine the solution, column 3. In row 1, the antecedent, $\sim p$, is false and the consequent, $\sim q$, is also false. Row 1 is F → F, which according to row 4 of Table 3.16, is T. Likewise, row 2 of Table 3.17 is F → T, which is T. Row 3 is T → F, which is F. Row 4 is T → T, which is T. ∎

Example 2 *A Conditional Truth Table with Three Simple Statements*

Construct a truth table for the statement $p \rightarrow (\sim q \land r)$.

Solution Because this statement is a conditional, the answer will lie under the → . Work within the parentheses first. Place the truth values under $\sim q$, column 1, and r, column 2 (Table 3.18). Then take the conjunction of columns 1 and 2 to obtain column 3. Next, place the truth values under p in column 4. To determine the answer, column 5, use columns 3 and 4 and the information of the conditional statement given in Table 3.16. Column 4 represents the truth values of the antecedent, and column 3 represents the truth values of the consequent. Remember that the conditional is false only when the antecedent is true and the consequent is false, as in cases (rows) 1, 2, and 4 of column 5. ∎

Example 3 *Examining an Advertisement*

An advertisement for Perky Morning coffee makes the following claim: "If you drink Perky Morning coffee, then you will not be sluggish and you will have a great day." Translate the statement into symbolic form and construct a truth table.

Solution Let

p: You drink Perky Morning coffee.

q: You will be sluggish.

r: You will have a great day.

In symbolic form, the claim is

$$p \rightarrow (\sim q \land r)$$

This symbolic statement is identical to the statement in Table 3.18, and the truth tables are the same. Column 3 represents the truth values of $(\sim q \land r)$, which corresponds to the statement "You will not be sluggish and you will have a great day." Note that column 3 is true in cases (rows) 3 and 7. In case 3, since p is true, you drank Perky Morning coffee. In case 7, however, since p is false, you did not drink Perky Morning coffee. From this information we can conclude that it is possible for you to not be sluggish and for you to have a great day without drinking Perky Morning coffee. ∎

A truth table cannot by itself determine whether a compound statement is true or false. However, a truth table does allow us to examine all possible cases for compound statements.

Biconditional

The *biconditional statement* $p \leftrightarrow q$ means that $p \rightarrow q$ and $q \rightarrow p$, or, symbolically, $(p \rightarrow q) \land (q \rightarrow p)$. To determine the truth table for $p \leftrightarrow q$, we will construct the truth table for $(p \rightarrow q) \land (q \rightarrow p)$ (Table 3.19 on page 120). Table 3.20 on page 120 shows the truth values for the biconditional statement.

Table 3.19

p	q	$(p$	$\rightarrow$	$q)$	$\wedge$	$(q$	$\rightarrow$	$p)$
T	T	T	T	T	T	T	T	T
T	F	T	F	F	F	F	T	T
F	T	F	T	T	F	T	F	F
F	F	F	T	F	T	F	T	F
		1	3	2	7	4	6	5

Table 3.20 Biconditional

p	q	$p \leftrightarrow q$
T	T	T
T	F	F
F	T	F
F	F	T

From Table 3.20 we see that the biconditional statement is true when the antecedent and the consequent have the same truth value and false when the antecedent and consequent have different truth values.

The **biconditional statement** $p \leftrightarrow q$ is true only when p and q have the same truth value, that is, when both are true or both are false.

Example 4 *A Truth Table Using a Biconditional*

Construct a truth table for the statement $\sim p \leftrightarrow (\sim q \rightarrow r)$.

Solution Since there are three letters, there must be eight cases. The parentheses indicate that the answer must be under the biconditional, as shown in Table 3.21. Use columns 1 and 4 to obtain the answer in column 5. When columns 1 and 4 have the same truth values, place a T in column 5. When columns 1 and 4 have different truth values, place an F in column 5.

Table 3.21

p	q	r	$\sim p$	$\leftrightarrow$	$(\sim q$	$\rightarrow$	$r)$
T	T	T	F	F	F	T	T
T	T	F	F	F	F	T	F
T	F	T	F	F	T	T	T
T	F	F	F	T	T	F	F
F	T	T	T	T	F	T	T
F	T	F	T	T	F	T	F
F	F	T	T	T	T	T	T
F	F	F	T	F	T	F	F
			1	5	2	4	3

In Section 3.2, we showed that finding the truth value of a compound statement for a specific case does not require constructing an entire truth table. Examples 5 and 6 illustrate this technique for the conditional and the biconditional.

Example 5 *Determine the Truth Value of a Compound Statement*

Determine the truth value of the statement $(\sim p \leftrightarrow q) \rightarrow (\sim q \leftrightarrow r)$ when p is false, q is true, and r is false.

Solution Substitute the truth value for each simple statement:

$$(\sim p \leftrightarrow q) \rightarrow (\sim q \leftrightarrow r)$$
$$(T \leftrightarrow T) \ \rightarrow \ (F \leftrightarrow F)$$
$$T \quad \rightarrow \quad T$$
$$T$$

For this specific case, the statement is true.

Example 6 *Determine the Truth Value of a Compound Statement*

Determine the truth value for each simple statement. Then use the truth values to determine the truth value of the compound statement.

a) If 15 is an even number, then 29 is an even number.

b) Vanderbilt University is in Tennessee and Wake Forest University is in Alaska, if and only if Syracuse University is in Alabama.

Solution

a) Let

$$p: \quad \text{15 is an even number.}$$
$$q: \quad \text{29 is an even number.}$$

Then the statement "If 15 is an even number, then 29 is an even number" can be written $p \rightarrow q$. Since 15 is not an even number, p is a false statement. Also, since 29 is not an even number, q is a false statement. We substitute F for p and F for q and evaluate the statement:

$$p \rightarrow q$$
$$F \rightarrow F$$
$$T$$

Therefore, "If 15 is an even number, then 29 is an even number" is a true statement.

b) Let

$$p: \quad \text{Vanderbilt University is in Tennessee.}$$
$$q: \quad \text{Wake Forest University is in Alaska.}$$
$$r: \quad \text{Syracuse University is in Alabama.}$$

The original compound statement can be written $(p \wedge q) \leftrightarrow r$. By checking the Internet or other references we can find that Vanderbilt University is in Tennessee, Wake Forest University is in North Carolina, and Syracuse University is in New York. Therefore, p is a true statement, but q and r are false statements. We will substitute T for p, F for q, and F for r and evaluate the compound statement:

$$(p \wedge q) \leftrightarrow r$$
$$(T \wedge F) \leftrightarrow F$$
$$F \quad \leftrightarrow F$$
$$T$$

Therefore, the original compound statement is true.

▲ *Vanderbilt University*

Example 7 *Using Real Data in Compound Statements*

The graph in Fig. 3.2 on page 122 represents the student population by age group in 2009 for the State College of Florida (SCF). Use this graph to determine the truth value of the following compound statements.

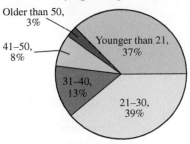

State College of Florida Population by Age Group

Older than 50, 3%
41–50, 8%
31–40, 13%
Younger than 21, 37%
21–30, 39%

Source: www.scf.edu

Figure 3.2

a) If 37% of the SCF population is younger than 21 or 26% of the SCF population is age 21–30, then 13% of the SCF population is age 31–40.

b) 3% of the SCF population is older than 50 and 8% of the SCF population is age 41–50, if and only if 19% of the SCF population is age 21–30.

Solution

a) Let

p: 37% of the SCF population is younger than 21.
q: 26% of the SCF population is age 21–30.
r: 13% of the SCF population is age 31–40.

Then the original statement can be written $(p \lor q) \to r$. We can see from Fig. 3.2 that both p and r are true statements and that q is a false statement. Substitute T for p, F for q, and T for r and evaluate the statement:

$$(p \lor q) \to r$$
$$(T \lor F) \to T$$
$$T \quad \to T$$
$$T$$

Therefore, "If 37% of the SCF population is younger than 21 or 26% of the SCF population is age 21–30, then 13% of the SCF population is age 31–40" is a true statement.

b) Let

p: 3% of the SCF population is older than 50.
q: 8% of the SCF population is age 41–50.
r: 19% of the SCF population is age 21–30.

Then the original statement can be written $(p \land q) \leftrightarrow r$. We can see from Fig. 3.2 that p and q are both true statements and r is a false statement. Substitute T for p, T for q, and F for r and evaluate the statement:

$$(p \land q) \leftrightarrow r$$
$$(T \land T) \leftrightarrow F$$
$$T \quad \leftrightarrow F$$
$$F$$

Therefore, the original statement, "3% of the SCF population is older than 50 and 8% of the SCF population is age 41–50, if and only if 19% of the SCF population is age 21–30," is a false statement. ∎

Self-Contradictions, Tautologies, and Implications

Two special situations can occur in the truth table of a compound statement: The statement may always be false, or the statement may always be true. We give such statements special names.

> **Definition: Self-contradiction**
>
> A **self-contradiction** is a compound statement that is always false.

When every truth value in the answer column of the truth table is false, then the statement is a self-contradiction.

Table 3.22

p	q	$(p \leftrightarrow q)$	$\wedge$	$(p$	$\leftrightarrow$	$\sim q)$
T	T	T	F	T	F	F
T	F	F	F	T	T	T
F	T	F	F	F	T	F
F	F	T	F	F	F	T
		1	5	2	4	3

⌐ Example **8** *All Falses, a Self-Contradiction*

Construct a truth table for the statement $(p \leftrightarrow q) \wedge (p \leftrightarrow \sim q)$.

Solution See Table 3.22. In this example, the truth values are false in each case of column 5. This statement is an example of a self-contradiction or a *logically false statement*.   ∎

> **Definition: Tautology**
>
> A **tautology** is a compound statement that is always true.

When every truth value in the answer column of the truth table is true, the statement is a tautology.

⌐ Example **9** *All Trues, a Tautology*

Construct a truth table for the statement $(p \wedge q) \rightarrow (p \vee r)$.

Solution The answer is given in column 3 of Table 3.23. The truth values are true in every case. Thus, the statement is an example of a tautology or a *logically true statement*.

Table 3.23

p	q	r	$(p \wedge q)$	$\rightarrow$	$(p \vee r)$
T	T	T	T	T	T
T	T	F	T	T	T
T	F	T	F	T	T
T	F	F	F	T	T
F	T	T	F	T	T
F	T	F	F	T	F
F	F	T	F	T	T
F	F	F	F	T	F
			1	3	2

▲ *"Heads I win, tails you lose." Do you think that this statement is a tautology, self-contradiction, or neither? See Exercise 77 on page 126.*

The conditional statement $(p \wedge q) \rightarrow (p \vee r)$ is a tautology. Conditional statements that are tautologies are called *implications*. In Example 9, we can say that $p \wedge q$ implies $p \vee r$.

Definition: Implication
An **implication** is a conditional statement that is a tautology.

In any implication the antecedent of the conditional statement implies the consequent. In other words, if the antecedent is true, then the consequent must also be true. That is, the consequent will be true whenever the antecedent is true.

Table 3.24

p	q	[(p ∧ q)	∧	p]	→	q
T	T	T	T	T	T	T
T	F	F	F	T	T	F
F	T	F	F	F	T	T
F	F	F	F	F	T	F
		1	3	2	5	4

Example 10 An Implication?

Determine whether the conditional statement $[(p \wedge q) \wedge p] \to q$ is an implication.

Solution If the conditional statement is a tautology, the conditional statement is an implication. Because the conditional statement is a tautology (see Table 3.24), the conditional statement is an implication. The antecedent $[(p \wedge q) \wedge p]$ implies the consequent q. Note that the antecedent is true only in case 1 and that the consequent is also true in case 1. ∎

SECTION 3.3   *Exercises*

Warm Up Exercises

In Exercises 1–6, fill in the blanks with an appropriate word, phrase, or symbol(s).

1. The conditional statement $p \to q$ is _____ only when p is true and q is false.

2. In the conditional statement $p \to q$,
   a) The lower-case letter p represents the _____.
   b) The lower-case letter q represents the _____.

3. The biconditional statement $p \leftrightarrow q$ is _____ only when p and q have the same truth value.

4. A compound statement that is always true is known as a _____.

5. A compound statement that is always false is known as a _____.

6. A conditional statement that is a tautology is known as an _____.

Practice the Skills

In Exercises 7–16, construct a truth table for the statement.

7. $\sim p \to q$

8. $\sim p \to \sim q$

9. $\sim(p \to \sim q)$

10. $\sim(\sim p \leftrightarrow q)$

11. $\sim q \leftrightarrow p$

12. $(p \leftrightarrow q) \to p$

13. $p \leftrightarrow (q \vee p)$

14. $(\sim q \wedge p) \to \sim q$

15. $q \to (p \to \sim q)$

16. $(p \vee q) \leftrightarrow (p \wedge q)$

In Exercises 17–24, construct a truth table for the statement.

17. $\sim p \to (q \wedge r)$

18. $q \vee (p \to \sim r)$

19. $(q \vee \sim r) \leftrightarrow \sim p$

20. $(p \wedge r) \to (q \vee r)$

21. $(\sim r \vee \sim q) \to p$

22. $[r \wedge (q \vee \sim p)] \leftrightarrow \sim p$

23. $(p \to q) \leftrightarrow (\sim q \to \sim r)$

24. $(\sim p \leftrightarrow \sim q) \to (\sim q \leftrightarrow r)$

In Exercises 25–30, write the statement in symbolic form. Then construct a truth table for the symbolic statement.

25. If it is raining, then the baseball game is canceled and we can eat dinner together.

26. We advance in the tournament if and only if Max plays, or Pondo does not show up.

27. The election was fair if and only if the polling station stayed open until 8 P.M., or we will request a recount.

28. If the dam holds then we can go fishing, if and only if the pole is not broken.

29. If Mary Andrews does not send me an e-mail then we can call her, or we can write to Mom.

30. It is false that if Eileen Jones went to lunch, then she cannot take a message and we will have to go home.

In Exercises 31–36, determine whether the statement is a tautology, self-contradiction, or neither.

31. $\sim p \rightarrow p$

32. $(\sim p \vee q) \leftrightarrow \sim q$

33. $\sim p \wedge (q \leftrightarrow \sim q)$

34. $(p \wedge \sim q) \rightarrow q$

35. $(\sim q \rightarrow p) \vee \sim q$

36. $[(p \rightarrow q) \vee r] \leftrightarrow [(p \wedge q) \rightarrow r]$

In Exercises 37–42, determine whether the statement is an implication.

37. $\sim p \rightarrow p$

38. $p \rightarrow (p \vee q)$

39. $\sim p \rightarrow \sim (p \wedge q)$

40. $(p \vee q) \rightarrow (p \vee \sim r)$

41. $[(p \rightarrow q) \wedge (q \rightarrow p)] \rightarrow (p \leftrightarrow q)$

42. $[(p \vee q) \wedge r] \rightarrow (p \vee q)$

In Exercises 43–52, if p is true, q is false, and r is true, find the truth value of the statement.

43. $p \rightarrow (q \rightarrow r)$

44. $(p \wedge \sim q) \rightarrow \sim r$

45. $(p \wedge q) \leftrightarrow (q \vee r)$

46. $r \rightarrow (\sim p \leftrightarrow \sim q)$

47. $(\sim p \wedge \sim q) \vee \sim r$

48. $\sim [p \rightarrow (q \wedge r)]$

49. $(\sim p \leftrightarrow r) \vee (\sim q \leftrightarrow r)$

50. $(r \rightarrow \sim p) \wedge (q \rightarrow \sim r)$

51. $\sim [(p \vee q) \leftrightarrow (p \rightarrow \sim r)]$

52. $[(\sim r \rightarrow \sim q) \vee (p \wedge \sim r)] \rightarrow q$

Problem Solving

In Exercises 53–60, determine the truth value for each simple statement. Then, using the truth values, determine the truth value of the compound statement.

53. If $\sqrt{25} = 5$, then $\sqrt{49} = 7$.

54. If $5 < 1$, then $7 > 10$.

55. If a cat has whiskers or a fish can swim, then a dog lays eggs.

56. If Dallas is in Texas and St. Louis is in Missouri, then Detroit is in California.

57. Apple makes computers, if and only if Nike makes sports shoes or Rolex makes watches.

58. Spike Lee is a movie director, or if Halle Berry is a school teacher then George Clooney is a circus clown.

59. Mother's Day is in May and Father's Day is in December, if and only if Thanksgiving is in April.

60. Honda makes automobiles or Honda makes motorcycles, if and only if Toyota makes cereal.

In Exercises 61–64, use the information provided about the moons for the planets Jupiter and Saturn to determine the truth values of the simple statements. Then determine the truth value of the compound statement.

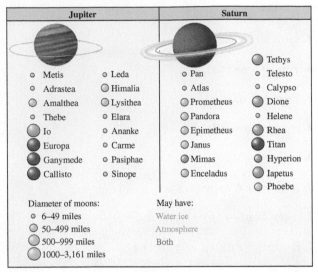

Source: Data from *Time* Magazine

61. Jupiter's Moons Io has a diameter of 1000–3161 miles or Thebe may have water, and Io may have atmosphere.

62. Moons of Saturn Titan may have water and Titan may have atmosphere, if and only if Janus may have water.

63. Moon Comparisons Phoebe has a larger diameter than Rhea if and only if Callisto may have water ice, and Calypso has a diameter of 6–49 miles.

64. Moon Comparisons If Jupiter has 16 moons or Saturn does not have 18 moons, then Saturn has 7 moons that may have water ice.

College Credits *In Exercises 65 and 66, use the graph to determine the truth value of each simple statement. Then determine the truth value of the compound statement.*

The following graph shows the number of credits in various categories needed by Jose Silva to earn his Associate in Arts degree from Keiser University.

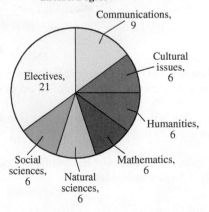

Credits Needed for an A.A. Degree

65. The number of communications credits needed is more than the number of mathematics credits needed and the number of cultural issues credits needed is equal to the number of humanities credits needed, if and only if the number of social sciences credits needed is more than the number of natural sciences credits needed.

66. If the number of elective credits needed is 21 or the number of communications credits needed is 15, then the number of humanities credits needed is equal to the number of mathematics credits needed.

In Exercises 67–72, suppose both of the following statements are false.

p: Muhundan spoke at the teachers' conference.

q: Muhundan received the outstanding teacher award.

Find the truth values of each compound statement.

67. If Muhundan received the outstanding teacher award, then Muhundan spoke at the teachers' conference.

68. If Muhundan spoke at the teachers' conference, then Muhundan did not receive the outstanding teacher award.

69. If Muhundan did not receive the outstanding teacher award, then Muhundan spoke at the teachers' conference.

70. Muhundan did not receive the outstanding teacher award if and only if Muhundan spoke at the teachers' conference.

71. Muhundan received the outstanding teacher award if and only if Muhundan spoke at the teachers' conference.

72. If Muhundan did not receive the outstanding teacher award, then Muhundan did not speak at the teachers' conference.

73. A New Computer Your parents make the following statement to your sister, "If you get straight A's this semester, then we will buy you a new computer." At the end of the semester your parents buy your sister a new computer. Can you conclude that your sister got straight A's? Explain.

74. Job Interview Consider the statement "If your interview goes well, then you will be offered the job." If you are interviewed and then offered the job, can you conclude that your interview went well? Explain.

Challenge Problems/Group Activities

In Exercises 75 and 76, construct truth tables for the symbolic statement.

75. $[p \lor (q \to \sim r)] \leftrightarrow (p \land \sim q)$

76. $[(r \to \sim q) \to \sim p] \lor (q \leftrightarrow \sim r)$

77. Is the statement "Heads I win, tails you lose" a tautology, a self-contradiction, or neither? Explain your answer.

78. Construct a truth table for

   a) $(p \lor q) \rightarrow (r \land s)$.

   b) $(q \rightarrow \sim p) \lor (r \leftrightarrow s)$.

Recreational Mathematics

79. *Satisfiability Problem* Refer to the Recreational Mathematics box on page 122 and then solve the following satisfiability problem. Allen, Booker, Chris, and Dennis all were born in the same year—one in January, one in February, one in March, and one in April. Chris was born before Dennis. Dennis was born two months after Booker. Booker was born after Allen, but before Chris. Find out who was born in each month.

80. *Cat Puzzle* Solve the following puzzle. The Joneses have four cats. The parents are Tiger and Boots, and the kittens are Sam and Sue. Each cat insists on eating out of its own bowl. To complicate matters, each cat will eat only its own brand of cat food. The colors of the bowls are red, yellow, green, and blue. The different types of cat food are Whiskas, Friskies, Nine Lives, and Meow Mix. Tiger will eat Meow Mix if and only if it is in a yellow bowl. If Boots is to eat her food, then it must be in a yellow bowl.

Mrs. Jones knows that the label on the can containing Sam's food is the same color as his bowl. Boots eats Whiskas. Meow Mix and Nine Lives are packaged in a brown paper bag. The color of Sue's bowl is green if and only if she eats Meow Mix. The label on the Friskies can is red. Match each cat with its food and the bowl of the correct color.

81. *The Youngest Triplet* The Barr triplets have an annoying habit: Whenever a question is asked of the three of them, two tell the truth and the third lies. When I asked them which of them was born last, they replied as follows.

   Mary: Katie was born last.
   Katie: I am the youngest.
   Annie: Mary is the youngest.

Which of the Barr triplets was born last?

Internet/Research Activity

82. Select an advertisement from the Internet, a newspaper, or a magazine that makes or implies a conditional statement. Analyze the advertisement to determine whether the consequent necessarily follows from the antecedent. Explain your answer. (See Example 3.)

SECTION 3.4   Equivalent Statements

▲ *Which statement is equivalent to* If it is sunny, then we go to the beach?

Suppose your friend makes the following statements:

   If it is sunny, then we go to the beach.

   If we go to the beach, then it is sunny.

   If it is not sunny, then we do not go to the beach.

   If we do not go to the beach, then it is not sunny.

Are these statements all saying the same thing, or does each one say something completely different from the others? In this section, we will study how we can answer this question by using logic symbols and truth tables. We also will learn to identify variations of conditional statements.

> **Why** **This is Important** Understanding when two statements are equivalent is important to understanding advertisers' claims, political statements, and legal documents.

Equivalent statements are an important concept in the study of logic.

Definition: **Equivalent**
Two statements are **equivalent**, symbolized ⇔,* if both statements have exactly the same truth values in the answer columns of the truth tables.

Sometimes the words *logically equivalent* are used in place of the word *equivalent*.

---

*The symbol $\equiv$ is also used to indicate equivalent statements.

To determine whether two statements are equivalent, construct a truth table for each statement and compare the answer columns of the truth tables. If the answer columns are identical, the statements are equivalent. If the answer columns are not identical, the statements are not equivalent.

Example 1 *Equivalent Statements*

Determine whether the following two statements are equivalent.

$$p \wedge (q \vee r)$$
$$(p \wedge q) \vee (p \wedge r)$$

Solution Construct a truth table for each statement (see Table 3.25).

Table 3.25

p	q	r	p	$\wedge$	$(q \vee r)$	$(p \wedge q)$	$\vee$	$(p \wedge r)$
T	T	T	T	T	T	T	T	T
T	T	F	T	T	T	T	T	F
T	F	T	T	T	T	F	T	T
T	F	F	T	F	F	F	F	F
F	T	T	F	F	T	F	F	F
F	T	F	F	F	T	F	F	F
F	F	T	F	F	T	F	F	F
F	F	F	F	F	F	F	F	F
			1	3	2	1	3	2

Because the truth tables have the same answer (column 3 for both tables), the statements are equivalent. Therefore, we can write

$$p \wedge (q \vee r) \Leftrightarrow (p \wedge q) \vee (p \wedge r)$$

Example 2 *Are the Following Equivalent Statements?*

Determine whether the following statements are equivalent.

a) If your homework is finished and you have washed the dishes, then you can watch television.

b) If your homework is not finished or you have not washed the dishes, then you cannot watch television.

Solution First write each statement in symbolic form, then construct a truth table for each statement. If the answer columns of both truth tables are identical, then the statements are equivalent. If the answer columns are not identical, then the statements are not equivalent.

Let

p:	Your homework is finished.
q:	You have washed the dishes.
r:	You can watch television.

In symbolic form, the statements are

a) $(p \wedge q) \rightarrow r$.   b) $(\sim p \vee \sim q) \rightarrow \sim r$.

The truth tables for these statements are given in Tables 3.26 and 3.27, respectively. The answers in the columns labeled 5 are not identical, so the statements are not equivalent.

Table 3.26

p	q	r	$(p \wedge q)$	$\rightarrow$	r
T	T	T	T	T	T	T	T
T	T	F	T	T	T	F	F
T	F	T	T	F	F	T	T
T	F	F	T	F	F	T	F
F	T	T	F	F	T	T	T
F	T	F	F	F	T	T	F
F	F	T	F	F	F	T	T
F	F	F	F	F	F	T	F
			1	3	2	5	4

Table 3.27

p	q	r	$(\sim p \vee \sim q)$	$\rightarrow$	$\sim r$
T	T	T	F	F	F	T	F
T	T	F	F	F	F	T	T
T	F	T	F	T	T	F	F
T	F	F	F	T	T	T	T
F	T	T	T	T	F	F	F
F	T	F	T	T	F	T	T
F	F	T	T	T	T	F	F
F	F	F	T	T	T	T	T
			1	3	2	5	4

Example 3 *Which Statements Are Logically Equivalent?*

Determine which statement is logically equivalent to "It is not true that the tire is both out of balance and flat."

a) If the tire is not flat, then the tire is not out of balance.

b) The tire is not out of balance or the tire is not flat.

c) The tire is not flat and the tire is not out of balance.

d) If the tire is not out of balance, then the tire is not flat.

Solution To determine whether any of the choices are equivalent to the given statement, first write the given statement and the choices in symbolic form. Then construct truth tables and compare the answer columns of the truth tables. Let

$$p: \quad \text{The tire is out of balance.}$$
$$q: \quad \text{The tire is flat.}$$

The given statement may be written "It is not true that the tire is out of balance and the tire is flat." The statement is expressed in symbolic form as $\sim (p \wedge q)$. Using p and q as indicated, choices (a) through (d) may be expressed symbolically as

a) $\sim q \rightarrow \sim p$.   b) $\sim p \vee \sim q$.   c) $\sim q \wedge \sim p$.   d) $\sim p \rightarrow \sim q$.

Now construct a truth table for the given statement (Table 3.28) and for each statement (a) through (d), given in Table 3.29 (a) through (d). By examining the truth tables, we see that the given statement, $\sim (p \wedge q)$, is logically equivalent to choice (b), $\sim p \vee \sim q$. Therefore, the correct answer is "The tire is not out of balance or the tire is not flat." This statement is logically equivalent to the statement "It is not true that the tire is both out of balance and flat."

Table 3.28

p	q	$\sim$	$(p$	$\wedge$	$q)$
T	T	F	T	T	T
T	F	T	T	F	F
F	T	T	F	F	T
F	F	T	F	F	F
		4	1	3	2

Table 3.29

p	q	$\sim q$	$\rightarrow$	$\sim p$	$\sim p$	$\vee$	$\sim q$	$\sim q$	$\wedge$	$\sim p$	$\sim p$	$\rightarrow$	$\sim q$
T	T	F	T	F	F	F	F	F	F	F	F	T	F
T	F	T	F	F	F	T	T	T	F	F	F	T	T
F	T	F	T	T	T	T	F	F	F	T	T	F	F
F	F	T	T	T	T	T	T	T	T	T	T	T	T

De Morgan's Laws

Example 3 showed that a statement of the form $\sim (p \wedge q)$ is equivalent to a statement of the form $\sim p \vee \sim q$. Thus, we may write $\sim (p \wedge q) \Leftrightarrow \sim p \vee \sim q$. This equivalent statement is one of two special laws called De Morgan's laws. The laws, named after Augustus De Morgan, an English mathematician, were first introduced in Section 2.4, where they applied to sets.

De Morgan's Laws

1. $\sim (p \wedge q) \Leftrightarrow \sim p \vee \sim q$
2. $\sim (p \vee q) \leftrightarrow \sim p \wedge \sim q$

You can demonstrate that De Morgan's second law is true by constructing and comparing truth tables for $\sim(p \lor q)$ and $\sim p \land \sim q$. Do so now.

When using De Morgan's laws, if it becomes necessary to negate an already negated statement, use the fact that $\sim(\sim p)$ is equivalent to p. For example, the negation of the statement "Today is not Monday" is "Today is Monday."

Example 4   *Use De Morgan's Laws*

Select the statement that is logically equivalent to "I do not have investments, but I do not have debts."

a) I do not have investments or I do not have debts.

b) It is false that I have investments and I have debts.

c) It is false that I have investments or I have debts.

d) I have investments or I have debts.

Solution To determine which statement is equivalent, write each statement in symbolic form.

Let

p: I have investments.

q: I have debts.

The statement "I do not have investments, but I do not have debts" written symbolically is $\sim p \land \sim q$. Recall that the word *but* means the same thing as *and*. Now, write parts (a) through (d) symbolically.

a) $\sim p \lor \sim q$ b) $\sim(p \land q)$ c) $\sim(p \lor q)$ d) $p \lor q$

De Morgan's law shows that $\sim p \land \sim q$ is equivalent to $\sim(p \lor q)$. Therefore, the answer is (c): "It is false that I have investments or I have debts."

Example 5   *Using De Morgan's Laws to Write an Equivalent Statement*

Write a statement that is logically equivalent to "It is not true that tomatoes are poisonous or eating peppers cures the common cold."

Solution Let

p: Tomatoes are poisonous.

q: Eating peppers cures the common cold.

The given statement is of the form $\sim(p \lor q)$. Using the second of De Morgan's laws, we see that an equivalent statement in symbols is $\sim p \land \sim q$. Therefore, an equivalent statement in words is "Tomatoes are not poisonous and eating peppers does not cure the common cold."

Consider $\sim(p \land q) \Leftrightarrow \sim p \lor \sim q$, one of De Morgan's laws. To go from $\sim(p \land q)$ to $\sim p \lor \sim q$, we negate both the p and the q within parentheses; change the conjunction, $\land$, to a disjunction, $\lor$; and remove the negation symbol preceding the left parentheses and the parentheses themselves. We can use a similar procedure to obtain equivalent statements. For example,

$$\sim(\sim p \land q) \Leftrightarrow p \lor \sim q$$
$$\sim(p \land \sim q) \Leftrightarrow \sim p \lor q$$

We can use a similar procedure to obtain equivalent statements when a disjunction is within parentheses. Note that

$$\sim(\sim p \lor q) \Leftrightarrow p \land \sim q$$
$$\sim(p \lor \sim q) \Leftrightarrow \sim p \land q$$

▲ *Taylor Swift*

Profile In Mathematics

Augustus De Morgan

Augustus De Morgan (1806–1871), the son of a member of the East India Company, was born in India and educated at Trinity College, Cambridge (UK). One of the great reformers of logic in the nineteenth century, De Morgan made his greatest contribution to the subject by realizing that logic as it had come down from Aristotle was narrow in scope and could be applied to a wider range of arguments. His work laid the foundation for modern, symbolic logic.

Example 6   *Using De Morgan's Laws to Write an Equivalent Statement*

Use De Morgan's laws to write a statement logically equivalent to "Taylor Swift did not win an Academy of Country Music award, but she had a top-selling record."

Solution Let

p: Taylor Swift won an Academy of Country Music award.

q: Taylor Swift had a top-selling record.

The statement written symbolically is $\sim p \wedge q$. Earlier we showed that

$$\sim p \wedge q \Leftrightarrow \sim (p \vee \sim q)$$

Therefore, the statement "It is false that Taylor Swift won an Academy of Country Music award or Taylor Swift did not have a top-selling record" is logically equivalent to the given statement.

There are strong similarities between the topics of sets and logic. We can see them by examining De Morgan's laws for sets and logic.

De Morgan's laws: set theory	De Morgan's laws: logic
$(A \cap B)' = A' \cup B'$	$\sim (p \wedge q) \Leftrightarrow \sim p \vee \sim q$
$(A \cup B)' = A' \cap B'$	$\sim (p \vee q) \Leftrightarrow \sim p \wedge \sim q$

The complement in set theory, ', is similar to the negation, $\sim$, in logic. The intersection, $\cap$, is similar to the conjunction, $\wedge$; and the union, $\cup$, is similar to the disjunction, $\vee$. If we were to interchange the set symbols with the logic symbols, De Morgan's laws would remain, but in a different form.

Both ' and $\sim$ can be interpreted as *not*.

Both $\cap$ and $\wedge$ can be interpreted as *and*.

Both $\cup$ and $\vee$ can be interpreted as *or*.

For example, the set statement $A' \cup B$ can be written as a statement in logic as $\sim a \vee b$.

Statements containing connectives other than *and* and *or* may have equivalent statements. To illustrate this point, construct truth tables for $p \rightarrow q$ and for $\sim p \vee q$. The truth tables will have the same answer columns and therefore the statements are equivalent. We summarize this as follows.

The Conditional Statement Written As a Disjunction

$$p \rightarrow q \Leftrightarrow \sim p \vee q$$

With these equivalent statements, we can write a conditional statement as a disjunction or a disjunction as a conditional statement. For example, the statement "If the game is polo, then you ride a horse" can be equivalently stated as "The game is not polo or you ride a horse."

To change a conditional statement to a disjunction, negate the antecedent, change the conditional symbol to a disjunction symbol, and keep the consequent the same. To change a disjunction statement to a conditional statement, negate the first statement, change the disjunction symbol to a conditional symbol, and keep the second statement the same.

Example 7   *Rewriting a Disjunction as a Conditional Statement*

Write a conditional statement that is logically equivalent to "The Oregon Ducks will win or the Oregon State Beavers will lose." Assume that the negation of winning is losing.

Solution Let

p: The Oregon Ducks will win.

q: The Oregon State Beavers will win.

The original statement may be written symbolically as $p \lor \sim q$. To write an equivalent conditional statement, negate the first statement, p, change the disjunction symbol to a conditional symbol, and keep the second statement the same. Symbolically, the equivalent statement is $\sim p \to \sim q$. The equivalent statement in words is "If the Oregon Ducks lose, then the Oregon State Beavers will lose." ∎

Negation of the Conditional Statement

Now we will discuss how to negate a conditional statement. To negate a conditional statement we use the fact that $p \to q \Leftrightarrow \sim p \lor q$ and De Morgan's laws. Examples 8 and 9 show the process.

Example 8   *The Negation of a Conditional Statement*

Determine a statement equivalent to $\sim(p \to q)$.

Solution Begin with $p \to q \Leftrightarrow \sim p \lor q$, negate both statements, and use De Morgan's laws.

$$p \to q \Leftrightarrow \sim p \lor q$$
$$\sim(p \to q) \Leftrightarrow \sim(\sim p \lor q) \qquad \text{Negate both statements.}$$
$$\Leftrightarrow p \land \sim q \qquad \text{De Morgan's laws}$$

Therefore, $\sim(p \to q)$ is equivalent to $p \land \sim q$. ∎

We summarize the result of Example 8 as follows.

The Negation of the Conditional Statement Written As a Conjunction

$$\sim(p \to q) \Leftrightarrow p \land \sim q$$

Example 9   *Write an Equivalent Statement*

Write a statement that is equivalent to "It is false that if you hang the picture then it will be crooked."

Solution Let

p: You hang the picture.

q: The picture will be crooked.

The given statement can be represented symbolically as $\sim(p \to q)$. We illustrated in Example 8 that $\sim(p \to q)$ is equivalent to $p \land \sim q$. Therefore, an equivalent statement is "You hang the picture and the picture will not be crooked." ∎

Using the fact that $\sim(p \to q) \Leftrightarrow p \land \sim q$, can you determine what $\sim(p \to \sim q)$ is equivalent to as a conjunction? If you answered $p \land q$ you answered correctly.

Variations of the Conditional Statement

We know that $p \rightarrow q$ is equivalent to $\sim p \vee q$. Are any other statements equivalent to $p \rightarrow q$? Yes, there are many. Now let's look at the variations of the conditional statement to determine whether any are equivalent to the conditional statement. *The variations of the conditional statement are made by switching and/or negating the antecedent and the consequent of a conditional statement.* The variations of the conditional statement are the *converse* of the conditional, the *inverse* of the conditional, and the *contrapositive* of the conditional.

Listed here are the variations of the conditional with their symbolic form and the words we say to read each one.

Variations of the Conditional Statement

Name	Symbolic form	Read
Conditional	$p \rightarrow q$	"If p, then q"
Converse of the conditional	$q \rightarrow p$	"If q, then p"
Inverse of the conditional	$\sim p \rightarrow \sim q$	"If not p, then not q"
Contrapositive of the conditional	$\sim q \rightarrow \sim p$	"If not q, then not p"

> **TIMELY TIP**
>
> The contrapositive statement is always equivalent to the original conditional statement.

To write the converse of the conditional statement, switch the order of the antecedent and the consequent. To write the inverse, negate both the antecedent and the consequent. To write the contrapositive, switch the order of the antecedent and the consequent and then negate both of them.

Are any of the variations of the conditional statement equivalent? To determine the answer, we can construct a truth table for each variation, as shown in Table 3.30. It reveals that *the conditional statement is equivalent to the contrapositive statement and that the converse statement is equivalent to the inverse statement.*

Table 3.30

p	q	Conditional $p \rightarrow q$	Contrapositive $\sim q \rightarrow \sim p$	Converse $q \rightarrow p$	Inverse $\sim p \rightarrow \sim q$
T	T	T	T	T	T
T	F	F	F	T	T
F	T	T	T	F	F
F	F	T	T	T	T

Example 10 *The Converse, Inverse, and Contrapositive*

For the conditional statement "If the song contains sitar music, then the song was written by George Harrison," write the

a) converse.   b) inverse.   c) contrapositive.

Solution

a) Let

p: The song contains sitar music.

q: The song was written by George Harrison.

The conditional statement is of the form $p \rightarrow q$, so the converse must be of the form $q \rightarrow p$. Therefore, the converse is "If the song was written by George Harrison, then the song contains sitar music."

▲ *A sitar.*

b) The inverse is of the form $\sim p \rightarrow \sim q$. Therefore, the inverse is "If the song does not contain sitar music, then the song was not written by George Harrison."

c) The contrapositive is of the form $\sim q \rightarrow \sim p$. Therefore, the contrapositive is "If the song was not written by George Harrison, then the song does not contain sitar music." ∎

RECREATIONAL MATH

Kakuro

Like Sudoku (see the *Recreational Mathematics* box on Sudoku on page 97), Kakuro is a puzzle that requires logic. The puzzle resembles a crossword puzzle but uses numbers for clues instead of words. The aim of the game is to fill all the blank squares in the grid with only the digits 1–9 so that the numbers you enter add up to the corresponding clues. For example, in the puzzle shown below, the 17 near the upper left corner of the puzzle is a clue that indicates that the two numbers that you place in the two squares to the right of the 17 must add up to equal 17. The 9 near the upper left corner of the puzzle is a clue that indicates that the two numbers that you place in the two squares below the 9 must add up to equal 9.

In addition, you may not repeat any digits in any given "word" or string of numbers.

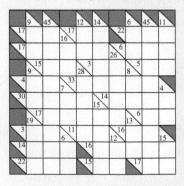

For more information and more puzzles, see www.kakuro.com. The solution to the above puzzle can be found in the answer section in the back of this book. For an additional puzzle, see Exercise 83 on page 140.

Example 11 *Determine the Truth Values*

Let

> p: The number is divisible by 10.
>
> q: The number is divisible by 5.

Write the following statements and determine which are true.

a) The conditional statement, $p \rightarrow q$

b) The converse of $p \rightarrow q$

c) The inverse of $p \rightarrow q$

d) The contrapositive of $p \rightarrow q$

Solution

a) The conditional statement in symbols is $p \rightarrow q$. Therefore, in words the conditional statement is *If the number is divisible by 10, then the number is divisible by 5*. This statement is true. A number divisible by 10 must also be divisible by 5, since 5 is a divisor of 10.

b) The converse of the conditional statement in symbols is $q \rightarrow p$. Therefore, in words the converse is *If the number is divisible by 5, then the number is divisible by 10*. This statement is false. For example, 15 is divisible by 5, but 15 is not divisible by 10.

c) The inverse of the conditional statement in symbols is $\sim p \rightarrow \sim q$. Therefore, in words the inverse is *If the number is not divisible by 10, then the number is not divisible by 5*. This statement is false. For example, 25 is not divisible by 10, but 25 is divisible by 5.

d) The contrapositive of the conditional statement in symbols is $\sim q \rightarrow \sim p$. Therefore, in words the contrapositive is *If the number is not divisible by 5, then the number is not divisible by 10*. This statement is true. Any number that is not divisible by 5 cannot be divisible by 10, since 5 is a divisor of 10. ∎

Because the contrapositive statement is always equivalent to the original conditional statement, in Example 11 d) we should have expected the answer to be a true statement because the original conditional statement was also a true statement.

Example 12 *Use the Contrapositive*

Use the contrapositive to write a statement logically equivalent to "If you don't eat your meat, then you can't have any pudding."

Solution Let

> p: You do eat your meat.
>
> q: You can have any pudding.

The given statement written symbolically is

$$\sim p \rightarrow \sim q$$

The contrapositive of the statement is

$$q \rightarrow p$$

Therefore, an equivalent statement is "If you can have any pudding, then you do eat your meat."   ∎

The contrapositive of the conditional is very important in mathematics. Consider the statement "If a^2 is not a whole number, then a is not a whole number." Is this statement true? You may find this question difficult to answer. Writing the statement's contrapositive may enable you to answer the question. The contrapositive is "If a is a whole number, then a^2 is a whole number." Since the contrapositive is a true statement, the original statement must also be true.

Example 13 *Which Are Equivalent?*

Determine which, if any, of the following statements are equivalent. You may use De Morgan's laws, the fact that $p \rightarrow q \Leftrightarrow \sim p \vee q$, information from the variations of the conditional, or truth tables.

a) If you leave by 9 A.M., then you will get to your destination on time.
b) You do not leave by 9 A.M. or you will get to your destination on time.
c) It is false that you will get to your destination on time or you did not leave by 9 A.M.
d) If you do not get to your destination on time, then you did not leave by 9 A.M.

Solution Let

p: You leave by 9 A.M.
q: You will get to your destination on time.

In symbolic form, the four statements are

a) $p \rightarrow q$.   b) $\sim p \vee q$.   c) $\sim (q \vee \sim p)$.   d) $\sim q \rightarrow \sim p$.

Which of these statements are equivalent? Earlier in this section, you learned that $p \rightarrow q$ is equivalent to $\sim p \vee q$. Therefore, statements (a) and (b) are equivalent. Statement (d) is the contrapositive of statement (a). Therefore, statement (d) is also equivalent to statement (a) and statement (b). Statements (a), (b), and (d) all have the same truth table (Table 3.31).

Table 3.31

p	q	$p \rightarrow q$ (a)	$\sim p \vee q$ (b)	$\sim q \rightarrow \sim p$ (d)
T	T	T	T	T
T	F	F	F	F
F	T	T	T	T
F	F	T	T	T

Now let's look at statement (c). To determine whether $\sim (q \vee \sim p)$ is equivalent to the other statements, we will construct its truth table (Table 3.32) and compare the answer column with the answer columns in Table 3.31.

Table 3.32   (c)

p	q	$\sim$	$(q$	$\vee$	$\sim p)$
T	T	F	T	T	F
T	F	T	F	F	F
F	T	F	T	T	T
F	F	F	F	T	T
		4	1	3	2

> None of the three answer columns of the truth table in Table 3.31 is the same as the answer column of the truth table in Table 3.32. Therefore $\sim(q \vee \sim p)$ is not equivalent to any of the other statements. Therefore, only statements (a), (b), and (d) are equivalent to each other. ∎

SECTION 3.4 *Exercises*

Warm Up Exercises

In Exercises 1–8, fill in the blanks with an appropriate word, phrase, or symbol(s).

1. Statements that have exactly the same truth values in the answer columns of their truth tables are called _____ statements.

2. DeMorgan's laws state that

   a) $\sim(p \wedge q)$ is equivalent to _____, and

   b) $\sim(p \vee q)$ is equivalent to _____.

3. The conditional statement $p \rightarrow q$ is equivalent to the following disjunction statement: _____.

4. The negation of the conditional statement $\sim(p \rightarrow q)$ is equivalent to the following conjunction statement: _____.

5. Given the conditional statement $p \rightarrow q$, the converse of the conditional statement in symbolic form is _____.

6. Given the conditional statement $p \rightarrow q$, the inverse of the conditional statement in symbolic form is _____.

7. Given the conditional statement $p \rightarrow q$, the contrapositive of the conditional statement in symbolic form is _____.

8. Of the converse, inverse, and contrapositive, only the contrapositive of the conditional statement is _____ to the conditional statement.

Practice the Skills

In Exercises 9–18, use De Morgan's laws to determine whether the two statements are equivalent.

9. $\sim(p \wedge q)$, $\sim p \wedge \sim q$

10. $\sim(p \wedge q)$, $\sim p \vee \sim q$

11. $\sim(p \vee q)$, $\sim p \wedge \sim q$

12. $\sim(p \vee q)$, $\sim p \vee \sim q$

13. $\sim(\sim p \wedge q)$, $p \wedge \sim q$

14. $\sim(\sim p \wedge q)$, $p \vee \sim q$

15. $(\sim p \vee \sim q) \rightarrow r$, $\sim(p \wedge q) \rightarrow r$

16. $q \rightarrow \sim(p \wedge \sim r)$, $q \rightarrow \sim p \vee r$

17. $\sim(p \rightarrow \sim q)$, $p \wedge q$

18. $\sim(\sim p \rightarrow q)$, $\sim p \wedge \sim q$

In Exercises 19–30, use a truth table to determine whether the two statements are equivalent.

19. $p \rightarrow q$, $\sim p \vee q$

20. $\sim(p \rightarrow q)$, $p \wedge \sim q$

21. $\sim q \rightarrow \sim p$, $p \rightarrow q$

22. $q \rightarrow p$, $\sim p \rightarrow \sim q$

23. $(p \vee q) \vee r$, $p \vee (q \vee r)$

24. $p \vee (q \wedge r)$, $\sim p \rightarrow (q \wedge r)$

25. $p \wedge (q \vee r)$, $(p \wedge q) \vee r$

26. $\sim(q \rightarrow p) \vee r$, $(p \vee q) \wedge \sim r$

27. $(p \rightarrow q) \wedge (q \rightarrow p)$, $(p \leftrightarrow q)$

28. $[\sim(p \rightarrow q)] \wedge [\sim(q \rightarrow p)]$, $\sim(p \leftrightarrow q)$

Problem Solving

In Exercises 29–34, use De Morgan's laws to write an equivalent statement for the sentence.

29. It is false that Oregon borders the Atlantic Ocean and Delaware borders the Pacific Ocean.

30. It is false that Greg Dietrich selects formulas or Moana Karsteter applies concepts.

31. The dog was neither a bulldog nor was the dog a boxer.

32. The pot roast is hot, but it is not well done.

33. If Ashley Tabai takes the new job, then she will not move or she will buy a new house in town.

34. If Phil Murphy buys us dinner, then we will not go to the top of the CN Tower but we will be able to walk to the Red Bistro Restaurant.

In Exercises 35–40, use the fact that $p \rightarrow q$ is equivalent to $\sim p \vee q$ to write an equivalent form of the given statement.

35. If Janette Campbell buys a new car, then she sells her old car.

36. Byron Dyce did not walk to the meeting or we started late.

37. Bob the Tomato visited the nursing home or he did not visit the Cub Scout meeting.

38. If Joanne Ernst goes to the Lightning game, then she will not go to the Rays game.

39. Chase is not hiding or the pitcher is broken.

40. If Weezer is not on the radio, then Tim Ollendick is working.

In Exercises 41–48, use the fact that $\sim (p \rightarrow q)$ is equivalent to $p \wedge \sim q$ to write the statement in an equivalent form.

41. It is false that if we go to Chicago, then we will go to Navy Pier.

▲ *Navy Pier in Chicago*

42. It is false that if General Electric makes the telephone, then the telephone is made in the United States.

43. I am cold and the heater is not working.

44. The Badgers beat the Nittany Lions and the Bucks beat the 76ers.

45. It is not true that if Amazon has a sale then we will buy $100 worth of books.

46. Thompson is sick today but Allen didn't go to school.

47. John Deere will hire new workers and the city of Dubuque will retrain the workers.

48. My cell phone is not a Blackberry but my cell phone has a keyboard.

In Exercises 49–54, write the converse, inverse, and contrapositive of the statement. (For Exercise 54, use De Morgan's laws.)

49. If Nanette Berry teaches macramé, then she needs extra yarn.

50. If the water is running, then Linus is getting a drink.

51. If I go to Mexico, then I buy silver jewelry.

52. If Bob Dylan records a new CD, then he will go on tour.

53. If that annoying paper clip shows up on my computer screen, then I will scream.

54. If the sun is shining, then we will go down to the marina and we will take out the sailboat.

In Exercises 55–60, write the contrapositive of the statement. Use the contrapositive to determine whether the conditional statement is true or false.

55. If a natural number is divisible by 14, then the natural number is divisible by 7.

56. If the quadrilateral is a parallelogram, then the opposite sides are parallel.

57. If a natural number is divisible by 3, then the natural number is divisible by 6.

58. If $1/n$ is not a natural number, then n is not a natural number.

59. If two lines do not intersect in at least one point, then the two lines are parallel.

60. If $\dfrac{m \cdot a}{m \cdot b} \neq \dfrac{a}{b}$, then m is not a counting number.

In Exercises 61–74, determine which, if any, of the three statements are equivalent (see Example 13).

61. a) If the ball lands in foul territory, then the runner returns to the base.

b) If the runner returns to the base, then the ball lands in foul territory.

c) The runner does not return to the base or the ball lands in foul territory.

62. a) If Fido is our dog's name, then Rex is not our dog's name.

   b) It is false that Fido is our dog's name and Rex is not our dog's name.

   c) Fido is not our dog's name or Rex is our dog's name.

63. a) The office is not cool and the copier is jammed.

   b) If the office is not cool, then the copier is not jammed.

   c) It is false that the office is cool or the copier is not jammed.

64. a) The test is not written or the review sheet is not ready.

   b) If the test is written, then the review sheet is ready.

   c) It is false that the review sheet is ready and the test is not written.

65. a) Today is not Sunday or the library is open.

   b) If today is Sunday, then the library is not open.

   c) If the library is open, then today is not Sunday.

66. a) If you are fishing at 1 P.M., then you are driving a car at 1 P.M.

   b) You are not fishing at 1 P.M. or you are driving a car at 1 P.M.

   c) It is false that you are fishing at 1 P.M. and you are not driving a car at 1 P.M.

67. a) The grass grows and the trees are blooming.

   b) If the trees are blooming, then the grass does not grow.

   c) The trees are not blooming or the grass does not grow.

68. a) Johnny Patrick is chosen as department chair if and only if he is the only candidate.

   b) If Johnny Patrick is chosen as department chair then he is the only candidate, and if Johnny Patrick is the only candidate then he is chosen as department chair.

   c) Johnny Patrick is not chosen as department chair and he is not the only candidate.

69. a) If the corn bag goes in the hole, then you are awarded three points.

   b) It is false that the corn bag goes in the hole and you are awarded three points.

   c) The corn bag does not go in the hole and you are not awarded three points.

70. a) Fitz and the Tantrums will not go on tour if and only if James King does not play the saxophone.

   b) It is false that Fitz and the Tantrums will go on tour if and only if James King does not play the saxophone.

   c) If Fitz and the Tantrums go on tour, then James King plays saxophone.

71. a) If the pay is good and today is Monday, then I will take the job.

   b) If I do not take the job, then it is false that the pay is good or today is Monday.

   c) The pay is good and today is Monday, or I will take the job.

72. a) If you are 18 years old and a citizen of the United States, then you can vote in the presidential election.

   b) You can vote in the presidential election, if and only if you are a citizen of the United States and you are 18 years old.

   c) You cannot vote in the presidential election, or you are 18 years old and you are not a citizen of the United States.

73. a) The package was sent by Federal Express, or the package was not sent by United Parcel Service but the package arrived on time.

b) The package arrived on time, if and only if it was sent by Federal Express or it was not sent by United Parcel Service.

c) If the package was not sent by Federal Express, then the package was not sent by United Parcel Service but the package arrived on time.

74. a) The mortgage rate went down, if and only if Tim purchased the house and the down payment was 10%.

b) The down payment was 10%, and if Tim purchased the house then the mortgage rate went down.

c) If Tim purchased the house, then the mortgage rate went down and the down payment was not 10%.

Concept/Writing Exercises

75. If p and q represent two simple statements, and if $p \to q$ is a false statement, what must be the truth value of the converse, $q \to p$? Explain.

76. If p and q represent two simple statements, and if $p \to q$ is a false statement, what must be the truth value of the inverse, $\sim p \to \sim q$? Explain.

77. If p and q represent two simple statements, and if $p \to q$ is a false statement, what must be the truth value of the contrapositive, $\sim q \to \sim p$? Explain.

78. If p and q represent two simple statements, and if $p \to q$ is a true statement, what must be the truth value of the contrapositive, $\sim q \to \sim p$? Explain.

Challenge Problems/Group Activities

79. We learned that $p \to q \Leftrightarrow \sim p \lor q$. Determine a conjunction that is equivalent to $p \to q$. (*Hint:* There are many answers.)

80. Determine whether $\sim[\sim(p \lor \sim q)] \Leftrightarrow p \lor \sim q$. Explain the method(s) you used to determine your answer.

81. In an appliance or device that uses fuzzy logic, a change in one condition causes a change in a second condition. For example, in a camera, if the brightness increases, the lens aperture automatically decreases to get the proper exposure. Name at least 10 appliances or devices that make use of fuzzy logic and explain how fuzzy logic is used in each appliance or device. See the *Mathematics Today* box on page 135.

82. In symbolic logic, a statement is either true or false (consider true to have a value of 1 and false a value of 0). In fuzzy logic, nothing is true or false, but everything is a matter of degree. For example, consider the statement "The sun is shining." In fuzzy logic, this statement may have a value between 0 and 1 and may be constantly changing. For example, if the sun is partially blocked by clouds, the value of this statement may be 0.25. In fuzzy logic, the values of connective statements are found as follows for statements p and q.

Not p has a truth value of $1 - p$.

$p \land q$ has a truth value equal to the lesser of p and q.

$p \lor q$ has a truth value equal to the greater of p and q.

$p \to q$ has a truth value equal to the lesser of 1 and $1 - p + q$.

$p \leftrightarrow q$ has a truth value equal to $1 - |p - q|$, that is, 1 minus the absolute value* of p minus q.

Suppose the statement "p: The sun is shining" has a truth value of 0.25 and the statement "q: Mary is getting a tan" has a truth value of 0.20. Find the truth value of

a) $\sim p$ **b)** $\sim q$

c) $p \land q$ **d)** $p \lor q$

e) $p \to q$ **f)** $p \leftrightarrow q$

*Absolute values are discussed in Section 13.8.

Recreational Exercises

83. Kakuro Refer to the *Recreational Mathematics* box on page 134. Complete the following Kakuro puzzle.

Internet/Research Activities

84. Do research and write a report on fuzzy logic.

85. Read one of Lewis Carroll's books and write a report on how he used logic in the book. Give at least five specific examples.

86. Do research and write a report on the life and achievements of Augustus De Morgan. Indicate in your report his contributions to sets and logic.

SECTION 3.5   Symbolic Arguments

Consider the following statements.

> If Carrie Underwood sings the national anthem, then The Who will play at halftime.

> Carrie Underwood sings the national anthem.

If you accept these two statements as true, then what logical conclusion could you draw? Do you agree that you can logically conclude that The Who will play at halftime? In this section, we will use our knowledge of logic to study the structure of such statements to draw logical conclusions.

▲ *The Who plays during halftime of Super Bowl XLIV.*

Why *This is Important* Drawing logical conclusions from a given set of statements is an important application of logic. Also, we use logic daily in decision making after considering all the facts we know to be true.

Previously in this chapter, we used symbolic logic to determine the truth value of a compound statement. We now extend those basic ideas to determine whether we can draw logical conclusions from a set of given statements. Consider once again the two statements.

> If Carrie Underwood sings the national anthem, then The Who will play at halftime.

> Carrie Underwood sings the national anthem.

These statements in the following form constitute what we will call a *symbolic argument*.

Premise 1:	If Carrie Underwood sings the national anthem, then The Who will play at halftime.
Premise 2:	Carrie Underwood sings the national anthem
Conclusion:	The Who will play at halftime.

A *symbolic argument* consists of a set of *premises* and a *conclusion*. It is called a symbolic argument because we generally write it in symbolic form to determine its validity.

Definition: Valid and Invalid Arguments

An **argument is valid** when its conclusion necessarily follows from a given set of premises.

An **argument is invalid** or a **fallacy** when the conclusion does not necessarily follow from the given set of premises.

An argument that is not valid is invalid. The argument just presented is an example of a valid argument, as the conclusion necessarily follows from the premises. Now we will discuss a procedure to determine whether an argument is valid or invalid. We begin by writing the argument in symbolic form. To write the argument in symbolic form, we let p and q be

> p: Carrie Underwood sings the national anthem.
>
> q: The Who will play at halftime.

Symbolically, the argument is written

> Premise 1: $p \rightarrow q$
> Premise 2: p
> Conclusion $\therefore q$ (The three-dot-triangle is read "therefore.")

Write the argument in the following form.

> If   [*premise 1*   **and**   *premise 2*]   **then**   *conclusion*
> [$(p \rightarrow q)$ $\wedge$ p] $\rightarrow$ q

Then construct a truth table for the statement $[(p \rightarrow q) \wedge p] \rightarrow q$ (Table 3.33). *If the truth table answer column is true in every case, then the statement is a tautology, and the argument is valid. If the truth table is not a tautology, then the argument is invalid.* Since the statement is a tautology (see column 5), the conclusion necessarily follows from the premises and the argument is valid.

Table 3.33

p	q	$[(p \rightarrow q)$	$\wedge$	$p]$	$\rightarrow$	q
T	T	T	T	T	T	T
T	F	F	F	T	T	F
F	T	T	F	F	T	T
F	F	T	F	F	T	F
		1	3	2	5	4

Once we have demonstrated that an argument in a particular form is valid, all arguments with exactly the same form will also be valid. In fact, many of these forms have been assigned names. The argument form just discussed,

$$p \rightarrow q$$
$$\underline{p}$$
$$\therefore q$$

is called the *law of detachment*, or *modus ponens*.

▲ *Alaska*

Example 1 *Determining Validity Without a Truth Table*

Determine whether the following argument is valid or invalid.

> If Canada is north of the United States, then Alaska is in Mexico.
> Canada is north of the United States.
> _____
> ∴ Alaska is in Mexico.

Solution Translate the argument into symbolic form.

Let

> c: Canada is north of the United States.
> a: Alaska is in Mexico.

In symbolic form, the argument is

$$c \rightarrow a$$
$$c$$
$$\overline{}$$
$$\therefore a$$

This argument is also the law of detachment. Therefore, it is a valid argument. ■

Note that the argument in Example 1 is valid even though the conclusion, "Alaska is in Mexico," is a false statement. It is also possible to have an invalid argument in which the conclusion is a true statement. *When an argument is valid, the conclusion necessarily follows from the premises. It is not necessary for the premises or the conclusion to be true statements in an argument.*

PROCEDURE   TO DETERMINE WHETHER AN ARGUMENT IS VALID

1. Write the argument in symbolic form.

2. Compare the form of the argument with forms that are known to be valid or invalid. If there are no known forms to compare it with, or you do not remember the forms, go to step 3.

3. If the argument contains two premises, write a conditional statement of the form

    [(premise 1) ∧ (premise 2)] → conclusion

4. Construct a truth table for the statement in step 3.

5. If the answer column of the truth table has all trues, the statement is a tautology, and the argument is valid. If the answer column does not have all trues, the argument is invalid.

Examples 1 through 4 contain two premises. When an argument contains more than two premises, step 3 of the procedure will change slightly, as will be explained shortly.

Example 2 *Determining the Validity of an Argument With a Truth Table*

Determine whether the following argument is valid or invalid.

> If you watch *Good Morning America*, then you see Robin Roberts.
> You did not see Robin Roberts.
> _____
> ∴ You did not watch *Good Morning America*.

▲ *Robin Roberts*

Solution We first write the argument in symbolic form.

Let

>   *p*:   You watch *Good Morning America*.
>   *q*:   You see Robin Roberts.

In symbolic form, the argument is

$$p \rightarrow q$$
$$\frac{\sim q}{\therefore \sim p}$$

As we have not tested an argument in this form, we will construct a truth table to determine whether the argument is valid or invalid. We write the argument in the form $[(p \rightarrow q) \land \sim q] \rightarrow \sim p$, and construct a truth table (Table 3.34). Since the answer, column 5, has all T's, the argument is valid.

Table 3.34

p	*q*	[(*p* → *q*)	∧	~ *q*]	→	~*p*
T	T	T	F	F	T	F
T	F	F	F	T	T	F
F	T	T	F	F	T	T
F	F	T	T	T	T	T
		1	3	2	5	4

The argument form in Example 2 is an example of the *law of contraposition*, or *modus tollens*.

Example 3 *Another Symbolic Argument*

Determine whether the following argument is valid or invalid.

>   The grass is green or the grass is full of weeds.
>   The grass is not green.
>   ∴ The grass is full of weeds.

Solution Let

>   *p*:   The grass is green.
>   *q*:   The grass is full of weeds.

In symbolic form, the argument is

$$p \lor q$$
$$\frac{\sim p}{\therefore q}$$

As this form is not one of those we are familiar with, we will construct a truth table. We write the argument in the form $[(p \lor q) \land \sim p] \rightarrow q$. Next we construct a truth table, as shown in Table 3.35 on page 144. The answer to the truth table, column 5, is true in *every case*. Therefore, the statement is a tautology, and the argument is valid.

Table 3.35

p	q	$[(p \lor q)$	$\land$	$\sim p]$	$\rightarrow$	q
T	T	T	F	F	T	T
T	F	T	F	F	T	F
F	T	T	T	T	T	T
F	F	F	F	T	T	F
		1	3	2	5	4

The argument form in Example 3 is an example of a *disjunctive syllogism*. Other standard forms of arguments are given in the following chart.

Standard Forms of Arguments

Valid Arguments	Law of Detachment	Law of Contraposition	Law of Syllogism	Disjunctive Syllogism
	$p \rightarrow q$	$p \rightarrow q$	$p \rightarrow q$	$p \lor q$
	p	$\sim q$	$q \rightarrow r$	$\sim p$
	$\therefore q$	$\therefore \sim p$	$\therefore p \rightarrow r$	$\therefore q$

Invalid Arguments	Fallacy of the Converse	Fallacy of the Inverse
	$p \rightarrow q$	$p \rightarrow q$
	q	$\sim p$
	$\therefore p$	$\therefore \sim q$

As we saw in Example 1, it is not always necessary to construct a truth table to determine whether or not an argument is valid. The next two examples will show how we can identify an argument as one of the standard arguments given in the chart above.

Example 4 *Identifying a Standard Argument*

Determine whether the following argument is valid or invalid.

> If you are on Facebook, then you see my pictures.
> If you see my pictures, then you know I have a dog.
> _____
> ∴ If you are on Facebook, then you know I have a dog.

Solution Let

p: You are on Facebook.
q: You see my pictures.
r: You know I have a dog.

In symbolic form, the argument is

$$p \rightarrow q$$
$$q \rightarrow r$$
$$\therefore p \rightarrow r$$

The argument is in the form of the law of syllogism. Therefore, the argument is valid, and there is no need to construct a truth table.

Example 5 *Identifying Common Fallacies in Arguments*

Determine whether the following arguments are valid or invalid.

a)

If it is snowing, then we put salt on the driveway.
We put salt on the driveway.

∴ It is snowing.

b)

If it is snowing, then we put salt on the driveway.
It is not snowing.

∴ We do not put salt on the driveway.

Solution

a) Let

p: It is snowing.
q: We put salt on the driveway.

In symbolic form, the argument is

$$p \to q$$
$$\underline{q}$$
$$\therefore p$$

This argument is in the form of the fallacy of the converse. Therefore, the argument is a fallacy, or invalid.

b) Using the same symbols defined in the solution to part (a), in symbolic form, the argument is

$$p \to q$$
$$\underline{\sim p}$$
$$\therefore \sim q$$

This argument is in the form of the fallacy of the inverse. Therefore, the argument is a fallacy, or invalid. ∎

TIMELY TIP
If you are not sure whether an argument with two premises is one of the standard forms or if you do not remember the standard forms, you can always determine whether a given argument is valid or invalid by using a truth table. To do so, follow the boxed procedure on page 142.
  In Example 5(b), if you did not recognize that this argument was of the same form as the fallacy of the inverse you could construct the truth table for the conditional statement

$$[(p \to q) \land \sim p] \to \sim q$$

The true–false values under the conditional column, $\to$, would be T, T, F, T. Since the statement is not a tautology, the argument is invalid.

Now we consider an argument that has more than two premises. When an argument contains more than two premises, the statement we test, using a truth table, is formed by taking the conjunction of all the premises as the antecedent of a conditional statement and the conclusion as the consequent of the conditional statement. One example is an argument of the form

$$p_1$$
$$p_2$$
$$\underline{p_3}$$
$$\therefore c$$

We evaluate the truth table for $[p_1 \land p_2 \land p_3] \to c$. When we evaluate $[p_1 \land p_2 \land p_3]$, it makes no difference whether we evaluate $[(p_1 \land p_2) \land p_3]$ or $[p_1 \land (p_2 \land p_3)]$ because both give the same answer. In Example 6, we evaluate $[p_1 \land p_2 \land p_3]$ from left to right; that is, $[(p_1 \land p_2) \land p_3]$.

Example 6   *An Argument with Three Premises*

Use a truth table to determine whether the following argument is valid or invalid.

If my cell phone company is Verizon, then I can call you free of charge.
I can call you free of charge or I can send you a text message.
I can send you a text message or my cell phone company is Verizon.

∴ My cell phone company is Verizon.

Solution   This argument contains three simple statements.

Let

p: My cell phone company is Verizon.
q: I can call you free of charge.
r: I can send you a text message.

In symbolic form, the argument is

$$p \rightarrow q$$
$$q \lor r$$
$$r \lor p$$
$$\overline{}$$
$$\therefore p$$

Write the argument in the form

$$[(p \rightarrow q) \land (q \lor r) \land (r \lor p)] \rightarrow p.$$

Now construct the truth table (Table 3.36). The answer, column 7, is not true in every case. Thus, the argument is a fallacy, or invalid.

Table 3.36

p	q	r	$[(p \rightarrow q)$	$\land$	$(q \lor r)$	$\land$	$(r \lor p)]$	$\rightarrow$	p
T	T	T	T	T	T	T	T	T	T
T	T	F	T	T	T	T	T	T	T
T	F	T	F	F	T	F	T	T	T
T	F	F	F	F	F	F	T	T	T
F	T	T	T	T	T	T	T	F	F
F	T	F	T	T	T	F	F	T	F
F	F	T	T	T	T	T	T	F	F
F	F	F	T	F	F	F	F	T	F
			1	3	2	5	4	7	6

Let's now investigate how we can arrive at a valid conclusion from a given set of premises.

Example 7   *Determine a Logical Conclusion*

Determine a logical conclusion that follows from the given statements. "If the price of gas is below $4.00 per gallon, then we will drive to the Offspring concert. We will not drive to the Offspring concert. Therefore … "

Solution   If you recognize a specific form of an argument, you can use your knowledge of that form to draw a logical conclusion.

Let

p: The price of gas is below $4.00 per gallon.
q: We will drive to the Offspring concert.

The argument is of the following form.

$$p \rightarrow q$$
$$\frac{\sim q}{\therefore ?}$$

If the question mark is replaced with a $\sim p$, this argument is of the form of the law of contraposition. Thus, a logical conclusion is "Therefore, the price of gas is not below $4.00 per gallon."

SECTION 3.5   *Exercises*

Warm Up Exercises

In Exercises 1–6, fill in the blanks with an appropriate word, phrase, or symbol(s).

1. When the conclusion of an argument necessarily follows from the given set of premises it is a(n) _____ argument.

2. When the conclusion of an argument does not necessarily follow from the given set of premises it is a(n) _____ argument.

3. An argument that is invalid is also known as a(n) _____.

4. To determine the validity of an argument with two premises, construct a truth table for a conditional statement of the form [(premise 1) $\wedge$ (premise 2)] $\rightarrow$ _____.

5. If the conditional statement referred to in Exercise 4 is a tautology, then the argument is a(n) _____ argument.

6. If the conditional statement referred to in Exercise 4 is not a tautology, then the argument is a(n) _____ argument.

For Exercises 7–12, identify the standard form of the argument.

7. $p \rightarrow q$ Fallacy of the _____.
$$\frac{\sim p}{\therefore \sim q}$$

8. $p \rightarrow q$ Law of _____.
$$\frac{p}{\therefore q}$$

9. $p \vee q$ Disjunctive _____.
$$\frac{\sim p}{\therefore q}$$

10. $p \rightarrow q$ Fallacy of the _____.
$$\frac{q}{\therefore p}$$

11. $p \rightarrow q$ Law of _____.
$$\frac{q \rightarrow r}{\therefore p \rightarrow r}$$

12. $p \rightarrow q$ Law of _____.
$$\frac{\sim q}{\therefore \sim p}$$

Practice the Skills

In Exercises 13–32, determine whether the argument is valid or invalid. You may compare the argument to a standard form, given on page 144, or use a truth table.

13. $a \rightarrow b$
$$\frac{\sim a}{\therefore \sim b}$$

14. $c \vee d$
$$\frac{\sim c}{\therefore d}$$

15. $e \rightarrow f$
$$\frac{e}{\therefore f}$$

16. $g \rightarrow h$
$$\frac{h \rightarrow i}{\therefore g \rightarrow i}$$

17. $j \vee k$
$$\frac{\sim k}{\therefore j}$$

18. $l \rightarrow m$
$$\frac{\sim m}{\therefore \sim l}$$

19. $n \rightarrow o$
$$\frac{o}{\therefore n}$$

20. $r \rightarrow s$
$$\frac{r}{\therefore s}$$

21. $t \rightarrow u$
$\underline{\sim t}$
$\therefore \sim u$

22. $v \rightarrow w$
$\underline{w}$
$\therefore v$

23. $x \rightarrow y$
$\underline{y \rightarrow z}$
$\therefore x \rightarrow z$

24. $x \rightarrow y$
$\underline{\sim x}$
$\therefore \sim y$

25. $p \leftrightarrow q$
$\underline{q \wedge r}$
$\therefore p \vee r$

26. $p \leftrightarrow q$
$\underline{q \rightarrow r}$
$\therefore \sim r \rightarrow \sim p$

27. $r \leftrightarrow p$
$\underline{\sim p \wedge q}$
$\therefore p \wedge r$

28. $p \vee q$
$\underline{r \wedge p}$
$\therefore q$

29. $p \rightarrow q$
$q \vee r$
$\underline{r \vee p}$
$\therefore p$

30. $p \rightarrow q$
$q \rightarrow r$
$\underline{r \rightarrow p}$
$\therefore q \rightarrow p$

31. $p \rightarrow q$
$r \rightarrow \sim p$
$\underline{p \vee r}$
$\therefore q \vee \sim p$

32. $p \leftrightarrow q$
$p \vee r$
$\underline{q \rightarrow r}$
$\therefore q \vee r$

Problem Solving

In Exercises 33–48, (a) translate the argument into symbolic form and (b) determine if the argument is valid or invalid. You may compare the argument to a standard form or use a truth table.

33. If the lighthouse works, then the boat can stay out late.
The boat cannot stay out late.
$\therefore$ The lighthouse does not work.

34. If the car is a Road Runner, then the car is fast.
The car is fast.
$\therefore$ The car is a Road Runner.

35. If the baby is a boy, then we will name him Alexander Martin.
The baby is a boy.
$\therefore$ We will name him Alexander Martin.

36. If I can get my child to preschool by 8:45 A.M., then I can take the 9:00 A.M. class.
If I can take the 9:00 A.M. class, then I can be done by 2:00 P.M.
$\therefore$ If I can get my child to preschool by 8:45 A.M., then I can be done by 2:00 P.M.

37. If the guitar is a Les Paul model, then the guitar is made by Gibson.
The guitar is not made by Gibson.
$\therefore$ The guitar is not a Les Paul model.

38. We will go for a bike ride or we will go shopping.
We will not go shopping.
$\therefore$ We will go for a bike ride.

39. If we planted the garden by the first Friday in April, then we will have potatoes by the Fourth of July.
We will have potatoes by the Fourth of July.
$\therefore$ We planted the garden by the first Friday in April.

40. If you pass general chemistry, then you can take organic chemistry.
You pass general chemistry.
$\therefore$ You can take organic chemistry.

41. Erica Kane will marry Samuel Woods or Erica Kane will marry David Hayward.
Erica Kane will not marry Samuel Woods.
$\therefore$ Erica Kane will marry David Hayward.

42. If Nicholas Thompson teaches this course, then I will get a passing grade.
I did not get a passing grade.
$\therefore$ Nicholas Thompson did not teach this course.

43. If it is cold, then graduation will be held indoors.
If graduation is held indoors, then the fireworks will be postponed.
$\therefore$ If it is cold, then the fireworks will be postponed.

44. If the canteen is full, then we can go for a walk.
We can go for a walk and we will not get thirsty.
∴ If we go for a walk, then the canteen is not full.

45. Marie works at the post office and Jim works for Target.
If Jim works for Target, then Tommy gets an internship.
∴ If Tommy gets an internship, then Marie works at the post office.

46. Vitamin C helps your immune system or niacin helps reduce cholesterol.
If niacin helps reduce cholesterol, then vitamin E enhances your skin.
∴ Vitamin C helps your immune system and vitamin E enhances your skin.

47. It is snowing and I am going skiing.
If I am going skiing, then I will wear a coat.
∴ If it is snowing, then I will wear a coat.

48. The garden has vegetables or the garden has flowers.
If the garden does not have flowers, then the garden has vegetables.
∴ The garden has flowers or the garden has vegetables.

In Exercises 49–58, translate the argument into symbolic form. Then determine whether the argument is valid or invalid.

49. If you read *The Order of the Phoenix* then you can understand *The Half-Blood Prince.* You cannot understand *The Half-Blood Prince.* Therefore, you did not read *The Order of the Phoenix.*

50. The printer has a clogged nozzle or the printer does not have toner. The printer has toner. Therefore, the printer has a clogged nozzle.

51. Max is playing Game Boy with the sound off or Max is wearing headphones. Max is not playing Game Boy with the sound off. Therefore, Max is wearing headphones.

52. If the cat is in the room, then the mice are hiding. The mice are not hiding. Therefore, the cat is not in the room.

53. The test was easy and I received a good grade. The test was not easy or I did not receive a good grade. Therefore, the test was not easy.

54. If Bonnie passes the bar exam, then she will practice law. Bonnie will not practice law. Therefore, Bonnie did not pass the bar exam.

55. The baby is crying but the baby is not hungry. If the baby is hungry then the baby is crying. Therefore, the baby is hungry.

56. If the car is new, then the car has air conditioning. The car is not new and the car has air conditioning. Therefore, the car is not new.

57. If you liked *This Is Spinal Tap* then you liked *Best in Show.* If you liked *Best in Show* then you did not like *A Mighty Wind.* Therefore, if you liked *This Is Spinal Tap* then you liked *A Mighty Wind.*

58. The engineering courses are difficult and the chemistry labs are long. If the chemistry labs are long, then the art tests are easy. Therefore, the engineering courses are difficult and the art tests are not easy.

In Exercises 59–64, using the standard forms of arguments and other information you have learned, supply what you believe is a logical conclusion to the argument. Verify that the argument is valid for the conclusion you supplied.

59. If you throw more than 60 pitches, then you must rest for three days. You throw more than 60 pitches.
Therefore, …

60. If the temperature hits 100°, then we will go swimming.
We did not go swimming.
Therefore, …

61. I am stressed out or I have the flu.
I do not have the flu.
Therefore, …

62. If I can get Nick to his piano lesson by 3:30 P.M., then I can do my shopping.
If I can do my shopping, then we do not need to order pizza again.
Therefore, …

63. If you close the deal, then you will get a commission.
You did not get a commission.
Therefore, …

64. If Katherine is at her ballet lesson, then Allyson will take a nap.
Katherine is at her ballet lesson.
Therefore, ...

Concept/Writing Exercises

65. Is it possible for an argument to be invalid if its conclusion is true? Explain your answer.

66. Is it possible for an argument to be valid if its conclusion is false? Explain your answer.

67. Is it possible for an argument to be invalid if the premises are all true? Explain your answer.

68. Is it possible for an argument to be valid if the premises are all false? Explain your answer.

Challenge Problems/Group Activities

69. Determine whether the argument is valid or invalid.

If Lynn wins the contest or strikes oil, then she will be rich.
If Lynn is rich, then she will stop working.

∴ If Lynn does not stop working, then she did not win the contest.

70. Is it possible for an argument to be invalid if the conjunction of the premises is false in every case of the truth table? Explain your answer.

Recreational Mathematics

71. René Descartes was a seventeenth-century French mathematician and philosopher. One of his most memorable statements is, "I think, therefore, I am." This statement is the basis for the following joke.

Descartes walks into an inn. The innkeeper asks Descartes if he would like something to drink. Descartes replies, "I think not," and promptly vanishes into thin air!

This joke can be summarized in the following argument: If I think, then I am. I think not. Therefore, I am not.

a) Represent this argument symbolically.

b) Is it a valid argument?

c) Explain your answer using either a standard form of argument or using a truth table.

Internet/Research Activities

72. Show how logic is used in advertising. Discuss several advertisements and show how logic is used to persuade the reader.

73. Find examples of valid (or invalid) arguments in printed matter such as newspaper or magazine articles. Explain why the arguments are valid (or invalid).

Euler Diagrams and Syllogistic Arguments

▲ *Ben Stiller*

While trying to select a movie to watch, you think, "All Ben Stiller movies are comedies. Ben Stiller is in the movie *The Hardy Men*. Therefore, *The Hardy Men* is a comedy." This type of argument will be discussed in this section.

Why *This is Important*   Understanding arguments is an important part of the study of logic, and it is useful in making real-life decisions.

In Section 3.5, we showed how to determine the validity of *symbolic arguments* using truth tables and comparing the arguments to standard forms. This section presents another form of argument called a *syllogistic argument*, better known by the shorter name *syllogism*. The validity of a syllogistic argument is determined by using Euler (pronounced "oiler") diagrams, as is explained shortly.

Syllogistic logic, a deductive process of arriving at a conclusion, was developed by Aristotle in about 350 B.C. Aristotle considered the relationships among the four types of statements that follow.

All _____ are _____.
No _____ are _____.
Some _____ are _____.
Some _____ are not _____.

Swiss mathematician Leonhard Euler (pronounced "oiler"; 1707–1783) produced such a large volume of work that not all of it has yet been compiled. It has been estimated that a complete edition of his work would make up over 60 volumes. Although his greatest contribution was made in the field of modern analysis, his work also explored physics, astronomy, trigonometry, and calculus. Euler also had a great influence on the notation and symbolism of mathematics, and it was through his work that the symbols e and π came into common use. His facility for mental calculation and his uncommon memory allowed him to continue his prolific career even after he lost his vision in both eyes.

Examples of these statements are as follows: *All doctors are tall. No doctors are tall. Some doctors are tall. Some doctors are not tall.* Since Aristotle's time, other types of statements have been added to the study of syllogistic logic, two of which are

Examples of these statements are as follows: *Maria is a doctor. Maria is not a doctor.*

The difference between a symbolic argument and a syllogistic argument can be seen in the following chart. Symbolic arguments use the connectives *and, or, not, if–then,* and *if and only if.* Syllogistic arguments use the quantifiers *all, some,* and *none,* which were discussed in Section 3.1.

Symbolic Arguments Versus Syllogistic Arguments

	Words or phrases used	*Method of determining validity*
Symbolic argument	and, or, not, if–then, if and only if	Truth tables or by comparison with standard forms of arguments
Syllogistic argument	all are, some are, none are, some are not	Euler diagrams

As with symbolic logic, the premises and the conclusion together form an argument. An example of a syllogistic argument is

> All German shepherds are dogs.
> All dogs bark.
> _____
> ∴ All German shepherds bark.

This is an example of a valid argument. Recall from Section 3.5 that an argument is *valid* when its conclusion necessarily follows from a given set of premises. Recall that an argument in which the conclusion does not necessarily follow from the given premises is said to be an *invalid argument* or a *fallacy.*

Before we give another example of a syllogism, let's review the Venn diagrams discussed in Section 2.3 in relationship with Aristotle's four statements.

All *A*s are *B*s	No *A*s are *B*s	Some *A*s are *B*s	Some *A*s are not *B*s
			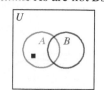
If an element is in set *A*, then it is in set *B*.	If an element is in set *A*, then it is not in set *B*.	There is at least one element that is in both set *A* and set *B*.	There is at least one element that is in set *A* that is not in set *B*.

One method used to determine whether an argument is valid or is a fallacy is by means of an *Euler diagram*, named after Leonhard Euler, who used circles to represent sets in syllogistic arguments. The technique of using Euler diagrams is illustrated in Example 1.

Example 1 *Using an Euler Diagram*

Determine whether the following syllogism is valid or invalid.

> All keys are made of brass.
> All things made of brass are valuable.
> _____
> ∴ All keys are valuable.

Solution   To determine whether this syllogism is valid or not valid, we will construct an Euler diagram. We begin with the first premise, "All keys are made of brass." As shown in Fig. 3.3, the inner blue circle labeled *K* represents the set of all keys and the outer red circle labeled *B* represents the set of all brass objects. The first premise requires that the inner blue circle must be entirely contained within the outer red circle. Next, we will represent the second premise, "All things made of brass are valuable." As shown in Fig. 3.4, the outermost black circle labeled *V* represents the set of all valuable objects. The second premise dictates that the red circle, representing the set of brass objects, must be entirely contained within the black circle, representing the set of valuable objects. Now, examine the completed Euler diagram in Fig. 3.4. Note that the premises force the set of keys to be within the set of valuable objects. Therefore, the argument is valid since the conclusion, "All keys are valuable," necessarily follows from the set of premises. ∎

Figure 3.3

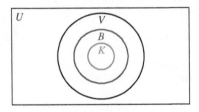

Figure 3.4

The syllogism in Example 1 is valid even though the conclusion, "All keys are valuable," is not a true statement. Similarly, a syllogism can be invalid, or a fallacy, even if the conclusion is a true statement.

When we determine the validity of an argument, we are determining whether the conclusion necessarily follows from the premises. When we say that an argument is valid, we are saying that if all the premises are true statements, then the conclusion must also be a true statement.

The form of the argument determines its validity, not the particular statements. For example, consider the syllogism

> All Earth people have two heads.
> All people with two heads can fly.
> _____
> ∴ All Earth people can fly.

The form of this argument is the same as that of the previous valid argument in Example 1. Therefore, this argument is also valid.

Example 2 *Analyzing a Syllogism*

Determine whether the following syllogism is valid or invalid.

> All patriots are Americans.
> Betsy is a patriot.
> _____
> ∴ Betsy is an American.

Solution   The statement "All patriots are Americans" is illustrated in Fig. 3.5. Note that the *P* circle must be completely inside the *A* circle. The second premise, "Betsy is a patriot," tells us that Betsy must be placed in the inner circle labeled *P* (Fig. 3.6). The Euler diagram illustrates, that by placing Betsy inside the *P* circle, Betsy must also be inside the *A* circle. Therefore, the conclusion "Betsy is an American" necessarily follows from the premises and the argument is valid. ∎

Figure 3.5

Figure 3.6

In both Example 1 and Example 2, we had no choice as to where the second premise was to be placed in the Euler diagram. In Example 1, the set of brass objects had to be placed inside the set of valuable objects. In Example 2, Betsy had to be placed inside the set of patriots. Often when determining the truth value of a syllogism, a premise can be placed in more than one area in the diagram. *We always try to draw the Euler diagram so that the conclusion* **does not necessarily** *follow from the premises. If that can be done, then the conclusion* **does not necessarily** *follow from the premises and the argument is invalid.* If we cannot show that the argument is invalid, only then do we accept the argument as valid. We illustrate this process in Example 3.

Example 3 *Ballerinas and Athletes*

Determine whether the following syllogism is valid or is invalid.

> All ballerinas are athletic.
> Keyshawn is athletic.
> _____
> ∴ Keyshawn is a ballerina.

Solution The premise "All ballerinas are athletic" is illustrated in Fig. 3.7(a). The next premise, "Keyshawn is athletic," tells us that Keyshawn must be placed in the set of athletic people. Two diagrams in which both premises are satisfied are shown in Fig. 3.7(b) and (c). By examining Fig. 3.7(b), however, we see that Keyshawn is not a ballerina. Therefore, the conclusion "Keyshawn is a ballerina" does not necessarily follow from the set of premises. Thus, the argument is invalid, or a fallacy.

    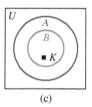

(a)   (b)   (c)

Figure 3.7

Example 4 *Parrots and Chickens*

Determine whether the following syllogism is valid or invalid.

> No parrots eat chicken.
> Fletch does not eat chicken.
> _____
> ∴ Fletch is a parrot.

Solution The first premise tells us that parrots and things that eat chicken are disjoint sets—that is, sets that do not intersect. The diagram in Fig. 3.8 satisfies the two given premises and also shows that Fletch is not a parrot. Therefore, the argument is invalid, or is a fallacy.

Example 5 *A Syllogism Involving the Word Some*

Determine whether the following syllogism is valid or invalid.

> All *A*s are *B*s.
> Some *B*s are *C*s.
> _____
> ∴ Some *A*s are *C*s.

Figure 3.8

TIMELY TIP

Note that in Example 4 if we placed Fletch in circle *P*, the argument would appear to be valid. Remember that *whenever testing the validity of an argument, always try to show that the argument is invalid.* If there is any way of showing that the conclusion does not necessarily follow from the premises, then the argument is invalid.

Figure 3.9

Solution The premise "All *A*s are *B*s" is illustrated in Fig. 3.9. The premise "Some *B*s are *C*s" means that there is at least one *B* that is a *C*. We can illustrate this set of premises in four ways, as illustrated in Fig. 3.10.

            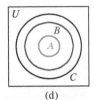

    (a)   (b)   (c)   (d)

Figure 3.10

In all four illustrations, we see that (1) all *A*s are *B*s and (2) some *B*s are *C*s. The conclusion is "Some *A*s are *C*s." Since at least one of the illustrations, Fig. 3.10(a), shows that the conclusion does not necessarily follow from the given premises, the argument is invalid.   ■

Example 6 *Fish and Cows*

Determine whether the following syllogism is valid or invalid.

> No fish are mammals.
> All cows are mammals.
> ─────────────────
> ∴ No fish are cows.

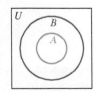

Figure 3.11

Solution The first premise tells us that fish and mammals are disjoint sets, as shown in Fig. 3.11. The second premise tells us that the set of cows is a subset of the set of mammals. Therefore, the circle representing the set of cows must go within the circle representing the set of mammals.

    Note that the set of fish and the set of cows cannot be made to intersect without violating a premise. Thus, the conclusion "No fish are cows" necessarily follows from the premises and the argument is valid. Note that we did not say that this conclusion is true, only that the argument is valid.   ■

SECTION 3.6   *Exercises*

Warm Up Exercises

In Exercises 1–6, fill in the blanks with an appropriate word, phrase, or symbol(s).

1. The validity of a syllogistic argument can be determined using a(n) _____ diagram.

2. If an Euler diagram can only be drawn in a way in which the conclusion necessarily follows from the premises, the syllogistic argument is a(n) _____ argument.

3. If an Euler diagram can be drawn in a way in which the conclusion does not necessarily follow from the premises, the syllogistic argument is a(n) _____ argument.

4. The following Euler diagram can represent the statement _____ *A*s are *B*s.

5. The following Euler diagram can represent the statement _____ *A*s are *B*s.

6. The following Euler diagram can represent the statement
_____ As are Bs.

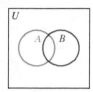

Practice the Skills/Problem Solving

In Exercises 7–28, use an Euler diagram to determine whether the syllogism is valid or invalid.

7. All gingerbread men can sing.

Gingy is a gingerbread man.

∴ Gingy can sing.

8. All cats have whiskers.

All things with whiskers are dogs.

∴ All cats are dogs.

9. No PCs are Macs.

All Dells are PCs.

∴ No Dells are Macs.

10. All dolphins are mammals.

All mammals are vertebrates.

∴ All dolphins are vertebrates.

11. All fishermen wear boots.

Percy wears boots.

∴ Percy is a fisherman.

12. All golfers have rain gear.

John Pearse has rain gear.

∴ John Pearse is a golfer.

13. No horses buck.

Palominos are horses.

∴ Palominos do not buck.

14. No jockeys weigh more than 200 pounds.

Deb Otto is not a jockey.

∴ Deb Otto weighs more than 200 pounds.

15. Some mushrooms are poisonous.

A morel is a mushroom.

∴ A morel is poisonous.

16. Some skunks are tame.

Pepé is a skunk.

∴ Pepé is not tame.

17. Some stamps are collectors' items.

Some collectors' items are valuable.

∴ Some stamps are valuable.

18. Some professional golfers give golf lessons.

All people who belong to the PGA are professional golfers.

∴ All people who belong to the PGA give golf lessons.

19. No lawn weeds are flowers.

Sedge is not a flower.

∴ Sedge is a lawn weed.

20. Some caterpillars are furry.

All furry things are mammals.

∴ Some caterpillars are mammals.

21. Some flowers love sunlight.

All things that love sunlight love water.

∴ Some flowers love water.

22. Some CD players are MP3 players.

All iPods are MP3 players.

∴ Some CD players are iPods.

23. No scarecrows are tin men.

No tin men are lions.

∴ No scarecrows are lions.

24. All pilots can fly.

All astronauts can fly.

∴ Some pilots are astronauts.

25. Some dogs wear glasses.

Fido wears glasses.

∴ Fido is a dog.

26. All rainy days are cloudy.

Today it is cloudy.

∴ Today is a rainy day.

27. All sweet things taste good.

All things that taste good are fattening.

All things that are fattening put on pounds.

∴ All sweet things put on pounds.

28. All books have red covers.

All books that have red covers contain 200 pages.

Some books that contain 200 pages are novels.

∴ All books that contain 200 pages are novels.

Concept/Writing Exercises

29. Can an argument be valid if the conclusion is a false statement? Explain your answer.

30. Can an argument be invalid if the conclusion is a true statement? Explain.

Challenge Problem/Group Activity

31. *Sets and Logic* Statements in logic can be translated into set statements: For example, $p \wedge q$ is similar to $P \cap Q$; $p \vee q$ is similar to $P \cup Q$; and $p \rightarrow q$ is equivalent to $\sim p \vee q$, which is similar to $P' \cup Q$. Euler diagrams can also be used to show that arguments similar to those discussed in Section 3.5 are valid or invalid. Use Euler diagrams to show that the following symbolic argument is invalid.

$$p \rightarrow q$$
$$p \vee q$$
$$\overline{\therefore \sim p}$$

Internet/Research Activity

32. Leonhard Euler is considered one of the greatest mathematicians of all time. Do research and write a report on Euler's life. Include information on his contributions to sets and to logic. Also indicate other areas of mathematics in which he made important contributions. References include encyclopedias, history of mathematics books, and the Internet.

SECTION 3.7   Switching Circuits

Suppose you are sitting at your desk and want to turn on a lamp so you can read a book. If a wall switch controls the power to the outlet that the lamp is plugged into and the lamp has an on/off switch, what conditions must be true for the lamp's bulb to light? The wiring in our homes can be explained and described using logic.

Why *This is Important* Analyzing electrical circuits is one of the most important applications of logic.

▲ *What must be true for a lamp to produce light?*

Using Symbolic Statements to Represent Circuits

A common application of logic is switching circuits. To understand the basic concepts of switching circuits, let us examine a few simple circuits that are common in most homes. The typical lamp has a cord, which is plugged into a wall outlet. Somewhere between the bulb in the lamp and the outlet is a switch to turn the lamp on and off. A switch is often referred to as being on or off. When the switch is in the *on* position, the current flows through the switch and the bulb lights up. When the switch is in the *on* position, we can say that the switch is *closed* and that current will flow through the switch. When the switch is in the *off* position, the current does not flow through the switch and the bulb does not light. When the switch is in the *off* position, we can say that the switch is *open*, and the current does not flow through the switch. The basic configuration of a switch is shown in Fig. 3.12.

Figure 3.12

Table 3.37

Switch	Lightbulb
T	on (switch closed)
F	off (switch open)

Figure 3.13

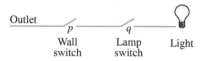

Figure 3.14

Table 3.38

p	q	Light	p ∧ q
T	T	on (T)	T
T	F	off (F)	F
F	T	off (F)	F
F	F	off (F)	F

Figure 3.15

Table 3.39

p	q	Light	p ∨ q
T	T	on (T)	T
T	F	on (T)	T
F	T	on (T)	T
F	F	off (F)	F

Electric circuits can be expressed as logical statements. We represent switches as letters, using T to represent a closed switch (or current flow) and F to represent an open switch (or no current flow). This relationship is indicated in Table 3.37.

Occasionally, we have a wall switch connected to a wall outlet and a lamp plugged into the wall outlet (Fig. 3.13). We then say that the wall switch and the switch on the lamp are in *series*, meaning that for the bulb in the lamp to light, both switches must be on at the same time (Fig. 3.14). On the other hand, the bulb will not light if either switch is off or if both switches are off. In either of these conditions, the electricity will not flow through the circuit. In a *series circuit*, the current can take only one path. If any switch in the path is open, the current cannot flow.

To illustrate this situation symbolically, let p represent the wall switch and q the lamp switch. The letter T will be used to represent both a closed switch and the bulb lighting. The letter F will represent an open switch and the bulb not lighting. Thus, we have four possible cases.

CASE 1: Both switches are closed; that is, p is T and q is T. The light is on, T.

CASE 2: Switch p is closed and switch q is open; that is, p is T and q is F. The light is off, F.

CASE 3: Switch p is open and switch q is closed; that is, p is F and q is T. The light is off, F.

CASE 4: Both switches are open; that is, p is F and q is F. The light is off, F.

Table 3.38 summarizes the results. The on–off results are the same as the truth table for the conjunction p ∧ q if we think of "on" as true and "off" as false.

Series Circuits
Switches in **series** will always be represented with a conjunction, ∧.

Another type of electric circuit used in the home is the *parallel circuit*, in which there are two or more paths that the current can take. If the current can pass through either path or both (see Fig. 3.15), the light will go on. The letter T will be used to represent both a closed switch and the bulb lighting. The letter F will represent an open switch and the bulb not lighting. Thus, we have four possible cases.

CASE 1: Both switches are closed; that is, p is T and q is T. The light is on, T.

CASE 2: Switch p is closed and switch q is open; that is, p is T and q is F. The light is on, T.

CASE 3: Switch p is open and switch q is closed; that is, p is F and q is T. The light is on, T.

CASE 4: Both switches are open; that is, p is F and q is F. The light is off, F.

Table 3.39 summarizes the results. The on–off results are the same as the $p ∨ q$ truth table if we think of "on" as true and "off" as false.

Parallel Circuits
Switches in **parallel** will always be represented with a disjunction, ∨.

Sometimes it is necessary to have two or more switches in the same circuit that will both be open at the same time and both be closed at the same time. In such circuits, we will use the same letter to represent both switches. For example, in the circuit shown in Fig. 3.16, there are two switches labeled p. Therefore, both of these switches must be open at the same time and both must be closed at the same time. One of the p switches cannot be open at the same time the other p switch is closed.

We can now combine some of these basic concepts to analyze more circuits.

Figure 3.16

Example 1 *Representing a Switching Circuit with Symbolic Statements*

a) Write a symbolic statement that represents the circuit shown in Fig. 3.16.

b) Construct a truth table to determine when the light will be on.

Solution

a) In Fig. 3.16, there is a blue switch p on the left, and to the right there is a branch containing a red switch p and a switch q. The current must flow through the blue switch p into the branch on its right. Therefore, the blue switch p is in series with the branch containing the red switch p and switch q. After the current flows through the blue switch p it reaches the branch on its right. At this point, the current has the option of flowing into the red switch p, switch q, or both of these switches. Therefore, the branch containing the red switch p and switch q is a parallel branch. We say these two switches are in parallel. The entire circuit in symbolic form is $p \wedge (p \vee q)$. Note that the parentheses are very important. Without parentheses, the symbolic statement could be interpreted as $(p \wedge p) \vee q$. The diagram for $(p \wedge p) \vee q$ is illustrated in Fig. 3.17. We shall see later in this section that the circuits in Fig. 3.16 and Fig. 3.17 are not the same.

b) The truth table for the statement (Table 3.40) indicates that the light will be on only in the cases in which p is true or when switch p is closed. ∎

Figure 3.17

Table 3.40

p	q	p	$\wedge$	$(p \vee q)$
T	T	T	T	T
T	F	T	T	T
F	T	F	F	T
F	F	F	F	F
		1	3	2

Example 2 *Representing a Switching Circuit with Symbolic Statements*

a) Write a symbolic statement that represents the circuit in Fig. 3.18.

b) Construct a truth table to determine when the light will be on.

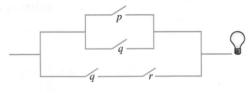

Figure 3.18

Solution

a) The upper branch of the circuit contains two switches, p and q, in parallel. We can represent that branch with the statement $p \vee q$. The lower branch of the circuit has two switches, q and r, in series. We can represent that branch with the statement $q \wedge r$. The upper branch is in parallel with the lower branch. Putting the two branches together, we get the statement $(p \vee q) \vee (q \wedge r)$.

b) The truth table for the statement (Table 3.41 on page 159) shows that cases 7 and 8 are false. Thus, the light will be off in these two cases and on in all the other cases. In examining the truth values, we see that the statement is false only in the cases in which both p and q are false, or when both switches p and q are open. By examining the diagram or truth table, we can see that the current will flow if switch p is closed or switch q is closed.

Table 3.41

p	*q*	*r*	*(p ∨ q)*	∨	*(q ∧ r)*
T	T	T	T	T	T
T	T	F	T	T	F
T	F	T	T	T	F
T	F	F	T	T	F
F	T	T	T	T	T
F	T	F	T	T	F
F	F	T	F	F	F
F	F	F	F	F	F
			1	3	2

Drawing Switching Circuits that Represent Symbolic Statements

Figure 3.19

We will next study how to draw a switching circuit that represents a given symbolic statement. Suppose we are given the statement $(p \wedge q) \vee r$ and are asked to construct a circuit corresponding to it. Remember that $\wedge$ indicates a series branch and $\vee$ indicates a parallel branch. Working first within parentheses, we see that switches p and q are in series. This series branch is in parallel with switch r, as indicated in Fig. 3.19.

Figure 3.20

Occasionally, it is necessary to have two switches in the same circuit such that when one switch is open, the other switch is closed; and when one switch is closed, the other switch is open. Therefore, the two switches will never both be open together and never be closed together. This situation can be represented by using p for one of the switches and $\bar{p}$ for the other switch. The switch labeled $\bar{p}$ corresponds to $\sim p$ in a logic statement. For example, in a series circuit, $p \wedge \sim p$ would be represented by Fig. 3.20. In this case, the light would never go on; the switches would counteract each other. When switch p is closed, switch $\bar{p}$ is open; and when p is open, $\bar{p}$ is closed.

┌ **Example 3** *Representing a Symbolic Statement as a Switching Circuit*

Draw a switching circuit that represents $[(p \wedge \sim q) \vee (r \vee q)] \wedge s$.

Solution In the statement, p and $\sim q$ have $\wedge$ between them, so switches p and $\bar{q}$ are in series, as represented in Fig. 3.21. Also in the statement, r and q have $\vee$ between them, so switches r and q are in parallel, as represented in Fig. 3.22.

Because $(p \wedge \sim q)$ and $(r \vee q)$ are connected with $\vee$, the two branches are in parallel with each other. The parallel branches are represented in Fig. 3.23. Finally, s in the statement is connected to the rest of the statement with $\wedge$. Therefore, switch s is in series with the entire rest of the circuit, as illustrated in Fig. 3.24.

Figure 3.21

Figure 3.22

Figure 3.23   Figure 3.24

Equivalent Circuits

Sometimes two circuits that look very different will actually have the exact same conditions under which the light will be on. If we were to analyze the truth tables for the corresponding symbolic statements for such circuits, we would find that they have identical answer columns. In other words, the corresponding symbolic statements are equivalent.

Definition: Equivalent Circuits

Equivalent circuits are two circuits that have equivalent corresponding symbolic statements.

To determine whether two circuits are equivalent, we will analyze the answer columns of the truth tables of their corresponding symbolic statements. If the answer columns from their corresponding symbolic statements are identical, then the circuits are equivalent.

Example 4 *Are the Circuits Equivalent?*

Determine whether the two circuits are equivalent.

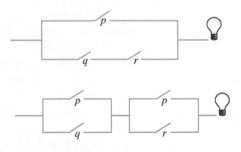

Solution The symbolic statement that represents the first circuit is $p \vee (q \wedge r)$. The symbolic statement that represents the second circuit is $(p \vee q) \wedge (p \vee r)$. The truth tables for these statements are shown in Table 3.42.

Table 3.42

p	q	r	p	$\vee$	$(q \wedge r)$	$(p \vee q)$	$\wedge$	$(p \vee r)$
T	T	T	T	T	T	T	T	T
T	T	F	T	T	F	T	T	T
T	F	T	T	T	F	T	T	T
T	F	F	T	T	F	T	T	T
F	T	T	F	T	T	T	T	T
F	T	F	F	F	F	T	F	F
F	F	T	F	F	F	F	F	T
F	F	F	F	F	F	F	F	F

Note that the answer columns for the two statements are identical. Therefore, $p \vee (q \wedge r)$ is equivalent to $(p \vee q) \wedge (p \vee r)$ and the two circuits are equivalent.

SECTION 3.7

Exercises

Warm Up Exercises

In Exercises 1–4, fill in the blanks with an appropriate word, phrase, or symbol(s).

1. A conjunction, $\wedge$, is used to represent switches in a(n) _____ circuit.

2. A disjunction, $\vee$, is used to represent switches in a(n) _____ circuit.

3. When a switch labeled as p is open, a switch labeled as $\bar{p}$ is _____.

4. Two circuits are equivalent if they have equivalent _____ statements.

Practice the Skills/Problem Solving

In Exercises 5–12, (a) write a symbolic statement that represents the circuit and (b) construct a truth table to determine when the lightbulb will be on. That is, determine which switches must be open and which switches must be closed for the lightbulb to be on.

5.

6.

7.

8.

9.

10.

11.

12.

In Exercises 13–20, draw a switching circuit that represents the symbolic statement.

13. $p \wedge q$

14. $p \vee (q \wedge r)$

15. $(p \vee q) \wedge r$

16. $\sim p \wedge (q \vee r)$

17. $(p \vee q) \wedge (r \vee s)$

18. $(p \wedge q) \vee (r \wedge s)$

19. $[(p \vee q) \vee (r \wedge q)] \wedge (\sim p)$

20. $[(p \vee q) \wedge r] \vee (\sim p \wedge q)$

In Exercises 21–26, represent each circuit with a symbolic statement. Then use a truth table to determine if the circuits are equivalent.

21.

22.

23.

24.

25.

26.

Concept/Writing Exercises

27. Explain why the lightbulb will never go on in the following circuit.

28. Explain why the lightbulb will always be on in the following circuit.

Challenge Problems/Group Activities

29. Design a circuit that can be represented by

a) $p \to q$ **b)** $\sim(p \to q)$

(*Hint*: See Section 3.4.)

30. Design two circuits that each involve switches labeled p, q, r, and s that appear to be different but are actually equivalent circuits.

Internet/Research Activities

31. Digital computers use gates that work like switches to perform calculations. (See *Did You Know?* box on page 160.) Information is fed into the gates and information leaves the gates, according to the type of gate. The three basic gates used in computers are the NOT gate, the AND gate, and or OR gate. Do research on the three types of gates.

a) Explain how each gate works.

b) Explain the relationship between each gate and the corresponding logic connectives *not*, *and*, and *or*.

c) Illustrate how two or more gates can be combined to form a more complex gate.

CHAPTER 3   Summary

Important Facts and Concepts

Examples

Section 3.1
Quantifiers

Example 1, page 96

Form of Statement	Form of Negation
All are.	Some are not.
None are.	Some are.
Some are.	None are.
Some are not.	All are.

Summary of Connectives

Examples 2–8, pages 97–101

Formal Name	Symbol	Read	Symbolic Form
Negation	$\sim$	not	$\sim p$
Conjunction	$\wedge$	and	$p \wedge q$
Disjunction	$\vee$	or	$p \vee q$
Conditional	$\to$	if–then	$p \to q$
Biconditional	$\leftrightarrow$	if and only if	$p \leftrightarrow q$

Section 3.2 & Section 3.3
Basic Truth Tables

Examples 1–10, pages 107–114
Examples 1–10, pages 118–124

p	$\sim p$	p	q	$p \wedge q$	$p \vee q$	$p \to q$	$p \leftrightarrow q$
T	F	T	T	T	T	T	T
F	T	T	F	F	T	F	F
		F	T	F	T	T	F
		F	F	F	F	T	T

Section 3.4
De Morgan's Laws

Examples 4–6, pages 130–131

$$\sim(p \wedge q) \Leftrightarrow \sim p \vee \sim q$$
$$\sim(p \vee q) \Leftrightarrow \sim p \wedge \sim q$$

Section 3.4
Other Equivalent Forms

$$p \rightarrow q \Leftrightarrow \sim p \ \lor \ q$$
$$\sim(p \rightarrow q) \Leftrightarrow p \land \sim q$$
$$p \leftrightarrow q \Leftrightarrow [(p \rightarrow q) \land (q \rightarrow p)]$$

Examples 7–9, pages 131–132

Variations of the Conditional Statement

Examples 10–12, pages 133–135

Name	Symbolic Form	Read
Conditional	$p \rightarrow q$	If p, then q.
Converse of the conditional	$q \rightarrow p$	If q, then p.
Inverse of the conditional	$\sim p \rightarrow \sim q$	If not p, then not q.
Contrapositive of the conditional	$\sim q \rightarrow \sim p$	If not q, then not p.

Section 3.5
Standard Forms of Valid Arguments

Examples 1–4, pages 142–144

Law of Detachment	Law of Contraposition	Law of Syllogism	Disjunctive Syllogism
$p \rightarrow q$	$p \rightarrow q$	$p \rightarrow q$	$p \ \lor \ q$
p	$\sim q$	$q \rightarrow r$	$\sim p$
$\therefore q$	$\therefore \sim p$	$\therefore p \rightarrow r$	$\therefore q$

Standard Forms of Invalid Arguments

Example 5, page 145

Fallacy of the Converse	Fallacy of the Inverse
$p \rightarrow q$	$p \rightarrow q$
q	$\sim p$
$\therefore p$	$\therefore \sim q$

Section 3.5 & Section 3.6
Symbolic Argument vs. Syllogistic Argument

Examples 1–5, pages 142–145
Examples 1–6, pages 152–154

	Words or Phrases Used	Method of Determining Validity
Symbolic argument	and, or, not, if–then, if and only if	Truth tables or by comparison with standard forms of arguments
Syllogistic argument	all are, some are, none are, some are not	Euler diagrams

Section 3.7
Switching Circuits as Symbolic Statements

Examples 1–4, pages 158–160

Switches in series will always be represented with a conjunction, $\land$.

Switches in parallel will always be represented with a disjunction, $\lor$.

CHAPTER 3) *Review Exercises*

3.1

In Exercises 1–4, write the negation of the statement.

1. All Scions are Toyotas.

2. No pets are allowed in this park.

3. Some women are presidents.

4. Some pine trees are not green.

In Exercises 5–10, write each compound statement in words.

> *p:*   The coffee is Maxwell House.
> *q:*   The coffee is hot.
> *r:*   The coffee is strong.

5. $p \vee q$

6. $\sim q \wedge r$

7. $q \rightarrow (r \wedge \sim p)$

8. $p \leftrightarrow \sim r$

9. $\sim p \leftrightarrow (r \wedge \sim q)$

10. $(p \vee \sim q) \wedge \sim r$

3.2

In Exercises 11–16, use the statements for p, q, and r as in Exercises 5–10 to write the statement in symbolic form.

11. The coffee is Maxwell House or the coffee is strong.

12. If the coffee is strong, then the coffee is not Maxwell House.

13. If the coffee is strong then the coffee is hot, or the coffee is not Maxwell House.

14. The coffee is hot if and only if the coffee is Maxwell House, and the coffee is not strong.

15. The coffee is strong and the coffee is hot, or the coffee is not Maxwell House.

16. It is false that the coffee is strong and the coffee is hot.

In Exercises 17–22, construct a truth table for the statement.

17. $(p \vee q) \wedge \sim p$

18. $q \leftrightarrow (p \vee \sim q)$

19. $(p \vee q) \leftrightarrow (p \vee r)$

20. $p \wedge (\sim q \vee r)$

21. $p \rightarrow (q \wedge \sim r)$

22. $(p \wedge q) \rightarrow \sim r$

3.2, 3.3

In Exercises 23–26, determine the truth value of the statement. You may need to use a reference such as the Internet or an encyclopedia.

23. If ESPN is a sports network then CNN is a news network, if and only if Nickelodeon is a cooking network.

24. President's Day is in February, or Memorial Day is in May and Labor Day is in December.

25. If Oregon borders the Pacific Ocean or California borders the Atlantic Ocean, then Minnesota is south of Texas.

26. $15 - 7 = 22$ or $4 + 9 = 13$, and $9 - 8 = 1$.

3.3

In Exercises 27–30, determine the truth value of the statement when p is T, q is F, and r is F.

27. $(\sim p \rightarrow q) \wedge \sim (q \vee r)$

28. $(p \leftrightarrow q) \rightarrow (\sim p \vee r)$

29. $\sim r \leftrightarrow [(p \vee q) \leftrightarrow \sim p]$

30. $\sim [(q \wedge r) \rightarrow (\sim p \vee r)]$

3.4

In Exercises 31–34, determine whether the pairs of statements are equivalent. You may use De Morgan's laws, the fact that $(p \rightarrow q) \Leftrightarrow (\sim p \vee q)$, the fact that $\sim (p \rightarrow q) \Leftrightarrow (p \wedge \sim q)$, truth tables, or equivalent forms of the conditional statement.

31. $\sim (p \wedge \sim q), \ \sim p \wedge q$

32. $p \vee q, \ \sim p \rightarrow q$

33. $\sim p \vee (q \wedge r), \ \ (\sim p \vee q) \wedge (\sim p \vee r)$

34. $(\sim q \rightarrow p) \wedge p, \ \ \sim (\sim p \leftrightarrow q) \vee p$

In Exercises 35–39, use De Morgan's laws, the fact that $(p \rightarrow q) \Leftrightarrow (\sim p \vee q)$, or the fact that $\sim (p \rightarrow q) \Leftrightarrow (p \wedge \sim q)$, to write an equivalent statement for the given statement.

35. Lady Gaga sang "Poker Face" and Jay-Z did not sing "Beamer, Benz, or Bentley."

36. Lynn Swann played for the Steelers or Jack Tatum played for the Raiders.

37. It is not true that Altec Lansing only produces speakers or Harman Kardon only produces stereo receivers.

38. Travis Tritt did not win an Academy Award and Randy Jackson does not do commercials for Milk Bone Dog Biscuits.

39. If the temperature is not above 32°, then we will go ice fishing at O'Leary's Lake.

In Exercises 40–44, write the (a) converse, (b) inverse, and (c) contrapositive for the given statement.

40. If you listen to Jim Rome, then you know Jay Stu.

41. If we take the table to *Antiques Roadshow*, then we will learn the table's value.

42. If you do not advertise, then you do not sell more doughnuts.

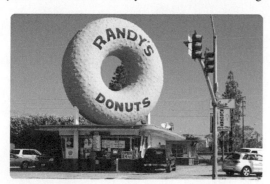

43. If the desk is made by Winner's Only and the desk is in the Rose catalog, then we will not buy a desk at Miller's Furniture.

44. If you get straight A's on your report card, then I will let you attend the prom.

In Exercises 45–48, determine which, if any, of the three statements are equivalent.

45. a) If you swim every day, then you lose five pounds.

 b) You do not swim every day or you lose five pounds.

 c) It is false that you swim every day and you do not lose five pounds.

46. a) The screwdriver is on the workbench if and only if the screwdriver is not on the counter.

 b) If the screwdriver is not on the counter, then the screwdriver is not on the workbench.

 c) It is false that the screwdriver is on the counter and the screwdriver is not on the workbench.

47. a) If $2 + 3 = 6$, then $3 + 1 = 5$.

 b) $2 + 3 = 6$ if and only if $3 + 1 \neq 5$.

 c) If $3 + 1 \neq 5$, then $2 + 3 \neq 6$.

48. a) If the sale is on Tuesday and I have money, then I will go to the sale.

 b) If I go to the sale, then the sale is on Tuesday and I have money.

 c) I go to the sale, or the sale is on Tuesday and I have money.

3.5

In Exercises 49–52, determine whether the argument is valid or invalid. You may compare the argument to a standard form or use a truth table.

49. $p \rightarrow q$
$\dfrac{q}{\therefore p}$

50. $p \wedge q$
$\dfrac{q \rightarrow r}{\therefore p \rightarrow r}$

51. If Jose Macias is the manager, then Kevin Geis is the coach.

If Kevin Geis is the coach, then Tim Weisman is the umpire.

∴ If Jose Macias is the manager, then Tim Weisman is the umpire.

52. If the astronaut visits the space station, then the astronaut uses the space shuttle. The astronaut uses the space shuttle or the astronaut uses the Soyuz spacecraft. Therefore, the astronaut does not use the Soyuz spacecraft.

▲ *The International Space Station*

3.6

In Exercises 53–56, use an Euler diagram to determine whether the argument is valid or invalid.

53. All registered nurses went to college.

Some bookkeepers went to college.

∴ Some bookkeepers are registered nurses.

54. All hackysack players are students.

Joel Knutson is a hackysack player.

∴ Joel Knutson is a student.

55. No Beatles are Rolling Stones.

Some Rolling Stones are Small Faces.

∴ No Beatles are Small Faces.

56. All bears are furry.

Teddy is furry.

∴ Teddy is a bear.

3.7

57. a) Write the corresponding symbolic statement of the circuit shown.

b) Construct a truth table to determine when the lightbulb will be on.

58. Construct a diagram of a circuit that corresponds to the symbolic statement $(p \vee q) \vee (p \wedge q)$.

59. Determine whether the circuits shown are equivalent.

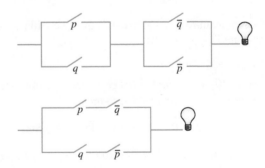

CHAPTER 3) *Test*

In Exercise 1–3, write the statement in symbolic form

p: Phobos is a moon of Mars.
q: Callisto is a moon of Jupiter.
r: Rosalind is a moon of Uranus.

▲ *Callisto, a moon of Jupiter*

1. Phobos is a moon of Mars and Rosalind is a moon of Uranus, or Callisto is not a moon of Jupiter.

2. If Rosalind is a moon of Uranus then Callisto is a moon of Jupiter, or Phobos is not a moon of Mars.

3. It is false that Rosalind is a moon of Uranus if and only if Callisto is not a moon of Jupiter.

In Exercises 4 and 5, use p, q, and r as above to write each symbolic statement in words.

4. $(\sim p \wedge r) \leftrightarrow \sim q$ 5. $(p \vee \sim q) \rightarrow r$

In Exercises 6 and 7, construct a truth table for the given statement.

6. $[\sim(p \rightarrow r)] \wedge q$ 7. $(q \leftrightarrow \sim r) \vee p$

In Exercises 8 and 9, find the truth value of the statement.

8. $2 + 6 = 8$ or $7 - 12 = 5$.

9. Harrison Ford is an actor or Gerald Ford was a president, if and only if the Mississippi is a river.

In Exercises 10 and 11, given that p is true, q is false, and r is true, determine the truth value of the statement.

10. $(r \vee q) \leftrightarrow (p \wedge \sim q)$

11. $[\sim(r \rightarrow \sim p)] \wedge (q \rightarrow p)$

12. Determine whether the pair of statements are equivalent.

$$\sim p \vee q, \quad \sim(p \wedge \sim q)$$

In Exercises 13 and 14, determine which, if any, of the three statements are equivalent.

13. a) If the bird is red, then it is a cardinal.

   b) The bird is not red or it is a cardinal.

   c) If the bird is not red, then it is not a cardinal.

14. a) It is not true that the test is today or the concert is tonight.

   b) The test is not today and the concert is not tonight.

   c) If the test is not today, then the concert is not tonight.

15. *Translate the following argument into symbolic form. Determine whether the argument is valid or invalid by comparing the argument to a recognized form or by using a truth table.*

   If the soccer team wins the game, then Sue played fullback. If Sue played fullback, then the team is in second place. Therefore, if the soccer team wins the game, then the team is in second place.

16. *Use an Euler diagram to determine whether the syllogism is valid or is a fallacy.*

   All living things contain carbon.
   Roger contains carbon.
   _____

   ∴ Therefore, Roger is a living thing.

In Exercises 17 and 18, write the negation of the statement.

17. All highways are roads.

18. Nick played football and Max played baseball.

19. Write the converse, inverse, and contrapositive of the conditional statement "If the garbage truck comes, then today is Saturday."

20. Construct a diagram of a circuit that corresponds to $(p \wedge q) \vee (\sim p \vee \sim q)$

GROUP PROJECTS

Computer Gates

1. Gates in computers work on the same principles as switching circuits. The three basic types of gate are the NOT gate, the AND gate, and the OR gate. Each is illustrated along with a table that indicates current flow entering and exiting the gate. If current flows into a NOT gate, then no current exits, and vice versa. Current exits an AND gate only when both inputs have a current flow. Current exits an OR gate if current flows through either, or both, inputs. In the table, a 1 represents a current flow and a 0 indicates no current flow. For example, in the AND gate, if there is a current flow in input A (I_a has a value of 1) and no current flow in input B (I_b has a value of 0), there is no current flow in the output (O has a value of 0); see row 2 of the AND Gate table.

NOT gate

Input ─▷○─ Output

NOT gate

I	O
1	0
0	1

AND gate

Input A ─┐
Input B ─┘ ─ Output

AND gate

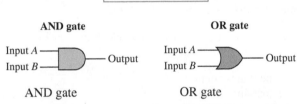

OR gate

Input A ─┐
Input B ─┘ ─ Output

OR gate

I_a	I_b	O
1	1	1
1	0	0
0	1	0
0	0	0

I_a	I_b	O
1	1	1
1	0	1
0	1	1
0	0	0

a) If 1 is considered true and 0 is considered false, explain how these tables are similar to the *not, and,* and *or* truth tables.

For the inputs indicated in the following figures determine whether the output is 1 or 0.

b) I_a 1, I_b 0 ─ Output

c) I_a 1, I_b 0 ─ Output

d) I_a 1, I_b 1 ─ Output

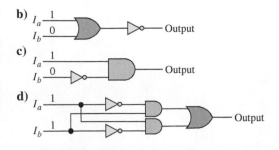

e) What values for I_a and I_b will give an output of 1 in the figure in part (d)? Explain how you determined your answer.

f) Construct a truth table using 1's and 0's for the following gate. Your truth table should have columns I_a, I_b, and O and should indicate the four possible cases for the inputs and each corresponding output.

Logic Game

2. a) Shown is a photograph of a logic game at the Ontario Science Centre. There are 12 balls on top of the game board, numbered from left to right, with ball 1 on the extreme left and ball 12 on the extreme right. On the platform in front of the players are 12 buttons. Button 1 corresponds to ball 1, button 2 corresponds to ball 2, and so on. When 6 buttons are pushed, the 6 respective balls are released. When 1 or 2 balls reach an *and* gate or an *or* gate, a single ball may or may not pass through the gate. The object of the game is to select a proper combination of 6 buttons that will allow 1 ball to reach the bottom. Using your knowledge of *and* and *or*, select a combination of 6 buttons that will result in a win. (There is more than one answer.) Explain how you determined your answer.

b) Construct a game similar to this one where 15 balls are at the top and 8 balls must be selected to allow 1 ball to reach the bottom.

c) Indicate all solutions to the game you constructed in part (c).

5

Number Theory and the Real Number System

Why This is Important

Every time we use a computer, make a telephone call, or watch television we use a device that relies on numbers to operate. In addition to playing many roles in our everyday lives, numbers are also used to describe the natural world, communicate information, and model problems facing scientists and researchers. In this chapter, we will see how number theory, the study of numbers and their properties, makes all these roles possible.

Number theory has many applications that help scientists and researchers solve problems in many areas including communications, biology medicine, computers, and other modern technical devices.

◀ *Number theory helps scientists and researchers model problems.*

209

▲ *There are many ways to display 48 pieces of chocolate.*

Suppose you decide to start your own chocolate candy company. You would like to sell boxes containing 48 pieces of candy. You must decide how to arrange the pieces within the box. You could have six rows with eight pieces in each row, or four rows with twelve pieces in each row, or three layers with four rows each with four pieces in each row. Each of these possibilities involves writing the number 48 as the product of two or more smaller numbers. In this section, we will discuss many other similar problems related to the writing of numbers as the product of smaller numbers.

Why *This is Important* Writing numbers as the product of smaller numbers has many applications to the branch of mathematics we know as number theory.

This chapter introduces *number theory*, the study of numbers and their properties. The numbers we use to count are called the *counting numbers* or *natural numbers*. Because we begin counting with the number 1, the set of natural numbers begins with 1. The set of natural numbers is frequently denoted by *N*:

$$N = \{1, 2, 3, 4, 5, \dots\}$$

Any natural number can be expressed as a product of two or more natural numbers. For example, $8 = 2 \times 4$, $16 = 4 \times 4$, and $19 = 1 \times 19$. The natural numbers that are multiplied together are called *factors* of the product. For example,

$$2 \times 4 = 8$$
$$\uparrow \quad \uparrow$$
Factors

A natural number may have many factors. For example, what pairs of numbers have a product of 18?

$$1 \cdot 18 = 18$$
$$2 \cdot 9 = 18$$
$$3 \cdot 6 = 18$$

The numbers 1, 2, 3, 6, 9, and 18 are all factors of 18. Each of these numbers divides 18 without a remainder.

If *a* and *b* are natural numbers, we say that *a* is a *divisor* of *b* or *a divides b*, symbolized $a \mid b$ if the quotient of *b* divided by *a* has a remainder of 0. If *a* divides *b*, then *b* is *divisible* by *a*. For example, 4 divides 12, symbolized $4 \mid 12$, since the quotient of 12 divided by 4 has a remainder of 0. Note that 12 is divisible by 4. The notation $7 \nmid 12$ means that 7 does not divide 12. Note that every factor of a natural number is also a divisor of the natural number. *Caution:* Do not confuse the symbols $a \mid b$ and a / b; $a \mid b$ means "*a* divides *b*" and a / b means "*a* divided by *b*" ($a \div b$). The symbols a / b and $a \div b$ indicate that the operation of division is to be performed, and *b* may or may not be a divisor of *a*.

Prime and Composite Numbers

Every natural number greater than 1 can be classified as either a prime number or a composite number.

Definition: Prime Number

A **prime number** is a natural number greater than 1 that has exactly two factors (or divisors), itself and 1.

The number 5 is a prime number because it is divisible only by the factors 1 and 5. The first eight prime numbers are 2, 3, 5, 7, 11, 13, 17, and 19. The number 2 is the only even prime number. All other even numbers have at least three divisors: 1, 2, and the number itself.

Definition: Composite Number

A **composite number** is a natural number that is divisible by a number other than itself and 1.

Any natural number greater than 1 that is not prime is composite. The first eight composite numbers are 4, 6, 8, 9, 10, 12, 14, and 15.

The number 1 is neither prime nor composite; it is called a *unit*. The number 38 has at least three divisors, 1, 2, and 38, and hence is a composite number. In contrast, the number 23 is a prime number since its only divisors are 1 and 23.

More than 2000 years ago, the ancient Greeks developed a technique for determining which numbers are prime numbers and which are not. This technique is known as the *sieve of Eratosthenes*, for the Greek mathematician Eratosthenes of Cyrene, who first used it.

To find the prime numbers less than or equal to any natural number, say, 50, using this method, list the first 50 counting numbers (Fig. 5.1). Cross out 1 since it is not a prime number. Circle 2, the first prime number. Then cross out all the multiples of 2: 4, 6, 8, ..., 50. Circle the next prime number, 3. Cross out all multiples of 3 that are not already crossed out. Continue this process of crossing out multiples of prime numbers until you reach the prime number p, such that $p \cdot p$, or p^2, is greater than the last number listed, in this case 50. Therefore, we next circle 5 and cross out its multiples. Then circle 7 and cross out its multiples. The next prime number is 11, and $11 \cdot 11$, or 121, is greater than 50, so you are done. At this point, circle all the remaining numbers to obtain the prime numbers less than or equal to 50. The prime numbers less than or equal to 50 are 2, 3, 5, 7, 11, 13, 17, 19, 23, 29, 31, 37, 41, 43, and 47.

Figure 5.1

Now we turn our attention to composite numbers and their factors. The rules of divisibility given in the chart on page 212 are helpful in finding divisors (or factors) of composite numbers.

The test for divisibility by 6 is a particular case of the general statement that the product of two prime divisors of a number is a divisor of the number. Thus, for example, if both 3 and 7 divide a number, then 21 will also divide the number.

Rules of Divisibility

Divisible by	Test	Example
2	The number is even.	924 is divisible by 2 since 924 is even.
3	The sum of the digits of the number is divisible by 3.	924 is divisible by 3 since the sum of the digits, $9 + 2 + 4 = 15$, and 15 is divisible by 3.
4	The number formed by the last two digits of the number is divisible by 4.	924 is divisible by 4 since the number formed by the last two digits, 24, is divisible by 4.
5	The number ends in 0 or 5.	265 is divisible by 5 since the number ends in 5.
6	The number is divisible by both 2 and 3.	924 is divisible by 6 since it is divisible by both 2 and 3.
8	The number formed by the last three digits of the number is divisible by 8.	5824 is divisible by 8 since the number formed by the last three digits, 824, is divisible by 8.
9	The sum of the digits of the number is divisible by 9.	837 is divisible by 9 since the sum of the digits, 18, is divisible by 9.
10	The number ends in 0.	290 is divisible by 10 since the number ends in 0.

Note that the chart does not list rules for the divisibility for the number 7. The rule for 7 is given in Exercise 92 on page 220. You may find after using the rule that the easiest way to check divisibility by 7 is simply to perform the division.

Example 1   Using the Divisibility Rules

Determine whether 384,540 is divisible by

a) 2   b) 3   c) 4   d) 5   e) 6   f) 8   g) 9   h) 10

Solution

a) 2: since 384,540 is even, it is divisible by 2.

b) 3: the sum of the digits of 384,540 is $3 + 8 + 4 + 5 + 4 + 0 = 24$. Since 24 is divisible by 3, the number 384,540 is divisible by 3.

c) 4: the number formed by the last two digits is 40. Since 40 is divisible by 4, the number 384,540 is divisible by 4.

d) 5: since 384,540 has 0 as the last digit, the number 384,540 is divisible by 5.

e) 6: since 384,540 is divisible by both 2 and 3, the number 384,540 is divisible by 6.

f) 8: the number formed by the last three digits is 540. Since 540 is not divisible by 8, the number 384,540 is not divisible by 8.

g) 9: the sum of the digits of 384,540 is 24. Since 24 is not divisible by 9, the number 384,540 is not divisible by 9.

h) 10:. since 384,540 has 0 as the last digit, the number 384,540 is divisible by 10. ∎

Every composite number can be expressed as a product of prime numbers. The process of breaking a given composite number down into a product of prime numbers is called *prime factorization*. The prime factorization of 18 is $3 \times 3 \times 2$. No other natural number listed as a product of primes will have the same prime factorization as 18. The *fundamental theorem of arithmetic* states this concept formally. (A *theorem* is a statement or proposition that can be proven true.)

The Fundamental Theorem of Arithmetic

Every composite number can be expressed as a *unique* product of prime numbers.

In writing the prime factorization of a number, the order of the factors is immaterial. For example, we may write the prime factors of 18 as $3 \times 3 \times 2$ or $2 \times 3 \times 3$ or $3 \times 2 \times 3$.

A number of techniques can be used to find the prime factorization of a number. Two methods are illustrated.

Method 1: Branching

To find the prime factorization of a number, select any two numbers whose product is the number to be factored. If the factors are not prime numbers, continue factoring each composite number until all factors are prime.

Example 2 *Prime Factorization by Branching*

Write 1500 as a product of primes.

Solution Select any two numbers whose product is 1500. Among the many choices, two possibilities are $15 \cdot 100$ and $30 \cdot 50$. First consider $15 \cdot 00$. Since neither 15 nor 100 is a prime number, find any two numbers whose product is 15 and any two numbers whose product is 100. Continue branching as shown in Fig. 5.2 until the numbers in the last row are all prime numbers. To determine the answer, write the product of all the prime factors. The branching diagram is sometimes called a *factor tree*.

Figure 5.2

Figure 5.3

We see that the numbers in the last row of factors in Fig. 5.2 are all prime numbers. Thus, the prime factorization of 1500 is $3 \cdot 5 \cdot 2 \cdot 5 \cdot 2 \cdot 5 = 2 \cdot 2 \cdot 3 \cdot 5 \cdot 5 \cdot 5 = 2^2 \cdot 3 \cdot 5^3$. Note from Fig. 5.3 that choosing 30 and 50 as the first pair of factors also leads to the same prime factorization of $2^2 \cdot 3 \cdot 5^3$. ■

Method 2: Division

To obtain the prime factorization of a number by this method, divide the given number by the smallest prime number by which it is divisible. Place the quotient under the given number. Then divide the quotient by the smallest prime number by which it is divisible and again record the quotient. Repeat this process until the quotient is a prime number. The prime factorization is the product of all the prime divisors and the prime (or last) quotient. This procedure is illustrated in Example 3.

Profile In Mathematics

Srinivasa Ramanujan

One of the most interesting mathematicians of modern times is Srinivasa Ramanujan (1887–1920). Born to an impoverished middle-class family in India, he virtually taught himself higher mathematics. He went to England to study with the number theorist G. H. Hardy. Hardy tells the story of a taxicab ride he took to visit Ramanujan. The cab had the license plate number 1729, and he challenged the young Indian to find anything interesting in that. Without hesitating, Ramanujan pointed out that it was the smallest positive integer that could be represented in two different ways as the sum of two cubes: $1^3 + 12^3$ and $9^3 + 10^3$.

Example 3 *Prime Factorization by Division*

Write 1500 as a product of prime numbers.

Solution Because 1500 is an even number, the smallest prime number that divides it is 2. Divide 1500 by 2. Place the quotient, 750, below the 1500. Continue to divide each quotient by the smallest prime number that divides it.

2	1500
2	750
3	375
5	125
5	25
	5

The final quotient, 5, is a prime number, so we stop. The prime factorization is determined by multiplying all divisors on the left side and the final prime number quotient as shown by the shaded arrow. Thus, the prime factorization of 1500 is

$$2 \cdot 2 \cdot 3 \cdot 5 \cdot 5 \cdot 5 = 2^2 \cdot 3 \cdot 5^3.$$

Note that despite the different methods used in Examples 2 and 3, the answer is the same.

Greatest Common Divisor

The discussion in Section 5.3 of how to reduce fractions makes use of the greatest common divisor (GCD). We will now discuss how to determine the GCD of a set of numbers. One technique of finding the GCD is to use prime factorization.

Definition: Greatest Common Divisor

The **greatest common divisor (GCD)** of a set of natural numbers is the largest natural number that divides (without remainder) every number in that set.

What is the GCD of 12 and 18? One way to determine the GCD is to list the divisors (or factors) of 12 and 18:

Divisors of 12   {**1, 2, 3**, 4, **6**, 12}

Divisors of 18   {**1, 2, 3, 6**, 9, 18}

The common divisors are 1, 2, 3, and 6. Therefore, the greatest common divisor is 6.

If the numbers are large, this method of finding the GCD is not practical. The GCD can be found more efficiently by using prime factorization.

PROCEDURE   TO DETERMINE THE GREATEST COMMON DIVISOR OF TWO OR MORE NUMBERS

1. Determine the prime factorization of each number.
2. List each prime factor with the *smallest* exponent that appears in each of the prime factorizations.
3. Determine the product of the factors found in Step 2.

Example 4 illustrates this procedure.

Example 4 *Using Prime Factorization to Determine the GCD*

Determine the GCD of 54 and 90.

Solution The branching method of finding the prime factors of 54 and 90 is illustrated in Fig. 5.4.

a) The prime factorization of 54 is $2 \cdot 3^3$, and the prime factorization of 90 is $2 \cdot 3^2 \cdot 5$.

b) The prime factors with the smallest exponents that appear in each of the factorizations of 54 and 90 are 2 and 3^2. Note that because 5 is not in the prime factorization of 54, it is not included when determining the GCD.

c) The product of the factors found in Step 2 is $2 \cdot 3^2 = 2 \cdot 9 = 18$. The GCD of 54 and 90 is 18. Eighteen is the largest natural number that divides both 54 and 90. ∎

Example 5 *Determining the GCD*

Determine the GCD of 315 and 450.

Solution

a) The prime factorization of 315 is $3^2 \cdot 5 \cdot 7$, and the prime factorization of 450 is $2 \cdot 3^2 \cdot 5^2$. You should verify these answers using either the branching method or the division method.

b) The prime factors with the smallest exponents that appear in each of the factorizations of 315 and 450 are 3^2 and 5.

c) The product of the factors found in Step 2 is $3^2 \cdot 5 = 9 \cdot 5 = 45$. The greatest common divisor of 315 and 450 is 45. It is the largest natural number that will evenly divide both 315 and 450. ∎

Least Common Multiple

To perform addition and subtraction of fractions (Section 5.3), we use the least common multiple (LCM). We will now discuss how to determine the LCM of a set of numbers.

Definition: Least Common Multiple
The **least common multiple (LCM)** of a set of natural numbers is the smallest natural number that is divisible (without remainder) by each element of the set.

What is the least common multiple of 12 and 18? One way to determine the LCM is to list the multiples of each number:

Multiples of 12 {12, 24, **36**, 48, 60, **72**, 84, 96, **108**, 120, 132, **144**, ... }
Multiples of 18 {18, **36**, 54, **72**, 90, **108**, 126, **144**, 162, ... }

Some common multiples of 12 and 18 are 36, 72, 108, and 144. The least common multiple, 36, is the smallest number that is divisible by both 12 and 18. Usually, the most efficient method of finding the LCM is to use prime factorization.

PROCEDURE TO DETERMINE THE LEAST COMMON MULTIPLE OF TWO OR MORE NUMBERS

1. Determine the prime factorization of each number.
2. List each prime factor with the *greatest* exponent that appears in any of the prime factorizations.
3. Determine the product of the factors found in Step 2.

Figure 5.4

Example 6 illustrates this procedure.

Example 6   *Using Prime Factorization to Determine the LCM*

Determine the LCM of 54 and 90.

Solution

a) Determine the prime factors of each number. In Example 4, we determined that

$$54 = 2 \cdot 3^3 \quad \text{and} \quad 90 = 2 \cdot 3^2 \cdot 5$$

b) List each prime factor with the greatest exponent that appears in either of the prime factorizations: $2, 3^3, 5$.

c) Determine the product of the factors found in Step 2:

$$2 \cdot 3^3 \cdot 5 = 2 \cdot 27 \cdot 5 = 270$$

Thus, 270 is the LCM of 54 and 90. It is the smallest natural number that is divisible by both 54 and 90.   ◼

Example 7   *Determining the LCM*

Determine the LCM of 315 and 450.

Solution

a) Determine the prime factorization of each number. In Example 5, we determined that

$$315 = 3^2 \cdot 5 \cdot 7 \quad \text{and} \quad 450 = 2 \cdot 3^2 \cdot 5^2$$

b) List each prime factor with the greatest exponent that appears in either of the prime factorizations: $2, 3^2, 5^2, 7$.

c) Determine the product of the factors from Step (b)

$$2 \cdot 3^2 \cdot 5^2 \cdot 7 = 2 \cdot 9 \cdot 25 \cdot 7 = 3150$$

Thus, 3150 is the least common multiple of 315 and 450. It is the smallest natural number that is evenly divisible by both 315 and 450.   ◼

The Search For Larger Prime Numbers

More than 2000 years ago, the Greek mathematician Euclid proved that there is no largest prime number. Mathematicians, however, continue to strive to find larger and larger prime numbers.

Marin Mersenne (1588–1648), a seventeenth-century monk, found that numbers of the form $2^n - 1$ are often prime numbers when n is a prime number. For example,

$$2^2 - 1 = 4 - 1 = 3 \qquad 2^3 - 1 = 8 - 1 = 7$$
$$2^5 - 1 = 32 - 1 = 31 \qquad 2^7 - 1 = 128 - 1 = 127$$

Numbers of the form $2^n - 1$ that are prime are referred to as *Mersenne primes*. The first 10 Mersenne primes occur when $n = 2, 3, 5, 7, 13, 17, 19, 31, 61, 89$.

GIMPS

The Great Internet Mersenne Prime Search (GIMPS) was started by George Woltman in 1996 to coordinate the computing efforts of thousands of people interested in finding new Mersenne prime numbers. Anyone with a computer and Internet access can join the project. GIMPS uses idle time on the participants' computers to search for prime numbers. As of this writing, the largest prime number discovered so far was found by Edson Smith, a computer resource manager at UCLA, in conjunction with GIMPS on August 23, 2008. The number, $2^{43,112,609} - 1$, was the forty-fifth known Mersenne prime number and the eleventh found by GIMPS participants. Since then, two smaller Mersenne prime numbers have also been found using GIMPS.

Why **This is Important** Finding larger and larger prime numbers is a major part of the history of mathematics that continues to this day.

The first time the expression $2^n - 1$ does not generate a prime number, for prime number n, is when n is 11. The number $2^{11} - 1$ is a composite number (see Exercise 90 on page 220).

Scientists frequently use Mersenne primes in their search for larger and larger primes. The largest prime number found to date was discovered on August 23, 2008, by Edson Smith, a computer resource manager at UCLA. Smith and his team worked in conjunction with the Great Internet Mersenne Prime Search (GIMPS; see *Mathematics Today*, at left) to use the university's computers during down time to conduct the search. The number is the Mersenne prime $2^{43,112,609} - 1$. This record prime number is the forty-fifth known Mersenne prime (two more, smaller, Mersenne primes have been found since). When written out, it is 12,978,189 digits long. When written using a standard 12-point font, the number is more than 17 miles long!

More About Prime Numbers

Another mathematician who studied prime numbers was Pierre de Fermat (1601–1665). A lawyer by profession, Fermat became interested in mathematics as a hobby. He became one of the finest mathematicians of the seventeenth century. Fermat conjectured that each number of the form $2^{2^n} + 1$, now referred to as a *Fermat number*, was prime for each natural number n. Recall that a *conjecture* is a supposition that has not been proved or disproved. In 1732, Leonhard Euler proved that for $n = 5$, $2^{32} + 1$ was a composite number, thus disproving Fermat's conjecture.

Since Euler's time, mathematicians have been able to evaluate only the sixth, seventh, eighth, ninth, tenth, and eleventh Fermat numbers to determine whether they are prime or composite. Each of these numbers has been shown to be composite. The eleventh Fermat number was factored by Richard Brent and François Morain in 1988. The sheer magnitude of the numbers involved makes it difficult to test these numbers, even with supercomputers.

In 1742, Christian Goldbach conjectured in a letter to Euler that every even number greater than or equal to 4 can be represented as the sum of two (not necessarily distinct) prime numbers (for example, $4 = 2 + 2$, $6 = 3 + 3$, $8 = 3 + 5$, $10 = 5 + 5$, $12 = 5 + 7$). This conjecture became known as *Goldbach's conjecture*, and it remains unproven to this day. The *twin prime conjecture* is another famous long-standing conjecture. *Twin primes* are primes of the form p and $p + 2$ (for example, 3 and 5, 5 and 7, 11 and 13). This conjecture states that there are an infinite number of pairs of twin primes. At the time of this writing, the largest known twin primes are of the form $65,516,468,355 \cdot 2^{333,333} \pm 1$, which was found by a collaborative effort of two research groups, *Twin Prime Search* and *PrimeGrid*, on August 6, 2009.

Exercises

Warm Up Exercises

In Exercises 1–12, fill in the blanks with an appropriate word, phrase, or symbol(s).

1. The study of numbers and their properties is known as number _____.

2. If a is a factor of b, then $b \div a$ is a(n) _____.

3. If a is divisible by b, then $a \div b$ has a remainder of _____.

4. A natural number greater than 1 that has exactly two factors, itself and 1, is known as a(n) _____ number.

5. A natural number that is divisible by a number other than itself and 1 is known as a(n) _____ number.

6. The largest natural number that divides (without remainder) each number in a set of numbers is known as the greatest common _____ of the set of numbers.

7. The smallest natural number that is divisible (without remainder) by each number in a set of numbers is known as the least common _____ of the set of numbers.

8. Prime numbers of the form $2^n - 1$, where n is a prime number, are known as _____ prime numbers.

9. A supposition or hypothesis that has not been proved or disproved is known as a(n) _____.

10. Goldbach's conjecture states that every even number greater than or equal to 4 can be written as the sum of two (not necessarily) distinct _____ numbers.

11. Numbers of the form $2^{2^n} + 1$, where n is a natural number, are known as _____ numbers.

12. Prime numbers of the form p and $p + 2$, where p is a prime number, are known as _____ prime numbers.

Practice The Skills

13. Use the sieve of Eratosthenes to find the prime numbers up to 100.

14. Use the sieve of Eratosthenes to find the prime numbers up to 150.

In Exercises 15–26, determine whether the statement is true or false. Modify each false statement to make it a true statement.

15. 5 is a factor of 15.

16. $24 \mid 3$

17. 7 is a multiple of 28.

18. 6 is a divisor of 18.

19. 8 is divisible by 56.

20. 15 is a factor of 45.

21. If a number is not divisible by 5, then it is not divisible by 10.

22. If a number is not divisible by 10, then it is not divisible by 5.

23. If a number is divisible by 3, then every digit of the number is divisible by 3.

24. If every digit of a number is divisible by 3, then the number itself is divisible by 3.

25. If a number is divisible by 2 and 3, then the number is divisible by 6.

26. If a number is divisible by 3 and 5, then the number is divisible by 15.

In Exercises 27–32, determine whether the number is divisible by each of the following numbers: 2, 3, 4, 5, 6, 8, 9, and 10.

27. 5390

28. 30,870

29. 72,216

30. 170,820

31. 1,882,320

32. 3,941,221

33. Determine a number that is divisible by 2, 3, 4, 5, and 6.

34. Determine a number that is divisible by 3, 4, 5, 9, and 10.

In Exercises 35–46, find the prime factorization of the number.

35. 36	36. 52
37. 140	38. 315
39. 332	40. 399
41. 513	42. 663
43. 1336	44. 1313
45. 2001	46. 3190

In Exercises 47–56, find (a) the greatest common divisor (GCD) and (b) the least common multiple (LCM).

47. 6 and 14	48. 18 and 21
49. 15 and 25	50. 32 and 224
51. 40 and 900	52. 120 and 240
53. 96 and 212	54. 240 and 285
55. 24, 48, and 128	56. 18, 78, and 198

Problem Solving

57. *Relatively Prime* Two numbers with a greatest common divisor of 1 are said to be *relatively prime*. For example, the numbers 9 and 14 are relatively prime, since their GCD is 1. Determine whether the following pairs of numbers are relatively prime. Write yes or no as your answer.

    a) 8, 9   b) 21, 30   c) 39, 52   d) 177, 178

58. The primes 2 and 3 are consecutive natural numbers. Is there another pair of consecutive natural numbers both of which are prime? Explain.

59. Find the next two sets of twin primes that follow the set 11, 13.

60. Find the first five Mersenne prime numbers.

61. Find the first three Fermat numbers and determine whether they are prime or composite.

62. Show that Goldbach's conjecture is true for the even numbers 4 through 20.

63. *Lawn Maintenance* Brenda Sax cuts her grass every six days and trims her shrubs every 16 days. If Brenda cut her grass and trimmed her shrubs on June 1, how many days will it be before she cuts her grass and trims her shrubs on the same day again?

64. *U.S. Senate Committees* The U.S. Senate consists of 100 members. Senate committees are to be formed so that each of the committees contains the same number of senators and each senator is a member of exactly one committee. The committees are to have more than 2 members but fewer than 50 members. There are various ways that these committees can be formed.

    a) What size committees are possible?

    b) How many committees are there for each size?

65. *Setting Up Chairs* Jerrett Dumouchel is setting up chairs for his school band concert. He needs to put 120 chairs on the gymnasium floor in rows of equal size, and there must be at least 2 chairs in each row. List the number of rows and the number of chairs in each row that are possible.

66. *Barbie and Ken* Mary Lois King collects Barbie dolls and Ken dolls. She has 390 Barbie dolls and 468 Ken dolls. Mary Lois wishes to display the dolls in groups so that the same number of dolls are in each group and that each doll belongs to one group. If each group is to consist only of Barbie dolls or only of Ken dolls, what is the largest number of dolls Mary Lois can have in each group?

67. *Toy Car Collection* Martha Goshaw collects Matchbox® and HotWheels® toy cars. She has 70 red cars and 175 blue cars. She wants to line up her cars in groups so that each group has the same number of cars and each group contains only red cars or only blue cars. What is the largest number of cars she can have in a group?

68. *Stacking Trading Cards* Desmond Freeman collects trading cards. He has 432 baseball cards and 360 football cards. He wants to make stacks of cards on a table so that each stack contains the same number of cards and each card belongs to one stack. If the baseball and football cards must not be mixed in the stacks, what is the largest number of cards that he can have in a stack?

69. *Tree Rows* Elizabeth Dwyer is the manager at Queen Palm Nursery and is in charge of displaying potted trees in rows. Elizabeth has 150 citrus trees and 180 palm trees. She wants to make rows of trees so that each row has the same number of trees and each tree is in a row. If the citrus trees and the palm trees must not be mixed in the rows, what is the largest number of trees that she can have in a row?

70. *Car Maintenance* For many sport utility vehicles, it is recommended that the oil be changed every 3500 miles and that the tires be rotated every 6000 miles. If Carmella Gonzalez just had the oil changed and tires rotated on her SUV during the same visit to her mechanic, how many miles will she drive before she has the oil changed and tires rotated again during the same visit?

71. *Work Schedules* Sara Pappas and Harry Kinnan both work the 3:00 P.M. to 11:00 P.M. shift. Sara has every fifth night off and Harry has every sixth night off. If they both have tonight off, how many days will pass before they have the same night off again?

72. *Prime Numbers* Consider the first eight prime numbers greater than 3. The numbers are 5, 7, 11, 13, 17, 19, 23, and 29.

    a) Determine which of these prime numbers differs by 1 from a multiple of the number 6.

    b) Use inductive reasoning and the results obtained in part (a) to make a conjecture regarding prime numbers.

    c) Select a few more prime numbers and determine whether your conjecture appears to be correct.

73. State a procedure that defines a divisibility test for 15.

74. State a procedure that defines a divisibility test for 22.

Euclidean Algorithm *Another method that can be used to find the greatest common divisor is known as the* Euclidean algorithm. *We illustrate this procedure by finding the GCD of 60 and 220.*

First divide 220 by 60 as shown below. Disregard the quotient 3 and then divide 60 by the remainder 40. Continue this process of dividing the divisors by the remainders until you obtain a remainder of 0. The divisor in the last division, in which the remainder is 0, is the GCD.

$$
\begin{array}{ccc}
3 & 1 & 2 \\
60\overline{)220} & 40\overline{)60} & 20\overline{)40} \\
\underline{180} & \underline{40} & \underline{40} \\
40 & 20 & 0
\end{array}
$$

Since 40/20 had a remainder of 0, the GCD is 20.

In Exercises 75–80, use the Euclidean algorithm to find the GCD.

75. 15, 40

76. 12, 28

77. 35, 105

78. 78, 104

79. 150, 180

80. 210, 560

Perfect Numbers *A number whose* proper factors *(factors other than the number itself) add up to the number is called a* perfect number. *For example, 6 is a perfect number because its proper factors are 1, 2, and 3, and 1 + 2 + 3 = 6. Determine which, if any, of the following numbers are perfect.*

81. 28

82. 32

83. 56

84. 496

Challenge Problems/Group Activities

85. ***Number of Factors*** The following procedure can be used to determine the *number of factors* (or *divisors*) of a composite number. Write the number in prime factorization form. Examine the exponents on the prime numbers in the prime factorization. Add 1 to each exponent and then find the product of these numbers. This product gives the number of positive divisors of the composite number. For example, the prime factorization of 75 is $3 \cdot 5^2$. The exponents on the prime factors are 1 and 2. Therefore, 75 has $(1 + 1) \cdot (2 + 1) = 2 \cdot 3$ or 6 factors (the factors are 1, 3, 5, 15, 25, and 75).

a) Use this procedure to determine the number of divisors of 60.

b) To check your answer, list all the divisors of 60. You should obtain the same number of divisors found in part (a).

86. Recall that if a number is divisible by both 2 and 3, then the number is divisible by 6. If a number is divisible by

both 2 and 4, is the number necessarily divisible by 8? Explain your answer.

87. The product of any three consecutive natural numbers is divisible by 6. Explain why.

88. A number in which each digit except 0 appears exactly three times is divisible by 3. For example, 888,444,555 and 714,714,714 are both divisible by 3. Explain why this outcome must be true.

89. Use the fact that if $a\,|\,b$ and $a\,|\,c$, then $a\,|\,(b + c)$ to determine whether 54,036 is divisible by 18. (*Hint:* Write 54,036 as 54,000 + 36.)

90. Show that the $2^n - 1$ is a (Mersenne) prime for $n = 2, 3, 5$, and 7 but composite for $n = 11$.

91. Goldbach also conjectured in his letter to Euler that *every* integer greater than 5 is the sum of three prime numbers. For example, $6 = 2 + 2 + 2$ and $7 = 2 + 2 + 3$. Show that this conjecture is true for integers 8 through 20.

92. ***Divisibility by Seven*** The following describes a procedure to determine whether a number is divisible by 7. We will demonstrate the procedure with the number 203.

i) Remove the units digit from the number, double the units digit, and subtract it from the remaining number. For 203, we will remove the 3, double it to get 6, and then subtract $20 - 6$ to get 14.

ii) If this new number is divisible by 7, then so is the original number. In our case, since 14 is divisible by 7, then 203 is also divisible by 7.

iii) If you are not sure if the new number obtained in Step ii is divisible by 7, you can repeat the process described in the first step.

Use the procedure described above to determine whether the following numbers are divisible by 7.

a) 329

b) 553

c) 583

d) 4823

Research Activities

93. Conduct an Internet search on the GIMPS project. (See *Mathematics Today* on page 217.) Write a report describing the history and development of the project. Include a current update of the project's findings.

94. Do research and explain what *deficient numbers* and *abundant numbers* are. Give an example of each type of number. References include history of mathematics books, encyclopedias, and the Internet.

The Integers

▲ *Fahrenheit temperatures can be positive, negative, or zero.*

Answer the question, What is the temperature, to the nearest degree Fahrenheit, outside right now? Depending on where you are and what time of year it is, you may have answered with a positive number, a negative number, or zero. These numbers are examples of the group of numbers called the *integers* that we will study in this section. We will also study the operations of addition, subtraction, multiplication, and division using the integers.

Why *This is Important*   We all use integers daily. An understanding of the integers and their properties is important to successfully complete our everyday tasks.

In Sections 1.1 and 5.1, we defined the natural or counting numbers:

$$N = \{1, 2, 3, 4, \dots\}$$

Another important set of numbers, the *whole numbers*, help to answer the question, How many?

$$\text{Whole numbers} = \{0, 1, 2, 3, 4, \dots\}$$

Note that the set of whole numbers contains the number 0 but that the set of counting numbers does not. If a farmer were asked how many chickens were in a coop, the answer would be a whole number. If the farmer had no chickens, he or she would answer zero. Although we use the number 0 daily and take it for granted, the number 0 as we know it was not used and accepted until the sixteenth century.

If the temperature is 12°F and drops 20°, the resulting temperature is −8°F. This type of problem shows the need for negative numbers. The set of *integers* consists of the negative integers, 0, and the positive integers.

$$\text{Integers} = \{\underbrace{\dots, -4, -3, -2, -1}, 0, \underbrace{1, 2, 3, \dots}\}$$

Negative integers   Positive integers

The term *positive integers* is yet another name for the natural numbers or counting numbers.

An understanding of addition, subtraction, multiplication, and division of the integers is essential in understanding algebra (Chapter 6). To aid in our explanation of addition and subtraction of integers, we introduce the real number line (Fig. 5.5). To construct the real number line, arbitrarily select a point for zero to serve as the starting point. Place the positive integers to the right of 0, equally spaced from one another. Place the negative integers to the left of 0, using the same spacing. The real number line contains the integers and all the other real numbers that are not integers. Some examples of real numbers that are not integers are indicated in Fig. 5.5, namely, $-\frac{5}{2}, \frac{1}{2}, \sqrt{2}$, and π. We discuss real numbers that are not integers in the next two sections.

Figure 5.5

The arrows at the ends of the real number line indicate that the line continues indefinitely in both directions. Note that for any natural number, n, on the number line, the *opposite of* that number, $-n$, is also on the number line. This real number line was drawn horizontally, but it could just as well have been drawn vertically. In fact, in the next chapter, we show that the axes of a graph are the union of two number lines, one horizontal and the other vertical.

Did You Know?

Triangular Numbers

One very simple reason that the ancient Greek mathematicians thought of mathematics in terms of whole numbers and their ratios (the rational numbers) was that they were still working with numbers that were represented by objects, such as squares and triangles, not number symbols. Still, that did not prevent them from drawing some conclusions about number theory. Consider two consecutive triangular numbers (introduced in Section 1.1), for instance, 3 and 6. You can see from the diagram that the sum of the two triangular numbers is equal to the square number 9, the square of a side of the larger triangle.

The number line can be used to determine the greater (or lesser) of two integers. Two *inequality symbols* that we will use in this chapter are $>$ and $<$. The symbol $>$ is read "is greater than," and the symbol $<$ is read "is less than." Expressions that contain an inequality symbol are called *inequalities*. On the number line, the numbers increase from left to right. The number 3 is greater than 2, written $3 > 2$. Observe that 3 is to the right of 2. Similarly, we can see that $0 > -1$ by observing that 0 is to the right of -1 on the number line.

Instead of stating that 3 is greater than 2, we could state that 2 is less than 3, written $2 < 3$. Note that 2 is to the left of 3 on the number line. We can also see that $-1 < 0$ by observing that -1 is to the left of 0. The inequality symbol always points to the smaller of the two numbers when the inequality is true.

Example 1 *Writing an Inequality*

Insert either $>$ or $<$ in the shaded area between the paired numbers to make the statement correct.

a) $-7 \quad 8$ b) $-7 \quad -8$ c) $-7 \quad 0$ d) $-7 \quad -4$

> Solution

a) $-7 < 8$ since -7 is to the left of 8 on the number line.
b) $-7 > -8$ since -7 is to the right of -8 on the number line.
c) $-7 < 0$ since -7 is to the left of 0 on the number line.
d) $-7 < -4$ since -7 is to the left of -4 on the number line.   ∎

Addition of Integers

Addition of integers can be represented geometrically using a number line. To do so, begin at 0 on the number line. Represent the first addend (the first number to be added) by an arrow starting at 0. Draw the arrow to the right if the addend is positive. If the addend is negative, draw the arrow to the left. From the tip of the first arrow, draw a second arrow to represent the second addend. Draw the second arrow to the right or left, as just explained. The sum of the two integers is found at the tip of the second arrow.

Example 2 *Adding Integers*

Evaluate the following using the number line.

a) $3 + (-5)$ b) $-1 + (-4)$ c) $-6 + 4$ d) $3 + (-3)$

> Solution

a)

Thus, $3 + (-5) = -2$.

b)

Thus, $-1 + (-4) = -5$.

c)

Thus, $-6 + 4 = -2$.

d)

Thus, $3 + (-3) = 0$. ■

In Example 2(d), the number -3 is said to be the additive inverse of 3 and 3 is the additive inverse of -3 because their sum is 0. In general, the *additive inverse* of the number n is $-n$ since $n + (-n) = 0$. Inverses are discussed more formally in Chapter 10.

Subtraction of Integers

Any subtraction problem can be rewritten as an addition problem. To do so, we use the following rule of subtraction.

Subtraction

$$a - b = a + (-b)$$

The rule for subtraction indicates that to subtract b from a, *add* the additive inverse of b to a. For example,

$$3 - 5 = 3 + (-5)$$

$\quad\quad\quad\uparrow\quad\quad\quad\quad\uparrow\quad\quad\uparrow$

Subtraction   Addition   Additive inverse of 5

Now we can determine the value of $3 + (-5)$.

Thus, $3 - 5 = 3 + (-5) = -2$.

┌ Example **3** *Subtracting Integers*

Evaluate $-4 - (-3)$ using the number line.

│ Solution │ We are subtracting -3 from -4. The additive inverse of -3 is 3; therefore, we add 3 to -4. We now add $-4 + 3$ on the number line to obtain the answer -1.

$\quad\quad\quad\quad\quad\quad\quad$ -4

$\quad\quad\quad\quad\quad\quad\quad\quad$ 3

-5 -4 -3 -2 -1   0   1   2   3   4   5   6

Thus, $-4 - (-3) = -4 + 3 = -1$. ■

In Example 3, we found that $-4 - (-3) = -4 + 3$. In general, $a - (-b) = a + b$. As you get more proficient in working with integers, you should be able to answer questions involving them without drawing a number line.

┌ Example **4** *Subtracting: Adding the Inverse*

Evaluate.

a) $-7 - 3$ b) $-7 - (-3)$ c) $7 - (-3)$ d) $7 - 3$

Solution

a) $-7 - 3 = -7 + (-3) = -10$ b) $-7 - (-3) = -7 + 3 = -4$
c) $7 - (-3) = 7 + 3 = 10$ d) $7 - 3 = 7 + (-3) = 4$ ∎

Example 5 *Elevation Difference*

The highest point on Earth is Mount Everest, in the Himalayas, at a height of 29,035 ft above sea level. The lowest point on Earth is the Mariana Trench, in the Pacific Ocean, at a depth of 36,198 ft below sea level ($-36,198$ ft). Find the vertical height difference between Mount Everest and the Mariana Trench.

Solution We obtain the vertical difference by subtracting the lower elevation from the higher elevation.

$$29,035 - (-36,198) = 29,035 + 36,198 = 65,233$$

The vertical difference is 65,233 ft.   ∎

Multiplication of Integers

The multiplication property of zero is important in our discussion of multiplication of integers. It indicates that the product of 0 and any number is 0.

Multiplication Property of Zero
$$a \cdot 0 = 0 \cdot a = 0$$

We will develop the rules for multiplication of integers using number patterns. The four possible cases are

1. positive integer × positive integer,

2. positive integer × negative integer,

3. negative integer × positive integer, and

4. negative integer × negative integer.

CASE 1: *POSITIVE INTEGER × POSITIVE INTEGER* The product of two positive integers can be defined as repeated addition of a positive integer. Thus, $3 \cdot 2$ means $2 + 2 + 2$. This sum will always be positive. Thus, *a positive integer times a positive integer is a positive integer.*

CASE 2: *POSITIVE INTEGER × NEGATIVE INTEGER* Consider the following patterns:

$$3(3) = 9$$
$$3(2) = 6$$
$$3(1) = 3$$

Note that each time the second factor is reduced by 1, the product is reduced by 3. Continuing the process gives

$$3(0) = 0$$

What comes next?

$$3(-1) = -3$$
$$3(-2) = -6$$

The pattern indicates that *a positive integer times a negative integer is a negative integer.*

We can confirm this result by using the number line. The expression $3(-2)$ means $(-2) + (-2) + (-2)$. Adding $(-2) + (-2) + (-2)$ on the number line, we obtain a sum of -6.

CASE 3: *NEGATIVE INTEGER × POSITIVE INTEGER* A procedure similar to that used in case 2 will indicate that *a negative integer times a positive integer is a negative integer.*

CASE 4: *NEGATIVE INTEGER × NEGATIVE INTEGER* We have illustrated that a positive integer times a negative integer is a negative integer. We make use of this fact in the following pattern:

$$4(-4) = -16$$
$$3(-4) = -12$$
$$2(-4) = -8$$
$$1(-4) = -4$$

In this pattern, each time the first term is decreased by 1, the product is increased by 4. Continuing this process gives

$$0(-4) = 0$$
$$(-1)(-4) = 4$$
$$(-2)(-4) = 8$$

This pattern illustrates that *a negative integer times a negative integer is a positive integer.*

The examples were restricted to integers. The rules for multiplication, however, can be used for any numbers. We summarize them as follows.

Rules for Multiplication

1. The product of two numbers with *like signs* (positive × positive or negative × negative) is a *positive number.*
2. The product of two numbers with *unlike signs* (positive × negative or negative × positive) is a *negative number.*

Example 6 *Multiplying Integers*

Evaluate.
a) $5 \cdot 6$ b) $5 \cdot (-6)$ c) $(-5) \cdot 6$ d) $(-5) \cdot (-6)$

Solution

a) $5 \cdot 6 = 30$ b) $5 \cdot (-6) = -30$
c) $(-5) \cdot 6 = -30$ d) $(-5) \cdot (-6) = 30$ ∎

Division of Integers

You may already realize that a relationship exists between multiplication and division.

$$6 \div 2 = 3 \quad \text{means that} \quad 3 \cdot 2 = 6$$
$$\frac{20}{10} = 2 \quad \text{means that} \quad 2 \cdot 10 = 20$$

These examples demonstrate that division is the reverse process of multiplication.

Division

For any a, b, and c where $b \neq 0$, $\dfrac{a}{b} = c$ means that $c \cdot b = a$.

We discuss the four possible cases for division of integers, which are similar to those for multiplication.

CASE 1: *POSITIVE INTEGER ÷ POSITIVE INTEGER* *A positive integer divided by a positive integer is positive.*

$$\frac{6}{2} = 3 \quad \text{since} \quad 3(2) = 6$$

CASE 2: *POSITIVE INTEGER ÷ NEGATIVE INTEGER* *A positive integer divided by a negative integer is negative.*

$$\frac{6}{-2} = -3 \quad \text{since} \quad (-3)(-2) = 6$$

CASE 3: *NEGATIVE INTEGER ÷ POSITIVE INTEGER* *A negative integer divided by a positive integer is negative.*

$$\frac{-6}{2} = -3 \quad \text{since} \quad (-3)(2) = -6$$

CASE 4: *NEGATIVE INTEGER ÷ NEGATIVE INTEGER* *A negative integer divided by a negative integer is positive.*

$$\frac{-6}{-2} = 3 \quad \text{since} \quad 3(-2) = -6$$

The examples were restricted to integers. The rules for division, however, can be used for any numbers. You should realize that division of integers does not always result in an integer. The rules for division are summarized as follows.

Rules for Division

1. The quotient of two numbers with *like signs* (positive ÷ positive or negative ÷ negative) is a *positive number*.
2. The quotient of two numbers with *unlike signs* (positive ÷ negative or negative ÷ positive) is a *negative number*.

Example 7 *Dividing Integers*

Evaluate.

a) $\dfrac{63}{9}$ b) $\dfrac{-63}{9}$ c) $\dfrac{63}{-9}$ d) $\dfrac{-63}{-9}$

Solution

a) $\dfrac{63}{9} = 7$ b) $\dfrac{-63}{9} = -7$ c) $\dfrac{63}{-9} = -7$ d) $\dfrac{-63}{-9} = 7$ ∎

In the definition of division, we stated that the denominator could not be 0. Why not? Suppose we are trying to find the quotient $\frac{5}{0}$. Let's say that this quotient is equal to some number x. Then we would have $\frac{5}{0} = x$. If true, it would mean that $5 = x \cdot 0$. The right side of the equation is $x \cdot 0$, which is equal to 0 for any real value of x. That leads us to conclude that $5 = 0$, which is false. Thus, there is no number that can replace x that makes the equation $\frac{5}{0} = x$ true. Therefore, in mathematics, division by 0 is not allowed and we say that a quotient of any number divided by zero is *undefined*.

SECTION 5.2 Exercises

Warm Up Exercises

In Exercises 1–4, fill in the blanks with an appropriate word, phrase, or symbol(s).

1. The set of numbers {0,1,2,3,4,...} is known as the _____ numbers.

2. The rule for subtraction indicates that to subtract b from a, _____ the additive inverse of b to a.

3. a) The product of two numbers with *like* signs is a _____ number.

   b) The product of two numbers with *unlike* signs is a _____ number.

4. a) The quotient of two numbers with *unlike* signs is a _____ number.

   b) The quotient of two numbers with *like* signs is a _____ number.

In Exercises 5–6, insert either $>$ or $<$ in the shaded area between the paired numbers to make the statement correct.

5. a) $-3 \; 2$ b) $-3 \; -2$

   c) $-3 \; 0$ d) $-3 \; -4$

6. a) $-5 \; -8$ b) $-5 \; 8$

   c) $-5 \; -1$ d) $-5 \; 0$

Practice the Skills

In Exercises 7–16, evaluate the expression.

7. $-3 + 5$ 8. $5 + (-8)$

9. $-10 + 3$ 10. $-5 + (-5)$

11. $[6 + (-11)] + 0$ 12. $(2 + 5) + (-4)$

13. $[(-3) + (-4)] + 9$ 14. $[8 + (-3)] + (-2)$

15. $[(-23) + (-9)] + 11$ 16. $[5 + (-13)] + 18$

In Exercises 17–26, evaluate the expression.

17. $3 - 5$ 18. $-3 - 7$

19. $-6 - 2$ 20. $9 - (-4)$

21. $-5 - (-3)$ 22. $-4 - 4$

23. $14 - 20$ 24. $8 - (-3)$

25. $[5 + (-3)] - 4$ 26. $6 - (8 + 6)$

In Exercises 27–36, evaluate the expression.

27. $-7 \cdot 8$

28. $8(-4)$

29. $(-9)(-9)$

30. $-6(13)$

31. $[(-8)(-2)] \cdot 6$

32. $4(-5)(-6)$

33. $(5 \cdot 6)(-2)$

34. $(-9)(-1)(-2)$

35. $[(-3)(-6)] \cdot [(-5)(8)]$

36. $[(-8 \cdot 4) \cdot 5](-2)$

In Exercises 37–46, evaluate the expression.

37. $-16 \div (-2)$ 38. $-54 \div 6$

39. $\dfrac{15}{-15}$ 40. $\dfrac{-90}{9}$

41. $56/-8$ 42. $-75/15$

43. $-210/14$ 44. $186/-6$

45. $144 \div (-3)$ 46. $(-900) \div (-4)$

In Exercises 47–56, determine whether the statement is true or false. Modify each false statement to make it a true statement.

47. Every whole number is an integer.

48. Every integer is a whole number.

49. The difference of any two negative integers is a negative integer.

50. The sum of any two negative integers is a negative integer.

51. The product of any two positive integers is a positive integer.

52. The difference of a positive integer and a negative integer is always a negative integer.

53. The quotient of a negative integer and a positive integer is always a negative number.

54. The quotient of any two negative integers is a negative number.

55. The sum of a positive integer and a negative integer is always a positive integer.

56. The product of a positive integer and a negative integer is always a positive integer.

In Exercises 57–66, evaluate the expression.

57. $(5 + 7) \div 4$

58. $(-15) \div \left[35 \div (-7)\right]$

59. $\left[(-12)(-3)\right] - 3$

60. $\left[7(-4)\right] - 8$

61. $(4 - 8)(3)$

62. $[18 \div (-2)](-3)$

63. $[2 + (-17)] \div 3$

64. $(5 - 9) \div (-4)$

65. $[(-22)(-3)] \div (2 - 13)$

66. $[15(-4)] \div (-6)$

In Exercises 67–70, write the numbers in increasing order from left to right.

67. $0, -3, 3, -6, 6, -9$

68. $100, -10, 1, 0, -1, 10$

69. $-5, -2, -3, -1, -4, -6$

70. $106, 33, -47, -108, 72, -76$

Problem Solving

71. *Submarine Depth* The *USS Virginia* submarine is at an underwater depth of 600 feet. It then rises 200 feet, dives 400 feet, and finally dives another 300 feet. What is the *USS Virginia's* final depth?

▲ *USS Virginia*

72. *Dow Jones Industrial Average* On May 25, 2010, the Dow Jones Industrial Average (DJIA) opened at 10,067

points. During that day it lost 23 points. On May 26 it lost 70 points. On May 27 it gained 285 points. On May 28 it lost 122 points. Determine the DJIA at closing on May 28, 2010.

73. *Elevation Difference* Mount Whitney, in the Sierra Nevada mountains of California, is the highest point in the contiguous United States. It is 14,495 ft above sea level. Death Valley, in California and Nevada, is the lowest point in the United States, 282 ft below sea level. Find the vertical height difference between Mount Whitney and Death Valley.

74. *Extreme Temperatures* The hottest temperature ever recorded in the United States was 134°F, which occurred at Greenland Ranch, California, in Death Valley on July 10, 1913. The coldest temperature ever recorded in the United States was −80°F, which occurred at Prospect Creek Camp, Alaska, in the Endicott Mountains on January 23, 1971. Determine the difference between these two temperatures.

75. *Time Zone Calculations* Part of a World Standard Time Zones chart used by airlines and the United States Navy is shown. The scale along the bottom is just like a number line with the integers $-12, -11, \ldots, 11, 12$ on it.

  a) Find the difference in time between Amsterdam (zone $+1$) and Los Angeles (zone -8).

  b) Find the difference in time between Boston (zone -5) and Puerto Vallarta (zone -7).

76. *Bus Stops* A city bus currently has 23 people on it. At the next stop, 10 people get off the bus, and 8 people get on the bus. At the next stop, 15 people get off the bus, and 6 people get on the bus. At the next stop, 2 people get off the bus, and 17 people get on the bus. At this point, how many people are on the bus?

Concept/Writing Exercises

77. Explain why the quotient of a number divided by 0 is undefined.

78. Explain why $\dfrac{a}{b} = \dfrac{-a}{-b}$.

Challenge Problems/Group Activities

79. Find the quotient:

$$\frac{-1 + 2 - 3 + 4 - 5 + \cdots - 99 + 100}{1 - 2 + 3 - 4 + 5 - \cdots + 99 - 100}$$

80. *Pentagonal Numbers* Triangular numbers and square numbers were introduced in the Section 1.1 Exercises. There are also **pentagonal numbers**, which were also studied by the Greeks. Four pentagonal numbers are 1, 5, 12, and 22.

1   5   12   22

a) Determine the next three pentagonal numbers.

b) Describe a procedure to determine the next five pentagonal numbers without drawing the figures.

c) Is 72 a pentagonal number? Explain how you determined your answer.

81. Place the appropriate plus or minus signs between each digit so that the total will equal 1.

0 1 2 3 4 5 6 7 8 9 = 1

Recreational Mathematics

82. *Four 4's* Refer to the *Recreational Mathematics* box on page 225.

a) Use the rules given on page 225 to obtain the following whole numbers: 12, 15, 16, 17, 20.

b) We will now change our rules to allow the number 44 to count as two of the four 4's. Use the number 44 and two other fours to obtain the whole number 10.

Internet/Research Activity

83. Do research and write a report on the history of the number 0 in the Hindu–Arabic numeration system.

SECTION 5.3 The Rational Numbers

Among the ingredients called for in a recipe for chocolate chip cookies are $2\frac{1}{4}$ cups flour, $\frac{1}{2}$ teaspoon salt, $1\frac{1}{3}$ teaspoons baking soda, $\frac{3}{4}$ cup sugar, and $\frac{3}{4}$ cup brown sugar. How much of each of these ingredients would you need to use if you wish to double the recipe? In this section, we will review the use of fractions such as those in the chocolate chip cookie recipe. We will also learn about the operations of addition, subtraction, multiplication, and division using fractions.

▲ *Rational numbers are frequently used in baking recipes.*

Why *This is Important* Fractions are everywhere in our everyday lives. Kitchen measurements, tool sizes, and many other real-life applications all involve fractions.

We introduced the number line and discussed the integers in Section 5.2. The numbers that fall between the integers on the number line are either rational or irrational numbers. In this section, we discuss the rational numbers, and in Section 5.4, we discuss the irrational numbers.

Any number that can be expressed as a quotient of two integers (denominator not 0) is a rational number.

Definition: Rational Numbers
The set of **rational numbers**, denoted by Q, is the set of all numbers of the form p/q, where p and q are integers and $q \neq 0$.

The following numbers are examples of rational numbers:

$$\frac{1}{3}, \quad \frac{3}{4}, \quad -\frac{7}{8}, \quad 1\frac{2}{3}, \quad 2, \quad 0, \quad \frac{15}{7}$$

The integers 2 and 0 are rational numbers because each can be expressed as the quotient of two integers: $2 = \frac{2}{1}$ and $0 = \frac{0}{1}$. In fact, every integer n is a rational number because it can be written in the form of $\frac{n}{1}$.

Many properties of fractions can be demonstrated by folding a sheet of paper. For example, take a sheet of white paper, fold it in half, unfold it, and color half of the sheet of paper. The colored portion of the paper represents the fraction $\frac{1}{2}$. Next, return the sheet of paper to its folded state and then fold the sheet of paper in half again. You should now have two creases on your paper and the paper should be divided into four equal regions. Since two of the regions are colored, the colored portion of the paper represents the fraction $\frac{2}{4}$. Also, since the colored portion still takes up half of the paper, we can see that $\frac{2}{4}$ is equivalent to $\frac{1}{2}$. Paper folding can also be used to demonstrate addition, subtraction, multiplication, and division of fractions. The Web site www.superteacherworksheets.com describes many such activities. Exercise 123 on page 243 includes some other activities with paper folding.

Numbers such as $\frac{1}{3}$ and $-\frac{7}{8}$ are also called *fractions*. The number above the fraction line is called the *numerator*, and the number below the fraction line is called the *denominator*.

Reducing Fractions

Sometimes the numerator and denominator in a fraction have a common divisor (or common factor). For example, both the numerator and denominator of the fraction $\frac{6}{10}$ have the common divisor 2. When a numerator and denominator have a common divisor, we can *reduce the fraction to its lowest terms*.

A fraction is said to be in its lowest terms (or reduced) when the numerator and denominator are relatively prime (that is, have no common divisors other than 1). To reduce a fraction to its lowest terms, divide both the numerator and the denominator by the greatest common divisor. Recall that a procedure for finding the greatest common divisor was discussed in Section 5.1.

The fraction $\frac{6}{10}$ is reduced to its lowest terms as follows.

$$\frac{6}{10} = \frac{6 \div 2}{10 \div 2} = \frac{3}{5}$$

Example 1 *Reducing a Fraction to Lowest Terms*

Reduce $\frac{54}{90}$ to its lowest terms.

Solution On page 215 in Example 4 of Section 5.1, we determined that the GCD of 54 and 90 is 18. Divide the numerator and the denominator by GCD, 18.

$$\frac{54}{90} = \frac{54 \div 18}{90 \div 18} = \frac{3}{5}$$

Since there are no common divisors of 3 and 5 other than 1, the fraction $\frac{3}{5}$ is in its lowest terms. ∎

Mixed Numbers and Improper Fractions

Consider the number $2\frac{3}{4}$. It is an example of a *mixed number*. It is called a mixed number because it consists of an integer, 2, and a fraction, $\frac{3}{4}$. The mixed number $2\frac{3}{4}$ means $2 + \frac{3}{4}$. The mixed number $-4\frac{1}{4}$ means $-\left(4 + \frac{1}{4}\right)$. Rational numbers greater than 1 or less than -1 that are not integers may be represented as mixed numbers, or as *improper fractions*. An improper fraction is a fraction whose numerator is greater than its denominator. An example of an improper fraction is $\frac{8}{5}$. Figure 5.6 shows both mixed numbers and improper fractions indicated on a number line. In this section, we show how to convert mixed numbers to improper fractions and vice versa.

Figure 5.6

We begin by limiting our discussion to positive mixed numbers and positive improper fractions.

> **PROCEDURE** **CONVERTING A POSITIVE MIXED NUMBER TO AN IMPROPER FRACTION**
>
> 1. Multiply the denominator of the fraction in the mixed number by the integer preceding it.
> 2. Add the product obtained in Step 1 to the numerator of the fraction in the mixed number. This sum is the numerator of the improper fraction we are seeking. The denominator of the improper fraction we are seeking is the same as the denominator of the fraction in the mixed number.

Example 2 *Converting Mixed Numbers to Improper Fractions*

Convert the following mixed numbers to improper fractions.

a) $1\dfrac{3}{4}$ b) $3\dfrac{7}{8}$

Solution

a) $1\dfrac{3}{4} = \dfrac{4 \cdot 1 + 3}{4} = \dfrac{4 + 3}{4} = \dfrac{7}{4}$

b) $3\dfrac{7}{8} = \dfrac{8 \cdot 3 + 7}{8} = \dfrac{24 + 7}{8} = \dfrac{31}{8}$

Notice that both $\frac{7}{4}$ and $\frac{31}{8}$ have numerators that are larger than their denominators; therefore, both numbers are improper fractions.   ∎

Now let's discuss converting an improper fraction to a mixed number.

> **PROCEDURE** **CONVERTING A POSITIVE IMPROPER FRACTION TO A MIXED NUMBER**
>
> 1. Divide the numerator by the denominator. Identify the quotient and the remainder.
> 2. The quotient obtained in Step 1 is the integer part of the mixed number. The remainder is the numerator of the fraction in the mixed number. The denominator in the fraction of the mixed number will be the same as the denominator in the original fraction.

Example 3 *From Improper Fraction to Mixed Number*

Convert the following improper fractions to mixed numbers.

a) $\dfrac{8}{5}$ b) $\dfrac{225}{8}$

Solution

a) Divide the numerator, 8, by the denominator, 5.

$$
\begin{array}{r}
1 \quad \leftarrow \text{Quotient} \\
\text{Divisor} \rightarrow \quad 5)\overline{8} \quad \leftarrow \text{Dividend} \\
\underline{5} \\
3 \quad \leftarrow \text{Remainder}
\end{array}
$$

Therefore,

$$\frac{8}{5} = 1\frac{3}{5}$$

Quotient ↓ ← Remainder ← Divisor

The mixed number is $1\frac{3}{5}$.

b) Divide the numerator, 225, by the denominator, 8.

$$\begin{array}{r} 28 \\ 8)\overline{225} \\ \underline{16} \\ 65 \\ \underline{64} \\ 1 \end{array}$$

Divisor → ← Quotient ← Dividend ← Remainder

Therefore,

$$\frac{225}{8} = 28\frac{1}{8}$$

Quotient ↓ ← Remainder ← Divisor

The mixed number is $28\frac{1}{8}$.

Up to this point, we have only worked with positive mixed numbers and positive improper fractions. When converting a negative mixed number to an improper fraction, or a negative improper fraction to a mixed number, it is best to ignore the negative sign temporarily. Perform the calculation as described earlier and then reattach the negative sign.

Example 4   Negative Mixed Numbers and Improper Fractions

a) Convert $-1\frac{3}{4}$ to an improper fraction.

b) Convert $-\frac{8}{5}$ to a mixed number.

Solution

a) First, ignore the negative sign and examine $1\frac{3}{4}$. We learned in Example 2(a) that $1\frac{3}{4} = \frac{7}{4}$. To convert $-1\frac{3}{4}$ to an improper fraction, we reattach the negative sign. Thus, $-1\frac{3}{4} = -\frac{7}{4}$.

b) We learned in Example 3(a) that $\frac{8}{5} = 1\frac{3}{5}$. Therefore, $-\frac{8}{5} = -1\frac{3}{5}$.

Terminating or Repeating Decimal Numbers

Note the following important property of the rational numbers. *Every rational number when expressed as a decimal number will be either a terminating or a repeating decimal number.*

Examples of terminating decimal numbers are 0.5, 0.75, and 4.65. Examples of repeating decimal numbers are $0.333\ldots$, $0.2323\ldots$, and $8.13456456\ldots$. One way to indicate that a number or group of numbers repeats is to place a bar above the number or group of numbers that repeats. Thus, $0.333\ldots$ may be written $0.\overline{3}$, $0.2323\ldots$ may be written $0.\overline{23}$, and $8.13456456\ldots$ may be written $8.13\overline{456}$.

⌜ Example **5** *Terminating Decimal Numbers*

Show that the following rational numbers can be expressed as terminating decimal numbers.

a) $\dfrac{3}{5}$ b) $-\dfrac{13}{20}$ c) $\dfrac{23}{16}$

Solution   To express the rational number in decimal form, divide the numerator by the denominator. If you use a calculator or long division, you will obtain the following results.

a) $\dfrac{3}{5} = 0.6$ b) $-\dfrac{13}{20} = -0.65$ c) $\dfrac{23}{16} = 1.4375$ ∎

⌜ Example **6** *Repeating Decimal Numbers*

Show that the following rational numbers can be expressed as repeating decimal numbers.

a) $\dfrac{2}{3}$ b) $\dfrac{14}{99}$ c) $1\dfrac{5}{36}$

Solution   If you use a calculator or long division, you will see that each fraction results in a repeating decimal number.

a) $2 \div 3 = 0.6666\ldots$ or $0.\overline{6}$

b) $14 \div 99 = 0.141414\ldots$ or $0.\overline{14}$

c) $1\frac{5}{36} = \frac{41}{36} = 1.138888\ldots$ or $1.13\overline{8}$ ∎

Note that in each part of Example 6, the quotient when expressed as a decimal number has no final digit and continues indefinitely. Each number is a repeating decimal number.

When a fraction is converted to a decimal number, the maximum number of digits that can repeat is $n - 1$, where n is the denominator of the fraction. For example, when $\frac{2}{7}$ is converted to a decimal number, the maximum number of digits that can repeat is $7 - 1$, or 6.

Converting Decimal Numbers to Fractions

We can convert a terminating or repeating decimal number into a quotient of integers. The explanation of the procedure will refer to the positional values to the right of the decimal point, as illustrated here:

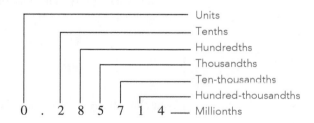

Example 7 demonstrates how to convert from a decimal number to a fraction.

⌜ Example **7** *Converting Decimal Numbers to Fractions*

Convert the following terminating decimal numbers to a quotient of integers. If necessary, reduce the quotient to lowest terms.

a) 0.7   b) 0.35   c) 0.016   d) 3.41

Solution When converting a terminating decimal number to a quotient of integers, we observe the last digit to the right of the decimal point. The position of this digit will indicate the denominator of the quotient of integers.

a) $0.7 = \frac{7}{10}$ because the 7 is in the tenths position.

b) $0.35 = \frac{35}{100}$ because the right-most digit, 5, is in the hundredths position. We finish by reducing the fraction to lowest terms:

$$\frac{35}{100} = \frac{35 \div 5}{100 \div 5} = \frac{7}{20}$$

c) $0.016 = \frac{16}{1000}$ because the right-most digit, 6, is in the thousandths position. We finish by reducing the fraction to lowest terms:

$$\frac{16}{1000} = \frac{16 \div 8}{1000 \div 8} = \frac{2}{125}$$

d) We begin by writing 3.41 as the mixed number, $3\frac{41}{100}$ because the right-most digit, 1, is in the hundredths position. To write the mixed number as a ratio of two integers, we follow the procedure shown in Example 2, on page 231:

$$3\frac{41}{100} = \frac{100 \cdot 3 + 41}{100} = \frac{341}{100}$$

The fraction $\frac{341}{100}$ cannot be reduced further.   ■

Converting a repeating decimal number to a quotient of integers is more difficult than converting a terminating decimal number to a quotient of integers. To do so, we must "create" another repeating decimal number with the same repeating digits so that when one repeating decimal number is subtracted from the other repeating decimal number, the difference will be a whole number. To create a number with the same repeating digits, multiply the original repeating decimal number by 10 if one digit repeats, by 100 if two digits repeat, by 1000 if three digits repeat, and so on. Examples 8 through 10 demonstrate this procedure.

Example 8 *Converting a Repeating Decimal Number to a Fraction*

Convert $0.\overline{3}$ to a quotient of integers.

Solution $0.\overline{3} = 0.3\overline{3} = 0.33\overline{3}$, and so on.

Let the original repeating decimal number be n; thus, $n = 0.\overline{3}$. Because one digit repeats, we multiply both sides of the equation by 10, which gives $10n = 3.\overline{3}$. Then we subtract.

$$\begin{array}{r} 10n = 3.\overline{3} \\ - \quad n = 0.\overline{3} \\ \hline 9n = 3.0 \end{array}$$

Note that $10n - n = 9n$ and $3.\overline{3} - 0.\overline{3} = 3.0$.

Next, we solve for n by dividing both sides of the equation by 9.

$$\frac{9n}{9} = \frac{3.0}{9}$$

$$n = \frac{3}{9} = \frac{1}{3}$$

Therefore, $0.\overline{3} = \frac{1}{3}$. Evaluate $1 \div 3$ on a calculator now and see what value you get.   ■

Example **9** *Converting a Repeating Decimal Number to a Fraction*

Convert $0.\overline{35}$ to a quotient of integers.

Solution Let $n = 0.\overline{35}$. Since two digits repeat, multiply both sides of the equation by 100. Thus, $100n = 35.\overline{35}$. Now we subtract n from $100n$.

$$
\begin{array}{r}
100n = 35.\overline{35} \\
-\quad n = 0.\overline{35} \\
\hline
99n = 35
\end{array}
$$

Finally, we divide both sides of the equation by 99.

$$\frac{99n}{99} = \frac{35}{99}$$

$$n = \frac{35}{99}$$

Therefore, $0.\overline{35} = \frac{35}{99}$. Evaluate $35 \div 99$ on a calculator now and see what value you get. ∎

Example **10** *Converting a Repeating Decimal Number to a Fraction*

Convert $12.14\overline{2}$ to a quotient of integers.

Solution This example is different from the two preceding examples in that the repeating digit, 2, is not directly to the right of the decimal point. When this situation arises, move the decimal point to the right until the repeating terms are directly to its right. For each place the decimal point is moved, the number is multiplied by 10. In this example, the decimal point must be moved two places to the right. Thus, the number must be multiplied by 100.

$$n = 12.14\overline{2}$$
$$100n = 100 \times 12.14\overline{2} = 1214.\overline{2}$$

Now proceed as in the previous two examples. Since one digit repeats, multiply both sides by 10.

$$100n = 1214.\overline{2}$$
$$10 \times 100n = 10 \times 1214.\overline{2}$$
$$1000n = 12142.\overline{2}$$

Now subtract $100n$ from $1000n$ so that the repeating part will drop out.

$$
\begin{array}{r}
1000n = 12142.\overline{2} \\
-\quad 100n = 1214.\overline{2} \\
\hline
900n = 10928
\end{array}
$$

$$n = \frac{10{,}928}{900} = \frac{2732}{225}$$

Therefore, $12.14\overline{2} = \frac{2732}{225}$. Evaluate $2732 \div 225$ on a calculator now and see what value you get. ∎

Multiplication and Division of Fractions

The product of two fractions is found by multiplying the numerators together and multiplying the denominators together.

Multiplication of Fractions

$$\frac{a}{b} \cdot \frac{c}{d} = \frac{a \cdot c}{b \cdot d} = \frac{ac}{bd}, \quad b \neq 0, \quad d \neq 0$$

Example 11 Multiplying Fractions

Evaluate.

a) $\dfrac{3}{5} \cdot \dfrac{7}{8}$ b) $\left(\dfrac{-2}{3}\right)\left(\dfrac{-4}{9}\right)$ c) $\left(1\dfrac{7}{8}\right)\left(2\dfrac{1}{4}\right)$

Solution

a) $\dfrac{3}{5} \cdot \dfrac{7}{8} = \dfrac{3 \cdot 7}{5 \cdot 8} = \dfrac{21}{40}$ b) $\left(\dfrac{-2}{3}\right)\left(\dfrac{-4}{9}\right) = \dfrac{(-2)(-4)}{(3)(9)} = \dfrac{8}{27}$

c) $\left(1\dfrac{7}{8}\right)\left(2\dfrac{1}{4}\right) = \dfrac{15}{8} \cdot \dfrac{9}{4} = \dfrac{135}{32} = 4\dfrac{7}{32}$ ∎

To divide fractions we make use of the *reciprocal* of a number. The *reciprocal* of any number is 1 divided by that number. The product of a number and its reciprocal must equal 1. Examples of some numbers and their reciprocals follow.

Number		Reciprocal		Product
3	·	$\dfrac{1}{3}$	=	1
$\dfrac{3}{5}$	·	$\dfrac{5}{3}$	=	1
−6	·	$-\dfrac{1}{6}$	=	1

To find the quotient of two fractions, multiply the first fraction by the reciprocal of the second fraction.

Division of Fractions

$$\frac{a}{b} \div \frac{c}{d} = \frac{a}{b} \cdot \frac{d}{c} = \frac{ad}{bc}, \quad b \neq 0, \quad d \neq 0, \quad c \neq 0$$

Example 12 Dividing Fractions

Evaluate.

a) $\dfrac{5}{7} \div \dfrac{3}{4}$ b) $\left(-\dfrac{3}{5}\right) \div \dfrac{7}{8}$

Solution

a) $\dfrac{5}{7} \div \dfrac{3}{4} = \dfrac{5}{7} \cdot \dfrac{4}{3} = \dfrac{5 \cdot 4}{7 \cdot 3} = \dfrac{20}{21}$

b) $\left(-\dfrac{3}{5}\right) \div \dfrac{7}{8} = \dfrac{-3}{5} \cdot \dfrac{8}{7} = \dfrac{-3 \cdot 8}{5 \cdot 7} = \dfrac{-24}{35} = -\dfrac{24}{35}$ ∎

Addition and Subtraction of Fractions

Before we can add or subtract fractions, the fractions must have a common denominator. A common denominator is another name for a common multiple of the denominators. The *lowest common denominator (LCD)* is the least common multiple of the denominators.

To add or subtract two fractions with a common denominator, we add or subtract their numerators and retain the common denominator.

Addition and Subtraction of Fractions

$$\frac{a}{c} + \frac{b}{c} = \frac{a+b}{c}, \quad c \neq 0; \quad \frac{a}{c} - \frac{b}{c} = \frac{a-b}{c}, \quad c \neq 0$$

Example 13   *Adding and Subtracting Fractions*

Evaluate.

a) $\frac{1}{8} + \frac{3}{8}$ b) $\frac{19}{24} - \frac{5}{24}$

Solution

a) $\frac{1}{8} + \frac{3}{8} = \frac{1+3}{8} = \frac{4}{8} = \frac{1}{2}$

b) $\frac{19}{24} - \frac{5}{24} = \frac{19-5}{24} = \frac{14}{24} = \frac{7}{12}$

Note that in Example 13, the denominators of the fractions being added or subtracted were the same; that is, they have a common denominator. *When adding or subtracting two fractions with unlike denominators, first rewrite each fraction with a common denominator. Then add or subtract the fractions.*

Writing fractions with a common denominator is accomplished with the *fundamental law of rational numbers.*

Fundamental Law of Rational Numbers

If a, b, and c are integers, with $b \neq 0$ and $c \neq 0$, then

$$\frac{a}{b} = \frac{a}{b} \cdot \frac{c}{c} = \frac{a \cdot c}{b \cdot c}$$

The terms $\frac{a}{b}$ and $\frac{a \cdot c}{b \cdot c}$ are called *equivalent fractions*. For example, since $\frac{5}{12} = \frac{5 \cdot 5}{12 \cdot 5} = \frac{25}{60}$, the fractions $\frac{5}{12}$ and $\frac{25}{60}$ are equivalent fractions. We will see the importance of equivalent fractions in the next two examples.

Example 14   *Subtracting Fractions with Unlike Denominators*

Evaluate $\frac{13}{15} - \frac{5}{6}$.

Solution   Using prime factorization (Section 5.1), we find that the LCM of 15 and 6 is 30. We will therefore express each fraction as an equivalent fraction with a denominator of 30. First, consider $\frac{13}{15}$. To obtain a denominator of 30, we must multiply the denominator, 15, by 2. If the denominator is multiplied by 2, the numerator must also be multiplied by 2 to obtain an equivalent fraction. Next, consider $\dfrac{5}{6}$. To obtain a denominator of 30, we must multiply the denominator, 6, by 5. Therefore, we must multiply both numerator and denominator by 5 to obtain an equivalent fraction.

$$\frac{13}{15} - \frac{5}{6} = \left(\frac{13}{15} \cdot \frac{2}{2}\right) - \left(\frac{5}{6} \cdot \frac{5}{5}\right)$$

$$= \frac{26}{30} - \frac{25}{30}$$

$$= \frac{1}{30}$$

Example 15 *Adding Fractions with Unlike Denominators*

Evaluate $\dfrac{1}{54} + \dfrac{1}{90}$.

Solution On page 216, in Example 6 of Section 5.1, we determined that the LCM of 54 and 90 is 270. Rewrite each fraction as an equivalent fraction using the LCM as the common denominator.

$$\frac{1}{54} + \frac{1}{90} = \left(\frac{1}{54} \cdot \frac{5}{5}\right) + \left(\frac{1}{90} \cdot \frac{3}{3}\right)$$

$$= \frac{5}{270} + \frac{3}{270}$$

$$= \frac{8}{270}$$

Now we reduce $\frac{8}{270}$ by dividing both 8 and 270 by 2, their greatest common factor.

$$\frac{8}{270} = \frac{8 \div 2}{270 \div 2} = \frac{4}{135}$$

Example 16 *Rice Preparation*

Following are the instructions given on a box of Minute Rice. Determine the amount of (a) rice and water, (b) salt, and (c) butter or margarine needed to make 3 servings of rice.

Directions
1. Bring water, salt, and butter (or margarine) to a boil.
2. Stir in rice. Cover; remove from heat. Let stand 5 minutes. Fluff with fork.

To Make	Rice & Water (Equal Measures)	Salt	Butter or Margarine (If Desired)
2 servings	$\frac{2}{3}$ cup	$\frac{1}{4}$ tsp	1 tsp
4 servings	$1\frac{1}{3}$ cups	$\frac{1}{2}$ tsp	2 tsp

Solution Since 3 is halfway between 2 and 4, we can find the amount of each ingredient by finding the average of the amount for 2 and 4 servings. To do so, we add the amounts for 2 servings and 4 servings and divide the sum by 2.

a) Rice and water: $\dfrac{\frac{2}{3} + 1\frac{1}{3}}{2} = \dfrac{\frac{2}{3} + \frac{4}{3}}{2} = \dfrac{\frac{6}{3}}{2} = \dfrac{2}{2} = 1$ cup

b) Salt: $\dfrac{\frac{1}{4} + \frac{1}{2}}{2} = \dfrac{\frac{1}{4} + \frac{2}{4}}{2} = \dfrac{\frac{3}{4}}{2} = \dfrac{3}{4} \cdot \dfrac{1}{2} = \dfrac{3}{8}$ tsp

c) Butter or margarine: $\dfrac{1 + 2}{2} = \dfrac{3}{2}$, or $1\frac{1}{2}$ tsp

The solution to Example 16 can be found in other ways. Suggest two other procedures for solving the same problem.

SECTION 5.3   *Exercises*

Warm Up Exercises

In Exercises 1–12, fill in the blanks with an appropriate word, phrase, or symbol(s).

1. The set of rational numbers is the set of numbers of the form $\dfrac{p}{q}$, where p and q are _____ and $q \neq 0$.

2. For the rational number $\dfrac{p}{q}$, p is called the _____.

3. For the rational number $\dfrac{p}{q}$, q is called the _____.

4. Rational numbers such as $2\frac{3}{4}$ and $-1\frac{1}{2}$ are examples of _____ numbers.

5. Rational numbers such as $\frac{11}{4}$ and $-\frac{3}{2}$ are examples of _____ fractions.

6. The number $\frac{1}{2}$ can be represented as a(n) _____ decimal number.

7. The number $\frac{1}{3}$ can be represented as a(n) _____ decimal number.

8. In the decimal number 0.285714, the 2 is in the _____ position.

9. In the decimal number 0.285714, the 8 is in the _____ position.

10. The product of a number and its _____ must equal 1.

11. When adding or subtracting two fractions with unlike denominators, first rewrite each fraction with the _____ common denominator.

12. The rational numbers $\frac{1}{2}$ and $\frac{5}{10}$ are examples of _____ fractions.

Practice the Skills

In Exercises 13–22, reduce each fraction to lowest terms.

13. $\dfrac{3}{6}$

14. $\dfrac{15}{20}$

15. $\dfrac{28}{63}$

16. $\dfrac{36}{56}$

17. $\dfrac{95}{125}$

18. $\dfrac{13}{221}$

19. $\dfrac{112}{176}$

20. $\dfrac{120}{135}$

In Exercises 21–26, convert each mixed number to an improper fraction.

21. $2\dfrac{3}{7}$

22. $3\dfrac{5}{6}$

23. $-1\dfrac{15}{16}$

24. $-7\dfrac{1}{5}$

25. $-4\dfrac{15}{16}$

26. $11\dfrac{9}{16}$

In Exercises 27–30, write the number of inches indicated by the arrows as an improper fraction.

27.

28.

29.

30.

In Exercises 31–36, convert each improper fraction to a mixed number.

31. $\dfrac{8}{3}$

32. $\dfrac{19}{7}$

33. $-\dfrac{73}{6}$

34. $-\dfrac{157}{12}$

35. $-\dfrac{878}{15}$

36. $\dfrac{1028}{21}$

In Exercises 37–44, express each rational number as terminating or repeating decimal number.

37. $\dfrac{3}{10}$ **38.** $\dfrac{7}{8}$ **39.** $\dfrac{2}{3}$ **40.** $\dfrac{1}{6}$

41. $\dfrac{3}{8}$ **42.** $\dfrac{23}{7}$ **43.** $\dfrac{13}{6}$ **44.** $\dfrac{115}{15}$

In Exercises 45–52, express each terminating decimal number as a quotient of two integers. If possible, reduce the quotient to lowest terms.

45. 0.25   **46.** 0.13

47. 0.175   **48.** 0.375

49. 0.2   **50.** 0.251

51. 0.0131   **52.** 0.2345

In Exercises 53–60, express each repeating decimal number as a quotient of two integers. If possible, reduce the quotient to lowest terms.

53. $0.\overline{2}$ **54.** $0.\overline{7}$

55. $0.\overline{9}$ **56.** $0.\overline{23}$

57. $1.\overline{36}$ **58.** $0.\overline{135}$

59. $2.0\overline{5}$ **60.** $2.4\overline{9}$

In Exercises 61–70, perform the indicated operation and reduce your answer to lowest terms.

61. $\dfrac{1}{3} \cdot \dfrac{6}{7}$ **62.** $\dfrac{1}{4} \div \dfrac{5}{8}$

63. $\left(\dfrac{-3}{8}\right)\left(\dfrac{-16}{15}\right)$ **64.** $\left(-\dfrac{3}{5}\right) \div \dfrac{10}{21}$

65. $\dfrac{7}{8} \div \dfrac{8}{7}$ **66.** $\dfrac{3}{7} \div \dfrac{3}{7}$

67. $\left(\dfrac{3}{5} \cdot \dfrac{4}{7}\right) \div \dfrac{1}{3}$ **68.** $\left(\dfrac{4}{7} \div \dfrac{4}{5}\right) \cdot \dfrac{1}{7}$

69. $\left[\left(-\dfrac{2}{3}\right)\left(\dfrac{5}{8}\right)\right] \div \left(-\dfrac{7}{16}\right)$

70. $\left(\dfrac{7}{15} \cdot \dfrac{5}{8}\right) \div \left(\dfrac{7}{9} \cdot \dfrac{5}{2}\right)$

In Exercises 71–80, perform the indicated operation and reduce your answer to lowest terms.

71. $\dfrac{2}{5} + \dfrac{1}{3}$ **72.** $\dfrac{5}{6} - \dfrac{3}{4}$

73. $\dfrac{2}{11} + \dfrac{5}{22}$ **74.** $\dfrac{5}{12} + \dfrac{7}{36}$

75. $\dfrac{5}{9} - \dfrac{7}{54}$ **76.** $\dfrac{17}{25} - \dfrac{43}{100}$

77. $\dfrac{1}{12} + \dfrac{1}{48} + \dfrac{1}{72}$ **78.** $\dfrac{3}{5} + \dfrac{7}{15} + \dfrac{9}{75}$

79. $\dfrac{1}{30} - \dfrac{3}{40} - \dfrac{7}{50}$ **80.** $\dfrac{4}{25} - \dfrac{9}{100} - \dfrac{7}{40}$

Problem Solving

Alternative methods for adding and subtracting two fractions are shown below. These methods may not result in a solution in its lowest terms.

$$\frac{a}{b} + \frac{c}{d} = \frac{ad + bc}{bd} \quad \text{and} \quad \frac{a}{b} - \frac{c}{d} = \frac{ad - bc}{bd}$$

In Exercises 81–86, use the appropriate formula to evaluate the expression.

81. $\dfrac{5}{8} + \dfrac{1}{3}$ **82.** $\dfrac{4}{7} + \dfrac{2}{5}$ **83.** $\dfrac{5}{6} - \dfrac{7}{8}$

84. $\dfrac{7}{3} - \dfrac{5}{12}$ **85.** $\dfrac{3}{8} + \dfrac{5}{12}$ **86.** $\left(\dfrac{2}{3} + \dfrac{1}{4}\right) - \dfrac{3}{5}$

In Exercises 87–92, evaluate each expression.

87. $\left(\dfrac{1}{3} \cdot \dfrac{6}{7}\right) + \dfrac{1}{4}$ **88.** $\left(\dfrac{1}{6} \div \dfrac{2}{3}\right) - \dfrac{1}{7}$

89. $\left(\dfrac{3}{4} + \dfrac{1}{6}\right) \div \left(2 - \dfrac{7}{6}\right)$ **90.** $\left(\dfrac{1}{3} \cdot \dfrac{3}{7}\right) + \left(\dfrac{3}{5} \cdot \dfrac{10}{11}\right)$

91. $\left(3 - \dfrac{4}{9}\right) \div \left(4 + \dfrac{2}{3}\right)$ **92.** $\left(\dfrac{2}{5} \div \dfrac{4}{9}\right)\left(\dfrac{3}{5} \cdot 6\right)$

In Exercises 93–104, write an expression that will solve the problem and then evaluate the expression.

93. *Height Increase* When David Conway finished his first year of high school, his height was $69\tfrac{7}{8}$ inches. When he returned to school after the summer, David's height was $71\tfrac{5}{8}$ inches. How much did David's height increase over the summer?

94. *Thistles* Diane Helbing has four different varieties of thistles invading her pasture. She estimates that of these thistles, $\tfrac{1}{2}$ are Canada thistles, $\tfrac{1}{4}$ are bull thistles, $\tfrac{1}{6}$ are plumeless thistles, and the rest are musk thistles. What fraction of the thistles are musk thistles?

95. *Stairway Height* A stairway consists of 14 stairs, each $8\tfrac{5}{8}$ inches high. What is the vertical height of the stairway?

96. Alphabet Soup Margaret Cannata's recipe for alphabet soup calls for (among other items) $\frac{1}{4}$ cup snipped parsley, $\frac{1}{8}$ teaspoon pepper, and $\frac{1}{2}$ cup sliced carrots. Margaret is expecting company and needs to multiply the amounts of the ingredients by $1\frac{1}{2}$ times. Determine the amount of (a) snipped parsley, (b) pepper, and (c) sliced carrots she needs for the soup.

97. Sprinkler System To repair his sprinkler system, Tony Gambino needs a total of $20\frac{5}{16}$ inches of PVC pipe. He has on hand pieces that measure $2\frac{1}{4}$ inches, $3\frac{7}{8}$ inches, and $4\frac{1}{4}$ inches in length. If he can combine these pieces and use them in the repair, how long a piece of PVC pipe will Tony need to purchase to repair his sprinkler system?

98. Crop Storage Todd Schroeder has a silo on his farm in which he can store silage made from his various crops. He currently has a silo that is $\frac{1}{4}$ full of corn silage, $\frac{2}{5}$ full of hay silage, and $\frac{1}{3}$ full of oats silage. What fraction of Todd's silo is currently in use?

99. Department Budget Jaime Bailey is chair of the humanities department at Santa Fe Community College. Jaime has a budget in which $\frac{1}{2}$ of the money is for photocopying, $\frac{2}{5}$ of the money is for computer-related expenses, and the rest of the money is for student tutors in the foreign languages lab. What fraction of Jaime's budget is for student tutors?

100. Art Supplies Denise Viale teaches kindergarten and is buying supplies for her class to make papier-mâché piggy banks. Each piggy bank to be made requires $1\frac{1}{4}$ cups of flour. If Denise has 15 students who are going to make piggy banks, how much flour does Denise need to purchase?

101. Height of a Computer Stand The instructions for assembling a computer stand include a diagram illustrating its dimensions. Find the total height of the stand.

102. Width of a Picture The width of a picture is $24\frac{7}{8}$ in., as shown in the diagram. Find x, the distance from the edge of the frame to the center.

103. Traveling Interstate 5 While on vacation, Janet Mazerella traveled the full length of Interstate Highway 5 from the U.S.–Canadian border to the U.S.–Mexican border. She recorded the following travel times between cities: Blaine, Washington, to Seattle: 1 hour 49 minutes; Seattle to Portland: 2 hours 48 minutes; Portland to Sacramento: 9 hours 6 minutes; Sacramento to Los Angeles: 6 hours 3 minutes; Los Angeles to San Diego: 2 hours 9 minutes; San Diego to San Ysidro, California: 22 minutes.

a) Write each of these times as a fraction or as a mixed number with minutes represented as a fraction with a denominator of 60. Do not reduce the fractional part of the mixed number.

b) What is Janet's total driving time from Blaine, Washington, to San Ysidro, California? Give your answer as a mixed number and in terms of hours and minutes.

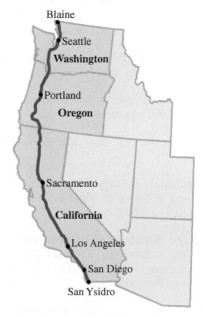

▲ Interstate Highway 5

104. Traveling Across Texas While on vacation, Omar Rodriguez traveled the entire length of Interstate Highway 10 in Texas. Omar recorded the following travel times between cities on his trip. Anthony to El Paso: 25 minutes; El Paso to San Antonio: 7 hours

54 minutes; San Antonio to Houston: 3 hours 1 minute; Houston to Beaumont: 1 hour 23 minutes; Beaumont to Orange: 28 minutes.

a) Write each of these times as a fraction or as a mixed number with minutes represented as a fraction with a denominator of 60. Do not reduce the fractional part of the mixed number.

b) What is Omar's total driving time from Anthony to Orange? Give your answer as a mixed number and in terms of hours and minutes.

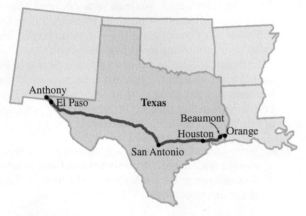

▲ *Interstate Highway 10*

Challenge Problems/Group Activities

105. *Cutting Lumber* If a piece of wood $8\frac{3}{4}$ ft long is to be cut into four equal pieces, find the length of each piece. (Allow $\frac{1}{8}$ in. for each saw cut.)

106. *Dimensions of a Room* A rectangular room measures 8 ft 3 in. by 10 ft 8 in. by 9 ft 2 in. high.

a) Determine the perimeter of the room in feet. Write your answer as a mixed number.

b) Calculate the area of the floor of the room in square feet.

c) Calculate the volume of the room in cubic feet. Use volume = length × width × height. Write your answer as a mixed number.

107. *Hanging a Picture* The back of a framed picture that is to be hung is shown above on the right. A nail is to be hammered into the wall, and the picture will be hung by the wire on the nail.

a) If the center of the wire is to rest on the nail and a side of the picture is to be 20 in. from the window, how far from the window should the nail be placed?

b) If the top of the frame is to be $26\frac{1}{4}$ in. from the ceiling, how far from the ceiling should the nail be placed? (Assume the wire will not stretch.)

c) Repeat part (b) if the wire will stretch $\frac{1}{4}$ in. when the picture is hung.

108. *Increasing a Book Size* The dimensions of the cover of a book have been increased from $8\frac{1}{2}$ in. by $9\frac{1}{4}$ in. to $8\frac{1}{2}$ in. by $10\frac{1}{4}$ in. By how many square inches has the surface area increased? Use area = length × width.

Dense Set of Numbers *A set of numbers is said to be a* dense set *if between any two distinct members of the set there exists a third distinct member of the set. The set of integers is not dense since between any two consecutive integers there is not another integer. For example, between 1 and 2 there are no other integers. The set of rational numbers is dense because between any two distinct rational numbers there exists a third distinct rational number. For example, we can find a rational number between 0.243 and 0.244. The number 0.243 can be written as 0.2430, and 0.244 can be written as 0.2440. There are many numbers between these two. Some of them are 0.2431, 0.2435, and 0.243912. In Exercises 109–114, find a rational number between the two numbers in each pair. Many answers are possible.*

109. 0.21 and 0.22

110. 4.005 and 4.05

111. −2.176 and −2.175

112. 1.3457 and 1.34571

113. 4.872 and 4.873

114. −3.7896 and −3.7895

Halfway Between Two Numbers *To find a rational number halfway between any two rational numbers given in fraction form, add the two numbers together and divide their sum by 2. In Exercises 115–120, find a rational number halfway between the two fractions in each pair.*

115. $\frac{1}{4}$ and $\frac{3}{4}$ **116.** $\frac{1}{5}$ and $\frac{2}{5}$

117. $\frac{1}{100}$ and $\frac{1}{10}$ **118.** $\frac{7}{13}$ and $\frac{8}{13}$

119. $\frac{1}{99}$ and $\frac{1}{9}$ **120.** $\frac{1}{2}$ and $\frac{2}{3}$

121. *Cooking Oatmeal* Following are the instructions given on a box of oatmeal. Determine the amount of water (or milk) and oats needed to make $1\frac{1}{2}$ servings by:

a) Adding the amount of each ingredient needed for 1 serving to the amount needed for 2 servings and dividing by 2.

b) Adding the amount of each ingredient needed for 1 serving to half the amount needed for 1 serving.

Directions

1. Boil water or milk and salt (if desired).
2. Stir in oats.
3. Stirring occasionally, cook over medium heat for 5 minutes.

Servings	1	2
Water (or milk)	1 cup	$1\frac{3}{4}$ cup
Oats	$\frac{1}{2}$ cup	1 cup
Salt (optional)	dash	$\frac{1}{8}$ tsp

122. Consider the rational number $0.\overline{9}$.

a) Use the method from Example 8 on page 234 to convert $0.\overline{9}$ to a quotient of integers.

b) Find a number halfway between $0.\overline{9}$ and 1 by adding the two numbers and dividing by 2.

c) Find $\frac{1}{3} + \frac{2}{3}$ by adding the fractions. Now express $\frac{1}{3}$ and $\frac{2}{3}$ as repeating decimals and find the sum using the decimal representation of $\frac{1}{3}$ and $\frac{2}{3}$.

d) What conclusion can you draw from parts (a), (b), and (c)?

Recreational Mathematics

123. *Paper Folding* Read the *Recreational Mathematics* box on page 230. Next, take a clean sheet of white paper and fold it in half, fold it in half again, and fold it in half a third time. Now unfold the paper. You should have eight equal regions of the paper.

a) What fraction does each region represent?

b) Next, color three of the regions red and one of the regions blue, as shown in the diagram below.

Use the paper to determine the following sum; $\frac{3}{8} + \frac{1}{8}$ Write your answer in reduced form.

c) Next, return the paper to its folded state and then fold the paper in half again. Use the blue region of the paper to determine the following product: $\frac{1}{16} \times 2$.

d) Use the blue region of the paper to determine the following quotient: $\frac{1}{8} \div 2$.

Internet/Research Activity

124. The ancient Greeks are often considered the first true mathematicians. Write a report summarizing the ancient Greeks' contributions to rational numbers. Include in your report what they learned and believed about the rational numbers. References include encyclopedias, history of mathematics books, and Internet Web sites.

SECTION 5.4

The Irrational Numbers and the Real Number System

▲ *The distance from the northwest corner of a football field to the southeast corner is an irrational number.*

A football field is 160 ft wide and 360 ft long. A football player catches the football from a kickoff in the northwest corner of one end zone and runs across the field to the southeast corner of the other end zone, as shown by the dashed line in the diagram.

How far did the football player run? The answer to this question is an example of an *irrational* number. In this section, we will introduce irrational numbers along with the operations of addition, subtraction, multiplication, and division of irrational numbers. The answer to the above question is $40\sqrt{97}$ feet, or about 394 feet.

Why *This is Important* Irrational numbers play an important role in many areas of mathematics, science, business, and other fields.

Hypotenuse
(longest side
of right triangle)

b c

a

$a^2 + b^2 = c^2$

Figure 5.7

Pythagoras (ca. 585–500 B.C.), a Greek mathematician, is credited with providing a written proof that in any *right triangle* (a triangle with a 90° angle; see Fig. 5.7), the square of the length of one side (a^2) added to the square of the length of the other side (b^2) equals the square of the length of the hypotenuse (c^2). The formula $a^2 + b^2 = c^2$ is now known as the *Pythagorean theorem.** Pythagoras found that when using the formula, with $a = 1$ and $b = 1$, the value of c was not a rational number.

$$a^2 + b^2 = c^2$$
$$1^2 + 1^2 = c^2$$
$$1 + 1 = c^2$$
$$2 = c^2$$

There is no rational number that when squared will equal 2. This fact prompted a need for a new set of numbers, the irrational numbers.

In Section 5.2, we introduced the real number line. The points on the real number line that are not rational numbers are referred to as irrational numbers. Recall that every rational number is either a terminating or a repeating decimal number. Therefore, irrational numbers, when represented as decimal numbers, will be nonterminating, nonrepeating decimal numbers.

Definition: **Irrational Number**
An **irrational number** is a real number whose decimal representation is a nonterminating, nonrepeating decimal number.

A nonrepeating decimal number such as 5.12639537... can be used to indicate an irrational number. Notice that no number or set of numbers repeat on a continuous basis, and the three dots at the end of the number indicate that the number continues indefinitely. Nonrepeating number patterns can be used to indicate irrational numbers. For example, 6.1011011101111... and 0.525225222... are both irrational numbers.

The expression $\sqrt{2}$ is read "the square root of 2" or "radical 2." The symbol $\sqrt{}$ is called the *radical sign*, and the number or expression inside the radical sign is called the *radicand*. In $\sqrt{2}$, 2 is the radicand.

The square roots of some numbers are rational, whereas the square roots of other numbers are irrational. The *principal* (or *positive*) *square root* of a number n, written $\sqrt{n}$, is the positive number that, when multiplied by itself, gives n. Whenever we mention the term "square root" in this text, we mean the principal square root. For example,

$$\sqrt{9} = 3 \quad \text{since} \quad 3 \cdot 3 = 9$$
$$\sqrt{36} = 6 \quad \text{since} \quad 6 \cdot 6 = 36$$

Both $\sqrt{9}$ and $\sqrt{36}$ are examples of numbers that are rational numbers because 3 and 6, respectively, are terminating decimal numbers.

We return to the problem faced by Pythagoras: If $c^2 = 2$, then it can be shown that c has a value of $\sqrt{2}$, but what is $\sqrt{2}$ equal to? The $\sqrt{2}$ is an irrational number, and it cannot be expressed as a terminating or repeating decimal number. It can only

---

*The Pythagorean theorem is discussed in more detail in Section 9.3.

be approximated by a decimal number: $\sqrt{2}$ is approximately 1.4142136 (to seven decimal places). Later in this section, we will discuss using a calculator to approximate irrational numbers.

Other irrational numbers include $\sqrt{3}$, $\sqrt{5}$, and $\sqrt{37}$. Another important irrational number used to represent the ratio of a circle's circumference to its diameter is pi, symbolized π. Pi is approximately 3.1415927.

We have discussed procedures for performing the arithmetic operations of addition, subtraction, multiplication, and division with rational numbers. We can perform the same operations with the irrational numbers. Before we can proceed, however, we must understand the numbers called perfect squares. Any number that is the square of a natural number is said to be a *perfect square*. Some perfect squares are shown in the following chart.

Natural numbers	1,	2,	3,	4,	5,	6,...
Squares of the natural numbers	1^2,	2^2,	3^2,	4^2,	5^2,	6^2,...
or perfect squares	1,	4,	9,	16,	25,	36,...

The numbers 1, 4, 9, 16, 25, and 36 are some of the perfect square numbers. Can you determine the next two perfect square numbers? How many perfect square numbers are there? The square root of a perfect square number will be a natural number. For example, $\sqrt{1} = 1$, $\sqrt{4} = 2$, $\sqrt{9} = 3$, $\sqrt{16} = 4$, $\sqrt{25} = 5$, and so on.

The number that multiplies a radical is called the radical's *coefficient*. For example, in $3\sqrt{5}$, the 3 is the coefficient of the radical.

Some irrational numbers can be simplified by determining whether there are any perfect square factors in the radicand. If there are, the following rule can be used to simplify the radical.

Product Rule for Radicals

$$\sqrt{a \cdot b} = \sqrt{a} \cdot \sqrt{b}, \quad a \geq 0, \quad b \geq 0$$

To simplify a radical, write the radical as a product of two radicals. One of the radicals should contain the greatest perfect square that is a factor of the radicand in the original expression. Then simplify the radical containing the perfect square factor.

For example,

$$\sqrt{18} = \sqrt{9 \cdot 2} = \sqrt{9} \cdot \sqrt{2} = 3 \cdot \sqrt{2} = 3\sqrt{2}$$

and

$$\sqrt{75} = \sqrt{25 \cdot 3} = \sqrt{25} \cdot \sqrt{3} = 5 \cdot \sqrt{3} = 5\sqrt{3}$$

Example 1 *Simplifying Radicals*

Simplify.

a) $\sqrt{18}$ b) $\sqrt{80}$

Solution

a) Since 9 is a perfect square factor of 18, we write

$$\sqrt{18} = \sqrt{9 \cdot 2} = \sqrt{9} \cdot \sqrt{2} = 3 \cdot \sqrt{2} = 3\sqrt{2}$$

Since 2 has no perfect square factors, $\sqrt{2}$ cannot be simplified.

b) Since 16 is a perfect square factor of 80, we write

$$\sqrt{80} = \sqrt{16 \cdot 5} = \sqrt{16} \cdot \sqrt{5} = 4 \cdot \sqrt{5} = 4\sqrt{5}$$

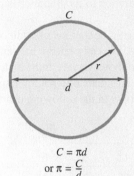
In Example 1(b), you can obtain the correct answer if you start out factoring differently:

$$\sqrt{80} = \sqrt{4 \cdot 20} = \sqrt{4} \cdot \sqrt{20} = 2 \cdot \sqrt{20} = 2\sqrt{20}$$

Note that 20 has 4 as a perfect square factor.

$$2\sqrt{20} = 2\sqrt{4 \cdot 5} = 2 \cdot \sqrt{4} \cdot \sqrt{5} = 2 \cdot 2 \cdot \sqrt{5} = 4\sqrt{5}$$

The second method will eventually give the same answer, but it requires more work. It is best to try to factor out the *largest* perfect square factor from the radicand.

Addition and Subtraction of Irrational Numbers

To add or subtract two or more square roots with the same radicand, add or subtract their coefficients while keeping the common radicand. The answer is the sum or difference of the coefficients multiplied by the common radical.

Example 2 *Adding and Subtracting Radicals with the Same Radicand*

Simplify.

a) $3\sqrt{2} + 7\sqrt{2}$ b) $5\sqrt{7} - 3\sqrt{7} + \sqrt{7}$

Solution

a) $3\sqrt{2} + 7\sqrt{2} = (3 + 7)\sqrt{2} = 10\sqrt{2}$

b) $5\sqrt{7} - 3\sqrt{7} + \sqrt{7} = (5 - 3 + 1)\sqrt{7} = 3\sqrt{7}$

Note that $\sqrt{7} = 1\sqrt{7}$. ∎

Example 3 *Subtracting Radicals with Different Radicands*

Simplify $5\sqrt{3} - \sqrt{12}$.

Solution These radicals cannot be subtracted in their present form because they contain different radicands. When that occurs, determine whether one or more of the radicals can be simplified so that they have the same radicand.

$$
\begin{aligned}
5\sqrt{3} - \sqrt{12} &= 5\sqrt{3} - \sqrt{4 \cdot 3} \\
&= 5\sqrt{3} - \sqrt{4} \cdot \sqrt{3} \\
&= 5\sqrt{3} - 2\sqrt{3} \\
&= (5 - 2)\sqrt{3} = 3\sqrt{3}
\end{aligned}
$$
∎

Multiplication of Irrational Numbers

When multiplying irrational numbers, we again make use of the product rule for radicals, as introduced on page 245. After the radicands are multiplied, simplify the remaining radical when possible.

Example 4 *Multiplying Radicals*

Simplify.

a) $\sqrt{2} \cdot \sqrt{8}$ b) $\sqrt{5} \cdot \sqrt{11}$ c) $\sqrt{10} \cdot \sqrt{15}$

Solution

a) $\sqrt{2} \cdot \sqrt{8} = \sqrt{2 \cdot 8} = \sqrt{16} = 4$ b) $\sqrt{5} \cdot \sqrt{11} = \sqrt{5 \cdot 11} = \sqrt{55}$

c) $\sqrt{10} \cdot \sqrt{15} = \sqrt{10 \cdot 15} = \sqrt{150} = \sqrt{25 \cdot 6} = \sqrt{25} \cdot \sqrt{6} = 5\sqrt{6}$ ∎

Division of Irrational Numbers

To divide irrational numbers, use the following rule. After performing the division, simplify when possible.

Quotient Rule for Radicals

$$\frac{\sqrt{a}}{\sqrt{b}} = \sqrt{\frac{a}{b}}, \quad a \geq 0, \quad b > 0$$

Example **5**   *Dividing Radicals*

Divide.

a) $\dfrac{\sqrt{8}}{\sqrt{2}}$ b) $\dfrac{\sqrt{96}}{\sqrt{2}}$

Solution

a) $\dfrac{\sqrt{8}}{\sqrt{2}} = \sqrt{\dfrac{8}{2}} = \sqrt{4} = 2$

b) $\dfrac{\sqrt{96}}{\sqrt{2}} = \sqrt{\dfrac{96}{2}} = \sqrt{48} = \sqrt{16 \cdot 3} = \sqrt{16} \cdot \sqrt{3} = 4\sqrt{3}$

Rationalizing the Denominator

A denominator of a fraction is *rationalized* when it contains no radical expressions. To rationalize a denominator that contains only a square root, multiply both the numerator and denominator of the fraction by a number that will result in the radicand in the denominator becoming a perfect square. (This action is the equivalent of multiplying the fraction by 1 because the value of the fraction does not change.) Then simplify the fractions when possible.

Example **6**   *Rationalizing the Denominator*

Rationalize the denominator of the following.

a) $\dfrac{5}{\sqrt{2}}$ b) $\dfrac{5}{\sqrt{12}}$ c) $\dfrac{\sqrt{5}}{\sqrt{10}}$

Solution

a) Multiply the numerator and denominator by a number that will make the radicand in the denominator a perfect square.

$$\frac{5}{\sqrt{2}} = \frac{5}{\sqrt{2}} \cdot \frac{\sqrt{2}}{\sqrt{2}} = \frac{5\sqrt{2}}{\sqrt{4}} = \frac{5\sqrt{2}}{2}$$

Note that the 2's in the answer cannot be divided out because one 2 is a radicand and the other is not.

b) $\dfrac{5}{\sqrt{12}} = \dfrac{5}{\sqrt{12}} \cdot \dfrac{\sqrt{3}}{\sqrt{3}} = \dfrac{5\sqrt{3}}{\sqrt{36}} = \dfrac{5\sqrt{3}}{6}$

You could have obtained the same answer to this problem by multiplying both the numerator and denominator by $\sqrt{12}$ and then simplifying. Try to do so now.

c) Write $\dfrac{\sqrt{5}}{\sqrt{10}}$ as $\sqrt{\dfrac{5}{10}}$ and reduce the fraction to obtain $\sqrt{\dfrac{1}{2}}$. By the quotient rule

for radicals, $\sqrt{\dfrac{1}{2}} = \dfrac{\sqrt{1}}{\sqrt{2}}$ or $\dfrac{1}{\sqrt{2}}$. Now rationalize the denominator of $\dfrac{1}{\sqrt{2}}$.

$$\frac{1}{\sqrt{2}} = \frac{1}{\sqrt{2}} \cdot \frac{\sqrt{2}}{\sqrt{2}} = \frac{\sqrt{2}}{2}$$

Estimating Square Roots Without a Calculator

Consider the irrational number $\sqrt{17}$. The radicand 17 is between the two perfect squares 16 and 25. Since $\sqrt{16} = 4$ and $\sqrt{25} = 5$, we can reason that $\sqrt{17}$ is between 4 and 5. We summarize this discussion as follows.

$$16 < 17\ \ < 25$$
$$\sqrt{16} < \sqrt{17} < \sqrt{25}$$
$$4 < \sqrt{17} < 5$$

Furthermore, since 17 is closer to 16 than it is to 25, we can further estimate that $\sqrt{17}$ is closer to 4 than it is to 5. In other words, $\sqrt{17}$ is between 4 and 4.5.

Example 7 *Estimating Square Roots*

The following diagram is a sketch of a 16-in. ruler marked using $\dfrac{1}{2}$ inches.

Indicate between which two adjacent ruler marks each of the following irrational numbers will fall.
a) $\sqrt{7}$ b) $\sqrt{89}$

Solution

a) $4 < 7\ \ < 9$
$$\sqrt{4} < \sqrt{7} < \sqrt{9}$$
$$2 < \sqrt{7} < 3$$

Furthermore, since 7 is closer to 9 than it is to 4, $\sqrt{7}$ is closer to 3 than it is to 2. Thus, $\sqrt{7}$ is between 2.5 and 3.

b) $81 < 89\ \ < 100$
$$\sqrt{81} < \sqrt{89} < \sqrt{100}$$
$$9 < \sqrt{89} < 10$$

Furthermore, since 89 is closer to 81 than it is to 100, $\sqrt{89}$ is closer to 9 than it is to 10. Thus, $\sqrt{89}$ is between 9 and 9.5.

Approximating Square Roots on a Scientific Calculator

Consider the irrational number the square root of two. We use the symbol $\sqrt{2}$ to represent the *exact value* of this number. Although exact values are important, approximations are also important, especially when working with application problems. We can use a scientific calculator to obtain approximations for square roots. Scientific calculators generally have one of the following square root keys:[*]

$\boxed{\sqrt{\ \ }}$ or $\boxed{\sqrt{x}}$

---

[*]If your calculator has the $\sqrt{\ }$ symbol printed *above* the key instead of on the face of the key, you can access the square root function by first pressing the "2nd" or the "inverse" key.

For simplicity, we will refer to the square root key with the $\boxed{\sqrt{}}$ symbol. To approximate $\sqrt{2}$, perform the following keystrokes:

$$\boxed{2} \quad \boxed{\sqrt{}}$$

or, depending on your model of calculator, you may have to do the following:

$$\boxed{\sqrt{}} \quad \boxed{2} \quad \boxed{\text{ENTER}}$$

The display on your calculator may read 1.414213562. Your calculator may display more or fewer digits. It is important to realize that 1.414213562 is a rational number *approximation* for the irrational number $\sqrt{2}$. The symbol $\approx$ means *is approximately equal to,* and we write

$$\sqrt{2} \approx 1.414213562$$

$\qquad\qquad\qquad \uparrow \qquad\qquad\qquad\qquad \uparrow$

Exact value (irrational number)   Approximation (rational number)

Example 8 Approximating Square Roots

Use a scientific calculator to approximate the following square roots. Round each answer to two decimal places.

a) $\sqrt{7}$ b) $\sqrt{89}$

Solution

a) $\sqrt{7} \approx 2.65$ b) $\sqrt{89} \approx 9.43$

Note that these approximations confirm the estimates that were made in Example 7. ∎

SECTION 5.4   *Exercises*

Warm Up Exercises

In Exercises 1–8, fill in the blanks with an appropriate word, phrase, or symbol(s).

1. A real number whose decimal representation is a nonterminating, nonrepeating decimal number is known as a(n) _____ number.

2. The symbol $\sqrt{}$ is called the _____ sign.

3. In the expression $5\sqrt{7}$, the 7 is called the _____.

4. In the expression $5\sqrt{7}$, the 5 is called the radical's _____.

5. The principal (or positive) square root of a number n, written $\sqrt{n}$, is the positive number that, when multiplied by _____, gives n.

6. Any number that is the square of a natural number is called a(n) _____ square.

7. When the denominator of a fraction contains no radical expressions, it is said to be _____.

8. Consider the irrational number the square root of two.

a) We use the symbol $\sqrt{2}$ to represent the _____ value of the number.

b) The number 1.414213562 is a(n) _____ of the number $\sqrt{2}$.

Practice the Skills

In Exercises 9–18, determine whether the number is rational or irrational.

9. $\sqrt{9}$

10. $\sqrt{10}$

11. $\dfrac{2}{3}$

12. $0.212112111\ldots$

13. $3.575775777\ldots$

14. π

15. $\dfrac{22}{7}$

16. 3.14159

17. $3.14159\ldots$

18. $\dfrac{\sqrt{5}}{\sqrt{5}}$

In Exercises 19–26, evaluate the expression.

19. $\sqrt{0}$ **20.** $\sqrt{1}$ **21.** $\sqrt{36}$ **22.** $-\sqrt{121}$

23. $-\sqrt{169}$ **24.** $\sqrt{25}$ **25.** $-\sqrt{81}$ **26.** $-\sqrt{36}$

In Exercises 27–36, classify the number as a member of one or more of the following sets: the rational numbers, the integers, the natural numbers, the irrational numbers.

27. 0

28. -5

29. $\sqrt{9}$

30. $\dfrac{3}{8}$

31. 0.040040004

32. 2.718

33. $-\dfrac{7}{8}$

34. 0.123123123

35. $0.\overline{123}$

36. 0.123112311123…

In Exercises 37–44, simplify the radical.

37. $\sqrt{18}$ **38.** $\sqrt{24}$

39. $\sqrt{45}$ **40.** $\sqrt{50}$

41. $\sqrt{63}$ **42.** $\sqrt{75}$

43. $\sqrt{84}$ **44.** $\sqrt{90}$

In Exercises 45–52, perform the indicated operation.

45. $2\sqrt{3} + 5\sqrt{3}$ **46.** $5\sqrt{3} - 7\sqrt{3}$

47. $3\sqrt{20} - 2\sqrt{45}$ **48.** $2\sqrt{18} - 3\sqrt{50}$

49. $4\sqrt{12} - 7\sqrt{27}$ **50.** $2\sqrt{7} + 5\sqrt{28}$

51. $5\sqrt{3} + 7\sqrt{12} - 3\sqrt{75}$

52. $\sqrt{63} + 13\sqrt{98} - 5\sqrt{112}$

In Exercises 53–60, perform the indicated operation. Simplify the answer when possible.

53. $\sqrt{2}\sqrt{8}$ **54.** $\sqrt{3}\sqrt{21}$

55. $\sqrt{6}\sqrt{14}$ **56.** $\sqrt{2}\sqrt{10}$

57. $\dfrac{\sqrt{20}}{\sqrt{5}}$ **58.** $\dfrac{\sqrt{125}}{\sqrt{5}}$

59. $\dfrac{\sqrt{72}}{\sqrt{8}}$ **60.** $\dfrac{\sqrt{145}}{\sqrt{5}}$

In Exercises 61–68, rationalize the denominator.

61. $\dfrac{1}{\sqrt{2}}$ **62.** $\dfrac{2}{\sqrt{2}}$

63. $\dfrac{\sqrt{7}}{\sqrt{5}}$ **64.** $\dfrac{\sqrt{2}}{\sqrt{7}}$

65. $\dfrac{\sqrt{20}}{\sqrt{3}}$ **66.** $\dfrac{\sqrt{50}}{\sqrt{14}}$

67. $\dfrac{\sqrt{10}}{\sqrt{6}}$ **68.** $\dfrac{\sqrt{2}}{\sqrt{27}}$

Problem Solving

Approximating Radicals *The following diagram is a sketch of a 16-in. ruler marked using $\frac{1}{2}$ inches.*

In Exercises 69–74, without using a calculator, indicate between which two adjacent ruler marks each of the following irrational numbers will fall. Support your answer by obtaining an approximation with a calculator.

69. $\sqrt{11}$ **70.** $\sqrt{67}$

71. $\sqrt{107}$ in.   **72.** $\sqrt{135}$ in.

73. $\sqrt{170}$ in.   **74.** $\sqrt{200}$ in.

In Exercises 75–80, determine whether the statement is true or false. Rewrite each false statement to make it a true statement. A false statement can be modified in more than one way to be made a true statement.

75. $\sqrt{c}$ is a rational number for any composite number c.

76. $\sqrt{p}$ is a rational number for any prime number p.

77. The sum of any two rational numbers is always a rational number.

78. The product of any two rational numbers is always a rational number.

79. The product of an irrational and a rational number is always an irrational number.

80. The product of any two irrational numbers is always an irrational number.

In Exercises 81–84, give an example to show that the stated case can occur.

81. The sum of two irrational numbers may be an irrational number.

82. The sum of two irrational numbers may be a rational number.

83. The product of two irrational numbers may be an irrational number.

84. The product of two irrational numbers may be a rational number.

85. *Height of Boys* The median height of boys less than 5 years old can be estimated using the formula $H = 2.9\sqrt{x} + 20.1$, where H is the height in inches and x is the boys' age in months. Estimate the median height of boys who are 30 months old. Round your answer to the nearest tenth of an inch.

86. *A Swinging Pendulum* The time T required for a pendulum to swing back and forth may be found by the formula

$$T = 2\pi\sqrt{\frac{l}{g}}$$

where l is the length of the pendulum and g is the acceleration of gravity. Determine the time in seconds for the pendulum to swing back and forth if $l = 35$ cm and $g = 980$ cm/sec^2. Round your answer to the nearest tenth of a second.

87. *Estimating Speed of a Vehicle* The speed that a vehicle was traveling, s, in miles per hour, when the brakes were first applied, can be estimated using the formula $s = \sqrt{\dfrac{d}{0.04}}$ where d is the length of the vehicle's skid marks, in feet.

a) Estimate the speed of a car that made skid marks 4 ft long.

b) Estimate the speed of a car that made skid marks 16 ft long.

c) Estimate the speed of a car that made skid marks 64 ft long.

d) Estimate the speed of a car that made skid marks 256 ft long.

88. *Dropping an Object* The formula $t = \dfrac{\sqrt{d}}{4}$ can be used to estimate the time, t, in seconds it takes for an object dropped to travel d feet.

a) Estimate the time it takes for an object to drop 100 ft.

b) Estimate the time it takes for an object to drop 400 ft.

c) Estimate the time it takes for an object to drop 900 ft.

d) Estimate the time it takes for an object to drop 1600 ft.

Concept/Writing Exercises

89. Without doing any calculations, determine whether $\sqrt{2} = 1.414$.

90. Without doing any calculations, determine whether $\sqrt{17} = 4.123$.

91. The number π is an irrational number. Often the values 3.14 or $\frac{22}{7}$ are used for π. Does π equal either 3.14 or $\frac{22}{7}$?

92. Give an example to show that $\sqrt{a + b} \neq \sqrt{a} + \sqrt{b}$.

93. Give an example to show that $\sqrt{a \cdot b} = \sqrt{a} \cdot \sqrt{b}$.

94. Give an example to show that for $b \neq 0$, $\sqrt{\dfrac{a}{b}} = \dfrac{\sqrt{a}}{\sqrt{b}}$.

Challenge Problems/Group Activities

95. a) Is $\sqrt{0.04}$ rational or irrational? Explain.

b) Is $\sqrt{0.7}$ rational or irrational? Explain.

96. One way to find a rational number between two distinct rational numbers is to add the two distinct rational numbers and divide by 2. Do you think that this method will work for finding an irrational number between two distinct irrational numbers? Explain.

Recreational Mathematics

97. *More Four 4's* In the *Recreational Mathematics* box on page 225 and in Exercise 82 on page 229, we introduced some of the basic rules of the game Four 4's. We now expand our operations to include square roots. For example, one way to obtain the whole number 8 is $\sqrt{4} + \sqrt{4} + \sqrt{4} + \sqrt{4} = 2 + 2 + 2 + 2 = 8$. Using at least one square root of 4, $\sqrt{4}$, play Four 4's to obtain the following whole numbers:

a) 11

b) 13

c) 14

d) 18

Internet/Research Activities

In Exercises 98 and 99, references include history of mathematics books, encyclopedias, and Internet Web sites.

98. Write a report on the history of the development of the irrational numbers.

99. Write a report on the history of pi. In your report, indicate when the symbol π was first used and list the first 10 digits of π.

SECTION 5.5 Real Numbers and Their Properties

▲ *Real number properties are often learned as we learn arithmetic facts.*

Evaluate $10 + 5$ and then evaluate $5 + 10$. Evaluate 10×5 and then evaluate 5×10. Evaluate $10 - 5$ and then evaluate $5 - 10$. Finally, evaluate $10 \div 5$ and then evaluate $5 \div 10$. You will notice that $10 + 5 = 5 + 10$ and that $10 \times 5 = 5 \times 10$. On the other hand, $10 - 5 \neq 5 - 10$ and $10 \div 5 \neq 5 \div 10$. These simple examples demonstrate a certain property that holds for addition and multiplication, but not for subtraction and division. In this section, we will study the set of *real* numbers and their properties.

Why *This is Important* Understanding the properties of real numbers is vital to learning algebra and many other areas of mathematics.

Now that we have discussed both the rational and irrational numbers, we can discuss the real numbers and the properties of the real number system. The union of the rational numbers and the irrational numbers is the *set of real numbers*, symbolized by $\mathbb{R}$.

Figure 5.8 illustrates the relationship among various sets of numbers. It shows that the natural numbers are a subset of the whole numbers, the integers, the rational numbers, and the real numbers. For example, since the number 3 is a natural or counting number, it is also a whole number, an integer, a rational number, and a real number. Since the rational number $\frac{1}{4}$ is outside the set of integers, it is not an integer, a whole number, or a natural number. The number $\frac{1}{4}$ is a real number, however, as is the irrational number $\sqrt{2}$. Note that the real numbers are the union of the rational numbers and the irrational numbers.

Did You Know?

An Important Number

Some years ago, a group of French mathematicians who worked under the collective pseudonym "Monsieur Nicholas Bourbaki" embarked on the development of an encyclopedic description of all mathematics. They devoted 200 pages simply to introduce the innocent-looking concept, the number 1.

Figure 5.8

The relationship between the various sets of numbers in the real number system can also be illustrated with a tree diagram, as in Fig. 5.9 on page 253.

Daniel Tammet

MATHEMATICS TODAY

Brain Man

In a segment of *60 Minutes* on January 29, 2007, Morley Safer interviewed Daniel Tammet, who has a mysterious disorder of the brain called savant syndrome. Tammet is called "Brain Man" in his native England. Unlike most savants, however, he has no obvious mental disability, and most important to scientists, he can describe his own thought process. In a period of a few weeks before he appeared on *60 Minutes*, Tammet memorized 23,514 decimal digits of pi. He recited them at Oxford University; it took more than 5 hours, and he made no mistakes. Tammet can also perform complicated calculations, such as 31^4, instantly. He has developed a rare crossing of the senses called synesthesia. Tammet said, "I see numbers in my head as colors, shapes, and textures." For example, when Daniel says he sees pi and does instant computations, he says he is not calculating, but, rather, says the answer appears to him as a landscape of colorful shapes. Tammet is working with scientists at the California Center for Brain Study, who are trying to unlock the secrets of the brain.

Why *This is Important* By learning how the human brain works, scientists can develop better methods of education—especially for those with learning disabilities.

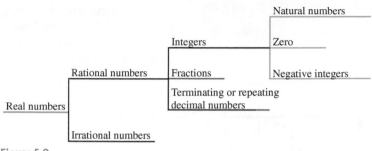

Figure 5.9

Figure 5.9 shows that, for example, the natural numbers are a subset of the integers, the rational numbers, and the real numbers. We can also see, for example, the natural numbers, zero, and the negative integers together form the integers.

Properties of the Real Number System

We are now prepared to consider the properties of the real number system. The first property we will discuss is *closure*.

Definition: Closure

If an operation is performed on any two elements of a set and the result is an element of the set, we say that the set has **closure** or is **closed** under that given operation.

Is the sum of any two natural numbers a natural number? The answer is yes. Thus, we say that the natural numbers are closed under the operation of addition.

Are the natural numbers closed under the operation of subtraction? If we subtract one natural number from another natural number, must the difference always be a natural number? The answer is no. For example, $3 - 5 = -2$, and -2 is not a natural number. Therefore, the natural numbers are not closed under the operation of subtraction.

Example 1 *Closure of Sets*

Determine whether the set of whole numbers is closed under the operations of (a) multiplication and (b) division.

Solution

a) If we multiply any two whole numbers, will the product always be a whole number? You may want to try multiplying several whole numbers. You will see that yes, the product of any two whole numbers is a whole number. Thus, the set of whole numbers is closed under the operation of multiplication.

b) If we divide any two whole numbers, will the quotient always be a whole number? The answer is no. For example $1 \div 2 = \frac{1}{2}$, and $\frac{1}{2}$ is not a whole number. Therefore, the set of whole numbers is not closed under the operation of division. ∎

Next we will discuss three important properties: the commutative property, the associative property, and the distributive property. A knowledge of these properties is essential for the understanding of algebra. We begin with the commutative property.

Commutative Property

Addition	Multiplication
$a + b = b + a$	$a \cdot b = b \cdot a$

for any real numbers a and b.

KenKen

Like Sudoku and Kakuro (see the *Recreational Mathematics* boxes on page 97 and page 134), KenKen is a puzzle that requires logic. However, KenKen® also requires you to use arithmetic facts. To play KenKen®, fill in the blank squares with the digits 1 through the number of rows or columns contained in the puzzle. For example, the puzzle above has 4 rows and 4 columns; therefore, you fill in the blank squares with the digits 1 through 4. Like Sudoku, you are not allowed to repeat a digit in any row or column. The heavily outlined sets of squares are called cages. The numbers placed in each cage must combine, *in any order*, to produce the given number using the given mathematical operation. For example, the cage in the upper left-hand corner of the puzzle above must contain two digits whose product is 8. The cage in the upper right-hand corner must contain two digits whose sum is 4. Cages with just one box should be filled in with the given number in the top corner. A number can be repeated within a cage as long as it is not in the same row or column. For more information and more puzzles, see www.kenken.com. Complete the above puzzle.

The solution to the above puzzle can be found in the answer section in the back of this book. For an additional puzzle, see Exercise 84 on page 258.

Note: KenKen® is a registered trademark of Nextoy, LLC. Puzzle content © 2011 KenKen Puzzle LLC. All rights reserved.

The commutative property states that the *order* in which two numbers are added or multiplied is not important. For example, $4 + 5 = 5 + 4 = 9$ and $3 \cdot 6 = 6 \cdot 3 = 18$. Note that the commutative property does not hold for the operations of subtraction or division. For example,

$$4 - 7 \neq 7 - 4 \quad \text{and} \quad 9 \div 3 \neq 3 \div 9$$

Now we introduce the associative property.

Associative Property

Addition	**Multiplication**
$(a + b) + c = a + (b + c)$	$(a \cdot b) \cdot c = a \cdot (b \cdot c)$

for any real numbers a, b, and c.

The associative property states that when adding or multiplying three real numbers, we may place parentheses around any two adjacent numbers. The result is the same regardless of the placement of parentheses. For example,

$$(3 + 4) + 5 = 3 + (4 + 5) \quad (3 \cdot 4) \cdot 5 = 3 \cdot (4 \cdot 5)$$
$$7 + 5 = 3 + 9 \qquad\qquad 12 \cdot 5 = 3 \cdot 20$$
$$12 = 12 \qquad\qquad\qquad 60 = 60$$

The associative property does not hold for the operations of subtraction or division. For example,

$$(10 - 6) - 2 \neq 10 - (6 - 2) \quad \text{and} \quad (27 \div 9) \div 3 \neq 27 \div (9 \div 3)$$

Note the difference between the commutative property and the associative property. The commutative property involves a change in *order*, whereas the associative property involves a change in *grouping* (or the *association* of numbers that are grouped together).

Another property of the real numbers is the distributive property of multiplication over addition.

Distributive Property of Multiplication Over Addition

$$a \cdot (b + c) = a \cdot b + a \cdot c$$

for any real numbers a, b, and c.

For example, if $a = 3$, $b = 4$, and $c = 5$, then

$$3 \cdot (4 + 5) = (3 \cdot 4) + (3 \cdot 5)$$
$$3 \cdot 9 = 12 + 15$$
$$27 = 27$$

This result indicates that, when using the distributive property, you may either add first and then multiply or multiply first and then add. Note that the distributive property involves two operations, addition and multiplication. Although positive integers were used in the example, any real numbers could have been used.

We frequently use the commutative, associative, and distributive properties without realizing that we are doing so. To add $13 + 4 + 6$, we may add the $4 + 6$ first to get 10. To this sum we then add 13 to get 23. Here we have done the equivalent of placing parentheses around the $4 + 6$. We can do so because of the associative property of addition.

To multiply 102×11 in our heads, we might multiply $100 \times 11 = 1100$ and $2 \times 11 = 22$ and add these two products to get 1122. We are permitted to do so because of the distributive property.

$$102 \times 11 = (100 + 2) \times 11 = (100 \times 11) + (2 \times 11)$$

$$= 1100 + 22 = 1122$$

Example 2 *Identifying Properties of Real Numbers*

Name the property illustrated.

a) $2 + 5 = 5 + 2$

b) $(x + 3) + 5 = x + (3 + 5)$

c) $4 \cdot (3 \cdot y) = (4 \cdot 3) \cdot y$

d) $9(w + 3) = 9 \cdot w + 9 \cdot 3$

e) $5 + (z + 3) = 5 + (3 + z)$

f) $(2p) \cdot 5 = 5 \cdot (2p)$

Solution

a) Commutative property of addition

b) Associative property of addition

c) Associative property of multiplication

d) Distributive property of multiplication over addition

e) The only change between the left and right sides of the equal sign is the order of the z and 3 within the parentheses. The order is changed from $z + 3$ to $3 + z$ using the commutative property of addition.

f) The order of 5 and $(2p)$ is changed by using the commutative property of multiplication. ∎

Example 3 *Simplifying by Using the Distributive Property*

Simplify.

a) $5(2 + \sqrt{3})$ b) $\sqrt{7}(4 + \sqrt{2})$

Solution

a) $5(2 + \sqrt{3}) = (5 \cdot 2) + (5 \cdot \sqrt{3})$

$$= 10 + 5\sqrt{3}$$

b) $\sqrt{7}(4 + \sqrt{2}) = (\sqrt{7} \cdot 4) + \sqrt{7} \cdot \sqrt{2}$

$$= 4\sqrt{7} + \sqrt{14}$$

Note that $\sqrt{7} \cdot 4$ is written $4\sqrt{7}$ ∎

Example 4 *Distributive Property*

Use the distributive property to multiply $2(x + 5)$. Then simplify the result.

Solution $2(x + 5) = 2 \cdot x + 2 \cdot 5$

$$= 2x + 10$$ ∎

Example 5 *Name the Property Used*

Name the property used to go from step to step when simplifying the expression.

a) $3(a + 2) + 5 = (3 \cdot a + 3 \cdot 2) + 5$

$$= (3a + 6) + 5$$

b) $= 3a + (6 + 5)$

$$= 3a + 11$$

Solution

a) In this step we rewrote $3(a + 2)$ as $(3 \cdot a + 3 \cdot 2)$, which we then simplified to $(3a + 6)$. This is an example of the *distributive property*.

b) In this step we rewrote $(3a + 6) + 5$ as $3a + (6 + 5)$, which we then simplified to $(3a + 11)$.

This is an example of the *associative property of addition*.   ∎

We summarize the properties mentioned in this section as follows, where a, b, and c are any real numbers.

The Properties of Real Numbers

Commutative property of addition	$a + b = b + a$
Commutative property of multiplication	$a \cdot b = b \cdot a$
Associative property of addition	$(a + b) + c = a + (b + c)$
Associative property of multiplication	$(a \cdot b) \cdot c = a \cdot (b \cdot c)$
Distributive property of multiplication over addition	$a \cdot (b + c) = a \cdot b + a \cdot c$

SECTION 5.5   *Exercises*

Warm Up Exercises

In Exercises 1–8, fill in the blanks with an appropriate word, phrase, or symbol(s).

1. The union of the rational numbers and the irrational numbers is the set of _____ numbers.

2. The symbol used to represent the set of real numbers is _____.

3. If an operation is performed on any two elements of a set and the result is still an element of the set, we say that the set is _____ under that given operation.

4. The equation $2 + 3 = 3 + 2$ demonstrates the _____ property of addition.

5. The equation $4 \cdot 5 = 5 \cdot 4$ demonstrates the _____ property of multiplication.

6. The equation $(2 + 3) + 4 = 2 + (3 + 4)$ demonstrates the _____ property of addition.

7. The equation $(5 \cdot 6) \cdot 7 = 5 \cdot (6 \cdot 7)$ demonstrates the _____ property of multiplication.

8. The equation $2 \cdot (3 + 4) = 2 \cdot 3 + 2 \cdot 4$ demonstrates the _____ property of multiplication over addition.

Practice the Skills

In Exercises 9–12, determine whether the natural numbers are closed under the given operation.

9. Addition

10. Division

11. Subtraction

12. Multiplication

In Exercises 13–16, determine whether the integers are closed under the given operation.

13. Division

14. Addition

15. Multiplication

16. Subtraction

In Exercises 17–20, determine whether the rational numbers are closed under the given operation.

17. Addition

18. Subtraction

19. Division

20. Multiplication

In Exercises 21–24, determine whether the irrational numbers are closed under the given operation.

21. Multiplication

22. Addition

23. Subtraction

24. Division

In Exercises 25–28, determine whether the real numbers are closed under the given operation.

25. Addition   **26.** Subtraction

27. Division   **28.** Multiplication

29. Does $(5 + x) + 6 = (x + 5) + 6$ illustrate the commutative property or the associative property? Explain your answer.

30. Does $(x + 5) + 6 = x + (5 + 6)$ illustrate the commutative property or the associative property? Explain your answer.

31. Give an example to show that the commutative property of addition may be true for the negative integers.

32. Give an example to show that the commutative property of multiplication may be true for the negative integers.

33. Does the commutative property hold for the integers under the operation of subtraction? Give an example to support your answer.

34. Does the commutative property hold for the rational numbers under the operation of division? Give an example to support your answer.

35. Give an example to show that the associative property of addition may be true for the negative integers.

36. Give an example to show that the associative property of multiplication may be true for the negative integers.

37. Does the associative property hold for the integers under the operation of division? Give an example to support your answer.

38. Does the associative property hold for the integers under the operation of subtraction? Give an example to support your answer.

39. Does the associative property hold for the real numbers under the operation of division? Give an example to support your answer.

40. Does $a + (b \cdot c) = (a + b) \cdot (a + c)$? Give an example to support your answer.

In Exercises 41–52, state the name of the property illustrated.

41. $3(y + 5) = 3 \cdot y + 3 \cdot 5$

42. $6 + 7 = 7 + 6$

43. $(7 \cdot 8) \cdot 9 = 7 \cdot (8 \cdot 9)$

44. $c + d = d + c$

45. $(24 + 7) + 3 = 24 + (7 + 3)$

46. $4 \cdot (11 \cdot x) = (4 \cdot 11) \cdot x$

47. $\sqrt{3} \cdot 7 = 7 \cdot \sqrt{3}$

48. $\dfrac{3}{8} + \left(\dfrac{1}{8} + \dfrac{3}{2}\right) = \left(\dfrac{3}{8} + \dfrac{1}{8}\right) + \dfrac{3}{2}$

49. $-1(x + 4) = (-1) \cdot x + (-1) \cdot 4$

50. $(r + s) \cdot t = (r \cdot t) + (s \cdot t)$

51. $(r + s) + t = t + (r + s)$

52. $g \cdot (h + i) = (h + i) \cdot g$

In Exercises 53–64, use the distributive property to multiply. Then, if possible, simplify the resulting expression.

53. $4(z + 1)$ **54.** $-1(a + b)$

55. $-\dfrac{3}{4}(x - 12)$ **56.** $-x(-y + z)$

57. $6\left(\dfrac{x}{2} + \dfrac{2}{3}\right)$ **58.** $24\left(\dfrac{x}{3} - \dfrac{1}{8}\right)$

59. $32\left(\dfrac{1}{16}x - \dfrac{1}{32}\right)$ **60.** $15\left(\dfrac{2}{3}x - \dfrac{4}{5}\right)$

61. $\sqrt{2}(\sqrt{8} - \sqrt{2})$ **62.** $-3(2 - \sqrt{3})$

63. $5(\sqrt{2} + \sqrt{3})$ **64.** $\sqrt{5}(\sqrt{15} - \sqrt{20})$

In Exercises 65–70, name the property used to go from step to step. You only need to name the properties indicated by an a), b), c), or d). For example, in Exercise 65, you need to supply an answer for part a), and an answer to go from the second step of part a) to part b).

65. a) $4(x + 1) + 6 = (4 \cdot x + 4 \cdot 1) + 6$
$= (4x + 4) + 6$

   b) $= 4x + (4 + 6)$
$= 4x + 10$

66. a) $2(b + 4) + 1 = (2 \cdot b + 2 \cdot 4) + 1$
$= (2b + 8) + 1$

   b) $= 2b + (8 + 1)$
$= 2b + 9$

67. a) $7(k + 1) + 2k = (7 \cdot k + 7 \cdot 1) + 2k$
$= (7k + 7) + 2k$

   b) $= 7k + (7 + 2k)$

   c) $= 7k + (2k + 7)$

   d) $= (7k + 2k) + 7$
$= 9k + 7$

68. a) $11(h + 6) + 5h = (11 \cdot h + 11 \cdot 6) + 5h$
$\qquad\qquad\qquad\quad = (11h + 66) + 5h$

b) $\qquad\qquad\quad = 11h + (66 + 5h)$

c) $\qquad\qquad\quad = 11h + (5h + 66)$

d) $\qquad\qquad\quad = (11h + 5h) + 66$
$\qquad\qquad\qquad = 16h + 66$

69. a) $9 + 2(t + 3) + 7t = 9 + (2 \cdot t + 2 \cdot 3) + 7t$
$\qquad\qquad\qquad\qquad = 9 + (2t + 6) + 7t$

b) $\qquad\qquad\qquad = 9 + (6 + 2t) + 7t$

c) $\qquad\qquad\qquad = (9 + 6) + 2t + 7t$
$\qquad\qquad\qquad\quad = 15 + 9t$

d) $\qquad\qquad\qquad = 9t + 15$

70. a) $7 + 5(s + 4) + 3s = 7 + (5 \cdot s + 5 \cdot 4) + 3s$
$\qquad\qquad\qquad\qquad = 7 + (5s + 20) + 3s$

b) $\qquad\qquad\qquad = 7 + (20 + 5s) + 3s$

c) $\qquad\qquad\qquad = (7 + 20) + 5s + 3s$
$\qquad\qquad\qquad\quad = 27 + 8s$

d) $\qquad\qquad\qquad = 8s + 27$

In Exercises 71–74, determine whether the activity can be used to illustrate the commutative property. For the property to hold, the end result must be identical, regardless of the order in which the actions are performed.

71. Feeding your cats and giving your cats water

72. Putting your wallet in your back pocket and putting your keys in your front pocket

73. Washing clothes and drying clothes

74. Turning on a computer and typing a term paper on the computer

In Exercises 75–80, determine whether the activity can be used to illustrate the associative property. For the property to hold, doing the first two actions followed by the third

would produce the same end result as doing the second and third actions followed by the first.

75. Putting batteries in your calculator, pressing the ON key, and pressing the 7 key

76. Filling your car with gas, washing the windshield, and checking the tire pressure

77. Sending a holiday card to your grandmother, sending one to your parents, and sending one to your teacher

78. Mowing the lawn, trimming the bushes, and removing dead limbs from trees

79. Brushing your teeth, washing your face, and combing your hair

80. Cracking an egg, pouring out the egg, and cooking the egg

Challenge Problems/Group Activities

81. Describe two other activities that can be used to illustrate the commutative property (see Exercises 71–74).

82. Describe three other activities that can be used to illustrate the associative property (see Exercises 75–80).

83. Does $0 \div a = a \div 0$ (assume $a \neq 0$)? Explain.

Recreational Math

84. *KenKen* Refer to the *Recreational Mathematics* box on page 254. Complete the following KenKen puzzle.

2	2−	2÷	24×
3−			
	7+		
1−		5+	

85. a) Consider the three words *man eating tiger*. Does (*man eating*) *tiger* mean the same as *man* (*eating tiger*)?

b) Does (*horse riding*) *monkey* mean the same as *horse* (*riding monkey*)?

c) Can you find three other nonassociative word triples?

Internet/Research Activity

86. A set of numbers that was not discussed in this chapter is the set of *complex numbers*. Write a report on complex numbers. Include their relationship to the real numbers.

Rules of Exponents and Scientific Notation

What is the current world population? What is the diameter of an atom? What is the diameter of a galaxy? What is the wavelength of an x-ray? What is the current national federal debt? All these questions have answers that may involve either very large numbers or very small numbers. One way to accurately represent such numbers is with *scientific notation*. In this section, we will study how to use scientific notation when answering questions such as those posed above.

▲ *The diameter of an atom may be given in scientific notation.*

Why *This is Important*   Scientific notation is used in many fields of study, including economics, physics, chemistry, and astronomy. Items such as a hard drive's capacity, measured in gigabytes, can also be represented using scientific notation.

An understanding of exponents is important in solving problems in algebra. In the expression 5^2, the 2 is referred to as the *exponent* and the 5 is referred to as the *base*. We read 5^2 as 5 to the second power, or 5 squared, which means

$$5^2 = \underbrace{5 \cdot 5}_{\text{2 factors of 5}}$$

The number 5 to the third power, or 5 cubed, written 5^3, means

$$5^3 = \underbrace{5 \cdot 5 \cdot 5}_{\text{3 factors of 5}}$$

In general, the number b to the nth power, written b^n, means

$$b^n = \underbrace{b \cdot b \cdot b \cdot \cdots \cdot b}_{n \text{ factors of } b}$$

Example **1**   *Evaluating the Power of a Number*

Evaluate

a) 5^2 b) $(-3)^2$ c) 3^4 d) 1^{1000} e) 1000^1

Solution

a) $5^2 = 5 \cdot 5 = 25$
b) $(-3)^2 = (-3) \cdot (-3) = 9$
c) $3^4 = 3 \cdot 3 \cdot 3 \cdot 3 = 81$
d) $1^{1000} = 1$
   The number 1 multiplied by itself any number of times equals 1.
e) $1000^1 = 1000$
   Any number with an exponent of 1 equals the number itself.   ■

Did You Know?

A Very Large Number

170,141,183,460,469,231,731,687,303,715,884,105,727 is a very large number. How would you read this number? Take a breath.

170 undecillion, 141 decillion, 183 nonillion, 460 octillion, 469 septillion, 231 sextillion, 731 quintillion, 687 quadrillion, 303 trillion, 715 billion, 884 million, 105 thousand, 727.

Often numbers this large can be represented with an approximation involving scientific notation. This number, however, is a prime number, and its exact representation is very important. Mathematicians frequently represent such large numbers by using exponents. Here, another exact, and more efficient, representation of this number is $2^{127} - 1$.

Example **2** *The Importance of Parentheses*

Evaluate.

a) $(-2)^4$ b) -2^4 c) $(-2)^5$ d) -2^5

Solution

a) $(-2)^4 = (-2)(-2)(-2)(-2) = 4(-2)(-2) = -8(-2) = 16$
b) -2^4 means take the opposite of 2^4 or $-1 \cdot 2^4$.
   $-1 \cdot 2^4 = -1 \cdot 2 \cdot 2 \cdot 2 \cdot 2 = -1 \cdot 16 = -16$
c) $(-2)^5 = (-2)(-2)(-2)(-2)(-2) = 4(-2)(-2)(-2) = -8(-2)(-2)$
   $= 16(-2) = -32$
d) $-2^5 = -1 \cdot 2^5 = -1 \cdot 2 \cdot 2 \cdot 2 \cdot 2 \cdot 2 = -1 \cdot 32 = -32$ ■

From Example 2, we can see that $(-x)^n \neq -x^n$, where n is an even natural number.

Rules of Exponents

Now that we know how to evaluate powers of numbers, we can discuss the rules of exponents. Consider

$$2^2 \cdot 2^3 = \underbrace{2 \cdot 2}_{\text{2 factors}} \cdot \underbrace{2 \cdot 2 \cdot 2}_{\text{3 factors}} = 2^5$$

This example illustrates the product rule for exponents.

Product Rule for Exponents
$$a^m \cdot a^n = a^{m+n}$$

Therefore, by using the product rule, $2^2 \cdot 2^3 = 2^{2+3} = 2^5$.

Example **3** *Using the Product Rule for Exponents*

Use the product rule to simplify.

a) $3^3 \cdot 3^2$ b) $5 \cdot 5^3$

Solution

a) $3^3 \cdot 3^2 = 3^{3+2} = 3^5 = 243$
b) $5 \cdot 5^3 = 5^1 \cdot 5^3 = 5^4 = 625$ ■

Consider

$$\frac{2^5}{2^2} = \frac{2 \cdot 2 \cdot 2 \cdot 2 \cdot 2}{2 \cdot 2} = 2 \cdot 2 \cdot 2 = 2^3$$

This example illustrates the quotient rule for exponents.

Quotient Rule for Exponents
$$\frac{a^m}{a^n} = a^{m-n}, \quad a \neq 0$$

Therefore, $\dfrac{2^5}{2^2} = 2^{5-2} = 2^3$.

Example 4 *Using the Quotient Rule for Exponents*

Use the quotient rule to simplify.

a) $\dfrac{3^7}{3^5}$ b) $\dfrac{5^9}{5^5}$

Solution

a) $\dfrac{3^7}{3^5} = 3^{7-5} = 3^2 = 9$ b) $\dfrac{5^9}{5^5} = 5^{9-5} = 5^4 = 625$

Consider $2^3 \div 2^3$. The quotient rule gives

$$\frac{2^3}{2^3} = 2^{3-3} = 2^0$$

But $\dfrac{2^3}{2^3} = \dfrac{8}{8} = 1$. Therefore, 2^0 must equal 1. This example illustrates the zero exponent rule.

Zero Exponent Rule

$$a^0 = 1, \quad a \neq 0$$

Note that 0^0 is not defined by the zero exponent rule.

Example 5 *The Zero Power*

Use the zero exponent rule to simplify. Assume $x \neq 0$.

a) 2^0 b) $(-2)^0$ c) -2^0 d) $(5x)^0$ e) $5x^0$

Solution

a) $2^0 = 1$ b) $(-2)^0 = 1$ c) $-2^0 = -1 \cdot 2^0 = -1 \cdot 1 = -1$
d) $(5x)^0 = 1$ e) $5x^0 = 5 \cdot x^0 = 5 \cdot 1 = 5$

Consider $2^3 \div 2^5$. The quotient rule yields

$$\frac{2^3}{2^5} = 2^{3-5} = 2^{-2}$$

But $\dfrac{2^3}{2^5} = \dfrac{2 \cdot 2 \cdot 2}{2 \cdot 2 \cdot 2 \cdot 2 \cdot 2} = \dfrac{1}{2^2}$. Since $\dfrac{2^3}{2^5}$ equals both 2^{-2} and $\dfrac{1}{2^2}$, then 2^{-2} must equal $\dfrac{1}{2^2}$. This example illustrates the negative exponent rule.

Negative Exponent Rule

$$a^{-m} = \frac{1}{a^m}, \quad a \neq 0$$

Example 6 *Using the Negative Exponent Rule*

Use the negative exponent rule to simplify.

a) 2^{-3} b) 5^{-1}

Solution

a) $2^{-3} = \dfrac{1}{2^3} = \dfrac{1}{8}$ b) $5^{-1} = \dfrac{1}{5^1} = \dfrac{1}{5}$

Consider $(2^3)^2$.

$$(2^3)^2 = (2^3)(2^3) = 2^{3+3} = 2^6$$

This example illustrates the power rule for exponents.

Power Rule for Exponents

$$(a^m)^n = a^{m \cdot n}$$

Thus, $(2^3)^2 = 2^{3 \cdot 2} = 2^6$.

Example 7 *Evaluating a Power Raised to Another Power*

Use the power rule to simplify.
a) $(5^4)^3$ b) $(7^2)^5$

Solution

a) $(5^4)^3 = 5^{4 \cdot 3} = 5^{12}$
b) $(7^2)^5 = 7^{2 \cdot 5} = 7^{10}$

Summary of the Rules of Exponents

$a^m \cdot a^n = a^{m+n}$	Product rule for exponents
$\dfrac{a^m}{a^n} = a^{m-n}, \quad a \neq 0$	Quotient rule for exponents
$a^0 = 1, \quad a \neq 0$	Zero exponent rule
$a^{-m} = \dfrac{1}{a^m}, \quad a \neq 0$	Negative exponent rule
$(a^m)^n = a^{m \cdot n}$	Power rule for exponents

Scientific Notation

Often scientific problems deal with very large and very small numbers. For example, the distance from Earth to the sun is about 93,000,000 miles. The wavelength of a yellow color of light is about 0.0000006 meter. Because working with many zeros is difficult, scientists developed a notation that expresses such numbers with exponents. For example, consider the distance from Earth to the sun, 93,000,000 miles.

$$93{,}000{,}000 = 9.3 \times 10{,}000{,}000$$
$$= 9.3 \times 10^7$$

The wavelength of a yellow color of light is about 0.0000006 meter.

$$0.0000006 = 6.0 \times 0.0000001$$
$$= 6.0 \times 10^{-7}$$

The numbers 9.3×10^7 and 6.0×10^{-7} are written in a form called *scientific notation*. Each number written in scientific notation is written as a number greater than or equal to 1 and less than 10 multiplied by some power of 10.

Some examples of numbers in scientific notation are

$$3.7 \times 10^3, \quad 2.05 \times 10^{-3}, \quad 5.6 \times 10^8, \quad \text{and} \quad 1.00 \times 10^{-5}$$

The following is a procedure for writing a number in scientific notation.

PROCEDURE TO WRITE A NUMBER IN SCIENTIFIC NOTATION

1. Move the decimal point in the original number to the right or left until you obtain a number greater than or equal to 1 and less than 10.

2. Count the number of places you have moved the decimal point to obtain the number in Step 1. If the decimal point was moved to the left, the count is to be considered positive. If the decimal point was moved to the right, the count is to be considered negative.

3. Multiply the number obtained in Step 1 by 10 raised to the count found in Step 2. (Note that the count determined in Step 2 is the exponent on the base 10.)

Example 8 *Converting from Decimal Notation to Scientific Notation*

Write each number in scientific notation.

a) In 2010, the population of the United States was about 309,500,000.

b) In 2010, the population of China was about 1,348,000,000.

c) In 2010, the population of the world was about 6,828,000,000.

d) The diameter of a hydrogen atom nucleus is about 0.0000000000011 millimeter.

e) The wavelength of an x-ray is about 0.000000000492 meter.

Solution

a) $309,500,000 = 3.095 \times 10^8$

b) $1,348,000,000 = 1.348 \times 10^9$

c) $6,828,000,000 = 6.828 \times 10^9$

d) $0.0000000000011 = 1.1 \times 10^{-12}$

e) $0.000000000492 = 4.92 \times 10^{-10}$

To convert from a number given in scientific notation to decimal notation, we reverse the procedure.

PROCEDURE TO CHANGE A NUMBER IN SCIENTIFIC NOTATION TO DECIMAL NOTATION

1. Observe the exponent on the 10.

2. a) If the exponent is positive, move the decimal point in the number to the right the same number of places as the exponent. Adding zeros to the number might be necessary.

   b) If the exponent is negative, move the decimal point in the number to the left the same number of places as the exponent. Adding zeros might be necessary.

Example 9 *Converting from Scientific Notation to Decimal Notation*

Write each number in decimal notation.

a) The average distance from Mars to the sun is about 1.4×10^8 miles.

b) The half-life of uranium-235 is about 4.5×10^9 years.

c) The average grain size in siltstone is about 1.35×10^{-3} inch.

d) A *millimicron* is a unit of measure used for very small distances. One millimicron is about 3.94×10^{-8} inch.

Solution

a) $1.4 \times 10^8 = 140{,}000{,}000$
b) $4.5 \times 10^9 = 4{,}500{,}000{,}000$
c) $1.35 \times 10^{-3} = 0.00135$
d) $3.94 \times 10^{-8} = 0.0000000394$

In scientific journals and books, we occasionally see numbers like 10^{15} and 10^{-6}. We interpret these numbers as 1×10^{15} and 1×10^{-6}, respectively, when converting the numbers to decimal form.

Example 10 *Multiplying Numbers in Scientific Notation*

Multiply $(2.1 \times 10^5)(9 \times 10^{-3})$. Write the answer in scientific notation and in decimal notation.

Solution We begin by rewriting the product so that 2.1 and 9 are multiplied together and the powers of 10 are multiplied together.

$$(2.1 \times 10^5)(9 \times 10^{-3}) = (2.1 \times 9)(10^5 \times 10^{-3})$$
$$= 18.9 \times 10^2$$
$$= 1.89 \times 10^3 \quad \text{Scientific notation}$$
$$= 1890 \quad \text{Decimal notation}$$

Example 11 *Dividing Numbers Using Scientific Notation*

Divide $\dfrac{0.000000000048}{24{,}000{,}000{,}000}$. Write the answer in scientific notation.

Solution First write each number in scientific notation.

$$\frac{0.000000000048}{24{,}000{,}000{,}000} = \frac{4.8 \times 10^{-11}}{2.4 \times 10^{10}} = \left(\frac{4.8}{2.4}\right)\left(\frac{10^{-11}}{10^{10}}\right)$$
$$= 2.0 \times 10^{-11-10}$$
$$= 2.0 \times 10^{-21}$$

Scientific Notation on the Scientific Calculator

One advantage of using scientific notation when working with very large and very small numbers is the ease with which you can perform operations. Performing these operations is even easier with the use of a scientific calculator. Most scientific calculators have a scientific notation key labeled "Exp," "EXP," or "EE." We will refer to the scientific notation key as EXP. The following keystrokes reading downward can be used to enter the number 4.3×10^6.

Keystroke(s)	Calculator display
4.3	4.3
EXP	4.3^{00}
6	4.3^{06}

Your calculator may have some variations to the display shown here. The display 4.3^{06} means 4.3×10^6. We now will use our calculators to perform some computations using scientific notation.

Example 12 *Use Scientific Notation on a Calculator to Find a Product*

Multiply $(4.3 \times 10^6)(2 \times 10^{-4})$ using a scientific calculator. Write the answer in decimal notation.

Solution Our sequence of keystrokes, reading downward, is as follows:

Keystroke(s)	Display	
4.3	4.3	
EXP	4.3^{00}	
6	4.3^{06}	
×	4300000	4.3×10^6 is now entered in the calculator. Most calculators will convert to decimal notation (if the display can show the number)
2	2.	
EXP	2.^{00}	
4	2.^{04}	Enter the positive form of the exponent
+/−	2.$^{-04}$	Make the exponent negative*
=	860.	Press [=] to obtain the answer of 860† ∎

Example 13 *Use Scientific Notation on a Calculator to Find a Quotient*

Divide $\dfrac{0.000000000048}{24,000,000,000}$ using a scientific calculator. Write the answer in scientific notation.

Solution We first rewrite the numerator and denominator using scientific notation. See Example 11.

$$\frac{0.000000000048}{24,000,000,000} = \frac{4.8 \times 10^{-11}}{2.4 \times 10^{10}}$$

Next we use a scientific calculator to perform the computation. The keystrokes are as follows:

4.8 [EXP] 11 [+/−] [÷] 2.4 [EXP] 10 [=]

The display on the calculator is 2.$^{-21}$, which means 2.0×10^{-21}. ∎

Example 14 *U.S. Debt per Person*

On June 18, 2010, the U.S. Department of the Treasury estimated the U.S. federal debt to be about \$13.08 trillion. On this same day, the U.S. Bureau of the Census estimated the U.S. population to be about 309.5 million people. Determine the average debt, per person, by dividing the U.S. federal debt by the U.S. population.

---

*Some calculators will require you to enter the negative sign before entering the exponent.
†Some calculators will display the answer in scientific notation. In this case, the display will show 8.6 ^{02}, which means 8.6×10^2 and equals 860.

> **Solution** We first write the numbers involved using decimal notation. We then convert them to scientific notation.

$$13.08 \text{ trillion} = 13{,}080{,}000{,}000{,}000 = 1.308 \times 10^{13}$$

$$309.5 \text{ million} = 309{,}500{,}000 = 3.095 \times 10^{8}$$

> Now we divide 1.308×10^{13} by 3.095×10^{8}, using a scientific calculator. The keystrokes are

$$1.308 \boxed{\text{EXP}} \; 13 \; \boxed{\div} \; 3.095 \boxed{\text{EXP}} \; 8 \; \boxed{=}$$

> The display then shows 42261.71244. This number indicates that on June 18, 2010, the U.S. government owed about $42,261.71 per man, woman, and child living in the United States. ∎

SECTION 5.6
Exercises

Warm Up Exercises

In Exercises 1–12, fill in the blanks with an appropriate word, phrase, or symbol(s).

1. In the expression 2^3, the 3 is known as the _____.

2. In the expression 2^3, the 2 is known as the _____.

3. The product $x \cdot x \cdot x \cdot x \cdot x$ can also be written as the exponential expression _____.

4. With the product rule for exponents, the expression $x^2 \cdot x^3$ can be simplified to _____.

5. With the quotient rule for exponents, the expression $\dfrac{x^7}{x^4}$ can be simplified to _____.

6. With the zero exponent rule, the expression 7^0 can be simplified to _____.

7. With the negative exponent rule, for $x \neq 0$, the expression x^{-5} can be simplified to _____.

8. With the power rule for exponents, the expression $(x^2)^3$ can be simplified to _____.

9. When written in scientific notation, the number 2013 is _____.

10. When written in scientific notation, the number 0.0034 is _____.

11. When written in decimal notation, the number 5.73×10^{-5} is _____.

12. When written in decimal notation, the number 1.776×10^3 is _____.

Practice the Skills

In Exercises 13–40, evaluate the expression. Assume $x \neq 0$.

13. a) 3^2 b) 2^3

14. a) 2^5 b) 5^2

15. a) $(-5)^2$ b) -5^2

16. a) -3^2 b) $(-3)^2$

17. a) -2^4 b) $(-2)^4$

18. a) $(-3)^4$ b) -3^4

19. a) -4^3 b) $(-4)^3$

20. a) $(-2)^7$ b) -2^7

21. a) $-\left(\dfrac{1}{2}\right)^2$ b) $\left(-\dfrac{1}{2}\right)^2$

22. a) $-\left(\dfrac{1}{2}\right)^3$ b) $\left(-\dfrac{1}{2}\right)^3$

23. a) 100^1 b) 1^{100}

24. a) 2012^1 b) 1^{2012}

25. a) $3^2 \cdot 3^3$ b) $(-3)^2 \cdot (-3)^3$

26. a) $2^3 \cdot 2$ b) $(-2)^3 \cdot (-2)$

27. a) $\dfrac{5^7}{5^5}$ b) $\dfrac{(-5)^7}{(-5)^5}$

28. a) $\dfrac{4^5}{4^2}$ b) $\dfrac{(-4)^5}{(-4)^2}$

29. a) 6^0 b) -6^0

30. a) $(-6)^0$ **b)** $-(-6)^0$

31. a) $(6x)^0$ **b)** $6x^0$

32. a) $-6x^0$ **b)** $(-6x)^0$

33. a) 3^{-3} **b)** 7^{-2}

34. a) 5^{-1} **b)** 2^{-4}

35. a) -9^{-2} **b)** $(-9)^{-2}$

36. a) -5^{-2} **b)** $(-5)^{-2}$

37. a) $(2^2)^3$ **b)** $(2^3)^2$

38. a) $\left[\left(\dfrac{1}{2}\right)^2\right]^3$ **b)** $\left[\left(-\dfrac{1}{2}\right)^2\right]^3$

39. a) $4^3 \cdot 4^{-2}$ **b)** $2^{-2} \cdot 2^{-2}$

40. a) $(-5)^{-2}(-5)^{-2}$ **b)** $(-1)^{-5}(-1)^{-5}$

In Exercises 41–52, express the number in scientific notation.

41. 415,000   **42.** 923,000,000

43. 0.00275   **44.** 0.000034

45. 0.56   **46.** 0.00467

47. 19,000   **48.** 1,260,000,000

49. 0.000186   **50.** 0.0003

51. 0.00000423   **52.** 54,000

In Exercises 53–62, express the number in decimal notation.

53. 4.2×10^4 **54.** 3.9×10^5

55. 1.32×10^{-2} **56.** 4.003×10^7

57. 8.62×10^{-5} **58.** 2.19×10^{-4}

59. 3.12×10^{-1} **60.** 4.6×10^1

61. 9×10^6 **62.** 7.3×10^4

In Exercises 63–72, (a) perform the indicated operation without the use of a calculator and express each answer in decimal notation. (b) Confirm your answer from part (a) by using a scientific calculator to perform the operations. If the calculator displays the answer in scientific notation, convert the answer to decimal notation.

63. $(2 \times 10^3)(3.1 \times 10^2)$ **64.** $(4.9 \times 10^4)(2 \times 10^3)$

65. $(5.1 \times 10^1)(3 \times 10^{-4})$ **66.** $(1.6 \times 10^{-2})(4 \times 10^{-3})$

67. $\dfrac{7.5 \times 10^6}{3 \times 10^4}$ **68.** $\dfrac{5.2 \times 10^7}{4 \times 10^9}$

69. $\dfrac{8.4 \times 10^{-6}}{4 \times 10^{-3}}$ **70.** $\dfrac{25 \times 10^3}{5 \times 10^{-2}}$

71. $\dfrac{4 \times 10^5}{2 \times 10^4}$ **72.** $\dfrac{16 \times 10^3}{8 \times 10^{-3}}$

In Exercises 73–82, (a) perform the indicated operation without the use of a calculator and express each answer in scientific notation. (b) Confirm your answer from part (a) by using a scientific calculator to perform the operations. If the calculator displays the answer in decimal notation, convert the answer to scientific notation.

73. $(1,000,000)(230,000)$

74. $(2,000,000)(0.00025)$

75. $(0.003)(0.00015)$

76. $(230,000)(3000)$

77. $\dfrac{5,600,000}{80,000}$ **78.** $\dfrac{28,000}{0.004}$

79. $\dfrac{0.00004}{200}$ **80.** $\dfrac{0.0012}{0.000006}$

81. $\dfrac{150,000}{0.0005}$ **82.** $\dfrac{24,000}{8,000,000}$

Problem Solving

In Exercises 83–86, list the numbers from smallest to largest.

83. 1.03×10^4; 1.7; 3.6×10^{-3}; 9.8×10^2

84. 8.5×10^{-5}; 8.2×10^3; 1.3×10^{-1}; 6.2×10^4

85. $40,000$; 4.1×10^3; 0.00079; 8.3×10^{-5}

86. $267,000,000$; 3.14×10^7; $1,962,000$; 4.79×10^6

In Exercises 87–97, you may use a scientific calculator to perform the necessary operations.

87. *U.S. Debt per Person: 2006 Versus 2010* In Example 14 on page 265, the U.S. government debt was discussed. It was found that the debt in 2010 was about \$42,261.71 per person. In 2006, the U.S. government debt was about \$8.38 trillion, and the population of the United States was about 299 million.

a) Determine the amount of debt per person in 2006.

b) How much more per person did the U.S. government owe in 2010 than in 2006?

88. *United Kingdom Debt per Person* In 2010, the United Kingdom's government had a debt of about £923 billion (the pound, symbolized, £, is the United Kingdom's unit of currency). The United Kingdom's population in 2010 was about 62.8 million.

a) Determine the amount of debt per person in 2010 for the United Kingdom.

b) In 2010, £1 was worth about \$1.50. Convert the amount found in part (a) to dollars.

89. *U.S. Population* In June 2010, the population of the United States was about 309.5 million people, and the population of the world was about 6.830 billion people. Determine the ratio of the U.S. population to the world's population by dividing the U.S. population by the world's population. Write your answer as a decimal number and round to the nearest thousandth.

90. *China's Population* In June 2010, the population of China was about 1.319 billion people, and the population of the world was about 6.830 billion people. Determine the ratio of China's population to the world's population by dividing China's population by the world's population. Write your answer as a decimal number and round to the nearest thousandth.

91. *New York Population Density* In June 2010, the population of the metropolitan New York area was about 17,800,000 people, and the area was about 8683 square kilometers. Determine the metropolitan New York population density by dividing the population by the area.

92. *Mumbai Population Density* In June 2010, the population of the metropolitan Mumbai, India, area was about 14,350,000 people, and the area was about 484 square kilometers. Determine the metropolitan Mumbai population density by dividing the population by the area.

93. *Gross Domestic Product* The gross domestic product (GDP) of a country is the total national output of goods and services produced within that country. In 2009, the GDP of the United States was about $14.3 trillion, and the U.S. population was about 308 million people. Determine the U.S. GDP per person by dividing the GDP by the population. Round your answer to the nearest whole dollar.

94. *China's GDP* In 2009, the GDP (see Exercise 93) of China was about $4.91 trillion, and the population of China was about 1.335 billion people. Determine China's GDP per person by dividing the GDP by the population. Round your answer to the nearest whole dollar.

95. *Traveling to the Moon* The distance from Earth to the moon is approximately 239,000 mi. If a spacecraft travels at a speed of 20,000 mph, how many hours would the spacecraft need to travel from Earth to the moon? Use distance = rate × time.

▲ *The Moon*

96. *Traveling to Jupiter* The distance from Earth to the planet Jupiter is approximately 4.5×10^8 mi. If a spacecraft traveled at a speed of 25,000 mph, how many hours would the spacecraft need to travel from Earth to Jupiter? Use distance = rate × time.

97. *Traveling to Proxima Centauri* The star closest in distance to our own sun is Proxima Centauri. The distance from Earth to Proxima Centauri is approximately 2.5×10^{13} miles. If a spacecraft travels at a speed of 20,000 mph, how many hours would the spacecraft need to travel to Proxima Centauri? Use distance = rate × time and write your answer in scientific notation.

98. *Computer Speed* As of June 22, 2010, the fastest computer in the world was the Cray Jaguar located at Oak Ridge National Laboratory. This computer is capable of performing about 1.75 quadrillion (1.75×10^{15}) calculations per second. At this rate, how long would it take to perform a task requiring 7.6×10^{65} calculations? Write your answer in scientific notation.

▲ *The Cray Jaguar computer*

99. *1950 Niagara Treaty* The 1950 Niagara Treaty between the United States and Canada requires that during the tourist season a minimum of 100,000 cubic feet of water per second (ft³/sec) flow over Niagara Falls (another 130,000–160,000 ft³/sec are diverted for power generation). Find the minimum amount of water that will flow over the falls in a 24-hour period during the tourist season. Write your answer in scientific notation.

▲ *Niagara Falls*

100. *Bucket Full of Molecules* A drop of water contains about 40 billion molecules. If a bucket has half a million drops of water in it, how many molecules of water are in the bucket? Write your answer in scientific notation.

101. *Blood Cells in a Cubic Millimeter* If a cubic millimeter of blood contains 5,800,000 red blood cells, how many red blood cells are contained in 50 cubic millimeters of blood? Write your answer in scientific notation.

102. *Radioactive Isotopes* The half-life of a radioactive isotope is the time required for half the quantity of the isotope to decompose. The half-life of uranium-238 is 4.5×10^9 years, and the half-life of uranium-234 is 2.5×10^5 years. How many times greater is the half-life of uranium-238 than uranium-234?

103. *Mutual Fund Manager* Lauri Mackey is the fund manager for the Mackey Mutual Fund. This mutual fund has total assets of $1.2 billion. Lauri wants to maintain the investments in this fund according to the following pie chart.

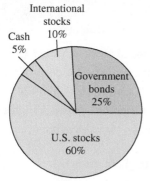

International stocks 10%

Cash 5%

Government bonds 25%

U.S. stocks 60%

a) How much of the $1.2 billion should be invested in U.S. stocks?

b) How much should be invested in government bonds?

c) How much should be invested in international stocks?

d) How much should remain in cash?

104. *Another Mutual Fund Manager* Susan Dratch is the fund manager for the Dratch Mutual Fund. This mutual fund has total assets of $3.4 billion. Susan wants to maintain the investments in this fund according to the following pie chart.

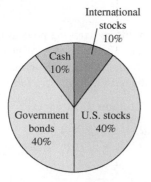

International stocks 10%

Cash 10%

Government bonds 40%

U.S. stocks 40%

a) How much of the $3.4 billion should be invested in U.S. stocks?

b) How much should be invested in government bonds?

c) How much should be invested in international stocks?

d) How much should remain in cash?

105. *Metric System Comparison* In the metric system, 1 meter $= 10^3$ millimeters. How many times greater is a meter than a millimeter?

106. *Milligrams and Kilograms* In the metric system, 1 gram $= 10^3$ milligrams and 1 gram $= 10^{-3}$ kilogram. What is the relationship between milligrams and kilograms?

107. *Earth to Sun Comparison* The mass of the sun is approximately 2×10^{30} kilograms, and the mass of Earth is approximately 6×10^{24} kilograms. How many times greater is the mass of the sun than the mass of Earth? Write your answer in decimal notation.

Challenge Problems/Group Activities

108. *Comparing a Million to a Billion* Many people have no idea of the difference in size between a million (1,000,000), a billion (1,000,000,000), and a trillion (1,000,000,000,000).

a) Write a million, a billion, and a trillion in scientific notation.

b) Determine how long it would take to spend one million dollars if you spent $1000 a day.

c) Repeat part (b) for one billion dollars.

d) Repeat part (b) for one trillion dollars.

e) How many times greater is one billion dollars than one million dollars?

109. *Speed of Light*

a) Light travels at a speed of 1.86×10^5 mi/sec. A *light-year* is the distance that light travels in 1 year. Determine the number of miles in a light-year.

b) Earth is approximately 93,000,000 mi from the sun. How long does it take light from the sun to reach Earth?

110. *Bacteria in a Culture* The exponential function $E(t) = 2^{10} \cdot 2^t$ approximates the number of bacteria in a certain culture after t hours.

a) The initial number of bacteria is determined when $t = 0$. What is the initial number of bacteria?

b) How many bacteria are there after $\frac{1}{2}$ hour?

Internet/Research Activities

111. Obtain data from the U.S. Department of the Treasury and from the U.S. Bureau of the Census Internet Web sites to calculate the current U.S. government debt per person. Write a report in which you compare your figure with those obtained in Exercise 87 and Example 14. Include in your report definitions of the following terms: revenues, expenditures, deficit, and surplus.

112. *John Allen Paulos* Read the *Profiles in Mathematics* box on page 264. Read one of Paulos's books and write a 500-word report on it.

113. Find an article in a newspaper or magazine that contains scientific notation. Write a paragraph explaining how scientific notation was used. Attach a copy of the article to your report.

SECTION 5.7   Arithmetic and Geometric Sequences

▲ *The modern study of diseases involves the use of mathematics to predict the size of bacteria populations.*

Under optimal laboratory conditions, the number of *Escherichia coli* (*E. coli*) bacteria will double every 17 minutes. If an experiment conducted under optimal conditions begins with 100 bacteria, how many bacteria will be present after 24 hours? Questions such as these are important to the modern study of diseases. In this section, we will study such questions by using lists of numbers known as *sequences*.

Why **This is Important** Sequences are used throughout many branches of mathematics to model real-life phenomena, such as population growth, disease control, and the inflation rates of currencies.

Now that you can recognize the various sets of real numbers and know how to add, subtract, multiply, and divide real numbers, we can discuss sequences. A *sequence* is a list of numbers that are related to each other by a rule. The numbers that form the sequence are called its *terms*. If your salary increases or decreases by a fixed amount over a period of time, the listing of the amounts, over time, would form an arithmetic sequence. When interest in a savings account is compounded at regular intervals, the listing of the amounts in the account over time will be a geometric sequence.

Arithmetic Sequences

A sequence in which each term after the first term differs from the preceding term by a constant amount is called an *arithmetic sequence*. The amount by which each pair of successive terms differs is called the *common difference*, *d*. The common difference can be found by subtracting any term from the term that directly follows it.

Examples of arithmetic sequences	**Common differences**
$1, 5, 9, 13, 17, \ldots$	$d = 5 - 1 = 4$
$-7, -5, -3, -1, 1, \ldots$	$d = -5 - (-7) = -5 + 7 = 2$
$\dfrac{5}{2}, \dfrac{3}{2}, \dfrac{1}{2}, -\dfrac{1}{2}, \ldots$	$d = \dfrac{3}{2} - \dfrac{5}{2} = -\dfrac{2}{2} = -1$

Example 1   *The First Five Terms of an Arithmetic Sequence*

Write the first five terms of the arithmetic sequence with first term 3 and a common difference of 7.

Solution   The first term is 3. The second term is $3 + 7$, or 10. The third term is $10 + 7$, or 17. The fourth term is $17 + 7$, or 24. The fifth term is $24 + 7$, or 31. Thus, the first five terms of the arithmetic sequence are 3, 10, 17, 24, 31. ∎

Example 2   *An Arithmetic Sequence with a Negative Difference*

Write the first five terms of the arithmetic sequence with first term 9 and a common difference of -4.

Solution   The first five terms of the sequence are

$$9, 5, 1, -3, -7$$

∎

When discussing a sequence, we often represent the first term as a_1 (read "*a* sub 1"), the second term as a_2, the fifteenth term as a_{15}, and so on. We use the notation a_n to represent the general or *n*th term of a sequence. Thus, a sequence may be symbolized as

$$a_1, a_2, a_3, a_4, \ldots, a_n, \ldots$$

For example, in the sequence 2, 5, 8, 11, 14, …, we have

$$a_1 = 2, a_2 = 5, a_3 = 8, a_4 = 11, a_5 = 14, \ldots.$$

The following formula can be used to determine the *n*th term of an arithmetic sequence.

General or *n*th Term of an Arithmetic Sequence

For an arithmetic sequence with first term a_1 and common difference d, the general or *n*th term can be found using the following formula.

$$a_n = a_1 + (n - 1)d$$

Example 3   *Determining the Twelfth Term of an Arithmetic Sequence*

Determine the twelfth term of the arithmetic sequence whose first term is -5 and whose common difference is 3.

Solution   To determine the twelfth term, or a_{12}, replace n in the formula with 12, a_1 with -5, and d with 3.

$$a_n = a_1 + (n - 1)d$$
$$a_{12} = -5 + (12 - 1)3$$
$$= -5 + (11)3$$
$$= -5 + 33$$
$$= 28$$

The twelfth term is 28. As a check, we have listed the first 12 terms of the sequence: $-5, -2, 1, 4, 7, 10, 13, 16, 19, 22, 25, 28$. ∎

Example 4 *Determining an Expression for the nth Term*

Write an expression for the general or nth term, a_n, for the sequence $1, 6, 11, 16, \ldots$.

Solution In this sequence, the first term, a_1, is 1 and the common difference, d, is 5. We substitute these values into $a_n = a_1 + (n - 1)d$ to obtain an expression for the nth term, a_n.

$$a_n = a_1 + (n - 1)d$$
$$= 1 + (n - 1)5$$
$$= 1 + 5n - 5$$
$$= 5n - 4$$

The expression is $a_n = 5n - 4$. Note that when $n = 1$, the first term is $5(1) - 4 = 1$. When $n = 2$, the second term is $5(2) - 4 = 6$, and so on. ■

We can use the following formula to find the sum of the first n terms in an arithmetic sequence.

Sum of the First *n* Terms in an Arithmetic Sequence

The sum of the first n terms of an arithmetic sequence can be found with the following formula where a_1 represents the first term and a_n represents the nth term.

$$s_n = \frac{n(a_1 + a_n)}{2}$$

In this formula, s_n represents the sum of the first n terms, a_1 is the first term, a_n is the nth term, and n is the number of terms in the sequence from a_1 to a_n.

Example 5 *Determining the Sum of an Arithmetic Sequence*

Determine the sum of the first 25 even natural numbers.

Solution The sequence we are discussing is

$$2, 4, 6, 8, 10, \ldots, 50$$

In this arithmetic sequence the first term is 2, the 25th term is 50, and there are 25 terms; therefore, $a_1 = 2$, $a_{25} = 50$, and $n = 25$. Thus, the sum of the first 25 terms is

$$s_n = \frac{n(a_1 + a_n)}{2}$$

$$s_{25} = \frac{25(2 + 50)}{2}$$

$$= \frac{25(52)}{2}$$

$$= \frac{1300}{2}$$

$$= 650$$

The sum of the first 25 even natural numbers, $2 + 4 + 6 + 8 + \cdots + 50$, is 650. ■

Geometric Sequences

The next type of sequence we will discuss is the geometric sequence. A *geometric sequence* is one in which the ratio of any term to the term that directly precedes it is a constant. This constant is called the *common ratio*. The common ratio, r, can be found by taking any term except the first and dividing that term by the preceding term.

Examples of geometric sequences	Common ratios
2, 4, 8, 16, 32, …	$r = 4 \div 2 = 2$; $r = 8 \div 4 = 2$; …
$-3, 6, -12, 24, -48, …$	$r = 6 \div (-3) = -2$; $r = (-12) \div 6 = -2$; …
$\dfrac{2}{3}, \dfrac{2}{9}, \dfrac{2}{27}, \dfrac{2}{81}, …$	$r = \dfrac{2}{9} \div \dfrac{2}{3} = \left(\dfrac{2}{9}\right)\left(\dfrac{3}{2}\right) = \dfrac{1}{3}$; $r = \dfrac{2}{27} \div \dfrac{2}{9} = \left(\dfrac{2}{27}\right)\left(\dfrac{9}{2}\right) = \dfrac{1}{3}$; …

To construct a geometric sequence when the first term, a_1, and common ratio, r, are known, multiply the first term by the common ratio to get the second term. Then multiply the second term by the common ratio to get the third term, and so on.

Example 6 *The First Five Terms of a Geometric Sequence*

Write the first five terms of the geometric sequence whose first term, a_1, is 5 and whose common ratio, r, is 2.

Solution The first term is 5. The second term, found by multiplying the first term by 2, is $5 \cdot 2$, or 10. The third term is $10 \cdot 2$, or 20. The fourth term is $20 \cdot 2$, or 40. The fifth term is $40 \cdot 2$, or 80. Thus, the first five terms of the geometric sequence are 5, 10, 20, 40, 80. ∎

The following formula can be used to determine the nth term of a geometric sequence.

General or nth Term of a Geometric Sequence

For a geometric sequence with first term a_1 and common ratio r, the general or nth term can be found using the following formula.

$$a_n = a_1 r^{n-1}$$

Example 7 *Determining the Twelfth Term of a Geometric Sequence*

Determine the twelfth term of the geometric sequence whose first term is -4 and whose common ratio is 2.

Solution In this sequence, $a_1 = -4$, $r = 2$, and $n = 12$. Substituting the values into the formula, we obtain

$$a_n = a_1 r^{n-1}$$
$$a_{12} = -4 \cdot 2^{12-1}$$
$$= -4 \cdot 2^{11}$$
$$= -4 \cdot 2048$$
$$= -8192$$

As a check, we have listed the first twelve terms of the sequence:

$-4, -8, -16, -32, -64, -128, -256, -512, -1024, -2048, -4096, -8192$ ∎

RECREATIONAL MATH

The Martingale System

The Martingale system is a strategy used by gamblers to determine the amount to bet while playing multiple rounds of a game of chance. The strategy requires the player to consistently bet a standard amount following a win and to double the previous bet following a loss. The underlying principle is that the first win will recover all the previous losses, thus ensuring that the player does not lose money in the long run. Let's use a standard bet of $1 as an example. In the first round, the player bets $1. If the player wins, the bet in the second round remains $1. If the player loses, the bet in the second round doubles to $2. Next, if the player wins in the second round, the bet in the third round returns to $1; however, if the player loses in the second round, the bet in the third round doubles to $4. The system continues with the player betting $1 following a win, and doubling the previous bet following a loss. Although the strategy may work in the short term, a player may have difficulty doubling the bet after several consecutive losses. Casinos generally place a maximum on the amount a person can bet. Exercise 90 on page 277 demonstrates why the Martingale system is a risky wagering strategy.

Example 8 *Determining an Expression for the nth Term*

Write an expression for the general or nth term, a_n, of the sequence 2, 6, 18, 54, ...

Solution In this sequence, the first term is 2, so $a_1 = 2$. Note that $\frac{6}{2} = 3$, so $r = 3$. We substitute $a_1 = 2$ and $r = 3$ into $a_n = a_1 r^{n-1}$ to obtain an expression for the nth term, a_n.

$$a_n = a_1 r^{n-1}$$
$$= 2(3)^{n-1}$$

The expression is $a_n = 2(3)^{n-1}$. Note that when $n = 1$, $a_1 = 2(3)^0 = 2(1) = 2$. When $n = 2$, $a_2 = 2(3)^1 = 6$, and so on. ∎

The following formula can be used to determine the sum of the first n terms of a geometric sequence.

Sum of the First *n* Terms of a Geometric Sequence

The sum of the first n terms of a geometric sequence can be found with the following formula where a_1 represents the first term and r represents the common ratio.

$$s_n = \frac{a_1(1 - r^n)}{1 - r}, \quad r \neq 1$$

Example 9 *Determining the Sum of a Geometric Sequence*

Determine the sum of the first five terms in the geometric sequence whose first term is 4 and whose common ratio is 2.

Solution In this sequence, $a_1 = 4$, $r = 2$, and $n = 5$. Substituting these values into the formula, we get

$$s_n = \frac{a_1(1 - r^n)}{1 - r}$$
$$s_5 = \frac{4[1 - (2)^5]}{1 - 2}$$
$$= \frac{4(1 - 32)}{-1}$$
$$= \frac{4(-31)}{-1} = \frac{-124}{-1} = 124$$

The sum of the first five terms of the sequence is 124. The first five terms of the sequence are 4, 8, 16, 32, 64. If you add these five numbers, you will obtain the sum 124. ∎

Example 10 *Pounds and Pounds of Silver*

As a reward for saving his kingdom from a band of thieves, a king offered a knight one of two options. The knight's first option was to be paid 100,000 pounds of silver all at once. The second option was to be paid over the course of a month. On the first day, he would receive one pound of silver. On the second day, he would receive two pounds of silver. On the third day, he would receive four pounds of silver, and so on, each day receiving double the amount given on the previous day. Assuming the month has 30 days, which option would provide the knight with more silver?

Solution The first option pays the knight 100,000 pounds of silver. The second option pays according to the geometric sequence 1, 2, 4, 8, 16, ... In this sequence,

$a_1 = 1$, $r = 2$, and $n = 30$. The sum of this sequence can be found by substituting these values into the formula to obtain

$$s_n = \frac{a_1(1 - r^n)}{1 - r}$$

$$s_{30} = \frac{1(1 - 2^{30})}{1 - 2}$$

$$= \frac{1 - 1{,}073{,}741{,}824}{-1}$$

$$= \frac{-1{,}073{,}741{,}823}{-1}$$

$$= 1{,}073{,}741{,}823$$

Thus, the knight would get 1,073,741,823 pounds of silver with the second option. Compared with the first option, the second would result in an additional 1,073,641,823 pounds of silver.

SECTION 5.7

Exercises

Warm Up Exercises

In Exercises 1–6, fill in the blanks with an appropriate word, phrase, or symbol(s).

1. A list of numbers that are related to each other by a rule is called a(n) _____.

2. The numbers that form a sequence are called its _____ .

3. A sequence in which each term differs from the preceding term by a constant amount is called a(n) _____ sequence.

4. The amount by which each pair of successive terms differ in an arithmetic sequence is called the common _____.

5. A sequence in which the ratio of any term to the term that directly precedes it is a constant is called a(n) _____ sequence.

6. The constant found by dividing any term in a geometric sequence by the term that directly precedes it is called the common _____.

Practice the Skills

In Exercises 7–14, write the first five terms of the arithmetic sequence with the first term, a_1, and common difference, d.

7. $a_1 = 3, d = 2$

8. $a_1 = 0, d = 3$

9. $a_1 = 25, d = -5$

10. $a_1 = -11, d = 5$

11. $a_1 = 5, d = -2$

12. $a_1 = -3, d = -4$

13. $a_1 = \frac{3}{4}, d = \frac{1}{4}$

14. $a_1 = \frac{5}{2}, d = -\frac{3}{2}$

In Exercises 15–22, determine the indicated term for the arithmetic sequence with the first term, a_1, and common difference, d.

15. Determine a_4 when $a_1 = 3, d = 1$.

16. Determine a_7 when $a_1 = 12, d = -2$.

17. Determine a_{11} when $a_1 = -20, d = 5$.

18. Determine a_{12} when $a_1 = 7, d = -3$.

19. Determine a_{20} when $a_1 = \frac{4}{5}, d = -1$.

20. Determine a_{14} when $a_1 = \frac{1}{3}, d = \frac{2}{3}$.

21. Determine a_{22} when $a_1 = -23, d = \frac{5}{7}$.

22. Determine a_{15} when $a_1 = \frac{4}{3}, d = \frac{1}{3}$.

In Exercises 23–30, write an expression for the general or nth term, a_n, for the arithmetic sequence.

23. $1, 2, 3, 4, \ldots$

24. $1, 3, 5, 7, \ldots$

25. $2, 4, 6, 8, \ldots$

26. $3, 6, 9, 12, \ldots$

27. $2, 6, 10, 14, \ldots$

28. $-7, -2, 3, 8, \ldots$

29. $-3, -\frac{3}{2}, 0, \frac{3}{2}, \ldots$

30. $-5, -2, 1, 4, \ldots$

In Exercises 31–38, determine the sum of the terms of the arithmetic sequence. The number of terms, n, is given.

31. $1, 2, 3, 4, \ldots, 50; n = 50$

32. $2, 4, 6, 8, \ldots, 100; n = 50$

33. $1, 3, 5, 7, \ldots, 99; n = 50$

34. $1, 4, 7, 10, \ldots, 100; n = 34$

35. $-10, -5, 0, 5, \ldots, 60; n = 15$

36. $100, 90, 80, 70, \ldots, -60; n = 17$

37. $\frac{1}{5}, \frac{2}{5}, \frac{3}{5}, \frac{4}{5}, \ldots, \frac{24}{5}; n = 24$

38. $-\frac{3}{4}, -\frac{1}{2}, -\frac{1}{4}, 0, \ldots, \frac{17}{4}; n = 21$

In Exercises 39–46, write the first five terms of the geometric sequence with the first term, a_1, and common ratio, r.

39. $a_1 = 1, r = 3$

40. $a_1 = 3, r = 1$

41. $a_1 = 5, r = 2$

42. $a_1 = 8, r = \frac{1}{2}$

43. $a_1 = -3, r = -1$

44. $a_1 = -6, r = -2$

45. $a_1 = 81, r = -\frac{1}{3}$

46. $a_1 = \frac{16}{15}, r = \frac{1}{2}$

In Exercises 47–54, determine the indicated term for the geometric sequence with the first term, a_1, and common ratio, r.

47. Determine a_5 when $a_1 = 7, r = 2$.

48. Determine a_5 when $a_1 = 2, r = 3$.

49. Determine a_3 when $a_1 = 3, r = \frac{1}{2}$.

50. Determine a_7 when $a_1 = -3, r = -3$.

51. Determine a_7 when $a_1 = -5, r = 3$.

52. Determine a_8 when $a_1 = \frac{1}{2}, r = -2$.

53. Determine a_{10} when $a_1 = -2, r = 3$.

54. Determine a_{18} when $a_1 = -5, r = -2$.

In Exercises 55–62, write an expression for the general or nth term, a_n, for the geometric sequence.

55. 5, 25, 125, 625 …

56. 1, 5, 25, 125, ….

57. −1, 1, −1, 1, …

58. −16, −8, −4, −2, …

59. 2, 1, $\frac{1}{2}$, $\frac{1}{4}$, …

60. −3, 6, −12, 24, …

61. 9, 3, 1, $\frac{1}{3}$, $\frac{1}{9}$, …

62. −4, −$\frac{8}{3}$, −$\frac{16}{9}$, −$\frac{32}{27}$, …

In Exercises 63–70, determine the sum of the first n terms of the geometric sequence for the values of a_1 and r.

63. $n = 6, a_1 = 3, r = 2$

64. $n = 7, a_1 = 1, r = 3$

65. $n = 6, a_1 = -3, r = 4$

66. $n = 9, a_1 = -3, r = 5$

67. $n = 11, a_1 = -7, r = 3$

68. $n = 15, a_1 = -1, r = 2$

69. $n = 15, a_1 = -1, r = -2$

70. $n = 10, a_1 = 512, r = \frac{1}{2}$

Problem Solving

71. Determine the sum of the first 100 natural numbers.

72. Determine the sum of the first 100 odd natural numbers.

73. Determine the sum of the first 100 even natural numbers.

74. Determine the sum of the first 50 multiples of 3.

75. *Pendulum Movement* Each swing of a pendulum (from far left to far right) is 3 in. shorter than the preceding swing. The first swing is 8 ft.

   a) Find the length of the twelfth swing.

   b) Determine the total distance traveled by the pendulum during the first 12 swings.

76. *Clock Strikes* A clock strikes once at 1 o'clock, twice at 2 o'clock, three times at 3 o'clock, and so on. How many times does it strike over a 12-hr period?

77. *Annual Pay Raises* Rita Fernandez is given a starting salary of $35,000 and promised a $1400 raise per year after each of the next 8 years.

   a) Determine her salary during her eighth year of work.

   b) Determine the total salary she received over the 8 years.

78. *A Bouncing Ball* Each time a ball bounces, the height attained by the ball is 6 in. less than the previous height attained. If on the first bounce the ball reaches a height of 6 ft, find the height attained on the eleventh bounce.

79. *Enrollment Increase* The current enrollment at Loras College is 8000 students. If the enrollment increases by 8% per year, determine the enrollment 10 years later.

80. *Samurai Sword Construction* While making a traditional Japanese samurai sword, the master sword maker prepares the blade by heating a bar of iron until it is white hot. He then folds it over and pounds it smooth. Therefore, after each folding, the number of layers of steel is doubled. Assuming the sword maker starts with a bar of one layer and folds it 15 times, how many layers of steel will the finished sword contain?

81. *Salary Increase* If your salary were to increase at a rate of 6% per year, find your salary during your 15th year if your original salary is $31,000.

82. *A Bouncing Ball* When dropped, a ball rebounds to four-fifths of its original height. How high will the ball rebound after the fourth bounce if it is dropped from a height of 30 ft?

83. *Value of a Stock* Ten years ago, Nancy Hart purchased $2000 worth of shares in RCF, Inc. Since then, the price of the stock has roughly tripled every 2 years. Approximately how much are Nancy's shares worth today?

84. *A Baseball Game* During a baseball game, the visiting team scored 1 run in the first inning, 2 runs in the second inning, 3 runs in the third inning, 4 runs in the fourth inning, and so on. The home team scored 1 run in the first inning, 2 runs in the second inning, 4 runs in the third inning, 8 runs in the fourth inning, and so on. What is the score of the game after eight innings?

Inning	1	2	3	4	5	6	7	8	9
Visitors	1	2	3	4					
Home	1	2	4	8					

Challenge Problems/Group Activities

85. A geometric sequence has $a_1 = 82$ and $r = \frac{1}{2}$; find s_6.

86. *Sums of Interior Angles* The sums of the interior angles of a triangle, a quadrilateral, a pentagon, and a hexagon are 180°, 360°, 540°, and 720°, respectively. Use this pattern to find a formula for the general term, a_n, where a_n represents the sum of the interior angles of an n-sided polygon.

87. *Divisibility by 6* Determine how many numbers between 7 and 1610 are divisible by 6.

88. Determine r and a_1 for the geometric sequence with $a_2 = 24$ and $a_5 = 648$.

89. *Total Distance Traveled by a Bouncing Ball* A ball is dropped from a height of 30 ft. On each bounce, it attains a height four-fifths of its original height (or of the previous bounce). Find the total vertical distance traveled by the ball after it has completed its fifth bounce (has therefore hit the ground six times).

Recreational Mathematics

90. *Martingale System* See the *Recreational Mathematics* box on page 274. Use the Martingale system to answer the following questions.

a) Assume a player is using a $1 standard bet and loses five times in a row. How much money should the player bet in the sixth round? How much money has the player lost at the end of the fifth round?

b) Assume a player is using a $10 standard bet and loses five times in a row. How much money should the player bet in the sixth round? How much money has the player lost at the end of the fifth round?

c) Assume a player is using a $1 standard bet and loses 10 times in a row. How much money should the player bet in the eleventh round? How much money has the player lost at the end of the tenth round?

d) Assume a player is using a $10 standard bet and loses 10 times in a row. How much money should the player bet in the eleventh round? How much money has the player lost at the end of the tenth round?

e) Why is this a risky strategy?

Internet/Research Activity

91. A topic generally associated with sequences is *series*.

a) Research *series* and explain what a series is and how it differs from a sequence. Also write a formal definition of series. Give examples of different kinds of series.

b) Write the arithmetic series associated with the arithmetic sequence 1, 4, 7, 10, 13, ...

c) Write the geometric series associated with the geometric sequence 3, 6, 12, 24, 48, ...

d) What is an infinite geometric series?

e) Determine the sum of the terms of the infinite geometric series $1 + \dfrac{1}{2} + \dfrac{1}{4} + \dfrac{1}{8} + \dfrac{1}{16} + \cdots$.

SECTION 5.8   Fibonacci Sequence

▲ *The number of ancestors of a male bee is among the numbers found in the Fibonacci sequence.*

Consider the following numbers found in nature: the number of petals on a daisy, the number of sunflower seeds in a sunflower, the number of scales on a pineapple, the number of ancestors of a male bee. In this section, we will find that all these numbers are part of a special sequence of numbers called the Fibonacci sequence.

Why *This is Important* The Fibonacci sequence and the related topic of the golden ratio appear in many places in nature and play an important role in geometry, art, and music.

Our discussion of sequences would not be complete without mentioning a sequence known as the *Fibonacci sequence*. The sequence is named after Leonardo of Pisa, also known as Fibonacci. He was one of the most distinguished mathematicians of the Middle Ages. This sequence is first mentioned in his book *Liber Abacci* (Book of the Abacus), which contained many interesting problems, such as: "A certain man put a pair of rabbits in a place surrounded on all sides by a wall. How many pairs of rabbits can be produced from that pair in a year if it is assumed that every month each pair begets a new pair which from the second month becomes productive?"

The solution to this problem (Fig. 5.10) led to the development of the sequence that bears its author's name: the Fibonacci sequence. The sequence is shown in Table 5.1. The numbers in the columns titled *Pairs of Adults* form the Fibonacci sequence.

Profile in Mathematics

Fibonacci

Leonardo of Pisa (1170–1250) is considered one of the most distinguished mathematicians of the Middle Ages. He was born in Italy and was sent by his father to study mathematics with an Arab master. When he began writing, he referred to himself as Fibonacci, or "son of Bonacci," the name by which he is known today. In addition to the famous sequence bearing his name, Fibonacci is also credited with introducing the Hindu–Arabic number system into Europe. His 1202 book, *Liber Abacci* (Book of the Abacus), explained the use of this number system and emphasized the importance of the number zero.

Table 5.1

Month	Pairs of Adults	Pairs of Babies	Total Pairs
1	1	0	1
2	1	1	2
3	2	1	3
4	3	2	5
5	5	3	8
6	8	5	13
7	13	8	21
8	21	13	34
9	34	21	55
10	55	34	89
11	89	55	144
12	144	89	233

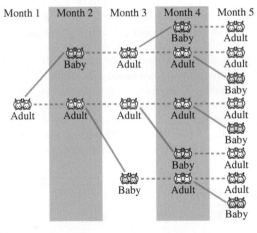

Figure 5.10

Following is the Fibonacci sequence

Fibonacci Sequence

$$1, 1, 2, 3, 5, 8, 13, 21, \ldots$$

In the Fibonacci sequence, the first and second terms are 1. The sum of these two terms is the third term. The sum of the second and third terms is the fourth term, and so on.

▲ *The head of a sunflower*

In the middle of the nineteenth century, mathematicians made a serious study of this sequence and found strong similarities between it and many natural phenomena. Fibonacci numbers appear in the seed arrangement of many species of plants and in the petal counts of various flowers. For example, when the flowering head of the sunflower matures to seed, the seeds' spiral arrangement becomes clearly visible. A typical count of these spirals may give 89 steeply curving to the right, 55 curving more shallowly to the left, and 34 again shallowly to the right. The largest known specimen to be examined had spiral counts of 144 right, 89 left, and 55 right. These numbers, like the other three mentioned, are consecutive terms of the Fibonacci sequence.

On the heads of many flowers, petals surrounding the central disk generally yield a Fibonacci number. For example, some daisies contain 21 petals, and others contain 34, 55, or 89 petals. (People who use a daisy to play the "love me, love me not" game will likely pluck 21, 34, 55, or 89 petals before arriving at an answer.)

Fibonacci numbers are also observed in the structure of pinecones and pineapples. The tablike or scalelike structures called bracts that make up the main body of the pinecone form a set of spirals that start from the cone's attachment to the branch. Two sets of oppositely directed spirals can be observed, one steep and the other more gradual. A count on the steep spiral will reveal a Fibonacci number, and a count on the gradual one will be the adjacent smaller Fibonacci number, or if not, the next smaller Fibonacci number. One investigation of 4290 pinecones from 10 species of pine trees found in California revealed that only 74 cones, or 1.7%, deviated from this Fibonacci pattern.

Like pinecone bracts, pineapple scales are patterned into spirals, and because they are roughly hexagonal in shape, three distinct sets of spirals can be counted. Generally, the number of pineapple scales in each spiral are Fibonacci numbers.

Fibonacci Numbers and Divine Proportions

In 1753, while studying the Fibonacci sequence, Robert Simson, a mathematician at the University of Glasgow, noticed that when he took the ratio of any term to the term that immediately preceded it, the value he obtained remained in the vicinity of one specific number. To illustrate this, we indicate in Table 5.2 the ratio of various pairs of sequential Fibonacci numbers.

The ratio of the 50th term to the 49th term is 1.6180. Simson proved that the ratio of the $(n + 1)$ term to the nth term as n gets larger and larger is the irrational number $(\sqrt{5} + 1)/2$, which begins 1.61803.... This number was already well known to mathematicians at that time as the *golden number*.

Many years earlier, Bavarian astronomer and mathematician Johannes Kepler wrote that for him the golden number symbolized the Creator's intention "to create like from like." The golden number $(\sqrt{5} + 1)/2$ is frequently referred to as "phi," symbolized by the Greek letter Φ.

The ancient Greeks, in about the sixth century B.C., sought unifying principles of beauty and perfection, which they believed could be described by using mathematics. In their study of beauty, the Greeks used the term *golden ratio*. To understand the golden ratio, let's consider the line segment AB in Fig. 5.11.

Figure 5.11

When this line segment is divided at a point C such that the ratio of the whole, AB, to the larger part, AC, is equal to the ratio of the larger part, AC, to the smaller

Table 5.2

Numbers	Ratio
1, 1	$\frac{1}{1} = 1$
1, 2	$\frac{2}{1} = 2$
2, 3	$\frac{3}{2} = 1.5$
3, 5	$\frac{5}{3} = 1.666\ldots$
5, 8	$\frac{8}{5} = 1.6$
8, 13	$\frac{13}{8} = 1.625$
13, 21	$\frac{21}{13} \approx 1.615$
21, 34	$\frac{34}{21} \approx 1.619$
34, 55	$\frac{55}{34} \approx 1.618$
55, 89	$\frac{89}{55} \approx 1.618$

▲ *The Great Pyramid of Gizeh*

Figure 5.12

Figure 5.13

▲ *The Parthenon*

part, *CB*, each ratio *AB/AC* and *AC/CB* is referred to as a *golden ratio*. The proportion these ratios form, *AB/AC = AC/CB*, is called the *golden proportion*. Furthermore, each ratio in the proportion will have a value equal to the golden number, $(\sqrt{5} + 1)/2$.

$$\frac{AB}{AC} = \frac{AC}{CB} = \frac{\sqrt{5} + 1}{2} \approx 1.618$$

The Great Pyramid of Gizeh in Egypt, built about 2600 B.C., is the earliest known example of use of the golden ratio in architecture. The ratio of any of its sides of the square base (775.75 ft) to its altitude (481.4 ft) is about 1.611. Other evidence of the use of the golden ratio appears in other Egyptian buildings and tombs.

In medieval times, people referred to the golden proportion as the *divine proportion*, reflecting their belief in its relationship to the will of God.

Twentieth-century architect Le Corbusier developed a scale of proportions for the human body that he called the Modulor (Fig. 5.12). Note that the navel separates the entire body into golden proportions, as do the neck and knee.

From the golden proportion, the *golden rectangle* can be formed, as shown in Fig. 5.13.

$$\frac{\text{Length}}{\text{Width}} = \frac{a + b}{a} = \frac{a}{b} = \frac{\sqrt{5} + 1}{2}$$

Note that when a square is cut off one end of a golden rectangle, as in Fig. 5.13, the remaining rectangle has the same properties as the original golden rectangle (creating "like from like" as Johannes Kepler had written) and is therefore itself a golden rectangle. Interestingly, the curve derived from a succession of diminishing golden rectangles, as shown in Fig. 5.14, is the same as the spiral curve of the chambered nautilus. The same curve appears on the horns of rams and some other animals. It is the same curve that is observed in the plant structures mentioned earlier: sunflowers, other flower heads, pinecones, and pineapples. You will recall that Fibonacci numbers were observed in each of these plant structures. The curve shown in Fig. 5.14 closely approximates what mathematicians call a *logarithmic spiral.*

Figure 5.14

Ancient Greek civilization used the golden rectangle in art and architecture. The main measurements of many buildings of antiquity, including the Parthenon in Athens, are governed by golden ratios and rectangles. Greek statues, vases, urns, and so on also exhibit characteristics of the golden ratio. It is for Phidas, considered the greatest of Greek sculptors, that the golden ratio was named "phi." The proportions can be found abundantly in his work.

The proportions of the golden rectangle can be found in the work of many artists, from the old masters to the moderns. For example, on page 281 the golden rectangle can be seen in the painting *Invitation to the Sideshow (La Parade de Cirque)*, 1887, by Georges Seurat, a French neoimpressionist artist.

▲ Fibonacci's Garden *by Caryl Bryer Fullert*

▲ Invitation to the Sideshow (La Parade de Cirque), *1887, by Georges Seurat*

In addition to using the golden rectangle in art, several artists have used Fibonacci numbers in art. One contemporary example is the 1995 work by Caryl Bryer Fallert called *Fibonacci's Garden* which is shown in the margin. This artwork is a quilt constructed from two separate fabrics that are put together in a pattern based on the Fibonacci sequence.

Fibonacci numbers are also found in another form of art, namely music. Perhaps the most obvious link between Fibonacci numbers and music can be found on the piano keyboard. An octave (Fig. 5.15) on a keyboard has 13 keys: 8 white keys and 5 black keys (the 5 black keys are in one group of 2 and one group of 3).

5 black

C D E F G A B C

8 white
13 total

Figure 5.15

In Western music, the most complete scale, the chromatic scale, consists of 13 notes (from C to the next higher C). Its predecessor, the diatonic scale, contains 8 notes (an octave). The diatonic scale was preceded by a 5-note pentatonic scale (*penta* is Greek for "five"). Each number is a Fibonacci number. In popular music, the song "Lateralas" by the band Tool uses the Fibonacci sequence in both the time signature and the lyric arrangement. The song also contains several references to the golden ratio and to the logarithmic spiral.

The visual arts deal with what is pleasing to the eye, and musical composition deals with what is pleasing to the ear. Whereas art achieves some of its goals by using division of planes and area, music achieves some of its goals by a similar division of time, using notes of various duration and spacing. The musical intervals considered by many to be the most pleasing to the ear are the major sixth and minor sixth. A major sixth, for example, consists of the note C, vibrating at about 264[†] vibrations per second, and note A, vibrating at about 440 vibrations per second. The ratio of 440 to 264 reduces to 5 to 3, or $\frac{5}{3}$, a ratio of two consecutive Fibonacci numbers. An example of a minor sixth is E (about 330 vibrations per second) and C (about 528 vibrations per second). The ratio 528 to 330 reduces to 8 to 5, or $\frac{8}{5}$, the next ratio of two consecutive Fibonacci numbers. The vibrations of any sixth interval reduce to a similar ratio.

[†]Frequencies of notes vary in different parts of the world and change over time.

Patterns that can be expressed mathematically in terms of Fibonacci relationships have been found in Gregorian chants and works of many composers, including Bach, Beethoven, and Bartók. A number of twentieth-century musical works, including Ernst Krenek's *Fibonacci Mobile*, were deliberately structured by using Fibonacci proportions.

A number of studies have tried to explain why the Fibonacci sequence and related items are linked to so many real-life situations. It appears that the Fibonacci numbers are a part of a natural harmony that is pleasing to both the eye and the ear. In the nineteenth century, German physicist and psychologist Gustav Fechner tried to determine which dimensions were most pleasing to the eye. Fechner, along with psychologist Wilhelm Wundt, found that most people do unconsciously favor golden dimensions when purchasing greeting cards, mirrors, and other rectangular objects. This discovery has been widely used by commercial manufacturers in their packaging and labeling designs, by retailers in their store displays, and in other areas of business and advertising.

SECTION 5.8   *Exercises*

Warm Up Exercises

In Exercises 1–6, fill in the blanks with an appropriate word, phrase, or symbol(s).

1. The sequence of numbers 1, 1, 2, 3, 5, 8, 13, 21, ... is known as the _____ sequence.

2. The irrational number $\frac{\sqrt{5}+1}{2}$ is known as the _____ number.

In Exercises 3–4, use the following diagram and assume that the ratio $\frac{AB}{AC}$ is equal to the ratio $\frac{AC}{CB}$

3. Each ratio $\frac{AB}{AC}$ and $\frac{AC}{CB}$ is referred to as a Golden _____.

4. The proportion $\frac{AB}{AC} = \frac{AC}{CB}$ is called the Golden _____.

5. In medieval times, people referred to the golden proportion as the _____ proportion.

6. A rectangle whose ratio of its length to its width is equal to the golden number is known as a golden _____.

Practice the Skills/Problem Solving

7. a) To what decimal value is $(\sqrt{5}+1)/2$ approximately equal?

   b) To what decimal value is $(\sqrt{5}-1)/2$ approximately equal?

   c) By how much do the results in parts (a) and (b) differ?

8. The sum of any six consecutive Fibonacci numbers is always divisible by 4. Select any six consecutive Fibonacci numbers and show that for your selection this statement is true.

9. The sum of any 10 consecutive Fibonacci numbers is always divisible by 11. Select any 10 consecutive Fibonacci numbers and show that for your selection this statement is true.

10. The greatest common factor of any two consecutive Fibonacci numbers is 1. Show that this statement is true for the first 15 Fibonacci numbers.

11. For any four consecutive Fibonacci numbers, the difference of the squares of the middle two numbers equals the product of the smallest and largest numbers. Select four consecutive Fibonacci numbers and show that this pattern holds for the numbers you selected.

12. Twice any Fibonacci number minus the next Fibonacci number equals the second number preceding the original number. Select a number in the Fibonacci sequence and show that this pattern holds for the number selected.

13. Determine the ratio of the length to width of various photographs and compare these ratios to Φ.

14. Determine the ratio of the length to the width of your television screen and compare this ratio to Φ.

15. Determine the ratio of the length to the width of a computer screen and compare this ratio to Φ.

16. Find three physical objects whose dimensions are very close to a golden rectangle.

   a) List the articles and record the dimensions.

   b) Compute the ratios of their lengths to their widths.

   c) Find the difference between the golden ratio and the ratio you obtain in part (b)—to the nearest tenth—for each object.

In Exercises 17–24, determine whether the sequence is a Fibonacci-type sequence (each term is the sum of the two preceding terms). If it is, determine the next two terms of the sequence.

17. 4, 5, 9, 18, 36, 72, …

18. 4, 5, 9, 14, 23, 37, …

19. 1, 5, 6, 11, 17, 28, …

20. 0, π, π, 2π, 3π, 5π, …

21. −1, 1, 0, 1, 1, 2, …

22. 1, 4, 9, 16, 25, 36, …

23. 5, 10, 15, 25, 40, 65, …

24. $\frac{1}{4}$, $\frac{1}{4}$, $\frac{1}{2}$, $\frac{3}{4}$, $1\frac{1}{4}$, 2, …

25. a) Select any two one-digit (nonzero) numbers and add them to obtain a third number. Continue adding the two previous terms to get a Fibonacci-type sequence.

b) Form ratios of successive terms to show how they will eventually approach the golden number.

26. a) Select any three consecutive terms of a Fibonacci sequence. Subtract the product of the terms on each side of the middle term from the square of the middle term. What is the difference?

b) Repeat part (a) with three different consecutive terms of the sequence.

c) Make a conjecture about what will happen when you repeat this process for any three consecutive terms of a Fibonacci sequence.

27. *Pascal's Triangle* One of the most famous number patterns involves *Pascal's triangle*. The Fibonacci sequence can be found by using Pascal's triangle. Can you explain how that can be done? A hint is shown.

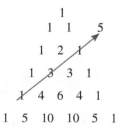

28. *Lucas Sequence* **a)** A sequence related to the Fibonacci sequence is the *Lucas sequence*. The Lucas sequence is formed in a manner similar to the Fibonacci sequence. The first two numbers of the Lucas sequence are 1 and 3. Write the first eight terms of the Lucas sequence.

b) Complete the next two lines of the following chart.

$$1 + 2 = 3$$
$$1 + 3 = 4$$
$$2 + 5 = 7$$
$$3 + 8 = 11$$
$$5 + 13 = 18$$

c) What do you observe about the first column in the chart in part (b)?

Concept/Writing Exercises

29. Explain how to construct the Fibonacci sequence.

30. Explain the relationship between the golden number, golden ratio, golden proportion, and golden rectangle.

31. Describe three examples of where Fibonacci numbers can be found

a) in nature.

b) in manufactured items.

32. The eleventh Fibonacci number is 89. Examine the first six digits in the decimal expression of its reciprocal, $\frac{1}{89}$. What do you find?

33. Find the ratio of the second to the first term of the Fibonacci sequence. Then find the ratio of the third to the second term of the sequence and determine whether this ratio was an increase or decrease from the first ratio. Continue this process for 10 ratios and then make a conjecture regarding the increasing or decreasing values in consecutive ratios.

34. A musical composition is described as follows. Explain why this piece is based on the golden ratio.

Entire Composition

34 measures	55 measures	21 measures	34 measures
Theme	Fast, Loud	Slow	Repeat of theme

Challenge Problems/Group Activities

35. *Fibonacci-Type Sequence* The following sequence represents a Fibonacci-type sequence (each term is the sum of the two preceding terms). Here x represents any natural number from 1 to 10:

$$-10, x, -10 + x, -10 + 2x, -20 + 3x, -30 + 5x, \ldots$$

For example, if $x = 2$, the first 10 terms of the sequence would be −10, 2, −8, −6, −14, −20, −34, −54, −88, −142.

Write out the first 10 terms of this Fibonacci-type sequence for x equal to the following.

a) 4   **b)** 5   **c)** 6   **d)** 7   **e)** 8

f) For values of x of 4, 5, and 6, you should have found that each term after the seventh term in the sequence was a negative number. For values of x of 7 and 8, you should have found that each term after the seventh term in the sequence was a positive number. Do you believe that for any value of x greater than or equal to 7, each term after the seventh term of the sequence will always be a positive number? Explain.

36. Draw a line of length 5 in. Determine and mark the point on the line that will create the golden ratio. Explain how you determined your answer.

37. The divine proportion is $(a + b)/a = a/b$ (see Fig. 5.13), which can be written $1 + (b/a) = a/b$. Now let $x = a/b$, which gives $1 + (1/x) = x$. Multiply both sides of this equation by x to get a quadratic equation and then use the quadratic formula (Section 6.9) to show that one answer is $x = (1 + \sqrt{5})/2$ (the golden ratio).

38. *Pythagorean Triples* A Pythagorean triple is a set of three whole numbers, $\{a, b, c\}$, such that $a^2 + b^2 = c^2$.

For example, since $6^2 + 8^2 = (10)^2$, $\{6, 8, 10\}$ is a Pythagorean triple. The following steps show how to find Pythagorean triples using any four consecutive Fibonacci numbers. Here we will demonstrate the process with the Fibonacci numbers 3, 5, 8, and 13.

1) Determine the product of 2 and the two inner Fibonacci numbers. We have $2(5)(8) = 80$, which is the first number in the Pythagorean triple. So $a = 80$.

2) Determine the product of the two outer numbers. We have $3(13) = 39$, which is the second number in the Pythagorean triple. So $b = 39$.

3) Determine the sum of the squares of the inner two numbers. We have $5^2 + 8^2 = 25 + 64 = 89$, which is the third number in the Pythagorean triple. So $c = 89$.

This process has produced the Pythagorean triple, $\{80, 39, 89\}$. To verify,

$$(80)^2 + (39)^2 = (89)^2$$
$$6400 + 1521 = 7921$$
$$7921 = 7921$$

Use this process to produce four other Pythagorean triples.

39. *Reflections* When two panes of glass are placed face to face, four interior reflective surfaces exist, labeled 1, 2, 3, and 4. If light is not reflected, it has just one path through the glass (see the figure below). If it has one reflection, it can be reflected in two ways. If it has two reflections, it can be reflected in three ways. Use this information to answer parts (a) through (c).

| 0 reflections | 1 reflection | 2 reflections |
| 1 path | 2 paths | 3 paths |

a) If a ray is reflected three times, there are five paths it can follow. Show the paths.

b) If a ray is reflected four times, there are eight paths it can follow. Show the paths.

c) How many paths can a ray follow if it is reflected five times? Explain how you determined your answer.

Internet/Research Activities

40. Write a report on the history and mathematical contributions of Fibonacci.

41. The digits 1 through 9 have evolved considerably since they appeared in Fibonacci's book *Liber Abacci*. Write a report tracing the history of the evolution of the digits 1 through 9 since Fibonacci's time.

42. Write a report indicating where the golden ratio and golden rectangle have been used in art and architecture. You may wish to include information on art and architecture related to the golden ratio and Fibonacci sequences.

CHAPTER 5 *Summary*

Important Facts and Concepts

Examples and Discussion

Section 5.1	
Fundamental Theorem of Arithmetic	Examples 2–7, pages 213–216
Every composite number can be expressed as a unique product of prime numbers.	

Sections 5.1–5.5

Sets of Numbers

Natural or counting numbers: $\{1, 2, 3, 4, \dots\}$
Whole numbers: $\{0, 1, 2, 3, 4, \dots\}$
Integers: $\{\dots, -3, -2, -1, 0, 1, 2, 3, \dots\}$
Rational numbers: Numbers of the form p/q, where p and q are integers, $q \neq 0$. Every rational number when expressed as a decimal number will be either a terminating or repeating decimal number.
Irrational number: A real number whose representation is a nonterminating, nonrepeating decimal number (not a rational number)
Real numbers: the union of the rational numbers and the irrational numbers.

Discussion pages 210, 221, 229, 244, and 252

Section 5.2

Definition of Subtraction

$a - b = a + (-b)$

Discussion page 223,
Examples 3–5, pages 223–224

Section 5.3

Fundamental Law of Rational Numbers

$\dfrac{a}{b} = \dfrac{a}{b} \cdot \dfrac{c}{c} = \dfrac{ac}{bc}$ $b \neq 0, \ c \neq 0$

Discussion page 237,
Examples 14–16, pages 237–239

Section 5.4

Rules of Radicals

Product rule for radicals:
$\sqrt{a \cdot b} = \sqrt{a} \cdot \sqrt{b}, \quad a \geq 0, \quad b \geq 0$

Quotient rule for radicals:

$\dfrac{\sqrt{a}}{\sqrt{b}} = \sqrt{\dfrac{a}{b}}, \quad a \geq 0, \quad b > 0$

Discussion pages 245 and 247,
Examples 1–6, pages 245–248

Section 5.5

Properties of Real Numbers

Commutative property of addition: $a + b = b + a$
Commutative property of multiplication: $a \cdot b = b \cdot a$
Associative property of addition:
$(a + b) + c = a + (b + c)$
Associative property of multiplication:
$(a \cdot b) \cdot c = a \cdot (b \cdot c)$
Distributive property: $a \cdot (b + c) = ab + ac$

Discussion pages 253–256,
Examples 1–5, pages 253–256

Section 5.6

Rules of Exponents

Product rule for exponents: $a^m \cdot a^n = a^{m+n}$
Quotient rule for exponents: $\dfrac{a^m}{a^n} = a^{m-n}, \quad a \neq 0$
Zero exponent rule: $a^0 = 1, \quad a \neq 0$
Negative exponent rule: $a^{-m} = \dfrac{1}{a^m}, \quad a \neq 0$
Power rule: $(a^m)^n = a^{m \cdot n}$

Examples 1–7, pages 259–262

Scientific Notation	
Scientific notation is used to write very small or very large numbers. Each number in scientific notation is written as a number greater than or equal to 1 and less than 10 multiplied by an integer power of 10.	Discussion page 262, Examples 8–14, pages 263–266
Section 5.7 **Arithmetic Sequence**	
General or nth term: $a_n = a_1 + (n - 1)d$ Sum of the first n terms: $s_n = \dfrac{n(a_1 + a_n)}{2}$	Discussion page 270, Examples 1–5, pages 271–272
Geometric Sequence	
General or nth term: $a_n = a_1 r^{n-1}$ Sum of the first n terms: $s_n = \dfrac{a_1(1 - r^n)}{1 - r},\quad r \neq 1$	Discussion page 272, Examples 6–10, pages 273–275
Section 5.8 **Fibonacci Sequence**	
1, 1, 2, 3, 5, 8, 13, 21, ...	Discussion pages 278–282
Golden Number	
$\dfrac{\sqrt{5} + 1}{2} \approx 1.618$	Discussion pages 278–282
Golden Proportion	
$\dfrac{a + b}{a} = \dfrac{a}{b}$	Discussion pages 278–282

CHAPTER 5) *Review Exercises*

5.1

In Exercises 1 and 2, determine whether the number is divisible by each of the following numbers: 2, 3, 4, 5, 6, 8, 9, and 10.

1. 60,060

2. 400,644

In Exercises 3–7, determine the prime factorization of the number.

3. 588

4. 840

5. 1452

In Exercises 6–9, determine the GCD and LCM of the numbers.

6. 30, 105

7. 63, 108

8. 45, 250

9. 90, 300

10. *Train Stops* From 1912 to 1971, the Milwaukee Road Railroad Company had a train stop every 15 days in Dubuque, Iowa. During this same period, the same train also stopped in Des Moines, Iowa, every 9 days. If on April 18, 1964, the train made a stop in Dubuque and a stop in Des Moines, how many days was it until the train again stopped in both cities on the same day?

▲ *Des Moines, Iowa*

5.2

In Exercises 11–16, use a number line to evaluate the expression.

11. $6 + (-9)$ **12.** $-2 + 5$

13. $-2 + (-4)$ **14.** $4 - 8$

15. $-5 - 4$ **16.** $-3 - (-6)$

In Exercises 17–21, evaluate the expression.

17. $-2 \cdot 12$ **18.** $(-2)(-12)$

19. $\dfrac{-35}{-7}$ **20.** $\dfrac{12}{-6}$

21. $[8 \div (-4)](-3)$

5.3

In Exercises 22–27, express the fraction as a terminating or repeating decimal.

22. $\dfrac{17}{20}$ **23.** $\dfrac{13}{4}$

24. $\dfrac{6}{7}$ **25.** $\dfrac{7}{12}$

26. $\dfrac{3}{8}$ **27.** $\dfrac{11}{16}$

In Exercises 28–31, express the decimal number as a quotient of two integers.

28. 1.4 **29.** $0.\overline{6}$

30. $0.\overline{51}$ **31.** 0.083

In Exercises 32–33, express each mixed number as an improper fraction.

32. $2\dfrac{5}{7}$ **33.** $-3\dfrac{1}{4}$

In Exercises 34–35, express each improper fraction as a mixed number.

34. $\dfrac{11}{5}$ **35.** $-\dfrac{136}{5}$

In Exercises 36–41, perform the indicated operation and reduce your answer to lowest terms.

36. $\dfrac{11}{12} - \dfrac{2}{3}$ **37.** $\dfrac{1}{6} + \dfrac{5}{4}$

38. $\dfrac{7}{16} \cdot \dfrac{12}{21}$ **39.** $\dfrac{5}{9} \div \dfrac{6}{7}$

40. $\left(\dfrac{4}{5} + \dfrac{5}{7}\right) \div \dfrac{4}{5}$

41. $\left(\dfrac{2}{3} \cdot \dfrac{1}{7}\right) \div \dfrac{4}{7}$

42. *Cajun Turkey* A recipe for Roasted Cajun Turkey calls for $\frac{1}{8}$ teaspoon of cayenne pepper per pound of turkey.

If Jennifer Sabo is preparing a turkey that weighs $17\frac{3}{4}$ pounds, how much cayenne pepper does she need?

5.4

In Exercises 43–54, simplify the expression. Rationalize the denominator when necessary.

43. $\sqrt{75}$ **44.** $\sqrt{2} - 4\sqrt{2}$

45. $\sqrt{8} + 6\sqrt{2}$ **46.** $\sqrt{3} - 7\sqrt{27}$

47. $\sqrt{28} + \sqrt{63}$ **48.** $\sqrt{3} \cdot \sqrt{6}$

49. $\sqrt{8} \cdot \sqrt{6}$ **50.** $\dfrac{\sqrt{300}}{\sqrt{3}}$

51. $\dfrac{4}{\sqrt{3}}$ **52.** $\dfrac{\sqrt{7}}{\sqrt{5}}$

53. $3(2 + \sqrt{7})$ **54.** $\sqrt{3}(4 + \sqrt{6})$

5.5

In Exercises 55–61, state the name of the property illustrated.

55. $3 + 8 = 8 + 3$

56. $5 \cdot m = m \cdot 5$

57. $(1 + 2) + 3 = 1 + (2 + 3)$

58. $9(x + 1) = 9 \cdot x + 9 \cdot 1$

59. $(3 \cdot a) \cdot b = 3 \cdot (a \cdot b)$

60. $a \cdot (2 + 3) = (2 + 3) \cdot a$

61. $2(x + 3) = (2 \cdot x) + (2 \cdot 3)$

In Exercises 62–66, determine whether the set of numbers is closed under the given operation.

62. Natural numbers, subtraction

63. Whole numbers, multiplication

64. Integers, division

65. Real numbers, subtraction

66. Irrational numbers, multiplication

5.6

In Exercises 67–72, evaluate each expression.

67. 5^3

68. 5^{-2}

69. $\dfrac{9^5}{9^3}$

70. $5^2 \cdot 5$

71. 7^0

72. $(3^2)^2$

In Exercises 73–74, write each number in scientific notation.

73. 8,200,000,000

74. 0.0000158

In Exercises 75–76, express each number in decimal notation.

75. 2.8×10^5

76. 1.39×10^{-4}

In Exercises 77–78, (a) perform the indicated operation and write your answer in scientific notation. (b) Confirm the result found in part (a) by performing the calculation on a scientific calculator.

77. $(3 \times 10^4)(2 \times 10^{-9})$

78. $\dfrac{1.5 \times 10^{-3}}{5 \times 10^{-4}}$

In Exercises 79–81, (a) perform the indicated calculation by first converting each number to scientific notation. Write your answer in decimal notation. (b) Confirm the result found in part (a) by performing the calculation on a scientific calculator.

79. (550,000)(2,000,000)

80. $\dfrac{8,400,000}{70,000}$

81. $\dfrac{0.000002}{0.0000004}$

82. *Space Distances* The distance from Earth to the sun is about 1.49×10^{11} meters. The distance from Earth to the moon is about 3.84×10^8 meters. The distance from Earth to the sun is how many times larger than the distance from Earth to the moon? Use a scientific calculator and round your answer to the nearest whole number.

▲ *Earth*

83. *Outstanding Debt* As a result of a recent water and sewer system improvement, the city of Galena, Illinois, has an outstanding debt of $20,000,000. If the population of Galena is 3600 people, how much would each person have to contribute to pay off the outstanding debt?

5.7

In Exercises 84–85, determine whether the sequence is arithmetic or geometric. Then determine the next two terms of the sequence.

84. $1, 5, 9, 13, \ldots$

85. $\frac{1}{2}, 1, 2, 4, \ldots$

In Exercises 86–89, determine the indicated term of the sequence with the given first term, a_1, and common difference, d, or common ratio, r.

86. Determine a_9 when $a_1 = -6, d = 2$.

87. Determine a_{10} when $a_1 = -20, d = 5$.

88. Determine a_5 when $a_1 = 3, r = 2$.

89. Determine a_4 when $a_1 = -6, r = 2$.

In Exercises 90–91, determine the sum of the arithmetic sequence. The number of terms, n, is given.

90. $3, 6, 9, 12, \ldots, 150; n = 50$

91. $0.5, 0.75, 1.00, 1.25, \ldots, 5.25; n = 20$

In Exercises 92–93, determine the sum of the first n terms of the geometric sequence for the values of a_1 and r.

92. $n = 4, a_1 = 3, r = 2$

93. $n = 6, a_1 = 1, r = -2$

In Exercises 94–97, first determine whether the sequence is arithmetic or geometric; then write an expression for the general or nth term, a_n.

94. $3, 6, 9, 12, \ldots$

95. $1, 4, 7, 10, \ldots$

96. $2, -2, 2, -2, \ldots$

97. $5, \frac{5}{3}, \frac{5}{9}, \frac{5}{27}, \ldots$

5.8

In Exercises 98–99, determine whether the sequence is a Fibonacci–type sequence. If so, determine the next two terms.

98. $0, 1, 1, 2, 2, 3, 3, 4, 4, \ldots$

99. $-1, 0, -1, -1, -2, -3, -5, \ldots$

CHAPTER 5 Test

1. Which of the numbers 2, 3, 4, 5, 6, 8, 9, and 10 divide 48,395?

2. Determine the prime factorization of 414.

3. Evaluate $[(-3) + 7] - (-4)$.

4. Evaluate $[(-70)(-5)] \div (8 - 10)$.

5. Convert $4\frac{5}{8}$ to an improper fraction.

6. Write $\frac{5}{8}$ as a terminating or repeating decimal.

7. Express 6.45 as a quotient of two integers.

8. Perform the operation and reduce the answer to lowest terms: $\frac{17}{24} - \frac{7}{12}$.

9. Simplify $\sqrt{75} + \sqrt{48}$.

10. Rationalize the denominator $\dfrac{\sqrt{2}}{\sqrt{7}}$.

11. Determine whether the integers are closed under the operation of multiplication. Explain your answer.

Name the property illustrated.

12. $(x + 3) + 5 = x + (3 + 5)$

Evaluate.

13. $\dfrac{4^5}{4^2}$

14. $4^3 \cdot 4^2$

15. 3^{-4}

16. Perform the operation by first converting the numerator and denominator to scientific notation. Write the answer in scientific notation.

$$\frac{7,200,000}{0.000009}$$

17. Write an expression for the general or nth term, a_n, of the sequence $-2, -6, -10, -14, \ldots$.

18. Determine the sum of the terms of the arithmetic sequence. The number of terms, n, is given.

$$-2, -5, -8, -11, \ldots, -32; n = 11$$

19. Write an expression for the general or nth term, a_n, of the sequence $3, 6, 12, 24, \ldots$.

20. Write the first 10 terms of the Fibonacci sequence.

GROUP PROJECTS

1. *Making Rice* The amounts of ingredients needed to make 3 and 5 servings of rice are:

To Make	Rice and Water	Salt	Butter
3 servings	1 cup	$\frac{3}{8}$ tsp	$1\frac{1}{2}$ tsp
5 servings	$1\frac{2}{3}$ cup	$\frac{5}{8}$ tsp	$2\frac{1}{2}$ tsp

Find the amount of each ingredient needed to make (a) 2 servings, (b) 1 serving, and (c) 29 servings. Explain how you determined your answers.

2. *Finding Areas*

a) Determine the area of the trapezoid shown by finding the area of the three parts indicated and finding the

sum of the three areas. The necessary geometric formulas are given in Chapter 9.

b) Determine the area of the trapezoid by using the formula for the area of a trapezoid given in Chapter 9.

c) Compare your answers from parts (a) and (b). Are they the same? If not, explain why they are different.

3. *Medical Insurance* On a medical insurance policy (such as Blue Cross/Blue Shield), the policyholder may need to make copayments for prescription drugs, office visits, and procedures until the total of all copayments reaches a specified amount. Suppose that the copayment on the Gattelaro's medical policy for prescription drugs is 50% of the cost; the copayment for office visits is $10; and the copayment for all medical tests, x-rays, and other procedures is 20% of the cost. After the family's copayment totals $500 in a calendar year, all medical and prescription bills are paid in full by the insurance company. The Gattelaros had the following medical expenses from January 1 through April 30.

Date	Reason	Cost before Copayment
January 10	Office visit	$40
	Prescription	$44
February 27	Office visit	$40
	Medical tests	$188
April 19	Office visit	$40
	X-rays	$348
	Prescription	$76

a) How much had the Gattelaros paid in copayments from January 1 through April 30?

b) How much had the medical insurance company paid?

c) What is the remaining copayment that must be paid by the Gattelaros before the $500 copayment limit is reached?

4. *A Branching Plant* A plant grows for two months and then adds a new branch. Each new branch grows for two months and then adds another branch. After the second month, each branch adds a new branch every month. Assume the growth begins in January.

a) How many branches will there be in February?

b) How many branches will there be in May?

c) How many branches will there be after 12 months?

d) How is this problem similar to the problem involving rabbits that appeared in Fibonacci's book *Liber Abacci* (see page 278)?

6

Algebra, Graphs, and Functions

Why This is Important

Algebra is one of the most practical tools for solving everyday problems. You use algebra daily without realizing it. For example, you use a coordinate system when you consult a map. To evaluate how much interest you will earn in a savings account or to determine how long it will take you to travel a given distance, you use common algebraic formulas. The symbolic language of algebra makes it an excellent tool for solving problems because it allows us to write lengthy expressions in compact form. English philosopher Alfred North Whitehead explained the power of algebra when he stated, "By relieving the brain of unnecessary work, a good notation sets the mind free to concentrate on more advanced problems."

◀ *Algebra is a tool for solving everyday problems such as changing a recipe to increase or decrease the number of servings.*

SECTION 6.1   Order of Operations

▲ *You can use algebra to determine the sales tax rate when purchasing items such as tires.*

Did You Know?

Broken Bones

Imagine yourself walking down a street in Spain during the Middle Ages. You see a sign over a door: "*Algebrista y Sangrador.*" Inside, you would find a person more ready to give you a haircut than help you with your algebra. The sign translates into "Bonesetter and Bloodletter," relatively simple medical treatments administered in barbershops of the day.

The root word *al-jabr*, which the Muslims (Moors) brought to Spain along with some concepts of algebra, suggests the restoring of broken parts. The parts might be bones, or they might be mathematical expressions that are broken into separate parts and the parts moved from one side of an equation to the other and reunited in such a way as to make a solution more obvious.

Knowing the order of operations is essential to solving problems algebraically. There are many everyday problems that can be easily solved if you have an understanding of algebra. Suppose you see an advertisement for tires that states: "Purchase Michelin All-Season Tires for $135 each. This price includes mounting." You purchase four tires and have them mounted on your car. Your total price, including sales tax, comes to $583.50. What is the sales tax rate? In this section, we will discuss how to use algebra to answer questions like the one above.

Why *This is Important* This is just one type of problem that can be solved algebraically. In this section and chapter you will see many more real-life applications of algebra.

Algebra is a generalized form of arithmetic. The word *algebra* is derived from the Arabic word *al-jabr* (meaning "reunion of broken parts"), which was the title of a book written by the mathematician Muhammed ibn-Musa al Khwarizmi in about A.D. 825.

Algebra uses letters of the alphabet called *variables* to represent numbers. Often the letters x and y are used to represent variables. However, any letter may be used as a variable. A symbol that represents a specific quantity is called a *constant*.

Multiplication of numbers and variables may be represented in several different ways in algebra. Because the "times" sign might be confused with the variable x, a dot between two numbers or variables indicates multiplication. Thus, $3 \cdot 4$ means 3 times 4, and $x \cdot y$ means x times y. Placing two letters or a number and a letter next to one another, with or without parentheses, also indicates multiplication. Thus, $3x$ means 3 times x, xy means x times y, and $(x)(y)$ means x times y.

An *algebraic expression* (or simply an *expression*) is a collection of variables, numbers, parentheses, and operation symbols. Some examples of algebraic expressions are

$$x, \qquad x + 2, \qquad 3(2x + 3), \qquad \frac{3x + 1}{2x - 3}, \qquad \text{and} \qquad x^2 + 7x + 3$$

Two algebraic expressions joined by an equal sign form an *equation*. Some examples of equations are

$$x + 2 = 4, \qquad 3x + 4 = 1, \qquad \text{and} \qquad x + 3 = 2x$$

The *solution to an equation* is the number or numbers that replace the variable to make the equation a true statement. For example, the solution to the equation $x + 3 = 4$ is 1. When we find the solution to an equation, we *solve the equation*.

We can determine if any number is a solution to an equation by *checking the solution*. To check the solution, we substitute the number for the variable in the equation. If the resulting statement is a true statement, that number is a solution to the equation. If the resulting statement is a false statement, the number is not a solution to the equation. To check the number 1 in the equation $x + 3 = 4$, we do the following.

$$x + 3 = 4$$
$$1 + 3 = 4 \qquad \text{Substitute 1 for } x.$$
$$4 = 4 \qquad \text{True}$$

The same number is obtained on both sides of the equal sign, so 1 is the solution. For the equation $x + 3 = 4$, the only solution is 1. Any other value of x would result in the check being a false statement.

To *evaluate an expression* means to find the value of the expression for a given value of the variable. To evaluate expressions and solve equations, you must have an understanding of exponents. Exponents (Section 5.6) are used to abbreviate repeated multiplication. For example, the expression 5^2 means $5 \cdot 5$. The 2 in the expression 5^2 is the *exponent*, and the 5 is the *base*. We read 5^2 as "5 to the second power" or "5 squared," and 5^2 means $5 \cdot 5$ or 25.

In general, the number b to the nth power, written b^n, means

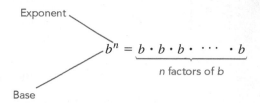

$$\underbrace{b^n = b \cdot b \cdot b \cdot \,\cdots\, \cdot b}_{n \text{ factors of } b}$$

An exponent refers only to its base. In the expression -5^2, the base is 5. In the expression $(-5)^2$, the base is -5.

$$-5^2 = -(5)^2 = -1(5)^2 = -1(5)(5) = -25$$
$$(-5)^2 = (-5)(-5) = 25$$

Note that $-5^2 \neq (-5)^2$ since $-25 \neq 25$.

Order of Operations

To evaluate an expression or to check the solution to an equation, we need to know the *order of operations* to follow. For example, suppose we want to evaluate the expression $2 + 3x$ when $x = 4$. Substituting 4 for x, we obtain $2 + 3 \cdot 4$. What is the value of $2 + 3 \cdot 4$? Does it equal 20, or does it equal 14? Some standard rules, called the order of operations, have been developed to ensure that there is only one correct answer. In mathematics, unless parentheses indicate otherwise, always perform multiplication before addition. Thus, the correct answer is 14.

$$2 + 3 \cdot 4 = 2 + (3 \cdot 4) = 2 + 12 = 14$$

The order of operations for evaluating an expression is as follows.

> **TIMELY TIP**
> Some students use the phrase "*P*lease *E*xcuse *M*y *D*ear *A*unt *S*ally" or the word "PEMDAS" (*P*arentheses, *E*xponents, *M*ultiplication, *D*ivision, *A*ddition, *S*ubtraction) to remind them of the order of operations. Remember: Multiplication and division are of the same order, and addition and subtraction are of the same order.

> **PROCEDURE   ORDER OF OPERATIONS**
> 1. First, perform all operations within parentheses or other grouping symbols (according to the following order).
> 2. Next, perform all exponential operations (that is, raising to powers or finding roots).
> 3. Next, perform all multiplications and divisions from left to right.
> 4. Finally, perform all additions and subtractions from left to right.

Example 1 *Evaluating an Expression*

Evaluate the expression $-x^2 + 4x + 16$ for $x = 3$.

Solution Substitute 3 for each x and use the order of operations to evaluate the expression.

$$-x^2 + 4x + 16$$
$$= -(3)^2 + 4(3) + 16$$
$$= -9 + 12 + 16$$
$$= 3 + 16$$
$$= 19$$

Example 2 *Finding the Height*

A diver jumps from a platform diving board that is 32 feet above water. The height of the diver above water, in feet, t seconds after jumping from the platform, can be determined by the expression $-16t^2 + 20t + 32$. Determine the diver's height above the water 2 seconds after jumping from the platform.

Solution Substitute 2 for each t.

$$-16t^2 + 20t + 32$$
$$= -16(2)^2 + 20(2) + 32$$
$$= -16(4) + 20(2) + 32$$
$$= -64 + 40 + 32$$
$$= -24 + 32$$
$$= 8$$

The diver is 8 feet above water 2 seconds after jumping from the platform.

Example 3 *Substituting for Two Variables*

Evaluate $-3x^2 + 2xy - 2y^2$ when $x = 2$ and $y = 3$.

Solution Substitute 2 for each x and 3 for each y; then evaluate using the order of operations.

$$-3x^2 + 2xy - 2y^2$$
$$= -3(2)^2 + 2(2)(3) - 2(3)^2$$
$$= -3(4) + 2(2)(3) - 2(9)$$
$$= -12 + 12 - 18$$
$$= 0 - 18$$
$$= -18$$

Example 4 *Is 2 a Solution?*

Determine whether 2 is a solution to the equation $3x^2 + 7x - 11 = 15$.

Solution To determine whether 2 is a solution to the equation, substitute 2 for each x in the equation. Then evaluate the left-hand side of the equation using the order of operations. If the left-hand side of the equation equals 15, then both sides of the equation have the same value and 2 is a solution. When checking the solution, we use $\overset{?}{=}$, which means we are not sure if the statement is true.

$$3x^2 + 7x - 11 = 15$$
$$3(2)^2 + 7(2) - 11 \overset{?}{=} 15 \quad \text{Substitute 2 for x.}$$
$$3(4) + 14 - 11 \overset{?}{=} 15$$
$$12 + 14 - 11 \overset{?}{=} 15$$
$$26 - 11 \overset{?}{=} 15$$
$$15 = 15 \quad \text{True}$$

Because 2 makes the equation a true statement, 2 is a solution to the equation. ∎

SECTION 6.1 Exercises

Warm Up Exercises

In Exercises 1–8, fill in the blank with an appropriate word, phrase, or symbol(s).

1. A letter of the alphabet used to represent numbers is called a(n) _____.

2. A symbol that represents a specific quantity is called a(n) _____.

3. A collection of variables, numbers, parentheses, and operation symbols is called an algebraic _____.

4. For the expression 4^5 the base is _____.

5. For the expression 8^3 the exponent is _____.

6. The number or numbers that replace the variable to make an equation a true statement is called the _____ to the equation.

7. To find the value of an expression for a given value of the variable means to _____ an expression.

8. To evaluate $8 + 16 \div 4$, we perform the operation of _____ first.

Practice the Skills

In Exercises 9–28, evaluate the expression for the given value(s) of the variable(s).

9. x^2, $x = -6$
10. x^2, $x = 5$
11. $-x^2$, $x = -4$
12. $-x^2$, $x = -2$
13. $-2x^3$, $x = -7$
14. $-x^3$, $x = -4$
15. $x - 7$, $x = 4$
16. $8x - 3$, $x = \frac{5}{2}$
17. $-3x + 7$, $x = -2$
18. $4x - 3$, $x = -1$

19. $x^2 - 5x + 12$, $x = 3$
20. $-x^2 + 3x - 10$, $x = -2$
21. $\frac{1}{2}x^2 - 5x + 2$, $x = \frac{2}{3}$
22. $\frac{2}{3}x^2 + x - 1$, $x = \frac{1}{2}$
23. $8x^3 - 4x^2 + 7$, $x = \frac{1}{2}$
24. $-x^2 + 5xy$, $x = 2$, $y = -3$
25. $3x^2 - xy + 2y^2$, $x = -2$, $y = 1$
26. $3x^2 + \frac{2}{5}xy - \frac{1}{5}y^2$, $x = 2$, $y = 5$
27. $4x^2 - 10xy + 3y^2$, $x = 2$, $y = -1$
28. $(2x - y)^2$, $x = 4$, $y = -2$

In Exercises 29–38, determine whether the value(s) is (are) a solution to the equation.

29. $5x + 2 = 17$, $x = 3$
30. $6x - 3 = -27$, $x = -4$
31. $x - 3y = 0$, $x = 6$, $y = 3$
32. $4x + 2y = -2$, $x = -2$, $y = 3$
33. $-x^2 + 3x + 6 = 5$, $x = 2$
34. $-2x^2 + x + 5 = 20$, $x = 3$
35. $3x^2 + 2x = 40$, $x = -4$
36. $y = x^2 + 3x - 6$, $x = -1$, $y = -8$
37. $y = -x^2 + 3x - 1$, $x = 3$, $y = -1$
38. $y = x^3 - 3x^2 + 1$, $x = 2$, $y = -3$

Problem Solving

39. *Cost of Reimbursement* When employees travel out of town on company business, the cost for reimbursement can be determined by the expression $0.55x$, where x is the number of miles driven. Determine the cost of reimbursement if an employee drives 120 miles on company business.

40. *8 Trillion Calculations* If a computer can do a calculation in 0.000002 sec, the time required to do n calculations can be determined by the expression $0.000002n$. Determine the number of seconds needed for the computer to do 8 trillion (8,000,000,000,000) calculations.

41. *Electronic Filing* The graph shows the number of taxpayers, in millions, filing their taxes electronically for the years 2004 through 2009. The number of taxpayers, in millions, filing their taxes electronically per year can be approximated by the expression $6.8x + 61$, where x is the number of years since 2004. For example, the year 2005 would correspond to $x = 1$. Assuming this trend continues, use the expression to approximate the number of taxpayers who will file their taxes electronically in 2012.

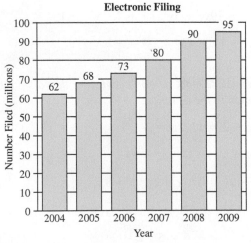

Electronic Filing

Source: *Internal Revenue Service*

42. *Cost of a Tour* The cost, in dollars, for Crescent City Tours to provide a tour for x people can be determined by the expression $220 + 2.75x$. Determine the cost for Crescent City Tours to provide a tour for 75 people.

43. *Drying Time* The time, in minutes, needed for clothes hanging on a line outdoors to dry, at a specific temperature and wind speed, depends on the humidity, h. The time can be approximated by the expression $2h^2 + 80h + 40$, where h is the percent humidity expressed as a decimal number. Find the length of time required for clothing to dry if there is 60% humidity.

44. *Stopping Distance* A typical car's stopping distance, in feet, on wet pavement can be approximated by the expression $0.08s^2 + 0.24s - 7.10$, where s is the speed of the car, in miles per hour (mph), before braking and $60 \leq s \leq 80$ miles per hour. Use the expression to approximate the car's stopping distance on wet pavement if the speed of the car before braking is 72 mph.

45. *Grass Growth* The rate of growth of grass, in inches per week, depends on a number of factors, including rainfall and temperature. For a certain area, this rate can be approximated by the expression $0.2R^2 + 0.003RT + 0.0001T^2$, where R is the weekly rainfall, in inches, and T is the average weekly temperature, in degrees Fahrenheit. Find the amount of growth of grass for a week in which the rainfall is 2 in. and the average temperature is 70°F.

Concept/Writing Exercises

46. Explain why $(-1)^n = 1$ for any even number n.

47. Does $(x + y)^2 = x^2 + y^2$? Complete the table and state your conclusion.

x	y	$(x + y)^2$	$x^2 + y^2$
2	3		
−2	−3		
−2	3		
2	−3		

48. Suppose n represents any natural number. Explain why 1^n equals 1.

49. a) Explain why $-x^2$ will always be a negative number for any nonzero real number selected for x.

   b) Explain why $(-x)^2$ will always be a positive number for any nonzero real number selected for x.

Internet/Research Activity

50. When were exponents first used? Write a paper explaining how exponents were first used and when mathematicians began writing them in the present form.

SECTION 6.2   Linear Equations in One Variable

▲ *A linear equation can be used to determine a salespersons weekly salary based upon weekly sales.*

While attending college, you work part time at a clothing store. You receive a weekly salary plus a commission on all clothing you sell. A linear equation can be written to determine your weekly salary based upon your weekly sales. In fact, many real-life situations can be expressed as linear equations.

Why *This is Important* Being able to solve equations algebraically will be very useful when solving application problems in this and later sections of this chapter and throughout life.

In Section 6.1, we stated that two algebraic expressions joined by an equal sign form an equation. The solution to some equations, such as $x + 3 = 4$, can be easily found by trial and error. Solving more difficult equations such as $60 = 0.51x + 40.1$ or $2x - 3 = 4(x + 3)$, however, requires us to understand some basic properties of equations.

The parts that are added or subtracted in an algebraic expression are called *terms*. The expression $0.51x + 40.1$ contains two terms: $0.51x$ and $+ 40.1$. The expression $4x - 3y - 5$ contains three terms: $4x$, $-3y$, and -5. The $+$ and $-$ signs that break the expression into terms are part of the terms. When listing the terms of an expression, however, it is not necessary to include the $+$ sign at the beginning of the term.

The numerical part of a term is called its *numerical coefficient* or, simply, its *coefficient*. In the term $4x$, the 4 is the numerical coefficient. In the term $-4y$, the -4 is the numerical coefficient.

Like terms are terms that have the same variables with the same exponents on the variables. *Unlike terms* have different variables or different exponents on the variables.

Like Terms	Unlike Terms
$2x$, $7x$ (same variable, x)	$2x$, 9 (only first term has a variable)
$-8y$, $3y$ (same variable, y)	$5x$, $6y$ (different variables)
-4, 10 (both constants)	x, 8 (only first term has a variable)
$-5x^2$, $6x^2$ (same variable with same exponent)	$2x^3$, $3x^2$ (different exponents)

To *simplify an expression* means to combine like terms by using the commutative, associative, and distributive properties discussed in Chapter 5. For convenience, we list these properties below.

Properties of the Real Numbers

$a(b + c) = ab + ac$ Distributive property
$a + b = b + a$ Commutative property of addition
$ab = ba$ Commutative property of multiplication
$(a + b) + c = a + (b + c)$ Associative property of addition
$(ab)c = a(bc)$ Associative property of multiplication

Example 1 *Combining Like Terms*

Combine like terms in each expression.
a) $8x + 4x$
b) $7y - 5y$
c) $x + 12 - 3x + 7$
d) $-2x + 4 - 6y - 11 - 5y + 3x$

François Viète

Greek philosopher Diophantus of Alexandria (A.D. 250), who invented notations for powers of a number and for multiplication and division of simple quantities, is thought to have made the first attempts at algebra. Not until the sixteenth century, however, did French mathematician François Viète (1540–1603) use symbols to represent numbers, the foundation of symbolic algebra. The work of René Descartes (1596–1660), though, is considered to be the starting point of modern-day algebra. In 1707, Sir Isaac Newton (1643–1727) gave symbolic mathematics the name *universal arithmetic*.

Solution

a) We use the distributive property (in reverse) to combine like terms.

$$8x + 4x = (8 + 4)x \qquad \text{Distributive property}$$
$$= 12x$$

b) $7y - 5y = (7 - 5)y = 2y$

c) $x + 12 - 3x + 7 = x - 3x + 12 + 7$ Rearrange terms; place like terms together.
$$= -2x + 19 \qquad \text{Combine like terms.}$$

d) $-2x + 4 - 6y - 11 - 5y + 3x$
$$= -2x + 3x - 6y - 5y + 4 - 11 \qquad \text{Rearrange terms; place like terms together.}$$
$$= x - 11y - 7 \qquad \text{Combine like terms.} \quad \blacksquare$$

We are able to rearrange the terms of an expression, as was done in Example 1(c) and (d) by the commutative and associative properties that were discussed in Section 5.5.

The order of the terms in an expression is not crucial. However, when listing the terms of an expression, we generally list the terms in alphabetical order, with the constant, the term without a variable, last.

Solving Equations

Recall that to solve an equation means to find the value or values for the variable that make(s) the equation true. In this section, we discuss solving *linear (or first-degree) equations*. A linear equation in one variable is one in which the exponent on the variable is 1. Examples of linear equations are $5x - 1 = 3$ and $2x + 4 = 6x - 5$.

Equivalent equations are equations that have the same solution. The equations $2x - 5 = 1$, $2x = 6$, and $x = 3$ are all equivalent equations since they all have the same solution, 3. When we solve an equation, we write the given equation as a series of simpler equivalent equations until we obtain an equation of the form $x = c$, where c is some real number.

To solve any equation, we have to *isolate the variable*. That means getting the variable by itself on one side of the equal sign. The four properties of equality that we are about to discuss are used to isolate the variable. The first is the addition property.

Addition Property of Equality
If $a = b$, then $a + c = b + c$ for all real numbers a, b, and c.

The addition property of equality indicates that the same number can be added to both sides of an equation without changing the solution.

Example 2 *Using the Addition Property of Equality*

Determine the solution to the equation $x - 9 = 15$.

Solution To isolate the variable, add 9 to both sides of the equation.

$$x - 9 = 15$$
$$x - 9 + 9 = 15 + 9$$
$$x + 0 = 24$$
$$x = 24$$

CHECK:
$$x - 9 = 15$$
$$24 - 9 \overset{?}{=} 15 \qquad \text{Substitute 24 for } x.$$
$$15 = 15 \qquad \text{True} \qquad \blacksquare$$

In Example 2, we showed the step $x + 0 = 24$. This step is usually done mentally, and the step is usually not listed.

Subtraction Property of Equality
If $a = b$, then $a - c = b - c$ for all real numbers a, b, and c.

The subtraction property of equality indicates that the same number can be subtracted from both sides of an equation without changing the solution.

Example 3 Using the Subtraction Property of Equality

Determine the solution to the equation $x + 11 = 19$.

Solution To isolate the variable, subtract 11 from both sides of the equation.

$$x + 11 = 19$$
$$x + 11 - 11 = 19 - 11$$
$$x = 8$$

Note in Example 3 that we did not subtract 19 from both sides of the equation, because doing so would not result in getting x on one side of the equal sign by itself. Now we discuss the multiplication property.

Multiplication Property of Equality
If $a = b$, then $a \cdot c = b \cdot c$ for all real numbers a, b, and c, where $c \neq 0$.

The multiplication property of equality indicates that both sides of the equation can be multiplied by the same nonzero number without changing the solution.

Example 4 Using the Multiplication Property of Equality

Determine the solution to $\dfrac{x}{4} = 8$.

Solution To solve this equation, multiply both sides of the equation by 4.

$$\frac{x}{4} = 8$$
$$4\left(\frac{x}{4}\right) = 4(8)$$
$$\frac{\overset{1}{\cancel{4}}x}{\underset{1}{\cancel{4}}} = 32$$
$$1x = 32$$
$$x = 32$$

In Example 4, we showed the steps $\dfrac{4x}{4} = 32$ and $1x = 32$. Usually, we will not illustrate these steps.

Division Property of Equality
If $a = b$, then $\dfrac{a}{c} = \dfrac{b}{c}$ for all real numbers a, b, and c, $c \neq 0$.

The division property of equality indicates that both sides of an equation can be divided by the same nonzero number without changing the solution. Note that the divisor, c, cannot be 0 because division by 0 is not permitted.

Example 5 *Using the Division Property of Equality*

Solve the equation $7x = 35$.

Solution To solve this equation, divide both sides of the equation by 7.

$$7x = 35$$

$$\frac{7x}{7} = \frac{35}{7}$$

$$x = 5$$

An *algorithm* is a general procedure for accomplishing a task. The following general procedure is an algorithm for solving linear (or first-degree) equations. Sometimes the solution to an equation may be found more easily by using a variation of this general procedure. Remember that the primary objective in solving any equation is to isolate the variable.

> **PROCEDURE**   **A GENERAL PROCEDURE FOR SOLVING LINEAR EQUATIONS**
>
> 1. If the equation contains fractions, multiply both sides of the equation by the lowest common denominator (or least common multiple). This step will eliminate all fractions from the equation.
> 2. Use the distributive property to remove parentheses when necessary.
> 3. Combine like terms on the same side of the equal sign when possible.
> 4. Use the addition or subtraction property to collect all terms with a variable on one side of the equal sign and all constants on the other side of the equal sign. It may be necessary to use the addition or subtraction property more than once. This process will eventually result in an equation of the form $ax = b$, where a and b are real numbers.
> 5. Solve for the variable using the division or multiplication property. The result will be an answer in the form $x = c$, where c is a real number.

Example 6 *Using the General Procedure*

Solve the equation $2x - 9 = 19$.

Solution Our goal is to isolate the variable; therefore, we start by getting the term $2x$ by itself on one side of the equation.

$$2x - 9 = 19$$

$$2x - 9 + 9 = 19 + 9 \quad \text{Add 9 to both sides of the equation (addition property) (Step 4).}$$

$$2x = 28$$

$$\frac{2x}{2} = \frac{28}{2} \quad \text{Divide both sides of the equation by 2 (division property) (Step 5).}$$

$$x = 14$$

A check will show that 14 is the solution to $2x - 9 = 19$.

Did You Know?

A New Concept

Well into the sixteenth century, mathematicians found it difficult to accept the idea that the solution to a problem (such as Example 7) could be a negative number because negative numbers could not be accepted as physically real. In the early days of algebra, someone working a problem did not isolate a variable by subtracting like terms. Instead, a problem would be put into a form that allowed only positive coefficients and answers. Albert Girard (1595–1637) contributed to the evolution of a correct understanding of negative quantities.

Example 7 *Solving a Linear Equation*

Solve the equation $4 = 5 + 2(t + 1)$ for t.

Solution Our goal is to isolate the variable t. To do so, follow the general procedure for solving equations.

$$4 = 5 + 2(t + 1)$$

$$4 = 5 + 2t + 2 \qquad \text{Distributive property (Step 2)}$$

$$4 = 2t + 7 \qquad \text{Combine like terms (Step 3).}$$

$$4 - 7 = 2t + 7 - 7 \qquad \text{Subtraction property (Step 4)}$$

$$-3 = 2t$$

$$\frac{-3}{2} = \frac{2t}{2} \qquad \text{Division property (Step 5)}$$

$$-\frac{3}{2} = t \qquad \blacksquare$$

Example 8 *Solving an Equation Containing Fractions*

Solve the equation $\dfrac{2x}{3} + \dfrac{1}{3} = \dfrac{3}{4}$.

Solution When an equation contains fractions, we generally begin by multiplying each term of the equation by the lowest common denominator, LCD (see page 237 in Chapter 5). In this example, the LCD is 12 because 12 is the smallest number that is divisible by both 3 and 4.

$$12\left(\frac{2x}{3} + \frac{1}{3}\right) = 12\left(\frac{3}{4}\right) \qquad \text{Multiply both sides of the equation by the LCD (Step 1).}$$

$$12\left(\frac{2x}{3}\right) + 12\left(\frac{1}{3}\right) = 12\left(\frac{3}{4}\right) \qquad \text{Distributive property (Step 2)}$$

$$\overset{4}{\cancel{12}}\left(\frac{2x}{\cancel{3}}\right) + \overset{4}{\cancel{12}}\left(\frac{1}{\cancel{3}}\right) = \overset{3}{\cancel{12}}\left(\frac{3}{\cancel{4}}\right) \qquad \text{Divide out common factors.}$$

$$8x + 4 = 9$$

$$8x + 4 - 4 = 9 - 4 \qquad \text{Subtraction property (Step 4)}$$

$$8x = 5$$

$$\frac{8x}{8} = \frac{5}{8} \qquad \text{Division property (Step 5)}$$

$$x = \frac{5}{8}$$

A check will show that $\frac{5}{8}$ is the solution to the equation. You could have worked the problem without first multiplying both sides of the equation by the LCD. Try it! $\blacksquare$

Example 9 *Variables on Both Sides of the Equation*

Solve the equation $6x + 8 = 10x + 12$.

Solution Note that the equation has an x on both sides of the equal sign. In equations of this type, you might wonder what to do first. It actually does not matter as long as you do not forget the goal of isolating the variable x. Let's collect the terms containing a variable on the left-hand side of the equation.

$$6x + 8 = 10x + 12$$

$$6x + 8 - 8 = 10x + 12 - 8 \qquad \text{Subtraction property (Step 4)}$$

$$6x = 10x + 4$$

$$6x - 10x = 10x - 10x + 4 \qquad \text{Subtraction property (Step 4)}$$

$$-4x = 4$$

$$\frac{-4x}{-4} = \frac{4}{-4} \qquad \text{Division property (Step 5)}$$

$$x = -1$$

In the solution to Example 9, the terms containing the variable were collected on the left-hand side of the equal sign. Now work Example 9, collecting the terms with the variable on the right-hand side of the equal sign. If you do so correctly, you will get the same result.

Example 10 *Solving an Equation Containing Decimals*

Solve the equation $4x - 0.48 = 0.8x + 4$ and check your solution.

Solution This equation may be solved with the decimals, or you may multiply each term by 100 and eliminate the decimals. We will solve the equation with the decimals.

$$4x - 0.48 = 0.8x + 4$$

$$4x - 0.48 + 0.48 = 0.8x + 4 + 0.48 \qquad \text{Addition property}$$

$$4x = 0.8x + 4.48$$

$$4x - 0.8x = 0.8x - 0.8x + 4.48 \qquad \text{Subtraction property}$$

$$3.2x = 4.48$$

$$\frac{3.2x}{3.2} = \frac{4.48}{3.2} \qquad \text{Division property}$$

$$x = 1.4$$

CHECK:
$$4x - 0.48 = 0.8x + 4$$

$$4(1.4) - 0.48 \overset{?}{=} 0.8(1.4) + 4 \qquad \text{Substitute 1.4 for each x in the equation.}$$

$$5.6 - 0.48 \overset{?}{=} 1.12 + 4$$

$$5.12 = 5.12 \qquad \text{True}$$

In Chapter 5, we explained that $a - b$ can be expressed as $a + (-b)$. We use this principle in Example 11.

Example 11 *Using the Definition of Subtraction*

Solve $12 = 2(3r - 4) - 4r$ for r.

TIMELY TIP
Remember that the goal in solving an equation is to get the variable alone on one side of the equal sign by using the general procedure for solving equations.

Solution Our goal is to isolate the variable r. To do so, follow the general procedure for solving equations.

$$12 = 2(3r - 4) - 4r$$

$$12 = 2[3r + (-4)] - 4r \qquad \text{Definition of subtraction}$$

$$12 = 2(3r) + 2(-4) - 4r \qquad \text{Distributive property}$$

$$12 = 6r - 8 - 4r$$

$$12 = 2r - 8 \qquad \text{Combine like terms.}$$

$$12 + 8 = 2r - 8 + 8 \qquad \text{Addition property}$$

$$20 = 2r$$

$$\frac{20}{2} = \frac{2r}{2} \qquad \text{Division property}$$

$$10 = r$$ ∎

So far, every equation has had exactly one solution. Some equations, however, have no solution, and others have more than one solution. Example 12 illustrates an equation that has no solution, and Example 13 illustrates an equation that has an infinite number of solutions.

Example 12 *An Equation with No Solution*

Solve $2(x - 4) + x + 5 = 5x - 2(x + 4)$.

Solution

$$2(x - 4) + x + 5 = 5x - 2(x + 4)$$

$$2x - 8 + x + 5 = 5x - 2x - 8 \qquad \text{Distributive property}$$

$$3x - 3 = 3x - 8 \qquad \text{Combine like terms.}$$

$$3x - 3x - 3 = 3x - 3x - 8 \qquad \text{Subtraction property}$$

$$-3 = -8 \qquad \text{False}$$

During the process of solving an equation, if you obtain a false statement like $-3 = -8$, or $5 = 0$, the equation has *no solution*. An equation that has no solution is called a *contradiction*. The equation $2(x - 4) + x + 5 = 5x - 2(x + 4)$ is a contradiction and thus has no solution.   ∎

Example 13 *An Equation with Infinitely Many Solutions*

Solve $2(x + 4) - 3(x - 5) = -x + 23$.

Solution

$$2(x + 4) - 3(x - 5) = -x + 23$$

$$2x + 8 - 3x + 15 = -x + 23 \qquad \text{Distributive property}$$

$$-x + 23 = -x + 23 \qquad \text{Combine like terms.}$$

Note that at this point both sides of the equation are the same. Every real number will satisfy this equation. This equation has an infinite number of solutions. An equation of this type is called an *identity*. When solving an equation, you can tell that the equation is an identity if you notice that the same expression appears on both sides of the equal sign. The solution to any linear equation with one variable that is an identity is *all real numbers*. If you continue to solve an equation that is an identity, you will end up with $0 = 0$, as follows.

$$-x + 23 = -x + 23$$

$$-x + x + 23 = -x + x + 23 \quad \text{Addition property}$$

$$23 = 23 \quad \text{Combine like terms.}$$

$$23 - 23 = 23 - 23 \quad \text{Subtraction property}$$

$$0 = 0 \quad \text{True for any value of } x$$

Proportions

A *ratio* is a quotient of two quantities. An example is the ratio of 2 to 5, which can be written $2 : 5$ or $\frac{2}{5}$ or 2/5. Ratios are used in proportions.

Definition: **Proportion**
A **proportion** is a statement of equality between two ratios.

An example of a proportion is $\dfrac{a}{b} = \dfrac{c}{d}$, where $b \neq 0$ and $d \neq 0$. Consider the proportion

$$\frac{x + 2}{5} = \frac{x + 5}{8}$$

We can solve this proportion by first multiplying both sides of the equation by the LCD, 40.

$$\frac{x + 2}{5} = \frac{x + 5}{8}$$

$$\overset{8}{\cancel{40}} \left(\frac{x + 2}{\cancel{5}} \right) = \overset{5}{\cancel{40}} \left(\frac{x + 5}{\cancel{8}} \right) \quad \text{Multiplication property}$$

$$8(x + 2) = 5(x + 5)$$

$$8x + 16 = 5x + 25$$

$$3x + 16 = 25$$

$$3x = 9$$

$$x = 3$$

A check will show that 3 is the solution.

Proportions can often be solved more easily by using cross multiplication.

Cross Multiplication

If $\dfrac{a}{b} = \dfrac{c}{d}$, then $ad = bc$, where $b \neq 0, d \neq 0$.

Let's use cross multiplication to solve the proportion $\dfrac{x+2}{5} = \dfrac{x+5}{8}$.

$$\frac{x+2}{5} = \frac{x+5}{8}$$

$$8(x+2) = 5(x+5) \quad \text{Cross multiplication}$$
$$8x + 16 = 5x + 25$$
$$3x + 16 = 25$$
$$3x = 9$$
$$x = 3$$

Notice we obtained the same answer as we did by multiplying both sides of the equation by the LCD, 40.

Many practical application problems can be solved using proportions.

PROCEDURE   **TO SOLVE APPLICATION PROBLEMS USING PROPORTIONS**

1. Represent the unknown quantity by a variable.

2. Set up the proportion by listing the given ratio on the left-hand side of the equal sign and the unknown and other given quantity on the right-hand side of the equal sign. When setting up the right-hand side of the proportion, the same respective quantities should occupy the same respective positions on the left and right. For example, an acceptable proportion might be

$$\frac{\text{miles}}{\text{hour}} = \frac{\text{miles}}{\text{hour}}$$

3. Once the proportion is properly written, drop the units and use cross multiplication to solve the equation.

4. Answer the question or questions asked using the appropriate units.

Example 14   *Water Usage*

The cost for water in the city of Tucson, Arizona is $1.75 per 750 gallons (gal) of water used. What is the water bill if 30,000 gallons are used?

Solution   This problem may be solved by setting up a proportion. One proportion that can be used is

$$\frac{\text{cost of 750 gal}}{750 \text{ gal}} = \frac{\text{cost of 30,000 gal}}{30,000 \text{ gal}}$$

The unknown quantity is the cost for 30,000 gallons of water, so we will call this quantity x. The proportion then becomes

$$\text{Given ratio} \left\{ \frac{1.75}{750} = \frac{x}{30,000} \right.$$

Now we solve for x by using cross multiplication.

$$(1.75)(30,000) = 750x$$
$$52,500 = 750x$$
$$\frac{52,500}{750} = \frac{750x}{750}$$
$$\$70 = x$$

▲ *Tucson, AZ*

The cost of 30,000 gallons of water is $70.

Example 15 Determining the Amount of Insulin

Insulin comes in 10-cubic-centimeter (cc) vials labeled in the number of units of insulin per cubic centimeter of fluid. A vial of insulin marked U40 has 40 units of insulin per cubic centimeter of fluid. If a patient needs 30 units of insulin, how much fluid should be drawn into the syringe from the U40 vial?

Solution The unknown quantity, x, is the number of cubic centimeters of fluid to be drawn into the syringe. Following is one proportion that can be used to find that quantity.

$$\text{Given ratio} \begin{cases} \dfrac{40 \text{ units}}{1 \text{ cc}} = \dfrac{30 \text{ units}}{x \text{ cc}} \end{cases}$$

$$40x = 30(1)$$
$$40x = 30$$
$$x = \frac{30}{40} = 0.75$$

The nurse or doctor putting the insulin in the syringe should draw 0.75 cc of the fluid.

SECTION 6.2 Exercises

Warm Up Exercises

In Exercises 1–12, fill in the blank with an appropriate word, phrase, or symbol(s).

1. The parts that are added or subtracted in an algebraic expression are called _____.

2. Terms that have the same variables with the same exponents on the variables are called _____ terms.

3. The numerical part of a term is called its numerical _____.

4. An equation in which the highest exponent on the variable is a 1, is called a(n) _____ equation.

5. To combine like terms by using the commutative, associative, and distributive properties means to _____ an expression.

6. A general procedure for accomplishing a task is called a(n) _____.

7. A quotient of two quantities is called a(n) _____.

8. A statement of equality between two ratios is called a(n) _____.

9. An equation that has an infinite number of solutions is called a(n) _____.

10. An equation that has no solution is called a(n) _____.

11. When solving an equation, getting a variable by itself on one side of the equal sign means to _____ the variable.

12. Equations that have the same solution are called _____ equations.

Practice the Skills

In Exercises 13–36, combine like terms.

13. $5x + 3x$

14. $7x - 2x$

15. $-8x - 3x + 12$

16. $-6x + 2x + 21$

17. $7x + 3y - 4x + 8y$

18. $x - 4x + 3$

19. $-3x + 2 - 5x$

20. $-3x + 4x - 2 + 5$

21. $2 - 3x - 2x + 1$

22. $-0.2x + 1.7x - 4$

23. $6.2x - 8.3 + 7.1x$

24. $4s + 3t + 8 - 2t$

25. $\frac{2}{3}x + \frac{1}{6}x - 5$

26. $\frac{1}{5}x - \frac{1}{3}x - 4$

27. $7x - 4y - 8y + 6x + 2$

28. $2p - 4q - 3p + 4q - 15$

29. $2(s + 3) + 6(s - 4) + 1$

30. $6(r - 3) - 2(r + 5) + 10$

31. $0.2(x + 4) + 1.2(x - 3)$

32. $0.9(2.3x - 2) + 1.7(3.2x - 5)$

33. $\frac{3}{5}(x + 1) - \frac{3}{10}x$

34. $\frac{2}{3}(3x + 9) - \frac{1}{4}(2x + 5)$

35. $\frac{1}{4}x + \frac{4}{5} - \frac{2}{3}x$ **36.** $n - \frac{3}{4} + \frac{5}{9}n - \frac{1}{6}$

In Exercises 37–62, solve the equation.

37. $y - 4 = 13$ **38.** $y + 6 = 12$

39. $21 = -2t + 9$ **40.** $12 = 3x + 6$

41. $\frac{3}{x} = \frac{7}{8}$ **42.** $\frac{x - 1}{5} = \frac{x + 5}{15}$

43. $\frac{1}{2}x + \frac{1}{3} = \frac{2}{3}$ **44.** $\frac{1}{2}y + \frac{1}{3} = \frac{1}{4}$

45. $0.9x - 1.2 = 2.4$ **46.** $5x + 0.050 = -0.732$

47. $6t - 8 = 4t - 2$ **48.** $6t - 7 = 8t + 9$

49. $\frac{x}{4} + 2x = \frac{1}{3}$ **50.** $\frac{r}{3} + 2r = 7$

51. $\frac{x - 3}{2} = \frac{x + 4}{3}$ **52.** $\frac{x - 5}{4} = \frac{x - 9}{3}$

53. $2(x + 3) - 4 = 2(x - 4)$

54. $3(x + 2) + 2(x - 1) = 5x - 7$

55. $4(x - 4) + 12 = 4(x - 1)$

56. $6(t + 2) - 14 = 6t - 2$

57. $\frac{1}{3}(x + 3) = \frac{2}{5}(x + 2)$ **58.** $\frac{2}{3}(x - 4) = \frac{1}{4}(x + 1)$

59. $3x + 2 - 6x = -x - 15 + 8 - 5x$

60. $6x + 8 - 22x = 28 + 14x - 10 + 12x$

61. $5(3n + 1) = 2(5n - 4) + 6n$

62. $4(t - 3) + 8 = 4(2t - 6)$

Problem Solving

In Exercises 63 and 64, use the water rate for Columbus, Ohio, which is $1.98 per 750 gallons of water.

63. *Water Bill* What is the water bill if a resident of Columbus uses 27,000 gal?

64. *Limiting the Cost* How many gallons of water can a customer use if the water bill is not to exceed $200?

65. *Paint* A gallon of paint covers 825 ft². How much paint is needed to paint a house with a surface area of 6600 ft²?

▲ *See Exercise 65*

66. *Watching Television* Nielsen Media Research determines the number of people who watch a television show. One rating point means that about 1,102,000 households watched the show. The top-rated television show for the week of February 14, 2011, was *American Idol*—with a rating of 21.0. About how many households watched *American Idol* that week?

67. *Fajitas* A recipe for six servings of beef fajitas requires 16 oz of beef sirloin.

   a) If the recipe were to be made for nine servings, how many ounces of beef sirloin would be needed?

   b) How many servings of beef fajitas can be made with 32 oz of beef sirloin?

68. *Topsoil* A 40-pound bag of topsoil will cover a surface area of 12 ft².

   a) How many pounds of topsoil are needed to cover a surface area of 480 ft²?

   b) How many bags of topsoil must be purchased to cover a surface area of 480 ft²?

69. *Speed Limit* When Jacob Abbott crossed over from Niagara Falls, New York, to Niagara Falls, Canada, he saw a sign that said 50 miles per hour (mph) is equal to 80 kilometers per hour (kph).

▲ *Niagara Falls, Canada*

   a) How many kilometers per hour are equal to 1 mph?

   b) On a stretch of the Queen Elizabeth Way, the speed limit is 90 kph. What is the speed limit in miles per hour?

70. *The Proper Dosage* A doctor asks a nurse to give a patient 250 milligrams (mg) of the drug Simethicone. The drug is available only in a solution whose concentration is 40 mg Simethicone per 0.6 milliliter ($m\ell$) of solution. How many milliliters of solution should the nurse give the patient?

Amount of Insulin In Exercises 71 and 72, how much insulin (in cc) would be given for the following doses? (Refer to Example 15 on page 306.)

71. 15 units of insulin from a vial marked U40

72. 35 units of insulin from a vial marked U40

73. a) Summarize the procedure to use to solve an equation.

b) Solve the equation $2(x + 3) = 4x + 3 - 5x$ with the procedure you outlined in part (a).

Challenge Problems/Group Activities

74. *Depth of a Submarine* The pressure, P, in pounds per square inch (psi) exerted on an object x ft below the sea is given by the formula $P = 14.70 + 0.43x$. The 14.70 represents the weight in pounds of the column of air (from sea level to the top of the atmosphere) standing over a 1 in. by 1 in. square of seawater. The $0.43x$ represents the weight in pounds of a column of water 1 in. by 1 in. by x ft (see Fig. 6.1).

This column
of air weighs
14.7 lb

This column
of water
weighs $0.43x$ lb

x ft

1 in. by 1 in. square

Figure 6.1

a) A submarine is built to withstand a pressure of 148 psi. How deep can that submarine go?

b) If the pressure gauge in the submarine registers a pressure of 128.65 psi, how deep is the submarine?

75. a) *Gender Ratios* If the ratio of males to females in a class is 2 : 3, what is the ratio of males to all the students in the class?

b) If the ratio of males to females in a class is $m : n$, what is the ratio of males to all the students in the class?

76. Determine whether the given equations are equivalent.

a) $\dfrac{x}{3} = \dfrac{x + 2}{6}$, $6x = 3x + 6$

b) $2x - 9 = 19$, $\dfrac{2x - 9}{4} = \dfrac{19}{4}$

Internet/Research Activities

77. Ratio and proportion are used in many different ways in everyday life. Submit two articles from newspapers, magazines, or the Internet in which ratios and/or proportions are used. Write a brief summary of each article explaining how ratio and/or proportion were used.

78. Write a report explaining how the ancient Egyptians used equations. Include in your discussion the forms of the equations used.

SECTION 6.3   # Formulas

▲ *A formula is used to determine the amount of carpet needed to cover the floor of a room.*

Suppose you need to purchase new carpet for your family room, which is in the shape of a rectangle. To determine the amount of carpet required, you would need to determine the area of the room by multiplying the length of the room by the width of the room. In this section, we will discuss a special kind of equation called a *formula*. Formulas are used to evaluate and determine the solution to many real world problems.

Why *This is Important* Using a formula can help us determine many quantities, such as how much carpet to purchase for a room and the interest you must pay when borrowing money.

A *formula* is an equation that typically has a real-life application. To *evaluate* a formula, substitute the given values for their respective variables and then evaluate using the order of operations given in Section 6.1. Many of the formulas given in this section are discussed in greater detail in other parts of the book.

Example 1 *Simple Interest*

The simple interest formula,* interest = principal $\times$ rate $\times$ time, or $i = prt$, is used to find the interest you must pay on a simple interest loan when you borrow principal, p, at simple interest rate, r, in decimal form, for time, t. Chris Campbell borrows $5000 at a simple interest rate of 6.5% for 3 years.

a) How much will Chris Campbell pay in interest at the end of 3 years?

b) What is the total amount he will repay the bank at the end of 3 years?

Solution

a) Substitute the values of p, r, and t into the formula; then evaluate.

$$i = prt$$
$$= 5000(0.065)(3)$$
$$= 975$$

Thus, Chris must pay $975 interest.

b) The total he must pay at the end of 3 years is the principal, $5000, plus the $975 interest, for a total of $5975.

Example 2 *Volume of an Ice-Cream Box*

The formula for the volume of a rectangular box† is volume = length $\times$ width $\times$ height, or $V = lwh$. Use the formula $V = lwh$ to find the width of a rectangular box of ice cream if $l = 7$ in., $h = 3.5$ in., and $V = 122.5$ in^3.

Solution We substitute the appropriate values into the volume formula and solve for the desired quantity, w.

$$V = lwh$$
$$122.5 = (7)w(3.5)$$
$$122.5 = 24.5w$$
$$\frac{122.5}{24.5} = \frac{24.5w}{24.5}$$
$$5 = w$$

Therefore, the width of the ice-cream box is 5 in.

In Example 1, we used the formula $i = prt$. In Example 2, we used the formula $V = lwh$. In these examples, we used a mathematical equation to represent real phenomena. When we represent real phenomena, such as finding simple interest, mathematically we say we have created a *mathematical model* or simply a *model* to represent the situation. A model may be a single formula, an equation, or a system of many equations. By using models we gain insight into real-life situations, such as how much interest you will accumulate in your savings account. We will use mathematical models throughout this chapter and elsewhere in the text. In some exercises in this and the next chapter, when you are asked to determine an equation to represent a real-life situation, we will sometimes write the word *modeling* in the instructions.

Many formulas contain Greek letters, such as μ (mu), σ (sigma), Σ (capital sigma), δ (delta), Δ (capital delta), ϵ (epsilon), π (pi), θ (theta), and λ (lambda).

---

*The simple interest formula is discussed in Section 11.2.

†The volume formula is discussed in Section 9.4.

Did You Know?

$$\cancel{L} = mc^2$$
$$E = mc^2$$

Albert Einstein

Many of you recognize the formula $E = mc^2$ used by Albert Einstein in 1912 to describe his groundbreaking theory of relativity. In the formula, E is energy, m is mass, and c is the speed of light. In his theory, Einstein hypothesized that time was not absolute and that mass and energy were related.

Einstein's 72-page handwritten manuscript, which went on display in 1999 at Jerusalem's Israel Museum, shows that Einstein toyed with using an L rather than an E to represent energy. He wrote $L = mc^2$, and then scratched out the L and replaced it with an E to produce the equation $E = mc^2$. Yisrail Galili at Jerusalem's Hebrew University said the L might have been a lambda, a Greek letter sometimes used in functions related to energy. He said it might also be related to Joseph-Louis Lagrange, an eighteenth-century Italian mathematician.

Example 3 *A Statistics Formula*

A formula used in the study of statistics to find a standard score (or z-score) is

$$z = \frac{\bar{x} - \mu}{\dfrac{\sigma}{\sqrt{n}}}$$

Find the value of z when $\bar{x}$ (read "x bar") $= 120$, $\mu = 100$, $\sigma = 16$, and $n = 4$.

Solution

$$z = \frac{\bar{x} - \mu}{\dfrac{\sigma}{\sqrt{n}}} = \frac{120 - 100}{\dfrac{16}{\sqrt{4}}} = \frac{20}{\dfrac{16}{2}} = \frac{20}{8} = 2.5$$

Some formulas contain *subscripts*. Subscripts are numbers (or letters) placed below and to the right of variables. They are used to help clarify a formula. For example, if two different amounts are used in a problem, they may be symbolized as A and A_0, or A_1 and A_2. Subscripts are read using the word *sub*; for example, A_0 is read "A sub zero" and A_1 is read "A sub one."

Solving for a Variable in a Formula or Equation

Often in mathematics and science courses, you are given a formula or an equation expressed in terms of one variable and asked to express it in terms of a different variable. For example, you may be given the formula $P = i^2 r$ and asked to solve the formula for r. To do so, treat each of the variables, except the one you are solving for, as if it were a constant. Then solve for the variable desired, using the properties previously discussed. Examples 4 through 6 show how to do this task.

When graphing equations in Section 6.7, you will sometimes have to solve the equation for the variable y, as is done in Example 4.

Example 4 *Solving for a Variable in an Equation*

Solve the equation $2x + 5y - 10 = 0$ for y.

Solution We need to isolate the term containing the variable y. Begin by moving the constant, -10, and the term $2x$ to the right-hand side of the equation.

$$2x + 5y - 10 = 0$$
$$2x + 5y - 10 + 10 = 0 + 10 \qquad \text{Addition property}$$
$$2x + 5y = 10$$
$$-2x + 2x + 5y = -2x + 10 \qquad \text{Subtraction property}$$
$$5y = -2x + 10$$
$$\frac{5y}{5} = \frac{-2x + 10}{5} \qquad \text{Division property}$$
$$y = \frac{-2x + 10}{5}$$
$$y = -\frac{2x}{5} + \frac{10}{5}$$
$$y = -\frac{2}{5}x + 2$$

Note that once you have found $y = \frac{-2x + 10}{5}$, you have solved the equation for y. The solution can also be expressed in the form $y = -\frac{2}{5}x + 2$. This form of the equation is convenient for graphing equations, as will be explained in Section 6.7. Example 4 can also be solved by moving the y term to the right-hand side of the equal sign. Do so now and note that you obtain the same answer.

Example 5 *Solving for a Variable in a Formula*

An important formula used in statistics is

$$z = \frac{x - \mu}{\sigma}$$

Solve this formula for x.

Solution To isolate the term x, use the general procedure for solving linear equations given in Section 6.2. Treat each letter, except x, as if it were a constant.

$$z = \frac{x - \mu}{\sigma}$$

$$z \cdot \sigma = \frac{x - \mu}{\sigma} \cdot \sigma \qquad \text{Multiply both sides of the equation by } \sigma.$$

$$z\sigma = x - \mu$$

$$z\sigma + \mu = x - \mu + \mu \qquad \text{Add } \mu \text{ to both sides of the equation.}$$

$$z\sigma + \mu = x$$

$$\text{or} \quad x = z\sigma + \mu$$

Example 6 *The Tax-Free Yield Formula*

A formula that may be important to you now or sometime in the future is the tax-free yield formula, $T_f = T_a(1 - F)$. This formula can be used to convert a taxable yield, T_a, into its equivalent tax-free yield, T_f, where F is the federal income tax bracket of the individual. A taxable yield is an interest rate for which income tax is paid on the interest made. A tax-free yield is an interest rate for which income tax does not have to be paid on the interest made.

a) For someone in a 25% tax bracket, find the equivalent tax-free yield of a 4% taxable investment.

b) Solve this formula for T_a. That is, write a formula for taxable yield in terms of tax-free yield.

Solution

a) $T_f = T_a(1 - F)$

$ = 0.04(1 - 0.25) = 0.04(0.75) = 0.03, \quad \text{or} \quad 3\%$

Thus, a taxable investment of 4% is equivalent to a tax-free investment of 3% for a person in a 25% income tax bracket.

b) $\qquad T_f = T_a(1 - F)$

$$\frac{T_f}{1 - F} = \frac{T_a(1 - F)}{1 - F} \qquad \text{Divide both sides of the equation by } 1 - F.$$

$$\frac{T_f}{1 - F} = T_a, \quad \text{or} \quad T_a = \frac{T_f}{1 - F}$$

Warm Up Exercises

In Exercises 1–2, fill in the blank with an appropriate word, phrase, or symbol(s).

1. An equation that typically has a real-life application is called a(n) _____.

2. Numbers or letters that are placed below and to the right of variables are called _____.

Practice the Skills

In Exercises 3–34, use the formula to determine the value of the indicated variable for the values given. Use a calculator when one is needed. When necessary, round answers to the nearest hundredth.

3. $A = bh$; determine A when $b = 12$ and $h = 4$ (geometry).

4. $P = a + b + c$; determine P when $a = 25$, $b = 53$, and $c = 32$ (geometry).

5. $P = 2l + 2w$; determine P when $l = 12$ and $w = 16$ (geometry).

6. $F = ma$; determine m when $F = 40$ and $a = 5$ (physics).

7. $K = \dfrac{1}{2}mv^2$; determine m when $v = 30$ and $K = 4500$ (physics).

8. $p = i^2r$; determine r when $p = 62{,}500$ and $i = 5$ (electronics).

9. $S = \pi r(r + h)$; determine S when $r = 8$, $\pi = 3.14$, and $h = 2$ (geometry).

10. $B = \dfrac{703w}{h^2}$; determine B when $w = 130$ and $h = 67$ (body mass index).

11. $z = \dfrac{x - \mu}{\sigma}$; determine μ when $z = 2.5$, $x = 42.1$, and $\sigma = 2$ (statistics).

12. $S = 4lw + 2wh$; determine l when $S = 336$, $h = 9$, and $w = 8$ (geometry).

13. $T = \dfrac{PV}{k}$; determine P when $T = 80$, $V = 20$, and $k = 0.5$ (physics).

14. $m = \dfrac{a + b + c}{3}$; determine a when $m = 85$, $b = 77$, and $c = 92$ (statistics).

15. $A = P(1 + rt)$; determine P when $A = 3600$, $r = 0.04$, and $t = 5$ (economics).

16. $V = -\dfrac{1}{2}at^2$; determine a when $V = 2304$ and $t = 12$ (physics).

17. $V = \pi r^2 h$; determine h when $V = 942$, $\pi = 3.14$, and $r = 5$ (geometry).

18. $F = \frac{9}{5}C + 32$; determine F when $C = 7$ (temperature conversion).

19. $C = \frac{5}{9}(F - 32)$; determine C when $F = 77$ (temperature conversion).

20. $K = \dfrac{F - 32}{1.8} + 273.1$; determine K when $F = 100$ (chemistry).

21. $m = \dfrac{y_2 - y_1}{x_2 - x_1}$; determine m when $y_2 = 8$, $y_1 = -4$, $x_2 = -3$, and $x_1 = -5$ (mathematics).

22. $z = \dfrac{\bar{x} - \mu}{\dfrac{\sigma}{\sqrt{n}}}$; determine z when $\bar{x} = 66$, $\mu = 60$, $\sigma = 15$, and $n = 25$ (statistics).

23. $S = R - rR$; determine R when $S = 186$ and $r = 0.07$ (for determining sale price when an item is discounted).

24. $S = C + rC$; determine C when $S = 115$ and $r = 0.15$ (for determining selling price when an item is marked up).

25. $E = a_1 p_1 + a_2 p_2 + a_3 p_3$; determine E when $a_1 = 5$, $p_1 = 0.2$, $a_2 = 7$, $p_2 = 0.6$, $a_3 = 10$, and $p_3 = 0.2$ (probability).

26. $x = \dfrac{-b + \sqrt{b^2 - 4ac}}{2a}$; determine x when $a = 2$, $b = -5$, and $c = -12$ (mathematics).

27. $s = -16t^2 + v_0 t + s_0$; determine s when $t = 4$, $v_0 = 30$, and $s_0 = 150$ (physics).

28. $R = O + (V - D)r$; determine O when $R = 670$, $V = 100$, $D = 10$, and $r = 4$ (economics).

29. $P = \dfrac{f}{1 + i}$; determine f when $i = 0.08$ and $P = 3000$ (investment banking).

30. $c = \sqrt{a^2 + b^2}$; determine c when $a = 5$ and $b = 12$ (geometry).

31. $R_T = \dfrac{R_1 R_2}{R_1 + R_2}$; determine R_T when $R_1 = 100$ and $R_2 = 200$ (electronics).

32. $P = \dfrac{nRT}{V}$; determine V when $P = 12, n = 10, R = 60$, and $T = 8$ (chemistry).

33. $S_n = \dfrac{a_1(1 - r^n)}{1 - r}$; determine S_n when $a_1 = 10, r = 1/2$, and $n = 4$ (mathematics).

34. $A = P\left(1 + \dfrac{r}{n}\right)^{nt}$; determine A when $P = 100, r = 6\%$, $n = 1$, and $t = 3$ (banking).

In Exercises 35–44, solve the equation for y.

35. $5x - 4y = 14$

36. $7x - 3y = 23$

37. $8x + 7y = 21$

38. $-9x + 4y = 11$

39. $2x - 3y + 6 = 0$

40. $10x - 3y = 0$

41. $-2x + 3y + z = 15$

42. $5x + 3y - 2z = 22$

43. $9x + 4z = 7 + 8y$

44. $2x - 3y + 5z = 0$

In Exercises 45–64, solve for the variable indicated.

45. $A = lw$, for w

46. $V = lwh$ for w

47. $p = a + b + c$ for a

48. $p = a + b + s_1 + s_2$ for s_1

49. $V = \frac{1}{3}Bh$ for B

50. $V = \pi r^2 h$ for h

51. $C = 2\pi r$ for r

52. $y = mx + b$ for m

53. $y = mx + b$ for b

54. $V = \frac{1}{3}\pi r^2 h$ for h

55. $P = 2l + 2w$ for w

56. $A = \frac{1}{2}bh$ for b

57. $L = \dfrac{c + 2d}{4}$ for d

58. $\dfrac{w_1}{w_2} = \dfrac{f_2 - f}{f - f_1}$ for w_1

59. $r = \dfrac{2gm}{c^2}$ for m

60. $\dfrac{P_1 V_1}{T_1} = \dfrac{P_2 V_2}{T_2}$ for V_2

61. $F = \frac{9}{5}C + 32$ for C

62. $C = \frac{5}{9}(F - 32)$ for F

63. $S = \pi r^2 + \pi r s$ for s

64. $A = \frac{1}{2}h(b_1 + b_2)$ for h_2

Problem Solving

In Exercises 65–69, when appropriate, round answers to the nearest hundredth.

65. **Driving Time** A family is planning to drive 549 miles from their home in Lincoln, Nebraska, to Mount Rushmore National Park. They plan to drive at an average speed of 61 miles per hour. How much time will they spend driving?

▲ Mount Rushmore, South Dakota

66. **Savings Account** Christine Chu borrowed $4500 from a bank at a simple interest rate of 2.5% for one year.

   a) Determine how much interest Christine paid at the end of 1 year.

   b) Determine the total amount Christine will repay the bank at the end of 1 year.

67. **Interest on a Loan** Jeff Hubbard borrowed $800 from his brother for 2 years. At the end of 2 years, he repaid the $800 plus $128 in interest. What simple interest rate did he pay?

68. **Volume of a Bucket** Determine the volume of a cylindrical bucket in cubic inches if the bucket's radius is 5 in. and the height is 12 in. The formula for the volume of a cylinder is $V = \pi r^2 h$. Use the π key on your calculator.

69. **Body Mass Index** A person's body mass index (BMI) is found by the formula $B = \dfrac{703w}{h^2}$, where w is the person's weight, in pounds, and h is the person's height, in inches. John Bass is 6 ft tall and weighs 200 lb.

   a) Determine his BMI.

   b) If John would like to have a BMI of 26, how much weight would he need to gain or lose?

Challenge Problem/Group Activity

70. Determine the volume of the block shown in Fig. 6.2, excluding the hole. The formula for the volume of a rectangular solid is $V = lwh$. The formula for the volume of a cylinder is $V = \pi r^2 h$.

Figure 6.2

▲ *An equation can be used to represent the base salary and the commission earned by a sales representative.*

Suppose your weekly salary as a sales representative consists of a weekly base salary of $400 and a 6% commission on the total dollar amount of all sales you make. How many dollars in sales would you need to make in a week to earn a total of $1000 a week? To answer this question you must first express the written problem as a mathematical equation. Then you can use the general procedure for solving linear equations discussed in Section 6.2 to obtain the answer. In this section, we will explain how to write mathematical equations to represent word problems.

Why **This Is Important** Being able to express a real-life problem as a mathematical equation is necessary in order to solve application problems like the one above.

One reason to study algebra is that it can be used to solve everyday problems. In this section, we will do two things: (1) show how to translate a written problem into a mathematical equation and (2) show how linear equations can be used in solving everyday problems. We begin by illustrating how English phrases can be written as mathematical expressions. When writing a mathematical expression, we may use any letter to represent the variable. In the following illustrations, we use the letter x.

Phrase	Mathematical expression
Six more than a number	$x + 6$
A number increased by 3	$x + 3$
Four less than a number	$x - 4$
A number decreased by 9	$x - 9$
Twice a number	$2x$
Four times a number	$4x$
3 decreased by a number	$3 - x$
The difference between a number and 5	$x - 5$

Sometimes the phrase that must be converted to a mathematical expression involves more than one operation.

Phrase	Mathematical expression
Four less than 3 times a number	$3x - 4$
Ten more than twice a number	$2x + 10$
The sum of 5 times a number and 3	$5x + 3$
Eight times a number, decreased by 7	$8x - 7$

The word *is* often represents the equal sign.

Phrase	Mathematical equation
Six more than a number is 10.	$x + 6 = 10$
Five less than a number is 20.	$x - 5 = 20$
Twice a number, decreased by 6 is 12.	$2x - 6 = 12$
A number decreased by 13 is 6 times the number.	$x - 13 = 6x$

The following is a general procedure for solving word problems.

PROCEDURE   TO SOLVE A WORD PROBLEM

1. Read the problem carefully at least twice to be sure that you understand it.
2. If possible, draw a sketch to help visualize the problem.
3. Determine which quantity you are being asked to find. Choose a letter to represent this unknown quantity. Write down exactly what this letter represents.
4. Write the word problem as an equation.
5. Solve the equation for the unknown quantity.
6. Answer the question or questions asked.
7. Check the solution.

This general procedure for solving word problems is illustrated in Examples 1 through 4. In these examples, the equations we obtain are mathematical models of the given situations.

Example 1 *House Cleaning Service*

A professional house cleaning service charges a base fee of $20 plus $32.50 per hour to clean the Munoz's house. If the Munoz's total bill for house cleaning services from this company was $117.50 before taxes, how many hours did it take to clean their house?

Solution In this problem, the unknown quantity is the number of hours it took to clean the Munoz's house. Let's select n to represent the number of hours. Then we construct an equation using the given information that will allow us to solve for n.

Let

$$n = \text{number of hours}$$

Then

$$\$32.50n = \text{cost for cleaning } n \text{ hours at } \$32.50 \text{ per hour}$$
$$\text{Base charge} + \text{hourly charge} = \text{total bill}$$
$$\$20 + \$32.50n = \$117.50$$

Now solve the equation.

$$20 + 32.50n = 117.50$$
$$20 - 20 + 32.50n = 117.50 - 20$$
$$32.50n = 97.5$$
$$\frac{32.50n}{32.50} = \frac{97.5}{32.50}$$
$$n = 3$$

Therefore, it took 3 hours to clean the Munoz's house.

CHECK: The check is made with the information given in the original problem.

$$\text{Total bill} = \text{base charge} + \text{hourly charge}$$
$$= 20 + 32.50(3)$$
$$= 20 + 97.50$$
$$= 117.50$$

Therefore, this answer checks.

Example **2** *Dividing Land*

Mark IV Construction Company purchased 100 acres of land to be split into three parcels of land on which to build houses. One parcel of land will be three times as large as each of the other two. How many acres of land will each parcel contain?

Solution Two parcels will contain the same number of acres, and the third parcel will contain three times that amount.

Let

$$x = \text{number of acres in the first parcel}$$
$$x = \text{number of acres in the second parcel}$$
$$3x = \text{number of acres in the third parcel}$$

Then

$$x + x + 3x = \text{total amount of land}$$
$$x + x + 3x = 100$$
$$5x = 100$$
$$x = 20$$

Thus, two parcels will contain 20 acres of land. The third parcel will contain 3(20), or 60, acres of land. A check in the original problem will verify that this answer is correct. ■

Example **3** *Dimensions of an Exercise Area*

Dr. Christine Seidel, a veterinarian, wants to fence in a large rectangular region in the yard behind her office for exercising dogs that are boarded overnight. She has 130 ft of fencing to use for the perimeter of the region. What should the dimensions of the region be if she wants the length to be 15 ft greater than the width?

Solution The formula for finding the perimeter of a rectangle is $P = 2l + 2w$, where P is the perimeter, l is the length, and w is the width. A diagram, such as the one shown below, is often helpful in solving problems of this type.

Let w equal the width of the region. The length is 15 ft more than the width, so $l = w + 15$. The total distance around the region P, is 130 ft.
Substitute the known quantities in the formula.

$$P = 2l + 2w$$
$$130 = 2(w + 15) + 2w$$
$$130 = 2w + 30 + 2w$$
$$130 = 4w + 30$$
$$100 = 4w$$
$$25 = w$$

The width of the region is 25 ft and the length of the region is $25 + 15 = 40$ ft. ■

In shopping and other daily activities, we are occasionally asked to solve problems using percents. The word *percent* means "per hundred." Thus, for example, 7% means 7 per hundred, or $\frac{7}{100}$. When $\frac{7}{100}$ is converted to a decimal number, we obtain 0.07. Thus, 7% = 0.07.

Let's look at one example involving percent. (See Section 11.1 for a more detailed discussion of percent.)

Example 4 *Craft Show*

Kim Stappenbeck is selling her homemade jewelry at a craft show. Determine the cost of a necklace before tax if the total cost of a necklace, including an 8% sales tax, is to be $34.56.

Solution   We are asked to find the cost of a necklace before sales tax.

Let

$$x = \text{cost of the necklace before sales tax}$$

Then

$$0.08x = 8\% \text{ of the cost of the necklace (the sales tax)}$$

$$\text{Cost of the necklace before tax } + \text{ tax on the necklace} = 34.56$$
$$x + 0.08x = 34.56$$
$$1.08x = 34.56$$
$$\frac{1.08x}{1.08} = \frac{34.56}{1.08}$$
$$x = \frac{34.56}{1.08}$$
$$x = 32$$

Thus, the cost of the necklace before tax is $32. ∎

SECTION 6.4   *Exercises*

Practice the Skills

In Exercises 1–4, write the mathematical expression as a phrase. (There are several acceptable answers.)

1. $x + 5$

2. $x - 2$

3. $2x - 3$

4. $3x + 5$

In Exercises 5–16, write the phrase as a mathematical expression.

5. 5 less than x

6. 2 more than y

7. 4 increased by 3 times z

8. 6 times x, decreased by 1

9. The product of 8 and w, increased by 9

10. 5 less than twice a number

11. 6 more than 4 times x

12. 8 increased by 5 times x

13. 12 decreased by s, divided by 4

14. The sum of 8 and t, divided by 2

15. Three times the sum of a number and 7

16. The quotient of 8 and y, decreased by 3 times x

In Exercises 17–28, write an equation and solve.

17. 7 more than a number is 15.

18. A number decreased by 3 is 8.

19. The difference between a number and 4 is 20.

20. Seven multiplied by a number is 56.

21. Ten less than four times a number is 42.

22. Fourteen increased by 6 times a number is 32.

23. Twelve more than 4 times a number is 32.

24. Eight less than 3 times a number is 6 times the number, increased by 10.

25. A number increased by 6 is 3 less than twice the number.

26. A number divided by 4 is 12 less than the number.

27. A number increased by 10 is 2 times the sum of the number and 3.

28. Three times the difference of a number and 4 is 6 more than the number.

Problem Solving

In Exercises 29–48, set up an equation that can be used to solve the problem. Solve the equation and determine the desired value(s).

29. MODELING—*Reimbursed Expenses* When sales representatives for Pfizer Pharmaceuticals drive to out-of-town meetings that require an overnight stay, they receive $150 for lodging plus $0.50 per mile driven. How many miles did Joe Kotaska drive if Pfizer reimbursed him $255 for an overnight trip?

30. MODELING—*Sales Commission* Tito Sanchez receives a weekly salary of $400 at Anderson's Appliances. He also receives a 6% commission on the total dollar amount of all sales he makes. What must his total sales be in a week if he is to make a total of $790?

31. MODELING—*Jet Skiing* At Action Water Sports of Ocean City, Maryland, the cost of renting a Jet Ski is $42 per half hour, which includes a 5% sales tax. Determine the cost of a half hour Jet Ski rental before tax.

32. MODELING—*Plumbing Supplies* Home Depot has a sale offering 10% off of all plumbing supplies. If Amanda Miller spent $46.98 on plumbing supplies before tax, what was the price of the plumbing supplies she purchased before the discount?

33. MODELING—*Copying* Ronnie McNeil pays 8¢ to make a copy of a page at a copy shop. She is considering purchasing a photocopy machine that is on sale for $250, including tax. How many copies would Ronnie have to make in the copy shop for her cost to equal the purchase price of the photocopy machine she is considering buying?

34. MODELING—*Investment* Marty Faegan received an inheritance of $12,000. If he wants to invest three times as much money in stocks as in mutual funds, how much money should Marty invest in mutual funds and in stocks?

35. MODELING—*Scholarship Donation* Each year, Andrea Choi donates a total of $1000 for scholarships at Mercer County Community College. This year, she wants the amount she donates for scholarships for liberal arts to be three times the amount she donates for scholarships for business. Determine the amount she will donate for each type of scholarship.

36. MODELING—*Homeowners Association* Cross Creek Townhouses Homeowners Association needs to charge each homeowner a supplemental assessment to help pay for some unexpected repairs to the townhouses. The association has $2000 in its reserve fund that it will use to help pay for the repairs. How much must the association charge each of the 50 homeowners if the total cost for the repairs is $13,350?

37. MODELING—*Floor Area* The total floor space in three barns is 45,000 ft^2. The two smaller ones have the same area, and the largest one has three times the area of the smaller ones.

a) Determine the floor space for each barn.

b) Can merchandise that takes up 8500 ft^2 of floor space fit into either of the smaller barns?

38. MODELING—*Dimensions of a Deck* Jim Yuhas is building a rectangular deck and wants the length to be 3 ft greater than the width. What will be the dimensions of the deck if the perimeter is to be 54 ft?

39. MODELING—*Endangered and Threatened Mammals* According to the U.S. Fish and Wildlife Service, in the United States in 2009 the number of species of endangered mammals was 10 more than 4 times the number of species of threatened mammals. The sum of the number of species of endangered mammals and the number of species of threatened mammals was 85. Determine the number of species of endangered mammals and the number of species of threatened mammal.

▲ *The panther is an endangered mammal.*

40. MODELING—*Counting Calories* According to *The Step Diet Book*, the number of steps it takes for a 150-lb person to burn off the calories from eating a cheeseburger and drinking a 12-oz soda is 11,040. The number of steps it takes to burn off the calories from eating a cheeseburger is 690 more than twice the number of steps it takes to burn off the calories from drinking a 12-oz soda. Determine the number of steps needed for a 150-lb person to burn off the calories from eating a cheeseburger, and from drinking a 12-oz soda.

41. MODELING—*Hurricanes* Since 1966, the total number of hurricanes formed in the Atlantic Ocean in the months of September and November is 127. The number of September hurricanes is seven more than five times the number of November hurricanes. Determine the number of hurricanes formed in September and the number of hurricanes formed in November.

42. MODELING—*Boat Purchase* The Nguyen's purchased a boat. If the total cost—including a 6% sales tax—was $18,232, determine the cost of the boat before tax.

43. MODELING—*Enclosing Two Pens* Chuck Salvador has 140 ft of fencing in which he wants to build two connecting, adjacent square pens (see the figure). What will be the dimensions if the length of the entire enclosed region is to be twice the width?

44. MODELING—*Dimensions of a Bookcase* A bookcase with three shelves, as shown in the diagram on the top right, is to be built by a woodworking student. If the height of the bookcase is to be 2 ft longer than the length of a shelf and the total amount of wood to be used is 32 ft, find the dimensions of the bookcase.

▲ *See Exercise 44*

45. MODELING—*Laundry Cost* The cost of doing the family laundry for a month at a local laundromat is $70. A new washer and dryer cost a total of $760. How many months would it take for the cost of doing the laundry at the laundromat to equal the cost of a new washer and dryer?

46. MODELING—*Car Antitheft System* Sandy Chang can save $92 per year off the price of her auto insurance premium by purchasing and installing a LoJack antitheft system. If the system costs $644, in how many years would the system pay for itself?

47. MODELING—*Airfare* Rachel James has been told that with her half-off airfare coupon, her airfare from New York to San Diego will be $257. The $257 includes a 7% tax *on the regular fare*. On the way to the airport, Rachel realizes that she has lost her coupon. What will her regular fare be before tax?

48. MODELING—*Golf Membership* Malcolm Nulton has two options for membership to a golf club. Option A has an annual cost of $3300 for unlimited golf. Option B has an annual cost of $1500 plus $40 for each round of golf. How many rounds of golf would Malcolm have to play in a year for the two options to cost the same?

Challenge Problems/Group Activities

49. *Income Tax* Some states allow a husband and wife to file individual tax returns (on a single form) even though they have filed a joint federal tax return. It is usually to the tax-payers' advantage to do so when both husband and wife work. The smallest amount of tax owed (or the largest refund) will occur when the husband's and wife's taxable incomes are the same.

Mr. McAdams's 2011 taxable income was $34,200, and Mrs. McAdams's taxable income for that year was $36,400. The McAdams's total tax deduction for the year was $3640. This deduction can be divided between Mr. and Mrs. McAdams any way they wish. How should the $3640 be divided between them to result in each individual having the same taxable income and therefore the greatest tax refund?

50. Write each equation as a sentence. There are many correct answers.

a) $x + 3 = 13$

b) $3x + 5 = 8$

c) $3x - 8 = 7$

51. Show that the sum of any three consecutive integers is 3 less than 3 times the largest.

52. *Auto Insurance* A driver education course at the East Lake School of Driving costs $45 but saves those under 25 years of age 10% of their annual insurance premiums until they are 25. Dan has just turned 18, and his insurance costs $100.00 per month.

a) When will the amount saved from insurance equal the price of the course?

b) Including the cost of the course, when Dan turns 25, how much will he have saved?

Recreational Mathematics

53. The relationship between Fahrenheit temperature (F) and Celsius temperature (C) is shown by the formula $F = \dfrac{9}{5}C + 32$. At what temperature will a Fahrenheit thermometer read the same as a Celsius thermometer?

SECTION 6.5   Variation

▲ *The computer in your stereo system uses the concept of variation when it automatically balances the sound.*

Suppose you purchase a new surround sound stereo system. When you set up the system, you place a microphone at the place you typically sit when watching television. The computer within the receiver then generates a series of sounds, and automatically adjusts the volume of all the speakers in the system to give the best balance of sounds from the speakers. Because the sound you hear from each speaker is dependent on (or varies with) your distance from the speaker, the computer is using a concept called variation when activating your sound system.

Why *This is Important* As you will see by the examples in this section, variation can be used to solve a wide variety of real-life problems.

Direct Variation

Many scientific formulas are expressed as variation equations. A *variation equation* is an equation that relates one variable to one or more other variables through the operations of multiplication or division (or both operations). There are essentially four types of variation problems: direct, inverse, joint, and combined variation.

In *direct variation*, the values of the two related variables increase together or decrease together; that is, as one increases so does the other, and as one decreases so does the other.

Consider a car traveling at 40 miles an hour. The car travels 40 miles in 1 hour, 80 miles in 2 hours, and 120 miles in 3 hours. Note that, as the time increases, the distance traveled increases, and, as the time decreases, the distance traveled decreases.

The formula used to calculate distance traveled is

$$\text{Distance} = \text{rate} \cdot \text{time}$$

Since the rate is a constant 40 miles per hour, the formula can be written

$$d = 40t$$

We say that distance *varies directly* as time or that distance is *directly proportional* to time.

The preceding equation is an example of direct variation.

Direct Variation

If a variable y varies directly with a variable x, then

$$y = kx$$

where k is the **constant of proportionality** (or the variation constant).

Examples 1 through 4 illustrate direct variation.

Example 1 *Direct Variation in Electronics*

The resistance of a wire, R, varies directly as its length, L. Write an equation for the resistance of a wire, R, if the constant of proportionality is 0.008.

Solution

$$R = kL \qquad \text{R varies directly as L.}$$
$$R = 0.008L \quad \text{Constant of proportionality, k, is 0.008.} \qquad\blacksquare$$

Example 2 *Direct Variation in Medicine*

The recommended dosage, d, of the antibiotic drug vancomycin is directly proportional to a person's weight, w.

a) Write this variation as an equation.

b) Find the recommended dosage, in milligrams, for Doug Kulzer, who weighs 192 lb. Assume the constant of proportionality for the dosage is 18.

Solution

a) $d = kw$

b) $d = 18(192) = 3456$

The recommended dosage for Doug Kulzer is 3456 mg. $\qquad\blacksquare$

In certain variation problems, the constant of proportionality, k, may not be known. In such cases, we can often find it by substituting the given values in the variation formula and solving for k.

Example 3 *Finding the Constant of Proportionality*

Suppose w varies directly as the square of y. If w is 60 when y is 20, find the constant of proportionality.

Solution Since w varies directly as the *square of y*, we begin with the formula $w = ky^2$. Since the constant of proportionality is not given, we must find k using the given information. Substitute 60 for w and 20 for y.

$$w = ky^2$$
$$60 = k(20)^2$$
$$60 = 400k$$
$$\frac{60}{400} = \frac{400k}{400}$$
$$0.15 = k$$

Thus, the constant of proportionality is 0.15. $\qquad\blacksquare$

Example 4 *Using the Constant of Proportionality*

The area, a, of a picture projected on a movie screen varies directly as the square of the distance, d, from the projector to the screen. If a projector at a distance of 25 feet projects a picture with an area of 100 square feet, what is the area of the projected picture when the projector is at a distance of 40 feet?

Solution We begin with the formula $a = kd^2$. Since the constant of proportionality is not given, we must determine k, using the given information.

$$a = kd^2$$
$$100 = k(25)^2$$
$$100 = k(625)$$
$$\frac{100}{625} = k$$
$$0.16 = k$$

We now use $k = 0.16$ to determine a when $d = 40$.

$$a = kd^2$$
$$a = 0.16d^2$$
$$a = 0.16(40)^2$$
$$a = 0.16(1600)$$
$$a = 256 \text{ ft}^2$$

Thus, the area of a projected picture is 256 ft^2 when the projector is at a distance of 40 ft.   ■

Inverse Variation

A second type of variation is *inverse variation*. When two quantities vary inversely, as one quantity increases the other quantity decreases, and vice versa.

To explain inverse variation, we use the formula distance = rate · time. If we solve for time, we get time = distance/rate. Assume the distance is fixed at 100 miles; then

$$\text{time} = \frac{100}{\text{rate}}$$

At 100 miles per hour, it would take 1 hour to cover this distance. At a rate of 50 miles an hour, it would take 2 hours. At a rate of 25 miles an hour, it would take 4 hours. Note that as the rate (or speed) decreases, the time increases and vice versa.

The preceding equation can be written

$$t = \frac{100}{r}$$

This equation is an example of an inverse variation equation. The time and rate are inversely proportional. The constant of proportionality in this case is 100.

Inverse Variation
If a variable y varies inversely with a variable x, then

$$y = \frac{k}{x}$$

where k is the constant of proportionality.

Two quantities *vary inversely*, or are *inversely proportional*, when as one quantity increases the other quantity decreases and vice versa. Examples 5 and 6 illustrate inverse variation.

Example 5 *Inverse Variation in Illuminance*

The illuminance, I, of a light source varies inversely as the square of the distance, d, from the source. If the illuminance is 80 units at a distance of 5 meters, determine the equation that expresses the relationship between the illuminance and the distance.

Solution Since the illuminance varies inversely as the square of the distance, the general form of the equation is

$$I = \frac{k}{d^2}$$

To determine k, we substitute the given values for I and d.

$$80 = \frac{k}{5^2}$$
$$80 = \frac{k}{25}$$
$$(80)(25) = k$$
$$2000 = k$$

Thus, the equation is $I = \dfrac{2000}{d^2}$

Example 6 *Using the Constant of Proportionality*

Suppose y varies inversely as x. If $y = 9$ when $x = 12$, determine y when $x = 4$.

Solution First write the inverse variation equation. Then solve for k.

$$y = \frac{k}{x}$$
$$9 = \frac{k}{12}$$
$$108 = k$$

Now substitute 108 for k in $y = \dfrac{k}{x}$ and determine y when $x = 4$.

$$y = \frac{108}{x} = \frac{108}{4} = 27$$

Thus, when x is 4, y is 27.

Joint Variation

One quantity may vary directly as a product of two or more other quantities. This type of variation is called *joint variation*.

Joint Variation
If a variable y varies jointly with variables x and z, then

$$y = kxz$$

where k is the constant of proportionality.

Example 7   *Joint Variation in Geometry*

The area, A, of a triangle varies jointly as its base, b, and height, h. If the area of a triangle is 48 in.^{2} when its base is 12 in. and its height is 8 in., find the area of a triangle whose base is 15 in. and whose height is 20 in.

Solution   First write the joint variation, then substitute the known values and solve for k.

$$A = kbh$$
$$48 = k(12)(8)$$
$$48 = k(96)$$
$$\frac{48}{96} = k$$
$$\tfrac{1}{2} = k$$

Now solve for the area of the given triangle.

$$A = kbh$$
$$= \tfrac{1}{2}(15)(20)$$
$$= 150 \text{ in.}^2$$

Summary of Variation Equations

Direct	Inverse	Joint
$y = kx$	$y = \dfrac{k}{x}$	$y = kxz$

Combined Variation

Often in real-life situations, one variable varies as a combination of variables. The following examples illustrate the use of *combined variation*.

Example 8   *Combined Variation in Engineering*

The load, L, that a horizontal beam can safely support varies jointly as the width, w, and the square of the depth, d, and inversely as the length, l. Express L in terms of w, d, l, and the constant of proportionality, k.

Solution

$$L = \frac{kwd^2}{l}$$

Example 9   *Hot Dog Price, Combined Variation*

The owners of Henrietta Hots find their weekly sales of hot dogs, S, vary directly with their advertising budget, A, and inversely with their hot dog price, P. When their advertising budget is $600 and the price of a hot dog is $1.50, they sell 5600 hot dogs a week.

a) Write a variation expressing S in terms of A and P. Include the value of the constant of proportionality.

b) Find the expected sales if the advertising budget is $800 and the hot dog price is $1.75.

Solution

a) Since S varies directly as A and inversely as P, we begin with the equation

$$S = \frac{kA}{P}$$

We now find k using the known values.

$$5600 = \frac{k(600)}{1.50}$$

$$5600 = 400k$$

$$14 = k$$

Therefore, the equation for the weekly sales of hot dogs is $S = \frac{14A}{P}$.

b)
$$S = \frac{14A}{P}$$

$$= \frac{14(800)}{1.75}$$

$$= 6400$$

Henrietta Hots can expect to sell 6400 hot dogs a week if the advertising budget is $800 and the hot dog price is $1.75. ∎

Example 10 Combined Variation

A varies jointly as B and C and inversely as the square of D. If $A = 1$ when $B = 9$, $C = 4$, and $D = 6$, find A when $B = 8$, $C = 12$, and $D = 5$.

Solution We begin with the equation

$$A = \frac{kBC}{D^2}$$

We must first find the constant of proportionality, k, by substituting the known values for A, B, C, and D and solving for k.

$$1 = \frac{k(9)(4)}{6^2}$$

$$1 = \frac{36k}{36}$$

$$1 = k$$

Thus, the constant of proportionality equals 1. Now we find A for the corresponding values of B, C, and D.

$$A = \frac{kBC}{D^2}$$

$$A = \frac{(1)(8)(12)}{5^2} = \frac{96}{25} = 3.84$$

∎

SECTION 6.5   *Exercises*

Warm Up Exercises

In Exercises 1–4, fill in the blank with an appropriate word, phrase, or symbol(s).

1. When one quantity increases while the other quantity decreases, it is an example of _____ variation.

2. When the values of two related variables increase together or decrease together, it is an example of _____ variation.

3. A variation equation that relates one variable to two or more other variables using the operation of multiplication is called a(n) _____ variation equation.

4. In the equation $y = kx$, k is called the constant of _____ .

In Exercises 5–20, use your intuition to determine whether the variation between the indicated quantities is direct or inverse.

5. The distance between two cities on a map and the actual distance between them

6. The time required to fill a pool with a hose and the volume of water coming from the hose

7. The time required to boil water on a burner and the temperature of the burner

8. A person's salary and the amount of money withheld from his or her salary for federal income taxes

9. The interest earned on an investment and the interest rate

10. The diameter of a hose and the volume of water coming out of the hose

11. The speed of a runner and the time it takes the runner to complete a 10-kilometer race

12. The time required to cool a warm room and the size of the air conditioning unit

13. The number of workers hired to install a fence and the time required to install the fence

14. The number of calories in a slice of pizza and the size of the slice

15. The time required to defrost a frozen hamburger in a room and the temperature of the room

16. On Earth, the weight and mass of an object

17. The number of people in line at a bank and the amount of time required for the last person to reach the teller

18. The time it takes an ice cube to melt in water and the temperature of the water

19. The amount of fertilizer needed to fertilize a lawn and the area of the lawn

20. The percent of light that filters through water and the depth of the water

In Exercises 21 and 22, use Exercises 5–20 as a guide.

21. Name two items that have not been mentioned in this section that vary directly.

22. Name two items that have not been mentioned in this section that vary inversely.

Practice the Skills

In Exercises 23–40, (a) write the variation equation and (b) determine the quantity indicated.

23. y varies directly as x. Determine y when $x = 20$ and $k = 7$.

24. x varies inversely as y. Determine x when $y = 9$ and $k = 27$.

25. m varies inversely as the square of n. Determine m when $n = 8$ and $k = 16$.

26. r varies directly as the square of s. Determine r when $s = 2$ and $k = 13$.

27. A varies directly as B and inversely as C. Determine A when $B = 5$, $C = 10$, and $k = 5$.

28. M varies directly as J and inversely as C. Determine M when $J = 12$, $C = 16$, and $k = 4$.

29. *F* varies jointly as *D* and *E*. Determine *F* when $D = 3$, $E = 10$, and $k = 7$.

30. *A* varies jointly as R_1 and R_2 and inversely as the square of *L*. Determine *A* when $R_1 = 120$, $R_2 = 8$, $L = 5$, and $k = \frac{3}{2}$.

31. *t* varies directly as the square of *d* and inversely as *f*. If $t = 192$ when $d = 8$ and $f = 4$, determine *t* when $d = 10$ and $f = 6$.

32. *y* varies directly as the square root of *t* and inversely as *s*. If $y = 12$ when $t = 36$ and $s = 2$, determine *y* when $t = 81$ and $s = 4$.

33. *Z* varies jointly as *W* and *Y*. If $Z = 12$ when $W = 9$ and $Y = 4$, determine *Z* when $W = 50$ and $Y = 6$.

34. *y* varies directly as the square of *R*. If $y = 4$ when $R = 4$, determine *y* when $R = 8$.

35. *H* varies directly as *L*. If $H = 12$ when $L = 40$, determine *H* when $L = 10$.

36. *C* varies inversely as *J*. If $C = 7$ when $J = 0.7$, determine *C* when $J = 12$.

37. *A* varies directly as the square of *B*. If $A = 245$ when $B = 7$, determine *A* when $B = 12$.

38. *F* varies jointly as M_1 and M_2 and inversely as the square of *d*. If $F = 20$ when $M_1 = 5$, $M_2 = 10$, and $d = 0.2$, determine *F* when $M_1 = 10$, $M_2 = 20$, and $d = 0.4$.

39. *F* varies jointly as q_1 and q_2 and inversely as the square of *d*. If $F = 80$ when $q_1 = 4$, $q_2 = 16$, and $d = 0.4$, determine *F* when $q_1 = 12$, $q_2 = 20$, and $d = 0.2$.

40. *S* varies jointly as *I* and the square of *T*. If $S = 4$ when $I = 10$ and $T = 4$, determine *S* when $I = 4$ and $T = 6$.

Problem Solving

In Exercises 41–49, (a) write the variation equation and (b) determine the quantity indicated.

41. *Profit* The profit, *p*, from selling lawn mowers is directly proportional to *n*, the number of lawn mowers sold. If the profit from selling 8 lawn mowers is $600, determine the profit from selling 15 lawn mowers.

42. *Property Tax* The property tax, *t*, on a home is directly proportional to the assessed value, *v*, of the home. If the property tax on a home with an assessed value of $140,000 is $2100, what is the property tax on a home with an assessed value of $180,000?

43. *Melting an Ice Cube* The time, *t*, for an ice cube to melt is inversely proportional to the temperature, *T*, of the water in which the ice cube is placed. If it takes an ice cube 2 minutes to melt in 75°F water, how long will it take an ice cube of the same size to melt in 80°F water?

44. *Pressure and Volume* The volume of a gas, *V*, varies inversely as its pressure, *P*. If the volume of a gas is 6400 cubic centimeters (cc) when the pressure is 25 millimeters (mm) of mercury, determine the volume when the pressure is 200 mm of mercury.

45. *Speaker Loudness* The loudness of a stereo speaker, *l*, measured in decibels (dB), is inversely proportional to the square of the distance, *d*, of the listener from the speaker. If the loudness is 20 dB when the listener is 6 ft from the speaker, what is the loudness when the listener is 3 ft from the speaker?

46. *Distance* The distance, *d*, that a rock falls when dropped from a cliff varies directly as the square of time, *t*, the rock is falling. If a rock falls 64 feet in 2 seconds, how far will it fall in 3 seconds?

47. *Electrical Resistance* The electrical resistance of a wire, *R*, varies directly as its length, *L*, and inversely as its crosssectional area, *A*. If the resistance of a wire is 0.2 ohm when the length is 200 ft and its cross-sectional area is 0.05 in.², what is the resistance of a wire whose length is 5000 ft with a cross-sectional area of 0.01 in.²?

48. *Guitar Strings* The number of vibrations per second, *v*, of a guitar string varies directly as the square root of the tension, *t*, and inversely as the length of the string, *l*. If the number of vibrations per second is 5 when the tension is 225 kg and the length of the string is 0.60 m, determine

the number of vibrations per second when the tension is 196 kg and the length of the string is 0.70 m.

49. *Wattage Rating* The wattage rating of an appliance, *W*, varies jointly as the square of the current, *I*, and the resistance, *R*. If the wattage is 6 watts when the current is 0.2 ampere and the resistance is 150 ohms, determine the wattage when the current is 0.3 ampere and the resistance is 100 ohms.

50. *Phone Calls* The number of phone calls between two cities during a given time period, *N*, varies directly as the populations p_1 and p_2 of the two cities and inversely to the distance, *d*, between them. If 100,000 calls are made between two cities 300 mi apart and the populations of the cities are 60,000 and 200,000, how many calls are made between two cities with populations of 125,000 and 175,000 that are 450 mi apart?

Concept/Writing Exercises

51. a) If *y* varies directly as *x* and the constant of proportionality is 2, does *x* vary directly or inversely as *y*?

   b) Give the new constant of proportionality as *x* varies directly as *y*.

52. a) If *y* varies inversely as *x* and the constant of proportionality is 0.3, does *x* vary directly or inversely as *y*?

   b) Give the new constant of proportionality as *x* varies inversely as *y*.

53. a) Assume *y* varies directly as *x*. If *x* is doubled, how will it affect *y*?

   b) Assume *y* varies inversely as *x*. If *x* is doubled, how will it affect *y*?

54. a) Assume *a* varies directly as b^2. If *b* is doubled, how will it affect *a*?

   b) Assume *a* varies inversely as b^2. If *b* is doubled, how will it affect *a*?

Challenge Problems/Group Activities

55. *Photography* An article in the magazine *Outdoor and Travel Photography* states, "If a surface is illuminated by a point-source of light, the intensity of illumination produced is inversely proportional to the square of the distance separating them. In practical terms, this means that foreground objects will be grossly overexposed if your background subject is properly exposed with a flash. Thus direct flash will not offer pleasing results if there are any intervening objects between the foreground and the subject."

If the subject you are photographing is 4 ft from the flash and the illumination on this subject is $\frac{1}{16}$ of the light of the flash, what is the intensity of illumination on an intervening object that is 3 ft from the flash?

56. *Water Cost* In a specific region of the country, the amount of a customer's water bill, *W*, is directly proportional to the average daily temperature for the month, *T*, the lawn area, *A*, and the square root of *F*, where *F* is the family size, and inversely proportional to the number of inches of rain, *R*.

In one month, the average daily temperature is 78°F and the number of inches of rain is 5.6. If the average family of four who has a thousand square feet of lawn pays $72.00 for water for that month, estimate the water bill in the same month for the average family of six who has 1500 ft^2 of lawn.

SECTION 6.6   Linear Inequalities

▲ *An inequality can be used to determine how many textbooks must be sold so that a bookstore's revenue is greater than its cost.*

Suppose your campus bookstore needs to determine how many textbooks for a particular course must be sold so that the bookstore's textbook revenue is greater than its cost. To determine this number, an inequality would be set up. In this section, we will discuss how to set up and how to solve an inequality.

Why *This is Important* Inequalities are used in industry in many different ways, including determining the profitability of a company.

The symbols of inequality are as follows.

Symbols of Inequality

$a < b$ means that a is less than b.
$a \le b$ means that a is less than or equal to b.
$a > b$ means that a is greater than b.
$a \ge b$ means that a is greater than or equal to b.

An *inequality* consists of two (or more) expressions joined by an inequality sign.

Examples of inequalities

$$3 < 5, \qquad x < 2, \qquad 3x - 2 \ge 5$$

A statement of inequality can be used to indicate a set of real numbers. For example, $x < 2$ represents the set of all real numbers less than 2. Listing all these numbers is impossible, but some are $-2, -1.234, -1, -\frac{1}{2}, 0, \frac{97}{163}, 1$.

Solving Inequalities

To indicate all real numbers less than 2, we can use the number line. The number line was discussed in Chapter 5.

To indicate the solution set of $x < 2$ on the number line, we draw an open circle at 2 and a line to the left of 2 with an arrow at its end. This technique indicates that all points to the left of 2 are part of the solution set. The open circle indicates that the solution set does not include the number 2.

To indicate the solution set of $x \le 2$ on the number line, we draw a closed (or darkened) circle at 2 and a line to the left of 2 with an arrow at its end. The closed circle indicates that the 2 is part of the solution.

Example 1 *Graphing a Less Than or Equal to Inequality*

Graph the solution set of $x \le 1$, where x is a real number, on the number line.

Solution The numbers less than or equal to 1 are all the points on the number line to the left of 1 and 1 itself. The closed circle at 1 shows that 1 is included in the solution set.

$$x \leq 1$$

The inequality statements $x < 2$ and $2 > x$ have the same meaning. Note that the inequality symbol points to the x in both cases. Thus, one inequality may be written in place of the other. Likewise, $x > 2$ and $2 < x$ have the same meaning. Note that the inequality symbol points to the 2 in both cases. We make use of this fact in Example 2.

Example 2 *Graphing a Less Than Inequality*

Graph the solution set of $3 < x$, where x is a real number, on the number line.

Solution We can restate $3 < x$ as $x > 3$. Both statements have identical solutions. Any number that is greater than 3 satisfies the inequality $x > 3$. The graph includes all the points to the right of 3 on the number line. To indicate that 3 is not part of the solution set, we place an open circle at 3.

$$\begin{array}{c} 3 < x \\ \text{or} \\ x > 3 \end{array}$$

We can find the solution to an inequality by adding, subtracting, multiplying, or dividing both sides of the inequality by the same number or expression. We use the procedure discussed in Section 6.2 to isolate the variable, with one important exception: ***When both sides of an inequality are multiplied or divided by a negative number, the direction of the inequality symbol is reversed.***

Example 3 *Multiplying by a Negative Number*

Solve the inequality $-x > 3$ and graph the solution set on the number line.

Solution To solve this inequality, we must eliminate the negative sign in front of the x. To do so, we multiply both sides of the inequality by -1 and change the direction of the inequality symbol.

$$-x > 3$$
$$-1(-x) < -1(3) \qquad \text{Multiply both sides of the inequality by } -1 \text{ and}$$
$$\qquad\qquad\qquad\quad \text{change the direction of the inequality symbol.}$$
$$x < -3$$

The solution set is graphed on the number line as follows.

$$x < -3$$

Example 4 *Dividing by a Negative Number*

Solve the inequality $-5x < 20$ and graph the solution set on the number line.

Solution Solving the inequality requires making the coefficient of the x term 1. To do so, divide both sides of the inequality by -5 and change the direction of the inequality symbol.

$$-5x < 20$$
$$\frac{-5x}{-5} > \frac{20}{-5} \qquad \text{Divide both sides of the inequality by } -5 \text{ and}$$
$$\qquad\qquad\qquad \text{change the direction of the inequality symbol.}$$
$$x > -4$$

The solution set is graphed on the number line as follows.

$x > -4$

Example 5 *Solving an Inequality*

Solve the inequality $2x + 5 > 15$ and graph the solution set on the number line.

Solution To find the solution set, isolate x on one side of the inequality symbol.

$$2x + 5 > 15$$

$$2x + 5 - 5 > 15 - 5 \qquad \text{Subtract 5 from both sides of the inequality.}$$

$$2x > 10$$

$$\frac{2x}{2} > \frac{10}{2} \qquad \text{Divide both sides of the inequality by 2.}$$

$$x > 5$$

Thus, the solution set to $2x + 5 > 15$ is all real numbers greater than 5.

$x > 5$

Note that in Example 5, the *direction of the inequality symbol* did not change when both sides of the inequality were divided by the positive number 2.

Example 6 *A Solution of Only Integers*

Solve the inequality $x - 1 < 3$, where x is an integer, and graph the solution set on the number line.

Solution To find the solution set, isolate x on one side of the inequality symbol.

$$x - 1 < 3$$

$$x - 1 + 1 < 3 + 1 \qquad \text{Add 1 to both sides of the inequality.}$$

$$x < 4$$

Since x is an integer and is less than 4, the solution set is the set of integers less than 4, or $\{ \dots, -2, -1, 0, 1, 2, 3 \}$. To graph the solution set, we make solid dots at the corresponding points on the number line. The ellipsis (the three dots) to the left of -3 indicate that all the integers to the left of -3 are included.

$x < 4,$
x an integer

Some linear inequalities have no solution. When solving an inequality, if you obtain a statement that is *always false*, such as $3 > 5$, the answer is *no solution*. There is no real number that makes the statement true.

Some linear inequalities have all real numbers as their solution. When solving an inequality, if you obtain a statement that is *always true*, such as $2 > 1$, the solution is *all real numbers.*

Solving Compound Inequalities

An inequality of the form $a < x < b$ is called a *compound inequality*. Consider the compound inequality $-3 < x \le 2$, which means that $-3 < x$ *and* $x \le 2$.

┌───
 Example **7** *A Compound Inequality*

Graph the solution set of the inequality $-3 < x \le 2$

a) where x is an integer.   b) where x is a real number.

Solution

a) The solution set is all the integers between -3 and 2, including the 2 but not including the -3, or $\{-2, -1, 0, 1, 2\}$.

$-3 < x \le 2$,
x an integer

b) The solution set consists of all the real numbers between -3 and 2, including the 2 but not including the -3.

$-3 < x \le 2$

■

┌───
 Example **8** *Solving a Compound Inequality*

Solve the compound inequality for x and graph the solution set.

$$-4 < \frac{x + 3}{2} \le 5$$

Solution To solve this compound inequality, we must isolate the x in the middle term. To do so, we use the same principles used to solve inequalities.

$$-4 < \frac{x + 3}{2} \le 5$$

$$2(-4) < 2\left(\frac{x + 3}{2}\right) \le 2(5) \qquad \text{Multiply each part of the inequality by 2.}$$

$$-8 < x + 3 \le 10$$

$$-8 - 3 < x + 3 - 3 \le 10 - 3 \qquad \text{Subtract 3 from each part of the inequality.}$$

$$-11 < x \le 7$$

■

The solution set is graphed on the number line as follows.

$-11 < x \le 7$

■

"In mathematics the art of posing problems is easier than that of solving them."

Georg Cantor

┌───
 Example **9** *Average Grade*

A student must have an average (the mean) on five tests that is greater than or equal to 80% but less than 90% to receive a final grade of B. Devon's grades on the first four tests were 98%, 76%, 86%, and 92%. What range of grades on the fifth test would give him a B in the course?

Solution The unknown quantity is the range of grades on the fifth test. First construct an inequality that can be used to find the range of grades on the fifth test. The average (mean) is found by adding the grades and dividing the sum by the number of tests.

Let $x =$ the fifth grade. Then

$$\text{Average} = \frac{98 + 76 + 86 + 92 + x}{5}$$

For Devon to obtain a B in this course, his average must be greater than or equal to 80 but less than 90.

$$80 \le \frac{98 + 76 + 86 + 92 + x}{5} < 90$$

$$80 \le \frac{352 + x}{5} < 90$$

$$5(80) \le 5\left(\frac{352 + x}{5}\right) < 5(90) \qquad \text{Multiply the three terms of the inequality by 5.}$$

$$400 \le 352 + x < 450$$

$$400 - 352 \le 352 - 352 + x < 450 - 352 \qquad \text{Subtract 352 from all three terms.}$$

$$48 \le x < 98$$

TIMELY TIP
Remember to change the direction of the inequality symbol when multiplying or dividing both sides of an inequality by a *negative* number.

Thus, a grade of 48% up to but not including a grade of 98% on the fifth test will result in a grade of B in this course. ■

SECTION 6.6

Exercises

Warm Up Exercises

In Exercises 1–8, fill in the blank with an appropriate word, phrase, or symbol(s).

1. Two or more expressions joined by an inequality sign is called a(n) _____.

2. a) $a < b$ means that a is _____ than b.

   b) $a > b$ means that a is _____ than b.

3. An inequality of the form $a < x < b$ is called a(n) _____ inequality.

4. When solving an inequality, if you obtain a statement that is always false, such as $3 > 5$, the answer is _____ solution.

5. When solving an inequality, if you obtain a statement that is always true, such as $2 > 1$, the solution is _____ real numbers.

6. When both sides of an inequality are multiplied or divided by a(n) _____ number, the direction of the inequality symbol is reversed.

7. To indicate the solution set of $x < 5$ on the number line, we draw a(n) _____ circle at 5.

8. To indicate the solution set of $x \le 5$ on the number line, we draw a(n) _____ circle at 5.

Practice the Skills

In Exercises 9–26, graph the solution set of the inequality, where x is a real number, on the number line.

9. $x \ge 5$

10. $x < 3$

11. $x + 7 \ge 2$

12. $x - 4 > -5$

13. $-3x \le 18$

14. $-4x < 12$

15. $\frac{x}{6} < 3$

16. $\frac{x}{5} > 2$

17. $\frac{-x}{3} \ge 3$

18. $\frac{-x}{2} \le -4$

19. $2x + 6 \ge 14$

20. $3x + 12 < 5x + 14$

21. $4(2x - 1) < 2(4x - 3)$

22. $-2(x - 3) \le 4x + 6$

23. $-1 \le x \le 3$

24. $-4 < x \le 1$

25. $2 < x - 4 \le 6$

26. $\frac{1}{2} < \frac{x + 4}{2} \le 4$

In Exercises 27–46, graph the solution set of the inequality, where x is an integer, on the number line.

27. $x > 2$

28. $-3 < x$

29. $-3x \le 27$

30. $3x \ge 27$

31. $x - 4 < -2$ **32.** $x + 6 > 2$

33. $\dfrac{x}{3} \le -2$ **34.** $\dfrac{x}{4} \ge -3$

35. $-\dfrac{x}{4} \ge 2$ **36.** $\dfrac{3x}{5} \le 3$

37. $-15 < -4x - 3$

38. $-5x - 1 < 17 - 2x$

39. $3(x + 4) \ge 4x + 13$

40. $-2(x - 1) < 3(x - 4) + 5$

41. $5(x + 4) - 6 \le 2x + 8$

42. $-2 \le x < 6$

43. $1 > -x > -6$

44. $-2 < 2x + 3 < 6$

45. $0.3 \le \dfrac{x + 2}{10} \le 0.5$

46. $-\dfrac{1}{3} < \dfrac{x - 2}{12} \le \dfrac{1}{4}$

Problem Solving

47. *Indianapolis 500* The following bar graph shows the average speed, in miles per hour (mph), of the winning driver of the Indianapolis 500 for the years 2004–2010.

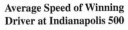

Source: *indianapolismotorspeedway.com*

In which years was the average speed of the winning driver

a) >150 mph?

b) ≤150 mph?

c) >160 mph?

d) ≤140 mph?

48. *Unemployment Rate* The following graph shows the unemployment rate in the United States for the years 2001–2009.

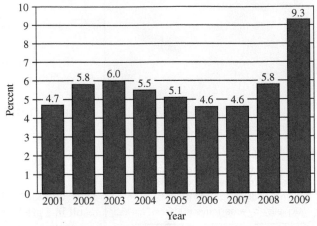

Source: *U.S. Department of Labor*

In which years was the unemployment rate in the United States

a) > 5%   **b)** < 5.5%

c) ≥ 5.5%   **d)** ≤ 5.0%

49. *DVD Rental* Movie Mania offers two rental plans. One has an annual fee, and the other has no annual fee. The annual membership fee and the daily charge per DVD for each plan are shown in the table. Determine the maximum number of DVDs that can be rented for the no fee plan to cost less than the annual fee plan.

Rental Plan	Yearly Fee	Daily Charge per DVD
Annual fee	$30	$1.49
No fee	None	$2.99

50. *Salary Plans* Bobby Exler recently accepted a sales position in Portland, Oregon. He can select between the two salary plans shown in the table. Determine the dollar amount of weekly sales that would result in Bobby earning more with Plan B than with Plan A.

Salary Plan	Weekly Salary	Commission on Sales
Plan A	$500	6%
Plan B	$400	8%

51. *College Employment* To be eligible for financial assistance for college, Samantha Lavin can earn no more than $3200 during her summer employment. She will earn $662.50 cutting lawns. She is also earning $7.25 per hour at an evening job as a cashier at a grocery store. What is the maximum number of hours Samantha can work at the grocery store without jeopardizing her financial assistance?

▲ See Exercise 51

52. *Anniversary* Patricia and Joe Kuby are celebrating their 75th wedding anniversary by having a party at the Diplomat Party House. They have budgeted $3000 for the party. If the party house charges a flat rate of $75 for set-up and clean-up, plus $25 per person, determine the maximum number of guests the Kubys can invite and remain within their budget.

53. *Parking Costs* A parking garage in Richmond, Virginia, charges $1.75 for the first hour and $0.50 for each additional hour or part of an hour. What is the maximum length of time Tom Shalhoub can park in the garage if he wishes to pay no more than $4.25?

54. *Making a Profit* For a business to realize a profit, its revenue, R, must be greater than its costs, C; that is, a profit will result only if $R > C$ (the company breaks even when $R = C$). A dry cleaning store has a weekly cost equation of $C = 0.25x + 1500$ and a weekly revenue of $R = 4x$, where x is the number of garments dry cleaned in a week. How many garments must be dry cleaned in a week for the company to make a profit?

55. *Finding Velocity* The velocity, v, in feet per second, t sec after a tennis ball is projected directly upward is given by the formula $v = 84 - 32t$. How many seconds after being projected upward will the velocity be between 36 ft/sec and 68 ft/sec?

56. *Speed Limit* The minimum speed for vehicles on a highway is 40 mph, and the maximum speed is 55 mph. If Philip Rowe has been driving nonstop along the highway for 4 hr, what range in miles could he have legally traveled?

57. *A Grade of B* In Example 9 on page 332, what range of grades on the fifth test would result in Devon receiving a grade of B if his grades on the first four tests were 78%, 64%, 88%, and 76%?

58. *Tent Rental* The Cuhayoga Community College Planning Committee wants to rent tents for the spring job fair. Rent-a-Tent charges $325 for setup and delivery of its tents. This fee is charged regardless of the number of tents delivered and set up. In addition, Rent-a-Tent charges $125 for each tent rented. If the minimum amount the planning committee wishes to spend is $950 and the maximum amount they wish to spend is $1200, determine the minimum and maximum number of tents the committee can rent.

Challenge Problems/Group Activities

59. *Painting a House* Donovan Davis is painting the exterior of his house. The instructions on the paint can indicate that 1 gal covers from 250 to 400 ft^2. The total surface of the house to be painted is 2750 ft^2. Determine the number of gallons of paint he could use and express the answer as an inequality.

60. *Final Exam* Teresa's five test grades for the semester are 86%, 78%, 68%, 92%, and 72%. Her final exam counts one-third of her final grade. What range of grades on her final exam would result in Teresa receiving a final grade of B in the course? (See Example 9.)

61. A student multiplied both sides of the inequality $-\frac{1}{3}x \le 4$ by -3 and forgot to reverse the direction of the inequality symbol. What is the relation between the student's incorrect solution set and the correct solution set? Is there any number in both the correct solution set and the student's incorrect solution set? If so, what is it?

Internet/Research Activity

62. Find a newspaper or a magazine article that contains the mathematical concept of inequality.

a) From the information in the article write a statement of inequality.

b) Summarize the article and explain how you arrived at the inequality statement in part (a).

SECTION 6.7   Graphing Linear Equations

▲ *The cost of mailing a package may depend on the weight of the package.*

The profit, *p*, of a company may depend on the amount of sales, *s*. The cost, *c*, of mailing a package may depend on the weight, *w*, of the package. Real-life problems, such as these two examples, often involve two or more variables. In this section, we will discuss how to graph equations with two variables.

Why *This is Important* We see and use graphs daily. If you read a newspaper or open a magazine, you are likely to see line graphs. Also, graphs are used to display information in businesses and industry.

To be able to work with equations with two variables requires understanding the *Cartesian* (or *rectangular*) *coordinate system*, named after the French mathematician René Descartes. The rectangular coordinate system consists of two perpendicular number lines (Fig. 6.3). The horizontal line is the *x-axis*, and the vertical line is the *y-axis*. The point of intersection of the *x*-axis and *y*-axis is called the *origin*. The numbers on the axes to the right and above the origin are positive. The numbers on the axes on the left and below the origin are negative. The axes divide the plane into four parts: the first, second, third, and fourth *quadrants*.

We indicate the location of a point in the rectangular coordinate system by means of an *ordered pair* of the form (x, y). The *x*-coordinate is always placed first, and the *y*-coordinate is always placed second in the ordered pair. Consider the point illustrated in Fig. 6.4. Since the *x*-coordinate of the point is 5 and the *y*-coordinate is 3, the ordered pair that represents this point is (5, 3).

Figure 6.3

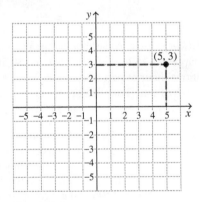

Figure 6.4

The origin is represented by the ordered pair (0, 0). Every point on the plane can be represented by one and only one ordered pair (x, y), and every ordered pair (x, y) represents one and only one point on the plane.

Example 1 *Plotting Points*

Plot the points $A(-2, 4)$, $B(-3, -1)$, $C(2, 0)$, $D(4, 2)$, and $E(0, -4)$.

Solution Point *A* has an *x*-coordinate of -2 and a *y*-coordinate of 4. Project a vertical line up from -2 on the *x*-axis and a horizontal line to the left from 4 on the

y-axis. The two lines intersect at the point denoted A (Fig. 6.5). The other points are plotted in a similar manner.

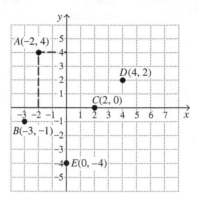

Figure 6.5

Example 2 A Parallelogram

The points, A, B, and C are three vertices of a parallelogram with two sides parallel to the x-axis. Plot the three points below and determine the coordinates of the fourth vertex, D.

$$A(1, 2) \quad B(2, 4) \quad C(7, 4)$$

Solution A parallelogram is a figure that has opposite sides that are of equal length and are parallel. (Parallel lines are two lines in the same plane that do not intersect.) The horizontal distance between points B and C is 5 units (see Fig. 6.6). Therefore, the horizontal distance between points A and D must also be 5 units. This problem has two possible solutions, as illustrated in Fig. 6.6. In each figure, we have indicated the given points in red.

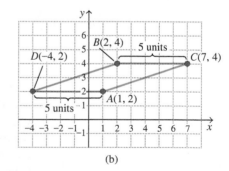

(a)   (b)

Figure 6.6

The solutions are the points $(6, 2)$ and $(-4, 2)$.

Graphing Linear Equations by Plotting Points

Consider the following equation in two variables: $y = x + 1$. Every ordered pair that makes the equation a true statement is a solution to, or satisfies, the equation. We can mentally find some ordered pairs that satisfy the equation $y = x + 1$ by picking some values of x and solving the equation for y. For example, suppose we let $x = 1$; then $y = 1 + 1 = 2$. The ordered pair $(1, 2)$ is a solution to the equation $y = x + 1$. We can make a chart of other ordered pairs that are solutions to the equation.

x	y	Ordered Pair
1	2	(1, 2)
2	3	(2, 3)
3	4	(3, 4)
4.5	5.5	(4.5, 5.5)
−3	−2	(−3, −2)

How many other ordered pairs satisfy the equation? Infinitely many ordered pairs satisfy the equation. Since we cannot list all the solutions, we show them by means of a graph. A *graph* is an illustration of all the points whose coordinates satisfy an equation.

The points $(1, 2)$, $(2, 3)$, $(3, 4)$, $(4.5, 5.5)$, and $(−3, −2)$ are plotted in Fig. 6.8. With a straightedge we can draw one line that contains all these points. This line, when extended indefinitely in either direction, passes through all the points in the plane that satisfy the equation $y = x + 1$. The arrows on the ends of the line indicate that the line extends indefinitely.

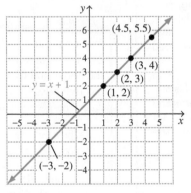

Figure 6.8

All equations of the form $ax + by = c$, $a \neq 0$ and $b \neq 0$, will be straight lines when graphed. Thus, such equations are called *linear equations in two variables*. The exponents on the variables x and y must be 1 for the equation to be linear. Since only two points are needed to draw a line, only two points are needed to graph a linear equation. It is always a good idea to plot a third point as a checkpoint. If no error has been made, all three points will be in a line, or *collinear*. One method that can be used to obtain points is to solve the equation for y, substitute values for x, and find the corresponding values of y.

Example 3 *Graphing an Equation by Plotting Points*

Graph $y = 2x + 2$.

Solution Since the equation is already solved for y, select values for x and find the corresponding values for y. The table on page 339 indicates values arbitrarily selected for x

and the corresponding values for y. The ordered pairs are $(0, 2)$, $(1, 4)$, and $(-1, 0)$. The graph is shown in Fig. 6.9.

x	y
0	2
1	4
-1	0

Figure 6.9

PROCEDURE   TO GRAPH LINEAR EQUATIONS BY PLOTTING POINTS

1. Solve the equation for y.
2. Select at least three values for x and find their corresponding values of y.
3. Plot the points.
4. The points should be in a straight line. Draw a line through the set of points and place arrow tips at both ends of the line.

In Step 4 of the procedure, if the points are not in a straight line, recheck your calculations and find your error.

Graphing by Using Intercepts

Example 3 contained two special points on the graph, $(-1, 0)$ and $(0, 2)$. At these points, the line crosses the x-axis and the y-axis, respectively. The ordered pairs $(-1, 0)$ and $(0, 2)$ represent the *x-intercept* and the *y-intercept*, respectively. Another method that can be used to graph linear equations is to find the x- and y-intercepts of the graph.

PROCEDURE   FINDING THE *X*- AND *Y*-INTERCEPTS

To find the x-intercept, set $y = 0$ and solve the equation for x.

To find the y-intercept, set $x = 0$ and solve the equation for y.

A linear equation may be graphed by finding the x- and y-intercepts, plotting the intercepts, and drawing a straight line through the intercepts. When graphing by this method, you should always plot a checkpoint before drawing your graph. To obtain a checkpoint, select a nonzero value for x and find the corresponding value of y. The checkpoint should be collinear with the x- and y-intercepts.

Example 4 *Graphing an Equation by Using Intercepts*

Graph $3x + 6y = 12$ by using the x- and y-intercepts.

Solution To determine the *x*-intercept, set $y = 0$ and solve for *x*.

$$3x + 6y = 12$$
$$3x + 6(0) = 12$$
$$3x = 12$$
$$x = 4$$

The *x*-intercept is (4, 0). To determine the *y*-intercept, set $x = 0$ and solve for *y*.

$$3x + 6y = 12$$
$$3(0) + 6y = 12$$
$$6y = 12$$
$$y = 2$$

The *y*-intercept is (0, 2). As a checkpoint, substitute $x = 2$ and determine the corresponding value for *y*.

$$3x + 6y = 12$$
$$3(2) + 6y = 12$$
$$6 + 6y = 12$$
$$6y = 6$$
$$y = 1$$

The checkpoint is the ordered pair (2, 1). The three points are plotted in Figure 6.10.

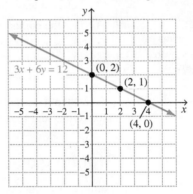

Figure 6.10

Since all three points are collinear, draw a line through the three points to obtain the graph. ■

Slope

Another useful concept when you are working with straight lines is slope, which is a measure of the "steepness" of a line. The *slope of a line* is a ratio of the vertical change to the horizontal change for any two points on the line. Consider Fig. 6.11. Point *A* has coordinates (x_1, y_1), and point *B* has coordinates (x_2, y_2). The vertical change between points *A* and *B* is $y_2 - y_1$. The horizontal change between points *A* and *B* is $x_2 - x_1$. Thus, the slope, which is often symbolized with the letter *m*, can be found as follows.

Figure 6.11

Slope of a Line

$$\textbf{Slope} = \frac{\text{vertical change}}{\text{horizontal change}}$$

$$m = \frac{y_2 - y_1}{x_2 - x_1}$$

The Greek capital letter delta, Δ, is often used to represent the words "the change in." Therefore, slope may be defined as

$$m = \frac{\Delta y}{\Delta x}$$

A line may have a positive slope, a negative slope, or a zero slope, or the slope may be undefined, as indicated in Fig. 6.12. A line with a positive slope rises from left to right, as shown in Fig. 6.12(a). A line with a negative slope falls from left to right, as shown in Fig. 6.12(b). A horizontal line, which neither rises nor falls, has a slope of zero, as shown in Fig. 6.12(c). Since a vertical line does not have any horizontal change (the x-value remains constant) and since we cannot divide by 0, the slope of a vertical line is undefined, as shown in Fig. 6.12(d).

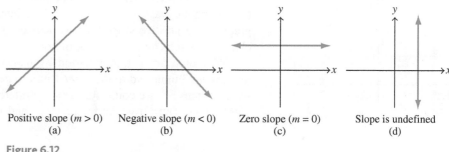

Positive slope $(m > 0)$ Negative slope $(m < 0)$ Zero slope $(m = 0)$ Slope is undefined
(a)   (b)   (c)   (d)

Figure 6.12

Example 5 *Finding the Slope of a Line*

Determine the slope of the line that passes through the points $(-1, -3)$ and $(1, 5)$.

Solution   Let's begin by drawing a sketch, illustrating the points and the line. See Fig. 6.13(a).

We will let (x_1, y_1) be $(-1, -3)$ and (x_2, y_2) be $(1, 5)$. Then

$$\text{Slope} = \frac{y_2 - y_1}{x_2 - x_1} = \frac{5 - (-3)}{1 - (-1)} = \frac{5 + 3}{1 + 1} = \frac{8}{2} = \frac{4}{1} = 4$$

The slope of 4 means that there is a vertical change of 4 units for each horizontal change of 1 unit; see Fig. 6.13(b). The slope is positive, and the line rises from left to right. Note that we would have obtained the same result if we let (x_1, y_1) be $(1, 5)$ and (x_2, y_2) be $(-1, -3)$. Try this method now and see.

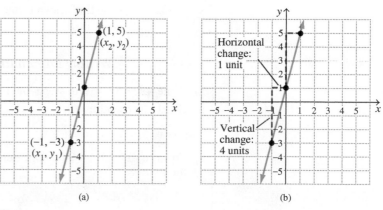

(a)   (b)

Figure 6.13

Graphing Linear Equations by Using the Slope and y-Intercept

A linear equation given in the form $y = mx + b$ is said to be in slope–intercept form.

Slope–Intercept Form of the Equation of a Line

$$y = mx + b$$

where m is the slope of the line and $(0, b)$ is the y-intercept of the line.

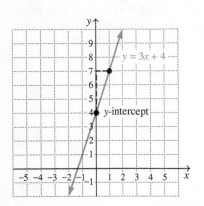

Figure 6.14

In the equation $y = mx + b$, b represents the value of y where the graph of the equation $y = mx + b$ crosses the y-axis.

Consider the graph of the equation $y = 3x + 4$, which appears in Fig. 6.14. By examining the graph, we can see that the y-intercept is $(0, 4)$. We can also see that the graph has a positive slope because it rises from left to right. Because the vertical change is 3 units for every 1 unit of horizontal change, the slope must be $\frac{3}{1}$ or 3.

We could graph this equation by marking the y-intercept at $(0, 4)$ and then moving *up* 3 units and to the *right* 1 unit to get another point. If the slope were -3, which means $\frac{-3}{1}$, we could start at the y-intercept and move *down* 3 units and to the *right* 1 unit. Thus, if we know the slope and y-intercept of a line, we can graph the line.

> **PROCEDURE   TO GRAPH LINEAR EQUATIONS BY USING THE SLOPE AND Y-INTERCEPT**
>
> 1. Solve the equation for y to place the equation in slope–intercept form.
> 2. Determine the slope and y-intercept from the equation.
> 3. Plot the y-intercept.
> 4. Obtain a second point using the slope.
> 5. Draw a straight line through the points.

Figure 6.15

Example 6 *Graphing an Equation by Using the Slope and y-Intercept*

Graph $y = -3x + 1$ by using the slope and y-intercept.

Solution The slope is -3 or $\frac{-3}{1}$ and the y-intercept is $(0, 1)$ (see Fig. 6.15). Plot $(0, 1)$ on the y-axis. Then plot the next point by moving *down* 3 units and to the *right* 1 unit. A third point has been plotted in the same way. The graph of $y = -3x + 1$ is the line drawn through these three points. ∎

Example 7 *Writing an Equation in Slope–Intercept Form*

a) Write $4x - 3y = 9$ in slope–intercept form.
b) Graph the equation.

Solution

a) To write $4x - 3y = 9$ in slope–intercept form, we solve the given equation for y.

$$4x - 3y = 9$$
$$4x - 4x - 3y = -4x + 9$$

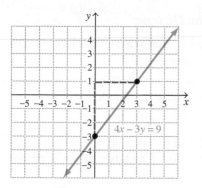

Figure 6.16

$$-3y = -4x + 9$$

$$\frac{-3y}{-3} = \frac{-4x + 9}{-3}$$

$$y = \frac{-4x}{-3} + \frac{9}{-3} \quad \text{or} \quad y = \frac{4}{3}x - 3$$

Thus, in slope–intercept form, the equation is $y = \frac{4}{3}x - 3$.

b) The y-intercept is $(0, -3)$, and the slope is $\frac{4}{3}$. Plot a point at $(0, -3)$ on the y-axis, then move *up* 4 units and to the *right* 3 units to obtain the second point (see Fig. 6.16). Draw a line through the two points.   ∎

Example 8   *Determining the Equation of a Line from Its Graph*

Determine the equation of the line in Fig. 6.17.

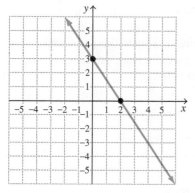

Figure 6.17

Solution   If we determine the slope and the y-intercept of the line, we can write the equation using slope–intercept form, $y = mx + b$. We see from the graph that the y-intercept is $(0, 3)$; thus, $b = 3$. The slope of the line is negative because the graph falls from left to right. The change in y is 3 units for every 2-unit change in x. Thus, m, the slope of the line, is $-\frac{3}{2}$.

$$y = mx + b$$

$$y = -\frac{3}{2}x + 3$$

The equation of the line is $y = -\frac{3}{2}x + 3$.   ∎

Example 9   *Horizontal and Vertical Lines*

In the Cartesian coordinate system, graph (a) $y = 2$ and (b) $x = -3$.

Solution

Figure 6.18

a) For any value of x, the value of y is 2. Therefore, the graph will be a horizontal line through $y = 2$ (Fig. 6.18).

b) For any value of y, the value of x is -3. Therefore, the graph will be a vertical line through $x = -3$ (Fig. 6.19).

Note that the graph of $y = 2$ has a slope of 0. The slope of the graph of $x = -3$ is undefined.   ∎

Figure 6.19

In graphing the equations in this section, we labeled the horizontal axis the x axis and the vertical axis the y-axis. For each equation, we can determine values for y by substituting values for x. Since the value of y depends on the value of x, we refer to y as the *dependent variable* and x as the *independent variable*. We label the *vertical axis* with the *dependent variable* and the *horizontal axis* with the *independent variable*. For the equation $C = 3n + 5$, the C is the dependent variable and n is the independent variable. Thus, to graph this equation, we label the vertical axis C and the horizontal axis n.

In many graphs, the values to be plotted on one axis are much greater than the values to be plotted on the other axis. When that occurs, we can use different scales on the horizontal and the vertical axes, as illustrated in Examples 10 and 11. The next two examples illustrate applications of graphing.

Figure 6.20

Example 10 *Using a Graph to Determine Distance*

The distance in miles, d, a car travels in t hours, traveling at a constant rate of 40 miles per hour, can be determined by the equation $d = 40t$.

a) Graph $d = 40t$, for $t \leq 6$.

b) Use the graph to estimate the distance the car travels in 4 hours.

Solution

a) Since $d = 40t$ is a linear equation, the graph will be a straight line. Select three values for t, determine the corresponding values for d, and then draw the graph (Fig 6.20).

$$d = 40t$$

Let $t = 0$, $d = 40(0) = 0$

Let $t = 2$, $d = 40(2) = 80$

Let $t = 6$, $d = 40(6) = 240$

t	d
0	0
2	80
6	240

b) By drawing a vertical line from $t = 4$ on the time axis up to the graph and then drawing a horizontal line across to the distance axis, we can estimate that the distance the car travels in 4 hours is about 160 miles.   ■

Example 11 *Using a Graph to Determine Profits*

Javier Mungro owns a business that sells mountain bicycles. He believes the profit (or loss) from the bicycles sold can be estimated by the formula $P = 60S - 90,000$, where S is the number of bicycles sold.

a) Graph $P = 60S - 90,000$, for $S \leq 5000$ bicycles.

b) From the graph, estimate the number of bicycles that must be sold for the business to break even (Fig. 6.21).

c) From the graph, estimate the number of bicycles sold if the profit from selling bicycles is about $150,000.

Solution

a) Select values for S and find the corresponding values of P.

S	P
0	−90,000
2000	30,000
5000	210,000

Figure 6.21

b) The break-even point is the number of bicycles that must be sold for the company to have neither a profit nor a loss. The break-even point is where the graph intercepts the horizontal, or S-axis, for that is where the profit, P, is 0. To break even, about 1500 bicycles must be sold. The actual value can be obtained by substituting 0 for P and solving the equation for S. Do this now.

c) We can estimate the answer by drawing a horizontal line from 150 on the profit axis. Since the horizontal line cuts the graph at 4000 on the S-axis, about 4000 bicycles were sold.   ■

Exercises

Warm Up Exercises

In Exercises 1–8, fill in the blank with an appropriate word, phrase, or symbols(s).

1. An illustration of all the points whose coordinates satisfy an equation is called a(n) _____.

2. To find the x-intercept of the graph of a linear equation, set _____ equal to zero and solve the equation for x.

3. To find the y-intercept of the graph of a linear equation, set _____ equal to zero and solve the equation for y.

4. The ratio of the vertical change to the horizontal change for any two points on a line is called the _____ of the line.

5. The three methods used to graph a linear equation given in this section are _____, _____, and _____.

6. The minimum number of points needed to graph a linear equation is _____.

7. In the equation $y = mx + b$, the slope of the line is represented by _____.

8. a) The point $(2, 7)$ is located in the _____ quadrant.

  b) The point $(-3, -5)$ is located in the _____ quadrant.

Practice the Skills

In Exercises 9–16, plot all the points on the same axes.

9. $(3, 1)$

10. $(-2, -4)$

11. $(-5, -1)$

12. $(4, 0)$

13. $(0, 2)$

14. $(0, 0)$

15. $(0, -5)$

16. $(2\frac{1}{2}, 5\frac{1}{2})$

In Exercises 17–24, plot all the points on the same axes.

17. $(5, 1)$

18. $(-4, 0)$

19. $(-2, -5)$

20. $(0, -1)$

21. $(0, 2)$

22. $(-4, 5)$

23. $(4, -1)$

24. $(4.5, 3.5)$

In Exercises 25–34 (indicated on Fig. 6.22), write the coordinates of the corresponding point.

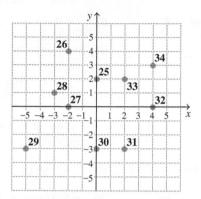

Figure 6.22

In Exercises 35–42, determine which ordered pairs satisfy the given equation.

35. $x + 4y = 13$ $(5, 2)$ $(1, 3)$ $(0, 5)$

36. $4x - y = 4$ $(0, -4)$ $(1, 0)$ $(2, -3)$

37. $3x - 2y = 10$ $(8, 7)$ $(-1, 4)$ $\left(\frac{10}{3}, 0\right)$

38. $3y = 4x + 2$ $(2, 1)$ $(1, 2)$ $\left(0, \frac{2}{3}\right)$

39. $6y = 3x + 6$ $(1, -1)$, $(4, 3)$, $(2, 5)$

40. $3x - 5y = -12$ $(1, 3)$, $(-1, 2)$, $(-4, 0)$

41. $\dfrac{x}{4} + \dfrac{2y}{3} = 2$ $(8, 0)$, $(1, \frac{1}{2})$, $(0, 3)$

42. $\dfrac{x}{2} + 3y = 4$ $\left(0, \frac{4}{3}\right)$ $(8, 0)$, $(10, -2)$

In Exercises 43–46, graph the equation and state the slope of the line if the slope exists (see Example 9).

43. $x = 3$ **44.** $x = -2$

45. $y = 3$ **46.** $y = -4$

In Exercises 47–56, graph the equation by plotting points, as in Example 3.

47. $y = x + 2$ **48.** $y = x - 3$

49. $y = 3x - 1$ **50.** $y = -2x + 4$

51. $y + 3x = 6$ **52.** $y - 4x = 8$

53. $y = \frac{1}{2}x + 4$ **54.** $3y = 2x - 3$

55. $y = \frac{1}{3}x$ **56.** $y = -\frac{2}{3}x$

In Exercises 57–66, graph the equation, using the x- and y-intercepts, as in Example 4.

57. $x + y = 2$

58. $x - y = 4$

59. $2x + y = 6$

60. $3x - y = -6$

61. $2x = -4y - 8$

62. $y = 4x + 4$

63. $y = 3x + 5$

64. $3x + 6y = 9$

65. $3x - y = 5$

66. $6x = 3y - 9$

In Exercises 67–76, determine the slope of the line through the given points. If the slope is undefined, so state.

67. (4, 7) and (8, 15)

68. (2, 3) and (3, 2)

69. (6, 5) and (2, 10)

70. (−5, 7) and (8, 9)

71. (5, 1) and (−3, 1)

72. (−3, −5) and (−1, −2)

73. (8, −3) and (8, 3)

74. (2, 6) and (2, −3)

75. (−3, −1) and (8, −9)

76. (2, 1) and (−5, −9)

In Exercises 77–86, graph the equation using the slope and y-intercept, as in Examples 6 and 7.

77. $y = x + 3$

78. $y = -x - 1$

79. $y = 3x + 1$

80. $y = 2x - 5$

81. $y = -\frac{1}{3}x + 2$

82. $y = \frac{1}{2}x - 2$

83. $7y = 4x - 7$

84. $3x + 2y = 6$

85. $3x - 2y + 6 = 0$

86. $3x + 4y - 8 = 0$

In Exercises 87–90, determine the equation of the graph.

87.

88.

89.

90.

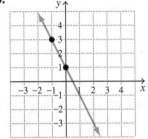

Problem Solving

In Exercises 91 and 92, points A, B, and C are three vertices of a rectangle (the points where two sides meet). Plot the three points. (a) Find the coordinates of the fourth point, D, to complete the rectangle. (b) Find the area of the rectangle; use A = lw.

91. $A(-1, 4)$, $B(4, 4)$, $C(-1, 2)$

92. $A(-4, 2)$, $B(7, 2)$, $C(7, 8)$

In Exercises 93 and 94, points A, B, and C are three vertices of a parallelogram with sides parallel to the x-axis. Plot the three points. Find the coordinates of the fourth point, D, to complete the parallelogram. Note: There are two possible answers for point D.

93. $A(3, 2)$, $B(5, 5)$, $C(9, 5)$

94. $A(-2, 2)$, $B(3, 2)$, $C(6, -1)$

In Exercises 95–98, for what value of b will the line joining the points P and Q be parallel to the indicated axis?

95. $P(2, -3)$, $Q(6, b)$;   x-axis

96. $P(4, 7)$, $Q(b, -2)$;   y-axis

97. $P(3b - 1, 5)$, $Q(8, 4)$;   y-axis

98. $P(-6, 2b + 3)$, $Q(7, -1)$;   x-axis

99. *Hanging Wallpaper* Tanisha Vizquez owns a wallpaper hanging business. Her charge, C, for hanging wallpaper is $40 plus $0.30 per square foot of wallpaper she hangs, or

$C = 40 + 0.30s$, where s is the number of square feet of wallpaper she hangs.

a) Graph $C = 40 + 0.30s$, for $s \leq 500$.

b) From the graph, estimate her charge if she hangs 300 square feet of wallpaper.

c) If her charge is $70, use the equation for C to determine how many square feet of wallpaper she hung.

100. *Selling Chocolates* Ryan Stewart sells chocolate on the Internet. His monthly profit, p, in dollars, can be estimated by $p = 15n - 300$, where n is the number of dozens of chocolates he sells in a month.

a) Graph $p = 15n - 300$, for $n \leq 60$.

b) From the graph, estimate his profit if he sells 40 dozen chocolates in a month.

c) How many dozens of chocolates must he sell in a month to break even?

101. *Earning Simple Interest* When $1000 is invested in a savings account paying simple interest for a year, the interest, i, in dollars, earned can be found by the formula $i = 1000r$, where r is the rate in decimal form.

a) Graph $i = 1000r$, for r up to and including a rate of 15%.

b) If the rate is 4%, what is the simple interest?

c) If the rate is 6%, what is the simple interest?

102. *Cable Cost* The Schwimmer's cost for cable television is given by $C = 75 + 25x$, where x is the number of months of service.

a) Graph $C = 75 + 25x$, for $x \leq 50$.

b) From the graph, estimate the Schwimmer's cost for 30 months of cable television.

c) If the Schwimmer's total cost for cable television is $975, estimate the number of months of service.

In Exercises 103 and 104, a set of points is plotted. Also shown is a straight line through the set of points that is called the line of best fit *(or a regression line, as will be discussed in Chapter 13, Statistics).*

103. *Determining the Number of Defects* The top graph on the right shows the daily number of workers absent from the assembly line at J. B. Davis Corporation and

the number of defects coming off the assembly line for 8 days. (The two points indicated on the line do not represent any of the 8 days.) The line of best fit, the blue line on the graph, can be used to approximate the number of defects coming off the assembly line per day for a given number of workers absent.

a) Determine the slope of the line of best fit using the two points indicated.

b) Using the slope determined in part (a) and the y-intercept, $(0, 9)$, determine the equation of the line of best fit.

c) Using the equation you determined in part (b), determine the approximate number of defects for a day if 3 workers are absent.

d) Using the equation you determined in part (b), approximate the number of workers absent for a day if there are 17 defects that day.

104. *Determining a Test Grade* The graph below shows the hours studied and the test grades on a biology test for six students. (The two points indicated on the line do not represent any of the six students.) The line of best fit, the red line on the graph, can be used to approximate the test grade the average student receives for the number of hours he or she studies.

a) Determine the slope of the line of best fit using the two points indicated.

b) Using the slope determined in part (a) and the *y*-intercept, (0, 53), determine the equation of the line of best fit.

c) Using the equation you determined in part (b), determine the approximate test grade for a student who studied for 3 hours.

d) Using the equation you determined in part (b), determine the amount of time a student would need to study to receive a grade of 80 on the biology test.

105. *Internet Access* The green graph shows the percentage of Americans who accessed the Internet, for the years 2004–2009. The red dashed line can be used to approximate the percentage of Americans who accessed the Internet. If we let 0 represent 2004, 1 represent 2005, and so on, then 2009 would be represented by 5. Using the ordered pairs (0, 73.19) and (5, 81.49),

a) determine the slope of the red dashed line.

b) determine the equation of the red dashed line, with (0, 73.19) as the *y*-intercept.

c) Using the equation you determined in part (b), estimate the percentage of Americans who accessed the Internet in 2006.

d) Using the equation you determined in part (b), determine the year in which 79.83% of Americans accessed the Internet.

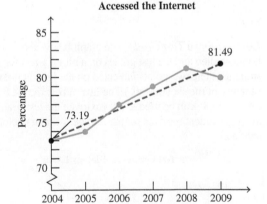

Percentage of Americans Who Accessed the Internet

Source: *Harris Interactive*

106. *Lead Poisoning* The blue graph above and to the right shows the actual number of 6-year-old children in Rochester, NY, who tested positive for lead poisoning for the years 1996–2008. The red dashed line can be used to

approximate the number of 6-year-old children in Rochester, NY, who tested positive for lead poisoning. If we let 0 represent 1996, 1 represent 1997, and so on, then 2008 would be represented by 12. Using the ordered pairs (0, 2747) and (12, 323),

a) determine the slope of the red dashed line.

b) determine the equation of the red dashed line, with (0, 2747) as the *y*-intercept of the graph.

c) Using the equation you determined in part (b), estimate the number of 6-year-old children in Rochester, NY, who tested positive for lead poisoning in 2006.

d) Assuming this trend continues, use the equation you determined in part (b) to determine the year in which the number of 6-year-old children in Rochester, NY, who test positive for lead poisoning is 120.

Number of 6-year-olds Who Tested Positive for Lead Poisoning in Rochester, NY

Challenge Problems/Group Activities

107. a) Two lines are parallel when they do not intersect no matter how far they are extended. Explain how you can determine, without graphing the equations, whether two equations will be parallel lines when graphed.

b) Determine whether the graphs of the equations $2x - 3y = 6$ and $4x = 6y + 6$ are parallel lines.

108. In which quadrants will the set of points that satisfy the equation $x + y = 1$ lie? Explain.

Internet/Research Activity

109. René Descartes is known for his contributions to algebra. Write a paper on his life and his contributions to algebra.

SECTION 6.8   Linear Inequalities in Two Variables

▲ *A linear inequality in two variables may be used to represent the number of grills that can be shipped to each of two stores.*

A manufacturer of gas grills needs to determine how many grills to ship to each of two stores. The manufacturer can ship at most 300 grills in total. A linear inequality in two variables can be used to represent the number of grills that can be shipped to each store. In this section, we will discuss how to solve linear inequalities in two variables.

Why *This is Important*   Linear inequalities are used to express many real-life applications mathematically. Linear inequalities are also used to perform linear programming, which is a tool used in many industries.

In Section 6.6, we introduced linear inequalities in one variable. Now we will introduce linear inequalities in two variables. Some examples of linear inequalities in two variables are $2x + 3y \leq 7$, $x + 7y \geq 5$, and $x - 3y < 6$.

The solution set of a linear inequality in one variable may be indicated on a number line. The solution set of a linear inequality in two variables is indicated on a coordinate plane.

An inequality that is strictly less than ($<$) or greater than ($>$) will have as its solution set a *half-plane*. A half-plane is the set of all the points on one side of a line. An inequality that is less than or equal to ($\leq$) or greater than or equal to ($\geq$) will have as its solution set the set of points that consists of a half-plane and a line. To indicate that the line is part of the solution set, we draw a solid line. To indicate that the line is not part of the solution set, we draw a dashed line.

PROCEDURE   TO GRAPH LINEAR INEQUALITIES IN TWO VARIABLES

1. Mentally substitute the equal sign for the inequality sign and plot points as if you were graphing the equation.

2. If the inequality is $<$ or $>$, draw a dashed line through the points. If the inequality is $\leq$ or $\geq$, draw a solid line through the points.

3. Select a test point not on the line and substitute the x- and y-coordinates into the inequality. If the substitution results in a true statement, shade in the area on the same side of the line as the test point. If the test point results in a false statement, shade in the area on the opposite side of the line as the test point.

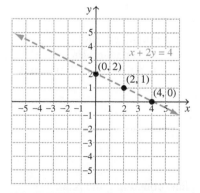

Figure 6.23

Example 1   *Graphing an Inequality*

Draw the graph of $x + 2y < 4$.

Solution   To obtain the solution set, start by graphing $x + 2y = 4$. Since the original inequality is strictly "less than," draw a dashed line (Fig 6.23). The dashed line indicates that the points on the line are not part of the solution set.

The line $x + 2y = 4$ divides the plane into three parts, the line itself and two *half-planes*. The line is the boundary between the two half-planes. The points in one half-plane will satisfy the inequality $x + 2y < 4$. The points in the other half-plane will satisfy the inequality $x + 2y > 4$.

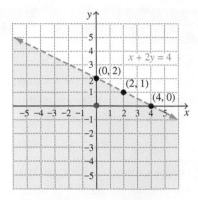

Figure 6.24

To determine the solution set to the inequality $x + 2y < 4$, pick any point on the plane that is not on the line. The simplest point to work with is the origin, $(0, 0)$. Substitute $x = 0$ and $y = 0$ into $x + 2y < 4$.

$$x + 2y < 4$$

$$\text{Is } 0 + 2(0) < 4?$$

$$0 + 0 < 4$$

$$0 < 4 \quad \text{True}$$

Since 0 is less than 4, the point $(0, 0)$ is part of the solution set. All the points on the same side of the graph of $x + 2y = 4$ as the point $(0, 0)$ are members of the solution set. We indicate that by shading the half-plane that contains $(0, 0)$. The graph is shown in Fig. 6.24. ∎

Example 2 *Graphing an Inequality*

Draw the graph of $2x - 3y \leq -6$.

Solution First draw the graph of the equation $2x - 3y = -6$. Use a solid line because the points on the boundary line are included in the solution set (see Fig. 6.25). Now pick a point that is not on the line. Take $(0, 0)$ as the test point.

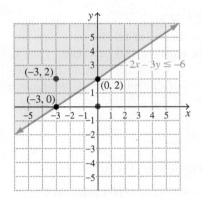

Figure 6.25

$$2x - 3y \leq -6$$

$$\text{Is } 2(0) - 3(0) \leq -6?$$

$$0 \leq -6 \quad \text{False}$$

Since 0 is not less than or equal to -6 $(0 \nleq -6)$, the solution set is the line and the half-plane that does not contain the point $(0, 0)$. This area is shaded in Fig. 6.25.

If you had arbitrarily selected the test point $(-3, 2)$ from the other half-plane, you would have found that the inequality would be true: $2(-3) - 3(2) \leq -6$, or $-12 \leq -6$. Because -12 is less than or equal to -6, the point $(-3, 2)$ would be in the half-plane containing the solution set. ∎

Example 3 *Graphing an Inequality*

Draw the graph of $y < x$.

Solution The inequality is strictly "less than," so the boundary line is not part of the solution set. In graphing the equation $y = x$, draw a dashed line (Fig. 6.26). Since $(0, 0)$ is *on* the line, it cannot serve as a test point. Let's pick the point $(1, -1)$.

$$y < x$$

$$-1 < 1 \quad \text{True}$$

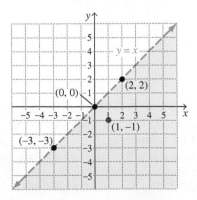

Figure 6.26

Since $-1 < 1$ is true, the solution set is the half-plane containing the point $(1, -1)$. ∎

SECTION 6.8

Exercises

Warm Up Exercises

In Exercises 1–2, fill in the blank with an appropriate word, phrase, or symbol(s).

1. The set of all points in a plane on one side of a line is called a(n) _____.

2. a) When graphing an inequality in two variables, if the inequality contains either $<$ or $>$ use a(n) _____ line.

   b) When graphing an inequality in two variables, if the inequality contains either $\leq$ or $\geq$ use a(n) _____ line.

Practice the Skills

3. For each inequality, determine whether (2, 1) is a solution to the inequality.

   a) $4x + 2y < 10$

   b) $4x + 2y \leq 10$

   c) $4x + 2y \geq 10$

   d) $4x + 2y > 10$

4. For each inequality, determine whether (−2, 4) is a solution to the inequality.

   a) $4x - 2y < -10$

   b) $4x - 2y \leq -10$

   c) $4x - 2y > -10$

   d) $4x - 2y \geq -10$

In Exercises 5–26, draw the graph of the inequality.

5. $x \leq 2$ 6. $y \geq -1$

7. $y > -x + 3$ 8. $y < x - 2$

9. $y \geq 2x - 6$ 10. $y < -2x + 2$

11. $3x - 4y > 12$ 12. $x + 2y > 4$

13. $3x - 4y \leq 8$ 14. $4y - 3x \geq 8$

15. $3x + 2y < 6$ 16. $-x + 2y < 2$

17. $x + y > 0$ 18. $x + 2y \leq 0$

19. $5x + 2y \geq 10$ 20. $y \geq -2x + 1$

21. $y \leq 3x - 4$ 22. $3x - 2y < 12$

23. $\frac{2}{5}x - \frac{1}{2}y \leq 1$ 24. $\frac{1}{2}x + \frac{2}{3}y \geq 1$

25. $0.1x + 0.3y \leq 0.4$ 26. $0.2x + 0.5y \leq 0.3$

Problem Solving

27. **Lawn Mowers** A company manufactures x walk-behind lawn mowers and y riding lawn mowers per week. The maximum number of lawn mowers the company can manufacture in a week is 25.

    a) Write an inequality in two variables that represents this problem.

    b) Graph the inequality.

28. **Buying CDs and DVDs** Reggie Wayne is allowed to spend a maximum of $100 for purchasing x DVDs and y CDs. Each DVD costs $20, and each CD costs $10.

    a) State this problem as an inequality in two variables.

    b) Graph the inequality.

Challenge Problems/Group Activities

29. **Men's Shirts** The Tommy Hilfiger Company must ship x men's shirts to one outlet and y men's shirts to a second outlet. The maximum number of shirts the manufacturer can produce and ship is 250. We can represent this situation with the inequality $x + y \leq 250$.

    a) Can x or y be negative? Explain.

    b) Graph the inequality.

    c) Write one or two paragraphs interpreting the information that the graph provides.

30. Which of the following inequalities have the same graph? Explain how you determined your answer.

    a) $2x - y < 8$ b) $-2x + y > -8$

    c) $2x - 4y < 16$ d) $y > 2x - 8$

Solving Quadratic Equations by Using Factoring and by Using the Quadratic Formula

You are adding a brick border of uniform width around your rectangular swimming pool. If you know the surface area of the pool and the area you would like the brick border to cover, you can determine the width of the border by solving a quadratic equation. In this section, we will learn two methods that can be used to solve quadratic equations.

Why *This is Important*   Quadratic equations are important in engineering, the sciences, statistics and research, and many other areas.

▲ *A quadratic equation can be used to determine the width of a border around a rectangular swimming pool.*

We begin this section by discussing binomials.

A *binomial* is an expression that contains two terms in which each exponent that appears on a variable is a whole number.

Examples of binomials

$$x + 3 \qquad\qquad x - 5$$
$$3x + 5 \qquad\qquad 4x - 2$$

To multiply two binomials, we can use the *FOIL method*. The name of the method, FOIL, is an acronym to help its users remember it as a method that obtains the products of the *F*irst, *O*uter, *I*nner, and *L*ast terms of the binomials.

$$(a + b)(c + d) = a \cdot c + a \cdot d + b \cdot c + b \cdot d$$

First   Outer   Inner   Last

After multiplying the first, outer, inner, and last terms, combine all like terms.

Example 1   *Multiplying Binomials*

Multiply $(x + 4)(x + 7)$.

Solution   The FOIL method of multiplication yields

$$(x + 4)(x + 7) = x \cdot x + x \cdot 7 + 4 \cdot x + 4 \cdot 7$$
$$= x^2 + 7x + 4x + 28$$
$$= x^2 + 11x + 28$$

Note that the like terms $7x$ and $4x$ were combined to get $11x$.   ■

Example 2   *Multiplying Binomials*

Multiply $(2x + 3)(x - 1)$.

Solution

$$\begin{array}{cccc} & \text{F} & \text{O} & \quad\text{I} \quad \text{L} \end{array}$$
$$(2x + 3)(x - 1) = 2x \cdot x + 2x \cdot (-1) + 3 \cdot x + 3 \cdot (-1)$$
$$= 2x^2 - 2x + 3x - 3$$
$$= 2x^2 + x - 3$$

∎

Factoring Trinomials of the Form $x^2 + bx + c$

The expression $x^2 + 8x + 15$ is an example of a trinomial. A *trinomial* is an expression containing three terms in which each exponent that appears on a variable is a whole number.

Example 1 showed that

$$(x + 4)(x + 7) = x^2 + 11x + 28$$

Since the product of $x + 4$ and $x + 7$ is $x^2 + 11x + 28$, we say that $x + 4$ and $x + 7$ are *factors* of $x^2 + 11x + 28$. *To factor* an expression means to write the expression as a product of its factors. For example, to factor $x^2 + 11x + 28$ we write

$$x^2 + 11x + 28 = (x + 4)(x + 7)$$

Let's look at the factors more closely.

$$\begin{array}{c} 4 + 7 = 11 \\ 4 \cdot 7 = 28 \end{array}$$
$$x^2 + 11x + 28 = (x + 4)(x + 7)$$

Note that the sum of the two numbers in the factors is $4 + 7$, or 11. The 11 is the coefficient of the x-term. Also note that the product of the numbers in the two factors is $4 \cdot 7$, or 28. The 28 is the constant in the trinomial. In general, when factoring an expression of the form $x^2 + bx + c$, we need to find two numbers whose product is c and whose sum is b. When we determine the two numbers, the factors will be of the form

$$(x + \boxed{}) \; (x + \boxed{})$$
$$\uparrow \qquad\qquad \uparrow$$
One   Other
number   number

Example 3 *Factoring a Trinomial*

Factor $x^2 + 6x + 8$.

Solution We need to find two numbers whose product is 8 and whose sum is 6. Since the product is $+8$, the two numbers must both be positive or both be negative. Because the coefficient of the x-term is positive, only the positive factors of 8 need to be considered. Can you explain why? We begin by listing the positive numbers whose product is 8.

Factors of 8	Sum of Factors
1(8)	$1 + 8 = 9$
2(4)	$2 + 4 = 6$

Since $2 \cdot 4 = 8$ and $2 + 4 = 6$, the numbers we are seeking are 2 and 4. Thus, we write

$$x^2 + 6x + 8 = (x + 2)(x + 4)$$

Note that $(x + 4)\,(x - 2)$ is also an acceptable answer.

∎

PROCEDURE **TO FACTOR TRINOMIAL EXPRESSIONS OF THE FORM**
$x^2 + bx + c$

1. Find two numbers whose product is c and whose sum is b.

2. Write factors in the form

$$(x + \blacksquare)\ (x + \blacksquare)$$

    ↑   ↑

One number Other number
from Step 1 from Step 1

3. Check your answer by multiplying the factors using the FOIL method.

If, for example, the numbers found in Step 1 of the above procedure were 6 and -4, the factors would be written $(x + 6)(x - 4)$.

Example 4 *Factoring a Trinomial*

Factor $x^2 - 6x - 16$.

Solution We must find two numbers whose product is -16 and whose sum is -6. Begin by listing the factors of -16.

Factors of -16	Sum of Factors
$-16(1)$	$-16 + 1 = -15$
$-8(2)$	$-8 + 2 = -6$
$-4(4)$	$-4 + 4 = 0$
$-2(8)$	$-2 + 8 = 6$
$-1(16)$	$-1 + 16 = 15$

The table lists all the factors of -16. The only factors listed whose product is -16 and whose sum is -6 are -8 and 2. We listed all factors in this example so that you could see, for example, that $-8(2)$ is a different set of factors than $-2(8)$. Once you find the factors you are looking for, there is no need to go any further. The trinomial can be written in factored form as

$$x^2 - 6x - 16 = (x - 8)(x + 2)$$ ∎

Factoring Trinomials of the Form $ax^2 + bx + c$, $a \neq 1$

Now we discuss how to factor an expression of the form $ax^2 + bx + c$, where a, the coefficient of the squared term, is not equal to 1.

Consider the multiplication problem $(2x + 1)(x + 3)$.

$$(2x + 1)(x + 3) = 2x \cdot x + 2x \cdot 3 + 1 \cdot x + 1 \cdot 3$$
$$= 2x^2 + 6x + x + 3$$
$$= 2x^2 + 7x + 3$$

Since $(2x + 1)(x + 3) = 2x^2 + 7x + 3$, the factors of $2x^2 + 7x + 3$ are $2x + 1$ and $x + 3$.

Let's study the coefficients more closely.

F = 2 · 1 = 2   O + I = (2 · 3) + (1 · 1) = 7   L = 1 · 3 = 3

Note that the product of the coefficient of the first terms in the multiplication of the binomials equals 2, the coefficient of the squared term. The sum of the products of the coefficients of the outer and inner terms equals 7, the coefficient of the x-term. The product of the last terms equals 3, the constant.

A procedure to factor expressions of the form $ax^2 + bx + c, a \neq 1$, follows.

PROCEDURE   TO FACTOR TRINOMIAL EXPRESSIONS OF THE FORM $ax^2 + bx + c, a \neq 1$

1. Write all pairs of factors of the coefficient of the squared term, a.

2. Write all pairs of factors of the constant, c.

3. Try various combinations of these factors until the sum of the products of the outer and inner terms is bx.

4. Check your answer by multiplying the factors using the FOIL method.

Example 5   *Factoring a Trinomial, a ≠ 1*

Factor $3x^2 + 17x + 10$.

Solution The only positive factors of 3 are 3 and 1. Therefore, we write

$$3x^2 + 17x + 10 = (3x \quad)(x \quad)$$

The number 10 has both positive and negative factors. However, since both the constant, 10, and the sum of the products of the outer and inner terms, 17, are positive, the two factors must be positive. Why? The positive factors of 10 are 1(10) and 2(5). The following is a list of the possible factors.

Possible Factors	Sum of Products of Outer and Inner Terms
$(3x + 1)(x + 10)$	$31x$
$(3x + 10)(x + 1)$	$13x$
$(3x + 2)(x + 5)$	$17x$ ← Correct middle term
$(3x + 5)(x + 2)$	$11x$

Thus, $3x^2 + 17x + 10 = (3x + 2)(x + 5)$.   ■

Note that factoring problems of this type may be checked by using the FOIL method of multiplication. We will check the results to Example 5:

$$(3x + 2)(x + 5) = 3x \cdot x + 3x \cdot 5 + 2 \cdot x + 2 \cdot 5$$
$$= 3x^2 + 15x + 2x + 10$$
$$= 3x^2 + 17x + 10$$

Since we obtained the expression we started with, our factoring is correct.

Example 6   *Factoring a Trinomial, $a \neq 1$*

Factor $6x^2 - 11x - 10$.

Solution The factors of 6 will be either $6 \cdot 1$ or $2 \cdot 3$. Therefore, the factors may be of the form $(6x\quad)(x\quad)$ or $(2x\quad)(3x\quad)$. When there is more than one set of factors for the first term, we generally try the medium-sized factors first. If that does not work, we try the other factors. Thus, we write

$$6x^2 - 11x - 10 = (2x\quad)(3x\quad)$$

The factors of -10 are $(-1)(10)$, $(1)(-10)$, $(-2)(5)$, and $(2)(-5)$. There will be eight different pairs of possible factors of the trinomial $6x^2 - 11x - 10$. Can you list them?

The correct factoring is $6x^2 - 11x - 10 = (2x - 5)(3x + 2)$. ∎

Note that in Example 6 we first tried factors of the form $(2x\quad)(3x\quad)$. If we had not found the correct factors using them, we would have tried $(6x\quad)(x\quad)$.

Solving Quadratic Equations by Factoring

In Section 6.2, we solved linear, or first-degree, equations. In those equations, the exponent on all variables was 1. Now we deal with the *quadratic equation*. The standard form of a quadratic equation in one variable is shown in the box.

Standard Form of a Quadratic Equation

$$ax^2 + bx + c = 0, \quad a \neq 0$$

Note that in the standard form of a quadratic equation, the greatest exponent on x is 2 and the right side of the equation is equal to zero. *To solve a quadratic equation* means to find the value or values that make the equation true. In this section, we will solve quadratic equations by factoring and by the quadratic formula.

To solve a quadratic equation by factoring, set one side of the equation equal to 0 and then use the *zero-factor* property.

Zero-Factor Property

$$\text{If } a \cdot b = 0, \text{ then } a = 0 \text{ or } b = 0.$$

The zero-factor property indicates that if the product of two factors is 0, then one (or both) of the factors must have a value of 0.

Example 7   *Using the Zero-Factor Property*

Solve the equation $(x + 5)(x - 4) = 0$.

Solution When we use the zero-factor property, either $(x + 5)$ or $(x - 4)$ must equal 0 for the product to equal 0. Thus, we set each individual factor equal to 0 and solve each resulting equation for x.

$$(x + 5)(x - 4) = 0$$
$$x + 5 = 0 \quad \text{or} \quad x - 4 = 0$$
$$x = -5 \qquad\qquad x = 4$$

Thus, the solutions are -5 and 4.

CHECK: $x = -5$ $x = 4$

$$(x + 5)(x - 4) = 0$$ $$(x + 5)(x - 4) = 0$$
$$(-5 + 5)(-5 - 4) = 0$$ $$(4 + 5)(4 - 4) = 0$$
$$0(-9) = 0$$ $$(9)(0) = 0$$
$$0 = 0 \quad \text{True}$$ $$0 = 0 \quad \text{True}$$ ■

PROCEDURE   TO SOLVE A QUADRATIC EQUATION BY FACTORING

1. Use the addition or subtraction property to make one side of the equation equal to 0.
2. Factor the side of the equation not equal to 0.
3. Use the zero-factor property to solve the equation.

Examples 8 and 9 illustrate this procedure.

Example 8 Solving a Quadratic Equation by Factoring

Solve the equation $x^2 - 8x = -15$.

Solution First add 15 to both sides of the equation to make the right-hand side of the equation equal to 0.

$$x^2 - 8x = -15$$
$$x^2 - 8x + 15 = -15 + 15$$
$$x^2 - 8x + 15 = 0$$

Factor the left-hand side of the equation. The object is to find two numbers whose product is 15 and whose sum is -8. Since the product of the numbers is positive and the sum of the numbers is negative, the two numbers must both be negative. The numbers are -3 and -5. Note that $(-3)(-5) = 15$ and $-3 + (-5) = -8$.

$$x^2 - 8x + 15 = 0$$
$$(x - 3)(x - 5) = 0$$

Now use the zero-factor property to find the solution.

$$x - 3 = 0 \quad \text{or} \quad x - 5 = 0$$
$$x = 3 \qquad\qquad x = 5$$

The solutions are 3 and 5.   ■

Example 9 Solving a Quadratic Equation by Factoring

Solve the equation $3x^2 - 7x - 6 = 0$.

Solution $3x^2 - 7x - 6$ factors into $(3x + 2)(x - 3)$. Thus, we write

$$3x^2 - 7x - 6 = 0$$
$$(3x + 2)(x - 3) = 0$$
$$3x + 2 = 0 \quad \text{or} \quad x - 3 = 0$$
$$3x = -2 \qquad\qquad x = 3$$
$$x = -\frac{2}{3}$$

The solutions are $-\frac{2}{3}$ and 3.   ■

TIMELY TIP
As stated on page 355, every factoring problem can be checked by multiplying the factors. If you have factored correctly, the product of the factors will be identical to the original expression that was factored. If we wished to check the factoring of Example 9, we would multiply $(3x + 2)(x - 3)$. Since the product of the factors is $3x^2 - 7x - 6$, which is the expression we started with, our factoring is correct.

Solving Quadratic Equations by Using the Quadratic Formula

Not all quadratic equations can be solved by factoring. When a quadratic equation cannot be easily solved by factoring, we can solve the equation with the *quadratic formula*. The quadratic formula can be used to solve any quadratic equation.

Quadratic Formula

For a quadratic equation in standard form, $ax^2 + bx + c = 0$, $a \neq 0$, the quadratic formula is

$$x = \frac{-b \pm \sqrt{b^2 - 4ac}}{2a}$$

In the quadratic formula, the plus or minus symbol, $\pm$, is used. If, for example, $x = 2 \pm 3$, then $x = 2 + 3 = 5$ or $x = 2 - 3 = -1$.

It is possible for a quadratic equation to have no real solution. In solving an equation, if the radicand (the expression inside the square root) is a negative number, the quadratic equation has *no real solution*.

To use the quadratic formula, first write the quadratic equation in standard form. Then determine the values for a (the coefficient of the squared term), b (the coefficient of the x term), and c (the constant). Finally, substitute the values of a, b, and c into the quadratic formula and evaluate the expression.

Example 10 *Solving a Quadratic Equation by Using the Quadratic Formula*

Solve the equation $x^2 - 5x - 14 = 0$ by using the quadratic formula.

Solution In this equation, $a = 1$, $b = -5$, and $c = -14$.

$$x = \frac{-b \pm \sqrt{b^2 - 4ac}}{2a} = \frac{-(-5) \pm \sqrt{(-5)^2 - 4(1)(-14)}}{2(1)}$$

$$= \frac{5 \pm \sqrt{25 + 56}}{2}$$

$$= \frac{5 \pm \sqrt{81}}{2}$$

$$= \frac{5 \pm 9}{2}$$

$$\frac{5 + 9}{2} = \frac{14}{2} = 7 \quad \text{or} \quad \frac{5 - 9}{2} = \frac{-4}{2} = -2$$

The solutions are 7 and -2.

Note that Example 10 can also be solved by factoring. We suggest you do so now.

Example 11 *Irrational Solutions to a Quadratic Equation*

Solve $4x^2 - 8x = -1$ by using the quadratic formula.

Solution   Begin by writing the equation in standard form by adding 1 to both sides of the equation, which gives the following.

$$4x^2 - 8x + 1 = 0$$

$$a = 4, \qquad b = -8, \qquad c = 1$$

$$x = \frac{-b \pm \sqrt{b^2 - 4ac}}{2a} = \frac{-(-8) \pm \sqrt{(-8)^2 - 4(4)(1)}}{2(4)}$$

$$= \frac{8 \pm \sqrt{64 - 16}}{8}$$

$$= \frac{8 \pm \sqrt{48}}{8}$$

Since $\sqrt{48} = \sqrt{16}\sqrt{3} = 4\sqrt{3}$ (see Section 5.4), we write

$$\frac{8 \pm \sqrt{48}}{8} = \frac{8 \pm 4\sqrt{3}}{8} = \frac{\overset{1}{\cancel{4}}(2 \pm \sqrt{3})}{\underset{2}{\cancel{8}}} = \frac{2 \pm \sqrt{3}}{2}$$

The solutions are $\dfrac{2 + \sqrt{3}}{2}$ and $\dfrac{2 - \sqrt{3}}{2}$.   ■

Note that the solutions to Example 11 are irrational numbers.

Example 12 *Brick Border*

Diane Cecero and her husband recently installed an inground rectangular swimming pool measuring 40 ft by 30 ft. They want to add a brick border of uniform width around all sides of the pool. How wide can they make the brick border if they purchased enough brick to cover an area of 296 ft^2?

Solution   Let's make a diagram of the pool and the brick border (Fig. 6.27). Let $x =$ the uniform width of the brick border. Then the total length of the larger rectangular area, the pool plus the border, is $2x + 40$. The total width of the larger rectangular area is $2x + 30$.

The area of the brick border can be found by subtracting the area of the pool from the area of the pool plus the brick border.

$$\text{Area of pool} = l \cdot w = (40)(30) = 1200 \text{ ft}^2$$

$$\text{Area of pool plus brick border} = l \cdot w = (2x + 40)(2x + 30)$$

$$= 4x^2 + 140x + 1200$$

$$\text{Area of the brick border} = \text{area of pool plus brick border} - \text{area of pool}$$

$$= (4x^2 + 140x + 1200) - 1200$$

$$= 4x^2 + 140x$$

The area of the brick border must be 296 ft^2. Therefore,

$$296 = 4x^2 + 140x$$

Figure 6.27

or

$$4x^2 + 140x - 296 = 0$$

$$4(x^2 + 35x - 74) = 0 \quad \text{Factor out 4 from each term.}$$

$$\frac{\cancel{4}}{\cancel{4}}(x^2 + 35x - 74) = \frac{0}{4} \quad \text{Divide both sides of the equation by 4.}$$

$$x^2 + 35x - 74 = 0$$

$$(x + 37)(x - 2) = 0 \quad \text{Factor trinomial.}$$

$$x + 37 = 0 \quad \text{or} \quad x - 2 = 0$$

$$x = -37 \qquad\qquad x = 2$$

Since lengths are positive, the only possible answer is $x = 2$. Thus, they can make a brick border 2 ft wide all around the pool. ∎

SECTION 6.9

Exercises

Warm Up Exercises

In Exercises 1–6, fill in the blank with an appropriate word, phrase, or symbol(s).

1. An expression that contains two terms in which each exponent that appears on a variable is a whole number is called a(n) _____.

2. An expression that contains three terms in which each exponent that appears on a variable is a whole number is called a(n) _____.

3. When multiplying two binomials, a method that obtains the products of the first, outer, inner, and last terms is called the _____ method.

4. The property that indicates that if the product of two factors is 0, then one or both of the factors must have a value of 0 is called the _____ property.

5. When a quadratic equation cannot be easily solved by factoring, the equation can be solved using the _____ formula.

6. For a quadratic equation in standard form $ax^2 + bx + c = 0$, $a \neq 0$, the quadratic formula is

   _____.

Practice the Skills

In Exercises 7–22, factor the trinomial. If the trinomial cannot be factored, so state.

7. $x^2 + 7x + 12$

8. $x^2 + 6x + 8$

9. $x^2 + x - 2$

10. $x^2 + 2x - 3$

11. $x^2 + 2x - 24$

12. $x^2 - 6x + 8$

13. $x^2 - 2x - 3$

14. $x^2 - 5x - 6$

15. $x^2 - 9x + 18$

16. $x^2 - x - 30$

17. $x^2 - 16$

18. $x^2 - 64$

19. $x^2 + 3x - 28$

20. $x^2 + 4x - 32$

21. $x^2 + 2x - 63$

22. $x^2 - 2x - 48$

In Exercises 23–34, factor the trinomial. If the trinomial cannot be factored, so state.

23. $2x^2 - 5x - 3$

24. $3x^2 - 13x + 4$

25. $5x^2 + 16x + 3$

26. $2x^2 - 3x - 20$

27. $5x^2 + 12x + 4$

28. $2x^2 - 9x + 10$

29. $4x^2 + 11x + 6$

30. $4x^2 + 20x + 21$

31. $4x^2 - 11x + 6$

32. $6x^2 - 11x + 4$

33. $8x^2 - 2x - 3$

34. $6x^2 - 13x + 2$

In Exercises 35–38, solve each equation, using the zero-factor property.

35. $(x - 7)(x + 2) = 0$

36. $(2x + 1)(x + 2) = 0$

37. $(3x + 4)(2x - 1) = 0$

38. $(x - 6)(5x - 4) = 0$

In Exercises 39–58, solve each equation by factoring.

39. $x^2 + 10x + 21 = 0$ **40.** $x^2 + x - 20 = 0$

41. $x^2 - 9x + 8 = 0$ **42.** $x^2 - 12x + 35 = 0$

43. $x^2 - 15 = 2x$ **44.** $x^2 - 7x = -6$

45. $x^2 = 4x - 3$ **46.** $x^2 - 13x + 40 = 0$

47. $x^2 - 81 = 0$ **48.** $x^2 - 64 = 0$

49. $x^2 + 5x - 36 = 0$ **50.** $x^2 + 12x + 20 = 0$

51. $3x^2 + 10x = 8$ **52.** $3x^2 - 5x = 2$

53. $5x^2 + 11x = -2$ **54.** $2x^2 = -5x + 3$

55. $3x^2 - 4x = -1$ **56.** $5x^2 + 16x + 12 = 0$

57. $6x^2 - 19x + 3 = 0$ **58.** $4x^2 + x - 3 = 0$

In Exercises 59–78, solve the equation, using the quadratic formula. If the equation has no real solution, so state.

59. $x^2 + 2x - 8 = 0$

60. $x^2 + 12x + 27 = 0$

61. $x^2 - 3x - 18 = 0$

62. $x^2 - 6x - 16 = 0$

63. $x^2 - 8x = 9$

64. $x^2 = -8x + 15$

65. $x^2 - 2x + 3 = 0$

66. $2x^2 - x - 3 = 0$

67. $x^2 - 4x + 2 = 0$

68. $2x^2 - 5x - 2 = 0$

69. $3x^2 - 8x + 1 = 0$

70. $2x^2 + 4x + 1 = 0$

71. $3x^2 - 6x - 5 = 0$

72. $4x^2 - 5x - 3 = 0$

73. $2x^2 + 7x + 5 = 0$

74. $3x^2 - 10x + 7 = 0$

75. $3x^2 = 9x - 5$

76. $4x^2 + 7x - 1 = 0$

77. $4x^2 + 6x = -5$

78. $5x^2 - 4x = -2$

Challenge Problems/Group Activities

79. *Flower Garden*   Karen and Kurt Ohliger's backyard has a width of 20 meters and a length of 30 meters. Karen and Kurt want to put a rectangular flower garden in the middle of the backyard, leaving a strip of grass of uniform width around all sides of the flower garden. If they want to have 336 square meters of grass, what will be the width and length of the garden?

80. *Height of a Ball*   A ball is projected upward from the ground. Its height h, above ground, in feet, can be determined by the equation

$$h = -16t^2 + 128t$$

where t is the number of seconds after the ball is projected. After how many seconds will the ball be 256 ft above ground?

81. a) Explain why solving $(x - 4)(x - 7) = 6$ by setting each factor equal to 6 is not correct.

   b) Determine the correct solution to $(x - 4)(x - 7) = 6$.

82. The radicand in the quadratic formula, $b^2 - 4ac$, is called the *discriminant*. How many real number solutions will the quadratic equation have if the discriminant is (a) greater than 0, (b) equal to 0, or (c) less than zero? Explain your answer.

83. Write an equation that has solutions -1 and 3.

Internet/Research Activities

84. Italian mathematician Girolamo Cardano (1501–1576) is recognized for his skill in solving equations. Write a paper about his life and his contributions to mathematics, in particular his contribution to solving equations.

85. Chinese mathematician Foo Ling Awong, who lived during the Pong dynasty, developed a technique, other than trial and error, to factor trinomials of the form $ax^2 + bx + c, a \neq 1$. Write a paper about his life and his contributions to mathematics, in particular his technique for factoring trinomials in the form $ax^2 + bx + c, a \neq 1$. (References include history of mathematics books, encyclopedias, and the Internet.)

SECTION 6.10   Functions and Their Graphs

▲ *The relationship between the number of songs purchased from iTunes and the cost is an example of a function.*

Assume that purchasing a song from iTunes costs $1.29. Thus, purchasing one song costs $1 \times \$1.29$, purchasing two songs costs $2 \times \$1.29 = \$2.58$, purchasing three songs costs $3 \times \$1.29 = \$3.87$, and so on. In this section we will discuss the relationships between two quantities, such as the number of songs purchased from iTunes and the cost of the songs.

Why *This is Important* Determining the relationship between two quantities is useful in many ways in real-life situations, from exchanging foreign currencies to many aspects of building a house. Functions, which we discuss in this section, express the relationship between two quantities. The concept of function is one of the most important concepts in mathematics.

*R*elations and *functions* are both extremely important mathematical concepts that we will introduce in this section. A *relation* is any set of ordered pairs. Every graph is a set of ordered pairs. Therefore, any graph will be a relation. We can indicate the relation between the number of songs purchased and the cost of the songs discussed in the section opening paragraph in a table of values.

Number of Songs	Cost
0	0.00
1	1.29
2	2.58
3	3.87
⋮	⋮
10	12.90
⋮	⋮

In general, the cost for purchasing *n* songs will be $1.29 times the number of songs, or $1.29n$ dollars. We can represent the cost, *c*, of *n* songs by the equation $c = 1.29n$. Since the value of *c* depends on the value of *n*, we refer to *c* as the *dependent variable* and *n* as the *independent variable*. *Note that for each value of the independent variable, n, there is one and only one value of the dependent variable, c.* An equation such as $c = 1.29n$ is called a **function**. In the equation $c = 1.29n$, the value of *c* depends on the value of *n*, so we say that "*c* is a function of *n*."

Definition: Function

A **function** is a special type of relation where each value of the independent variable corresponds to a unique value of the dependent variable.

The set of values that can be used for the independent variable is called the *domain* of the function, and the resulting set of values obtained for the dependent variable is called the *range*. The domain and range for the function $c = 1.29n$ are illustrated in Fig. 6.28 on page 363.

When we graphed equations of the form $ax + by = c$ in Section 6.7, we found that they were straight lines. For example, the graph of $y = 2x - 1$ is illustrated in Fig. 6.29 on page 363.

Figure 6.28

Figure 6.29

Is the equation $y = 2x - 1$ a function? To answer this question, we must ask, Does each value of x correspond to a unique value of y? The answer is yes; therefore, this equation is a function.

For the equation $y = 2x - 1$, we say that "y is a function of x" and write $y = f(x)$. The notation $f(x)$ is read "f of x." When we are given an equation that is a function, we may replace the y in the equation with $f(x)$ because $f(x)$ represents y. Thus, $y = 2x - 1$ may be written $f(x) = 2x - 1$.

To evaluate a function for a specific value of x, replace each x in the function with the given value, then evaluate. For example, to evaluate $f(x) = 2x - 1$ when $x = 8$, we do the following.

$$f(x) = 2x - 1$$
$$f(8) = 2(8) - 1 = 16 - 1 = 15$$

Thus, $f(8) = 15$. Since $f(x) = y$, when $x = 8, y = 15$. What is the domain and range of $f(x) = 2x - 1$? Because x can be any real number, the domain is the set of real numbers, symbolized $\mathbb{R}$; The range is also $\mathbb{R}$.

We can determine whether a graph represents a function by using the *vertical line test*: If a vertical line can be drawn so that it intersects the graph at more than one point, then each value of x does not have a unique value of y and the graph does not represent a function. If a vertical line cannot be made to intersect the graph in at least two different places, then the graph represents a function.

Example 1 Using the Vertical Line Test

Use the vertical line test to determine which of the graphs in Figure 6.30 represent functions.

a) b) c) d)

   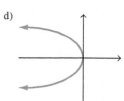

Figure 6.30

Solution (a), (b), and (c) represent functions, but (d) does not.

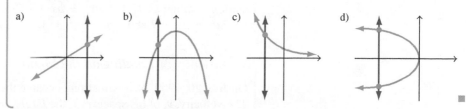

There are many real-life applications of functions. In fact, all the applications illustrated in Sections 6.2 through 6.4 are functions.

In this section, we will discuss three types of functions: linear functions, quadratic functions, and exponential functions.

Linear Functions

In Section 6.7, we graphed linear equations. The graph of any linear equation of the form $y = ax + b$ will pass the vertical line test, and so equations of the form $y = ax + b$ are *linear functions*. If we wished, we could write the linear function as $f(x) = ax + b$ since $f(x)$ means the same as y.

Example 2   *Salary as a Linear Function*

Celia Boroso's weekly salary as a real estate agent, s, is given by the function $s(x) = 100 + 0.03x$, where x is weekly sales, in dollars. What is Celia's weekly salary if she sells one house for $85,000 in a given week?

Solution   Substitute 85,000 for x in the function.

$$s(x) = 100 + 0.03x$$
$$s(85,000) = 100 + 0.03(85,000)$$
$$= 100 + 2550 = 2650$$

Thus, if Celia sells one house for $85,000 in a given week, her salary for that week will be $2650.   ∎

Graphs of Linear Functions

The graphs of linear functions are straight lines that will pass the vertical line test. In Section 6.7, we discussed how to graph linear equations. Linear functions can be graphed by plotting points, by using intercepts, or by using the slope and y-intercept.

Example 3   *Graphing a Linear Function*

Graph $f(x) = -2x + 3$ by using the slope and y-intercept.

Solution   Since $f(x)$ means the same as y, we can rewrite this function as $y = -2x + 3$. From Section 6.7, we know that the slope is -2 and the y-intercept is $(0, 3)$. Plot $(0, 3)$ on the y-axis. Then plot the next point by moving *down* 2 units and to the *right* 1 unit (see Fig. 6.31). A third point has been plotted in the same way. The graph of $f(x) = -2x + 3$ is the line drawn through these three points.   ∎

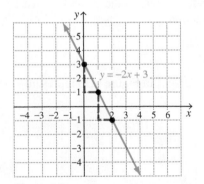

Figure 6.31

Quadratic Functions

The standard form of a quadratic equation is $y = ax^2 + bx + c, a \neq 0$. We will learn shortly that graphs of equations of this form always pass the vertical line test and are functions. Therefore, equations of the form $y = ax^2 + bx + c, a \neq 0$, may be referred to as *quadratic functions*. We may express quadratic functions using function notation as $f(x) = ax^2 + bx + c$. Two examples of quadratic functions are $y = 2x^2 + 5x - 7$ and $y = -\frac{1}{2}x^2 + 4$.

Example 4   *Landing on the Moon*

On July 20, 1969, Neil Armstrong became the first person to walk on the moon. The velocity, v, of his spacecraft, the *Eagle*, in meters per second, was a function of time before touchdown, t, given by

$$v = f(t) = 3.2t + 0.45$$

The height of the spacecraft, h, above the moon's surface, in meters, was also a function of time before touchdown, given by

$$h = g(t) = 1.6t^2 + 0.45t$$

What was the velocity of the spacecraft and its distance from the surface of the moon
a) at 3 seconds before touchdown?   b) at touchdown (0 seconds)?

Solution

a) $v = f(t) = 3.2t + 0.45,$
$f(3) = 3.2(3) + 0.45$
$= 9.6 + 0.45$
$= 10.05$

$h = g(t) = 1.6t^2 + 0.45t$
$g(3) = 1.6(3)^2 + 0.45(3)$
$= 1.6(9) + 1.35$
$= 14.4 + 1.35$
$= 15.75$

The velocity 3 seconds before touchdown was 10.05 meters per second, and the height 3 seconds before touchdown was 15.75 meters.

b) $v = f(t) = 3.2t + 0.45,$
$f(0) = 3.2(0) + 0.45$
$= 0 + 0.45$
$= 0.45$

$h = g(t) = 1.6t^2 + 0.45t$
$g(0) = 1.6(0)^2 + 0.45(0)$
$= 0 + 0$
$= 0$

The touchdown velocity was 0.45 meter per second. At touchdown, the *Eagle* is on the moon, and the distance from the surface of the moon is therefore 0 meter.   ■

Graphs of Quadratic Functions

The graph of every quadratic function is a *parabola*. Two parabolas are illustrated in Fig. 6.32. Note that both graphs represent functions since they pass the vertical line test. A parabola opens upward when the coefficient of the squared term, a, is greater than 0, as shown in Figure 6.32(a). A parabola opens downward when the coefficient of the squared term, a, is less than 0, as shown in Fig. 6.32(b).

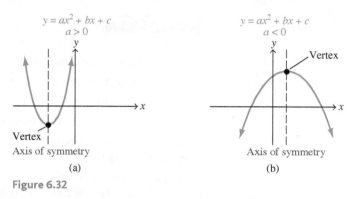

Figure 6.32

The *vertex* of a parabola is the lowest point on a parabola that opens upward and the highest point on a parabola that opens downward. Every parabola is *symmetric* with respect to a vertical line through its vertex. This line is called the *axis of symmetry* of the parabola.

Axis of Symmetry of a Parabola

The axis of symmetry of the graph of an equation of the form $y = ax^2 + bx + c$ can be determined by the following formula.

$$x = \frac{-b}{2a}$$

This formula also gives the x-coordinate of the vertex of a parabola.

Once the x-coordinate of the vertex has been determined, the y-coordinate can be found by substituting the value found for the x-coordinate into the quadratic equation and evaluating the equation. This procedure is illustrated in Example 5.

Example 5 *Describing the Graph of a Quadratic Equation*

Consider the equation $y = -2x^2 + 12x - 10$.

a) Determine whether the graph will be a parabola that opens upward or downward.

b) Determine the equation of the axis of symmetry of the parabola.

c) Determine the vertex of the parabola.

Solution

a) Since $a = -2$, which is less than 0, the parabola opens downward.

b) To find the axis of symmetry, we use the equation $x = -\frac{b}{2a}$. In the equation $y = -2x^2 + 12x - 10$, $a = -2$, $b = 12$, and $c = -10$, so

$$x = \frac{-b}{2a} = \frac{-(12)}{2(-2)} = \frac{-12}{-4} = 3$$

The equation of the axis of symmetry is $x = 3$.

c) The x-coordinate of the vertex is 3 from part (b). To find the y-coordinate, we substitute 3 for x in the equation and then evaluate.

$$
\begin{aligned}
y &= -2x^2 + 12x - 10 \\
&= -2(3)^2 + 12(3) - 10 \\
&= -2(9) + 36 - 10 \\
&= -18 + 36 - 10 \\
&= 8
\end{aligned}
$$

Therefore, the vertex of the parabola is located at the ordered pair $(3, 8)$ on the graph. ∎

PROCEDURE   GENERAL PROCEDURE TO SKETCH THE GRAPH OF A QUADRATIC EQUATION

1. Determine whether the parabola opens upward or downward.

2. Determine the equation of the axis of symmetry.

3. Determine the vertex of the parabola.

4. Determine the y-intercept by substituting $x = 0$ into the equation.

5. Determine the x-intercepts (if they exist) by substituting $y = 0$ into the equation and solving for x.

6. Draw the graph, making use of the information gained in Steps 1 through 5. Remember that the parabola will be symmetric with respect to the axis of symmetry.

In Step 5, you may use either factoring or the quadratic formula to determine the x-intercepts.

Example 6 *Graphing a Quadratic Equation*

Sketch the graph of the equation $y = x^2 - 6x + 8$.

Solution We follow the steps outlined in the general procedure.

1. Since $a = 1$, which is greater than 0, the parabola opens upward.

2. Axis of symmetry: $x = \dfrac{-b}{2a} = \dfrac{-(-6)}{2(1)} = \dfrac{6}{2} = 3$

   Thus, the axis of symmetry is $x = 3$.

3. y-coordinate of vertex:

$$y = x^2 - 6x + 8$$
$$= (3)^2 - 6(3) + 8 = 9 - 18 + 8 = -1$$

Thus, the vertex is at $(3, -1)$.

4. y-intercept:

$$y = x^2 - 6x + 8$$
$$y = (0)^2 - 6(0) + 8 = 8$$

Thus, the y-intercept is at $(0, 8)$.

5. x-intercepts:

$$0 = x^2 - 6x + 8, \text{ or } x^2 - 6x + 8 = 0$$

We can solve this equation by factoring.

$$x^2 - 6x + 8 = 0$$
$$(x - 4)(x - 2) = 0$$
$$x - 4 = 0 \quad \text{or} \quad x - 2 = 0$$
$$x = 4 \qquad\qquad x = 2$$

Thus, the x-intercepts are $(4, 0)$ and $(2, 0)$.

6. Plot the vertex $(3, -1)$, the y-intercept $(0, 8)$, and the x-intercepts $(4, 0)$ and $(2, 0)$. Then sketch the graph (Fig. 6.33).   ■

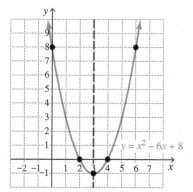

Figure 6.33

Note that the domain of the graph in Example 6, the possible x-values, is the set of all real numbers, $\mathbb{R}$. The range, the possible y-values, is the set of all real numbers greater than or equal to -1. When graphing parabolas, if you think you need additional points to graph the equation, you can always substitute values for x and find the corresponding values of y and plot those points. For example, if you substituted 1 for x, the corresponding value of y is 3. Thus, you could plot the point $(1, 3)$.

Example 7   *Domain and Range of a Quadratic Function*

a) Sketch the graph of the function $f(x) = -2x^2 + 3x + 4$.

b) Determine the domain and range of the function.

Solution

a) Since $f(x)$ means y, we can replace $f(x)$ with y to obtain $y = -2x^2 + 3x + 4$. Now graph $y = -2x^2 + 3x + 4$ using the steps outlined in the general procedure.

1. Since $a = -2$, which is less than 0, the parabola opens downward.

2. Axis of symmetry:

$$x = \frac{-b}{2a} = \frac{-(3)}{2(-2)} = \frac{-3}{-4} = \frac{3}{4}$$

Thus, the axis of symmetry is $x = \frac{3}{4}$.

3. y-coordinate of vertex:

$$y = -2x^2 + 3x + 4$$
$$= -2\left(\frac{3}{4}\right)^2 + 3\left(\frac{3}{4}\right) + 4$$
$$= -2\left(\frac{9}{16}\right) + \frac{9}{4} + 4$$
$$= -\frac{9}{8} + \frac{9}{4} + 4$$
$$= -\frac{9}{8} + \frac{18}{8} + \frac{32}{8} = \frac{41}{8} \quad \text{or} \quad 5\frac{1}{8}$$

Thus, the vertex is at $\left(\frac{3}{4}, 5\frac{1}{8}\right)$.

4. y-intercept: $y = -2x^2 + 3x + 4$

$$= -2(0)^2 + 3(0) + 4 = 4$$

Thus, the y-intercept is $(0, 4)$.

5. x-intercepts: $y = -2x^2 + 3x + 4$

$$0 = -2x^2 + 3x + 4 \quad \text{or} \quad -2x^2 + 3x + 4 = 0$$

This equation cannot be factored, so we will use the quadratic formula to solve it.

$$a = -2, \quad b = 3, \quad c = 4$$

$$x = \frac{-b \pm \sqrt{b^2 - 4ac}}{2a}$$

$$= \frac{-3 \pm \sqrt{3^2 - 4(-2)(4)}}{2(-2)}$$

$$= \frac{-3 \pm \sqrt{9 + 32}}{-4}$$

$$= \frac{-3 \pm \sqrt{41}}{-4}$$

Since $\sqrt{41} \approx 6.4$,

$$x \approx \frac{-3 + 6.4}{-4} \approx \frac{3.4}{-4} \approx -0.85 \quad \text{or} \quad x \approx \frac{-3 - 6.4}{-4} \approx \frac{-9.4}{-4} \approx 2.35$$

Thus, the x-intercepts are about $(-0.85, 0)$ and $(2.35, 0)$.

6. Plot the vertex $\left(\frac{3}{4}, 5\frac{1}{8}\right)$, the y-intercept $(0, 4)$, and the x-intercepts $(-0.85, 0)$ and $(2.35, 0)$. Then sketch the graph (Fig. 6.34).

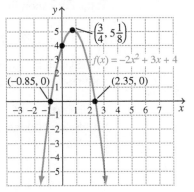

Figure 6.34

b) The domain, the values that can be used for x, is the set of all real numbers, $\mathbb{R}$. The range, the values of y, is $y \le 5\frac{1}{8}$.

When we use the quadratic formula to find the x-intercepts of a graph, if the radicand, $b^2 - 4ac$, is a negative number, the graph has no x-intercepts. The graph will lie totally above or below the x-axis.

Exponential Functions

Many real-life problems, including population growth, growth of bacteria, and decay of radioactive substances, increase or decrease at a very rapid rate. For example, the graph in Fig. 6.35 on page 369 shows the growth of the world population. Notice how the graph is increasing rapidly. This is an example in which the graph is increasing *exponentially*. The equation of a graph that increases or decreases exponentially is called an *exponential equation* or an *exponential function*. An exponential equation or exponential function is of the form $y = a^x$ or $f(x) = a^x$, where in both cases $a > 0, a \neq 1$. When graphing exponential functions we often use the form $y = a^x$, and when working with applications we often use the form $f(x) = a^x$. However, since $y = f(x)$, we can use either form to represent exponential functions.

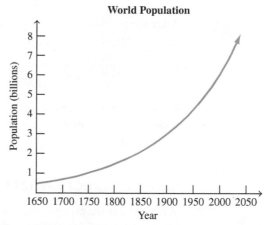

World Population

Source: *U.S. Census Bureau*

Figure 6.35

In an exponential function, letters other than x and y may be used for the variables. The following are examples of exponential functions: $f(x) = 2^x$, $A(r) = \left(\frac{1}{2}\right)^r$ and $P(t) = 2.3^t$. Note in exponential functions that the *variable is the exponent* of some positive constant that is not equal to 1. In many real-life applications, the variable t will be used to represent time. Problems involving exponential functions can be evaluated much more easily if you use a calculator containing a $\boxed{y^x}$, $\boxed{x^y}$, or $\boxed{\wedge}$ key.

The following function, referred to as the *exponential growth* or *decay formula*, is used to solve many real-life problems.

Exponential Growth or Decay Formula

$$P(t) = P_0 a^{kt}, \qquad a > 0, \quad a \neq 1$$

In the formula, P_0 represents the original amount present, $P(t)$ represents the amount present after t years, and a and k are constants.

When $k > 0$, $P(t)$ increases as t increases and we have exponential growth. When $k < 0$, $P(t)$ decreases as t increases and we have exponential decay.

Example 8   *Using an Exponential Decay Formula*

Carbon dating is used by scientists to find the age of fossils, bones, and other items. The formula used in carbon dating is

$$P(t) = P_0 2^{-t/5600}$$

where P_0 represents the original amount of carbon 14 (C_{14}) present and $P(t)$ represents the amount of C_{14} present after t years. If 10 mg of C_{14} is present in an animal bone recently excavated, how many milligrams will be present in 3000 years?

Solution Substituting the values in the formula gives

$$
\begin{aligned}
P(t) &= P_0 2^{-t/5600} \\
&= 10(2)^{-3000/5600} \\
&\approx 10(2)^{-0.54} \qquad \text{(Recall that } \approx \text{ means "is approximately equal to.")} \\
&\approx 10(0.69) \\
&\approx 6.9 \text{ mg}
\end{aligned}
$$

Thus, in 3000 years, approximately 6.9 mg of the original 10 mg of C_{14} will remain. ■

In Example 8, we used a calculator to evaluate $(2)^{-3000/5600}$. The steps used to find this quantity on a calculator with a $\boxed{y^x}$ key are

$$2 \;\boxed{y^x}\; \boxed{(}\; 3000 \;\boxed{+/-}\; \boxed{\div}\; 5600 \;\boxed{)}\; \boxed{=}\; .6898170602$$

After the $\boxed{=}$ key is pressed, the calculator displays the answer 0.6898170602. To evaluate $10(2)^{-3000/5600}$ on a scientific calculator, we can press the following keys.

$$10 \;\boxed{\times}\; 2 \;\boxed{y^x}\; \boxed{(}\; 3000 \;\boxed{+/-}\; \boxed{\div}\; 5600 \;\boxed{)}\; \boxed{=}\; 6.898170602$$

Notice that the answer obtained using the calculator steps shown above is a little more accurate than the answer we gave when we rounded the values before the final answer in Example 8.

Natural Exponential Functions

When the a in the exponential function $f(x) = a^x$ is replaced with a very special letter e, we get the *natural exponential function* $f(x) = e^x$. The exponential growth or decay formula is $P(t) = P_0 a^{kt}$. Replacing the letter a with the letter e in the exponential growth or decay formula leads us to the *natural exponential growth or decay formula*,

Natural Exponential Growth or Decay Formula

$$P(t) = P_0 e^{kt} \quad a > 0, \quad a \neq 1$$

The letter e represents an irrational number called the natural base whose value is approximately 2.7183. The number e plays an important role in mathematics and is used in finding the solution to many application problems.

To evaluate $e^{0.0116(8)}$ on a calculator, as will be needed in Example 9, press*

$$\boxed{(}\; .0116 \;\boxed{\times}\; 8 \;\boxed{)}\; \boxed{inv}\; \boxed{ln}\; \boxed{=}\; 1.097242265$$

$\nearrow \qquad \nwarrow$

Inverse   Natural
key   logarithm
key

After the $\boxed{ln}$ key is pressed, the calculator displays the answer 1.097242265.
To evaluate $7{,}882{,}590 e^{0.0116(8)}$ on a calculator, press

$$7882590 \;\boxed{\times}\; \boxed{(}\; .0116 \;\boxed{\times}\; 8 \;\boxed{)}\; \boxed{inv}\; \boxed{ln}\; \boxed{=}\; 8649110.905$$

In this calculation, after the $\boxed{=}$ key is pressed, the calculator displays the answer 8649110.905. This calculation will be used in Example 9.

Example 9   *Evaluating an Exponential Growth Function*

The population of Virginia is growing exponentially at the rate of about 1.16% per year. In 2009, the population of Virginia was about 7,882,590. Virginia's expected population, t years after 2009, is given by the formula $P(t) = 7{,}882{,}590 e^{0.0116t}$. Assuming that the population continues to grow at the same rate, determine the expected population of Virginia in 2017.

---

*Keys to press may vary on some calculators.

Solution Since 2017 is 8 years after 2009, $t = 8$.

$$P(t) = 7{,}882{,}590e^{0.0116t}$$

$$P(7) = 7{,}882{,}590e^{0.0116(8)}$$

$$= 7{,}882{,}590e^{0.0928}$$

$$\approx 7{,}882{,}590(1.097242265)$$

$$\approx 8{,}649{,}110.905$$

Thus, in 2017, the population of Virginia is expected to be about 8,649,111 people. ∎

Example 10 *Evaluating an Exponential Decay Function*

Plutonium, a radioactive material used in most nuclear reactors, decays exponentially at a rate of 0.003% per year. If there are originally 2000 grams of plutonium, the amount of plutonium, P, remaining after t years is $P(t) = 2000e^{-0.00003t}$. How much plutonium will remain after 50 years?

Solution Substitute 50 years for t in the function, then evaluate using a calculator as described in Section 6.3.

$$P(t) = 2000e^{-0.00003t}$$

$$P(50) = 2000e^{-0.00003(50)}$$

$$= 2000e^{-0.0015}$$

$$\approx 2000(0.9985011244)$$

$$\approx 1997.0 \text{ grams}$$

Thus, after 50 years, the amount of plutonium remaining will be about 1997 grams. ∎

Graphs of Exponential Functions

What does the graph of an *exponential function* of the form $y = a^x$, $a > 0$, $a \neq 1$, look like? Examples 11 and 12 illustrate graphs of exponential functions.

Example 11 *Graphing an Exponential Function with a Base Greater Than 1*

a) Graph $y = 2^x$.

b) Determine the domain and range of the function.

Solution

a) Substitute values for x and find the corresponding values of y. The graph is shown in Fig. 6.36.

$$y = 2^x$$

$x = -3,$	$y = 2^{-3} = \dfrac{1}{2^3} = \dfrac{1}{8}$
$x = -2,$	$y = 2^{-2} = \dfrac{1}{2^2} = \dfrac{1}{4}$
$x = -1,$	$y = 2^{-1} = \dfrac{1}{2^1} = \dfrac{1}{2}$
$x = 0,$	$y = 2^0 = 1$
$x = 1,$	$y = 2^1 = 2$
$x = 2,$	$y = 2^2 = 4$
$x = 3,$	$y = 2^3 = 8$

x	y
-3	$\dfrac{1}{8}$
-2	$\dfrac{1}{4}$
-1	$\dfrac{1}{2}$
0	1
1	2
2	4
3	8

MATHEMATICS TODAY

Population Growth

Population growth during certain time periods can be described by an exponential function. Whether it is a population of bacteria, fish, flowers, or people, the same general trend emerges: a period of rapid (exponential) growth, which is then followed by a leveling-off period.

Why This is Important Knowing the population growth rate helps government agencies determine the number of people for whom they will need to provide future services.

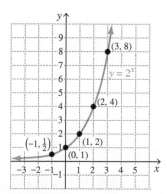

Figure 6.36

b) The domain is all real numbers, $\mathbb{R}$. The range is $y > 0$. Note that y can never have a value of 0. ∎

All exponential functions of the form $y = a^x, a > 1$, will have the general shape of the graph illustrated in Fig. 6.36. Since $f(x)$ is the same as y, the graphs of functions of the form $f(x) = a^x, a > 1$, will also have the general shape of the graph illustrated in Fig. 6.36. Can you now predict the shape of the graph of $y = e^x$? Remember: e has a value of about 2.7183.

Example 12 *Graphing an Exponential Function with a Base Between 0 and 1*

a) Graph $y = \left(\frac{1}{2}\right)^x$.
b) Determine the domain and range of the function.

Solution

a) We begin by substituting values for x and calculating values for y. We then plot the ordered pairs and use these points to sketch the graph. To evaluate a fraction with a negative exponent, we use the fact that

$$\left(\frac{a}{b}\right)^{-x} = \left(\frac{b}{a}\right)^{x}$$

For example,

$$\left(\frac{1}{2}\right)^{-3} = \left(\frac{2}{1}\right)^{3} = 8$$

Then

$$y = \left(\frac{1}{2}\right)^x$$

$$x = -3, \qquad y = \left(\frac{1}{2}\right)^{-3} = 2^3 = 8$$

$$x = -2, \qquad y = \left(\frac{1}{2}\right)^{-2} = 2^2 = 4$$

$$x = -1, \qquad y = \left(\frac{1}{2}\right)^{-1} = 2^1 = 2$$

$$x = 0, \qquad y = \left(\frac{1}{2}\right)^{0} = 1$$

$$x = 1, \qquad y = \left(\frac{1}{2}\right)^{1} = \frac{1}{2}$$

$$x = 2, \qquad y = \left(\frac{1}{2}\right)^{2} = \frac{1}{4}$$

$$x = 3, \qquad y = \left(\frac{1}{2}\right)^{3} = \frac{1}{8}$$

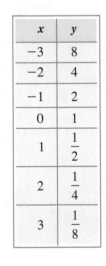

x	y
-3	8
-2	4
-1	2
0	1
1	$\frac{1}{2}$
2	$\frac{1}{4}$
3	$\frac{1}{8}$

The graph is illustrated in Fig. 6.37.
b) The domain is the set of all real numbers, $\mathbb{R}$. The range is $y > 0$. ∎

Figure 6.37

All exponential functions of the form $y = a^x$ or $f(x) = a^x, 0 < a < 1$, will have the general shape of the graph illustrated in Fig. 6.37.

Example 13 *Is the Growth Exponential?*

The graph below shows the population, in millions, of people age 85 and older in the United States for selected years from 1960 to 2010 and projected to 2050.

a) Does the graph approximate the graph of an exponential function?

b) Estimate the number of U.S. people age 85 and older in 2000.

Solution

U.S. Population Age 85 and Older

Source: *U.S. Census Bureau*

a) Yes, the graph has the approximate shape of an exponential function. A function that increases rapidly with this general shape is, or approximates, an exponential function.

b) From the graph, we see that there were about 5 million people in the United States who were age 85 and older in 2000. ∎

SECTION 6.10 *Exercises*

Warm Up Exercises

In Exercises 1–8, fill in the blank with an appropriate word, phrase, or symbol(s).

1. Any set of ordered pairs is called a(n) _____.

2. A special type of relation where each value of the independent variable corresponds to a unique value of the dependent variable is called a(n) _____.

3. The set of values that can be used for the independent variable is called the _____ of the function.

4. The set of values obtained for the dependent variable is called the _____ of the function.

5. In a quadratic function of the form $f(x) = ax^2 + bx + c$, if a is greater than 0, then the graph of $f(x)$ is a parabola that opens _____.

6. In a quadratic function of the form $f(x) = ax^2 + bx + c$, if a is less than 0, then the graph of $f(x)$ is a parabola that opens _____.

7. The formula used to determine the equation for the axis of symmetry of a parabola is _____.

8. A test that is used to determine whether a graph represents a function is called the _____ line test.

Practice the Skills

In Exercises 9–26, determine whether the graph represents a function. If it does represent a function, give its domain and range.

9.

10.

11.

12.

23.

24.

13.

14.

25.

26.

15.

16.

In Exercises 27–32, determine whether the set of ordered pairs is a function.

27. {(3, 7), (4, 9), (2, 1), (8, 0)}

28. {(5, −1), (6, −2), (8, −4), (10, −5)}

29. {(2, 5), (2, 7), (2, −1), (2, 2)}

30. {(−1, 2), (−1, 4), (−1, 6), (−1, 9)}

31. {(−1, −1), (0, −1), (3, −1)}

32. {(4, 2), (4, −3), (4, 5)}

17.

18.

In Exercises 33–46, evaluate the function for the given value of x.

33. $f(x) = x + 6, \quad x = 3$

34. $f(x) = 2x - 5, \quad x = 1$

35. $f(x) = -2x - 7, \quad x = -4$

36. $f(x) = -5x + 3, \quad x = -1$

37. $f(x) = 10x - 6, \quad x = 0$

38. $f(x) = 7x - 6, \quad x = 4$

19.

20.

39. $f(x) = x^2 - 3x + 1, \quad x = 4$

40. $f(x) = x^2 - 5, \quad x = 7$

41. $f(x) = -x^2 - 2x + 1, \quad x = 4$

42. $f(x) = 2x^2 + 3x - 1, \quad x = 3$

43. $f(x) = 4x^2 - 6x - 9, \quad x = -3$

21.

22.

44. $f(x) = 3x^2 + 2x - 5, \quad x = -4$

45. $f(x) = -5x^2 + 3x - 9, \quad x = -1$

46. $f(x) = -3x^2 - 6x + 10, \quad x = -2$

In Exercises 47–52, graph the function by using the slope and y-intercept.

47. $f(x) = 2x + 3$

48. $f(x) = -x - 1$

49. $f(x) = -3x + 2$

50. $f(x) = 2x + 5$

51. $f(x) = \frac{3}{2}x - 1$

52. $f(x) = -\frac{1}{2}x + 3$

In Exercises 53–68,

    a) *determine whether the parabola will open upward or downward.*

    b) *find the equation of the axis of symmetry.*

    c) *find the vertex.*

    d) *find the y-intercept.*

    e) *find the x-intercepts if they exist.*

    f) *sketch the graph.*

    g) *find the domain and range of the function.*

53. $y = x^2 - 1$

54. $y = x^2 - 9$

55. $y = -x^2 + 4$

56. $y = -x^2 + 16$

57. $y = -2x^2 - 8$

58. $f(x) = -x^2 - 4$

59. $y = 2x^2 - 3$

60. $f(x) = -3x^2 - 6$

61. $f(x) = x^2 + 4x - 4$

62. $y = x^2 - 8x + 1$

63. $y = x^2 + 5x + 6$

64. $y = x^2 - 7x - 8$

65. $y = -x^2 + 4x - 6$

66. $y = -x^2 + 8x - 8$

67. $y = -2x^2 + 3x - 2$

68. $y = -4x^2 - 6x + 4$

In Exercises 69–80, draw the graph of the function and state the domain and range.

69. $y = 3^x$

70. $f(x) = 4^x$

71. $y = \left(\frac{1}{3}\right)^x$

72. $y - \left(\frac{1}{4}\right)^x$

73. $f(x) = 2^x + 1$

74. $y = 3^x - 1$

75. $y = 4^x + 1$

76. $y = 2^x - 1$

77. $y = 3^{x-1}$

78. $y = 3^{x+1}$

79. $f(x) = 4^{x+1}$

80. $y = 4^{x-1}$

Problem Solving

81. *Yearly Profit* Marta Rivera is a part owner of a newly opened candy company. Marta's yearly profit, in dollars, is given by the function $p(x) = 3.5x - 15,000$, where x is the number of pounds of candy sold per year. If Marta sells 20,000 pounds of candy a year, determine her yearly profit.

82. *Finding Distances* The distance a car travels, $d(t)$, at a constant 60 mph is given by the function $d(t) = 60t$, where t is the time in hours. Find the distance traveled in

    a) 3 hours.

    b) 7 hours.

83. *U.S. Foreign-Born Population* The graph on the top of page 376 indicates the percentage of the U.S. population that was foreign-born for each decade between 1930 and 2000, and projected percentage for 2010. The function $f(x) = 0.005x^2 - 0.36x + 11.8$ can be used to estimate the percentage of the U.S. population that was foreign-born, where x is the number of years since 1930 and $0 \le x \le 80$.

    a) Use the function $f(x)$ to estimate the percentage of the U.S. population that was foreign-born in 2004. Round your answer to the nearest percent.

    b) Of the years illustrated on the graph, determine the year in which the percentage of the U.S. population that was foreign-born was a minimum.

    c) Determine the x-coordinate of the vertex of the graph of the function $f(x)$. Then use this value in the function $f(x)$ to estimate the minimum percentage of the U.S. population that was foreign-born. Round your answer for the vertex to the nearest whole number. Round your answer for the population to the nearest percent.

Percentage of U.S. Population That is Foreign-Born

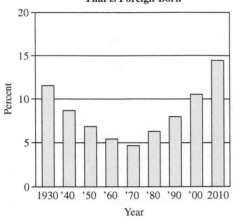

Source: *Bureau of the Census, U.S. Dept. of Commerce*

84. *Hourly Temperature* The following graph indicates the hourly temperature, in degrees fahrenheit, in Rochester, New York, from 2 A.M. through 12 noon on Friday, February 10, 2011. The function $t(x) = 0.17x^2 - 1.75x + 15.35$ can be used to estimate the hourly temperature in Rochester, where x is the number of hours after 2 A.M on February 10, 2011 and $0 \leq x \leq 10$.

a) Use the function $t(x)$ to estimate the temperature in Rochester at 8 A.M. on February 10, 2011. Round your answer to the nearest degree.

b) Use the graph to determine the hour(s) that the temperature was a minimum.

c) Determine the x-coordinate of the vertex of the graph of the function $t(x)$. Then use this value in the function $t(x)$ to estimate the minimum temperature. Round your answer for the vertex to the nearest hour. Round your answer for the temperature to the nearest degree.

Hourly Temperature in Rochester, NY February 10, 2011

Source: *Weather.com*

85. *Bacteria* The number of a certain type of bacteria, y, present in a culture is determined by the equation $y = 2000(3)^x$, where x is the number of days the culture

has been growing. Find the number of bacteria present after 5 days.

86. *Adjusting for Inflation* If P is the price of an item today, the price of the same item n years from today, P_n, is $P_n = P(1 + r)^n$, where r is the constant rate of inflation. Determine the price of a movie ticket 10 years from today if the price today is $8.00 and the annual rate of inflation is constant at 3%.

87. *Expected Growth* The town of Lockport currently has 4000 residents. The expected future population can be approximated by the function $P(x) = 4000(1.3)^{0.1x}$, where x is the number of years in the future. Determine the expected population of Lockport in

a) 10 years.

b) 50 years.

88. *Value of an SUV* The cost of a new SUV is $30,000. If it depreciates at a rate of 18% per year, the value of the SUV in t years can be approximated by the function $V(t) = 30,000(0.82)^t$. Determine the value of the SUV in 4 years. Round your answer to the nearest cent.

89. *Population of China* The population of China in April 2011, was about 1.34 billion people. Assume that the population of China continues to grow exponentially at the growth rate of 0.6% per year. Thus, the expected population of China, in billions of people, t years after 2011, is given by the function $P(t) = 1.34e^{0.006t}$. Determine the expected population of China in 2016.

90. *Value of New York City* Assume the value of the island of Manhattan has grown at an exponential rate of 8% per year since 1626 when Peter Minuit of the Dutch West India Company purchased the island for $24. The value of the island, V, at any time, t, in years after 1626, can be found by the formula $V(t) = 24e^{0.08t}$. What is the value of the island in 2012, 386 years after Minuit purchased it? Use a scientific calculator and give your answer in scientific notation as provided by your calculator.

91. *Radioactive Decay* Radium-226 is a radioactive isotope that decays exponentially at a rate of 0.0428% per year. The amount of radium-226, Rt, remaining after t years can be found by the formula $R(t) = R_0 e^{-0.000428t}$, where R_0 is the original amount present. If there are originally 10 grams of radium-226, determine the amount of radium-226 remaining after 1000 years.

92. *Radioactive Decay* Strontium-90 is a radioactive isotope that decays exponentially at a rate of 2.8% per year. The amount of strontium-90, S, remaining after t years can be found by the function $S(t) = S_0 e^{-0.028t}$, where S_0 is the original amount present. If there are originally 1000 grams of strontium-90, determine the amount of strontium-90 remaining after 40 years. Round your answer to the nearest gram.

93. *U.S. Cellular Telephone Subscribers* The graph on the top of page 377 shows the number of U.S. cellular subscribers, in thousands, for the years 1989 through 2008.

a) Does the graph approximate the graph of an exponential function?

b) Estimate the number of U.S. cellular subscribers in 2008.

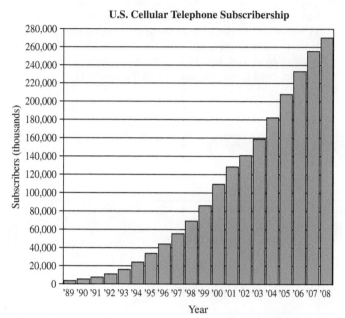

U.S. Cellular Telephone Subscribership

Source: *The CTIA Semi-Annual Wireless Industry Survey, 1989–2008*

94. *U.S. Gross Domestic Product* The following graph shows the U.S. gross domestic product (GDP), the market value of all goods and services produced within the United States, for every 5 years between 1965 and 2010.

a) Does the graph approximate the graph of an exponential function?

b) Estimate the U.S. gross domestic product in 2005.

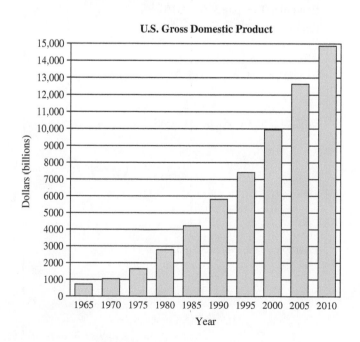

U.S. Gross Domestic Product

95. The spacing of the frets on the neck of a classical guitar is determined from the equation $d = (21.9)(2)^{(20-x)/12}$, where $x =$ the fret number and $d =$ the distance in centimeters of the xth fret from the bridge.

a) Determine how far the 19th fret should be from the bridge (rounded to one decimal place).

b) Determine how far the 4th fret should be from the bridge (rounded to one decimal place).

c) The distance of the nut from the bridge can be found by letting $x = 0$ in the given exponential equation. Find the distance from the nut to the bridge (rounded to one decimal place).

Challenge Problems/Group Activities

96. *Appreciation of a House* A house initially cost $150,000. The value, V, of the house after n years if it appreciates at a constant rate of 4% per year can be determined by the function $V = f(n) = \$150{,}000(1.04)^n$.

a) Determine $f(8)$ and explain its meaning.

b) After how many years is the value of the house greater than $250,000? (Find by trial and error.)

97. *Target Heart Rate* While exercising, a person's recommended target heart rate is a function of age. The recommended number of beats per minute, y, is given by the function $y = f(x) = -0.85x + 187$, where x represents a person's age in years. Determine the number of recommended heart beats per minute for the following ages and explain the results.

a) 20

b) 30

c) 50

d) 60

e) What is the age of a person with a recommended target heart rate of 85?

98. *Speed of Light*   Light travels at about 186,000 miles per second through space. The distance, d, in miles that light travels in t seconds can be determined by the function $d(t) = 186,000t$.

a) Light reaches the moon from Earth in about 1.3 sec. Determine the approximate distance from Earth to the moon.

b) Express the distance in miles, d, traveled by light in t minutes as a function of time, t.

c) Light travels from the sun to Earth in about 8.3 min. Determine the approximate distance from the sun to Earth.

Internet/Research Activity

99. The idea of using variables in algebraic equations was introduced by the French mathematician François Viète (1540–1603). Write a paper about his life and his contributions to mathematics. In particular, discuss his work with algebra equations. References include history of mathematics books, encyclopedias, and the Internet.

CHAPTER 6   *Summary*

Important Facts and Concepts	Examples
Section 6.1	
Order of Operations	Examples 1–4, pages 293–295
Section 6.2	
Properties Used to Solve Equations	Examples 2–13, pages 298–304
Addition property of equality	
$\quad$ If $a = b$, then $a + c = b + c$.	
Subtraction property of equality	
$\quad$ If $a = b$, then $a - c = b - c$.	
Multiplication property of equality	
$\quad$ If $a = b$, then $ac = bc$.	
Division property of equality	
$\quad$ If $a = b$, then $a/c = b/c$, $c \neq 0$.	
Section 6.3	
Evaluating a formula	Examples 1–3, pages 309–310
Solving for a variable in a formula	Examples 4–6, pages 310–311
Section 6.4	
Applications of Linear Equations	Examples 1–4, pages 315–317
Section 6.5	
Variation	Examples 1–10, pages 321–325
Direct: $y = kx$	
Inverse: $y = \dfrac{k}{x}$	
Joint: $y = kxz$	
Section 6.6	
Inequality Symbols	Examples 1–9, pages 329–333
$a < b$ means that a is less than b.	
$a \leq b$ means that a is less than or equal to b.	
$a > b$ means that a is greater than b.	
$a \geq b$ means that a is greater than or equal to b.	

Section 6.7

CHAPTER 6) Review Exercises

6.1

In Exercises 1–4, evaluate the expression for the given value(s) of the variable.

1. $x^2 + 12$, $x = 3$

2. $-x^2 - 8$, $x = -2$

3. $4x^2 - 2x + 5$, $x = 2$

4. $4x^3 - 7x^2 + 3x + 1$, $x = -1$

6.2

In Exercises 5–6, combine like terms.

5. $4x - 2 + x + 9$

6. $2x + 3(x - 2) + 7x$

In Exercises 7–10, solve the equation for the given variable.

7. $3s + 10 = -32$

8. $2t + 15 = -6t - 9$

9. $\dfrac{x + 5}{2} = \dfrac{x - 3}{4}$

10. $4(x - 2) = 3 + 5(x + 4)$

11. **Making Oatmeal** A recipe for Hot Oats Cereal calls for 2 cups of water and for $\frac{1}{3}$ cup of dry oats. How many cups of dry oats would be used with 3 cups of water?

12. **Laying Blocks** A mason lays 120 blocks in 1 hr 40 min. How long will it take her to lay 300 blocks?

6.3

In Exercises 13–16, use the formula to find the value of the indicated variable for the values given.

13. $F = ma$
    Determine F when $m = 40$ and $a = 5$ (physics).

14. $v = lwh$
    Determine v when $l = 7$, $w = 4$, and $h = 3$ (*geometry*).

15. $z = \dfrac{\bar{x} - \mu}{\dfrac{\sigma}{\sqrt{n}}}$

    Determine $\bar{x}$ when $z = 2$, $\mu = 100$, $\sigma = 3$, and $n = 16$ (statistics).

16. $E = mc^2$
    Determine m when $E = 400$ and $c = 4$ (physics).

In Exercises 17–18, solve for y.

17. $6x - 3y = 24$ 18. $2x + 9y = 17$

In Exercises 19–22, solve for the variable indicated.

19. $A = lw$,   for w

20. $P = 2l + 2w$,   for w

21. $L = 2(wh + lh)$,   for l

22. $a_n = a_1 + (n - 1)d$,   for d

6.4

In Exercises 23–26, write the phrase in mathematical terms.

23. 7 decreased by 2 times x

24. 3 times y, increased by 4

25. 10 increased by 3 times r

26. The difference between 9 divided by q and 15

In Exercises 27–30, write an equation that can be used to solve the problems. Solve the equation and find the desired value(s).

27. Two increased by 8 times a number is 18.

28. The product of 3 and a number, increased by 8, is 6 less than the number.

29. Five times the difference of a number and 4 is 45.

30. Fourteen more than 10 times a number is 8 times the sum of the number and 12.

In Exercises 31–34, write the equation and then find the solution.

31. **MODELING – Investing**   Jim Lawton received an inheritance of $15,000. If he wants to invest twice as much money in mutual funds as in bonds, how much should he invest in mutual funds?

32. **MODELING – Lawn Chairs**   Larry's Lawn Chair Company has fixed costs of $15,000 per month and variable costs of $9.50 per lawn chair manufactured. The company has $95,000 available to meet its total monthly expenditures. What is the maximum number of lawn chairs the company can manufacture in a month? (Fixed costs, such as rent and insurance, are those that occur regardless of the level of production. Variable costs, such as those for materials, depend on the level of production.)

33. **MODELING – National Parks**   The area of Crater Lake National Park is 4049 acres more than 5 times the area of Bryce Canyon National Park. The total area of Crater Lake National park and Bryce Canyon National Park is 219,059 acres. Determine the area, in acres, of Crater

Lake National Park and the area of Bryce Canyon National Park.

▲ *Carter Lake National Park, Oregon*

34. MODELING – *Restaurant Profit* John Smith owns two restaurants. His profit for a year at restaurant A is $12,000 greater than his profit at restaurant B. The total profit from both restaurants is $68,000. Determine the profit at each restaurant.

6.5

In Exercises 35–38, find the quantity indicated.

35. s is directly proportional to t. If $s = 30$ when $t = 10$, find s when $t = 8$.

36. J is inversely proportional to the square of A. If $J = 25$ when $A = 2$, find J when $A = 5$.

37. W is directly proportional to L and inversely proportional to A. If $W = 80$ when $L = 100$ and $A = 20$, find W when $L = 50$ and $A = 40$.

38. z is jointly proportional to x and y and inversely proportional to the square of r. If $z = 12$ when $x = 20$, $y = 8$, and $r = 8$, find z when $x = 10$, $y = 80$, and $r = 3$.

39. *Buying Fertilizer*

a) A 30-lb bag of fertilizer will cover an area of 2500 ft². How many pounds of fertilizer are needed to cover an area of 12,500 ft²?

b) How many bags of fertilizer are needed?

40. *Property Tax* The property tax, t, on a house is directly proportional to the assessed value, v, of the house. If the property tax on a house with an assessed value of $155,000 is $2325, what is the property tax on a house with an assessed value of $210,000?

41. *Electric Bill* An electric company charges $0.162 per kilowatt-hour (kWh). What is the electric bill if 740 kWh are used in a month?

42. *Stretching a Spring* The length that a spring will stretch, S, varies directly with the weight, w, attached to the spring. If a spring stretches 4.2 in. when a 60-lb weight is attached, how far will the spring stretch when a 25-lb weight is attached?

▲ *See Exercises 42*

6.6

In Exercises 43–49, graph the solution set for the set of real numbers on the real number line.

43. $8 + 9x \le 6x - 4$

44. $3x + 8 \ge 7x + 12$

45. $3(x + 9) \le 4x + 11$

46. $-3 \le x + 1 < 7$

In Exercises 47–50, graph the solution set for the set of integers on the real number line.

47. $4 + 2x > -10$

48. $5x + 13 \ge -22$

49. $-1 < x \le 9$

50. $-8 \le x + 2 \le 7$

6.7

In Exercises 51–54, graph the ordered pair in the Cartesian coordinate system.

51. $(-2, 1)$

52. $(2, -2)$

53. $(-4, 3)$

54. $(5, 3)$

In Exercises 55 and 56, points A, B, and C are vertices of a rectangle. Plot the points. Find the coordinates of the fourth point, D, to complete the rectangle. Find the area of the rectangle.

55. $A(-3, 3)$, $B(2, 3)$, $C(2, -1)$

56. $A(-3, 1)$, $B(-3, -2)$, $C(4, -2)$

In Exercises 57–58, graph the equation by plotting points.

57. $x - y = 2$

58. $2x + 3y = 12$

In Exercises 59–60, graph the equation, using the x- and y-intercepts.

59. $x - 2y = 6$

60. $4x - 3y = 12$

In Exercises 61–64, find the slope of the line through the given points.

61. $(1, 3), (4, 7)$

62. $(3, -1), (5, -4)$

63. $(-1, -4), (2, 3)$

64. $(6, 2), (6, -2)$

In Exercises 65–66, graph the equation by plotting the y-intercept and then plotting a second point by making use of the slope.

65. $y = 2x - 5$

66. $2y - 4 = 3x$

In Exercises 67 and 68, determine the equation of the graph.

67. **68.**

69. *Car Wash Profit* The weekly profit, p, in dollars, at Delta Sonic Car Wash can be estimated by $p = 20n - 400$, where n is the number of cars washed in 1 week.

a) Draw a graph of weekly profit versus number of cars washed for up to and including 100 cars.

b) Use the function to determine the weekly profit if 50 cars are washed.

c) If the weekly profit was $1000, use the function to determine how many cars were washed.

70. **MODELING—***Taxi Business Cost* Tony Li's weekly cost, C, in dollars, of operating a taxi business can be approximated by the equation $C = 0.20m + 80$, where m is the number of miles driven in a week.

a) Draw a graph of weekly cost versus the number of miles driven for up to and including 500 miles driven per week.

b) If, during one week, Tony drove the taxi 150 miles, what would be the cost?

c) How many miles would Tony have to drive for the weekly cost to be $104?

6.8

In Exercises 71–74, graph the inequality.

71. $2x + 3y \leq 12$

72. $4x + 2y \geq 12$

73. $2x - 3y > 12$

74. $-7x - 2y < 14$

6.9

In Exercises 75–78, factor the trinomial. If the trinomial cannot be factored, so state.

75. $x^2 + 9x + 20$

76. $x^2 + x - 12$

77. $x^2 - 10x + 24$

78. $6x^2 + 7x - 3$

In Exercises 79–82, solve the equation by factoring.

79. $x^2 + 6x + 5 = 0$

80. $x^2 + 3x = 10$

81. $3x^2 - 17x + 10 = 0$

82. $3x^2 = -7x - 2$

In Exercises 83–86, solve the equation using the quadratic formula. If the equation has no real solution, so state.

83. $x^2 - 6x - 16 = 0$

84. $2x^2 - x - 3 = 0$

85. $2x^2 - 3x + 4 = 0$

86. $x^2 - 3x - 2 = 0$

6.10

In Exercises 87–90, determine whether the graph represents a function. If it does represent a function, give its domain and range.

87. **88.**

89. **90.**

In Exercises 91–94, evaluate $f(x)$ for the given value of x.

91. $f(x) = 5x - 2$, $x = 4$

92. $f(x) = -3x + 7$, $x = -3$

93. $f(x) = 2x^2 - 3x + 4$, $x = 5$

94. $f(x) = -4x^2 + 7x + 9$, $x = -2$

In Exercises 95 and 96, for each function

  a) *determine whether the parabola will open upward or downward.*

  b) *determine the equation of the axis of symmetry.*

  c) *determine the vertex.*

  d) *determine the y-intercept.*

  e) *determine the x-intercepts if they exist.*

  f) *sketch the graph.*

  g) *determine the domain and range.*

95. $y = -x^2 - 4x + 21$

96. $f(x) = 2x^2 + 8x + 6$

In Exercises 97 and 98, draw the graph of the function and state the domain and range.

97. $y = 4^x$ **98.** $y = \left(\dfrac{1}{2}\right)^x$

6.2, 6.3, 6.10

99. *Gas Mileage* The gas mileage, m, of a specific car can be estimated by the equation (or function)

$$m = 30 - 0.002n^2, \quad 20 \le n \le 80$$

where n is the speed of the car in miles per hour. Estimate the gas mileage when the car travels at 60 mph.

100. *Filtered Light* The percent of light filtering through Swan Lake, P, can be approximated by the function $P(x) = 100(0.92)^x$, where x is the depth in feet. Find the percent of light filtering through at a depth of 4.5 ft.

CHAPTER 6   *Test*

1. Evaluate $3x^2 + 6x - 1$, when $x = -2$.

In Exercises 2 and 3, solve the equation.

2. $4x + 6 = 2(3x - 7)$

3. $-2(x - 3) + 6x = 2x + 3(x - 4)$

In Exercises 4 and 5, write an equation to represent the problem. Then solve the equation.

4. The product of 3 and a number, increased by 5, is 17.

5. *Salary* Mary Gilligan's salary is $350 per week plus a 6% commission of sales. How much in sales must Mary make to earn a total of $710 per week?

6. Evaluate $L = ah + bh + ch$ when $a = 2, b = 5, c = 4$, and $h = 7$.

7. Solve $3x + 5y = 11$ for y.

8. L varies jointly as M and N and inversely as P. If $L = 12$ when $M = 8, N = 3$, and $P = 2$, find L when $M = 10, N = 5$, and $P = 15$.

9. For a constant area, the length, l, of a rectangle varies inversely as the width, w. If $l = 15$ ft when $w = 9$ ft, find the length of a rectangle with the same area if the width is 20 ft.

10. Graph the solution set of $-5x + 14 \le 2x + 35$ on the real number line.

11. Determine the slope of the line through the points $(-2, 8)$ and $(1, 14)$.

In Exercises 12 and 13, graph the equation.

12. $y = 2x - 4$ **13.** $2x - 3y = 15$

14. Graph the inequality $3y \ge 5x - 12$.

15. Factor the following trinomial: $x^2 + 11x + 18$. If the trinomial cannot be factored, so state.

16. Solve the equation $x^2 + 7x = -6$ by factoring.

17. Solve the equation $3x^2 + 2x = 8$ by using the quadratic formula.

18. Determine whether the graph is a function. Explain your answer.

19. Evaluate $f(x) = -2x^2 - 8x + 7$ when $x = -2$.

20. For the equation $y = x^2 - 2x + 4$,

  a) determine whether the parabola will open upward or downward.

  b) determine the equation of the axis of symmetry.

  c) determine the vertex.

  d) determine the y-intercept.

  e) determine the x-intercepts if they exist.

  f) sketch the graph.

  g) determine the domain and range of the function.

GROUP PROJECTS

Archeology: Gaining Information From Bones

1. Archeologists have developed formulas to predict the height and, in some cases, the age at death of the deceased by knowing the lengths of certain bones in the body. The long bones of the body grow at approximately the same rate. Thus, a linear relationship exists between the length of the bones and the person's height. If the length of one of these major bones—the femur (F), the tibia (T), the humerus (H), and the radius (R)— is known, the height, h, of a person can be calculated with one of the following formulas. The relationship between bone length and height is different for males and females.

Male	Female
$h = 2.24F + 69.09$	$h = 2.23F + 61.41$
$h = 2.39T + 81.68$	$h = 2.53T + 72.57$
$h = 2.97H + 73.57$	$h = 3.14H + 64.98$
$h = 3.65R + 80.41$	$h = 3.88R + 73.51$

All measurements are in centimeters.

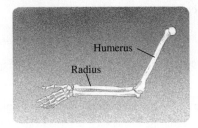

a) Measure your humerus and use the appropriate formula to predict your height in centimeters. How close is this predicted height to your actual height? (The result is an approximation because measuring a bone covered with flesh and muscle is difficult.)

b) Determine and describe where the femur and tibia bones are located.

c) Dr. Juarez, an archeologist, had one female humerus that was 29.42 cm in length. He concluded that the height of the entire skeleton would have been 157.36 cm. Was his conclusion correct?

d) If a 21-year-old woman is 167.64 cm tall, about how long should her tibia be?

e) Sometimes the age of a person may be determined by using the fact that the height of a person, and the length of his or her long bones, decreases at the rate of 0.06 cm per year after the age of 30.

i. At age 30, Jolene is 168 cm tall. Estimate the length of her humerus.

ii. Estimate the length of Jolene's humerus when she is 60 years old.

f) Select six people of the same gender and measure their height and one of the bones for which an equation is given (the same bone on each person). Each measurement should be made to the nearest 0.5 cm. For each person, you will have two measurements, which can be considered an ordered pair (bone length, height). Plot the ordered pairs on a piece of graph paper, with the bone length on the horizontal axis and the height on the vertical axis. Start the scale on both axes at zero. Draw a straight line that you feel is the best approximation, or best fit, through these points. Determine where the line crosses the y-axis and the slope of the line. Your y-intercept and slope should be close to the values in the given equation for that bone. (Reference: M. Trotter and G. C. Gleser, "Estimation of Stature from Long Bones of American Whites and Negroes," *American Journal of Physical Anthropology,* 1952, 10:463–514.)

Graphing Calculator

2. The functions that we graphed in this chapter can be easily graphed with a graphing calculator (or grapher). If you do not have a graphing calculator, borrow one from your instructor or a friend.

a) Explain how you would set the domain and range. The calculator key to set the domain and range may be labeled *range* or *window*. Set the grapher with the following range or window settings:

$$Xmin = -12, Xmax = 12, Xscl = 1,$$
$$Ymin = -13, Ymax = 6, \text{ and } Yscl = 1.$$

b) Explain how to enter a function in the graphing calculator. Enter the function $y = 3x^2 - 7x - 8$ in the calculator.

c) Graph the function you entered in part (b).

d) Learn how to use the *trace feature*. Then use it to estimate the x-intercepts. Record the estimated values for the x-intercepts.

e) Learn how to use the *zoom feature* to obtain a better approximation of the x-intercepts. Use the zoom feature twice and record the x-intercepts each time.

9

Geometry

◄ Baseballs and baseball diamonds are examples of geometric objects.

478

SECTION 9.1   Points, Lines, Planes, and Angles

▲ *Billiard games involve many geometric concepts.*

Profile In Mathematics

Euclid

Euclid (320–275 B.C.) lived in Alexandria, Egypt, and was a teacher and scholar at Alexandria's school called the *Museum*. It was here that Euclid collected and arranged many of the mathematical results known at the time. This collection of works became his 13-volume masterpiece known as *Elements*. Beginning with a list of definitions, postulates, and axioms, Euclid proved one theorem after another, using only previously proven results. This method of proof became a model of mathematical and scientific investigation that survives today. Remarkably, the geometry in *Elements* does not rely on making exact geometric measurements using a ruler or protractor. Rather, the work is developed using only an unmarked straightedge and a drawing compass. Next to the Bible, Euclid's *Elements* may be the most translated, published, and studied of all the books produced in the Western world.

Playing billiards involves many geometric concepts. In this section, we will introduce the geometric terms *points*, *lines*, *planes*, and *angles*. In a typical billiard game, each of these terms is evident. The billiard balls rest on specific points on the table, which is part of a plane. After being struck with a cue, the ball travels along a path that is part of a line. Angles are involved in the path the ball takes when the ball hits a table bumper or another ball. The concepts we will discuss in this section form an important basis for the study of geometry.

Why This is Important Geometry is used in our everyday lives to describe the world around us. An understanding of fundamental geometric concepts can help us better understand our world.

Human beings recognized shapes, sizes, and physical forms long before geometry was developed. Geometry as a science is said to have begun in the Nile Valley of ancient Egypt. The Egyptians used geometry to measure land and to build pyramids and other structures.

The word *geometry* is derived from two Greek words: *ge*, meaning earth, and *metron*, meaning measure. Thus, geometry means "earth measure" or "measurement of the earth."

Unlike the Egyptians, the Greeks were interested in more than just the applied aspects of geometry. The Greeks attempted to apply their knowledge of logic to geometry. In about 600 B.C., Thales of Miletus was the first to be credited with using deductive methods to develop geometric concepts. Another outstanding Greek mathematician, Pythagoras, continued the systematic development of geometry that Thales had begun.

In about 300 B.C., Euclid (see *Profile in Mathematics* in the margin) collected and summarized much of the Greek mathematics of his time. In a set of 13 books called *Elements*, Euclid laid the foundation for plane geometry, which is also called *Euclidean geometry*.

Euclid is credited with being the first mathematician to use the *axiomatic method* in developing a branch of mathematics. First, Euclid introduced *undefined terms* such as point, line, plane, and angle. He related these to physical space by such statements as "A line is length without breadth" so that we may intuitively understand them. Because such statements play no further role in his system, they constitute primitive or undefined terms.

Second, Euclid introduced certain *definitions*. The definitions are introduced when needed and are often based on the undefined terms. Some terms that Euclid introduced and defined include triangle, right angle, and hypotenuse.

Third, Euclid stated certain primitive propositions called *postulates* (now called *axioms**) about the undefined terms and definitions. The reader is asked to accept these statements as true on the basis of their "obviousness" and their relationship with the physical world. For example, the Greeks accepted all right angles as being equal, which is Euclid's fourth postulate.

Fourth, Euclid proved, using deductive reasoning (see Section 1.1), other propositions called *theorems*. One theorem that Euclid proved is known as the Pythagorean

---

*The concept of the axiom has changed significantly since Euclid's time. Now any statement may be designated as an axiom, whether it is self-evident or not. All axioms are *accepted* as true. A set of axioms forms the foundation for a mathematical system.

Straightedge   Compass

Geometric constructions were central to ancient Greek mathematics. Although these constructions are often referred to as *Euclidean constructions*, they were used centuries before Euclid wrote his classic work, *Elements*. The tools *allowed* in geometric constructions are a pencil, an unmarked straightedge, and a drawing compass. The straightedge is used to draw line segments, and the compass is used to draw circles and arcs. The Internet has many sites devoted to classic geometric constructions. Exercise 107 on page 489 shows you how to construct a triangle with sides of equal length (an equilateral triangle).

theorem: "The sum of the areas of the squares constructed on the arms of a right triangle is equal to the area of the square constructed on the hypotenuse." He also proved that the sum of the angles of a triangle is 180°.

Using only 10 axioms, Euclid deduced 465 propositions (or theorems) in plane and solid geometry, number theory, and Greek geometric algebra.

Point and Line

Three basic terms in geometry are *point*, *line*, and *plane*. These three terms are not given a formal definition, but we recognize points, lines, and planes when we see them.

Let's consider some properties of a line. Assume that a line means a straight line unless otherwise stated.

1. A line is a set of points. Each point is on the line and the line passes through each point. When we wish to refer to a specific point, we will label it with a single capital letter. For example, in Fig. 9.1(a) three points are labeled A, B, and C, respectively.
2. Any two distinct points determine a unique line. Figure 9.1(a) illustrates a line. The arrows at both ends of the line indicate that the line continues in each direction. The line in Fig. 9.1(a) may be symbolized with any two points on the line by placing a line with a double-sided arrow above the letters that correspond to the points, such as $\overleftrightarrow{AB}$, $\overleftrightarrow{BA}$, $\overleftrightarrow{AC}$, $\overleftrightarrow{CA}$, $\overleftrightarrow{BC}$, or $\overleftrightarrow{CB}$.
3. Any point on a line separates the line into three parts: the point itself and two *half lines* (neither of which includes the point). For example, in Fig. 9.1(a) point B separates the line into the point B and two half lines. Half line BA, symbolized $\overset{\circ}{\overrightarrow{BA}}$, is illustrated in Fig. 9.1(b). The open circle above the B indicates that point B is not included in the half line. Figure 9.1(c) illustrates half line BC, symbolized $\overset{\circ}{\overrightarrow{BC}}$.

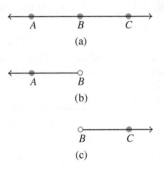

Figure 9.1

Look at the half line $\overset{\circ}{\overrightarrow{AB}}$ in Fig. 9.2(b) on page 481. If the *end point*, A, is included with the set of points on the half line, the result is called a *ray*. Ray AB, symbolized $\overrightarrow{AB}$, is illustrated in Fig. 9.2(c). Ray BA, symbolized $\overrightarrow{BA}$, is illustrated in Fig. 9.2(d).

A *line segment* is that part of a line between two points, including the end points. Line segment AB, symbolized $\overline{AB}$, is illustrated in Fig. 9.2(e).

An open line segment is the set of points on a line between two points, excluding the end points. Open line segment AB, symbolized $\overset{\circ}{\overline{AB}}\overset{\circ}{}$, is illustrated in Fig. 9.2(f).

Figure 9.2(g) illustrates two half open line segments, symbolized $\overline{AB}\overset{\circ}{}$ and $\overset{\circ}{\overline{AB}}$.

Recall from Chapter 2 that the intersection (symbolized $\cap$) of two sets is the set of elements (points in this case) common to both sets. Consider the rays $\overrightarrow{AB}$ and $\overrightarrow{BA}$ in Fig. 9.3(a) on page 481. The intersection of $\overrightarrow{AB}$ and $\overrightarrow{BA}$ is $\overline{AB}$. Thus, $\overrightarrow{AB} \cap \overrightarrow{BA} = \overline{AB}$.

Description	Diagram	Symbol
(a) Line AB		$\overleftrightarrow{AB}$
(b) Half line AB		$\overset{\circ\longrightarrow}{AB}$
(c) Ray AB		$\overrightarrow{AB}$
(d) Ray BA		$\overleftarrow{BA}$
(e) Line segment AB		$\overline{AB}$
(f) Open line segment AB		$\overset{\circ\!-\!\circ}{AB}$
(g) Half open line segments AB		$\overline{AB}^{\circ}$ $\overset{\circ}{\overline{AB}}$

Figure 9.2

Also recall from Chapter 2 that the union (symbolized ∪) of two sets is the set of elements (points in this case) that belong to either of the sets or both sets. The union of $\overrightarrow{AB}$ and $\overrightarrow{BA}$ is $\overleftrightarrow{AB}$ (Fig. 9.3b). Thus, $\overrightarrow{AB} \cup \overrightarrow{BA} = \overleftrightarrow{AB}$.

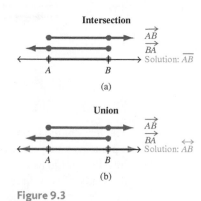

Figure 9.3

Example 1 *Unions and Intersections of Parts of a Line*

Using line AD, determine the solution to each part.

a) $\overrightarrow{AB} \cap \overrightarrow{DC}$ b) $\overrightarrow{AB} \cup \overrightarrow{DC}$ c) $\overrightarrow{AB} \cap \overrightarrow{CD}$ d) $\overline{AD} \cup \overset{\circ}{CA}\!\!\rightarrow$

Solution

a) $\overrightarrow{AB} \cap \overrightarrow{DC}$

Ray AB and ray DC are shown below. The intersection of these two rays is that part of line AD that is a part of *both* ray AB and ray DC. The intersection of ray AB and ray DC is line segment AD.

$$\overrightarrow{AB} \cap \overrightarrow{DC} = \overline{AD}$$

b) $\overrightarrow{AB} \cup \overrightarrow{DC}$

Once again ray AB and ray DC are shown below. The union of these two rays is that part of line AD that is part of *either* ray AB *or* ray DC. The union of ray AB and ray DC is the entire line AD.

$$\overrightarrow{AB} \cup \overrightarrow{DC} = \overleftrightarrow{AD}$$

c) $\overline{AB} \cap \overrightarrow{CD}$

Line segment AB and ray CD have no points in common, so their intersection is empty.

$$\overline{AB} \cap \overrightarrow{CD} = \varnothing$$

d) $\overline{AD} \cup \overset{\circ}{\overrightarrow{CA}}$

The union of line segment AD and half line CA is ray DA (or equivalently, $\overrightarrow{DB}$ or $\overrightarrow{DC}$).

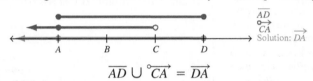

$$\overline{AD} \cup \overset{\circ}{\overrightarrow{CA}} = \overrightarrow{DA}$$ ▪

Plane

The term *plane* is one of Euclid's undefined terms. For our purposes, we can think of a plane as a two-dimensional surface that extends infinitely in both directions, like an infinitely large blackboard. Euclidean geometry is called *plane geometry* because it is the study of two-dimensional figures in a plane.

Two lines in the same plane that do not intersect are called *parallel lines*. Figure 9.4(a) illustrates two parallel lines in a plane ($\overleftrightarrow{AB}$ is parallel to $\overleftrightarrow{CD}$).

Properties of planes include the following:

1. Any three points that are not on the same line (noncollinear points) determine a unique plane (Fig. 9.4b).
2. A line in a plane divides the plane into three parts, the line and two half planes (Fig. 9.4c).
3. Any line and a point not on the line determine a unique plane.
4. The intersection of two distinct planes is a line (Fig. 9.4d).

Two planes that do not intersect are said to be *parallel planes*. For example, in Fig. 9.5 plane ABE is parallel to plane GHF.

Two lines that do not lie in the same plane and do not intersect are called *skew lines*. Figure 9.5 illustrates many skew lines (for example, $\overleftrightarrow{AB}$ and $\overleftrightarrow{CD}$).

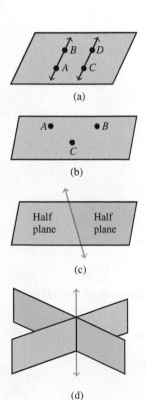

(a)

(b)

(c)

(d)

Figure 9.4

Figure 9.5

Angles

An *angle*, denoted ⦟, is the union of two rays with a common end point (Fig. 9.6):

$$\overrightarrow{BA} \cup \overrightarrow{BC} = \text{⦟}ABC \text{ (or ⦟}CBA)$$

An angle can be formed by the rotation of a ray about a point. An angle has an initial side and a terminal side. The initial side indicates the position of the ray prior to rotation; the terminal side indicates the position of the ray after rotation. The point common to both rays is called the *vertex* of the angle. The letter designating the vertex is always the middle one of the three letters designating an angle. The rays that make up the angle are called its *sides*.

There are several ways to name an angle. The angle in Fig. 9.6 may be denoted

$$\text{⦟}ABC, \qquad \text{⦟}CBA, \qquad \text{or} \qquad \text{⦟}B$$

An angle divides a plane into three distinct parts: the angle itself, its interior, and its exterior. In Fig. 9.6, the angle is represented by the blue lines, the interior of the angle is shaded pink, and the exterior is shaded green.

The *measure of an angle*, symbolized m, is the amount of rotation from its initial side to its terminal side. In Fig. 9.6, the letter x represents the measure of ⦟ABC; therefore, we may write $m\text{⦟}ABC = x$.

Angles can be measured in *degrees*, radians, or gradients. In this text, we will discuss only the degree unit of measurement. An angle of 45 degrees is written 45°. A *protractor* is used to measure angles. The angle shown being measured by the protractor in Fig. 9.7 is 50°.

Figure 9.6

Figure 9.7

Example 2 *Union and Intersection*

Refer to Fig. 9.8. Determine the following.

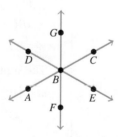

Figure 9.8

a) $\overrightarrow{BC} \cup \overrightarrow{BG}$ b) $\overrightarrow{AB} \cap \overrightarrow{CB}$ c) $\overrightarrow{BE} \cap \overrightarrow{BF}$ d) ⦟$DBG \cap$ ⦟ABD

Solution

a) $\overrightarrow{BC} \cup \overrightarrow{BG} = $ ⦟CBG or ⦟GBC b) $\overrightarrow{AB} \cap \overrightarrow{CB} = \overline{AC}$

c) $\overrightarrow{BE} \cap \overrightarrow{BF} = \{B\}$ d) ⦟$DBG \cap$ ⦟$ABD = \overrightarrow{BD}$

Figure 9.10

Consider a circle whose circumference is divided into 360 equal parts. If we draw a line from each mark on the circumference to the center of the circle, we get 360 wedge-shaped pieces. The measure of an angle formed by the straight sides of each wedge-shaped piece is defined to be $1°$.

Angles are classified by their degree measurement, as shown in the following summary. A *right angle* has a measure of $90°$, an *acute angle* has a measure less than $90°$, an *obtuse angle* has a measure greater than $90°$ but less than $180°$, and a *straight angle* has a measure of $180°$.

Right Angle	Acute Angle	Obtuse Angle	Straight Angle

$x = 90°$ $0° < x < 90°$ $90° < x < 180°$ $x = 180°$

The symbol ∟ is used to indicate right angles.

Two angles in the same plane are *adjacent angles* when they have a common vertex and a common side but no common interior points. In Fig. 9.9, $\angle DBC$ and $\angle CBA$ are adjacent angles, but $\angle DBA$ and $\angle CBA$ are not adjacent angles.

Two angles are called *complementary angles* if the sum of their measures is $90°$. Two angles are called *supplementary angles* if the sum of their measures is $180°$.

Figure 9.9

Example 3 *Determining Complementary and Supplementary Angles*

In Fig. 9.10, we see that $m\angle ABC = 28°$.

a) $\angle ABC$ and $\angle CBD$ are complementary angles. Determine $m\angle CBD$.

b) $\angle ABC$ and $\angle CBE$ are supplementary angles. Determine $m\angle CBE$.

Solution

a) The sum of two complementary angles must be $90°$, so

$$m\angle ABC + m\angle CBD = 90°$$
$$28° + m\angle CBD = 90°$$
$$m\angle CBD = 90° - 28° = 62°$$

Subtract 28° from each side of the equation.

b) The sum of two supplementary angles must be $180°$, so

$$m\angle ABC + m\angle CBE = 180°$$
$$28° + m\angle CBE = 180°$$
$$m\angle CBE = 180° - 28° = 152°$$

Subtract 28° from each side of the equation.

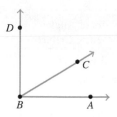

Figure 9.11

┌ Example **4** *Determining Complementary Angles*

If $\angle ABC$ and $\angle CBD$ are complementary angles and $m\angle ABC$ is 26° less than $m\angle CBD$, determine the measure of each angle (Fig. 9.11).

Solution Let $m\angle CBD = x$. Then $m\angle ABC = x - 26$ since it is 26° less than $m\angle CBD$. Because these angles are complementary, we have

$$m\angle CBD + m\angle ABC = 90°$$
$$x + (x - 26) = 90°$$
$$2x - 26 = 90°$$
$$2x = 116°$$
$$x = 58°$$

Therefore, $m\angle CBD = 58°$ and $m\angle ABC = 58° - 26°$, or 32°. Note that $58° + 32° = 90°$, which is what we expected. ■

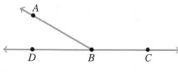

Figure 9.12

┌ Example **5** *Determining Supplementary Angles*

If $\angle ABC$ and $\angle ABD$ are supplementary and $m\angle ABC$ is five times larger than $m\angle ABD$, determine $m\angle ABC$ and $m\angle ABD$ (Fig. 9.12).

Solution Let $m\angle ABD = x$, then $m\angle ABC = 5x$. Since these angles are supplementary, we have

$$m\angle ABD + m\angle ABC = 180°$$
$$x + 5x = 180°$$
$$6x = 180°$$
$$x = 30°$$

Thus, $m\angle ABD = 30°$ and $m\angle ABC = 5(30°) = 150°$. Note that $30° + 150° = 180°$, which is what we expected. ■

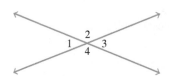

Figure 9.13

When two straight lines intersect, the nonadjacent angles formed are called *vertical angles*. In Fig. 9.13, $\angle 1$ and $\angle 3$ are vertical angles, and $\angle 2$ and $\angle 4$ are vertical angles. We can show that vertical angles have the same measure; that is, they are equal. For example, Fig. 9.13 shows that

$$m\angle 1 + m\angle 2 = 180°. \qquad \text{Why?}$$
$$m\angle 2 + m\angle 3 = 180°. \qquad \text{Why?}$$

Since $\angle 2$ has the same measure in both cases, $m\angle 1$ must equal $m\angle 3$.

Vertical Angles
Vertical angles have the same measure.

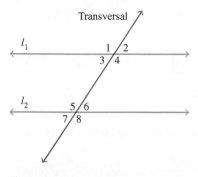

Figure 9.14

A line that intersects two different lines, l_1 and l_2, at two different points is called a *transversal*. Figure 9.14 illustrates that when two parallel lines are cut by a transversal, eight angles are formed. Angles 3, 4, 5, and 6 are called *interior angles*, and angles 1, 2, 7, and 8 are called *exterior angles*. Eight pairs of supplementary angles are formed. Can you list them?

Special names are given to the angles formed by a transversal crossing two parallel lines. We describe these angles on page 486.

Name	Description	Illustration	Pairs of Angles Meeting Criteria
Alternate interior angles	Interior angles on opposite sides of the transversal		∡3 and ∡6 ∡4 and ∡5
Alternate exterior angles	Exterior angles on opposite sides of the transversal		∡1 and ∡8 ∡2 and ∡7
Corresponding angles	One interior and one exterior angle on the same side of the transversal		∡1 and ∡5 ∡2 and ∡6 ∡3 and ∡7 ∡4 and ∡8

Parallel Lines Cut by a Transversal

When two parallel lines are cut by a transversal,
1. alternate interior angles have the same measure.
2. alternate exterior angles have the same measure.
3. corresponding angles have the same measure.

Example 6 *Determining Angle Measures*

Figure 9.15 shows two parallel lines cut by a transversal. Determine the measure of ∡1 through ∡7.

Figure 9.15

Solution

$m∡6 = 49°$	∡8 and ∡6 are vertical angles.
$m∡5 = 131°$	∡8 and ∡5 are supplementary angles.
$m∡7 = 131°$	∡5 and ∡7 are vertical angles.
$m∡1 = 131°$	∡1 and ∡7 are alternate exterior angles.
$m∡4 = 49°$	∡4 and ∡6 are alternate interior angles.
$m∡2 = 49°$	∡6 and ∡2 are corresponding angles.
$m∡3 = 131°$	∡3 and ∡1 are vertical angles.

In Example 6, the angles could have been determined in alternate ways. For example, we mentioned $m∡1 = 131°$ because ∡1 and ∡7 are alternate exterior angles. We could have also stated that $m∡1 = 131°$ because ∡1 and ∡5 are corresponding angles.

SECTION 9.1   *Exercises*

Warm Up Exercises

In Exercises 1–12, fill in the blanks with an appropriate word, phrase, or symbol(s).

1. Two lines in the same plane that do not intersect are called _____ lines.

2. Two lines that do not lie in the same plane and do not intersect are called _____ lines.

3. The union of two rays with a common endpoint is called a(n) _____.

4. Two angles, the sum of whose measures is 90°, are called _____ angles.

5. Two angles, the sum of whose measures is 180°, are called _____ angles.

6. Two angles in the same plane that have a common vertex and a common side, but no common interior points, are called _____ angles.

7. An angle whose measure is 180° is called a(n) _____ angle.

8. An angle whose measure is 90° is called a(n) _____ angle.

9. An angle whose measure is greater than 90° but less than 180° is called a(n) _____ angle.

10. An angle whose measure is less than 90° is called a(n) _____ angle.

11. When two straight lines intersect, the nonadjacent angles formed are called _____ angles.

12. A line that intersects two different lines at two different points is called a(n) _____.

Practice the Skills

In Exercises 13–20, identify the figure as a line, half line, ray, line segment, open line segment, or half open line segment. Denote the figure by its appropriate symbol.

13.

14.

15.

16.

17.

18.

19.

20.

In Exercises 21–32, use the figure to find the following:

21. $\overrightarrow{AB} \cap \overrightarrow{DC}$

22. $\overset{\circ}{FE} \cup \overrightarrow{FG}$

23. $\overline{BC} \cup \overset{\circ}{CD}$

24. $\overline{AB} \cup \overline{BD}$

25. $\angle ICA \cap \overleftrightarrow{EG}$

26. $\angle IFG \cap \angle EFH$

27. $\overset{\circ}{AB} \cap \overline{HC}$

28. $\overset{\circ}{BD} \cap \overset{\circ}{CB}$

29. $\overrightarrow{BC} \cup \overrightarrow{BF}$

30. $\overline{BC} \cup \overline{CF} \cup \overline{FB}$

31. $\overset{\circ}{BD} \cup \overset{\circ}{CB}$

32. $\{C\} \cap \overset{\circ}{CH}$

In Exercises 33–44, use the figure to find the following.

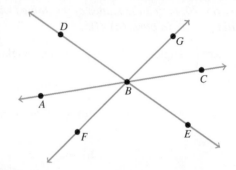

33. $\overrightarrow{DB} \cup \overrightarrow{EB}$

34. $\angle ABD \cap \angle CBG$

35. $\angle GBC \cap \angle CBE$

36. $\overleftrightarrow{DE} \cup \overleftrightarrow{BE}$

37. $\angle ABE \cup \overset{\circ}{AB}$

38. $\overset{\circ}{BF} \cup \overline{BE}$

39. $\overrightarrow{FG} \cap \overrightarrow{BF}$

40. $\overline{BE} \cup \overline{BD}$

41. $\overset{\circ}{AC} \cap \overline{AC}$

42. $\overset{\circ}{AC} \cap \overset{\circ}{BE}$

43. $\overrightarrow{EB} \cap \overline{BE}{}^{\circ}$

44. $\overline{FB} \cup \overline{BG}$

In Exercises 45–52, classify the angle as acute, right, straight, obtuse, or none of these angles.

45.

46.

47.

48.

49.

50.

51.

52.

In Exercises 53–58, find the complementary angle of the given angle.

53. 10°

54. 15°

55. $32\frac{3}{4}°$

56. $31\frac{2}{5}°$

57. 64.7°

58. 0.01°

In Exercises 59–64, find the supplementary angle of the given angle.

59. 80°   **60.** 150°

61. 20.5°   **62.** 148.7°

63. $43\frac{5}{7}$°   **64.** $64\frac{7}{16}$°

In Exercises 65–70, match the names of the angles with the corresponding figure in parts (a)–(f).

65. Complementary angles   **66.** Supplementary angles

67. Vertical angles   **68.** Corresponding angles

69. Alternate exterior angles   **70.** Alternate interior angles

a)

b)

c)

d)

e)

f)

Problem Solving

71. MODELING - *Complementary Angles* If $\angle 1$ and $\angle 2$ are complementary angles and if the measure of $\angle 1$ is five times the measure of $\angle 2$, determine the measures of $\angle 1$ and $\angle 2$.

72. MODELING - *Complementary Angles* The difference between the measures of two complementary angles is 22°. Determine the measures of the two angles.

73. MODELING - *Supplementary Angles* The difference between the measures of two supplementary angles is 88°. Determine the measures of the two angles.

74. MODELING - *Supplementary Angles* If $\angle 1$ and $\angle 2$ are supplementary angles and if the measure of $\angle 2$ is 17 times the measure of $\angle 1$, determine the measures of the two angles.

In Exercises 75–78, parallel lines are cut by the transversal shown. Determine the measures of $\angle 1$ through $\angle 7$.

75.

76.

77.

78.

In Exercises 79–82, the angles are complementary angles. Determine the measures of $\angle 1$ and $\angle 2$.

79.

80.

81.

82.

In Exercises 83–86, the angles are supplementary angles. Determine the measures of $\angle 1$ and $\angle 2$.

83.

84.

85.

86.

The figure below suggests a number of lines and planes. The lines may be described by naming two points, and the planes may be described by naming three points. In Exercises 87–94, use the figure to name the following.

87. Two parallel planes

88. Two parallel lines

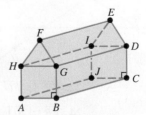

89. Two lines that intersect at right angles

90. Two planes that intersect at right angles

91. Three planes whose intersection is a single point

92. Three planes whose intersection is a line

93. A line and a plane whose intersection is a point

94. A line and a plane whose intersection is a line

Concept/Writing Exercises

95. a) What are the four key parts in the axiomatic method used by Euclid?

   b) Discuss each of the four parts.

96. What is the difference between an axiom and a theorem?

97. a) How many lines can be drawn through a given point?

   b) How many planes can be drawn through a given point?

98. What is the intersection of two distinct nonparallel planes?

99. How many planes can be drawn through a given line?

100. a) Will three noncollinear points *A*, *B*, and *C* always determine a plane? Explain.

   b) Is it possible to determine more than one plane with three noncollinear points? Explain.

   c) How many planes can be constructed through three collinear points?

In Exercises 101–106, determine whether the statement is always true, sometimes true, or never true. Explain your answer.

101. Two lines that are both parallel to a third line must be parallel to each other.

102. A triangle contains exactly two acute angles.

103. Vertical angles are complementary angles.

104. Alternate exterior angles are supplementary angles.

105. Alternate interior angles are complementary angles.

106. A triangle contains two obtuse angles.

Challenge Problems/Group Activities

107. Use a straightedge and a compass to construct a triangle with sides of equal length (an equilateral triangle) by doing the following:

   a) Use the straightedge to draw a line segment of any length and label the end points *A* and *B* (Fig. a).

b) Place one end of the compass at point *A* and the other end at point *B* and draw an arc as shown (Fig. b).

c) Now turn the compass around and draw another arc as shown. Label the point of intersection of the two arcs *C* (Fig. c).

d) Draw line segments *AC* and *BC*. This completes the construction of equilateral triangle *ABC* (Fig. d).

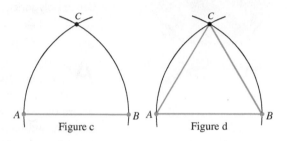

Figure a   Figure b

Figure c   Figure d

108. If lines *l* and *m* are parallel lines and if lines *l* and *n* are skew lines, is it true that lines *m* and *n* must also be skew? (*Hint:* Look at Fig. 9.5 on page 482.) Explain your answer and include a sketch to support your answer.

109. Two lines are *perpendicular* if they intersect at right angles. If lines *l* and *m* are perpendicular and if lines *m* and *n* are perpendicular, is it true that lines *l* and *n* must also be perpendicular? Explain your answer and include a sketch to support your answer.

110. Suppose you have three distinct lines, all lying in the same plane. Find all the possible ways in which the three lines can be related. Sketch each case (four cases).

111. If two straight lines intersect at a point, determine the sum of the measures of the 4 angles formed.

112. $\angle ABC$ and $\angle CBD$ are complementary and $m\angle CBD$ is twice the $m\angle ABC$. $\angle ABD$ and $\angle DBE$ are supplementary angles.

   a) Draw a sketch illustrating $\angle ABC$, $\angle CBD$, and $\angle DBE$.

   b) Determine $m\angle ABC$.

   c) Determine $m\angle CBD$.

   d) Determine $m\angle DBE$.

Internet/Research Activities

113. Using the Internet and other sources, write a research paper on Euclid's contributions to geometry.

114. Using the Internet and other sources, write a research paper on the three classic geometry problems of Greek antiquity (see the *Did You Know?* on page 484).

115. Search the Internet or other sources such as a geometry textbook to study the geometric constructions that use a straightedge and a compass only. Prepare a poster demonstrating five of these basic constructions.

SECTION 9.2   Polygons

▲ *The shapes of these road signs are examples of polygons.*

What shape would you use to best describe the following road signs: a stop sign, a yield sign, a speed limit sign? In this section, we will study the shapes of these and other geometric figures that can be classified as *polygons*.

Why *This is Important* Polygons appear in many aspects of our daily lives. The properties of polygons can be used in many problem-solving applications.

A *polygon* is a closed figure in a plane determined by three or more straight line segments. Examples of polygons are given in Fig. 9.16.

The straight line segments that form the polygon are called its *sides*, and a point where two sides meet is called a *vertex* (plural, *vertices*). The union of the sides of a polygon and its interior is called a *polygonal region*. A *regular polygon* is one whose sides are all the same length and whose interior angles all have the same measure. Figures 9.16(b) and (d) are regular polygons.

(a)   (b)   (c)   (d)

Figure 9.16

Polygons are named according to their number of sides. The names of some polygons are given in Table 9.1.

Table 9.1

Number of Sides	Name	Number of Sides	Name
3	Triangle	8	Octagon
4	Quadrilateral	9	Nonagon
5	Pentagon	10	Decagon
6	Hexagon	12	Dodecagon
7	Heptagon	20	Icosagon

One of the most important polygons is the triangle. The sum of the measures of the interior angles of a triangle is 180°. To illustrate, consider triangle *ABC* given in Fig. 9.17. The triangle is formed by drawing two transversals through two parallel lines l_1 and l_2 with the two transversals intersecting at a point on l_1.

Figure 9.17

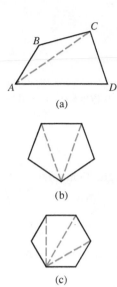

(a)

(b)

(c)

Figure 9.18

In Fig. 9.17, notice that $\angle A$ and $\angle A'$ are corresponding angles. Recall from Section 9.1 that corresponding angles are equal, so $m\angle A = m\angle A'$. Also, $\angle C$ and $\angle C'$ are corresponding angles; therefore, $m\angle C = m\angle C'$. Next, we notice that $\angle B$ and $\angle B'$ are vertical angles. In Section 9.1, we learned that vertical angles are equal; therefore, $m\angle B = m\angle B'$. Figure 9.17 shows that $\angle A'$, $\angle B'$, and $\angle C'$ form a straight angle; therefore, $m\angle A' + m\angle B' + m\angle C' = 180°$. Since $m\angle A = m\angle A'$, $m\angle B = m\angle B'$, and $m\angle C = m\angle C'$, we can reason that $m\angle A + m\angle B + m\angle C = 180°$. This example illustrates that the sum of the interior angles of a triangle is $180°$.

Consider the quadrilateral $ABCD$ (Fig. 9.18a). Drawing a straight line segment between any two vertices forms two triangles. Since the sum of the measures of the angles of a triangle is $180°$, the sum of the measures of the interior angles of a quadrilateral is $2 \cdot 180°$, or $360°$.

Now let's examine a pentagon (Fig. 9.18b). We can draw two straight line segments to form three triangles. Thus, the sum of the measures of the interior angles of a five-sided figure is $3 \cdot 180°$, or $540°$. Figure 9.18(c) shows that four triangles can be drawn in a six-sided figure. Table 9.2 summarizes this information.

Table 9.2

Sides	Triangles	Sum of the Measures of the Interior Angles
3	1	$1(180°) = 180°$
4	2	$2(180°) = 360°$
5	3	$3(180°) = 540°$
6	4	$4(180°) = 720°$

If we continue this procedure, we can see that for an n-sided polygon the sum of the measures of the interior angles is $(n - 2)180°$.

Sum of the Measures of Interior Angles

The **sum** of the measures of the interior angles of an n-sided polygon is $(n - 2)180°$.

Figure 9.19

Example 1   *Angles of a Hexagon*

The surfaces of the heads of many bolts are in the shape of regular hexagons. A regular hexagon is a six-sided figure with all the sides the same length and all interior angles with the same measure. See Fig. 9.19. Determine

a) the measure of an interior angle.

b) the measure of exterior $\angle 1$.

Solution

a) Using the formula $(n - 2)180°$, we can determine the sum of the measures of the interior angles of a hexagon as follows.

$$\begin{aligned} \text{Sum} &= (6 - 2)180° \\ &= 4(180°) \\ &= 720° \end{aligned}$$

The measure of an interior angle of a regular polygon can be determined by dividing the sum of the interior angles by the number of angles.

The measure of an interior angle of a regular hexagon is determined as follows:

$$\text{Measure} = \frac{720°}{6} = 120°$$

b) Since $\measuredangle 1$ is the supplement of an interior angle,

$$m\measuredangle 1 = 180° - 120° = 60°$$

To discuss area in the next section, we must be able to identify various types of triangles and quadrilaterals. The following is a summary of certain types of triangles and their characteristics.

Triangles

Acute Triangle

All angles are acute angles.

Obtuse Triangle

One angle is obtuse.

Right Triangle

One angle is a right angle.

Isosceles Triangle

Two equal sides
Two equal angles

Equilateral Triangle

Three equal sides
Three equal angles
(60° each)

Scalene Triangle

No two sides are equal in length.

Similar Figures

In everyday living, we often have to deal with geometric figures that have the "same shape" but are of different sizes. For example, an architect will make a small-scale drawing of a floor plan or a photographer will make an enlargement of a photograph. Figures that have the same shape but may be of different sizes are called *similar figures*. Two similar figures are illustrated in Fig. 9.20.

Similar figures have *corresponding angles* and *corresponding sides*. In Fig. 9.20, triangle *ABC* has angles *A*, *B*, and *C*. Their respective corresponding angles in triangle *DEF* are angles *D*, *E*, and *F*. Sides $\overline{AB}$, $\overline{BC}$, and $\overline{AC}$ in triangle *ABC* have corresponding sides $\overline{DE}$, $\overline{EF}$, and $\overline{DF}$, respectively, in triangle *DEF*.

Definition: Similar Figures
Two figures are **similar** if their corresponding angles have the same measure and the lengths of their corresponding sides are in proportion.

In Figure 9.20, $\measuredangle A$ and $\measuredangle D$ have the same measure, $\measuredangle B$ and $\measuredangle E$ have the same measure, and $\measuredangle C$ and $\measuredangle F$ have the same measure. Also, the lengths of corresponding sides of similar triangles are in proportion.

When we refer to the line segment *AB*, we place a line over the *AB* and write $\overline{AB}$. **When we refer to the *length* of a line segment, we do not place a bar above the two letters**. For example, if we write $AB = 12$, we are indicating the length of line segment $\overline{AB}$ is 12. The proportion below shows that the lengths of the corresponding sides of the similar triangles in Fig. 9.20 are in proportion.

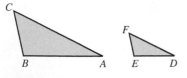

Figure 9.20

$$\frac{AB}{DE} = \frac{BC}{EF} = \frac{AC}{DF}$$

The molecular structure of C_{60} resembles the patterns found on a soccer ball.

Buckminsterfullerenes, known as buckyballs, are a class of pure carbon molecules. Along with graphite and diamond, buckyballs are the only naturally occurring forms of pure carbon. Named after American architect–engineer F. Buckminster Fuller, who designed hemispherical geodesic domes from hexagonal and pentagonal faces, fullerenes are the most spherical molecules known. Discovered in 1985 at Rice University, buckyballs are used primarily as microscopic lubricant and have potential applications in molecular medical engineering, electrical superconductivity, and computer chip design. The most common form of buckminsterfullerene contains 60 carbon atoms and has the chemical symbol C_{60}. The molecular structure of C_{60} contains 12 pentagons and 20 hexagons arranged in a pattern similar to that found on a soccer ball.

Example 2 *Similar Figures*

Consider the similar figures in Fig. 9.21.

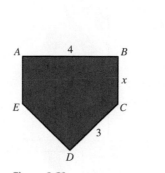

Figure 9.21

Determine

a) the length of side $\overline{BC}$. b) the length of side $\overline{PQ}$.

Solution

a) We will represent the length of side $\overline{BC}$ with the variable x. Because the corresponding sides of similar figures must be in proportion, we can write a proportion (as explained in Section 6.2) to determine the length of side $\overline{BC}$. Corresponding sides $\overline{CD}$ and $\overline{RS}$ are known, so we use them as one ratio in the proportion. The side corresponding to $\overline{BC}$ is $\overline{QR}$.

$$\frac{BC}{QR} = \frac{CD}{RS}$$

$$\frac{x}{3} = \frac{3}{4.5}$$

Now we solve for x.

$$x \cdot 4.5 = 3 \cdot 3$$
$$4.5x = 9$$
$$x = 2$$

Thus, the length of side $\overline{BC}$ is 2 units.

b) We will represent the length of side $\overline{PQ}$ with the variable y. The side corresponding to $\overline{PQ}$ is $\overline{AB}$. We will work part (b) in a manner similar to part (a).

$$\frac{PQ}{AB} = \frac{RS}{CD}$$

$$\frac{y}{4} = \frac{4.5}{3}$$

$$y \cdot 3 = 4 \cdot 4.5$$
$$3y = 18$$
$$y = 6$$

Thus, the length of side $\overline{PQ}$ is 6 units. ∎

Example 3 *Using Similar Triangles to Find the Height of a Tree*

Monique Currie plans to remove a tree from her backyard. She needs to know the height of the tree. Monique is 6 ft tall and determines that when her shadow is 9 ft long, the shadow of the tree is 45 ft long (see Fig. 9.22 on page 494). How tall is the tree?

Figure 9.22

Solution We will let *x* represent the height of the tree. From Fig. 9.22, we can see that the triangle formed by the sun's rays, Monique, and her shadow is similar to the triangle formed by the sun's rays, the tree, and its shadow. To find the height of the tree, we will set up and solve the following proportion:

$$\frac{\text{height of the tree}}{\text{height of Monique}} = \frac{\text{length of tree's shadow}}{\text{length of Monique's shadow}}$$

$$\frac{x}{6} = \frac{45}{9}$$

$$9x = 270$$

$$x = 30$$

Therefore, the tree is 30 ft tall. ∎

Congruent Figures

If the corresponding sides of two similar figures are the same length, the figures are called *congruent figures*. Corresponding angles of congruent figures have the same measure, and the corresponding sides are equal in length. Two congruent figures coincide when placed one upon the other.

Example 4 *Congruent Triangles*

Triangles *ABC* and *A′B′C′* in Fig. 9.23 are congruent. Determine
a) the length of side *A′C′*.   b) the length of side $\overline{AB}$.
c) $m\angle C'A'B'$.   d) $m\angle ACB$.
e) $m\angle ABC$.

Figure 9.23

Solution Because $\triangle ABC$ is congruent to $\triangle A'B'C'$, we know that the corresponding side lengths are equal and corresponding angle measures are equal.
a) $A'C' = AC = 13$ b) $AB = A'B' = 10.6$
c) $m\angle C'A'B' = m\angle CAB = 60°$ d) $m\angle ACB = m\angle A'C'B' = 50°$
e) The sum of the angles of a triangle is 180°. Since $m\angle BAC = 60°$ and $m\angle ACB = 50°$, $m\angle ABC = 180° - 60° - 50° = 70°$. ∎

Earlier we learned that *quadrilaterals* are four-sided polygons, the sum of whose interior angles is 360°. Quadrilaterals may be classified according to their characteristics, as illustrated in the summary box on page 495.

Quadrilaterals

Trapezoid

Two sides are parallel.

Parallelogram

Both pairs of opposite sides are parallel. Both pairs of opposite sides are equal in length.

Rhombus

Both pairs of opposite sides are parallel. The four sides are equal in length.

Rectangle

Both pairs of opposite sides are parallel. Both pairs of opposite sides are equal in length. The angles are right angles.

Square

Both pairs of opposite sides are parallel. The four sides are equal in length. The angles are right angles.

Figure 9.24

Example 5 *Angles of a Trapezoid*

Trapezoid *ABCD* is shown in Fig. 9.24.

a) Determine the measure of the interior angle, *x*.
b) Determine the measure of the exterior angle, *y*.

Solution

a) We know that each of the two right angles in trapezoid *ABCD* has a measure of 90°. We also know that the sum of the interior angles in any quadrilateral is 360°. Therefore, we have

$$m\angle DAB + m\angle ABC + m\angle BCD + m\angle x = 360°$$
$$130° + 90° + 90° + m\angle x = 360°$$
$$310° + m\angle x = 360°$$
$$m\angle x = 50°$$

Thus, the measure of the interior angle, *x*, is 50°.

b) Angle *x* and angle *y* are supplementary angles. Therefore, $m\angle x + m\angle y = 180°$ and $m\angle y = 180° - m\angle x = 180° - 50° = 130°$. Thus, the measure of the exterior angle, *y*, is 130°.

Note that in Example 5 part (b) we could also have determined the measure of angle *y* as follows. By the definition of a trapezoid, sides $\overline{AB}$ and $\overline{CD}$ must be parallel. Therefore, side $\overline{AD}$ may be considered a transversal and $\angle BAD$ and $\angle ADE$ are alternate interior angles. Recall from Section 9.1 that alternate interior angles are equal. Thus, $m\angle BAD = m\angle ADE$ and $m\angle y = 130°$.

SECTION 9.2   *Exercises*

Warm Up Exercises

In Exercises 1–6, fill in the blanks with an appropriate word, phrase, or symbol(s).

1. A closed figure in a plane determined by three or more straight line segments is called a(n) _____.

2. A polygon whose sides are all the same length and whose interior angles all have the same measure is called a(n) _____ polygon.

3. Two polygons are similar if their corresponding angles have the same measure and the lengths of their corresponding sides are in _____.

4. The sum of the measures of the interior angles of a triangle is _____.

5. If the corresponding sides of two similar figures are the same length, the figures are called _____ figures.

6. The sum of the measures of the interior angles of a quadrilateral is _____.

In Exercises 7–14, (a) name the polygon. If the polygon is a quadrilateral, give its specific name. (b) State whether or not the polygon is a regular polygon.

7.

8.

9.

10.

11.

12.

13.

14.

In Exercises 15–22, identify the triangle as (a) scalene, isosceles, or equilateral and as (b) acute, obtuse, or right. The

parallel markings (the two small parallel lines) on two or more sides indicate that the marked sides are of equal length.

15.

16.

17.

18.

19.

20.

21.

22.

In Exercises 23–28, identify the quadrilateral.

23.

24.

25.

26.

27.

28.

In Exercises 29–32, find the measure of $\angle x$.

29.

30.

31.

32.

In Exercises 33–34, lines l_1 and l_2 are parallel. Determine the measures of ∡1 through ∡12.

33.   **34.**

In Exercises 35–40, determine the sum of the measures of the interior angles of the indicated polygon.

35. Pentagon   **36.** Heptagon   **37.** Nonagon

38. Decagon   **39.** Icosagon   **40.** Dodecagon

In Exercises 41–46, (a) determine the measure of an interior angle of the named regular polygon. (b) If a side of the polygon is extended, determine the supplementary angle of an interior angle. See Example 1.

41. Triangle   **42.** Quadrilateral

43. Octagon   **44.** Nonagon

45. Decagon   **46.** Icosagon

In Exercises 47–52, the figures are similar. Find the length of side x and side y.

47.

48.

49.

50.

51.

52.

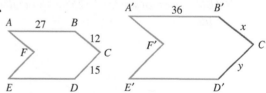

In Exercises 53–56, triangles ABC and DEC are similar figures. Determine the length of

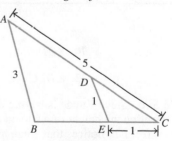

53. side $\overline{BC}$.   **54.** side $\overline{DC}$.

55. side $\overline{AD}$.   **56.** side $\overline{BE}$.

In Exercises 57–62, find the length of the sides and the measures of the angles for the congruent triangles ABC and A′B′C′.

57. The length of side $\overline{AC}$ **58.** The length of side $\overline{A'B'}$

59. The length of side $\overline{B'C'}$ **60.** $\angle B'A'C'$

61. $\angle ACB$ **62.** $\angle ABC$

In Exercises 63–68, determine the length of the sides and the measures of the angles for the congruent quadrilaterals ABCD and A′B′C′D′.

63. The length of side $\overline{AD}$ **64.** The length of side $\overline{B'C'}$

65. The length of side $\overline{A'B'}$ **66.** $\angle BCD$

67. $\angle A'D'C'$ **68.** $\angle DAB$

Problem Solving

In Exercises 69–72, determine the measure of the angle. In the figure, $\angle ABC$ makes an angle of 125° with the floor and l_1 and l_2 are parallel.

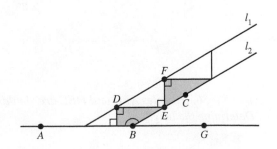

69. $\angle GBC$ **70.** $\angle EDF$

71. $\angle DFE$ **72.** $\angle DEC$

73. *Height of a Silo*   Steve Runde is buying a farm and needs to determine the height of a silo on the farm. Steve, who is 6 ft tall, notices that when his shadow is 9 ft long, the shadow of the silo is 105 ft long (see diagram above and to the right). How tall is the silo? Note that the diagram is not to scale.

74. *Angles on a Picnic Table*   The legs of a picnic table form an isosceles triangle as indicated in the figure. If $\angle ABC = 80°$, determine $m\angle x$ and $m\angle y$ so that the top of the table will be parallel to the ground.

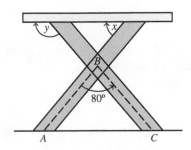

75. *Distances in Minnesota*   A triangle can be formed by drawing line segments on a map of Minnesota connecting the cities of Austin, Rochester, and St. Paul (see figure below). If the actual distance from Austin to Rochester is approximately 44 miles, use the lengths of the line segments indicated in the figure along with similar triangles to approximate

a) the actual distance from St. Paul to Austin.

b) the actual distance from St. Paul to Rochester.

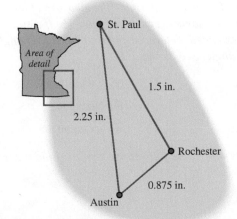

76. *Distances in Illinois*   A triangle can be formed by drawing line segments on a map of Illinois connecting the cities of Rockford, Chicago, and Bloomington (see figure below). If the actual distance from Chicago to Rockford is approximately 90 miles, use the lengths of the line segments indicated in the figure along with similar triangles to approximate

a) the actual distance from Chicago to Bloomington.

b) the actual distance from Bloomington to Rockford.

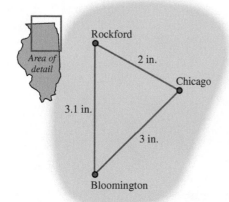

Concept/Writing Exercises

77. List six different types of triangles and in your own words describe the characteristics of each.

78. List five different types of quadrilaterals and in your own words describe the characteristics of each.

Challenge Problems/Group Activities

Scaling Factor   In Exercises 79 and 80 we use a scaling factor. Examine the similar triangles ABC and A'B'C' in the figure below.

*If we calculate the ratios $\dfrac{AB}{A'B'}$, $\dfrac{BC}{B'C'}$, and $\dfrac{CA}{C'A'}$, we see that each of these ratios is equal to 2. We call this common ratio the **scaling factor** of $\triangle ABC$ with respect to $\triangle A'B'C'$. If we calculate the reciprocal ratios $\dfrac{A'B'}{AB}$, $\dfrac{B'C'}{BC}$, and $\dfrac{C'A'}{CA}$, we see that each of these ratios is equal to $\frac{1}{2}$. We call this common ratio the scaling factor of $\triangle A'B'C'$ with respect to $\triangle ABC$. Every pair of similar figures has two*

scaling factors that show the relationship between the corresponding side lengths. Notice that the length of each side of $\triangle ABC$ is two times the length of the corresponding side in $\triangle A'B'C'$. We can also state that the length of each side of $\triangle A'B'C'$ is one-half the length of the corresponding side of $\triangle ABC$.

79. In the figure, $\triangle DEF$ is similar to $\triangle D'E'F'$. The length of the sides of $\triangle DEF$ is shown in the figure. If the scaling factor of $\triangle DEF$ with respect to $\triangle D'E'F'$ is 3, determine the length of the sides of triangle $\triangle D'E'F'$.

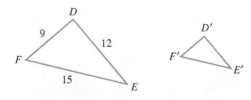

80. In the figure, quadrilateral $EFGH$ is similar to quadrilateral $E'F'G'H'$. The length of the sides of quadrilateral $EFGH$ is shown in the figure. If the scaling factor of quadrilateral $E'F'G'H'$ with respect to quadrilateral $EFGH$ is $\frac{1}{3}$, determine the length of the sides of quadrilateral $E'F'G'H'$.

81. *Height of a Wall*   You are asked to measure the height of an inside wall of a warehouse. No ladder tall enough to measure the height is available. You borrow a mirror from a salesclerk and place it on the floor. You then move away from the mirror until you can see the reflection of the top of the wall in it, as shown in the figure.

a) Explain why triangle HFM is similar to triangle TBM. (*Hint:* In the reflection of light the angle of incidence, $\angle HMF$, equals the angle of *reflection*, $\angle TMB$. Thus, $\angle HMF = \angle TMB$.)

b) If your eyes are $5\frac{1}{2}$ ft above the floor and you are $2\frac{1}{2}$ ft from the mirror and the mirror is 20 ft from the wall, how high is the wall?

Recreational Mathematics

82. *Distance Across a Lake*

a) In the figure, $m\angle CED = m\angle ABC$. Explain why triangles *ABC* and *DEC* must be similar.

b) Determine the distance across the lake, *DE*.

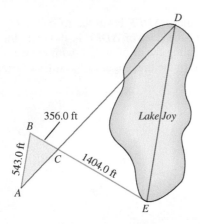

Internet/Research Activities

83. Using the Internet and history of mathematics texts, write a paper on the history and use of the theodolite, a surveying instrument.

84. Using the Internet and other sources, write a paper on the use of geometry in the photographic process. Include discussions on the use of similar figures.

SECTION 9.3 Perimeter and Area

▲ *We will study the perimeter and area of rectangles, such as those on which volleyball games are played.*

If you were to walk around the outside edge of a volleyball court, how far would you walk? If you had to place floor tiles that each measured 1 foot by 1 foot on a basketball court, how many tiles would you need? In this section, we will study the geometric concepts of perimeter and area that are used to answer these and other questions.

Why *This is Important* The concepts of area and perimeter are involved in many real-life applications of geometry. These include calculating the cost of flooring for your home, calculating the amount of fencing needed for your yard, and determining the best value when purchasing pizza!

Perimeter and Area

The *perimeter*, *P*, of a two-dimensional figure is the sum of the lengths of the sides of the figure. In Figs. 9.25 and 9.26, the sums of the lengths of the red line segments are the perimeters. Perimeters are measured in the same units as the sides. For example, if the sides of a figure are measured in feet, the perimeter will be measured in feet.

The *area*, *A*, is the region within the boundaries of the figure. The blue color in Figs. 9.25 and 9.26 indicates the areas of the figures. Area is measured in square units. For example, if the sides of a figure are measured in inches, the area of the

Figure 9.25   **Figure 9.26**

figure will be measured in square inches (in.^{2}). (See Table 8.7 on page 465 for common units of area in the U.S. customary and metric systems.)

Consider the rectangle in Fig. 9.26 on page 500. Two sides of the rectangle have length l, and two sides of the rectangle have width w. Thus, if we add the lengths of the four sides to get the perimeter, we find $P = l + w + l + w = 2l + 2w$.

Perimeter of a Rectangle

$$P = 2l + 2w$$

Figure 9.27

Consider a rectangle of length 5 units and width 3 units (Fig. 9.27). Counting the number of 1-unit by 1-unit squares within the figure, we obtain the area of the rectangle, 15 square units. The area can also be obtained by multiplying the number of units of length by the number of units of width, or 5 units $\times$ 3 units $=$ 15 square units. We can find the area of a rectangle by the formula area $=$ length $\times$ width.

Area of a Rectangle

$$A = l \times w$$

Using the formula for the area of a rectangle, we can determine the formulas for the areas of other figures.

A square (Fig. 9.28) is a rectangle that contains four equal sides. Therefore, the length equals the width. If we call both the length and the width of the square s, then

$$A = l \times w, \quad \text{so} \quad A = s \times s = s^2$$

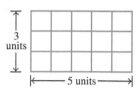

Figure 9.28

Area of a Square

$$A = s^2$$

A parallelogram with height h and base b is shown in Fig. 9.29(a).

 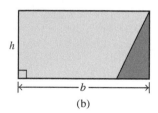

(a)   (b)

Figure 9.29

If we were to cut off the red portion of the parallelogram on the left, Fig. 9.29(a), and attach it to the right side of the figure, the resulting figure would be a rectangle, Fig. 9.29(b). Since the area of the rectangle is $b \times h$, the area of the parallelogram is also $b \times h$.

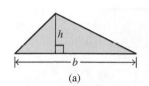

(a)

Area of a Parallelogram

$$A = b \times h$$

(b)

Figure 9.30

Consider the triangle with height, h, and base, b, shown in Fig. 9.30(a). Using this triangle and a second identical triangle, we can construct a parallelogram, Fig. 9.30(b). The area of the parallelogram is bh. The area of the triangle is one-half that of the parallelogram. Therefore, the area of the triangle is $\frac{1}{2} \times$ base $\times$ height.

Area of a Triangle

$$A = \tfrac{1}{2}bh$$

Now consider the trapezoid shown in Fig. 9.31(a). We can partition the trapezoid into two triangles by drawing diagonal $\overline{DB}$, as in Fig. 9.31(b). One triangle has base $\overline{AB}$ (called b_2) with height $\overline{DE}$, and the other triangle has base $\overline{DC}$ (called b_1) with height $\overline{FB}$. Note that the line used to measure the height of the triangle need not be inside the triangle. Because heights $\overline{DE}$ and $\overline{FB}$ are equal, both triangles have the same height, h. The area of triangles DCB and ADB are $\tfrac{1}{2}b_1 h$ and $\tfrac{1}{2}b_2 h$, respectively. The area of the trapezoid is the sum of the areas of the triangles, $\tfrac{1}{2}b_1 h + \tfrac{1}{2}b_2 h$, which can be written $\tfrac{1}{2}h(b_1 + b_2)$.

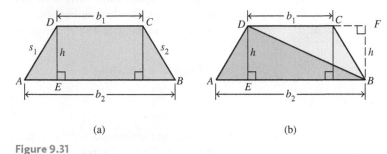

(a)   (b)

Figure 9.31

Area of a Trapezoid

$$A = \tfrac{1}{2}h(b_1 + b_2)$$

Following is a summary of the perimeters and areas of selected figures.

Perimeters and Areas

Triangle

$P = s_1 + s_2 + s_3 \ (s_3 = b)$
$A = \tfrac{1}{2}bh$

Square

$P = 4s$
$A = s^2$

Rectangle

$P = 2l + 2w$
$A = lw$

Parallelogram

$P = 2b + 2w$
$A = bh$

Trapezoid

$P = s_1 + s_2 + b_1 + b_2$
$A = \tfrac{1}{2}h(b_1 + b_2)$

Example 1 Sodding a Lacrosse Field

Rob Marshall wishes to replace the grass (sod) on a lacrosse field. One pallet of Bethel Farms sod costs $175 and covers 450 square feet. If the area to be covered is a rectangle with a length of 330 feet and a width of 270 feet, determine

a) the area to be covered with sod.

b) how many pallets of sod Rob needs to purchase.

c) the cost of the sod purchased.

Solution

a) The area to be covered is

$$A = l \cdot w = 330 \cdot 270 = 89{,}100 \text{ ft}^2$$

The area to be covered is in square feet because both the length and the width are measured in feet.

b) To determine the number of pallets of sod Rob needs, divide the area to be covered by the area covered by one pallet of sod.

$$\frac{\text{Area to be covered}}{\text{Area covered by one pallet}} = \frac{89{,}100}{450} = 198$$

Rob needs 198 pallets of sod.

c) The cost of 198 pallets of sod is 198 × $175, or $34,650. ∎

Pythagorean Theorem

We introduced the Pythagorean theorem in Chapter 5. Because this theorem is an important tool for finding the perimeter and area of triangles, we restate it here.

Pythagorean Theorem
The sum of the squares of the lengths of the legs of a right triangle equals the square of the length of the hypotenuse.

$$\text{leg}^2 + \text{leg}^2 = \text{hypotenuse}^2$$

Symbolically, if a and b represent the lengths of the legs and c represents the length of the hypotenuse (the side opposite the right angle), then

$$a^2 + b^2 = c^2$$

Example 2 *Crossing a Moat*

The moat surrounding a castle is 18 ft wide and the wall by the moat of the castle is 24 ft high (see Fig. 9.32). If an invading army wishes to use a ladder to cross the moat and reach the top of the wall, how long must the ladder be?

Figure 9.32

Solution The moat, the castle wall, and the ladder form a right triangle. The moat and the castle wall form the legs of the triangle (sides a and b), and the ladder forms the hypotenuse (side c). By the Pythagorean theorem,

$$c^2 = a^2 + b^2$$
$$c^2 = (18)^2 + (24)^2$$
$$c^2 = 324 + 576$$
$$c^2 = 900$$
$$\sqrt{c^2} = \sqrt{900} \qquad \text{Take the square root of both sides of the equation.}$$
$$c = 30$$

Therefore, the ladder would need to be at least 30 ft long. ∎

Circles

Circumference
$C = 2\pi r$

Area
$A = \pi r^2$

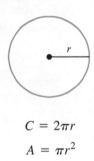

Figure 9.33

A commonly used plane figure that is not a polygon is a *circle*. A *circle* is a set of points equidistant from a fixed point called the center. A *radius*, r, of a circle is a line segment from the center of the circle to any point on the circle (Fig. 9.33). A *diameter*, d, of a circle is a line segment through the center of a circle with both end points on the circle. Note that the diameter of the circle is twice its radius. The *circumference* is the length of the simple closed curve that forms the circle. The formulas for the area and circumference of a circle are given in the box below.

Circumference and Area of a Circle

$$C = 2\pi r$$
$$A = \pi r^2$$

The symbol pi, π, was introduced in Chapter 5. Recall that π is approximately 3.14. However, when solving problems, you should use the $\boxed{\pi}$ key on your calculator to get a more accurate answer.

Example 3 *Comparing Pizzas*

Victoria Montoya wishes to order a large cheese pizza. She can choose among three pizza parlors in town: Antonio's, Steve's, and Dorsey's. Antonio's large cheese pizza is a round 16-in.-diameter pizza that sells for $15. Steve's large cheese pizza is a round 14-in.-diameter pizza that sells for $12. Dorsey's large cheese pizza is a square 12-in. by 12-in. pizza that sells for $10. All three pizzas have the same thickness. To get the most for her money, from which pizza parlor should Victoria order her pizza?

Solution To determine the best value, we will calculate the cost per square inch of pizza for each of the three pizzas. To do so, we will divide the cost of each pizza by its area. The areas of the two round pizzas can be determined using the formula for the area of a circle, $A = \pi r^2$. Since the radius is half the diameter, we will use $r = 8$ and $r = 7$ for Antonio's and Steve's large pizzas, respectively, and we will use the $\boxed{\pi}$ key on our calculator. The area for the square pizza can be determined using the formula for the area of a square, $A = s^2$. We will use $s = 12$.

$$\text{Area of Antonio's pizza} = \pi r^2 = \pi(8)^2 = \pi(64) \approx 201.06 \text{ in.}^2$$
$$\text{Area of Steve's pizza} = \pi r^2 = \pi(7)^2 = \pi(49) \approx 153.94 \text{ in.}^2$$
$$\text{Area of Dorsey's pizza} = s^2 = (12)^2 = 144 \text{ in.}^2$$

Now, to find the cost per square inch of pizza, we will divide the cost of the pizza by the area of the pizza.

$$\text{Cost per square inch of Antonio's pizza} \approx \frac{\$15}{201.06 \text{ in.}^2} \approx \$0.0746$$

Thus, Antonio's pizza costs about \$0.0746, or about 7.5 cents, per square inch.

$$\text{Cost per square inch of Steve's pizza} \approx \frac{\$12}{153.94 \text{ in.}^2} \approx \$0.0780$$

Thus, Steve's pizza costs about \$0.0780, or about 7.8 cents, per square inch.

$$\text{Cost per square inch of Dorsey's pizza} = \frac{\$10}{144 \text{ in.}^2} \approx \$0.0694$$

Thus, Dorsey's pizza costs about \$0.0694, or about 6.9 cents, per square inch.

Since the cost per square inch of pizza is the lowest for Dorsey's pizza, Victoria would get the most pizza for her money by ordering her pizza from Dorsey's. ∎

Example 4 Determining the Shaded Area

Determine the shaded area. Use the $\boxed{\pi}$ key on your calculator and round your answer to the nearest hundredth.

2 ft

10 ft

Solution To determine the area of the shaded region, we will first determine the area of the parallelogram and then subtract the area of the circle. Notice that the height of the parallelogram is equal to the diameter of the circle. Since the diameter of a circle is twice its radius, the height of the parallelogram = 2 · 2 feet, or 4 feet.

$$\text{Area of the parallelogram} = bh = 10 \cdot 4 = 40 \text{ ft}^2$$
$$\text{Area of the circle} = \pi r^2 = \pi(2)^2 = \pi \cdot 4 \approx 12.57 \text{ ft}^2$$
$$\text{Area of the shaded region} = \text{Area of the parallelogram} - \text{Area of the circle}$$
$$\approx 40 - 12.57 \approx 27.43 \text{ ft}^2$$

Thus, the area of the shaded region is approximately 27.43 ft^2. ∎

Example 5 Applying Lawn Fertilizer

Altay Özgener plans to fertilize his lawn. The shapes and dimensions of his lot, house, driveway, pool, and rose garden are shown in Fig. 9.34 on page 506. One bag of fertilizer costs \$29.95 and covers 5000 ft^2. Determine how many bags of fertilizer Altay needs and the total cost of the fertilizer.

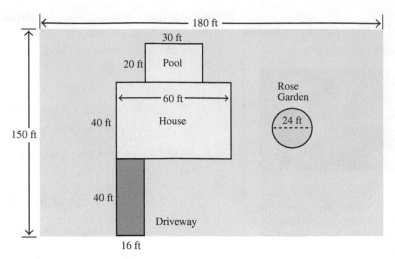

Figure 9.34

Solution   The total area of the lot is $150 \cdot 180$, or $27{,}000 \ \text{ft}^2$. To determine the area to be fertilized, subtract the area of house, driveway, pool, and rose garden from the total area.

$$\text{Area of house} = 60 \cdot 40 = 2400 \ \text{ft}^2$$
$$\text{Area of driveway} = 40 \cdot 16 = 640 \ \text{ft}^2$$
$$\text{Area of pool} = 20 \cdot 30 = 600 \ \text{ft}^2$$

The diameter of the rose garden is 24 ft, so its radius is 12 ft.

$$\text{Area of rose garden} = \pi r^2 = \pi(12)^2 = \pi(144) \approx 452.39 \ \text{ft}^2$$

The total area of the house, driveway, pool, and rose garden is approximately $2400 + 640 + 600 + 452.39$, or $4092.39 \ \text{ft}^2$. The area to be fertilized is $27{,}000 - 4092.39 \ \text{ft}^2$, or $22{,}907.61 \ \text{ft}^2$. The number of bags of fertilizer is found by dividing the total area to be fertilized by the number of square feet covered per bag.

The number of bags of fertilizer is $\dfrac{22{,}907.61}{5000}$, or about 4.58 bags. Therefore, Altay needs five bags. At \$29.95 per bag, the total cost is $5 \times \$29.95$, or \$149.75. ∎

Example 6 *Converting Between Square Feet and Square Inches*

a) Convert $1 \ \text{ft}^2$ to square inches.   b) Convert $37 \ \text{ft}^2$ to square inches.
c) Convert $432 \ \text{in}^2$ to square feet.   d) Convert $2196 \ \text{in}^2$ to square feet.

Solution

a) $1 \ \text{ft} = 12 \ \text{in}$. Therefore, $1 \ \text{ft}^2 = 12 \ \text{in} \times 12 \ \text{in} = 144 \ \text{in}^2$.

b) From part (a), we know that $1 \ \text{ft}^2 = 144 \ \text{in}^2$. Therefore,
$37 \ \text{ft}^2 = 37 \times 144 \ \text{in}^2 = 5328 \ \text{in}^2$.

c) In part (b), we converted from square feet to square inches by *multiplying* the number of square feet by 144. Now, to convert from square inches to square feet we will *divide* the number of square inches by 144. Therefore,
$432 \ \text{in}^2 = \frac{432}{144} \ \text{ft}^2 = 3 \ \text{ft}^2$.

d) As in part (c), we will divide the number of square inches by 144. Therefore,
$2196 \ \text{in}^2 = \frac{2196}{144} \ \text{ft}^2 = 15.25 \ \text{ft}^2$. ∎

Example 7 *Installing Ceramic Tile*

Rebecca Williams wishes to purchase ceramic tile for her family room, which measures 30 ft × 27 ft. The cost of the tile, including installation, is $72 per square yard.

a) Find the area of Rebecca's family room in square *yards*.

b) Determine Rebecca's cost of the ceramic tile for her family room.

Solution

a) The area of the family room in square feet is $30 \cdot 27 = 810$ ft². Since 1 yd = 3 ft, 1 yd² = 3 ft × 3 ft = 9 ft². To find the area of the family room in square yards, divide the area in square feet by 9 ft².

$$\text{Area in square yards} = \frac{810}{9} = 90$$

Therefore, the area is 90 yd².

b) The cost of 90 yd² of ceramic tile, including installation, is 90 · $72 = $6480. ■

When multiplying units of length, be sure that the units are the same. You can multiply feet by feet to get square feet or yards by yards to get square yards. However, you cannot get a valid answer if you multiply numbers expressed in feet by numbers expressed in yards.

SECTION 9.3 *Exercises*

Warm Up Exercises

In Exercises 1–4, fill in the blanks with an appropriate word, phrase, or symbol(s).

1. a) The sum of the lengths of the sides of a two-dimensional figure is called the _____ of the figure.

b) The region within the boundaries of a two-dimensional figure is called the _____ of the figure.

2. In a right triangle, the side that is opposite the right angle is called the _____.

3. A set of points equidistant from a fixed point is called a(n) _____.

4. a) A line segment from the center of a circle to any point on the circle is called the _____ of the circle.

b) A line segment through the center of the circle with both endpoints on the circle is called the _____ of the circle.

c) The length of the simple closed curve that forms a circle is called the _____ of the circle.

Practice the Skills

In Exercises 5–8, determine the area of the triangle.

5.

4 cm
6 cm

6.

9 ft
1 ft

7.

5 cm
7 cm

8.

$\sqrt{3}$ m 2 m

In Exercises 9–14, determine (a) the area and (b) the perimeter of the quadrilateral.

9.

5 ft
10 ft

10.

6 in. 8 in.
13 in.

11.

20 cm   27 cm
3 m

12.

2 yd
6 ft

13.

5 in.
25 in. 2 ft 25 in.
19 in.

14.

16 in.
13 in. 12 in. 13 in.
6 in.

In Exercises 15–18, determine (a) the area and (b) the circumference of the circle. Use the π *key on your calculator and round your answer to the nearest hundredth.*

15.

5 m

16.

16 yd

17.

13 ft

18.

13 mm

In Exercises 19–22, (a) use the Pythagorean theorem to determine the length of the unknown side of the triangle, (b) determine the perimeter of the triangle, and (c) determine the area of the triangle.

19.

c   15 yd
8 yd

20.

15 in.   12 in.
a

21.

5 km   13 km
b

22.

10 cm   24 cm
c

Problem Solving

In Exercises 23–32, determine the shaded area. When appropriate, use the π *key on your calculator and round your answer to the nearest hundredth.*

23.

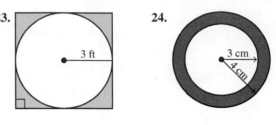

3 ft

24.

3 cm
4 cm

25.

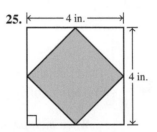

4 in.
4 in.

26.

10 in.
20 in.
30 in.

27.

9 yd   10 yd   11 yd
18 yd

28.

5 in.
10 in.

29.

20 in.
4 in.
9 in.

30.

31.

32.

In Exercises 33–36, one square yard equals 9 ft². Use this information to convert the following.

33. 72 ft² to square yards   **34.** 153 ft² to square yards

35. 14.7 yd² to square feet   **36.** 15.2 yd² to square feet

In Exercises 37–40, one square meter equals 10,000 cm². Use this information to convert the following.

37. 5 m² to square centimeters

38. 0.25 m² to square centimeters

39. 8625 cm² to square meters

40. 608 cm² to square meters

In Exercises 41–46, Nancy Wallin has just purchased a new house that is in need of new flooring. Use the measurements given on the floor plans of Nancy's house to obtain the answer.

Second floor

First floor

41. *Cost of Hardwood Flooring*   The cost of Thomasville Walnut hardwood flooring is $9.99 per square foot if Nancy installs the flooring herself or $11.99 per square foot if she has the flooring installed by the flooring company. Determine the cost for hardwood flooring in the living/dining room if

a) Nancy installs it herself.

b) Nancy has it installed by the flooring company.

42. *Cost of Laminate Flooring*   The cost of Prestige August Oak laminate flooring is $2.29 per square foot if Nancy installs the flooring herself or $4.29 per square foot if she has the flooring installed by the flooring company. Determine the cost for the flooring in the living/dining room if

a) Nancy installs it herself.

b) Nancy has it installed by the flooring company.

43. *Cost of Ceramic Tile*   The cost of Mohawk Porcelain ceramic tile is $8.99 per square foot. This price includes the cost of installation. Determine the cost for Nancy to have this ceramic tile installed in the kitchen and in both bathrooms.

44. *Cost of Linoleum*   The cost of Armstrong Marmorette Parchment linoleum is $2.59 per square foot. This price includes the cost of installation. Determine the cost for Nancy to have this linoleum installed in the kitchen and in both bathrooms.

45. *Cost of Berber Carpeting*   The cost of Shaw Golden Wheat Berber carpeting is $7.99 per square foot. This price includes the cost of installation. Determine the cost for Nancy to have this carpeting installed in all three bedrooms.

46. *Cost of Saxony Carpeting*   The cost of DuPont Stainmaster Saxony carpeting is $6.99 per square foot. This price includes the cost of installation. Determine the cost for Nancy to have this carpeting installed in all three bedrooms.

47. *Cost of a Lawn Service*   Clarence and Rose Cohen's home lot is illustrated here. Clarence and Rose wish to hire Picture Perfect Lawn Service to cut their lawn. How much will it cost Clarence and Rose to have their lawn cut if Picture Perfect charges $0.02 per square yard?

48. Cost of a Lawn Service Jim and Wendy Scott's home lot is illustrated here. The Scotts wish to hire a lawn service to cut their lawn. M&M Lawn Service charges $0.02 per square yard of lawn. How much will it cost the Scotts to have their lawn cut?

49. Area of a Basketball Court A National Basketball Association (NBA) basketball court is a rectangle that is 94 ft long and 50 ft wide.

a) If you were to walk around the outside edge of a basketball court, how far would you walk?

b) If you had to place floor tiles that each measured 1 foot by 1 foot on a basketball court, how many tiles would you need?

50. Quartz Countertops Larry Shedden wishes to have three Cambria Windsor quartz countertops installed in his new kitchen. The countertops are rectangular and have the following dimensions: $3\frac{1}{2}$ ft × 6 ft, $2\frac{1}{2}$ ft × 8 ft, and 3 ft × $11\frac{1}{2}$ ft. The cost of the countertops is $75 per square foot, which includes the cost of installation.

a) Determine the total area of the three countertops.

b) Determine the total cost to have all three countertops installed.

51. Ladder on a Wall Lorrie Morgan places a 29-ft ladder against the side of a building with the bottom of the ladder 20 ft away from the building (see figure). How high up on the wall does the ladder reach?

52. Docking a Boat Brian Murphy is bringing his boat into a dock that is 9 ft above the water level (see figure above and to the right). If a 41-ft rope is attached to the dock on

one side and to the boat on the other side, determine the horizontal distance from the dock to the boat.

53. The Green Monster In Fenway Park, home of baseball's Boston Red Sox, the left field wall is known as the *Green Monster*. The distance from home plate down the third baseline to the bottom of the wall is 310 feet (see photo). In left field, at the end of the baseline, the Green Monster is perpendicular to the ground and is 37 feet tall. Determine the distance from home plate to the top of the Green Monster along the third baseline. Round your answer to the nearest foot.

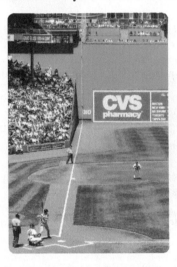

54. Plasma Television The screen of a plasma television is in the shape of a rectangle with a diagonal of length 43 in. If the height of the screen is 21 in., determine the width of the screen.

Challenge Problems/Group Activities

55. Doubling the Sides of a Square In the figure below, an original square with sides of length *s* is shown. Also shown is a larger square with sides double in length, or 2*s*.

a) Express the area of the original square in terms of *s*.

b) Express the area of the larger square in terms of *s*.

c) How many times larger is the area of the square in part (b) than the area of the square in part (a)?

56. Doubling the Sides of a Parallelogram In the figure below, an original parallelogram with base b and height h is shown. Also shown is a larger parallelogram with base and height double in length, or $2b$ and $2h$, respectively.

a) Express the area of the original parallelogram in terms of b and h.

b) Express the area of the larger parallelogram in terms of b and h.

c) How many times larger is the area of the parallelogram in part (b) than the area of the parallelogram in part (a)?

57. Heron's Formula A second formula for determining the area of a triangle (called Heron's formula) is

$$A = \sqrt{s(s - a)(s - b)(s - c)}$$

where $s = \frac{1}{2}(a + b + c)$ and a, b, and c are the lengths of the sides of the triangle. Use Heron's formula to determine the area of right triangle ABC and check your answer using the formula $A = \frac{1}{2}ab$.

58. Expansion of $(a + b)^2$ In the figure, one side of the largest square has length $a + b$. Therefore, the area of the largest square is $(a + b)^2$. Answer the following questions to find a formula for the expansion of $(a + b)^2$.

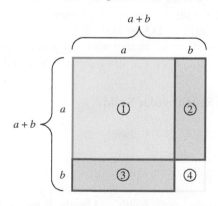

a) What is the area of the square marked ①?

b) What is the area of the rectangle marked ②?

c) What is the area of the rectangle marked ③?

d) What is the area of the square marked ④?

e) Add the four areas found in parts (a) through (d) to write a formula for the expansion of $(a + b)^2$.

Recreational Mathematics

59. Sports Areas Use the Internet to research the official dimensions of the playing surface of your favorite sport and determine the area of the playing surface. Choices may include a basketball court, volleyball court, tennis court, racquetball court, hockey rink, football field, soccer field, lacrosse field, and a baseball diamond.

60. Scarecrow's Error In the movie *The Wizard of Oz*, once the scarecrow gets his diploma he states the following: "In an isosceles triangle, the sum of the square roots of the two equal sides is equal to the square root of the third side." Discuss why this statement is incorrect.

Internet/Research Activities

For Exercises 61–63, references include the Internet, history of mathematics textbooks, and encyclopedias.

61. Research the proof of the Pythagorean theorem provided by President James Garfield. Write a brief paper and make a poster of this proof and the associated diagrams.

62. The early Babylonians and Egyptians did not know about π and had to devise techniques to approximate the area of a circle. Do research and write a paper on the techniques these societies used to approximate the area of a circle.

63. Write a paper on the contributions of Heron of Alexandria to geometry.

On the label of a can of Color Place paint is the following sentence: "One gallon will cover about 400 sq. ft." This sentence refers to the two main geometric topics that we will cover in this section. *One gallon* refers to volume of the paint in the can, and *400 sq. ft* refers to the surface area that the paint will cover.

Why *This is Important* The concepts of volume and surface area have many real-life applications. These include calculating the volume of a freezer, the displacement of an engine, and the amount of paint needed to paint a room.

▲ *The amount of paint in a can refers to volume, and the amount of wall space that the paint covers refers to surface area.*

When discussing a one-dimensional figure such as a line, we can find its length. When discussing a two-dimensional figure such as a rectangle, we can find its area and its perimeter. When discussing a three-dimensional figure such as a cube, we can find its volume and its surface area. *Volume* is a measure of the capacity of a three-dimensional figure. *Surface area* is the sum of the areas of the surfaces of a three-dimensional figure. Volume refers to the amount of material that you can put *inside* a three-dimensional figure, and surface area refers to the total area that is on the *outside* surface of the figure.

Solid geometry is the study of three-dimensional solid figures, also called *space figures*. Volumes of three-dimensional figures are measured in cubic units such as cubic feet or cubic meters. Surface areas of three-dimensional figures are measured in square units such as square feet or square meters.

Rectangular Solids, Cylinders, Cones, and Spheres

Rectangular Solid

If the length of a *rectangular solid* is 5 units, the width is 2 units, and the height is 3 units, the total number of cubes is 30 (Fig. 9.35). Thus, the volume is 30 cubic units. The volume of a rectangular solid can also be found by multiplying its length times width times height; in this case, 5 units $\times$ 2 units $\times$ 3 units = 30 cubic units. In general, the volume of any rectangular solid is $V = l \times w \times h$.

The surface area of the rectangular solid in Fig. 9.35 is the sum of the area of the surfaces of the rectangular solid. Notice that each surface of the rectangular solid is a rectangle. The left and right side of the rectangular solid each has an area of 5 units $\times$ 3 units, or 15 square units. The front and back sides of the rectangular solid each has an area of 2 units $\times$ 3 units, or 6 square units. The top and bottom sides of the rectangular solid each has an area of 5 units $\times$ 2 units, or 10 square units. Therefore, the surface area of the rectangular solid is $2(5 \times 3) + 2(2 \times 3) + 2(5 \times 2) = 2(15) + 2(6) + 2(10) = 30 + 12 + 20 = 62$ square units. In general, the surface area of any rectangular solid is $SA = 2lw + 2wh + 2lh$ (see the figure to the left).

Figure 9.35

Volume and Surface Area of a Rectangular Solid

$$V = lwh \qquad SA = 2lw + 2wh + 2lh$$

Cube

A *cube* is a rectangular solid with the same length, width, and height. If we call the length of the side of the cube s and use the volume and surface area formulas for a rectangular solid, substituting s in for l, w, and h, we obtain $V = s \cdot s \cdot s = s^3$ and $SA = 2 \cdot s \cdot s + 2 \cdot s \cdot s + 2 \cdot s \cdot s = 2s^2 + 2s^2 + 2s^2 = 6s^2$ (see the figure to the left).

Volume and Surface Area of a Cube

$$V = s^3 \qquad SA = 6s^2$$

Cylinder

Now consider the right circular cylinder shown in Fig. 9.36(a). When we use the term *cylinder* in this book, we mean a right circular cylinder. The volume of the cylinder is found by multiplying the area of the circular base, πr^2, by the height, h, to get $V = \pi r^2 h$.

The surface area of the cylinder is the sum of the area of the top, the area of the bottom, and the area of the side of the cylinder. Both the top and bottom of the cylinder are circles with an area of πr^2. To determine the area of the side of the cylinder, examine Fig. 9.36(b) and (c).

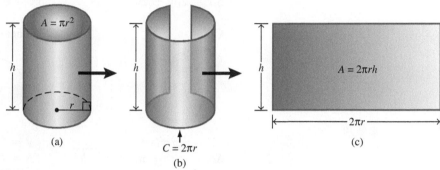

(a)

$C = 2\pi r$

(b)

(c)

Figure 9.36

Notice how when flattened, the side of the cylinder is a rectangle whose length is the circumference of the base of the cylinder and whose width is the height of the cylinder. Thus, the side of the cylinder has an area of $2\pi r \cdot h$, or $2\pi rh$. Therefore, the surface area of the cylinder is $\pi r^2 + \pi r^2 + 2\pi rh$, or $SA = 2\pi rh + 2\pi r^2$.

Volume and Surface Area of a Cylinder

$$V = \pi r^2 h \qquad SA = 2\pi rh + 2\pi r^2$$

Now consider the right circular cone illustrated in Fig. 9.37. When we use the term *cone* in this book, we mean a right circular cone. The volume of a cone is less than the volume of a cylinder that has the same base and the same height. In fact, the volume of the cone is one-third the volume of the cylinder. The formula for the surface area of a cone is the sum of the area of the circular base of the cone, πr^2, and the area of the side of the cone, $\pi r\sqrt{r^2 + h^2}$, or $SA = \pi r^2 + \pi r\sqrt{r^2 + h^2}$. The derivation of the area of the side of the cone is beyond the scope of this book.

Figure 9.37

Volume and Surface Area of a Cone

$$V = \tfrac{1}{3}\pi r^2 h \qquad SA = \pi r^2 + \pi r\sqrt{r^2 + h^2}$$

Sphere

Baseballs, tennis balls, and so on have the shape of a *sphere*. The formulas for the volume and surface area of a sphere are as follows. The derivation of the volume and surface area of a sphere are beyond the scope of this book (see the figure to the left).

Volume and Surface Area of a Sphere

$$V = \tfrac{4}{3}\pi r^3 \qquad SA = 4\pi r^2$$

Following is a summary of the formulas for the volumes and surface areas of the three-dimensional figures we have discussed thus far.

Volumes and Surface Areas

Rectangular Solid

$V = lwh$

$SA = 2lw + 2wh + 2lh$

Cube

$V = s^3$

$SA = 6s^2$

Cylinder

$V = \pi r^2 h$

$SA = 2\pi rh + 2\pi r^2$

Cone

$V = \frac{1}{3}\pi r^2 h$

$SA = \pi r^2 + \pi r\sqrt{r^2 + h^2}$

Sphere

$V = \frac{4}{3}\pi r^3$

$SA = 4\pi r^2$

Example 1 *Volume and Surface Area*

Determine the volume and surface area of each of the following three-dimensional figures. When appropriate, use the $\boxed{\pi}$ key on your calculator and round your answer to the nearest hundredths.

(a)

(b)

(c)

(d)

Solution

a) $V = lwh = 11 \cdot 3 \cdot 6 = 198 \text{ ft}^3$

$SA = 2lw + 2wh + 2lh = 2 \cdot 11 \cdot 3 + 2 \cdot 3 \cdot 6 + 2 \cdot 11 \cdot 6$

$= 66 + 36 + 132 = 234 \text{ ft}^2$

b) $V = \pi r^2 h = \pi \cdot 4^2 \cdot 8 = 128\pi \approx 402.12 \text{ in}^3$

$SA = 2\pi rh + 2\pi r^2 = 2\pi \cdot 4 \cdot 8 + 2\pi \cdot 4^2$

$= 64\pi + 32\pi = 96\pi \approx 301.59 \text{ in}^2$

c) $V = \frac{1}{3}\pi r^2 h = \frac{1}{3}\pi \cdot 3^2 \cdot 8 = \frac{1}{3}\pi \cdot 9 \cdot 8 = 24\pi \approx 75.40 \text{ m}^3$

$SA = \pi r^2 + \pi r\sqrt{r^2 + h^2} = \pi \cdot 3^2 + \pi \cdot 3 \cdot \sqrt{3^2 + 8^2}$

$= 9 \cdot \pi + 3 \cdot \pi \cdot \sqrt{73} \approx 108.80 \text{ m}^2$

d) $V = \frac{4}{3}\pi r^3 = \frac{4}{3} \cdot \pi \cdot 9^3 = \frac{4}{3} \cdot \pi \cdot 729 = 972\pi \approx 3053.63 \text{ cm}^3$

$SA = 4\pi r^2 = 4 \cdot \pi \cdot 9^2 = 4 \cdot \pi \cdot 81 = 324\pi \approx 1017.88 \text{ cm}^2$ ∎

Example 2   *Replacing a Sand Volleyball Court*

Robin Ayers is the manager at the Colony Apartments and needs to replace the sand in the rectangular sand volleyball court. The court is 30 ft wide by 60 ft long, and the sand has a uniform depth of 18 in. (see figure below). Sand sells for $27 per cubic yard.

18 in.

60 ft

30 ft

a) How many cubic yards of sand does Robin need?

b) How much will the sand cost?

Solution

a) Since we are asked to find the volume in cubic yards, we will convert each measurement to yards. There are 3 ft in a yard. Thus, 30 ft equals $\frac{30}{3}$, or 10 yd, and 60 ft equals $\frac{60}{3}$, or 20 yd. There are 36 in. in a yard, so 18 in. equals $\frac{18}{36}$, or $\frac{1}{2}$ yd. The amount of sand needed is determined using the formula for the volume of a rectangular solid, $V = l \cdot w \cdot h$. In this case, the height of the rectangular solid can be considered the depth of the sand.

$$V = l \cdot w \cdot h = 10 \cdot 20 \cdot \frac{1}{2} = 100 \text{ yd}^3$$

Note that since the measurements for length, width, and height are each in terms of yards, the answer is in terms of cubic yards.

b) One cubic yard of sand costs $27, so 100 yd^3 will cost 100 × $27, or $2700.   ∎

Example 3   *Homecoming Float*

The basketball team at Southwestern High School is building a float for the homecoming parade. On the float is a large papier-mâché basketball that has a radius of 4.5 ft. Team members need to know the surface area of the basketball so that they can determine how much paint they will need to buy to paint the basketball.

a) Determine the surface area of the basketball.

b) If 1 quart of paint covers approximately 100 sq. ft, how many quarts of paint will team members need to buy?

Solution

a) The basketball has the shape of a sphere. We will use the formula for the surface area of a sphere: $SA = 4\pi r^2 = 4 \cdot \pi \cdot (4.5)^2 = 81\pi \approx 254.47$ sq. ft.

b) Since each quart of paint will cover about 100 sq. ft, they will need about $\frac{254.47}{100} = 2.5447$ quarts. Since you cannot buy a portion of a quart of paint, the team will need to buy 3 quarts of paint to paint the basketball.   ∎

Example 4   *Silage Storage*

Gordon Langeneger has three silos on his farm. The silos are each in the shape of a right circular cylinder (see Fig. 9.38). One silo has a 12-ft diameter and is 40 ft tall. The second silo has a 14-ft diameter and is 50 ft tall. The third silo has an 18-ft diameter and is 60 ft tall.

Figure 9.38

a) What is the total capacity of the three silos in cubic feet?

b) If Gordon fills all three of his silos and then feeds his cattle 150 ft³ of silage per day, in how many days will all three silos be empty?

Solution

a) The capacity of each silo can be determined using the formula for the volume of a right circular cylinder, $V = \pi r^2 h$. Since the radius is half the diameter, the radii for the three silos are 6 ft, 7 ft, and 9 ft, respectively. Now let's determine the volumes.

$$\text{Volume of the first silo} = \pi r^2 h = \pi \cdot 6^2 \cdot 40$$
$$= \pi \cdot 36 \cdot 40 = 1440\pi \approx 4523.89 \text{ ft}^3$$

$$\text{Volume of the second silo} = \pi r^2 h = \pi \cdot 7^2 \cdot 50$$
$$= \pi \cdot 49 \cdot 50 = 2450\pi \approx 7696.90 \text{ ft}^3$$

$$\text{Volume of the third silo} = \pi r^2 h = \pi \cdot 9^2 \cdot 60$$
$$= \pi \cdot 81 \cdot 60 = 4860\pi \approx 15,268.14 \text{ ft}^3$$

Therefore, the total capacity of all three silos is about

$$4523.89 + 7696.90 + 15,268.14 \approx 27,488.93 \text{ ft}^3$$

b) To find how long it takes to empty all three silos, we will divide the total capacity by 150 ft³, the amount fed to Gordon's cattle every day.

$$\frac{27,488.93}{150} \approx 183.26$$

Thus, the silos will be empty in about 183 days.   ■

Polyhedra, Prisms, and Pyramids

A *polyhedron* (plural, *polyhedra*) is a closed surface formed by the union of polygonal regions. Figure 9.39 on page 517 illustrates some polyhedra.

Each polygonal region is called a *face* of the polyhedron. The line segment formed by the intersection of two faces is called an *edge*. The point at which two or more edges intersect is called a *vertex*. In Fig. 9.39(a), there are 6 faces, 12 edges, and 8 vertices.

Polyhedra

(a) (b) (c) (d)

Figure 9.39

Note that:

Number of vertices − number of edges + number of faces = 2

8 − 12 + 6 = 2

This formula, credited to Leonhard Euler, is true for any polyhedron.

Euler's Polyhedron Formula

Number of vertices − number of edges + number of faces = 2

We suggest that you verify that this formula holds for Fig. 9.39(b), (c), and (d).

Example 5 Using Euler's Polyhedron Formula

A certain polyhedron has 20 vertices and 12 faces. Determine the number of edges on the polyhedron.

Solution Since we are seeking the number of edges, we will let x represent the number of edges on the polyhedron. Next, we will use Euler's polyhedron formula to set up an equation:

Number of vertices − number of edges + number of faces = 2

20 − x + 12 = 2

$$32 - x = 2$$
$$-x = -30$$
$$x = 30$$

Therefore, the polyhedron has 30 edges. ∎

A *platonic solid*, also known as a *regular polyhedron*, is a polyhedron whose faces are all regular polygons of the same size and shape. There are exactly five platonic solids. All five platonic solids are illustrated in the *Did You Know?* at left.

A *prism* is a special type of polyhedron whose bases are congruent polygons and whose sides are parallelograms. These parallelogram regions are called the *lateral faces* of the prism. If all the lateral faces are rectangles, the prism is said to be a *right prism*. The prisms illustrated in Fig. 9.40 are all right prisms. When we use the word *prism* in this book, we are referring to a right prism.

Prisms

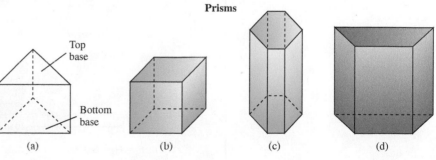

(a) (b) (c) (d)

Figure 9.40

Figure 9.41

The volume of any prism can be found by multiplying the area of the base, B, by the height, h, of the prism.

Volume of a Prism

$$V = Bh$$

where B is the area of a base and h is the height.

Example 6   *Volume of a Hexagonal Prism Fish Tank*

Frank Nicolzaao's fish tank is in the shape of a hexagonal prism as shown in Fig. 9.41. Use the dimensions shown in the figure and the fact that 1 gal = 231 in³ to

a) determine the volume of the fish tank in cubic inches.

b) determine the volume of the fish tank in gallons (round your answer to the nearest gallon).

Solution

a) First we will need to calculate the area of the hexagonal base of the fish tank. Notice from Fig. 9.41 that by drawing a diagonal as indicated, the base can be divided into two identical trapezoids. To find the area of the hexagonal base, we will calculate the area of one of these trapezoids and then multiply by 2.

$$\text{Area of one trapezoid} = \tfrac{1}{2}h(b_1 + b_2)$$
$$= \tfrac{1}{2}(8)(16 + 8) = 96 \text{ in}^2$$
$$\text{Area of the hexagonal base} = 2(96) = 192 \text{ in}^2$$

Now to determine the volume of the fish tank, we will use the formula for the volume of a prism, $V = Bh$. We already determined that the area of the base, B, is 192 in.².

$$V = B \cdot h = 192 \cdot 24 = 4608 \text{ in}^3$$

In the above calculation, the area of the base, B, was measured in square inches and the height was measured in inches. The product of square inches and inches is cubic inches, or in.³.

b) To determine the volume of the fish tank in gallons, we will divide the volume of the fish tank in cubic inches by 231.

$$V = \frac{4608}{231} \approx 19.95 \text{ gal}$$

Thus, the volume of the fish tank is approximately 20 gal. ∎

Example 7   *Volumes Involving Prisms*

Determine the volume of the remaining solid after the cylinder, triangular prism, and square prism have been cut from the solid (Fig. 9.42).

Figure 9.42

Solution To determine the volume of the remaining solid, first determine the volume of the rectangular solid. Then subtract the volume of the two prisms and the cylinder that were cut out.

$$\text{Volume of rectangular solid} = l \cdot w \cdot h$$
$$= 20 \cdot 3 \cdot 8 = 480 \text{ in}^3$$
$$\text{Volume of circular cylinder} = \pi r^2 h$$
$$= \pi(2^2)(3)$$
$$= \pi(4)(3) = 12\pi \approx 37.70 \text{ in}^3$$
$$\text{Volume of triangular prism} = \text{area of the base} \cdot \text{height}$$
$$= \tfrac{1}{2}(6)(4)(3) = 36 \text{ in}^3$$
$$\text{Volume of square prism} = s^2 \cdot h$$
$$= 4^2 \cdot 3 = 48 \text{ in}^3$$
$$\text{Volume of solid} \approx 480 - 37.70 - 36 - 48$$
$$\approx 358.30 \text{ in}^3$$

Another special category of polyhedra is the *pyramid*. Unlike prisms, pyramids have only one base. The figures illustrated in Fig. 9.43 are pyramids. Note that all but one face of a pyramid intersect at a common vertex.

Pyramids

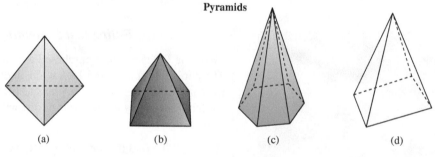

(a)   (b)   (c)   (d)

Figure 9.43

If a pyramid is drawn inside a prism, as shown in Fig. 9.44, the volume of the pyramid is less than that of the prism. In fact, the volume of the pyramid is one-third the volume of the prism.

Figure 9.44

Volume of a Pyramid

$$V = \tfrac{1}{3}Bh$$

where B is the area of the base and h is the height.

Example 8 *Volume of a Pyramid*

Determine the volume of the pyramid shown in Fig. 9.45.

Solution First find the area of the base of the pyramid. Since the base of the pyramid is a square,

$$\text{Area of base} = s^2 = 2^2 = 4 \text{ m}^2$$

Now use this information to find the volume of the pyramid.

$$V = \tfrac{1}{3} \cdot B \cdot h$$
$$= \tfrac{1}{3} \cdot 4 \cdot 3$$
$$= 4 \text{ m}^3$$

Thus, the volume of the pyramid is 4 m³.

Figure 9.45

Cubic Unit Conversions

In certain situations, converting volume from one cubic unit to a different cubic unit might be necessary. For example, when purchasing topsoil you might have to change the amount of topsoil from cubic feet to cubic yards prior to placing your order. Example 9 shows how that may be done.

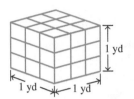

Figure 9.46

Example 9 *Cubic Yards and Cubic Feet*

a) Convert 1 yd^3 to cubic feet. (See Fig. 9.46.)

b) Convert 8.9 yd^3 to cubic feet.

c) Convert 749.25 ft^3 to cubic yards.

Solution

a) We know that 1 yd = 3 ft. Thus, 1 yd^3 = 3 ft $\times$ 3 ft $\times$ 3 ft = 27 ft^3.

b) In part (a), we learned that 1 yd^3 = 27 ft^3. Thus, 8.9 yd^3 = 8.9 $\times$ 27 = 240.3 ft^3.

c) In part (b), we converted from cubic yards to cubic feet by *multiplying* the number of cubic yards by 27. Now, to convert from cubic feet to cubic yards we will *divide* the number of cubic feet by 27. Therefore, 749.25 ft^3 = $\frac{749.25}{27}$ yd^3 = 27.75 yd^3. ∎

Example 10 *Filling in a Swimming Pool*

Madeline Bates recently purchased a home with a rectangular swimming pool. The pool is 30 ft long and 15 ft wide, and it has a uniform depth of 4.5 ft. Madeline lives in a cold climate, so she plans to fill the pool in with dirt to make a flower garden. How many cubic yards of dirt will Madeline have to purchase to fill in the swimming pool?

Solution   To find the amount of dirt, we will use the formula for the volume of a rectangular solid:

$$V = lwh$$
$$= (30)(15)(4.5)$$
$$= 2025 \ ft^3$$

Now we must convert this volume from cubic feet to cubic yards. In Example 9, we learned that 1 yd^3 = 27 ft^3. Therefore, 2025 ft^3 = $\frac{2025}{27}$ = 75 yd^3. Thus, Madeline needs to purchase 75 yd^3 of dirt to fill in her swimming pool. ∎

SECTION 9.4   *Exercises*

Warm Up Exercises

In Exercises 1–6, fill in the blanks with an appropriate word, phrase, or symbol(s).

1. A measure of the capacity of a three-dimensional figure is called the figure's _____.

2. The sum of the areas of the surfaces of a three-dimensional figure is called the figure's _____ area.

3. A regular polyhedron, whose faces are all regular polygons of the same size and shape, is also called a _____ solid.

4. A polyhedron whose bases are congruent polygons and whose sides are parallelograms is called a _____.

5. A prism whose sides are rectangles is called a _____ prism.

6. Euler's polyhedron formula states that, for any polyhedron, the number of vertices minus the number of edges plus the number of faces equals_____.

Practice the Skills

In Exercises 7–16, determine (a) the volume and (b) the surface area of the three-dimensional figure. When appropriate, use the $\boxed{\pi}$ *key on your calculator and round your answer to the nearest hundredth.*

7.

4 ft
2 ft
8 ft

8.

25 mm
6 mm
8 mm

9.

2 yd
2 yd
2 yd

10.

13 ft
13 ft
13 ft

11.

12 in.
2 in.

12.

24 in.
6 in.

13.

3 cm
14 cm

14.

24 ft
10 ft

15.

9 cm

16.

←7 mi→

In Exercises 17–20, determine the volume of the three-dimensional figure. When appropriate, round your answer to the nearest hundredth.

17.

10 m
10 m
15 m

18.

8 in.
10 in.
12 in.
24 in.
8 in.
10 in.
12 in.

19.

15 cm
12 cm
12 cm

20.

13 ft
15 ft
9 ft

Problem Solving

In Exercises 21–28, determine the volume of the shaded region. When appropriate, use the $\boxed{\pi}$ *key on your calculator and round your answer to the nearest hundredth.*

21.

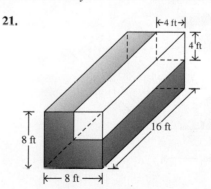

←4 ft→
4 ft
8 ft
16 ft
8 ft

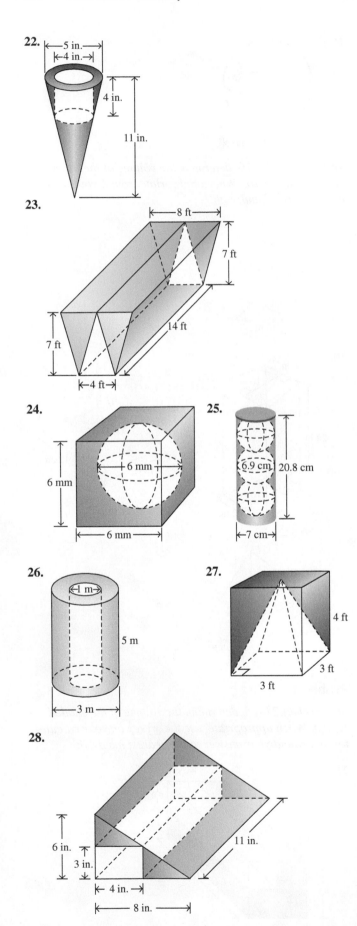

22.

23.

24.

25.

26.

27.

28.

In Exercises 29–32, use the fact that 1 yd³ equals 27 ft³ to make the conversion.

29. 3 yd³ to cubic feet   **30.** 7.25 yd³ to cubic feet

31. 153 ft³ to cubic yards   **32.** 2457 ft³ to cubic yards

In Exercises 33–36, use the fact that 1 m³ equals 1,000,000 cm³ to make the conversion.

33. 0.56 m³ to cubic centimeters

34. 17.6 m³ to cubic centimeters

35. 7,500,000 cm³ to cubic meters

36. 7,300,000 cm³ to cubic meters

37. *Playground Mulch* Bob Malena is building a backyard playground for his grandchildren and wishes to put down rubber mulch to provide safety from falls. Bob wishes to put the mulch in a pit in the shape of a rectangular solid 20 ft long, 15 ft wide, and 9 in deep.

  a) Determine the volume, in cubic feet, of mulch Bob will need.

  b) If mulch costs $11 per cubic foot, what will the cost of the mulch be?

38. *Volume of a Freezer* The dimensions of the interior of an upright freezer are height 46 in., width 25 in., and depth 25 in. Determine the volume of the freezer

  a) in cubic inches.   **b)** in cubic feet.

39. *CD Case* A compact disc case is a rectangular solid that is 142 mm long, 125 mm wide, and 10 mm high. Determine its surface area.

40. *Globe Surface Area* The Everest model globe has a diameter of 20 in. Determine the surface area of this globe. Round your answer to the nearest hundredth.

41. *Volume of a Bread Pan* A bread pan is 12 in. × 4 in. × 3 in. How many quarts does it hold, if 1 in³ ≈ 0.01736 qt?

42. *Ice-Cream Comparison* The Louisburg Creamery packages its homemade ice cream in tubs and in boxes. The tubs are in the shape of a right cylinder with a radius of 3 in. and height of 5 in. The boxes are in the shape of a cube with each side measuring 5 in. Determine the volume of each container.

43. *A Fish Tank*

a) How many cubic centimeters of water will a rectangular fish tank hold if the tank is 80 cm long, 50 cm wide, and 30 cm high?

b) If 1 cm^3 holds 1 mℓ of liquid, how many milliliters will the tank hold?

c) If 1 ℓ = 1000 mℓ, how many liters will the tank hold?

44. *The Pyramid of Cheops* The Pyramid of Cheops in Egypt has a square base measuring 720 ft on a side. Its height is 480 ft. What is its volume?

45. *Engine Capacity* The engine in a 1957 Chevrolet Corvette has eight cylinders. Each cylinder is a right cylinder with a bore (diameter) of 3.875 in. and a stroke (height) of 3 in. Determine the total displacement (volume) of this engine.

46. *Rose Garden Topsoil* Marisa Raffaele wishes to plant a rose garden in her backyard. The rose garden will be in the shape of a 9 ft by 18 ft rectangle. Marisa wishes to add a 4-in. layer of organic topsoil on top of the rectangular area. The topsoil sells for $42 per cubic yard. Determine

a) how many cubic yards of topsoil Marisa will need.

b) how much the topsoil will cost.

47. *Pool Toys* A Wacky Noodle Pool Toy, frequently referred to as a "noodle," is a cylindrical flotation device made from cell foam (see photo). One style of noodle is a cylinder that has a diameter of 2.5 in. and a length of 5.5 ft. Determine the volume of this style of noodle in

a) cubic inches.   **b)** cubic feet.

48. *Comparing Cake Pans* When baking a cake, you can choose between a round pan with a 9-in. diameter and a 7 in. × 9 in. rectangular pan.

a) Determine the area of the base of each pan.

b) If both pans are 2 in. deep, determine the volume of each pan.

c) Which pan has the larger volume?

49. *Cake Icing* A bag used to apply icing to a cake is in the shape of a cone with a diameter of 3 in. and a height of 6 in. How much icing will this bag hold when full?

50. *Flower Box* The flower box shown below is 4 ft long, and its ends are in the shape of a trapezoid. The upper and lower bases of the trapezoid measure 12 in. and 8 in., respectively, and the height is 9 in. Find the volume of the flower box

a) in cubic inches.   **b)** in cubic feet.

In Exercises 51–56, find the missing value indicated by the question mark. Use the following formula.

$$\left(\begin{array}{c}\text{Number of}\\\text{vertices}\end{array}\right) - \left(\begin{array}{c}\text{number of}\\\text{edges}\end{array}\right) + \left(\begin{array}{c}\text{number}\\\text{of faces}\end{array}\right) = 2$$

	Number of Vertices	Number of Edges	Number of Faces
51.	8	?	4
52.	12	16	?
53.	?	8	4
54.	11	?	5
55.	7	12	?
56.	?	10	4

Challenge Problems/Group Activities

57. *Earth and Moon Comparisons* The diameter of Earth is approximately 12,756.3 km. The diameter of the moon is approximately 3474.8 km. Assume that both Earth and the moon are spheres.

a) Determine the surface area of Earth.

b) Determine the surface area of the moon.

c) How many times larger is the surface area of Earth than the surface area of the moon?

d) Determine the volume of Earth.

e) Determine the volume of the moon.

f) How many times larger is the volume of Earth than the volume of the moon?

58. *Packing Orange Juice* A box is packed with six cans of orange juice. The cans are touching each other and the sides of the box, as shown. What percent of the volume of the interior of the box is not occupied by the cans?

59. *Doubling the Edges of a Cube* In this exercise, we will explore what happens to the volume of a cube if we double the length of each edge of the cube.

a) Choose a number between 1 and 10 and call this number *s*.

b) Calculate the volume of a cube with the length of each edge equal to *s*.

c) Now double *s* and call this number *t*.

d) Calculate the volume of a cube with the length of each edge equal to *t*.

e) Repeat parts (a) through (d) for a different value of *s*.

f) Compare the results from part (b) with the results from part (d) and explain what happens to the volume of a cube if we double the length of each edge.

60. *Doubling the Radius of a Sphere* In this exercise, we will explore what happens to the volume of a sphere if we double the radius of the sphere.

a) Choose a number between 1 and 10 and call this number *r*.

b) Calculate the volume of a sphere with radius *r* (use the $\boxed{\pi}$ key on your calculator).

c) Now double *r* and call this number *t*.

d) Calculate the volume of a sphere with radius *t*.

e) Repeat parts (a) through (d) for a different value of *r*.

f) Compare the results from part (b) with the results from part (d) and explain what happens to the volume of a sphere if we double the radius.

61. a) Explain how to demonstrate, using the cube shown below, that

$$(a + b)^3 = a^3 + 3a^2b + 3ab^2 + b^3$$

b) What is the volume in terms of *a* and *b* of each numbered piece in the figure?

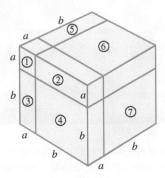

c) An eighth piece is not illustrated. What is its volume?

Recreational Mathematics

62. *More Pool Toys* Wacky Noodle Pool Toys (see Exercise 47) come in many different shapes and sizes.

Base for part (a)   Base for part (b)

a) Determine the volume, in cubic inches, of a noodle that is in the shape of a 5.5-ft-long solid octagonal prism whose base has an area of 5 in².

b) Determine the volume, in cubic inches, of a hollow noodle that has the same shape as the noodle described in part (a) except that a right circular cylinder of diameter 0.75 in. has been removed from the center.

Internet/Research Activities

63. *Air-Conditioner Selection* Calculate the volume of the room in which you sleep or study. Go to a store that sells room air conditioners and find out how many cubic feet can be cooled by the different models available. Describe the model that would be the proper size for your room. What is the initial cost? How much does that model cost to operate? If you moved to a room that had twice the amount of floor space and the same height, would the air conditioner you selected still be adequate? Explain.

64. Pappus of Alexandria (ca. A.D. 350) was the last of the well-known ancient Greek mathematicians. Write a paper on his life and his contributions to mathematics.

65. *Platonic Solids*   Construct cardboard models of one or more of the platonic solids. Visit the Web site www.mathsnet.net/geometry/solid/platonic.html or similar Web sites for patterns to follow.

SECTION 9.5 — Transformational Geometry, Symmetry, and Tessellations

▲ *Capital letters can be used to display symmetry.*

Consider the capital letters of the alphabet. Now consider a kindergarten-age child who is practicing to write capital letters. Usually, children will write some of the letters "backwards." However, some letters cannot be made backwards. For example, the capital letter A would look the same backwards as it does forwards, but the capital letters B and C would look different backwards than they do forwards. The capital letters that appear the same forwards as they do backwards have a property called *symmetry* that we will define and study in this section. Symmetry is part of another branch of geometry known as *transformational geometry*.

Why *This is Important*   Transformational geometry can be used to describe many natural phenomena in biology, physics, chemistry, and other scientific areas.

In our study of geometry, we have thus far focused on definitions, axioms, and theorems that are used in the study of *Euclidean geometry*. We will now introduce a second type of geometry called *transformational geometry*. In *transformational geometry*, we study various ways to move a geometric figure without altering the shape or size of the figure. When discussing transformational geometry, we often use the term *rigid motion*.

Definition: Rigid Motion or Transformation

The act of moving a geometric figure from some starting position to some ending position without altering its shape or size is called a **rigid motion** (or **transformation**).

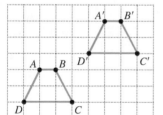

Figure 9.47

Consider trapezoid *ABCD* in Fig. 9.47. If we move each point on this trapezoid 4 units to the right and 3 units up, the trapezoid is in the location specified by trapezoid *A'B'C'D'*. This figure illustrates one type of rigid motion. When studying rigid motions, we are concerned only about the starting and ending positions of the figure and not what happens in between. When discussing rigid motions of two-dimensional figures, we note there are four basic types of rigid motions: reflections, rotations, translations, and glide reflections. We call these four types of rigid motions the *basic rigid motions in a plane*. After we discuss the four rigid motions, we will discuss symmetry of geometric figures and tessellations.

Reflections

The first rigid motion we will study is *reflection*. In our everyday life, we are quite familiar with the concept of reflection. In transformational geometry, a reflection is an image of a geometric figure that appears on the opposite side of a designated line.

Definition: **Reflection**

A **reflection** is a rigid motion that moves a geometric figure to a new position such that the figure in the new position is a mirror image of the figure in the starting position. In two dimensions, the figure and its mirror image are equidistant from a line called the **reflection line** or the **axis of reflection**.

Figure 9.48 shows trapezoid $ABCD$, a reflection line l, and the reflected trapezoid $A'B'C'D'$. Notice that vertex A is 6 units to the *left* of reflection line l and that vertex A' is 6 units to the *right* of reflection line l. Next notice that vertex B is 2 units to the *left* of l and that vertex B' is 2 units to the *right* of l. A similar relationship holds true for vertices C and C' and for vertices D and D'. It is important to see that the trapezoid is not simply *moved* to the other side of the reflection line, but instead it is *reflected*. Notice in the trapezoid $ABCD$ that the longer base $\overline{BC}$ is on the *right* side of the trapezoid, but in the reflected trapezoid $A'B'C'D'$ the longer base $\overline{B'C'}$ is on the *left* side of the trapezoid. Finally, notice the colors of the sides of the two trapezoids. Side $\overline{AB}$ in trapezoid $ABCD$ and side $\overline{A'B'}$ in the reflected trapezoid are both blue. Side $\overline{BC}$ and side $\overline{B'C'}$ are both red, sides $\overline{CD}$ and $\overline{C'D'}$ are both gold, and sides $\overline{DA}$ and $\overline{D'A'}$ are both green. In this section, we will occasionally use such color coding to help you visualize the effect of a rigid transformation on a figure.

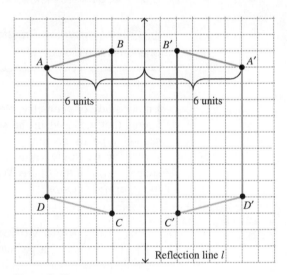

Figure 9.48

Example 1 *Reflection of a Triangle*

Construct the reflection of triangle *ABC,* shown in Fig. 9.49, about reflection line *l*.

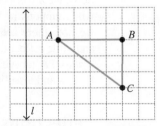

Figure 9.49

Solution   The reflection of triangle ABC will be called $A'B'C'$. To determine the position of the reflection, we first examine vertex A in Fig. 9.49. Notice that vertex A is 2 units to the *right* of line l. Thus, in the reflected triangle $A'B'C'$,

Figure 9.51

Figure 9.52

Figure 9.53

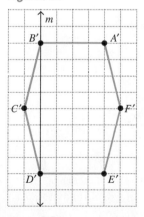

Figure 9.54

vertex A' must also be 2 units away from, but to the *left* of, reflection line l (see Fig 9.50 below). Next, notice that vertex B is 6 units to the right of line l. Thus, in the reflected triangle $A'B'C'$, vertex B' must also be 6 units away from, but to the *left* of, reflection line l. Next, notice that vertex C is 6 units to the right of line l. Thus, in the reflected triangle $A'B'C'$, vertex C' must also be 6 units away from, but to the *left* of, reflection line l. Figure 9.50 shows vertices A', B', and C'. Finally, we draw line segments between vertices A' and B', between B', and C', and between A' and C' to form the sides of the reflection triangle A' B' C', as illustrated in Fig. 9.50.

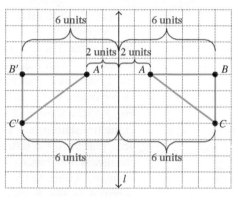

Figure 9.50

In Example 1, the reflection line did not intersect the figure being reflected. We will now study an example in which the reflection line goes directly through the figure to be reflected.

Example 2 *Reflection of a Hexagon*

Construct the reflection of hexagon *ABCDEF*, shown in Fig. 9.51, about reflection line l.

Solution From Fig. 9.51 (in the margin above), we see that vertex A in hexagon *ABCDEF* is 2 units to the left of reflection line l. Thus, vertex A' in the reflected hexagon will be 2 units to the right of l (see Fig. 9.52). Notice that vertex A' of the reflected hexagon is in the same location as vertex B of hexagon *ABCDEF* in Fig. 9.51.

We next see that vertex B in hexagon *ABCDEF* is 2 units to the right of l. Thus, vertex B' in the reflected hexagon will be 2 units to the left of l. Notice that vertex B' of the reflected hexagon is in the same location as vertex A of hexagon *ABCDEF*. We continue this process to determine the locations of vertices C', D', E', and F' of the reflected hexagon. Notice once again that each vertex of the reflected hexagon is in the same location as a vertex of hexagon *ABCDEF*. Finally, we draw the line segments to complete the reflected hexagon $A'B'C'D'E'F'$ (see Fig. 9.52). For this example, we see that other than the vertex labels, the positions of the hexagon before and after the reflection are identical.

In Example 2, the reflection line was in the center of the hexagon in the original position. As a result, the reflection line was also in the center of the reflected hexagon. In this particular case the reflected hexagon lies directly on top of the hexagon in its original position. We will revisit reflections such as that in Example 2 again when we discuss *reflective symmetry* later in this section.

Now consider hexagon *ABCDEF* in Fig. 9.53 and its reflection about line m, hexagon $A'B'C'D'E'F'$ in Fig. 9.54. Notice that the positions of the hexagon before and after the reflection, relative to line m, are not the same. Furthermore, if we line up reflection line m in Fig. 9.53 and Fig. 9.54, we would see that hexagon *ABCDEF* and hexagon $A'B'C'D'E'F'$ are in different positions.

Translations

The next rigid motion we will discuss is the *translation*. In a translation, we simply move a figure along a straight line to a new position.

Definition: **Translation or Glide**

A **translation** (or **glide**) is a rigid motion that moves a geometric figure by sliding it along a straight line segment in the plane. The direction and length of the line segment completely determine the translation.

After conducting a translation, we say the figure was *translated* to a new position.

A concise way to indicate the direction and the distance that a figure is moved during a translation is with a *translation vector*. In mathematics, vectors are typically represented with boldface letters. For example, in Fig. 9.55 we see trapezoid *ABCD* and a translation vector, **v**, which is pointing to the right and upward. This translation vector indicates a translation of 9 units to the right and 4 units upward. Notice that in Fig. 9.55 the translated vector appears on the right side of the polygon. The placement of the translation vector does not matter. Therefore, the translation vector could have been placed to the left, above, or below the polygon, and the translation would not change. When trapezoid *ABCD* is translated using **v**, every point on trapezoid *ABCD* is moved 9 units to the right and 4 units upward. This movement is demonstrated for vertex *A* in Fig. 9.56(a). Figure 9.56(b) shows trapezoid *ABCD* and the translated trapezoid *A'B'C'D'*. Notice in Fig. 9.56(b) that every point on trapezoid *A'B'C'D'* is 9 units to the right and 4 units up from its corresponding point on trapezoid *ABCD*.

Figure 9.55

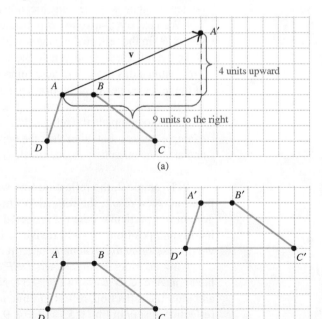

(a)

(b)

Figure 9.56

Example **3** *A Translated Square*

Given square *ABCD* and translation vector **v**, shown in Fig. 9.57, construct the translated square *A'B'C'D'*.

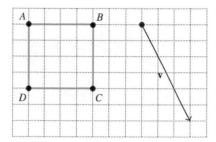

Figure 9.57

Solution The translated figure will be a square of the same size and shape as square *ABCD*. We notice that the translation vector, **v**, points 6 units downward and 3 units to the right. To determine the location of vertex *A'* of the translated square, start at vertex *A* of square *ABCD* and move down 6 units and to the right 3 units. We label this vertex *A'* (see Fig. 9.58a). We determine vertices *B'*, *C'*, and *D'* in a similar manner by moving down 6 units and to the right 3 units from vertices *B*, *C*, and *D,* respectively. Figure 9.58(b) shows square *ABCD* and the translated square *A'B'C'D'*. Notice in Fig. 9.58(b) that every point on square *A'B'C'D'* is 6 units down and 3 units to the right of its corresponding point on square *ABCD*.

(a)

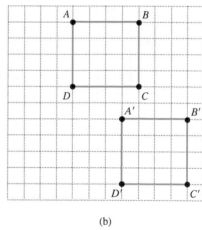

(b)

Figure 9.58

Rotations

The next rigid motion we will discuss is *rotation*. To help visualize a rotation, examine Fig. 9.59, which shows right triangle *ABC* and point *P* about which right triangle *ABC* is to be rotated.

Imagine that this page was removed from this book and attached to a bulletin board with a single pin through point *P*. Next imagine rotating the page 90° in the *counterclockwise* direction. The triangle would now appear as triangle *A'B'C'* shown in Fig. 9.60 on page 530. Next, imagine rotating the original triangle 180° in a counterclockwise direction. The triangle would now appear as triangle *A"B"C"* shown in Fig. 9.61 on page 530.

Now that we have an intuitive idea of how to determine a rotation, we give the definition of rotation.

Figure 9.59

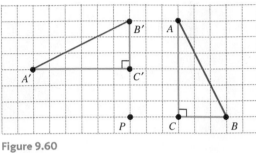

Figure 9.60

Figure 9.61

Definition: Rotation

A **rotation** is a rigid motion performed by rotating a geometric figure in the plane about a specific point, called the **rotation point** or the **center of rotation**. The angle through which the object is rotated is called the **angle of rotation**.

We will measure angles of rotation using degrees. In mathematics, generally, *counterclockwise angles have positive degree measures and clockwise angles have negative degree measures.*

Example 4 *A Rotated Rectangle*

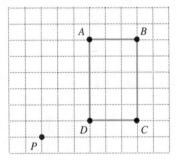

Figure 9.62

Given rectangle *ABCD* and rotation point *P*, shown in Fig. 9.62, construct rectangles that result from rotations through

a) 90°.   b) 180°.   c) 270°.

Solution

a) First, since 90 is a *positive* number, we will rotate the figure in a counterclockwise direction. We also note that the rotated rectangle will be the same size and shape as rectangle *ABCD*. To get an idea of what the rotated rectangle will look like, pick up this book and rotate it counterclockwise 90°. Figure 9.63 shows rectangle *ABCD* and rectangle *A'B'C'D'* which is rectangle *ABCD* rotated 90° about point *P*. Notice how line segment *AB* in rectangle *ABCD* is horizontal, but in the rotated rectangle in Fig. 9.63 line segment *A'B'* is vertical. Also notice that in rectangle *ABCD* vertex *D* is 3 units to the *right* and 1 unit *above* rotation point *P*, but in the rotated rectangle, vertex *D'* is 3 units *above* and 1 unit to the *left* of rotation point *P*.

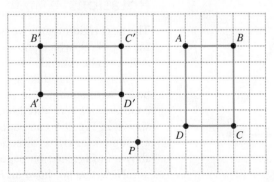

Figure 9.63

b) To gain some perspective on a 180° rotation, again pick up this book, but this time rotate the book 180° in the counterclockwise direction. The rotated rectangle *A″B″C″D″* is shown along with the rectangle *ABCD* in Fig. 9.64.

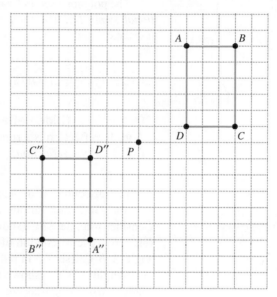

Figure 9.64

c) To gain some perspective on a 270° rotation, rotate this book 270° in the counterclockwise direction. The rotated rectangle *A‴B‴C‴D‴* is shown along with rectangle *ABCD* in Fig. 9.65.

Thus far in our examples of rotations, the rotation point was outside the figure being rotated. We now will study an example where the rotation point is inside the figure to be rotated.

┌ **Example 5** *A Rotation Point Inside a Polygon*

Given polygon *ABCDEFGH* and rotation point *P*, shown in Fig. 9.66, construct polygons that result from rotations through

a) 90°.   b) 180°.

Solution

a) We will rotate the polygon 90° in a counterclockwise direction. The resulting polygon will be the same size and shape as polygon *ABCDEFGH*. To visualize what the rotated polygon will look like, pick up this book and rotate it counterclockwise 90°. Figure 9.67 shows the polygon *ABCDEFGH,* in pale blue, and the rotated polygon *A′B′C′D′E′F′G′H′*, in deeper blue. Notice how line segments $\overline{AB}$, $\overline{CD}$, $\overline{EF}$, and $\overline{GH}$ in polygon *ABCDEFGH* are *horizontal*, but in the rotated polygon *A′B′C′D′E′F′G′H′*, line segments $\overline{A'B'}$, $\overline{C'D'}$, $\overline{E'F'}$, and $\overline{G'H'}$ are *vertical*. Also notice in polygon *ABCDEFGH* that line segment $\overline{GH}$ is 1 unit *above* rotation point *P*, but in the rotated polygon, line segment $\overline{G'H'}$ is 1 unit to the *left* of rotation point *P*.

b) To visualize the polygon obtained through a 180° rotation, we can pick up this book and rotate it 180° in the counterclockwise direction. Notice from Fig. 9.68 on page 532 that vertex *A″* of the rotated polygon is in the same position as vertex *E* of polygon *ABCDEFGH*. Also notice from Fig. 9.68 that vertex *B″* of the rotated polygon is in the same position as vertex *F* of polygon *ABCDEFGH*. In fact, each of the vertices in the rotated polygon is in the same position as a different vertex in polygon *ABCDEFGH*. From

Figure 9.65

Figure 9.66

Figure 9.67

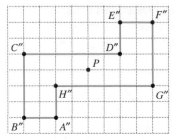

Figure 9.68

Fig. 9.68 we see that, other than vertex labels, the position of rotated polygon
$A''B''C''D''E''F''G''H''$ is the same as the position of polygon $ABCDEFGH$. ■

The polygon used in Example 5 will be discussed again later when we discuss *rotational symmetry*. The three rigid motions we have discussed thus far are reflection, translation, and rotation. Now we will discuss the fourth rigid motion, *glide reflection*.

Glide Reflections

Definition: Glide Reflection
A **glide reflection** is a rigid motion formed by performing a *translation* (or *glide*)
followed by a *reflection*.

A glide reflection, as its name suggests, is a translation (or glide) followed by a reflection. Both translations and reflections were discussed earlier in this section. Consider triangle ABC (shown in blue), translation vector **v**, and reflection line l in Fig. 9.69. The translation of triangle ABC, obtained using translation vector **v**, is triangle $A'B'C'$ (shown in red). The reflection of triangle $A'B'C'$ about reflection line l is triangle $A''B''C''$ (shown in green). Thus, triangle $A''B''C''$ is the glide reflection of triangle ABC using translation vector **v** and reflection line l.

Figure 9.69

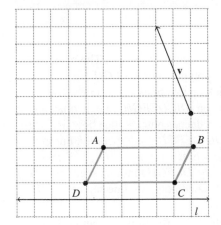

Figure 9.70

Example 6 *A Glide Reflection of a Parallelogram*

Construct a glide reflection of parallelogram $ABCD$, shown in Fig. 9.70, using
translation vector **v** and reflection line l.

Solution To construct the glide reflection of parallelogram $ABCD$, first translate
the parallelogram 2 units to the left and 5 units up, as indicated by translation vector
v. This translated parallelogram is labeled $A'B'C'D'$, shown in red in Fig. 9.71(a)
on page 533. Next, we will reflect parallelogram $A'B'C'D'$ about reflection line l.
Parallelogram $A'B'C'D'$, shown in red, and the reflected parallelogram, labeled
$A''B''C''D''$, shown in green, are shown in Fig. 9.71(b). The glide reflection of the
parallelogram $ABCD$ is parallelogram $A''B''C''D''$. ■

Symmetry

We are now ready to discuss symmetry. Our discussion of symmetry involves a rigid
motion of an object.

Figure 9.71

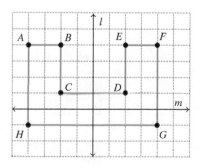

Figure 9.73

Definition: Symmetry

A **symmetry** of a geometric figure is a rigid motion that moves the figure back onto itself. That is, the beginning position and ending position of the figure must be identical.

Suppose we start with a figure in a specific position and perform a rigid motion on this figure. If the position of the figure after the rigid motion is identical to the position of the figure before the rigid motion (if the beginning and ending positions of the figure coincide), then the rigid motion is a symmetry and we say that the figure has symmetry. For a two-dimensional figure, there are four types of symmetries: reflective symmetry, rotational symmetry, translational symmetry, and glide reflective symmetry. In this textbook, however, we will discuss only reflective symmetry and rotational symmetry.

Consider the polygon and reflection line l shown in Fig. 9.72(a). If we use the rigid motion of reflection and reflect the polygon $ABCDEFGH$ about line l, we get polygon $A'B'C'D'E'F'G'H'$. Notice that the ending position of the polygon is identical to the starting position, as shown in Fig. 9.72(b). Compare Fig. 9.72(a) with Fig. 9.72(b). Although the vertex labels are different, the reflected polygon is in the same position as the polygon in the original position. Thus, we say that the polygon has *reflective symmetry* about line l. We refer to line l as a *line of symmetry*.

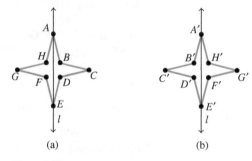

(a)   (b)

Figure 9.72

Recall Example 2 on page 527 in which hexagon $ABCDEF$ was reflected about reflection line l. Examine the hexagon in the original position (Fig. 9.51) and the hexagon in the final position after being reflected about line l (Fig. 9.52). Other than the labels of the vertices, the beginning and ending positions of the hexagon are identical. Therefore, hexagon $ABCDEF$ has reflective symmetry about line l.

Example 7 *Reflective Symmetries of Polygons*

Determine whether the polygon shown in Fig. 9.73 has reflective symmetry about each of the following lines.

a) Line l b) Line m

Solution

a) Examine the reflection of the polygon about line l as seen in Fig. 9.74(a) on page 534. Notice that other than the vertex labels, the beginning and ending positions of the polygon are identical. Thus, the polygon has reflective symmetry about line l.

b) Examine the reflection of the polygon about line m as seen in Fig. 9.74(b). Notice that the position of the reflected polygon is different from the original position of the polygon. Thus, the polygon does not have reflective symmetry about line m.

(a)

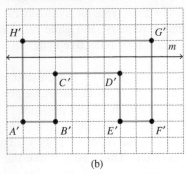

(b)

Figure 9.74

We will now discuss a second type of symmetry, rotational symmetry. Consider the polygon and rotation point P shown in Fig. 9.75(a). The rigid motion of rotation of polygon $ABCDEFGH$ through a 90° angle about point P gives polygon $A'B'C'D'E'F'G'H'$ shown in Fig. 9.75(b). Compare Fig. 9.75(a) with Fig. 9.75(b). Although the vertex labels are different, the position of the polygon before and after the rotation is identical. Thus, we say that the polygon has 90° *rotational symmetry* about point P. We refer to point P as the *point of symmetry*.

(a)   (b)

Figure 9.75

Recall Example 5 on page 531, in which polygon $ABCDEFGH$ was rotated 90° about point P in part (a) and 180° in part (b). First examine the polygon in the original position in Fig. 9.66 and the 90° rotated polygon in Fig. 9.67. Notice the position of the polygon after the 90° rotation is different from the original position of the polygon. Therefore, polygon $ABCDEFGH$ in Fig. 9.67 does not have 90° rotational symmetry about point P. Now examine the 180° rotated polygon in Fig. 9.68 on page 532. Notice that other than the vertex labels, the positions of the two polygons $ABCDEFGH$ and $A'B'C'D'E'F'G'H'$ are identical with respect to rotation about point P. Therefore, polygon $ABCDEFGH$ in Fig. 9.66 has 180° rotational symmetry about point P.

Example 8 *Rotational Symmetries*

Determine whether the polygon shown in Fig. 9.76 on page 533 has rotational symmetry about point P for rotations through each of the following angles.

a) 90°   b) 180°

Solution

a) To determine whether the polygon has 90° counterclockwise rotational symmetry about point P, we rotate the polygon 90° as shown in Fig. 9.77(a). Compare Fig. 9.77(a) with Fig. 9.76. Notice that the position of the polygon after the rotation in Fig. 9.77(a) is different than the original position of the polygon (Fig. 9.76). Therefore, the polygon does not have 90° rotational symmetry.

Figure 9.76

Figure 9.77   (a)   (b)

Symmetry can be found everywhere in nature. One type of symmetry in nature is reflective symmetry, or *bilateral* symmetry. For example, if you draw a line down the center of a maple leaf, you will often find that one half has the same shape as the other half.

Rotational symmetry, or *radial* symmetry, is also found in nature. Starfish, sand dollars, and many flowers all display rotational symmetry. For example, if you rotate a daisy 90°, 180°, or 270°, the rotated daisy will look identical to the original daisy. There are many other examples of symmetry in nature. In Exercise 63 on page 542 you are asked to find other examples of reflective symmetry and rotational symmetry.

b) To determine whether the polygon has 180° counterclockwise rotational symmetry about the point P, we rotate the polygon 180° as shown in Fig. 9.77(b) on page 534. Compare Fig. 9.77(b) with Fig. 9.76. Notice that other than vertex labels, the position of the polygon after the rotation in Fig. 9.77(b) is identical to the position of the polygon before the rotation (Fig. 9.76). Therefore, the polygon has 180° rotational symmetry. ∎

Tessellations

A fascinating application of transformational geometry is the creation of *tessellations*.

Definition: Tessellation or Tiling

A **tessellation** (or **tiling**) is a pattern consisting of the repeated use of the same geometric figures to entirely cover a plane, leaving no gaps. The geometric figures used are called the **tessellating shapes** of the tessellation.

Figure 9.78 shows an example of a tessellation from ancient Egypt. Perhaps the most famous person to incorporate tessellations into his work is M. C. Escher (see *Profiles in Mathematics* on page 536).

Figure 9.78

The simplest tessellations use one single regular polygon as the tessellating shape. Recall that a *regular polygon* is one whose sides are all the same length and whose interior angles all have the same measure. A tessellation that uses one single regular polygon as the tessellating shape is called a *regular tessellation*. It can be shown that only three regular tessellations exist: those that use an equilateral triangle, a square, or a regular hexagon as the tessellating shape. Figure 9.79 shows each of these regular tessellations. Notice that each tessellation can be obtained from a single tessellating shape through the use of reflections, translations, or rotations.

Figure 9.79

We will now learn how to create unique tessellations. We will do so by constructing a unique tessellating shape from a square. We could also construct other tessellating shapes, using an equilateral triangle or a regular hexagon. If you wish to follow along with our construction, you will need some lightweight cardboard, a ruler, cellophane tape, and a pair of scissors. We will start by measuring and cutting out a square 2 in. by 2 in. from the cardboard. We next cut the square into two parts by cutting it from top to bottom using any kind of cut. One example is shown in Fig. 9.80. We then rearrange the pieces and tape the two vertical edges together as shown in Fig. 9.81. Next we cut this new shape into two parts by cutting it from left to right using any kind of cut as shown in Fig. 9.82. We then rearrange the pieces and tape the two horizontal edges together as shown in Fig. 9.83. This completes our tessellating shape.

Figure 9.80

Figure 9.81

Figure 9.82

Figure 9.83

Figure 9.84

We now set the cardboard tessellating shape in the middle of a blank piece of paper (the tessellating shape can be rotated to any position as a starting point) and trace the outline of the shape onto the paper. Next move the tessellating shape so that it lines up with the figure already drawn and trace the outline again. Continue to do that until the page is completely covered. Once the page is covered with the tessellation, we can add some interesting colors or even some unique sketches to the tessellation. Figure 9.84 shows one tessellation created using the tessellation shape in Fig. 9.83. In Fig. 9.84, the tessellation shape was rotated about 45° counterclockwise.

An infinite number of different tessellations can be created using the method described by altering the cuts made. We could also create different tessellations using an equilateral triangle, a regular hexagon, or other types of polygons. There are also other, more complicated ways to create the tessellating shape. The Internet has many sites devoted to the creation of tessellations by hand. Many computer programs that generate tessellations are also available.

Profile In Mathematics

Maurits Cornelius Escher

In addition to being wonderfully engaging art, the work of M. C. Escher (1898–1972) also displays some of the more beautiful and intricate aspects of mathematics. Escher's work involves Euclidean, non-Euclidean (to be studied shortly), and transformational geometries. Amazingly, Escher had no formal training in mathematics.

In 1936, Escher became obsessed with tessellations, that is, with creating art that used objects to cover a plane so as to leave no gaps. Symmetry became a cornerstone of Escher's famous tessellations. In 1995, the mathematician Donald Coxeter published a paper in which he proved that the mathematics Escher displayed in the etching *Circle Limit III* (see page 557) was indeed perfectly consistent with mathematical theory.

Escher kept a notebook in which he kept background information for his artwork. In this notebook, Escher characterized all possible combinations of shapes, colors, and symmetrical properties of polygons in the plane. By doing so, Escher had unwittingly developed areas of a branch of mathematics known as *crystallography* years before any mathematician had done so!

Escher's *Self Portrait in Spherical Mirror*

SECTION 9.5   *Exercises*

Warm Up Exercises

In Exercises 1–14, fill in the blanks with an appropriate word, phrase, or symbol(s).

1. The act of moving a geometric figure from some starting position to some ending position without altering its shape or size is called a(n) _____ motion.

2. A rigid motion that moves a geometric figure to a new position such that the new position is a mirror image of the figure in the starting position is called a(n) _____.

3. In two dimensions, the geometric figure and its reflected image are equidistant from a line called the reflection line, or the _____ of reflection.

4. A rigid motion that moves a geometric figure by sliding it along a straight line segment in the plane is called a(n) _____.

5. A concise way to indicate the direction and the distance that a figure is moved during a translation is with a translation _____.

6. A rigid motion performed by rotating a geometric figure in the plane about a specific point is called a(n) _____.

7. The point about which a geometric figure is rotated during a rotation is called the rotation point, or the _____ of rotation.

8. The angle through which a geometric figure is rotated during a rotation is called the angle of _____.

9. A rigid motion formed by performing a translation followed by a reflection is called a(n) _____ reflection.

10. A rigid motion that moves the geometric figure back onto itself is called a(n) _____.

11. Rectangle *ABCD* shown below has _____ symmetry about line *l*.

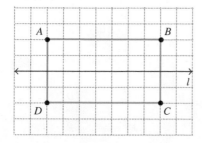

12. Rectangle *ABCD* shown below has 180° _____ symmetry about point *P*.

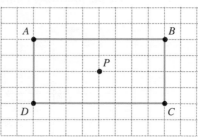

13. A pattern consisting of the repeated use of the same geometric figures to entirely cover a plane, leaving no gaps, is called a(n) _____.

14. The geometric figures used to cover a plane are called the _____ shapes of the tessellation.

Practice the Skills/Problem Solving

In Exercises 15–22, use the given figure and lines of reflection to construct the indicated reflections. Show the figure in the positions both before and after the reflection.

In Exercises 15 and 16, use the following figure. Construct

15. the reflection of rectangle *ABCD* about line *m*.

16. the reflection of rectangle *ABCD* about line *l*.

In Exercises 17 and 18, use the following figure. Construct

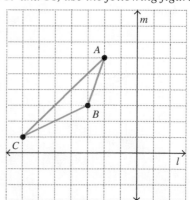

17. the reflection of triangle *ABC* about line *l*.

18. the reflection of triangle *ABC* about line *m*.

In Exercises 19 and 20, use the following figure. Construct

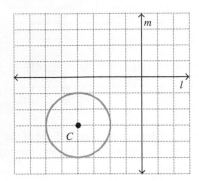

19. the reflection of circle *C* about line *l*.

20. the reflection of circle *C* about line *m*.

In Exercises 21 and 22, use the following figure. Construct

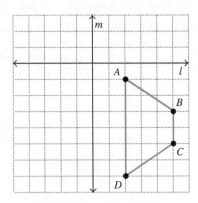

21. the reflection of trapezoid *ABCD* about line *m*.

22. the reflection of trapezoid *ABCD* about line *l*.

*In Exercises 23–30, use the translation vectors **v** and **w**, shown below, to construct the translations indicated in the exercises. Show the figure in the positions both before and after the translation.*

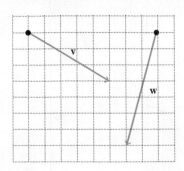

In Exercises 23 and 24, use the following figure. Construct

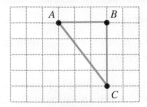

23. the translation of triangle *ABC* using translation vector **v**.

24. the translation of triangle *ABC* using translation vector **w**.

In Exercises 25 and 26, use the following figure. Construct

25. the translation of square *ABCD* using translation vector **w**.

26. the translation of square *ABCD* using translation vector **v**.

In Exercises 27 and 28, use the following figure. Construct

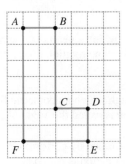

27. the translation of polygon *ABCDEF* using translation vector **v**.

28. the translation of polygon *ABCDEF* using translation vector **w**.

In Exercises 29 and 30, use the following figure. Construct

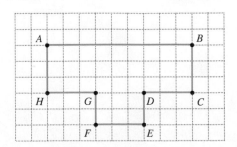

29. the translation of polygon *ABCDEFGH* using translation vector **w** (shown on page 538).

30. the translation of polygon *ABCDEFGH* using translation vector **v** (shown on page 538).

In Exercises 31–38, use the given figure and rotation point P to construct the indicated rotations. Show the figure in the positions both before and after the rotation.

In Exercises 31 and 32, use the following figure. Construct

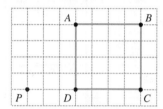

31. a 90° rotation of square *ABCD* about point *P*.

32. a 180° rotation of square *ABCD* about point *P*.

In Exercises 33 and 34, use the following figure. Construct

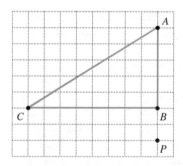

33. a 180° rotation of triangle *ABC* about point *P*.

34. a 270° rotation of triangle *ABC* about point *P*.

In Exercises 35 and 36, use the following figure. Construct

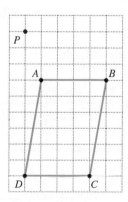

35. a 270° rotation of parallelogram *ABCD* about point *P*.

36. a 180° rotation of parallelogram *ABCD* about point *P*.

In Exercises 37 and 38, use the following figure. Construct

37. a 90° rotation of trapezoid *ABCD* about point *P*.

38. a 270° rotation of trapezoid *ABCD* about point *P*.

*In Exercises 39–46, use the given figure, translation vectors **v** and **w**, and reflection lines l and m to construct the indicated glide reflections. Show the figure in the positions before and after the glide reflection.*

In Exercises 39 and 40, use the following figure. Construct

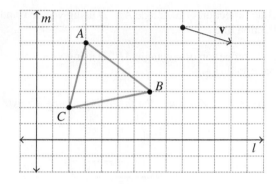

39. a glide reflection of triangle *ABC* using vector **v** and reflection line *l*.

40. a glide reflection of triangle *ABC* using vector **v** and reflection line *m*.

In Exercises 41 and 42, use the following figure. Construct

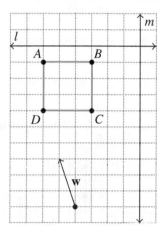

41. a glide reflection of square *ABCD* using vector **w** and reflection line *l*.

42. a glide reflection of square *ABCD* using vector **w** and reflection line *m*.

In Exercises 43 and 44, use the following figure. Construct

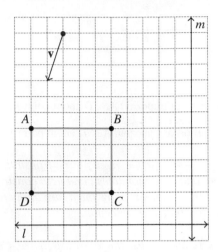

43. a glide reflection of rectangle *ABCD* using vector **v** and reflection line *l*.

44. a glide reflection of rectangle *ABCD* using vector **v** and reflection line *m*.

In Exercises 45 and 46, use the following figure. Construct

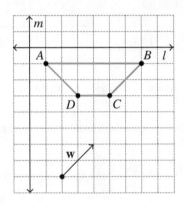

45. a glide reflection of trapezoid *ABCD* using vector **w** and reflection line *l*.

46. a glide reflection of trapezoid *ABCD* using vector **w** and reflection line *m*.

47. a) Reflect triangle *ABC*, shown below, about line *l*. Label the reflected triangle *A'B'C'*.

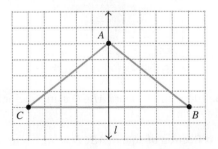

b) Other than vertex labels, is the position of triangle *A'B'C'* identical to the position of triangle *ABC*?

c) Does triangle *ABC* have reflective symmetry about line *l*?

48. a) Reflect rectangle *ABCD*, shown below, about line *l*. Label the reflected rectangle *A'B'C'D'*.

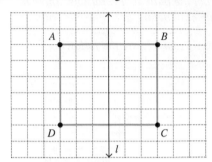

b) Other than vertex labels, is the position of rectangle *A'B'C'D'* identical to the position of rectangle *ABCD*?

c) Does rectangle *ABCD* have reflective symmetry about line *l*?

49. a) Reflect parallelogram *ABCD*, shown below, about line *l*. Label the reflected parallelogram *A'B'C'D'*.

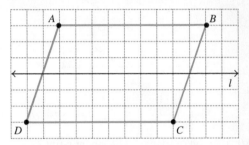

b) Other than vertex labels, is the position of parallelogram *A'B'C'D'* identical to the position of parallelogram *ABCD*?

c) Does parallelogram *ABCD* have reflective symmetry about line *l*?

50. a) Reflect triangle *ABC*, shown below, about line *l*. Label the reflected triangle *A'B'C'*.

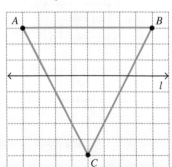

b) Other than vertex labels, is the position of triangle $A'B'C'$ identical to the position of triangle ABC?

c) Does triangle ABC have reflective symmetry about line l?

51. a) Rotate rectangle $ABCD$, shown below, 90° about point P. Label the rotated rectangle $A'B'C'D'$.

b) Other than vertex labels, is the position of rectangle $A'B'C'D'$ identical to the position of rectangle $ABCD$?

c) Does rectangle $ABCD$ have 90° rotational symmetry about point P?

d) Now rotate the rectangle in the original position, rectangle $ABCD$, 180° about point P. Label the rotated rectangle $A''B''C''D''$.

e) Other than vertex labels, is the position of rectangle $A''B''C''D''$ identical to the position of rectangle $ABCD$?

f) Does rectangle $ABCD$ have 180° rotational symmetry about point P?

52. a) Rotate parallelogram $ABCD$, shown below, 90° about point P. Label the rotated parallelogram $A'B'C'D'$.

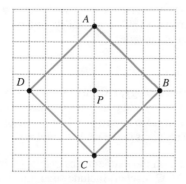

b) Other than vertex labels, is the position of parallelogram $A'B'C'D'$ identical to the position of parallelogram $ABCD$?

c) Does parallelogram $ABCD$ have 90° rotational symmetry about point P?

d) Now rotate the parallelogram in the original position, parallelogram $ABCD$, shown above, 180° about point P. Label the rotated parallelogram $A''B''C''D''$.

e) Other than vertex labels, is the position of parallelogram $A''B''C''D''$ identical to the position of parallelogram $ABCD$?

f) Does parallelogram $ABCD$ have 180° rotational symmetry about point P?

53. Consider the following figure.

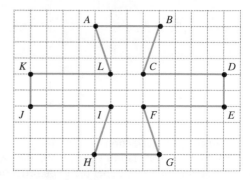

a) Insert a vertical line m through the figure so the figure has reflective symmetry about line m.

b) Insert a horizontal line l through the figure so the figure has reflective symmetry about line l.

c) Insert a point P within the figure so the figure has 180° rotational symmetry about point P.

d) Is it possible to insert a point P within the figure so the figure has 90° rotational symmetry about point P? Explain your answer.

54. Consider the following figure.

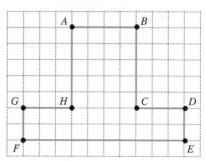

a) Insert a vertical line m through the figure so the figure has reflective symmetry about line m.

b) Is it possible to insert a horizontal line l through the figure so the figure has reflective symmetry about line l? Explain your answer.

c) Is it possible to insert a point P within the figure so the figure has 90° rotational symmetry about point P? Explain your answer.

d) Is it possible to insert a point P within the figure so the figure has 180° rotational symmetry about point P? Explain your answer.

Challenge Problems/Group Activities

55. *Glide Reflection, Order* Examine the figure below and then do the following:

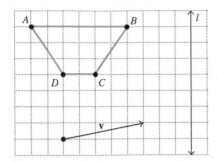

a) Determine a glide reflection of trapezoid *ABCD* by first applying translation vector **v** and then reflecting about the line *l*. Label the glide reflection *A′B′C′D′*.

b) In this step, we will reverse the order of the translation and the reflection. First reflect trapezoid *ABCD* about the line *l* and then translate the reflection using vector **v**. Label the resulting figure *A″B″C″D″*.

c) Is figure *A′B′C′D′* in the same position as figure *A″B″C″D″*?

d) What can be said about the order of the translation and the reflection used in a glide reflection? Is the figure obtained in part (a) or part (b) the glide reflection?

56. *Tessellation with a Square* Create a unique tessellation from a square piece of cardboard by using the method described on page 536. Be creative, using color and sketches to complete your tessellation.

57. *Tessellation with a Hexagon* Using the method described on page 536, create a unique tessellation using a regular hexagon like the one shown below. Be creative, using color and sketches to complete your tessellation.

58. *Tessellation with an Octagon?*

Trace the regular octagon, shown below, onto a separate piece of paper.

Try to create a regular tessellation by tracing this octagon repeatedly. Attempt to cover the entire piece of paper where no two octagons overlap each other. What conclusion can you draw about using a regular octagon as a tessellating shape?

59. *Tessellation with a Pentagon?* Repeat Exercise 58 using the regular pentagon below instead of a regular octagon.

Recreational Mathematics

60. Examine each capital letter in the alphabet and determine which letters have reflective symmetry about a horizontal line through the center of the letter.

61. Examine each capital letter in the alphabet and determine which letters have reflective symmetry about a vertical line through the center of the letter.

62. Examine each capital letter in the alphabet and determine which letters have 180° rotational symmetry about a point in the center of the letter.

Internet/Research Activities

63. In the study of biology, reflective symmetry is called *bilateral symmetry* and rotational symmetry is called *radial symmetry*. Do research and write a report on the role symmetry plays in the study of biology.

64. Write a paper on the mathematics displayed in the artwork of M. C. Escher. Include such topics as tessellations, optical illusions, perspective, and non-Euclidean geometry.

Topology

Examine the outline of the map of the continental United States shown below. Now suppose you were given four crayons, each of a different color. Could you color this map with the four crayons in a way so that no two bordering states have the same color? In this section, we will discuss this question and many other questions that are relevant to the branch of mathematics known as *topology*.

Why *This is Important* Topology is used in many applications in the fields of map making (cartography), computer science, robotics, and biology.

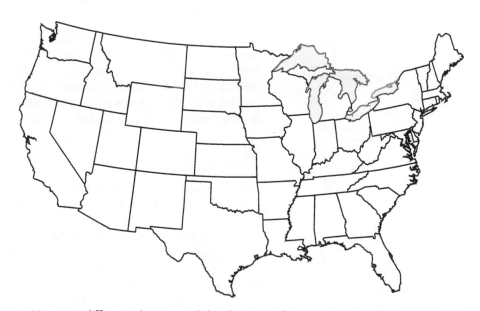

▲ *How many different colors are needed so that no two bordering states share the same color?*

The branch of mathematics called *topology* is sometimes referred to as "rubber sheet geometry" because it deals with bending and stretching of geometric figures.

One of the first pioneers of topology was the German astronomer and mathematician August Ferdinand Möbius (1790–1866). A student of Gauss, Möbius was the director of the University of Leipzig's observatory. He spent a great deal of time studying geometry and he played an essential part in the systematic development of projective geometry. He is best known for his studies of the properties of one-sided surfaces, including the one called the Möbius strip.

Möbius Strip

If you place a pencil on one surface of a sheet of paper and do not remove it from the sheet, you must cross the edge to get to the other surface. Thus, a sheet of paper has one edge and two surfaces. The sheet retains these properties even when crumpled into a ball. The *Möbius strip*, also called a *Möbius band*, is a one-sided, one-edged surface. You can construct one, as shown in Fig. 9.85, by (a) taking a strip of paper, (b) giving one end a half twist, and (c) taping the ends together.

The Möbius strip has some very interesting properties. To better understand these properties, perform the following experiments.

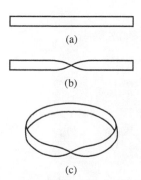

(a)

(b)

(c)

Figure 9.85

Figure 9.86

Figure 9.87

Figure 9.88

Figure 9.89

Experiment 1 Make a Möbius strip using a strip of paper and tape as illustrated in Fig. 9.85. Place the point of a felt-tip pen on the edge of the strip (Fig. 9.86). Pull the strip slowly so that the pen marks the edge; do not remove the pen from the edge. Continue pulling the strip and observe what happens.

Experiment 2 Make a Möbius strip. Place the tip of a felt-tip pen on the surface of the strip (Fig. 9.87). Pull the strip slowly so that the pen marks the surface. Continue and observe what happens.

Experiment 3 Make a Möbius strip. Use scissors to make a small slit in the middle of the strip. Starting at the slit, cut along the strip, keeping the scissors in the middle of the strip (Fig. 9.88). Continue cutting and observe what happens.

Experiment 4 Make a Möbius strip. Make a small slit at a point about one-third of the width of the strip. Cut along the strip, keeping the scissors the same distance from the edge (Fig. 9.89). Continue cutting and observe what happens.

If you give a strip of paper several twists, you get variations on the Möbius strip. To a topologist, the important distinction is between an odd number of twists, which leads to a one-sided surface, and an even number of twists, which leads to a two-sided surface. All strips with an odd number of twists are topologically the same as a Möbius strip, and all strips with an even number of twists are topologically the same as an ordinary cylinder, which has no twists.

Klein Bottle

Another topological object is the punctured *Klein bottle*; see Fig. 9.90. This object, named after Felix Klein (1849–1925), resembles a bottle but only has one side.

A punctured Klein bottle can be made by stretching a hollow piece of glass tubing. The neck is then passed through a hole and joined to the base.

Look closely at the model of the Klein bottle shown in Fig. 9.90. The punctured Klein bottle has only one edge and no outside or inside because it has just one side. Figure 9.91 shows a Klein bottle blown in glass by Alan Bennett of Bedford, England.

Imagine trying to paint a Klein bottle. You start on the "outside" of the large part and work your way down the narrowing neck. When you cross the self-intersection, you have to pretend temporarily that it is not there, so you continue to

Limericks from unknown writers:

"A mathematician confided
That a Möbius band is one-sided,
And you'll get quite a laugh
If you cut one in half
For it stays in one piece when divided."

"A mathematician named Klein
Thought the Möbius band was divine.
He said, 'If you glue
the edges of two
You'll get a weird bottle like mine.' "

Figure 9.90

Figure 9.91 *Klein bottle,* a one-sided surface, blown in glass by Alan Bennett.

follow the neck, which is now inside the bulb. As the neck opens up, to rejoin the bulb, you find that you are now painting the inside of the bulb! What appear to be the inside and outside of a Klein bottle connect together seamlessly since it is one-sided.

If a Klein bottle is cut along a curve, the results are two (one-twist) Möbius strips; see Fig. 9.92. Thus, a Klein bottle could also be made by gluing together two Möbius strips along the edges.

Figure 9.92 Two Möbius strips result from cutting a Klein bottle along a curve.

Maps

Mapmakers have known for a long time that regardless of the complexity of the map and whether it is drawn on a flat surface or a sphere, only four colors are needed to differentiate each country (or state) from its immediate neighbors. Thus, every map can be drawn by using only four colors, and no two countries with a common border will have the same color. Regions that meet at only one point (such as the states of Arizona, Colorado, Utah, and New Mexico) are not considered to have a common border. In Fig. 9.93(a), no two states with a common border are marked with the same color.

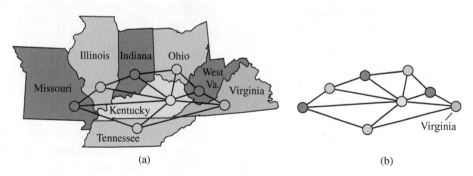

(a)   (b)

Figure 9.93

The "four-color" problem was first suggested by a student of Augustus DeMorgan in 1852. In 1976, Kenneth Appel and Wolfgang Haken of the University of Illinois—using their ingenuity, logic, and 1200 hours of computer time—succeeded in proving that only four colors are needed to draw a map. They solved the four-color map problem by reducing any map to a series of points and connecting line segments. They replaced each country with a point. They connected two countries having a common border with a straight line; see Fig. 9.93(b). They then showed that the points of any graph in the plane could be colored by using only four colors in such a way that no two points connected by the same line were the same color.

Mathematicians have shown that, on different surfaces, more than four colors may be needed to draw a map. For example, a map drawn on a Möbius strip requires a maximum of six colors, as in Fig. 9.94(a). A map drawn on a torus (the shape of a doughnut) requires a maximum of seven colors, as in Fig. 9.94(b).

Topological Paper Constructions

In addition to the Möbius strip, many other interesting surfaces can be made using paper, scissors, and cellophane tape. Shown above is a surface that shares some of the same characteristics as a Möbius strip, but is not topologically equivalent to a Möbius strip. Notice that, like a Möbius strip, this surface has 1 side and 1 edge.

Construct the surface shown above using two strips of paper, scissors, and tape. Attempt to cut the surface "in half" by making a small slit along a dashed line in the middle of the paper surface. Then cut along the dashed line shown in the figure, keeping the scissors the same distance from the edge. What happens? Exercise 45 on page 549 describes another topological construction.

Many Internet Web sites are devoted to topological constructions. One such Web site is www.woollythoughts.com/mobius.html. This Web site demonstrates a Möbius strip made with a zipper. This process allows you to "cut" the Möbius strip and then put the two parts back together again.

(a)   (b)

Figure 9.94

Jordan Curves

A *Jordan curve* is a topological object that can be thought of as a circle twisted out of shape; see Fig. 9.95 (a)–(d). Like a circle, it has an inside and an outside. To get from one side to the other, at least one line must be crossed. Consider the Jordan curve in Fig. 9.95(d). Are points A and B inside or outside the curve?

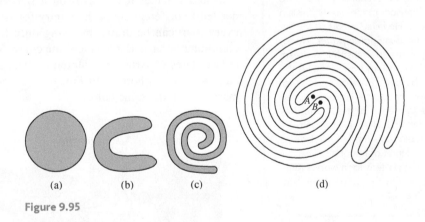

(a)   (b)   (c)   (d)

Figure 9.95

A quick way to tell whether the two dots are inside or outside the curve is to draw a straight line from each dot to a point that is clearly outside the curve. If the straight line crosses the curve an even number of times, the dot is outside. If the straight line crosses the curve an odd number of times, the dot is inside the curve. Can you explain why this procedure works? Determine whether point A and point B are inside or outside the curve (see Exercises 17 and 18 at the end of this section).

Topological Equivalence

Someone once said that a topologist is a person who does not know the difference between a doughnut and a coffee cup. Two geometric figures are said to be *topologically equivalent* if one figure can be elastically twisted, stretched, bent, or shrunk into the other figure without puncturing or ripping the original figure. If a doughnut is made of elastic material, it can be stretched, twisted, bent, shrunk, and distorted until it resembles a coffee cup with a handle, as shown in Fig. 9.96 on page 547. Thus, the doughnut and the coffee cup are topologically equivalent.

Figure 9.96

In topology, figures are classified according to their *genus*. The *genus* of an object is determined by the number of holes that go *through* the object. A cup and a doughnut each have one hole and are of genus 1 (and are therefore topologically equivalent). Notice that the cup's handle is considered a hole, whereas the opening at the rim of the cup is not considered a hole. For our purposes, we will consider an object's opening a hole if you could pour liquid *through* the opening. For example, a typical bowling ball has three openings in the surface into which you can put your fingers when preparing to roll the ball, but liquid cannot be poured *through* any of these openings. Therefore, a bowling ball has genus 0 and is topologically equivalent to a marble. Figure 9.97 illustrates the genus of several objects.

Genus 0	Genus 1	Genus 2	Genus 3 or more
Marble	Doughnut	Kettle	Strainer
Bowling Ball	Coffee Cup	Scissors	Grater

Figure 9.97

SECTION 9.6
Exercises

Warm Up Exercises

In Exercises 1–8, fill in the blanks with an appropriate word, phrase, or symbol(s).

1. Because it deals with bending and stretching of geometric figures, topology is sometimes referred to as _____ sheet geometry.

2. A one-sided, one-edged surface is a(n) _____ strip.

3. A topological object that resembles a bottle but has only one side is a(n) _____ bottle.

4. If you color a map of the United States, the maximum number of colors needed so that no two states that share a common border have the same color is _____.

5. A topological object that can be thought of as a circle twisted out of shape is a(n) _____ curve.

6. The number of holes that go through an object determines the _____ of the object.

7. A compact disc is an example of an object that has a genus of _____.

8. A pair of scissors is an example of an object that has a genus of _____.

Practice the Skills

In Exercises 9–12, color the map by using a maximum of four colors so that no two regions with a common border have the same color.

9.

10.

		3
1	2	4
		5
	6	
	7	
	8	

11.

12.

Using the Four-Color Theorem *In Exercises 13–16, maps show certain areas of the United States, Canada, and Mexico. Shade in the states (or provinces) using a maximum of four colors so that no two states (or provinces) with a common border have the same color.*

13.

14.

15.

16.

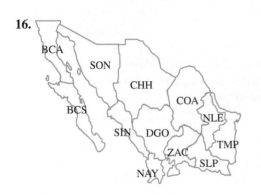

17. Determine whether point *A* in Fig. 9.95(d) on page 546 is inside or outside the Jordan curve.

18. Determine whether point *B* in Fig. 9.95(d) is inside or outside the Jordan curve.

At right is a Jordan curve. In Exercises 19–22, determine if the point is inside or outside the curve.

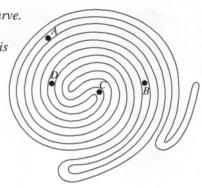

19. Point *A*

20. Point *B*

21. Point *C*

22. Point *D*

In Exercises 23–34, give the genus of the object. If the object has a genus larger than 5, write "larger than 5."

23.

24.

25.

26.

27.

28.

29.

30.

31.

32.

33.

34.

35. Name at least three objects not mentioned in this section that have

   a) genus 0.   **b)** genus 1.

   c) genus 2.   **d)** genus 3 or more.

36. Use the result of Experiment 1 on page 544 to find the number of edges on a Möbius strip.

37. Use the result of Experiment 2 on page 544 to find the number of surfaces on a Möbius strip.

38. How many separate strips are obtained in Experiment 3 on page 544?

39. How many separate strips are obtained in Experiment 4 on page 544?

40. Make a Möbius strip. Cut it one-third of the way from the edge, as in Experiment 4 on page 544. You should get two loops, one going through the other. Determine whether either (or both) of these loops is itself a Möbius strip.

41. a) Take a strip of paper, give it one full twist, and connect the ends. Is the result a Möbius strip with only one side? Explain.

   b) Determine the number of edges, as in Experiment 1.

   c) Determine the number of surfaces, as in Experiment 2.

   d) Cut the strip down the middle. What is the result?

42. Take a strip of paper, make one whole twist and another half twist, and then tape the ends together. Test by a method of your choice to determine whether this has the same properties as a Möbius strip.

Challenge Problems/Group Activities

43. Using clay (or glazing compound), make a doughnut. Without puncturing or tearing the doughnut, reshape it into a topologically equivalent figure, a cup with a handle.

44. Using at most four colors, color the following map of the counties of New Mexico. Do not use the same color for any two counties that share a common border.

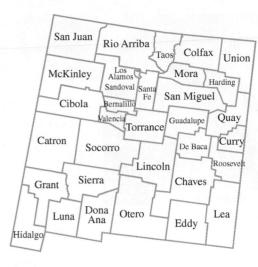

Recreational Math

45. *Topological Paper Constructions* Using paper, scissors, and tape, perform the construction described in the *Recreational Mathematics* box on page 546. Once you have completed the construction, cut along the dashed line as instructed. Set the result aside.

   In this exercise we will construct another interesting surface. We begin by constructing a "cross" shape from two strips of paper, as shown below, using scissors and tape. Note the red dashed line and the green dashed line and the ends of the strips labeled *A* or *B*.

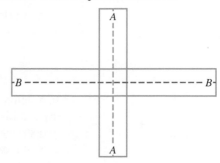

Next, using tape connect the two ends labeled *A without* twisting the ends. Then, connect the two ends labeled *B* by giving one end a half twist. The strip that connects the *B* ends should resemble a Möbius strip. Finally, cut the object first along the green dashed line and then along the red dashed line. Compare the result with that from the construction on page 546. What do you notice?

Internet/Research Activities

46. Use the Internet to find a map of your state that shows the outline of all the counties within your state. Print this map and, using at most four colors, color it. Do not use the same color for any two counties that share a common border.

47. The short story *Paul Bunyan versus the Conveyor Belt* (1947) by William Hazlett Upson focuses on a conveyor belt in the shape of a Möbius strip. The story can be found in several books that include mathematical essays. Read Upson's short story and write a 200-word description of what Paul Bunyan does to the conveyor belt. Confirm the outcome of the story by repeating Paul's actions with a paper Möbius strip.

▲ *Many branches of geometry are needed to accurately represent space.*

Ponder the following question: Given a line *l* and a point *P* not on the line *l*, how many lines can you draw through *P* that are parallel to *l*?

You may answer that only one line may be drawn through *P* parallel to *l*. This answer would be correct *provided* the setting of the problem is in a plane and not on the surface of a curved object. The study of this question led to the development of several new branches of geometry. It is now believed all of these branches of geometry, taken together, can be used to accurately represent space. In this section, we will study the geometry of surfaces other than the geometry of the plane.

Why *This is Important* Scientists now believe that space and time can best be represented using a combination of these different branches of geometry. In addition, many applications of the geometry described in this section are used in modern technology, such as cellular phones, computer memory, and medical imaging.

Non-Euclidean Geometry

In Section 9.1, we stated that postulates or axioms are statements to be accepted as true. In his book *Elements*, Euclid's fifth postulate was, "If a straight line falling on two straight lines makes the interior angles on the same side less than two right angles, the two straight lines, if produced indefinitely, meet on that side on which the angles are less than the two right angles."

Euclid's fifth axiom may be better understood by observing Fig. 9.98. The sum of angles *A* and *B* is less than the sum of two right angles (180°). Therefore, the two lines will meet if extended.

John Playfair (1748–1819), a Scottish physicist and mathematician, wrote a geometry book that was published in 1795. In his book, Playfair gave a logically equivalent interpretation of Euclid's fifth postulate. This version is often referred to as Playfair's postulate or the Euclidean parallel postulate.

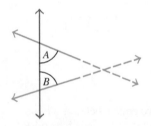

Figure 9.98

The Euclidean Parallel Postulate
Given a line and a point not on the line, one and only one line can be drawn through the given point parallel to the given line (Fig. 9.99).

The Euclidean parallel postulate may be better understood by looking at Fig. 9.99. Many mathematicians after Euclid believed that this postulate was not as self-evident as the other nine postulates given by Euclid. Others believed that this postulate could be proved from the other nine postulates and therefore was not needed at all. Of the many attempts to prove that the fifth postulate was not needed, the most noteworthy one was presented by Girolamo Saccheri (1667–1733), a Jesuit

Figure 9.99

MATHEMATICS TODAY

Mapping The Brain

Photograph courtesy of Dr. Monica K. Hurdal (mhurdal@math.fsu.edu), Dept. of Mathematics, Florida State University

Medical researchers and mathematicians are currently attempting to capture an image of the three-dimensional human brain on a two-dimensional map. In some respects, the task is like capturing the image of Earth on a two-dimensional map, but because of the many folds and fissures on the surface of the brain, the task is much more complex. Points of the brain that are at different depths can appear too close in a flat image. Therefore, to develop an accurate mapping, researchers use topology, hyperbolic geometry, and elliptical geometry to create an image known as a *conformal mapping*. Researchers use conformal mappings to precisely identify the parts of the brain that correspond to specific functions.

Why **This is Important** Medical imaging is just one application of the various branches of geometry described in this section.

priest in Italy. In the course of his elaborate chain of deductions, Saccheri proved many of the theorems of what is now called hyperbolic geometry. However, Saccheri did not realize what he had done. He believed that Euclid's geometry was the only "true" geometry and concluded that his own work was in error. Thus, Saccheri narrowly missed receiving credit for a great achievement: the founding of *non-Euclidean geometry*.

Over time, geometers became more and more frustrated at their inability to prove Euclid's fifth postulate. One of them, a Hungarian named Farkos Bolyai, in a letter to his son, Janos Bolyai, wrote, "I entreat you leave the science of parallels alone.... I have traveled past all reefs of this infernal dead sea and have always come back with a broken mast and torn sail." The son, refusing to heed his father's advice, continued to think about parallels until, in 1823, he saw the whole truth and enthusiastically declared, "I have created a new universe from nothing." He recognized that geometry branches in two directions, depending on whether Euclid's fifth postulate is applied. He recognized two different geometries and published his discovery as a 24-page appendix to a textbook written by his father. The famous mathematician George Bruce Halsted called it "the most extraordinary two dozen pages in the whole history of thought." Farkos Bolyai proudly presented a copy of his son's work to his friend Carl Friedrich Gauss, then Germany's greatest mathematician, whose reply to the father had a devastating effect on the son. Gauss wrote, "I am unable to praise this work.... To praise it would be to praise myself. Indeed, the whole content of the work, the path taken by your son, the results to which he is led, coincides almost entirely with my meditations which occupied my mind partly for the last thirty or thirty-five years." We now know from his earlier correspondence that Gauss had indeed been familiar with *hyperbolic geometry* even before Janos was born. In his letter, Gauss also indicated that it was his intention not to let his theory be published during his lifetime, but to record it so that the theory would not perish with him. It is believed that the reason Gauss did not publish his work was that he feared being ridiculed by other prominent mathematicians of his time.

At about the same time as Bolyai's publication, Nikolay Ivanovich Lobachevsky, a Russian, published a paper that was remarkably like Bolyai's, although it was quite independent of it. Lobachevsky made a deeper investigation and wrote several books. In marked contrast to Bolyai, who received no recognition during his lifetime, Lobachevsky received great praise and became a professor at the University of Kazan.

After the initial discovery, little attention was paid to the subject until 1854, when G. F. Bernhard Riemann (1826–1866), a student of Gauss, suggested a second type of non-Euclidean geometry, which is now called *spherical*, *elliptical*, or *Riemannian geometry*. The hyperbolic geometry of his predecessors was synthetic; that is, it was not based on or related to any concrete model when it was developed. Riemann's geometry was closely related to the theory of surfaces. A *model* may be considered a physical interpretation of the undefined terms that satisfies the axioms. A model may be a picture or an actual physical object.

The two types of non-Euclidean geometries we have mentioned are elliptical geometry and hyperbolic geometry. The major difference among the three geometries lies in the fifth axiom. The fifth axiom of the three geometries is summarized here.

The Fifth Axiom of Geometry

Euclidean	Elliptical	Hyperbolic
Given a line and a point not on the line, one and only one line can be drawn parallel to the given line through the given point	Given a line and a point not on the line, no line can be drawn through the given point parallel to the given line.	Given a line and a point not on the line, two or more lines can be drawn through the given point parallel to the given line.

To understand the fifth axiom of the two non-Euclidean geometries, remember that the term *line* is undefined. Thus, a line can be interpreted differently in different geometries. A model for Euclidean geometry is a plane, such as a blackboard (Fig. 9.100a). A model for elliptical geometry is a sphere (Fig. 9.100b). A model for hyperbolic geometry is a pseudosphere (Fig. 9.100c). A pseudosphere is similar to two trumpets placed bell to bell. Obviously, a line on a plane cannot be the same as a line on either of the other two figures.

(a) Plane   (b) Sphere   (c) Pseudosphere

Figure 9.100

Elliptical Geometry

A circle on the surface of a sphere is called a great circle if it divides the sphere into two equal parts. If we were to cut through a sphere along a great circle, we would have two identical pieces. If we interpret a line to be a great circle, then the two red curves in Fig. 9.101(a) are lines. Figure 9.101(a) shows that the fifth axiom of elliptical geometry is true. Two great circles on a sphere must intersect; hence, there can be no parallel lines (Fig. 9.101a).

If we were to construct a triangle on a sphere, the sum of its angles would be greater than 180° (Fig. 9.101b). The theorem "The sum of the measures of the angles of a triangle is greater than 180°" has been proven by means of the axioms of elliptical geometry. The sum of the measures of the angles varies with the area of the triangle and gets closer to 180° as the area decreases.

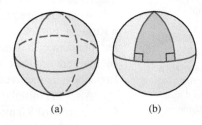

(a)   (b)

Figure 9.101

Hyperbolic Geometry

Lines in hyperbolic geometry*are represented by geodesics on the surface of a pseudosphere. A *geodesic* is the shortest and least-curved arc between two points on a surface. Figure 9.102 shows two different lines represented by geodesics on the surface of a pseudosphere. For simplicity of the diagrams, we only show one of the "bells" of the pseudosphere.

(a)   (b)

Figure 9.102

---

*A formal discussion of hyperbolic geometry is beyond the scope of this text.

Albert Einstein's general theory of relativity, published in 1916, approached space and time differently from our everyday understanding of them. Einstein's theory unites the three dimensions of space with one of time in a four-dimensional space–time continuum. His theory dealt with the path that light and objects take while moving through space under the force of gravity. Einstein conjectured that mass (such as stars and planets) caused space to be curved. The greater the mass, the greater the curvature.

To prove his conjecture, Einstein exposed himself to Riemann's non-Euclidean geometry. Einstein believed that the trajectory of a particle in space represents not a straight line but the straightest curve possible, a geodesic. Einstein's theory was confirmed by the solar eclipses of 1919 and 1922.

Space–time is now thought to be a combination of three different types of curvature: spherical (described by Riemannian geometry), flat (described by Euclidean geometry), and saddle-shaped (described by hyperbolic geometry).

"The Great Architect of the universe now appears to be a great mathematician."
British physicist Sir James Jeans

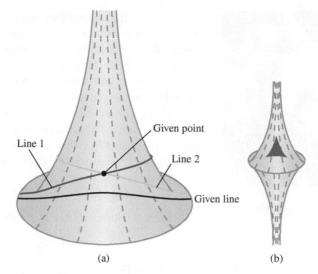

Figure 9.103

Figure 9.103(a) illustrates the fifth axiom of hyperbolic geometry. The diagram illustrates one way that, through the given point, two lines are drawn parallel to the given line. If we were to construct a triangle on a pseudosphere, the sum of the measures of the angles would be less than 180° (Fig. 9.103b). The theorem "The sum of the measures of the angles of a triangle is less than 180°" has been proven by means of the axioms of hyperbolic geometry.

We have stated that the sum of the measures of the angles of a triangle is 180°, is greater than 180°, and is less than 180°. Which statement is correct? Each statement is correct *in its own geometry.* Many theorems hold true for all three geometries; vertical angles still have the same measure, we can uniquely bisect a line segment with a straightedge and compass alone, and so on.

The many theorems based on the fifth postulate may differ in each geometry. It is important for you to realize that each theorem proved is true *in its own geometry* because each is logically deduced from the given set of axioms of the geometry. No one system is the "best" system. Euclidean geometry may appear to be the one to use in the classroom, where the blackboard is flat. In discussions involving Earth as a whole, however, elliptical geometry may be the most useful since Earth is a sphere. If the object under consideration has the shape of a saddle or pseudosphere, hyperbolic geometry may be the most useful.

Fractal Geometry

We are familiar with one-, two-, and three-dimensional figures. Many objects, however, are difficult to categorize as one-, two-, or three-dimensional. For example, how would you classify the irregular shapes we see in nature, such as a coastline, or the bark on a tree, or a mountain, or a path followed by lightning? For a long time mathematicians assumed that making realistic geometric models of natural shapes and figures was almost impossible, but the development of *fractal geometry* now makes it possible. Both color photos on the next page were made by using fractal geometry. The discovery and study of fractal geometry has been one of the most popular mathematical topics in recent times.

The word *fractal* (from the Latin word *fractus*, "broken up, fragmented") was first used in the mid-1970s by mathematician Benoit Mandelbrot to describe shapes that had several common characteristics, including some form of "self-similarity," as will be seen shortly in the Koch snowflake.

▲ *Fractal images*

Typical fractals are extremely irregular curves or surfaces that "wiggle" enough so that they are not considered one-dimensional. Fractals do not have integer dimensions; their dimensions are between 1 and 2. For example, a fractal may have a dimension of 1.26. Fractals are developed by applying the same rule over and over again, with the end point of each simple step becoming the starting point for the next step, in a process called *recursion*.

Using the recursive process, we will develop a famous fractal called the *Koch snowflake* named after Helga von Koch, a Swedish mathematician who first discovered its remarkable characteristics. The Koch snowflake illustrates a property of all fractals called *self-similarity*; that is, each smaller piece of the curve resembles the whole curve.

To develop the Koch snowflake:

1. Start with an equilateral triangle (Step 1, Fig. 9.104).

2. Whenever you see an edge ——— replace it with ⌃ (Steps 2–4).

What is the perimeter of the snowflake in Fig. 9.104, and what is its area? A portion of the boundary of the Koch snowflake known as the Koch curve, or the snowflake curve, is represented in Fig. 9.105.

The Koch curve consists of infinitely many pieces of the form ⌃. Notice that after each step, the perimeter is $\frac{4}{3}$ times the perimeter of the previous step. Therefore, the Koch snowflake has an infinite perimeter. It can be shown that the area of the snowflake is 1.6 times the area of the starting equilateral triangle. Thus, the area of the snowflake is finite. The Koch snowflake has a finite area enclosed by an infinite boundary! This fact may seem difficult to accept, but it is true. However, the Koch snowflake, like other fractals, is not an everyday run-of-the-mill geometric shape.

Step 1   Step 2

Step 3   Step 4

Figure 9.104   **Figure 9.105**

Let us look at a few more fractals made using the recursive process. We will now construct what is known as a *fractal tree*. Start with a tree trunk (Fig. 9.106a on page 555). Draw two branches, each one a bit smaller than the trunk (Fig. 9.106b). Draw two branches from each of those branches, and continue; see Fig. 9.106(c) and (d). Ideally, we continue the process forever.

If you take a little piece of any branch and zoom in on it, it will look exactly like the original tree. Fractals are *scale independent*, which means that you cannot really tell whether you are looking at something very big or something very small because the fractal looks the same whether you are close to it or far from it.

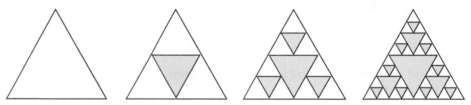

Figure 9.106 The fractal tree

In Figs. 9.107 and 9.108, we develop two other fractals through the process of recursion. Figure 9.107 shows a fractal called the Sierpinski triangle, and Fig. 9.108 shows a fractal called the Sierpinski carpet. Both fractals are named after Waclaw Sierpinski, a Polish mathematician who is best known for his work with fractals and space-filling curves.

Figure 9.107 Sierpinski triangle

Figure 9.108 Sierpinski carpet

Fractals provide a way to study natural forms such as coastlines, trees, mountains, galaxies, polymers, rivers, weather patterns, brains, lungs, and blood supply. Fractals also help explain that which appears chaotic. The blood supply in the body is one example. The branching of arteries and veins appears chaotic, but closer inspection reveals that the same type of branching occurs for smaller and smaller blood vessels, down to the capillaries. Thus, fractal geometry provides a geometric structure for chaotic processes in nature. The study of chaotic processes is called *chaos theory*.

Fractals nowadays have a potentially important role to play in characterizing weather systems and in providing insight into various physical processes such as the occurrence of earthquakes or the formation of deposits that shorten battery life. Some scientists view fractal statistics as a doorway to unifying theories of medicine, offering a powerful glimpse of what it means to be healthy.

Fractals lie at the heart of current efforts to understand complex natural phenomena. Unraveling their intricacies could reveal the basic design principles at work in our world. Until recently, there was no way to describe fractals. Today, we are beginning to see such features everywhere. Tomorrow, we may look at the entire universe through a fractal lens.

Warm Up Exercises

In Exercises 1–8, fill in the blanks with an appropriate word, phrase, or symbol(s).

1. The fifth axiom of Euclidean geometry states that given a line and a point not on the line, one and only one line can be drawn through the given point _____ to the given line.

2. The fifth axiom of elliptical geometry states that given a line and a point not on the line, _____ line can be drawn through the given point parallel to the given line.

3. The fifth axiom of hyperbolic geometry states that given a line and a point not on the line, _____ or more lines can be drawn through the given point parallel to the given line.

4. A model for Euclidean geometry is a(n) _____.

5. A model for elliptical geometry is a(n) _____.

6. A model for hyperbolic geometry is a(n) _____.

7. The shortest and least-curved arc between two points on a surface is a(n) _____.

8. The study of chaotic processes is known as _____ theory.

Practice the Skills

In the following, we show a fractal-like figure made using a recursive process with the letter "M." In Exercises 9–12, use this fractal-like figure as a guide in constructing fractal-like figures with the letter given. Show three steps, as is done here.

9. I   10. E   11. H   12. W

13. a) Develop a fractal by beginning with a square and replacing each side —— with a ⌐⌐. Repeat this process twice.

   b) If you continue this process, will the fractal's perimeter be finite or infinite? Explain.

   c) Will the fractal's area be finite or infinite? Explain.

Problem Solving/Group Activity

14. In forming the Koch snowflake in Figure 9.104 on page 554, the perimeter becomes greater at each step in the process. If each side of the original triangle is 1 unit, a general formula for the perimeter, L, of the snowflake at any step, n, may be found by the formula

$$L = 3\left(\frac{4}{3}\right)^{n-1}$$

For example, at the first step when $n = 1$, the perimeter is 3 units, which can be verified by the formula as follows:

$$L = 3\left(\frac{4}{3}\right)^{1-1} = 3\left(\frac{4}{3}\right)^{0} = 3 \cdot 1 = 3$$

At the second step, when $n = 2$, we find the perimeter as follows:

$$L = 3\left(\frac{4}{3}\right)^{2-1} = 3\left(\frac{4}{3}\right) = 4$$

Thus, at the second step the perimeter of the snowflake is 4 units.

a) Use the formula to complete the following table.

Step	Perimeter
1	
2	
3	
4	
5	
6	

b) Use the results of your calculations to explain why the perimeter of the Koch snowflake is infinite.

c) Explain how the Koch snowflake can have an infinite perimeter, but a finite area.

Concept/Writing Exercises

15. What do we mean when we say that no one axiomatic system of geometry is "best"?

16. List the three types of curvature of space and the types of geometry that correspond to them.

17. List at least five natural forms that appear chaotic that we can study using fractals.

18. State the theorem concerning the sum of the measures of the angles of a triangle in

    a) Euclidean geometry.

    b) Hyperbolic geometry.

    c) Elliptical geometry.

In Exercises 19–24 describe the accomplishments of the mathematician.

19. Benoit Mandelbrot

20. G. F. Bernhard Riemann

21. Nikolay Ivanovich Lobachevsky

22. Carl Friedrich Gauss

23. Janos Bolyai

24. Girolamo Saccheri

Internet/Research Activities

In Exercises 25–27, references include the Internet, books on art, encyclopedias, and history of mathematics books.

25. To complete his masterpiece *Circle Limit III*, M. C. Escher studied a model of hyperbolic geometry called

the *Poincaré disk*. Write a paper on the Poincaré disk and how it was used in Escher's art. Include representations of *infinity* and the concepts of *point* and *line* in hyperbolic geometry.

▲ Escher's *Circle Limit III*

26. To transfer his two-dimensional tiling known as *Symmetry Work 45* to a sphere, M. C. Escher used the spherical geometry of Bernhard Riemann. Write a paper on Escher's use of geometry to complete this masterpiece.

27. Go to the Web site *Fantastic Fractals* at www.fantastic-fractals.com and study the information about fractals given there. Print copies, in color if a color printer is available, of the Mandlebrot set and the Julia set.

CHAPTER 9) *Summary*

Important Facts and Concepts

Examples and Discussion

Section 9.1	
Point, line, plane, ray, half line, line segment, angle, and related terms and definitions are discussed throughout Section 9.1.	Discussion, pages 480–482, Examples 1 and 2, pages 481–483
Two angles are **complementary angles** if the sum of their measures is 90°. Two angles are **supplementary angles** if the sum of their measures is 180°.	Examples 3 and 4, pages 484 and 485
Vertical angles, alternate interior angles, alternate exterior angles, and **corresponding angles** and related terms are discussed in Section 9.1	Discussion, pages 485–486, Example 6, page 486
Section 9.2	
The sum of the measures of the interior angles of an *n*-sided polygon is $(n-2)\,180°$.	Discussion, page 491, Example 1, page 491
Two polygons are **similar** if their corresponding angles have the same measure and the lengths of their corresponding sides are in proportion.	Discussion, page 492, Examples 2–3, pages 493–494

Section 9.3
Perimeter, P, and Area, A

TRIANGLE

$P = s_1 + s_2 + s_3$ $(s_3 = b)$

$A = \frac{1}{2}bh$

SQUARE

$P = 4s$

$A = s^2$

RECTANGLE

$P = 2l + 2w$

$A = lw$

PARALLELOGRAM

$P = 2b + 2w$

$A = bh$

TRAPEZOID

$P = s_1 + s_2 + b_1 + b_2$

$A = \frac{1}{2}h(b_1 + b_2)$

Discussion, pages 500–502, Example 1, page 502,
Examples 3–5, pages 504–506

Pythagorean Theorem

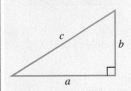

$a^2 + b^2 = c^2$

Example 2, page 503

Area, A, and Perimeter, P, of a Circle

$A = \pi r^2;\ C = 2\pi r$ or $C = \pi d$

Discussion, page 504, Examples 3–5, pages 504–506

Section 9.4
Volume, V, and Surface Area, SA

CUBE

$V = s^3$
$SA = 6s^2$

RECTANGULAR SOLID

$V = lwh$
$SA = 2lw + 2wh + 2lh$

Discussion, pages 512–514,
Examples 1–8, pages 514–519

CYLINDER

$V = \pi r^2 h$
$SA = 2\pi rh + 2\pi r^2$

CONE

$V = \frac{1}{3}\pi r^2 h$
$SA = \pi r^2 + \pi r\sqrt{r^2 + h^2}$

SPHERE

$V = \frac{4}{3}\pi r^3$
$SA = 4\pi r^2$

PYRAMID

$V = \frac{1}{3}Bh$, where
B is the area of the base

PRISM

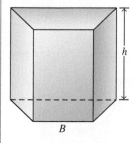

$V = Bh$, where B is the area of the base

Section 9.5
Rigid Motions

The **rigid motions: Reflections, translations, rotations,** and **glide reflections** are defined and discussed throughout Section 9.5.

Discussion, pages 525–526, 528, 529, 532,
Examples 1–6, pages 526–532

Reflective symmetry, rotational symmetry, and **tessellations** are described in Section 9.5.

Discussion, pages 532–533, Examples 7–8,
pages 533–534

Section 9.6
Topology

Möbius strip, Klein bottle, maps, Jordan curves, and **topological equivalence** are described in Section 9.6.

Discussion, pages 543–547

Section 9.7

The Fifth Axiom

Fifth axiom in Euclidean geometry: Given a line and a point not on the line, only one line can be drawn through the given point parallel to the given line.

Fifth axiom in elliptical geometry: Given a line and a point not on the line, no line can be drawn through the given point parallel to the given line.

Fifth axiom in hyperbolic geometry: Given a line and a point not on the line, two or more lines can be drawn through the given point parallel to the given line.

Discussion, pages 550–555

CHAPTER 9 *Review Exercises*

9.1

In Exercises 1–6, use the figure shown to determine the following.

1. $\angle ABF \cap \angle DBI$

2. $\overrightarrow{AB} \cap \overrightarrow{DC}$

3. $\overline{BF} \cup \overline{FC} \cup \overline{BC}$

4. $\overrightarrow{BH} \cup \overrightarrow{HB}$

5. $\overleftrightarrow{HI} \cap \overleftrightarrow{EG}$

6. $\overrightarrow{CF} \cap \overrightarrow{CG}$

7. $m\angle A = 35.4°$. Determine the measure of the complement of $\angle A$.

8. $m\angle B = 100.5°$. Determine the measure of the supplement $\angle B$.

9.2

In Exercises 9–12, use the similar triangles ABC and A'B'C shown to determine the following.

9. The length of $\overline{BC}$

10. The length of $\overline{A'B'}$

11. $m\angle BAC$

12. $m\angle ABC$

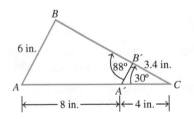

13. In the following figure, l_1 and l_2 are parallel lines. Determine $m\angle 1$ through $m\angle 6$.

14. Determine the sum of the measures of the interior angles of an octagon.

9.3

In Exercises 15–18, determine (a) the area and (b) the perimeter of the figure.

15.

9 mi

11 mi

16.

3.2 in. 2 in. 3.2 in.

4 in.

9 in.

17.

9 in. 7 in.

12 in.

18.

3 km

4 km

19. Determine (a) the area and (b) the circumference of the circle. Use the $\boxed{\pi}$ key on a calculator and round your answer to the nearest hundredth.

7 ft

In Exercises 20 and 21, determine the shaded area. When appropriate, use the $\boxed{\pi}$ key on your calculator and round your answer to the nearest hundredth.

20.

10 m

21.

12 yd

12 yd   6 yd

22. *Cost of Kitchen Tile* Determine the total cost of covering a 14-ft by 16-ft kitchen floor with ceramic tile. The cost of the tile selected is $5.25 per square foot.

9.4

In Exercises 23–26, determine (a) the volume and (b) the surface area of the figure. When appropriate, use the $\boxed{\pi}$ key on your calculator and round your answer to the nearest hundredth.

23.

4 cm

4 cm
10 cm
3 cm

24.

9 ft

3 ft

25.

12 mm

16 mm

26.

7 yd

In Exercises 27 and 28, determine the volume of the figure.

27.

9 m   12 m

8 m

15 m

28.

5 ft   7 ft

6 ft   5 ft

In Exercises 29 and 30, determine the volume of the shaded area. When appropriate, use the $\boxed{\pi}$ key and round your answer to the nearest hundredth.

29.

9 cm

←4 cm→

30.

← 5 in. →

← 10 in. →

31. *Water Trough* Steven Dale has a water trough whose ends are trapezoids and whose sides are rectangles, as illustrated. He is afraid that the base it is sitting on will not support the weight of the trough when it is filled with water. He knows that the base will support 4800 lb.

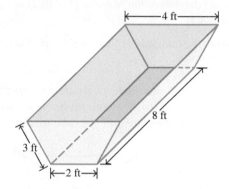

← 4 ft →

8 ft

3 ft

← 2 ft →

a) If the trough is filled with water, determine the number of cubic feet of water contained in the trough.

b) Determine the total weight, assuming that the trough weighs 375 lb and the water weighs 62.4 lb per cubic foot. Is the base strong enough to support the trough filled with water?

c) If 1 gal of water weighs 8.3 lb, how many gallons of water will the trough hold?

9.5

In Exercises 32 and 33, use the given triangle and reflection lines to construct the indicated reflections. Show the triangle in the positions both before and after the reflection.

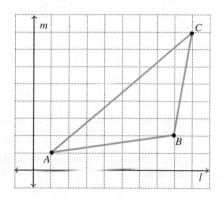

m   *C*

A   *B*

l

32. Construct the reflection of triangle *ABC* (see p. 561) about line *l*.

33. Construct the reflection of triangle *ABC* (see p. 561) about line *m*.

In Exercises 34 and 35, use translation vectors **v** *and* **w** *to construct the indicated translations. Show the rectangle in the positions both before and after the translation.*

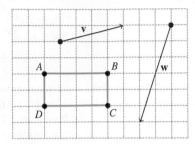

34. Construct the translation of rectangle *ABCD* using translation vector **v**.

35. Construct the translation of rectangle *ABCD* using translation vector **w**.

In Exercises 36–38, use the given figure and rotation point P to construct the indicated rotations. Show the trapezoid in the positions both before and after the rotation.

36. Construct a 90° rotation of trapezoid *ABCD* about point *P*.

37. Construct a 180° rotation of trapezoid *ABCD* about point *P*.

38. Construct a 270° rotation of trapezoid *ABCD* about point *P* .

In Exercises 39 and 40, use the given figure, translation vector **v**, *and reflection lines l and m to construct the indicated glide reflections. Show the triangle in the positions both before and after the glide reflection.*

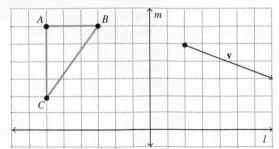

39. Construct a glide reflection of triangle *ABC* using vector **v** and reflection line *l*.

40. Construct a glide reflection of triangle *ABC* using vector **v** and reflection line *m*.

In Exercises 41 and 42, use the following figure to answer the following questions.

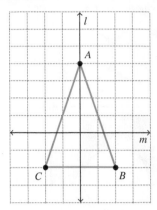

41. Does triangle *ABC* have reflective symmetry about line *l*? Explain.

42. Does triangle *ABC* have reflective symmetry about line *m*? Explain.

In Exercises 43 and 44, use the following figure to answer the following questions.

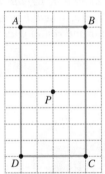

43. Does rectangle *ABCD* have 90° rotational symmetry about point *P*? Explain.

44. Does rectangle *ABCD* have 180° rotational symmetry about point *P*? Explain.

9.6

45. Give an example of an object that has

    a) genus 0.   **b)** genus 1.

    c) genus 2.   **d)** genus 3 or more.

46. Color the map by using a maximum of four colors so that no two regions with a common border have the same color.

47. Determine whether point A is inside or outside the Jordan curve.

48. State the fifth axiom of Euclidean, elliptical, and hyperbolic geometry.

49. Develop a fractal by beginning with a square and replacing each side ⎯⎯ with a ⌐⌐. Repeat this process twice.

50. Construct a Koch snowflake by beginning with an equilateral triangle and replacing each side with a ⋀. Repeat this process twice.

CHAPTER 9 Test

In Exercises 1–4, use the figure to describe the following sets of points.

1. $\overrightarrow{AF} \cap \overleftrightarrow{EF}$

2. $\overline{BC} \cup \overline{CD} \cup \overline{BD}$

3. $\sphericalangle EDF \cap \sphericalangle BDC$

4. $\overrightarrow{AC} \cup \overrightarrow{BA}$

5. $m\sphericalangle A = 74.9°$. Determine the measure of the complement of $\sphericalangle A$.

6. $m\sphericalangle B = 10.4°$. Determine the measure of the supplement of $\sphericalangle B$.

7. In the figure, determine the measure of $\sphericalangle x$.

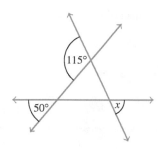

8. Determine the sum of the measures of the interior angles of a pentagon.

9. Triangles ABC and $A'B'C'$ are similar figures. Determine the length of side $\overline{B'C'}$.

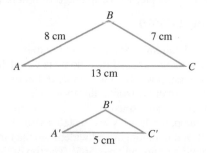

10. Right triangle ABC (see below) has one leg of length 12 in. and a hypotenuse of length 13 in.

   a) Determine the length of the other leg.

   b) Determine the perimeter of the triangle.

   c) Determine the area of the triangle.

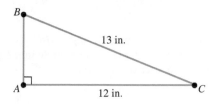

11. Determine (a) the volume and (b) the surface area of a sphere of diameter 14 cm.

12. Determine the volume of the shaded area. Use the $\boxed{\pi}$ key on your calculator and round your answer to the nearest hundredth.

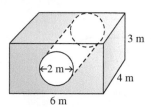

13. Determine the volume of the pyramid.

14. Construct a reflection of rectangle *ABCD*, shown below, about line *l*. Show the rectangle in the positions both before and after the reflection.

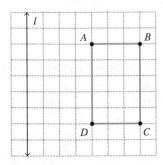

15. Construct a translation of quadrilateral *ABCD*, shown below, using translation vector **v**. Show the quadrilateral in the positions both before and after the translation.

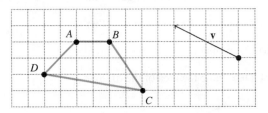

16. Construct a 180° rotation of triangle *ABC*, shown below, about rotation point *P*. Show the triangle in the positions both before and after the rotation.

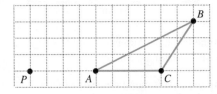

17. Construct a glide reflection of rectangle *ABCD*, shown below, using translation vector **v** and reflection line *l*. Show the rectangle in the positions both before and after the glide reflection.

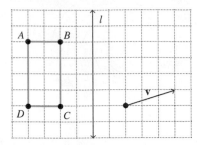

18. Use the figure below to answer the following questions.

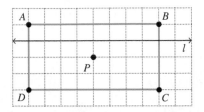

a) Does rectangle *ABCD* have reflective symmetry about line *l*? Explain.

b) Does rectangle *ABCD* have 180° rotational symmetry about point *P*? Explain.

19. What is a Möbius strip?

20. a) Sketch an object of genus 1.

b) Sketch an object of genus 2.

GROUP PROJECTS

Supporting a Hot Tub

1. Samantha Saraniti is thinking of buying a circular hot tub 12 ft in diameter, 4 ft deep, and weighing 475 lb. She wants to place the hot tub on a deck built to support 30,000 lb.

a) Determine the volume of the water in the hot tub in cubic feet.

b) Determine the number of gallons of water the hot tub will hold. (*Note:* 1 ft^3 ≈ 7.5 gal.)

c) Determine the weight of the water in the hot tub. (*Hint:* Fresh water weighs about 62.4 lb/ft^3.)

d) Will the deck support the weight of the hot tub and water?

e) Will the deck support the weight of the hot tub, water, and four people, whose average weight is 115 lb?

Designing a Ramp

2. David and Sandra Jessee are planning to build a ramp so that the front entrance of their home is wheelchair accessible. The ramp will be 3 feet wide. It will rise 2 in. for each foot of length of horizontal distance. Where the ramp meets the porch, the ramp must be 2 ft high. To provide stability for the ramp, the Jessees will install a slab of concrete 4 in. thick and 6 in. longer and wider than the ramp (see accompanying figure on page 565). The top of the slab will be level with the ground. The ramp may be constructed of concrete or pressure-treated lumber. You are to estimate the cost of materials for constructing the slab, the ramp of concrete, and the ramp of pressure-treated lumber.

Slab

a) Determine the length of the base of the ramp.

b) Determine the dimensions of the concrete slab on which the ramp will be set.

c) Determine the volume of the concrete in cubic yards needed to construct the slab.

d) If ready-mix concrete costs $45 per cubic yard, determine the cost of the concrete needed to construct the slab.

Concrete Ramp

e) To build the ramp of concrete, a form in the shape of the ramp must be framed. The two sides of the form are triangular, and the shape of the end, which is against the porch, is rectangular. The form will be framed from $\frac{3}{4}$-in. plywood, which comes in 4 ft × 8 ft sheets. Determine the number of sheets of plywood needed. Assume that the entire sheet(s) will be used to make the sides and the end of the form and that there is no waste.

f) If the plywood costs $18.95 for a 4 ft × 8 ft sheet, determine the cost of the plywood.

g) To brace the form, the Jessees will need two boards 2 in. × 4 in. × 8 ft (referred to as 8-ft 2 × 4's) and

six pieces of lumber 2 in. × 4 in. × 3 ft. These six pieces of lumber will be cut from 8-ft 2 × 4 boards. Determine the number of 8-ft 2 × 4 boards needed.

h) Determine the cost of the 8-ft 2 × 4 boards needed in part (g) if one board costs $2.14.

i) Determine the volume, in cubic yards, of concrete needed to fill the form.

j) Determine the cost of the concrete needed to fill the form.

k) Determine the total cost of materials for building the ramp of concrete by adding the results in parts (d), (f), (h), and (j).

Wooden Ramp

l) Determine the length of the top of the ramp.

m) The top of the ramp will be constructed of $\frac{5}{4}$-in. × 6 in. × 10 ft pressure-treated lumber. The boards will be butted end to end to make the necessary length and will be supported from underneath by a wooden frame. Determine the number of boards needed to cover the top of the ramp. The boards are laid lengthwise on the ramp.

n) Determine the cost of the boards to cover the top of the ramp if the price of a 10-ft length is $6.47.

o) To support the top of the ramp, the Jessees will need 10 pieces of 8-ft 2 × 4's. The price of a pressure-treated 8-ft 2 × 4 is $2.44. Determine the cost of the supports.

p) Determine the cost of the materials for building a wooden ramp by adding the amounts from parts (d), (n), and (o).

q) Are the materials for constructing a concrete ramp or a wooden ramp less expensive?

10

Mathematical Systems

Why This is Important

Mathematics plays a crucial role in the study of the interaction between many objects of interest to scientists. One branch of mathematics of particular importance to this study is group theory. Physicists and chemists rely on group theory to study the behavior of the tiniest particles that make up an atom in a scientific field known as *quantum mechanics*. Group theory can be used to predict the interactive behavior of subatomic particles within an atom, atoms within a molecule, and molecules within a chemical reaction. Group theory also plays an important role in robotics, computer graphics, weather forecasting, musical theory, and medical image analysis.

◄ *Group theory plays an important role in robotics and many other aspects of modern technology.*

▲ *The big bang theory uses groups to address questions relating to the size, structure, and future of the universe.*

How big is the universe? Is there an end to the universe? Does the universe continue to expand? Such questions are addressed by the scientific theory known as the *big bang theory*. In this section, we will introduce a mathematical structure known as a *group*. Many modern scientific theories, including the big bang theory, make use of groups and other mathematical topics discussed in this book.

Why *This is Important* The more we understand about our universe, the better prepared we are to answer questions regarding the history and future of planet Earth.

W e begin our discussion by introducing a mathematical system. As you will learn shortly, you already know and use many mathematical systems.

Definition: **Mathematical System**
A **mathematical system** consists of a set of elements and at least one binary operation.

TIMELY TIP
Throughout this section, we will work with many different sets of numbers, such as natural numbers, whole numbers, integers, rational numbers, and real numbers. A review of the numbers that make up each of these sets can be found on page 252–253 in Section 5.5.

In the above definition, we mention binary operation. A *binary operation* is an operation, or rule, that can be performed on two and only two elements of a set. The result is a single element. When we add *two* integers, the sum is *one* integer. When we multiply *two* integers, the product is *one* integer. Thus, addition and multiplication are both binary operations. Is finding the reciprocal of a number a binary operation? No, it is an operation on a single element of a set.

When you learned how to add integers, you were introduced to a mathematical system. The set of elements is the set of integers, and the binary operation is addition. When you learned how to multiply integers, you became familiar with a second mathematical system. The set of integers with the operation of subtraction and the set of integers with the operation of division are two other examples of mathematical systems since subtraction and division are also binary operations.

Some mathematical systems are used in solving everyday problems, such as planning work schedules. Others are more abstract and are used primarily in research, chemistry, physical structure, matter, the nature of genes, and other scientific fields.

Commutative and Associative Properties

Once a mathematical system is defined, its structure may display certain properties. Consider the set of integers

$$I = \{\ldots, -3, -2, -1, 0, 1, 2, 3, \ldots\}$$

Recall that the ellipsis, the three dots at each end of the set, indicates that the set continues in the same manner.

The set of integers can be studied with the operations of addition, subtraction, multiplication, and division as separate mathematical systems. For example, when we study the set of integers under the operations of addition or multiplication, we see that the commutative and associative properties hold. The general forms of the properties are shown here.

Commutative and Associative Properties

For any elements a, b, and c

	Addition	Multiplication
Commutative property	$a + b = b + a$	$a \cdot b = b \cdot a$
Associative property	$(a + b) + c = a + (b + c)$	$(a \cdot b) \cdot c = a \cdot (b \cdot c)$

The integers *are commutative* under the operations of *addition and multiplication*. For example,

Addition		Multiplication
$2 + 4 = 4 + 2$	and	$2 \cdot 4 = 4 \cdot 2$
$6 = 6$		$8 = 8$

The integers, however, *are not commutative* under the operations of *subtraction and division*. For example,

Subtraction		Division
$4 - 2 \neq 2 - 4$	and	$4 \div 2 \neq 2 \div 4$
$2 \neq -2$		$2 \neq \frac{1}{2}$

The integers *are associative* under the operations of *addition and multiplication*. For example,

Addition		Multiplication
$(1 + 2) + 3 = 1 + (2 + 3)$	and	$(1 \cdot 2) \cdot 3 = 1 \cdot (2 \cdot 3)$
$3 + 3 = 1 + 5$		$2 \cdot 3 = 1 \cdot 6$
$6 = 6$		$6 = 6$

The integers, however, *are not associative* under the operations of *subtraction and division*. See Exercises 21 and 22 at the end of this section.

To say that a set of elements is commutative under a given operation means that the commutative property holds for *any* elements a and b in the set. Similarly, to say that a set of elements is associative under a given operation means that the associative property holds for *any* elements a, b, and c in the set.

Consider the mathematical system consisting of the set of integers under the operation of addition. Because the set of integers is infinite, this mathematical system is an example of an *infinite mathematical system*. We will study certain properties of this mathematical system. The first property we will examine is closure.

Closure

The sum of any two integers is an integer. Therefore, the set of integers is said to be *closed*, or to satisfy the *closure property*, under the operation of addition.

> **Definition: Closure**
>
> If a binary operation is performed on any two elements of a set and the result is an element of the set, then that set is **closed** (or has **closure**) under the given binary operation.

Is the set of integers closed under the operation of multiplication? The answer is yes. When any two integers are multiplied, the product will be an integer.

Is the set of integers closed under the operation of subtraction? Again, the answer is yes. The difference of any two integers is an integer.

Is the set of integers closed under the operation of division? The answer is no because two integers may have a quotient that is not an integer. For example, if we select the integers 2 and 3, the quotient of 2 divided by 3 is $\frac{2}{3}$, which is not an integer. Thus, the integers are not closed under the operation of division.

We showed that the set of integers was not closed under the operation of division by finding two integers whose quotient was not an integer. A specific example illustrating that a specific property is not true is called a *counterexample*. Mathematicians and scientists often try to find a counterexample to confirm that a specific property is not always true.

Identity Element

Is there an element in the set of integers that, when added to any given integer, results in a sum that is the given integer? The answer is yes. The sum of 0 and any integer is the given integer. For example, $1 + 0 = 0 + 1 = 1, -4 + 0 = 0 + (-4) = -4$, and so on. For this reason, we call 0 the *additive identity element* for the set of integers. Note that for any integer a, $a + 0 = 0 + a = a$.

> **Definition: Identity Element**
> An **identity element** is an element in a set such that when a binary operation is performed on it and any given element in the set, the result is the given element.

Is there an identity element for the set of integers under the operation of multiplication? The answer is yes; it is the number 1. Note that $2 \cdot 1 = 1 \cdot 2 = 2$, $3 \cdot 1 = 1 \cdot 3 = 3$, and so on. For any integer a, $a \cdot 1 = 1 \cdot a = a$. For this reason, 1 is called the *multiplicative identity element* for the set of integers.

Inverses

What integer, when added to 4, gives a sum of 0; that is, $4 + \underline{\quad} = 0$? The shaded area is to be filled in with the integer -4: $4 + (-4) = 0$. We say that -4 is the additive inverse of 4 and that 4 is the additive inverse of -4. Note that the sum of the element and its additive inverse gives the additive identity element 0. What is the additive inverse of 12? Since $12 + (-12) = 0, -12$ is the additive inverse of 12.

Other examples of integers and their additive inverses are

Element	+	Additive Inverse	=	Identity Element
0	+	0	=	0
2	+	(−2)	=	0
−5	+	5	=	0

Note that for the operation of addition, every integer a has a unique inverse, $-a$, such that $a + (-a) = -a + a = 0$.

> **Definition: Inverse**
> When a binary operation is performed on two elements in a set and the result is the identity element for the binary operation, each element is said to be the **inverse** of the other.

TIMELY TIP

Note that the set of elements need *not* be commutative for the mathematical system to be a group. Also note that *every* element in the set must have an inverse for the mathematical system to be a group.

Does every integer have an inverse under the operation of multiplication? For multiplication, the product of an integer and its inverse must yield the multiplicative identity element, 1. What is the multiplicative inverse of 2? That is, 2 times what number gives 1?

$$2 \cdot \boxed{} = 1 \qquad 2 \cdot \tfrac{1}{2} = 1$$

However, since $\tfrac{1}{2}$ is not an integer, 2 does not have a multiplicative inverse in the set of integers.

Group

Let's review what we have learned about the mathematical system consisting of the set of integers under the operation of addition.

1. The set of integers is *closed* under the operation of addition.
2. The set of integers has an *identity element* under the operation of addition.
3. Each element in the set of integers has an *inverse* under the operation of addition.
4. The *associative property* holds for the set of integers under the operation of addition.

The set of integers under the operation of addition is an example of a *group*. The properties of a group can be summarized as follows.

Properties of a Group

Any mathematical system that meets the following four requirements is called a **group**.
1. The set of elements is *closed* under the given operation.
2. An *identity element* exists for the set under the given operation.
3. Every element in the set has an *inverse* under the given operation.
4. The set of elements is *associative* under the given operation.

It is often very time consuming to show that the associative property holds for all cases. In many of the examples that follow, we will state that the associative property holds for the given set of elements under the given operation.

Commutative Group

The commutative property does not need to hold for a mathematical system to be a group. However, if a mathematical system meets the four requirements of a group and is also commutative under the given operation, the mathematical system is a *commutative* (or *abelian*) *group*. The abelian group is named after Niels Abel (see the *Profiles in Mathematics* in the margin).

Definition: **Commutative Group**

A group that satisfies the commutative property is called a **commutative group** (or **abelian group**).

Because the commutative property holds for the set of integers under the operation of addition, the set of integers under the operation of addition is not only a group, but it is also a commutative group.

Properties of a Commutative Group

A mathematical system is a **commutative group** if all five of the following conditions hold.

1. The set of elements is *closed* under the given operation.
2. An *identity element* exists for the set under the given operation.
3. Every element in the set has an *inverse* under the given operation.
4. The set of elements is *associative* under the given operation.
5. The set of elements is *commutative* under the given operation.

To determine whether a mathematical system is a group under a given operation, *check, in the following order,* whether (1) the system is closed under the given operation, (2) there is an identity element in the set for the given operation, (3) every element in the set has an inverse under the given operation, and (4) the associative property holds under the given operation. If *any* of these four requirements is *not* met, stop and state that the mathematical system is not a group. If asked to determine whether the mathematical system is a commutative group, you also need to determine whether the commutative property holds for the given operation.

┌ Example **1** *Whole Numbers Under Addition*

Determine whether the mathematical system consisting of the set of whole numbers under the operation of addition forms a group.

Solution Recall from Chapter 5 that the set of whole numbers is $\{0, 1, 2, 3, \ldots\}$. We will check the properties required, using the operation of addition, to determine if the mathematical system is a group.

1. *Closure*: The sum of any two whole numbers is a whole number. Therefore, the set of whole numbers is closed under the operation of addition.
2. *Identity element*: The additive identity for the set of whole numbers is 0. For example, $1 + 0 = 0 + 1 = 1$, and $2 + 0 = 0 + 2 = 2$, and so on. For any whole number a, $a + 0 = 0 + a = a$. Thus, the mathematical system contains an identity element.
3. *Inverse elements*: For the mathematical system to be a group, each element must have an additive inverse *in the set*. Remember that the additive inverse of a number is the *opposite* of the number. For example, the additive inverse of 1 is -1, the additive inverse of 2 is -2, the additive inverse of 3 is -3, and so on. Since the numbers $-1, -2, -3, \ldots$ are *not* in the set of whole numbers, not every number has an inverse in the set. Therefore, this mathematical system is not a group.

Because we have already shown that the set of whole numbers under the operation of addition is not a group, there is no need to check the associative property. ∎

┌ Example **2** *Rational Numbers Under Multiplication*

Determine whether the set of rational numbers under the operation of multiplication forms a group.

Solution Recall from Chapter 5 that the rational numbers are the set of numbers of the form $\frac{p}{q}$, where p and q are integers and $q \neq 0$. The set of rational numbers includes all fractions and integers.

1. *Closure*: The product of any two rational numbers is a rational number. Therefore, the rational numbers are closed under the operation of multiplication.
2. *Identity element*: The multiplicative identity element for the set of rational numbers is 1. Note, for example, that $3 \cdot 1 = 1 \cdot 3 = 3$, and $\frac{3}{8} \cdot 1 = 1 \cdot \frac{3}{8} = \frac{3}{8}$. For any rational number a, $a \cdot 1 = 1 \cdot a = a$.

Group theory may be viewed as the study of the algebra of symmetry and transformations (see Section 9.5 for a discussion of transformational geometry). One of the best, and perhaps most entertaining, examples of this view is *Rubik's cube*. In 1974, Erno Rubik, a Hungarian teacher of architecture and design, presented the world with his popular puzzle. Each face of the cube is divided into nine squares, and each row and column of each face can rotate. The result is approximately 43 quintillion different arrangements of the colors on the cube. Rubik's cube is the most popular and best-selling puzzle in human history. Although the popularity of the puzzle peaked during the 1980s, clubs and annual contests are still devoted to solving the puzzle. For more information, visit the Web site www.rubiks.com.

3. *Inverse elements*: For the mathematical system to be a group under the operation of multiplication, *each and every* rational number must have a multiplicative inverse in the set of rational numbers. Remember that for the operation of multiplication, the product of a number and its inverse must give the multiplicative identity element, 1. Let's check a few rational numbers:

Rational Number $\cdot$ Inverse $=$ Identity Element

$$3 \cdot \frac{1}{3} = 1$$

$$\frac{2}{3} \cdot \frac{3}{2} = 1$$

$$-\frac{1}{5} \cdot -5 = 1$$

Looking at these examples you might deduce that each rational number does have an inverse. However, one rational number, 0, does not have an inverse.

$$0 \cdot ? = 1$$

Because there is no rational number that when multiplied by 0 gives 1, 0 does not have a multiplicative inverse. Since not *every* rational number has an inverse, this mathematical system is not a group.

There is no need at this point to check the associative property because we have already shown that the mathematical system of rational numbers under the operation of multiplication is not a group. ∎

Example 3 *Real Numbers Under Addition*

Determine whether the set of real numbers under the operation of addition forms a commutative group.

Solution Recall from Chapter 5 that the real numbers can be thought of as the numbers that correspond to *each* point on the real number line. The set of real numbers includes all rational numbers and all irrational numbers.

1. *Closure*: The sum of any two real numbers is a real number. Therefore, the real numbers are closed under the operation of addition.
2. *Identity element*: The additive identity element for the set of real numbers is 0. For example, $\frac{2}{3} + 0 = 0 + \frac{2}{3} = \frac{2}{3}$ and $\sqrt{5} + 0 = 0 + \sqrt{5} = \sqrt{5}$. For any real number a, $a + 0 = 0 + a = a$.
3. *Inverse elements*: For the set of real numbers under the operation of addition to be a commutative group, each and every real number must have an additive inverse in the set of real numbers. For the operation of addition, the sum of a real number and its additive inverse, or *opposite*, must be the additive identity element, 0. From Chapter 5, we saw that every real number a has an opposite $-a$ such that $a + (-a) = -a + a = 0$. Recall also that $0 + 0 = 0$; therefore, 0 is its own additive inverse. Thus, all real numbers have an additive inverse.
4. *Associative property*: From Chapter 5, we know that the real numbers are associative under the operation of addition. That is, for any real numbers a, b, and c, $(a + b) + c = a + (b + c)$.
5. *Commutative property*: From Chapter 5, we know that the real numbers are commutative under the operation of addition. That is, for any real numbers a and b, $a + b = b + a$.

Since all five properties (closure, identity element, inverse elements, associative property, and commutative property) hold, the set of real numbers under the operation of addition forms a commutative group. ∎

Exercises

Warm Up Exercises

In Exercises 1–14, fill in the blanks with an appropriate word, phrase, or symbol(s).

1. A mathematical system consists of a set of elements and at least one _____ operation.

2. A binary operation is an operation or rule that can be performed on exactly two elements of a set, with the result being a(n) _____ element.

3. The commutative property of addition states: $a + b =$ _____.

4. The commutative property of multiplication states: $a \cdot b =$ _____.

5. The associative property of multiplication states: $(a \cdot b) \cdot c =$ _____.

6. The associative property of addition states: $(a + b) + c =$ _____.

7. If a binary operation is performed on any two elements of a set and the result is an element of the set, then that set is _____ under the given binary operation.

8. A specific example illustrating that a property is not true is called a(n) _____.

9. Since the sum of 0 and any integer is the given integer, we say that 0 is the additive _____ element for the set of the integers under the operation of addition.

10. Since the product of 1 and any integer is the given integer, we say that 1 is the _____ identity element for the set of the integers under the operation of multiplication.

11. When a binary operation is performed on two elements in a set and the result is the identity element for the binary operation, each element is said to be the _____ of the other.

12. If a mathematical system possesses the following properties—closure, identity element, inverses, and the associative property—then the mathematical system is a(n) _____.

13. A group that also satisfies the commutative property is called a(n) _____ (or abelian) group.

14. Another name for a commutative group is a(n) _____ group.

Practice the Skills

15. Give the commutative property of multiplication and illustrate the property with an example.

16. Give the commutative property of addition and illustrate the property with an example.

17. Give the associative property of addition and illustrate the property with an example.

18. Give the associative property of multiplication and illustrate the property with an example.

19. Give an example to show that the commutative property does not hold for the set of integers under the operation of division.

20. Give an example to show that the commutative property does not hold for the set of integers under the operation of subtraction.

21. Give an example to show that the associative property does not hold for the set of integers under the operation of subtraction.

22. Give an example to show that the associative property does not hold for the set of integers under the operation of division.

Problem Solving

In Exercises 23–36, explain your answer.

23. Is the set of integers a commutative group under the operation of addition?

24. Is the set of integers a group under the operation of addition?

25. Is the set of positive integers a group under the operation of addition?

26. Is the set of positive integers a commutative group under the operation of addition?

27. Is the set of positive integers a group under the operation of subtraction?

28. Is the set of negative integers a group under the operation of division?

29. Is the set of negative integers a commutative group under the operation of addition?

30. Is the set of integers a group under the operation of multiplication?

31. Is the set of positive integers a commutative group under the operation of multiplication?

32. Is the set of negative integers a group under the operation of multiplication?

33. Is the set of rational numbers a group under the operation of addition?

34. Is the set of rational numbers a commutative group under the operation of multiplication?

35. Is the set of rational numbers a commutative group under the operation of division?

36. Is the set of rational numbers a group under the operation of subtraction?

Challenge Problems/Group Activities

In Exercises 37–40, explain your answer.

37. Is the set of real numbers a group under the operation of addition?

38. Is the set of real numbers a group under the operation of multiplication?

39. Is the set of irrational numbers a group under the operation of addition?

40. Is the set of irrational numbers a group under the operation of multiplication?

41. Create a mathematical system with two binary operations. Select a set of elements and two binary operations so that one binary operation with the set of elements meets the requirements for a group and the other binary operation does not. Explain why the one binary operation with the set of elements is a group. For the other binary operation and the set of elements, find counterexamples to show that it is not a group.

Internet/Research Activity

42. There are other classifications of mathematical systems besides groups. For example, there are *rings* and *fields*. Do research to determine the requirements that must be met for a mathematical system to be (a) a ring and (b) a field. (c) Is the set of real numbers, under the operations of addition and multiplication, a field? Ask your instructor for references to use.

SECTION 10.2   Finite Mathematical Systems

▲ *Many applications make use of mathematical systems.*

Suppose you decide to use your slow cooker to cook a roast for a dinner party. You would like to eat at 6:30 P.M., and it will take 10 hours for the roast to cook. What time should you begin to cook the roast in the slow cooker? Or, suppose you need to take medicine every eight hours. You last took the medicine at 7:45 A.M. When should you take the medicine again? Questions such as these involve the use of mathematical systems that we will study in this section.

Why **This is Important** Timekeeping is just one application of *finite mathematical systems*.

In the preceding section, we presented infinite mathematical systems. In this section, we present some finite mathematical systems. A *finite mathematical system* is one whose set contains a finite number of elements.

Clock Arithmetic

Figure 10.1

Let's develop a finite mathematical system called *clock 12 arithmetic*. The set of elements in this system will be the hours on a clock: $\{1, 2, 3, 4, 5, 6, 7, 8, 9, 10, 11, 12\}$. The binary operation that we will use is addition, which we define as movement of the hour hand in a clockwise direction. Assume that it is 4 o'clock. What time will it be in 9 hours? (See Fig. 10.1.) If we add 9 hours to 4 o'clock, the clock will read 1 o'clock. Thus, $4 + 9 = 1$ in clock arithmetic. Would $9 + 4$ be the same as $4 + 9$? Yes it will because $4 + 9 = 9 + 4 = 1$.

Table 10.1 on page 575 is the addition table for clock arithmetic. Its elements are based on the definition of addition as previously illustrated. For example, the sum of 4 and 9 is 1, so we put a 1 in the table where the row to the right of the 4 intersects the column below the 9. Likewise, the sum of 11 and 10 is 9, so we put a 9 in the table where the row to the right of the 11 intersects the column below the 10.

The binary operation of this system is defined by the table. It is denoted by the symbol $+$. To determine the value of $a + b$, where a and b are any two numbers in the set, find a in the left-hand column and find b along the top row. Assume that there is a horizontal line through a and a vertical line through b; the point of intersection of these two lines is where you find the value of $a + b$. For example, $10 + 4 = 2$ has been circled in Table 10.1. Note that $4 + 10$ also equals 2, but this result will not necessarily hold for all examples in this chapter.

Table 10.1   Clock 12 Arithmetic

+	1	2	3	4	5	6	7	8	9	10	11	12
1	2	3	4	5	6	7	8	9	10	11	12	1
2	3	4	5	6	7	8	9	10	11	12	1	2
3	4	5	6	7	8	9	10	11	12	1	2	3
4	5	6	7	8	9	10	11	12	1	2	3	4
5	6	7	8	9	10	11	12	1	2	3	4	5
6	7	8	9	10	11	12	1	2	3	4	5	6
7	8	9	10	11	12	1	2	3	4	5	6	7
8	9	10	11	12	1	2	3	4	5	6	7	8
9	10	11	12	1	2	3	4	5	6	7	8	9
10	11	12	1	②	3	4	5	6	7	8	9	10
11	12	1	2	3	4	5	6	7	8	9	10	11
12	1	2	3	4	5	6	7	8	9	10	11	12

Example 1   *A Commutative Group?*

Determine whether the clock 12 arithmetic system under the operation of addition is a commutative group.

Solution   Check the five requirements that must be satisfied for a commutative group.

1. *Closure*: Is the set of elements in clock 12 arithmetic closed under the operation of addition? Yes it is, since Table 10.1 contains only the elements in the set $\{1, 2, 3, 4, 5, 6, 7, 8, 9, 10, 11, 12\}$. If Table 10.1 had contained an element other than the numbers 1 through 12, the set would not have been closed under addition.

2. *Identity element*: Is there an identity element for clock 12 arithmetic? If the time is currently 4 o'clock, how many hours have to pass before it is 4 o'clock again? Twelve hours: $4 + 12 = 12 + 4 = 4$. In fact, given any hour, in 12 hours the clock will return to the starting point. Therefore, 12 is the additive identity element in clock 12 arithmetic.

   In examining Table 10.1, we see that the row of numbers next to the 12 in the left-hand column is identical to the row of numbers along the top. We also see that the column of numbers under the 12 in the top row is identical to the column of numbers on the left. The search for such a column and row is one technique for determining whether an identity element exists for a system defined by a table.

3. *Inverse elements*: Is there an inverse for the number 4 in clock 12 arithmetic for the operation of addition? Recall that the identity element in clock 12 arithmetic is 12. What number when added to 4 gives 12—that is, $4 +$ ▮ $= 12$? Table 10.1 shows that $4 + 8 = 12$ and also that $8 + 4 = 12$. Thus, 8 is the additive inverse of 4, and 4 is the additive inverse of 8.

   To find the additive inverse of 7, find 7 in the left-hand column of Table 10.1. Look to the right of the 7 until you come to the identity element 12. Then determine the number at the top of this column. The number is 5. Since $7 + 5 = 5 + 7 = 12$, 5 is the inverse of 7 and 7 is the inverse of 5. The other

This photo shows the famous clock at the Cathedral of St. Mark (called the Basilica) in Piazza San Marco (St. Mark's Plaza) in Venice, Italy. Construction of the basilica began in 830, but it has been rebuilt a number of times due to fires. The clock tower was built in the fifteenth century. Note that the clock displays all 24 hours in Roman numerals. Also note the position of the hours. Noon, or XII, is where we expect 9 o'clock to be.

In Florence, Italy, the oldest building is probably the Duomo (Cathedral House) in the Piazza del Duomo in the city's center. Florentines believe it was constructed in about 1000. The large clock in the cathedral also displays 24 hours using Roman numerals. What would be the additive identity of clock arithmetic if we used the 24-hour clock shown? What would be the additive inverse of VI?

inverses can be found in the same way. Table 10.2 shows each element in clock 12 arithmetic and its inverse. Note that each element in the set has an *inverse*.

Table 10.2 Clock 12 Inverses

Element	+	Inverse	=	Identity Element
1	+	11	=	12
2	+	10	=	12
3	+	9	=	12
4	+	8	=	12
5	+	7	=	12
6	+	6	=	12
7	+	5	=	12
8	+	4	=	12
9	+	3	=	12
10	+	2	=	12
11	+	1	=	12
12	+	12	=	12

4. *Associative property*: Now consider the associative property. Does $(a + b) + c = a + (b + c)$ for all values a, b, and c of the set? Remember to always evaluate the values within the parentheses first. Let's select some values for a, b, and c.

Let $a = 2$, $b = 6$, and $c = 8$. Then

$$(2 + 6) + 8 = 2 + (6 + 8)$$
$$8 + 8 = 2 + 2$$
$$4 = 4 \quad \text{True}$$

Let $a = 5$, $b = 12$, and $c = 9$. Then

$$(5 + 12) + 9 = 5 + (12 + 9)$$
$$5 + 9 = 5 + 9$$
$$2 = 2 \quad \text{True}$$

Randomly selecting *any* elements a, b, and c of the set reveals $(a + b) + c = a + (b + c)$. Thus, the system of clock 12 arithmetic is associative under the operation of addition. Note that if there is just one set of values a, b, and c such that $(a + b) + c \neq a + (b + c)$, the system is not associative. Usually, you will not be asked to check every case to determine whether the associative property holds. *If not every element in the set appears in every row and column of the table, however, you need to check the associative property carefully.*

5. *Commutative property*: Does the commutative property hold under the given operation? Does $a + b = b + a$ for all elements a and b of the set? Let's randomly select some values for a and b to determine whether the commutative property appears to hold. Let $a = 5$ and $b = 8$; then Table 10.1 shows that

$$5 + 8 = 8 + 5$$
$$1 = 1 \quad \text{True}$$

Let $a = 9$ and $b = 6$; then

$$9 + 6 = 6 + 9$$
$$3 = 3 \quad \text{True}$$

The commutative property holds for these two specific cases. In fact, if we were to select *any* values for a and b, we would find that $a + b = b + a$. Thus, the commutative property of addition is true in clock 12 arithmetic. Note that if there is just one set of values a and b such that $a + b \neq b + a$, the system is not commutative.

This system satisfies the five properties required for a mathematical system to be a commutative group. Thus, clock 12 arithmetic under the operation of addition is a commutative, or abelian, group. ∎

One method that can be used to determine whether a system defined by a table is commutative under the given operation is to determine whether the elements in the table are symmetric about the *main diagonal*. The main diagonal is the diagonal from the upper left-hand corner to the lower right-hand corner of the table. In Table 10.3, the main diagonal is shaded in color.

If the elements are symmetric about the main diagonal, then the system is commutative. If the elements are not symmetric about the main diagonal, then the system is not commutative. If you examine the system in Table 10.3, you see that its elements are symmetric about the main diagonal because the same numbers appear in the same relative positions on opposite sides of the main diagonal. Therefore, this mathematical system is commutative.

It is possible to have groups that are not commutative. Such groups are called *noncommutative* or *nonabelian groups*. However, a *noncommutative group defined by a table must be at least a six-element by six-element table*. Nonabelian groups are illustrated in Exercises 77 through 79 at the end of this section.

Now we will look at another finite mathematical system.

Table 10.3 Symmetry about the Main Diagonal

+	0	1	2	3	4
0	0	1	2	3	4
1	1	2	3	4	0
2	2	3	4	0	1
3	3	4	0	1	2
4	4	0	1	2	3

Table 10.4 A Four-Element System

©	2	4	6	8
2	6	8	2	4
4	8	2	4	6
6	2	4	6	8
8	4	6	8	2

Example 2 *A Finite Mathematical System*

Consider the mathematical system defined by Table 10.4. Assume that the associative property holds for the given operation.

a) List the elements in the set of this mathematical system.

b) Identify the binary operation.

c) Determine whether this mathematical system is a commutative group.

Solution

a) The set of elements for this mathematical system consists of the elements found in the top row or the left-hand column of the table: {2, 4, 6, 8}.

b) The binary operation is ©.

c) We will determine whether the five requirements for a commutative group are satisfied.

1. *Closure*: All the elements in the table are in the original set of elements {2, 4, 6, 8}, so the mathematical system is closed.

2. *Identity element*: The identity is 6. Note that the row of elements to the right of the 6 is identical to the top row *and* the column of elements under the 6 is identical to the left-hand column.

3. *Inverse elements*: When an element operates on its inverse element, the result is the identity element. For this example, the identity is 6. To determine the inverse of 2, determine which element from the set, {2, 4, 6, or 8} replaces the shaded area in the following equation and gives a true statement:

$$2 © \; \blacksquare \; = 6$$

From Table 10.4, we see that $2 © 2 = 6$. Thus, 2 is its own inverse.

To determine the inverse of 4, determine which element replaces the shaded area in the following equation and gives a true statement:

$$4 © \blacksquare = 6$$

From Table 10.4, we see that $4 © 8 = 8 © 4 = 6$. Therefore, 4 is the inverse of 8, and 8 is the inverse of 4. The elements and their inverses are shown in Table 10.5. Note that every element in the mathematical system has an inverse.

Table 10.5 Inverses Under ©

Element	©	Inverse	=	Identity Element
2	©	2	=	6
4	©	8	=	6
6	©	6	=	6
8	©	4	=	6

4. *Associative property*: It is given that the associative property holds for this binary operation, ©. One example of the associative property is

$$(2 © 8) © 4 = 2 © (8 © 4)$$
$$4 © 4 = 2 © 6$$
$$2 = 2 \quad \text{True}$$

5. *Commutative property*: The elements in Table 10.4 are symmetric about the main diagonal, so the commutative property holds for the operation of ©. One example of the commutative property is

$$2 © 4 = 4 © 2$$
$$8 = 8 \quad \text{True}$$

The five necessary properties hold. Thus, the mathematical system is a commutative group.

Mathematical Systems Without Numbers

Thus far, all the systems we have discussed have been based on sets of numbers. Example 3 illustrates a mathematical system of symbols rather than numbers.

Table 10.6 A System of Symbols

·	@	P	W
@	P	W	@
P	W	@	P
W	@	P	W

Example 3 *Investigating a System of Symbols*

Use the mathematical system defined by Table 10.6 and determine
a) the set of elements.
b) the binary operation.
c) closure or nonclosure of the system.
d) the identity element.
e) the inverse of @.
f) $(@ \boxdot P) \boxdot P$ and $@ \boxdot (P \boxdot P)$.
g) $W \boxdot P$ and $P \boxdot W$.

Solution
a) The set of elements of this mathematical system is $\{@, P, W\}$.
b) The binary operation is $\boxdot$.
c) Because the table does not contain any symbols other than @, P, and W, the system is closed under $\boxdot$.

d) The identity element is *W*. Note that the row next to *W* in the left-hand column is the same as the top row and that the column under *W* is identical to the left-hand column. We see that

$$@ \boxdot W = W \boxdot @ = @$$
$$P \boxdot W = W \boxdot P = P$$
$$W \boxdot W = W$$

e) We know that

element $\boxdot$ inverse element = identity element,

and since *W* is the identity element, to find the inverse of @ we write

$$@ \boxdot \blacksquare = W$$

To find the inverse of @, we must determine the element to replace the shaded area. Since $@ \boxdot P = W$ and $P \boxdot @ = W$, *P* is the inverse of @.

f) We first evaluate the information within parentheses.

$$(@ \boxdot P) \boxdot P = W \boxdot P \qquad \text{and} \qquad @ \boxdot (P \boxdot P) = @ \boxdot @$$
$$= P \qquad\qquad\qquad = P$$

g) $W \boxdot P = P$ and $P \boxdot W = P$ ∎

Example 4 *Is the System a Commutative Group?*

Determine whether the mathematical system defined by Table 10.7 is a commutative group. Assume that the associative property holds for the given operation.

Table 10.7

♪	α	β	γ	δ
α	δ	α	β	γ
β	α	β	γ	δ
γ	β	γ	δ	α
δ	γ	δ	α	β

Table 10.8 Inverses Under ♪

Element	♪	Inverse	=	Identity Element
α	♪	γ	=	β
β	♪	β	=	β
γ	♪	α	=	β
δ	♪	δ	=	β

Solution

1. *Closure*: The system is closed.
2. *Identity element*: The identity element is β.
3. *Inverse elements*: Each element has an inverse, as illustrated in Table 10.8.
4. *Associative property*: It is given that the associative property holds. An example illustrating the associative property is

$$(\gamma ♪ \delta) ♪ \alpha = \gamma ♪ (\delta ♪ \alpha)$$
$$\alpha ♪ \alpha = \gamma ♪ \gamma$$
$$\delta = \delta \quad \text{True}$$

5. *Commutative property*: By examining Table 10.7, we can see that the elements are symmetric about the main diagonal. Thus, the system is commutative under the given operation, ♪. One example of the commutative property is

$$\alpha ♪ \delta = \delta ♪ \alpha$$
$$\gamma = \gamma \quad \text{True}$$

All five properties are satisfied. Thus, the system is a commutative group. ∎

Example 5 *Another System to Study*

Determine whether the mathematical system in Table 10.9 is a commutative group under the operation of ☺.

Table 10.9

☺	x	y	z
x	x	z	y
y	z	y	x
z	y	x	z

Solution

1. The system is closed.

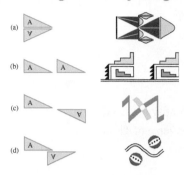
2. No row is identical to the top row, so there is no identity element. Therefore, this mathematical system is *not a group*. There is no need to go any further, but for practice, let's look at a few more items.

3. Since there is no identity element, there can be no inverses.

4. The associative property does not hold. The following counterexample illustrates the associative property does not hold for every case.

$$(x \odot y) \odot z \neq x \odot (y \odot z)$$
$$z \odot z \neq x \odot x$$
$$z \neq x$$

5. The table is symmetric about the main diagonal. Therefore, the commutative property does hold for the operation of $\odot$.

Note that the associative property does not hold even though the commutative property does hold. This outcome can occur when there is no identity element and every element does not have an inverse, as in this example. ∎

Example 6 *Is the System a Commutative Group?*

Determine whether the mathematical system in Table 10.10 is a commutative group under the operation of ▲.

Table 10.10

▲	A	B	C
A	A	B	C
B	B	B	A
C	C	A	C

Solution

1. The system is closed.

2. There is an identity element, A.

3. Each element has an inverse; A is its own inverse, and B and C are inverses of each other.

4. Every element in the set does not appear in every row and every column of the table, so we need to check the associative property carefully. There are many specific cases in which the associative property does hold. However, the following counterexample illustrates that the associative property does not hold for every case.

$$(B \blacktriangle B) \blacktriangle C \neq B \blacktriangle (B \blacktriangle C)$$
$$B \blacktriangle C \neq B \blacktriangle A$$
$$A \neq B$$

5. The commutative property holds because there is symmetry about the main diagonal.

Since we have shown that the associative property does not hold under the operation of ▲, this system is not a group. Therefore, it cannot be a commutative group. ∎

SECTION 10.2 *Exercises*

Warm Up Exercises

In Exercises 1–12, fill in the blanks with an appropriate word, phrase, or symbol(s).

1. In the mathematical system of clock 12 arithmetic, under the operation of addition, the set of elements is _____.

2. In clock 12 arithmetic, under the operation of addition, we define addition as a movement of the hour hand in a _____ direction.

3. Since clock 12 arithmetic, under the operation of addition, contains only the elements {1, 2, 3, 4, 5, 6, 7, 8, 9, 10, 11, 12}, the mathematical system is _____.

4. In clock 12 arithmetic, since $a + 12 = 12 + a = a$, for any element a, we say that 12 is the additive _____ element.

5. In clock 12 arithmetic, since $1 + 11 = 11 + 1 = 12$, we say that 1 and 11 are additive _____.

6. In clock 12 arithmetic, the additive inverse of 2 is _____.

7. In clock 12 arithmetic, for any elements a, b, and c, $(a + b) + c = a + (b + c)$; therefore, the _____ property holds under the operation of addition.

8. In clock 12 arithmetic, for any elements a and b, $a + b = b + a$; therefore, the _____ property holds under the operation of addition.

9. In clock 12 arithmetic under the operation of addition, since the system is closed, there is an identity element, each element has an inverse, and the associative and commutative properties hold, the mathematical system is a _____ group.

10. In a finite mathematical system, if every element does not appear in every row and every column of the table, you need to check the _____ property carefully.

11. In a finite mathematical system, if the elements are symmetric about the main diagonal, then the system is _____.

12. Groups that are not commutative are called noncommutative or _____ groups.

Practice the Skills

In Exercises 13 and 14, determine if the system is closed. Explain how you determined your answer.

13.

ψ	x	y	z
x	z	y	x
y	y	a	y
z	x	y	z

14.

∇	a	b	c
a	a	b	c
b	b	c	a
c	c	a	b

In Exercises 15 and 16, determine if the system has an identity element. If so, list the identity element. Explain how you determined your answer.

15.

W	A	B	C
A	C	B	A
B	B	C	B
C	A	B	C

16.

$\ominus$	$\square$	$\odot$	$\triangle$
$\square$	$\triangle$	$\square$	$\odot$
$\odot$	$\odot$	$\triangle$	$\square$
$\triangle$	$\square$	$\odot$	$\triangle$

In Exercises 17 and 18, the identity element is C. Determine the inverse of (a) A, (b) B, and (c) C.

17.

$\otimes$	A	B	C
A	B	C	A
B	C	A	B
C	A	B	C

18.

$\frac{\perp}{\top}$	A	B	C
A	C	B	A
B	B	C	B
C	A	B	C

In Exercises 19 and 20, determine if the system is commutative. Explain how you determined your answer.

19.

I	P	A	L
P	L	P	A
A	P	L	A
L	A	L	P

20.

$\boxminus$	A	$\otimes$	W
A	$\otimes$	W	A
$\otimes$	W	A	$\otimes$
W	A	$\otimes$	$\otimes$

In Exercises 21–30, use Table 10.1 on page 575 to determine the sum in clock 12 arithmetic.

21. $3 + 6$ **22.** $7 + 6$

23. $9 + 5$ **24.** $11 + 7$

25. $4 + 12$ **26.** $12 + 12$

27. $3 + (8 + 9)$ **28.** $(8 + 7) + 6$

29. $(6 + 4) + 8$ **30.** $(6 + 10) + 12$

In Exercises 31–40, determine the difference in clock 12 arithmetic by starting at the first number and counting counterclockwise on the clock the number of units given by the second number.

31. $10 - 4$ **32.** $9 - 8$ **33.** $2 - 4$

34. $8 - 11$ **35.** $4 - 10$ **36.** $1 - 12$

37. $6 - 10$ **38.** $5 - 8$ **39.** $5 - 5$

40. $12 - 12$

41. Use the following figure to develop an addition table for clock 6 arithmetic. The figure will also be used in Exercises 42–50.

In Exercises 42–50, determine the sum or difference in clock 6 arithmetic.

42. 5 + 2   **43.** 3 + 5   **44.** 4 + 6

45. 5 − 2   **46.** 4 − 5   **47.** 2 − 6

48. 3 − 4   **49.** (3 − 5) − 6   **50.** 2 + (1 − 3)

51. Use the following figure to develop an addition table for clock 7 arithmetic. The figure will also be used in Exercises 52–61.

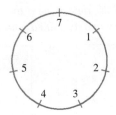

In Exercises 52–60, determine the sum or difference in clock 7 arithmetic.

52. 4 + 4   **53.** 3 + 6   **54.** 6 + 7

55. 5 + 5   **56.** 2 − 3   **57.** 3 − 6

58. 2 − 4   **59.** (4 − 5) − 6   **60.** 3 − (2 − 6)

61. Determine whether clock 7 arithmetic under the operation of addition is a commutative group. Explain.

62. A mathematical system is defined by a three-element by three-element table where every element in the set appears in each row and each column. Must the mathematical system be a commutative group? Explain.

63. Consider the mathematical system defined by the following table. Assume that the associative property holds for the given operation.

£	0	2	4	6
0	0	2	4	6
2	2	4	6	0
4	4	6	0	2
6	6	0	2	4

a) What are the elements of the set in this mathematical system?

b) What is the binary operation?

c) Is the system closed? Explain.

d) Is there an identity element for the system under the given operation? If so, what is it?

e) Does every element in the system have an inverse? If so, give each element and its corresponding inverse.

f) Give an example to illustrate the associative property.

g) Is the system commutative? Give an example to verify your answer.

h) Is the mathematical system a commutative group? Explain.

In Exercises 64–66, repeat parts (a)–(h) of Exercise 63 for the mathematical system defined by the following table. Assume that the associative property holds for the given operation.

64.

®	♣	♦	♥	♠
♣	♥	♠	♣	♦
♦	♠	♣	♦	♥
♥	♣	♦	♥	♠
♠	♦	♥	♠	♣

65.

$	*	5	L
*	5	L	*
5	L	*	5
L	*	5	L

66.

☿	3	5	8	4
3	5	8	4	3
5	8	4	3	5
8	4	3	5	8
4	3	5	8	4

67. For the mathematical system determine

~	f	r	o	m
f	f	r	o	m
r	r	o	m	f
o	o	m	f	r
m	m	f	r	o

a) the elements in the set.

b) the binary operation.

c) closure or nonclosure of the system.

d) $(r \sim o) \sim f$ e) $(f \sim r) \sim m$

f) the identity element.   g) the inverse of r.

h) the inverse of m.

68. a) Is the following mathematical system a group? Explain your answer.

b) Find an example showing that the associative property does not hold for the given set of elements.

⅋	1	2	3	4
1	2	3	4	1
2	3	4	1	2
3	4	1	2	3
4	1	4	3	2

In Exercises 69–74, for the mathematical system given, determine which of the five properties of a commutative group do not hold.

69.

‡	Δ	Φ	Γ
Δ	Δ	Φ	Γ
Φ	Φ	Γ	Δ
Γ	Γ	Δ	Π

70.

⊗	⊡	M	🔔
⊡	⊡	M	🔔
M	M	⊡	🔔
🔔	🔔	M	⊡

71.

⊡	⊙	*	?	T	P
⊙	T	P	⊙	*	*
*	P	⊙	*	⊙	T
?	⊙	*	?	T	P
T	*	⊙	T	P	?
P	*	T	P	?	⊙

72.

☺	a	b	π	0	Δ
a	Δ	a	b	π	0
b	a	b	π	0	Δ
π	b	π	0	Δ	a
0	π	0	Δ	a	b
Δ	0	Δ	π	b	a

73.

⇔	a	b	c	d	e
a	c	d	e	a	b
b	d	e	a	b	c
c	e	a	b	c	d
d	a	b	c	e	d
e	b	c	d	e	a

74.

▽	0	1	2	3	4	5
0	0	0	0	0	0	0
1	0	1	2	3	4	5
2	0	2	4	0	2	4
3	0	3	0	3	0	3
4	0	4	2	0	4	2
5	0	5	4	3	2	1

Problem Solving

75. a) Consider the set consisting of two elements $\{E, O\}$, where E stands for an even number and O stands for an odd number. For the operation of addition, complete the table.

+	E	O
E		
O		

b) Determine whether this mathematical system forms a commutative group under the operation of addition. Explain your answer.

76. a) Let E and O represent even numbers and odd numbers, respectively, as in Exercise 75. Complete the table for the operation of multiplication.

×	E	O
E		
O		

b) Determine whether this mathematical system forms a commutative group under the operation of multiplication. Explain your answer.

In Exercises 77 and 78 on page 584 the tables shown are examples of noncommutative, or nonabelian, groups. For each exercise, do the following.

a) *Show that the system under the given operation is a group. (It would be very time consuming to prove that the associative property holds, but you can give some examples to show that it appears to hold.)*

b) *Determine a counterexample to show that the commutative property does not hold.*

77.

∞	1	2	3	4	5	6
1	5	3	4	2	6	1
2	4	6	5	1	3	2
3	2	1	6	5	4	3
4	3	5	1	6	2	4
5	6	4	2	3	1	5
6	1	2	3	4	5	6

78.

⊖	*A*	*B*	*C*	*D*	*E*	*F*
A	*E*	*C*	*D*	*B*	*F*	*A*
B	*D*	*F*	*E*	*A*	*C*	*B*
C	*B*	*A*	*F*	*E*	*D*	*C*
D	*C*	*E*	*A*	*F*	*B*	*D*
E	*F*	*D*	*B*	*C*	*A*	*E*
F	*A*	*B*	*C*	*D*	*E*	*F*

Challenge Problems/Group Activities

79. Book Arrangements Suppose that three books numbered 1, 2, and 3 are placed next to one another on a shelf. If we remove volume 3 and place it before volume 1, the new order of books is 3, 1, 2. Let's call this replacement R. We can write

$$R = \begin{pmatrix} 1 & 2 & 3 \\ 3 & 1 & 2 \end{pmatrix}$$

which indicates the books were switched in order from 1, 2, 3 to 3, 1, 2. Other possible replacements are S, T, U, V, and I, as indicated.

$$S = \begin{pmatrix} 1 & 2 & 3 \\ 2 & 1 & 3 \end{pmatrix} \quad T = \begin{pmatrix} 1 & 2 & 3 \\ 3 & 2 & 1 \end{pmatrix} \quad U = \begin{pmatrix} 1 & 2 & 3 \\ 1 & 3 & 2 \end{pmatrix}$$

$$V = \begin{pmatrix} 1 & 2 & 3 \\ 2 & 3 & 1 \end{pmatrix} \quad I = \begin{pmatrix} 1 & 2 & 3 \\ 1 & 2 & 3 \end{pmatrix}$$

Replacement set I indicates that the books were removed from the shelves and placed back in their original order. Consider the mathematical system with the set of elements, $\{R, S, T, U, V, I\}$ with the operation of $*$.

To evaluate $R * S$, write

$$R \qquad\qquad S$$

$$R * S = \begin{pmatrix} 1 & 2 & 3 \\ 3 & 1 & 2 \end{pmatrix} * \begin{pmatrix} 1 & 2 & 3 \\ 2 & 1 & 3 \end{pmatrix}$$

As shown in Fig. 10.2, R replaces 1 with 3 and S replaces 3 with 3 (no change), so $R * S$ replaces 1 with 3. R

replaces 2 with 1 and S replaces 1 with 2, so $R * S$ replaces 2 with 2 (no change). R replaces 3 with 2 and S replaces 2 with 1, so $R * S$ replaces 3 with 1. $R * S$ replaces 1 with 3, 2 with 2, and 3 with 1.

$$R \qquad\qquad S$$

$$1 \longrightarrow 3 \longrightarrow 3$$

$$2 \longrightarrow 1 \longrightarrow 2$$

$$3 \longrightarrow 2 \longrightarrow 1$$

$$\uparrow \quad R \quad * \quad S \quad \uparrow$$

$$R * S = \begin{pmatrix} 1 & 2 & 3 \\ 3 & 2 & 1 \end{pmatrix} = T$$

Figure 10.2

Since this result is the same as replacement set T, we write $R * S = T$.

a) Complete the table for the operation using the procedure outlined.

*	*R*	*S*	*T*	*U*	*V*	*I*
R		*T*				
S						
T						
U						
V						
I						

b) Is this mathematical system a group? Explain.

c) Is this mathematical system a commutative group? Explain.

80. If a mathematical system is defined by a four-element by four-element table, how many specific cases must be illustrated to prove the set of elements is associative under the given operation?

Exercises 81–82 will help prepare you for the next section.

81. A table is shown below.

+	0	1	2	3	4
0	0		2		4
1	1		3		
2			4		1
3	3		0	1	2
4		0	1		

Fill in the blank areas of the table by performing the following operations.

1. Add the number in the left-hand column and the number in the top row.

2. Divide this sum by 5.

3. Place the *remainder* in the cell where the number in the left-hand column and the number in the top row would meet.

For example, in the table, the number 2 is in red. This 2 is found as follows:

$$(3 + 4) \div 5 = 1, \text{ remainder } 2$$

82. Using Exercise 81 as a guide, complete the following table by dividing the sum of the numbers by 6. Place the remainders in the table as explained in Exercise 81.

+	0	1	2	3	4	5
0						
1						
2						
3						
4						
5						

Recreational Mathematics

83. *A Tiny Group* Consider the mathematical system with the single element {1} under the operation of multiplication.

    a) Is this system closed?

    b) Does the system have an identity element?

    c) Does 1 have an inverse?

    d) Does the associative property hold?

    e) Does the commutative property hold?

    f) Is {1} under the operation of multiplication a commutative group?

Internet/Research Activities

84. a) *Matrices* In Section 7.3, we introduced matrices. Show that 2×2 matrices under the operation of addition form a commutative group.

    b) Show that 2×2 matrices under the operation of multiplication do not form a commutative group.

Modular Arithmetic

If your birthday is on a Monday this year, on what day of the week will it fall next year? What if next year is a leap year? When will your birthday next fall on a Saturday? These questions can be addressed with the type of arithmetic that we will study in this section.

Why *This is Important* Modular arithmetic is a fundamental part of many branches of mathematics. A wide variety of applications of modular arithmetic can be found in cryptography (the study of writing in secret codes), computer science, chemistry, music, and economics.

▲ *When will your birthday next land on a Saturday?*

The clock arithmetic we discussed in the previous section is similar to modular arithmetic. The set of elements {0, 1, 2, 3, 4, 5, 6, 7, 8, 9, 10, 11} together with the operation of addition is called a modulo 12 or mod 12 system. There is one difference in notation between clock 12 arithmetic and modulo 12 arithmetic. In the modulo 12 system, the symbol 12 is replaced with the symbol 0.

Modulo *m* Systems

A *modulo m system* consists of m elements, 0 through $m - 1$, and a binary operation. In this section, we will discuss modular arithmetic systems and their properties.

If today is Sunday, what day of the week will it be in 23 days? The answer, Tuesday, is arrived at by dividing 23 by 7. The quotient is 3 and the remainder is 2. Twenty-three days represent 3 weeks plus 2 days. Since we are interested only in the day of the week on which the twenty-third day will fall, the 3-week segment is unimportant to the answer. The remainder of 2 indicates the answer will be 2 days later than Sunday, which is Tuesday.

If we place the days of the week on a clock face as shown in Fig. 10.3, then in 23 days the hand would have made three complete revolutions and end on Tuesday. If we replace the days of the week with numbers, then a modulo 7 arithmetic system will result. See Fig. 10.4: Sunday = 0, Monday = 1, Tuesday = 2, and so on. If we start at 0 and move the hand 23 places, we will end at 2. Table 10.11 shows a modulo 7 addition table.

Table 10.11 Modular 7 Addition

+	0	1	2	3	4	5	6
0	0	1	2	3	4	5	6
1	1	2	3	4	5	6	0
2	2	3	4	5	6	0	1
3	3	4	5	6	0	1	2
4	4	5	6	0	1	2	③
5	5	6	0	1	2	3	4
6	6	0	1	2	3	4	5

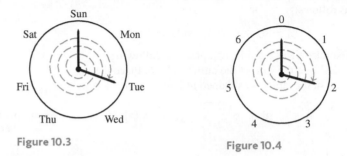

Figure 10.3   **Figure 10.4**

If we start at 4 and add 6, we end at 3 on the clock in Fig. 10.5. This number is circled in Table 10.11. The other numbers can be obtained in the same way.

A second method of determining the sum of 4 + 6 in modulo 7 arithmetic is to divide the sum, 10, by 7 and observe the remainder.

$$10 \div 7 = 1, \quad \text{remainder } 3$$

The remainder, 3, is the sum of 4 + 6 in a modulo 7 arithmetic system.

The concept of congruence is important in modular arithmetic.

Figure 10.5

Definition: **Congruent**
a is **congruent** to b modulo m, written, $a \equiv b$ (mod m), if a and b have the same remainder when divided by m.

We can show, for example, that $10 \equiv 3$ (mod 7) by dividing both 10 and 3 by 7 and observing that we obtain the same remainder in each case.

$$10 \div 7 = 1, \quad \text{remainder } 3 \quad \text{and} \quad 3 \div 7 = 0, \quad \text{remainder } 3$$

Since the remainders are the same, 3 in each case, 10 is congruent to 3 modulo 7, and we may write $10 \equiv 3$ (mod 7).

Now consider $37 \equiv 5$ (mod 8). If we divide both 37 and 5 by 8, each has the same remainder, 5.

In any modulo system, we can develop a set of *modulo classes* by placing all numbers with the same remainder in the appropriate modulo class. In a modulo 7 system, every number must have a remainder of either 0, 1, 2, 3, 4, 5, or 6. Thus, a modulo 7 system has seven modulo classes. The seven classes are presented in Table 10.12.

Every number is congruent to a number from 0 to 6 in modulo 7. For example, $24 \equiv 3$ (mod 7) because 24 is in the same modulo class as 3.

The solution to a problem in modular arithmetic, if it exists, will always be a number from 0 through $m - 1$, where m is the *modulus* of the system. For example, in a modulo 7 system, because 7 is the modulus, the solution will be a number from 0 through 6.

Table 10.12 Modulo 7 Classes

0	1	2	3	4	5	6
0	1	2	3	4	5	6
7	8	9	10	11	12	13
14	15	16	17	18	19	20
21	22	23	24	25	26	27
28	29	30	31	32	33	34
⋮	⋮	⋮	⋮	⋮	⋮	⋮

A cipher, or secret code, actually has group properties: A well-defined operation turns plain text into a cipher, and an inverse operation allows it to be deciphered. During World War II, the Germans used an encrypting device based on a modulo 26 system (for the 26 letters of the alphabet) known as the Enigma. It has four rotors, each with the 26 letters. The rotors were wired to one another so that if an A were typed into the machine, the first rotor would contact a different letter on the second rotor, which contacted a different letter on the third rotor, and so on. The French secret service obtained the wiring instructions, and Polish and British cryptoanalysts were able to crack the ciphers using group theory. This breakthrough helped to keep the Allies abreast of the deployment of the German Navy.

Example 1 *Congruence Modulo 7*

Determine which number, from 0 through 6, the following numbers are congruent to in modulo 7.

a) 47   b) 86   c) 133

Solution We could determine the answer by listing more entries in Table 10.12. Another method of finding the answer is to divide the given number by 7 and observe the remainder. In the solutions, we will use a question mark, ?, as a place holder. The ? will represent a number from 0 through 6. When we determine the answer, we will replace the ? with the answer.

a) $47 \equiv ? \pmod 7$

To determine the value that 47 is congruent to in mod 7, divide 47 by 7 and determine the remainder.

$$\begin{array}{r} 6 \\ 7\overline{)47} \\ \underline{42} \\ 5 \end{array} \leftarrow \text{remainder}$$

$$47 \div 7 = 6, \text{remainder } 5$$

Thus, $47 \equiv 5 \pmod 7$.

b) $86 \equiv ? \pmod 7$

$$86 \div 7 = 12, \text{remainder } 2$$

Thus, $86 \equiv 2 \pmod 7$.

c) $133 \equiv ? \pmod 7$

$$133 \div 7 = 19, \text{remainder } 0$$

Thus, $133 \equiv 0 \pmod 7$. ■

EXAMPLE 2 *Congruence Modulo 6*

Evaluate each of the following in modulo 6.

a) $3 + 5$ b) $5 - 2$ c) $3 \cdot 5$

Solution In each part, because we are working in modulo 6, the answer will be a number from 0 through 5.

a)
$$3 + 5 \equiv ? \pmod 6$$
$$8 \equiv ? \pmod 6$$

Since $8 \div 6 = 1$ with 2 as the remainder, $8 \equiv 2 \pmod 6$. Therefore, $3 + 5 \equiv 2 \pmod 6$.

b)
$$5 - 2 \equiv ? \pmod 6$$
$$3 \equiv ? \pmod 6$$
$$3 \equiv 3 \pmod 6$$

Remember that we want to replace the question mark with a number between 0 and 5, inclusive. Thus, $5 - 2 \equiv 3 \pmod 6$.

c)
$$3 \cdot 5 \equiv ? \pmod 6$$
$$15 \equiv ? \pmod 6$$

Since $15 \div 6 = 2$, remainder 3, $15 \equiv 3 \pmod 6$. Thus, $3 \cdot 5 \equiv 3 \pmod 6$. ■

Note in Table 10.12 on page 586 that every number in the same modulo class differs by a multiple of the modulus, in this case a multiple of 7. Adding (or subtracting) a multiple of the modulus to (or from) a given number does not change the modulo class or congruence of the given number. For example, $3, 3 + 1(7), 3 + 2(7), 3 + 3(7), \ldots, 3 + n(7)$ are all in the same modulo class, namely, 3. We use this fact in the solution to Example 3.

EXAMPLE 3 *Using Modulo Classes in Subtraction*

Determine the positive number replacement (less than the modulus) for the question mark that makes the statement true.

a) $3 - 5 \equiv ? \pmod 7$ b) $? - 4 \equiv 3 \pmod 5$ c) $5 - ? \equiv 7 \pmod 8$

Solution In each part, we wish to replace the question mark with a positive number less than the modulus. Therefore, in part (a) we wish to replace the ? with a positive number less than 7. In part (b), we wish to replace the ? with a positive number less than 5. In part (c), we wish to replace the ? with a positive number less than 8.

a) In mod 7, adding 7, or a multiple of 7, to a number results in a sum that is in the same modulo class. Thus, if we add 7, 14, 21, ... to 3, the result will be a number in the same modulo class. We want to replace 3 with an equivalent mod 7 number that is greater than 5. Adding 7 to 3 yields a sum of 10, which is greater than 5.

$$3 - 5 \equiv ? \pmod 7$$
$$(3 + 7) - 5 \equiv ? \pmod 7$$
$$10 - 5 \equiv ? \pmod 7$$
$$5 \equiv ? \pmod 7$$
$$5 \equiv 5 \pmod 7$$

Therefore, $? = 5$ and $3 - 5 \equiv 5 \pmod 7$.

b) We wish to replace the ? with a number less than 5. We know that $7 - 4 \equiv 3$ mod 5 because $3 \equiv 3$ mod 5. Therefore, we need to determine what number, less than 5, the number 7 is congruent to in mod 5. If we subtract the modulus, 5, from 7, we obtain 2. Thus, 2 and 7 are in the same modular class. Therefore, $? = 2$.

$$? - 4 \equiv 3 \pmod 5$$
$$7 - 4 \equiv 3 \pmod 5$$
$$2 - 4 \equiv 3 \pmod 5$$

Notice in the last equivalence that if we add 5 to 2, we get $7 - 4 \equiv 3 \pmod 5$, which is a true statement.

c) $5 - ? \equiv 7 \pmod 8$

In mod 8, adding 8, or a multiple of 8, to a number results in a sum that is in the same modulo class. Thus, we can add 8 to 5 so that the statement becomes

$$(8 + 5) - ? \equiv 7 \pmod 8$$
$$13 - ? \equiv 7 \pmod 8$$

We can see that $13 - 6 = 7$. Therefore, $? = 6$ and $5 - 6 \equiv 7 \pmod 8$. ∎

EXAMPLE 4 *Using Modulo Classes in Multiplication*

Determine all positive number replacements (less than the modulus) for the question mark that make the statement true.

a) $2 \cdot ? \equiv 3 \pmod 5$ b) $3 \cdot ? \equiv 0 \pmod 6$ c) $3 \cdot ? \equiv 2 \pmod 6$

Solution

a) One method of determining the solution is to replace the question mark with the numbers 0, 1, 2, 3, and 4 and then determine the equivalent modulo class of the product. We use the numbers 0–4 because we are working in modulo 5.

$$2 \cdot \, ? \equiv 3 \pmod 5$$
$$2 \cdot 0 \equiv 0 \pmod 5$$
$$2 \cdot 1 \equiv 2 \pmod 5$$
$$2 \cdot 2 \equiv 4 \pmod 5$$
$$2 \cdot 3 \equiv 1 \pmod 5$$
$$\boxed{2 \cdot 4 \equiv 3 \pmod 5}$$

Therefore, the question mark can be replaced with 4 since $2 \cdot 4 \equiv 3 \pmod 5$.

b) Since we are working in modulo 6, replace the question mark with the numbers 0–5 and follow the procedure used in part (a).

$$3 \cdot \, ? \equiv 0 \pmod 6$$
$$3 \cdot 0 \equiv 0 \pmod 6$$
$$3 \cdot 1 \equiv 3 \pmod 6$$
$$3 \cdot 2 \equiv 0 \pmod 6$$
$$3 \cdot 3 \equiv 3 \pmod 6$$
$$3 \cdot 4 \equiv 0 \pmod 6$$
$$3 \cdot 5 \equiv 3 \pmod 6$$

Therefore, replacing the question mark with 0, 2, or 4 results in true statements. The answers are 0, 2, and 4.

c) $3 \cdot \, ? \equiv 2 \pmod 6$

Examining the products in part (b) shows there are no values that satisfy the statement. The answer is "no solution." ■

Whenever a process is repetitive, modular arithmetic may be helpful in answering some questions about the process. Now let's look at an application of modular arithmetic.

Example 5 *Work Schedule*

Dusty is a chef at a restaurant. His working schedule is to work for 6 days, and then he gets 2 days off. If today is the third day that Dusty has been working, determine the following.

a) Will he be working 60 days from today?

b) Will he be working 82 days from today?

c) Was he working 124 days ago?

Solution

a) Since Dusty works for 6 days and then gets 2 days off, his working schedule may be considered a modular 8 system. That is, 8, 16, 24, … days from today will be just like today, the third day of the 8-day cycle.

    If we divide 60 by 8, we obtain

$$\begin{array}{r} 7 \\ 8\overline{)60} \\ \underline{56} \\ 4 \leftarrow \text{remainder} \end{array}$$

Therefore, in 60 days Dusty will go through 7 complete cycles and will be 4 days further into the next cycle. If we let W represent a working day and N represent a nonworking day, then Dusty's cycle may be represented as follows:

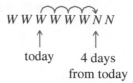

Notice that 4 days from today will be his first nonworking day. Therefore, Dusty will not be working 60 days from today.

b) We work this part in the same way we worked part (a). Divide 82 by 8 and determine the remainder.

$$\begin{array}{r} 10 \\ 8\overline{)82} \\ \underline{80} \\ 2 \end{array} \leftarrow \text{remainder}$$

Thus, in 82 days it will be 2 days later in the cycle than it is today. Because he is currently in day 3 of his cycle, Dusty will be in day 5 of his cycle and will be working.

c) This part is worked in the same way as parts (a) and (b), but once we find the remainder we must move backward in the cycle.

$$\begin{array}{r} 15 \\ 8\overline{)124} \\ \underline{120} \\ 4 \end{array} \leftarrow \text{remainder}$$

Thus, 124 days ago was 4 days earlier in the cycle. Marking day 3 of the cycle (indicated by the word *today*) and then moving 4 days backwards brings us to the first nonworking day. The two N's shown at the beginning of the letters below are actually the end days of the previous cycle.

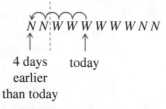

Therefore, 124 days ago Dusty was not working. ∎

Modular Arithmetic and Groups

Modular arithmetic systems under the operation of addition are commutative groups, as illustrated in Example 6.

EXAMPLE 6 *A Commutative Group*

Construct a mod 5 addition table and show that the mathematical system is a commutative group. Assume that the associative property holds for the given operation.

Profile in Mathematics

Amalie Emmy Noether (1882–1935)

Professor Amalie Emmy Noether was described by Albert Einstein as the "most significant creative mathematical genius thus far produced since the higher education of women began." Because she was a woman, she was never to be granted a regular professorship in her native Germany. In 1933, with the rise of the Nazis to power, she and many other mathematicians and scientists emigrated to the United States. That brought her to Bryn Mawr College, at the age of 51, to her first full-time faculty appointment. She was to die just 2 years later.

Her special interest lay in abstract algebra, which includes such topics as groups, rings, and fields. She developed a number of theories that helped draw together many important mathematical concepts. Her innovations in higher algebra gained her recognition as one of the most creative abstract algebraists of modern times.

Solution The set of elements in modulo 5 arithmetic is $\{0, 1, 2, 3, 4\}$; the binary operation is $+$.

+	0	1	2	3	4
0	0	1	2	3	4
1	1	2	3	4	0
2	2	3	4	0	1
3	3	4	0	1	2
4	4	0	1	2	3

For this system to be a commutative group, it must satisfy the five properties of a commutative group.

1. *Closure*: Every entry in the table is a member of the set $\{0, 1, 2, 3, 4\}$, so the system is closed under addition.

2. *Identity element*: An easy way to determine whether there is an identity element is to look for a row in the table that is identical to the elements at the top of the table. Note that the row next to 0 is identical to the top of the table, which indicates that 0 *might be* the identity element. Now look at the column under the 0 at the top of the table. If this column is identical to the left-hand column, then 0 is the identity element. Since the column under 0 is the same as the left-hand column, 0 is the additive identity in modulo 5 arithmetic.

Element	+	Identity	=	Element
0	+	0	=	0
1	+	0	=	1
2	+	0	=	2
3	+	0	=	3
4	+	0	=	4

3. *Inverse elements*: Does every element have an inverse? Recall that an element plus its inverse must equal the identity element. In this example, the identity element is 0. Therefore, for each of the given elements 0, 1, 2, 3, and 4, we must find the element that when added to it results in a sum of zero. These elements will be the inverses.

Element	+	Inverse	=	Identity	
0	+	?	=	0	Since $0 + 0 \equiv 0$, 0 is its own inverse.
1	+	?	=	0	Since $1 + 4 \equiv 0$, 4 is the inverse of 1.
2	+	?	=	0	Since $2 + 3 \equiv 0$, 3 is the inverse of 2.
3	+	?	=	0	Since $3 + 2 \equiv 0$, 2 is the inverse of 3.
4	+	?	=	0	Since $4 + 1 \equiv 0$, 1 is the inverse of 4.

Note that each element has an inverse.

4. *Associative property*: It is given that the associative property holds. One example that illustrates the associative property is

$$(2 + 3) + 4 = 2 + (3 + 4)$$
$$0 + 4 = 2 + 2$$
$$4 = 4 \quad \text{True}$$

5. *Commutative property*: Is $a + b = b + a$ for *all* elements a and b of the given set? The table shows that the system is commutative because the elements are symmetric about the main diagonal. We will give one example to illustrate the commutative property.

$$4 + 2 = 2 + 4$$
$$1 = 1 \quad \text{True}$$

All five properties are satisfied. Thus, modulo 5 arithmetic under the operation of addition is a commutative group. ∎

SECTION 10.3 Exercises

Warm Up Exercises

In Exercises 1–6, fill in the blanks with an appropriate word, phrase, or symbol(s).

1. The elements in a modulo m system consist of the m numbers, 0 through _____.

2. In a modulo m system, in addition to the m elements, there is also a(n) _____ operation.

3. In any modulo m system, we can develop a set of modulo classes by dividing the numbers by m and placing all numbers with the same _____ in the appropriate modulo class.

4. In a modulo m system, the number m is called the _____ of the system.

5. If a and b have the same remainder when divided by m, we say that a is _____ to b modulo m.

6. To determine the value that 45 is congruent to in modulo 7, we _____ 45 by 7 and determine the remainder.

Practice the Skills

In Exercises 7–16, assume that Sunday is represented as day 0, Monday is represented as day 1, and so on. If today is Thursday (day 4), determine the day of the week it will be in the specified number of days. Assume no leap years.

7. 11 days
8. 43 days
9. 101 days
10. 135 days
11. 365 days
12. 3 years
13. 3 years, 34 days
14. 463 days
15. 400 days
16. 3 years, 27 days

In Exercises 17–24, consider 12 months to be a modulo 12 system. If it is currently October, determine the month it will be in the specified number of months.

17. 19 months
18. 73 months
19. 2 years, 10 months
20. 4 years, 8 months
21. 83 months
22. 7 years
23. 105 months
24. 5 years, 9 months

In Exercises 25–36, determine what number the sum, difference, or product is congruent to in mod 5.

25. $4 + 3$
26. $2 + 3$
27. $1 + 2 + 3$
28. $9 - 3$
29. $5 - 12$
30. $8 \cdot 7$
31. $8 \cdot 9$
32. $1 - 4$
33. $4 - 8$
34. $3 - 7$
35. $(15 \cdot 4) - 8$
36. $(4 - 9) \cdot 7$

In Exercises 37–50, find the modulo class to which each number belongs for the indicated modulo system.

37. 5, mod 3
38. 28, mod 5
39. 60, mod 7
40. 43, mod 6
41. 41, mod 9
42. 75, mod 8
43. 30, mod 7
44. 53, mod 4
45. -1, mod 7
46. -7, mod 4
47. -13, mod 11
48. -11, mod 13
49. 205, mod 10
50. -12, mod 4

In Exercises 51–66, determine all positive number replacements (less than the modulus) for the question mark that make the statement true.

51. $4 + 5 \equiv ? \pmod{8}$
52. $? + 3 \equiv 2 \pmod{5}$
53. $6 + ? \equiv 2 \pmod{7}$
54. $4 + ? \equiv 3 \pmod{6}$
55. $4 - ? \equiv 5 \pmod{6}$
56. $2 \cdot 5 \equiv ? \pmod{7}$
57. $5 \cdot ? \equiv 7 \pmod{9}$
58. $3 \cdot ? \equiv 5 \pmod{6}$
59. $2 \cdot ? \equiv 1 \pmod{6}$
60. $3 \cdot ? \equiv 3 \pmod{12}$
61. $4 \cdot ? \equiv 4 \pmod{10}$
62. $? - 3 \equiv 4 \pmod{8}$
63. $? - 8 \equiv 9 \pmod{12}$
64. $6 - ? \equiv 8 \pmod{9}$
65. $3 \cdot ? \equiv 0 \pmod{10}$
66. $4 \cdot ? \equiv 5 \pmod{8}$

Problem Solving

67. *Presidential Elections* The upcoming presidential election years are 2012, 2016, 2020, ...

a) List the next five presidential election years after 2020.

b) What will be the first election year after the year 3000?

c) List the election years between the years 2550 and 2575.

68. *Flight Schedules* A pilot is scheduled to fly for 5 consecutive days and rest for 3 consecutive days. If today is the second day of her rest shift, determine whether she will be flying or resting

a) 60 days from today.   **b)** 90 days from today.

c) 240 days from today.   **d)** Was she flying 6 days ago?

e) Was she flying 20 days ago?

69. *Workout Schedule* A golf pro's workout schedule is to give both morning and afternoon lessons for 3 days, rest for 1 day, give only morning lessons for 2 days, rest for 2 days, and then start the cycle again. If the golf pro is on his rest for 1 day part of the schedule, determine what he will be doing

a) 28 days from today.

b) 60 days from today.

c) 127 days from today.

d) Will the golf pro have a day off 82 days from today?

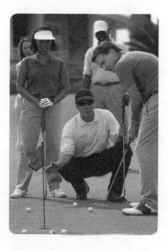

70. *Physical Therapy* A man has an Achilles' tendon injury and is receiving physical therapy. He must have physical therapy twice a day for 5 days, physical therapy once a day for 3 days, and then 2 days off; then the cycle begins again. If he is in his second day of his twice-a-day therapy cycle, determine what he will be doing

a) 20 days from today.   **b)** 49 days from today.

c) 103 days from today.

d) Will the man have a day off 78 days from today?

71. *The Weekend Off* A manager of a theater has both Saturday and Sunday off every 7 weeks. It is week 2 of the 7 weeks.

a) Determine the number of weeks before he will have both Saturday and Sunday off.

b) Will he have both Saturday and Sunday off 25 weeks from this week?

c) What is the first week, after 50 weeks from this week, that he will have both Saturday and Sunday off?

72. *Nursing Shifts* A nurse's work pattern at Community Hospital consists of working the 7 A.M.–3 P.M. shift for 3 weeks and then the 3 P.M.–11 P.M. shift for 2 weeks.

a) If it is the third week of the pattern, what shift will the nurse be working 6 weeks from now?

b) If it is the fourth week of the pattern, what shift will the nurse be working 7 weeks from now?

c) If it is the first week of the pattern, what shift will the nurse be working 11 weeks from now?

73. *Restaurant Rotation* A waiter at a restaurant works both daytime and evening shifts. He works daytime for 5 consecutive days, then evenings for 3 consecutive days, then daytime for 4 consecutive days, then evenings for 2 consecutive days. Then the rotation starts again. If it is day 2 of the 5-day consecutive daytime shift, determine whether he will be working the daytime or evening shift

a) 20 days from today.   **b)** 52 days from today.

c) 365 days from today.

74. *A Truck Driver's Schedule* A truck driver's routine is as follows: Drive 3 days from New York to Chicago, rest 1 day in Chicago, drive 3 days from Chicago to Los Angeles, rest 2 days in Los Angeles, drive 5 days to return to New York, rest 3 days in New York. Then the cycle begins again. If the truck driver is starting her trip to Chicago today, what will she be doing

a) 30 days from today?

b) 70 days from today?

c) 2 years from today?

75. a) Construct a modulo 3 addition table.

b) Is the system closed? Explain.

c) Is there an identity element for the system? If so, what is it?

d) Does every element in the system have an inverse? If so, list the elements and their inverses.

e) The associative property holds for the system. Give an example.

f) Does the commutative property hold for the system? Give an example.

g) Is the system a commutative group?

h) Will every modulo system under the operation of addition be a commutative group? Explain.

76. Construct a modulo 8 addition table. Repeat parts (b)–(h) in Exercise 75.

77. a) Construct a modulo 4 multiplication table.

b) Is the system closed under the operation of multiplication?

c) Is there an identity element in the system? If so, what is it?

d) Does every element in the system have an inverse? Make a list showing the elements that have a multiplicative inverse and list the inverses.

e) The associative property holds for the system. Give an example.

f) Does the commutative property hold for the system? Give an example.

g) Is this mathematical system a commutative group? Explain.

78. Construct a modulo 7 multiplication table. Repeat parts (b)–(g) in Exercise 77.

Challenge Problems/Group Activities

We have not discussed division in modular arithmetic. With what number or numbers, if any, can you replace the question marks to make the statement true? The question mark must be a number less than the modulus. Hint: Use the fact that $\frac{a}{b} \equiv c \ (mod \ m)$ means $a \equiv b \cdot c \ (mod \ m)$ and use trial and error to obtain your answer.

79. $? \div 3 \equiv 4 \ (mod \ 5)$ **80.** $3 \div 4 \equiv ? \ (mod \ 7)$

81. $? \div ? \equiv 1 \ (mod \ 4)$ **82.** $1 \div 2 \equiv ? \ (mod \ 5)$

In Exercises 83–85, solve for x where k is any counting number.

83. $8k \equiv x \ (mod \ 8)$ **84.** $7k + 1 \equiv x \ (mod \ 7)$

85. $4k - 2 \equiv x \ (mod \ 4)$

86. Find the smallest positive number divisible by 5 to which 2 is congruent in modulo 6.

87. *Birthday Question* During a certain year, Clarence Dee's birthday is on Monday, April 18.

a) If next year is *not* a leap year, on what day of the week will Clarence's birthday fall next year?

b) If next year *is* a leap year, on what day of the week will Clarence's birthday fall next year?

88. *More Birthday Questions* During a certain leap year, Josephine Emme's birthday is on Tuesday, May 18. In how many years will Josephine's birthday fall on a

a) Friday?   **b)** Saturday?

Recreational Math

89. *Cryptography* Read the *Recreational Mathematics* box on page 588. Using the same coding circle and a code key of the letter *e*, decipher the following message.

16	19	20	1	17	10	9	12	10
5	14	24	5	21	20	1	10	23

90. *Rolling Wheel* The wheel shown below is to be rolled. Before the wheel is rolled, it is resting on number 0. The wheel will be rolled at a uniform rate of one complete roll every 4 minutes. In exactly 1 year (not a leap year), what number will be at the bottom of the wheel?

Internet/Research Activity

91. *The Enigma Cipher Machine* Do research on the Enigma ciphering machine (see the *Did You Know?* box on page 587). Write a paper on the role the machine played prior to and during World War II.

92. The concept and notation for modular systems were introduced by Carl Friedrich Gauss in 1801. Write a paper on Gauss's contribution to modular systems.

CHAPTER 10   *Summary*

Important Facts and Concepts   **Examples and Discussion**

Section 10.1 A **mathematical system** consists of a set of elements and at least one binary operation.	Discussion, page 567
Commutative Property **Addition:** $a + b = b + a$ **Multiplication:** $a \cdot b = b \cdot a$	Discussion, pages 567–568
Associative Property **Addition:** $(a + b) + c = a + (b + c)$ **Multiplication:** $(a \cdot b) \cdot c = a \cdot (b \cdot c)$	Discussion, pages 567–568
Properties of a Group and a Commutative Group A mathematical system is a group if the first four following conditions hold, and a commutative group if all five conditions hold. 1. The set of elements is *closed* under the given operation. 2. An *identity element* exists for the set. 3. Every element in the set has an *inverse*. 4. The set of elements is *associative* under the given operation. 5. The set of elements is *commutative* under the given operation.	Discussion, pages 568–571, Examples 1–2, pages 571–572; Examples 1–6, pages 575–580; Example 6 pages 590–592
Section 10.2, 10.3 If the elements of a finite mathematical system are symmetric about the main diagonal, then the system is *commutative*.	Discussion, page 577, Examples 1–6, pages 575–580; Example 6, page 580
Section 10.3 a is **congruent** to b modulo m, written $a \equiv b \ (mod \ m)$, if a and b have the same remainder when divided by m.	Discussion, pages 585–586, Examples 1-6, pages 587–591

CHAPTER 10   *Review Exercises*

10.1, 10.2

1. What is a binary operation?

2. List the parts of a mathematical system.

3. Are the set of whole numbers closed under the operation of division? Explain.

4. Are the set of real numbers closed under the operation of subtraction? Explain.

Determine the sum or difference in clock 12 arithmetic.

5. $11 + 3$ **6.** $12 + 7$ **7.** $3 - 6$

8. $4 + 7 + 9$ **9.** $7 - 4 + 6$ **10.** $2 - 8 - 7$

11. List the properties of a group and explain what each property means.

12. What is another name for an abelian group?

In Exercises 13 and 14, explain your answer.

13. Determine whether the set of integers under the operation of addition forms a group.

14. Determine whether the set of integers under the operation of multiplication forms a group.

15. Determine whether the set of natural numbers under the operation of addition forms a group.

16. Determine whether the set of rational numbers under the operation of multiplication forms a group.

In Exercises 17–19, for the mathematical system, determine which of the five properties of a commutative group do not hold.

17.

∴	ρ	σ	ω
ρ	ρ	ω	σ
σ	ω	σ	ρ
ω	σ	ρ	ω

18.

?	4	#	L	P
4	P	4	#	L
#	4	#	L	P
L	#	L	P	4
P	L	P	4	L

19.

□	!	?	Δ	p
!	?	Δ	!	p
?	Δ	p	?	!
Δ	!	?	Δ	p
p	p	!	p	Δ

20. Consider the following mathematical system. Assume the associative property holds for the given operation.

△	☺	●	♀	♂
☺	☺	●	♀	♂
●	●	♀	♂	☺
♀	♀	♂	☺	●
♂	♂	☺	●	♀

a) What are the elements of the set in this mathematical system?

b) What is the binary operation? △

c) Is the system closed? Explain.

d) Is there an identity element for the system under the given operation?

e) Does every element in the system have an inverse? If so, give each element and its corresponding inverse.

f) Give an example to illustrate the associative property. △ △   △ △

g) Is the system commutative? Give an example. △   △

h) Is this mathematical system a commutative group? Explain.

10.3

In Exercises 21–30, find the modulo class to which the number belongs for the indicated modulo system.

21. 14, mod 7

22. 37, mod 6

23. 56, mod 9

24. 68, mod 8

25. 71, mod 12

26. 54, mod 4

27. 52, mod 12

28. 54, mod 14

29. 97, mod 11

30. 31, mod 20

In Exercises 31–40, determine all positive number replacements (less than the modulus) for the question mark that make the statement true.

31. $2 + 5 \equiv ?$ (mod 6)

32. $2 - ? \equiv 3$ (mod 7)

33. $7 \cdot ? \equiv 5$ (mod 8)

34. $5 \cdot ? \equiv 3$ (mod 8)

35. $? \cdot 4 \equiv 0$ (mod 8)

36. $10 \cdot 7 \equiv ?$ (mod 11)

37. $3 - 5 \equiv ?$ (mod 7)

38. $? \cdot 7 \equiv 3$ (mod 10)

39. $? \cdot 3 = 5$ (mod 6)

40. $7 \cdot ? \equiv 2$ (mod 9)

41. Construct a modulo 6 addition table. Then determine whether the modulo 6 system forms a commutative group under the operation of addition.

42. Construct a modulo 4 multiplication table. Then determine whether the modulo 4 system forms a commutative group under the operation of multiplication.

43. *Police Officer Shifts* Julie Francavilla, a police officer, has the following work pattern. She works 3 days, has 4 days off, then works 4 days, then has 3 days off, and then the pattern repeats. Assume that today is the first day of the work pattern.

a) Will Julie be working 30 days from today?

b) Julie's niece is getting married 45 days from today. Will Julie have the day off?

CHAPTER 10 Test

1. What is a mathematical system?

2. List the requirements needed for a mathematical system to be a commutative group.

3. Is the set of integers a commutative group under the operation of addition? Explain your answer completely.

4. Is the set of natural numbers a commutative group under the operation of subtraction? Explain your answer completely.

5. Develop a clock 5 arithmetic addition table.

6. Is clock 5 arithmetic under the operation of addition a commutative group? Assume that the associative property holds. Explain your answer completely.

In Exercises 7 and 8, determine the following in clock 5 arithmetic.

7. $2 + 4 + 1$ 8. $1 - 4$

9. Consider the mathematical system

□	W	S	T	R
W	T	R	W	S
S	R	W	S	T
T	W	S	T	R
R	S	T	R	W

a) What is the binary operation?

b) Is this system closed? Explain.

c) Is there an identity element for this system under the given operation? Explain.

d) What is the inverse of the element R?

e) What is $(T \,\square\, R) \,\square\, W$?

In Exercises 10 and 11, determine whether the mathematical system is a commutative group. Explain your answer completely.

10.

*	a	b	c
a	a	b	c
b	b	b	a
c	c	a	d

11.

?	1	2	3
1	3	1	2
2	1	2	3
3	2	3	1

12. Determine whether the mathematical system is a commutative group. Assume that the associative property holds. Explain your answer.

○	@	$	&	%
@	%	@	$	&
$	@	$	&	%
&	$	&	%	@
%	&	%	@	$

In Exercises 13 and 14, determine the modulo class to which the number belongs for the indicated modulo system.

13. 39, mod 4   14. 107, mod 11

In Exercises 15–19, determine all positive number replacements for the question mark, less than the modulus, that make the statement true.

15. $? + 5 \equiv 3 \pmod 6$ 16. $? - 3 \equiv 4 \pmod 5$

17. $3 - ? \equiv 7 \pmod 9$ 18. $4 \cdot 2 \equiv ? \pmod 6$

19. $3 \cdot ? \equiv 2 \pmod 6$

20. a) Construct a modulo 5 multiplication table.

    b) Is this mathematical system a commutative group? Explain your answer completely.

GROUP PROJECTS

1. **Rotating a Square** The square $ABCD$ below has a pin through it at point P so that the square can be rotated in a clockwise direction. The mathematical system consists of the set $\{A, B, C, D\}$ and the operation ♣. The elements of the set represent different rotations of the square clockwise, as follows.

A = rotate about the point P clockwise 90°

B = rotate about the point P clockwise 180°

C = rotate about the point P clockwise 270°

D = rotate about the point P clockwise 360°

The operation ♣ means *followed by*. For example, A ♣ B means a clockwise rotation of 90° followed by a clockwise rotation of 180° or a clockwise rotation of 270°. Since C represents a clockwise rotation of 270°, we write A ♣ $B = C$. This result and two other results are shown in the following table.

♣	A	B	C	D
A		C		
B			A	
C	D			
D				

Complete the table and determine if the mathematical system is a commutative group. Explain.

2. **Product of Zero** In arithmetic and algebra, the statement "If $a \cdot b = 0$, then $a = 0$ or $b = 0$" is true. That is, for the product of two numbers to be 0, at least one of the factors must be 0. Can the product of two nonzero numbers equal 0 in a specific modulo system? If so, in what type of modulo systems can this result occur?

a) Construct multiplication tables for modulo systems 3–9.

b) Which, if any, of the multiplication tables in part (a) have products equal to 0 when neither factor is 0?

c) Which, if any, of the multiplication tables in part (a) have products equal to 0 only when at least one factor is 0?

d) Using the results in parts (b) and (c), can you write a conjecture as to which modulo systems have a product of 0 when neither factor is 0?

3. **Conjecture About Multiplicative Inverses** Are there certain modulo systems where all numbers have multiplicative inverses?

a) If you have not worked Group Projects Exercise 2, construct multiplication tables for modulo systems 3–9.

b) Which of the multiplication tables in part (a) contain multiplicative inverses for all nonzero numbers?

c) Which, if any, of the multiplication tables in part (a) do not contain multiplicative inverses for all nonzero numbers?

d) Using the results in parts (b) and (c), can you write a conjecture as to which modulo systems contain multiplicative inverses for all nonzero numbers?

12
Probability

◄ Probability is involved in all games of chance, determining the cost of car insurance, and weather forecasting.

What You Will Learn

- Empirical probability and theoretical probability
- Compound probability, conditional probability, and binomial probability
- Odds against an event and odds in favor of an event
- Expected value
- Tree diagrams
- Mutually exclusive events and independent events
- The counting principle, permutations, and combinations

Why This is Important

Each year, millions of Americans play lotteries. If you play a lottery, your hope is to beat the odds and be the person with the winning numbers. Not satisfied with leaving things to chance, mathematicians of the sixteenth, seventeenth, and eighteenth centuries invented the study of probability to determine the likelihood of an event such as winning the lottery.

Although the rules of probability were first applied to gaming, they have many other applications. The cost of your car insurance, the weather forecast, the expected number of people who will attend an outdoor concert if it is raining all involve probability. In this chapter, we will learn many of the important concepts of probability that can help us make informed decisions in our lives.

The Nature of Probability

▲ *We can determine the probability of an event, such as the probability that a particular auto part will fail before the warranty expires, based on actual observations.*

How do researchers determine if a new potential drug is superior to a standard drug? How do automobile manufacturers determine the chance that a particular part will fail before the warranty expires? These and many other similar questions are answered through experimentation and observation of the results. Determining the chance of something happening in the future by observing past results is called empirical probability.

Why *This is Important* Understanding how to calculate probabilities based on past experience is essential to our daily lives. Empirical probability is used to determine insurance premiums and the length of a warranty. It is also used in medical and genetics research, as well as many other areas.

I n this section we introduce some basic concepts of probability including the Law of Large Numbers.

History

Probability is used in many areas, including public finance, medicine, insurance, elections, manufacturing, educational tests and measurements, genetics, weather forecasting, investments, opinion polls, the natural sciences, and games of chance. The study of probability originated from the study of games of chance. Archaeologists have found artifacts used in games of chance in Egypt dating from about 3000 B.C.

Mathematical problems relating to games of chance were studied by a number of mathematicians of the Renaissance. Italy's Girolamo Cardano (1501–1576) in his *Liber de Ludo Aleae* (book on the games of chance) presents one of the first systematic computations of probabilities. Although it is basically a gambler's manual, many consider it the first book ever written on probability. A short time later, two French mathematicians, Blaise Pascal (1623–1662) and Pierre de Fermat (1601–1665), worked together studying "the geometry of the die." In 1657, Dutch mathematician Christian Huygens (1629–1695) published *De Ratiociniis in Luno Aleae* (on ratiocination in dice games), which contained the first documented reference to the concept of mathematical expectation (see Section 12.4). Swiss mathematician Jacob Bernoulli (1654–1705), whom many consider the founder of probability theory, is said to have fused pure mathematics with the empirical methods used in statistical experiments. The works of Pierre-Simon de Laplace (1749–1827) dominated probability throughout the nineteenth century.

The Nature of Probability

Before we discuss the meaning of the word *probability* and learn how to calculate probabilities, we must introduce a few definitions.

Definition: Experiment
An **experiment** is a controlled operation that yields a set of results.

The process by which medical researchers administer experimental drugs to patients to determine their reaction is one type of experiment.

Definition: Outcomes
The possible results of an experiment are called its **outcomes**.

Profile In Mathematics

Jacob Bernoulli (1654–1705)

S wiss mathematician Jacob Bernoulli was considered a pioneer of probability theory. He was part of a famous family of mathematicians and scientists. In *Ars Conjectand*, published posthumously in 1713, he proposed that an increased degree of accuracy can be obtained by increasing the number of trials of an experiment. This theorem, called Bernoulli's theorem (of probability), is also known as the law of large numbers. Bernoulli's theorem of fluid dynamics, used in aircraft wing design, was developed by Daniel Bernoulli (1700–1782). Daniel was one of Jacob's younger brother Johann's three sons.

▲ *A die (one of a pair of dice) contains six surfaces, called faces. Each face contains a unique number of dots, from 1 to 6. The sum of the dots on opposite surfaces is 7.*

For example, the possible outcomes from administering an experimental drug may be a favorable reaction, no reaction, or an adverse reaction.

Definition: Event

An **event** is a subcollection of the outcomes of an experiment.

For example, when a die is rolled, the event of rolling a number greater than 2 can be satisfied by any one of four outcomes: 3, 4, 5, or 6. The event of rolling a 5 can be satisfied by only one outcome, the 5 itself. The event of rolling an even number can be satisfied by any of three outcomes: 2, 4, or 6.

Probability is classified as either *empirical* (experimental) or *theoretical* (mathematical). *Empirical probability* is the relative frequency of occurrence of an event and is determined by actual observations of an experiment. *Theoretical probability* is determined through a study of the possible *outcomes* that can occur for the given experiment. We will indicate the probability of an event E by $P(E)$, which is read "P of E."

Empirical Probability

In this section, we will briefly discuss empirical probability. The emphasis in the remaining sections is on theoretical probability. Following is the formula for computing empirical probability, or relative frequency.

Empirical Probability (Relative Frequency)

The empirical probability of an event, $P(E)$, can be determined by the following formula.

$$P(E) = \frac{\text{number of times event } E \text{ has occurred}}{\text{total number of times the experiment has been performed}}$$

The probability of an event, whether empirical or theoretical, is always a number between 0 and 1, inclusive, and may be expressed as a decimal number or a fraction. An empirical probability of 0 indicates that the event has never occurred. An empirical probability of 1 indicates that the event has always occurred.

Example 1 *Heads Up!*

In 100 tosses of a fair coin, 44 landed heads up. Determine the empirical probability of the coin landing heads up.

Solution Let E be the event that the coin lands heads up. Then

$$P(E) = \frac{44}{100} = 0.44$$

∎

Example 2 *Blood Pressure Reduction*

A pharmaceutical company is testing a drug that is supposed to help reduce high blood pressure. The drug is given to 500 individuals with the following outcomes.

Blood pressure reduced	Blood pressure unchanged	Blood pressure increased
379	62	59

**One Blue Eye,
One Brown Eye**

Seeing a dog or a person with different-colored eyes is unusual, but not that unusual. Features such as eye color are determined genetically, as are certain illnesses. Below is a chart listing some human genetic disorders and their rates of occurrence.

Disorder/Incidence

Cystic fibrosis:
1 out of 2500 Caucasian births

Down syndrome:
1 out of 800–1000 births

Duchenne muscular dystrophy:
1 out of 3300 male births

Fragile X syndrome:
1 out of 1500 male births
1 out of 2500 female births

Hemophilia A:
1 out of 8500 male births

Polycystic kidney disease:
1 out of 3000 births

Prader–Willi syndrome:
1 out of 12,000 births

Sickle-cell anemia:
1 out of 400–600 African-American births

Tay-Sachs disease:
1 out of 3600 Ashkenazi Jewish births

Why This is Important Genetics, which has its foundation in probability, is used in explaining the cause of these illnesses, and it plays an important role in research to find cures for genetic disorders.

If this drug is given to an individual, determine the empirical probability that the person's blood pressure is (a) reduced, (b) unchanged, (c) increased.

Solution

a) Let E be the event that the blood pressure is reduced.

$$P(E) = \frac{379}{500} = 0.758$$

b) Let E be the event that the blood pressure is unchanged.

$$P(E) = \frac{62}{500} = 0.124$$

c) Let E be the event that the blood pressure is increased.

$$P(E) = \frac{59}{500} = 0.118$$

Empirical probability is used when probabilities cannot be theoretically calculated. For example, life insurance companies use empirical probabilities to determine the chance of an individual in a certain profession, with certain risk factors, living to age 65.

Empirical Probability in Genetics

Using empirical probability, Gregor Mendel (1822–1884) developed the laws of heredity by crossbreeding different types of "pure" pea plants and observing the relative frequencies of the resulting offspring. These laws became the foundation for the study of genetics. For example, when he crossbred a pure yellow pea plant and a pure green pea plant, the resulting offspring (the first generation) were always yellow; see Fig. 12.1(a). When he crossbred a pure round-seeded pea plant and a pure wrinkled-seeded pea plant, the resulting offspring (the first generation) were always round; see Fig. 12.1(b).

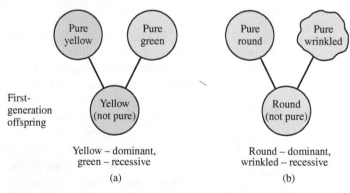

First-generation offspring

Yellow – dominant, green – recessive

(a)

Round – dominant, wrinkled – recessive

(b)

Figure 12.1

Mendel called traits such as yellow color and round seeds *dominant* because they overcame or "dominated" the other trait. He labeled the green color and the wrinkled traits *recessive*.

Mendel then crossbred the offspring of the first generation. The resulting second-generation offspring had both the dominant and the recessive traits of their grandparents; see Fig. 12.2(a) and 12.2(b) on page 678. What's more, these traits always appeared in approximately a 3 to 1 ratio of dominant to recessive.

"The laws of probability, so true in general, so fallacious in particular."
Edward Gibbon, 1796

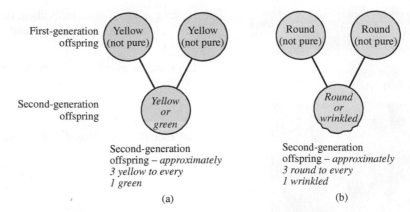

Figure 12.2

Table 12.1 lists some of the actual results of Mendel's experiments with pea plants. Note that the ratio of dominant trait to recessive trait in the second-generation offspring is about 3 to 1 for each experiment. The empirical probability of the dominant trait has also been calculated. How would you find the empirical probability of the recessive trait?

Table 12.1 Second-Generation Offspring

Dominant Trait	Number with Dominant Trait	Recessive Trait	Number with Recessive Trait	Ratio of Dominant to Recessive	P (Dominant Trait)
Yellow seeds	6022	Green seeds	2001	3.01 to 1	$\frac{6022}{8023} \approx 0.75$
Round seeds	5474	Wrinkled seeds	1850	2.96 to 1	$\frac{5474}{7324} \approx 0.75$

From his work, Mendel concluded that the sex cells (now called gametes) of the pure yellow (dominant) pea plant carried some factor that caused the offspring to be yellow and that the gametes of the green variety had a variant factor that "induced the development of green plants." In 1909, Danish geneticist W. Johannsen called these factors "genes." Mendel's work led to the understanding that each pea plant contains two genes for color, one that comes from the mother and the other from the father. If the two genes are alike—for instance, both for yellow plants or both for green plants—the plant will be that color. If the genes for color are different, the plant will grow the color of the dominant gene. Thus, if one parent contributes a gene for the plant to be yellow (dominant) and the other parent contributes a gene for the plant to be green (recessive), the plant will be yellow.

The Law of Large Numbers

Most of us accept that if a "fair coin" is tossed many, many times, it will land heads up approximately half of the time. Intuitively, we can guess that the probability that a fair coin will land heads up is $\frac{1}{2}$. Does that mean that if a coin is tossed twice, it will land heads up exactly once? If a fair coin is tossed 10 times, will there necessarily be five heads? The answer is clearly no. What, then, does it mean when we state that the probability that a fair coin will land heads up is $\frac{1}{2}$? To answer this question, let's examine Table 12.2, which shows what may occur when a fair coin is tossed a given number of times.

Table 12.2

Number of Tosses	Expected Number of Heads	Actual Number of Heads Observed	Relative Frequency of Heads
10	5	4	$\frac{4}{10} = 0.4$
100	50	45	$\frac{45}{100} = 0.45$
1000	500	546	$\frac{546}{1000} = 0.546$
10,000	5000	4852	$\frac{4852}{10,000} = 0.4852$
100,000	50,000	49,770	$\frac{49,770}{100,000} = 0.49770$

The far right column of Table 12.2, the relative frequency of heads, is a ratio of the number of heads observed to the total number of tosses of the coin. The relative frequency is the empirical probability, as defined earlier. Note that as the number of tosses increases, the relative frequency of heads gets closer and closer to $\frac{1}{2}$, or 0.5, which is what we expect.

The nature of probability is summarized by the law of large numbers.

Definition: Law of Large Numbers

The **law of large numbers** states that probability statements apply in practice to a large number of trials, not to a single trial. It is the relative frequency over the long run that is accurately predictable, not individual events or precise totals.

What does it mean to say that the probability of rolling a 2 on a die is $\frac{1}{6}$? It means that over the long run, on the average, one of every six rolls will result in a 2.

SECTION 12.1 *Exercises*

Warm Up Exercises

In Exercises 1–6, fill in the blank with an appropriate word, phrase, or symbol(s).

1. A controlled operation that yields a set of results is called a(n) _____.

2. The possible results of an experiment are called its _____.

3. A subcollection of the outcomes of an experiment is called a(n) _____.

4. Probability is classified as either theoretical probability or _____ probability.

5. Probability determined by the relative frequency of occurrence of an event, or actual observations of an experiment is called _____ probability.

6. Probability determined through a study of the possible outcomes that can occur for a given experiment is called _____ probability.

Practice the Skills

7. Flip a Coin Flip a coin 50 times and record the results. Determine the empirical probability of flipping

a) a head.   **b)** a tail.

c) Does the probability of flipping a head appear to be the same as flipping a tail?

8. Pair of Dice Roll a pair of dice 60 times and record the sums. Determine the empirical probability of rolling a sum of

a) 2.   **b)** 7.

c) Does the probability of rolling a sum of 2 appear to be the same as the probability of rolling a sum of 7?

9. Roll a Die Roll a die 50 times and record the results. Determine the empirical probability of rolling

a) a 1.   **b)** a 4.

c) Does the probability of rolling a 1 appear to be the same as the probability of rolling a 4? Explain.

10. Two Coins Flip two coins 50 times and record the number of times exactly one head was obtained. Determine the empirical probability of flipping exactly one head.

Problem Solving

11. Boat Rentals The last 30 boat rentals at Green Lakes Boat Rentals were 14 sunfish, 10 kayaks, and 6 rowboats. Use this information to determine the empirical probability that the next boat rental is a

a) sunfish.   **b)** kayak.   **c)** rowboat.

12. Music Purchases At the Virgin Music store in Times Square, 60 people entering the store were selected at random and were asked to choose their favorite type of music. Of the 60, 12 chose rock, 16 chose country, 8 chose classical, and 24 chose something other than rock, country, or classical. Determine the empirical probability that the next person entering the store favors

a) rock music.   **b)** country music.

c) something other than rock, country, or classical music.

13. Veterinarian In a given week, a veterinarian treated the following animals.

Animal	Number Treated
Dog	45
Cat	40
Bird	15
Rabbit	5

Determine the empirical probability that the next animal she treats is

a) a dog.   **b)** a cat.   **c)** a rabbit.

14. Prader–Willi Syndrome In a sample of 50,000 first-born babies, 5 were found to have Prader–Willi syndrome. Find the empirical probability that a family's first child will be born with this syndrome.

15. Studying Abroad The table below shows the 10 most popular destinations for U.S. college students studying abroad for the 2008–2009 school year.

Destination	Number of Students
United Kingdom	31,342
Italy	27,362
Spain	24,169
France	16,910
China	13,674
Australia	11,140
Germany	8330
Mexico	7320
Ireland	6858
Costa Rica	6363
Total	153,468

Source: *Institute of International Education*

If a student were selected at random from those who studied abroad in 2008–2009 at one of the destinations in the table, determine the empirical probability that the student studied in

a) China.   **b)** Italy.   **c)** Australia.

16. *Travel Web Sites* The following table shows the number of visitors to the five most frequently visited travel Web sites in October 2010.

Web Site	Number of Visitors
Trip Advisor	24,000,000
Yahoo! Travel	23,250,000
Expedia	23,000,000
Travelocity	16,000,000
Priceline	15,000,000
Total	101,250,000

Source: ebizmba.com

Assuming this trend continues, if a person chooses to visit only one of the listed Web sites, determine the empirical probability the person will visit

a) Priceline.   **b)** Expedia.   **c)** Trip Advisor.

17. *Top-Selling Video Games* The following table shows the number of video games sold worldwide for the five highest-selling video games in 2010.

▲ *Wii Fit Plus*

Title	Units Sold
Call of Duty: Black Ops	18,880,000
Wii Sports	16,600,000
Super Mario Bros. Wii	11,310,000
Wii Sports Resort	11,290,000
Wii Fit Plus	8,870,000
Total	66,950,000

Source: vgchartz.com

Assuming this trend continues, if a person chooses to purchase a video game, determine the empirical probability that the person will purchase

a) Wii Sports.   **b)** Wii Fit Plus.

c) Call of Duty: Black Ops.

18. *Grade Distribution* Mr. Doole's grade distribution over the past 3 years for a course in college algebra is shown in the chart below.

Grade	Number
A	43
B	182
C	260
D	90
F	62
I	8

If Sue Gilligan plans to take college algebra with Mr. Doole, determine the empirical probability that she receives a grade of

a) A.   **b)** C.   **c)** D or higher.

19. *Election* In an election for student council president at Russell Sage College, 80 students were polled and asked for whom they planned to vote. The table shows the results of the poll.

Candidate	Votes
Allison	22
Emily	18
Kimberly	20
Johanna	14
Other	6

If one student from Russell Sage College is selected at random, determine the empirical probability that the person planned to vote for

a) Allison.   **b)** Emily.

c) Kimberly.   **d)** Johanna.

e) Someone other than the four people-listed above.

20. *Volunteer Hours* The graph below shows the average number of hours volunteered per week by Americans in 2009.

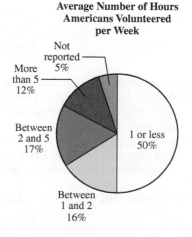

Average Number of Hours Americans Volunteered per Week

- Not reported 5%
- More than 5 12%
- Between 2 and 5 17%
- 1 or less 50%
- Between 1 and 2 16%

Source: CNCS (www.serve.gov)

If one American who participated in volunteer work is selected at random, determine the empirical probability the person volunteered

a) between 1 and 2 hours per week.

b) more than 5 hours per week.

c) between 2 and 5 hours per week.

21. *Hitting a Bull's-Eye* The pattern of hits shown on the target resulted from a marksman firing 20 rounds. For a single shot,

a) determine the empirical probability that the marksman hits the 50-point bull's-eye (the center of the target).

b) determine the empirical probability that the marksman does not hit the bull's-eye.

c) determine the empirical probability that the marksman scores at least 20 points.

d) determine the empirical probability that the marksman does not score any points (the area outside the large circle).

22. *Rock Toss* Jim Handy finds an irregularly shaped five-sided rock. He labels each side and tosses the rock 100 times. The results of his tosses are shown in the table. Determine the empirical probability that the rock will land on side 4 if tossed again.

Side	1	2	3	4	5
Frequency	32	18	15	13	22

23. *Cell Biology Experiment* An experimental serum was injected into 500 guinea pigs. Initially, 150 of the guinea pigs had circular cells, 250 had elliptical cells, and 100 had irregularly shaped cells. After the serum was injected, none of the guinea pigs with circular cells were affected, 50 with elliptical cells were affected, and all those with irregular cells were affected. Determine the empirical probability that a guinea pig with (a) circular cells, (b) elliptical cells, and (c) irregular cells will be affected by injection of the serum.

24. *Gender* In a large lecture hall there are 325 students of which 160 are male and 165 are female. If one student is

selected at random, determine the empirical probability the individual selected is

a) male.   b) female.

25. *Mendel's Experiment* In one of his experiments (see pages 677–678), Mendel crossbred nonpure purple flower pea plants. These purple pea plants had two traits for flowers, purple (dominant) and white (recessive). The result of this crossbreeding was 705 second-generation plants with purple flowers and 224 second-generation plants with white flowers. Determine the empirical probability of a second-generation plant having

a) white flowers.   b) purple flowers.

26. *Second-Generation Offspring* In another experiment, Mendel crossbred nonpure tall pea plants. As a result, the second-generation offspring were 787 tall plants and 277 short plants. Determine the empirical probability of a second-generation plant being

a) tall.   b) short.

Concept/Writing Exercises

27. The theoretical probability of a coin landing heads up is $\frac{1}{2}$. Does this probability mean that if a coin is flipped two times, one flip will land heads up? If not, what does it mean?

28. To determine premiums, life insurance companies must compute the probable date of death. On the basis of a great deal of research, Mr. Duncan, age 36, is expected to live another 43.21 years. Does this determination mean that Mr. Duncan will live until he is 79.21 years old? If not, what does it mean?

29. a) Explain how you would find the empirical probability of rolling a 5 on a die.

b) What do you believe is the empirical probability of rolling a 5?

c) Determine the empirical probability of rolling a 5 by rolling a die 40 times.

30. The theoretical probability of rolling a 4 on a die is $\frac{1}{6}$. Does this probability mean that if a die is rolled six times one 4 will appear? If not, what does it mean?

Challenge Problem/Group Activity

31. a) *Design an Experiment* Which do you believe is used more frequently in a magazine or newspaper article, the word *a* or the word *the*?

b) Design an experiment to determine the empirical prob-abilities (or relative frequencies) of the words *a* and *the* appearing in a magazine or newspaper article.

c) Perform the experiment in part (b) and determine the empirical probabilities.

d) Which word, *a* or *the*, appears to occur more frequently?

Recreational Mathematics

32. *Cola Preference* Can people selected at random distinguish Coke from Pepsi? Which do they prefer?

a) Design an experiment to determine the empirical probability that a person selected at random can select Coke when given samples of both Coke and Pepsi.

b) Perform the experiment in part (a) and determine the empirical probability.

c) Determine the empirical probability that a person selected at random will prefer Coke over Pepsi.

Internet/Research Activities

33. Write a paper on how insurance companies use empirical probabilities in determining insurance premiums. An insurance agent may be able to direct you to a source of information.

34. Write a paper on how Gregor Mendel's use of empirical probability led to the development of the science of genetics. You may want to check with a biology professor to determine references to use.

SECTION 12.2 Theoretical Probability

Should you spend the money for a stamp to return a sweepstakes ticket? What are your chances of winning a lottery? If you go to a carnival, bazaar, or casino, which games provide the greatest chance of winning? These and similar questions can be answered once you have an understanding of theoretical probability that we will discuss in this section.

Why *This is Important* Understanding how to calculate theoretical probability is essential to many real-life applications, including games of chance. Theoretical probability is also necessary to determine the odds of an event happening, and the expected gain or loss of business ventures.

▲ *We can use probability to determine the likelihood of winning games of chance.*

Recall from Section 12.1 that the results of an experiment are called outcomes. When you roll a die and observe the number of points that face up, the possible outcomes are 1, 2, 3, 4, 5, and 6. It is equally likely that you will roll any one of the possible numbers.

Definition: Equally Likely Outcomes
If each outcome of an experiment has the same chance of occurring as any other outcome, we say that the outcomes are **equally likely outcomes**.

Can you think of a second set of equally likely outcomes when a die is rolled? An odd number is as likely to be rolled as an even number. Therefore, odd and even numbers are another set of equally likely outcomes.

If an event E has *equally likely outcomes*, the theoretical probability of event E, symbolized by $P(E)$, may be calculated with the following formula.

Probability
The **theoretical probability** of an event can be calculated using the following formula.

$$P(E) = \frac{\text{number of outcomes favorable to } E}{\text{total number of possible outcomes}}$$

*In the remainder of this chapter, the word **probability** will refer to **theoretical probability**.*

TIMELY TIP

To be able to do the problems in this section and the remainder of the chapter, you must have a thorough understanding of fractions. If you have forgotten how to work with fractions, we strongly suggest that you review Section 5.3 before beginning this section.

Example 1 illustrates how to use this formula.

Example 1 *Determining Probabilities*

A die is rolled. Determine the probability of rolling

a) a 5.   b) an even number.   c) a number greater than 3.

d) a 7.   e) a number less than 7.

Solution

a) There are six possible equally likely outcomes: 1, 2, 3, 4, 5, and 6. The event of rolling a 5 can occur in only one way.

$$P(5) = \frac{\text{number of outcomes that will result in a 5}}{\text{total number of possible outcomes}} = \frac{1}{6}$$

b) The event of rolling an even number can occur in three ways: 2, 4, or 6.

$$P(\text{even number}) = \frac{\text{number of outcomes that result in an even number}}{\text{total number of possible outcomes}}$$

$$= \frac{3}{6} = \frac{1}{2}$$

c) Three numbers are greater than 3, namely, 4, 5 and 6.

$$P(\text{number greater than 3}) = \frac{3}{6} = \frac{1}{2}$$

d) No outcomes will result in a 7. Thus, the event cannot occur and the probability is 0.

$$P(7) = \frac{0}{6} = 0$$

e) All the outcomes 1 through 6 are less than 7. Thus, the event must occur and the probability is 1.

$$P(\text{number less than 7}) = \frac{6}{6} = 1$$

Four important facts about probability follow.

Important Probability Facts

1. The probability of an event that cannot occur is 0.
2. The probability of an event that must occur is 1.
3. Every probability is a number between 0 and 1 inclusive; that is, $0 \leq P(E) \leq 1$.
4. The sum of the probabilities of all possible outcomes of an experiment is 1.

Example 2 *Choosing One Bird from a List*

The names of 15 birds and their food preferences are listed in Table 12.3 on page 685. Each of the 15 birds' names is listed on a slip of paper, and the 15 slips are placed in a bag. One slip is to be selected at random from the bag. Determine the probability that the slip contains the name of

a) a finch (any type listed).

b) a bird that has a high attractiveness to cracked corn.

c) a bird that has a low attractiveness to peanut kernels, *and* a low attractiveness to cracked corn, *and* a high attractiveness to black-striped sunflower seeds.

d) a bird that has a high attractiveness to either peanut kernels *or* cracked corn (or both).

Table 12.3 Birds and Their Food Preferences

Bird	Peanut Kernels	Cracked Corn	Black-Striped Sunflower Seeds
American goldfinch	L	L	H
Blue jay	H	M	H
Chickadee	M	L	H
Common grackle	M	H	H
Evening grosbeak	L	L	H
House finch	M	L	H
House sparrow	L	M	M
Mourning dove	L	M	M
Northern cardinal	L	L	H
Purple finch	L	L	H
Scrub jay	H	L	H
Song sparrow	L	L	M
Tufted titmouse	H	L	H
White-crowned sparrow	H	M	H
White-throated sparrow	H	H	H

Source: *How to Attract Birds* (Ortho Books)

Note: H = high attractiveness; M = medium attractiveness; L = low attractiveness.

Solution

a) Three of the 15 birds listed are finches (American goldfinch, house finch, and purple finch).

$$P(\text{finch}) = \frac{3}{15} = \frac{1}{5}$$

b) Two of the 15 birds listed have a high attractiveness to cracked corn (common grackle and white-throated sparrow).

$$P(\text{high attractiveness to cracked corn}) = \frac{2}{15}$$

c) Reading across the rows reveals that 4 birds have a low attractiveness to peanut kernels, a low attractiveness to cracked corn, and a high attractiveness to black-striped sunflower seeds (American goldfinch, evening grosbeak, northern cardinal, and purple finch).

$$P\left(\begin{array}{c}\text{low attractiveness to peanuts, and low to} \\ \text{corn, and high to black-striped sunflower sweeds}\end{array}\right) = \frac{4}{15}$$

d) Six birds have a high attractiveness to either peanut kernels or to cracked corn (or both). They are the blue jay, common grackle, scrub jay, tufted titmouse, white-crowned sparrow, and white-throated sparrow.

$$P(\text{high attractiveness to peanut kernels or cracked corn}) = \frac{6}{15} = \frac{2}{5}$$

In any experiment, an event must either occur or not occur. *The sum of the probability that an event will occur and the probability that it will not occur is 1.* Thus, for any event A we conclude that

The Sum of the Probabilities Equals 1

$$P(A) + P(\text{not } A) = 1$$

or

$$P(\text{not } A) = 1 - P(A)$$

For example, if the probability that event A will occur is $\frac{5}{12}$, the probability that event A will not occur is $1 - \frac{5}{12}$, or $\frac{7}{12}$. Similarly, if the probability that event A will not occur is 0.3, the probability that event A will occur is $1 - 0.3 = 0.7$, or $\frac{7}{10}$. We make use of this concept in Example 3.

Example 3 *Selecting One Card from a Deck*

A standard deck of 52 playing cards is shown in Fig. 12.3. The deck consists of four suits: hearts, clubs, diamonds, and spades. Each suit has 13 cards, including numbered cards ace (1) through 10 and three picture (or face) cards, the jack, the queen, and the king. Hearts and diamonds are red cards; clubs and spades are black cards. There are 12 picture cards, consisting of 4 jacks, 4 queens, and 4 kings. One card is to be selected at random from the deck of cards. Determine the probability that the card selected is

a) a 7.

b) not a 7.

c) a diamond.

d) a jack *or* queen *or* king (a picture card).

e) a heart *and* a spade.

f) a card greater than 6 *and* less than 9.

Figure 12.3

Solution

a) There are four 7's in a deck of 52 cards.

$$P(7) = \frac{4}{52} = \frac{1}{13}$$

b) $P(\text{not a } 7) = 1 - P(7) = 1 - \frac{1}{13} = \frac{12}{13}$

This probability could also have been found by noting that there are 48 cards that are not 7's in a deck of 52 cards.

$$P(\text{not a } 7) = \frac{48}{52} = \frac{12}{13}$$

c) There are 13 diamonds in the deck.

$$P(\text{diamond}) = \frac{13}{52} = \frac{1}{4}$$

d) There are 4 jacks, 4 queens, and 4 kings, or a total of 12 picture cards.

$$P(\text{jack } or \text{ queen } or \text{ king}) = \frac{12}{52} = \frac{3}{13}$$

e) The word *and* means that *both* events must occur. Since it is not possible to select one card that is both a heart and a spade the probability is 0.

$$P(\text{heart and spade}) = \frac{0}{52} = 0$$

f) The cards that are both greater than 6 and less than 9 are 7's and 8's. There are four 7's and four 8's, or a total of eight cards.

$$P(\text{greater than 6 } and \text{ less than 9}) = \frac{8}{52} = \frac{2}{13}$$

SECTION 12.2 *Exercises*

Warm Up Exercises

In Exercises 1–10, fill in the blank with an appropriate word, phrase, or symbol(s).

1. If each outcome of an experiment has the same chance of occurring as any other outcome, the outcomes are _____ likely outcomes.

2. The probability of an event that cannot occur is _____.

3. The probability of an event that must occur is _____.

4. Every probability is a number between _____ and _____ inclusive.

5. The sum of the probabilities of all possible outcomes of an experiment is _____.

6. For any event A, $P(A) + P(\text{not } A) =$ _____.

7. If the probability that an event occurs is $\frac{3}{7}$, the probability that the event does not occur is _____.

8. If the probability that an event occurs is 0.2, the probability that the event does not occur is _____.

9. If the probability that an event does not occur is 0.9, the probability that the event occurs is _____.

10. If the probability that an event does not occur is $\frac{4}{9}$, the probability that the event occurs is _____.

Practice the Skills

11. **Multiple-Choice Test** A multiple-choice test has five possible choices for each question.

   a) If you randomly select one of the choices, what is the probability that you select the correct answer for one particular question?

   b) If you eliminate one of the five possible choices and guess from the remaining choices, what is the probability that you select the correct answer to that question?

12. **Remote Control** A TV remote control has keys for channels 0 through 9. If you select one key at random,

   a) what is the probability that you press channel 6?

   b) what is the probability that you press a key for an even number?

   c) what is the probability that you press a key for a number less than 7?

13. **Raffle** In a raffle where one number is chosen, determine the probability that you would win if you have a choice of 40 numbers to choose from.

14. **Raffle** In a raffle where one number is chosen, determine the probability that you would win if you have a choice of 52 numbers to choose from.

Select a Card In Exercises 15–24, one card is selected at random from a deck of cards. Determine the probability that the card selected is

15. a 5.

16. a 5 or a 10.

17. not a 5.

18. the five of diamonds.

19. a black card.

20. a diamond.

21. a red card or a black card.

22. a red card and a black card.

23. a card greater than 3 and less than 8.

24. a king and a club.

Spin the Spinner In Exercises 25–28, assume that the spinner cannot land on a line. Determine the probability that the spinner lands on (a) red, (b) green, (c) yellow, (d) blue.

25.

26.

27.

28.

Picnic In Exercises 29–32, a cooler at a picnic contains 100 cans of soda covered by ice. There are 30 cans of cola, 40 cans of orange soda, 10 cans of ginger ale, and 20 cans of root beer. The cans are all the same size and shape. If one can is selected at random from the cooler, determine the probability that the soda selected is

29. root beer.

30. cola or orange soda.

31. cola, root beer, or orange soda.

32. ginger ale.

Wheel of Fortune In Exercises 33–36, use the small replica of the Wheel of Fortune.

If the wheel is spun at random, determine the probability that the indicated sector will stop under the pointer.

33. $600

34. A number greater than $700

35. Lose a turn or Bankrupt

36. $2500 or Surprise

Basketballs In Exercises 37–40, 30 basketballs, including 15 Spalding, 10 Wilson, and 5 other brand-name balls, are on a basketball court. Barry Wood closes his eyes and arbitrarily picks up a ball from the court. Determine the probability that the ball selected is

37. a Spalding.

38. a Wilson.

39. not a Wilson.

40. a Wilson or a Spalding.

Traffic Light In Exercises 41–44, a traffic light is red for 25 sec, yellow for 5 sec, and green for 55 sec. What is the probability that when you reach the light,

41. the light is green.

42. the light is yellow.

43. the light is not red.

44. the light is not green.

TALLAHASSEE In Exercises 45–50, each individual letter of the word **TALLAHASSEE** is placed on a piece of paper and all 11 pieces of paper are placed in a hat. If one letter is selected at random from the hat, determine the probability that

45. the letter *S* is selected.

46. the letter *S* is not selected.

47. a consonant is selected.

48. the letter *T* or *E* is selected.

49. the letter *W* is selected.

50. the letter *V* is not selected.

National Parks In Exercises 51–54, use the list below which shows the 10 U.S. National Parks with the most visitors in 2010.

Park	Location	Visits
Great Smokey Mountains National Park	North Carolina/ Tennessee	9,463,538
Grand Canyon National Park	Arizona	4,388,386
Yosemite National Park	California	3,901,408
Yellowstone National Park	Wyoming	3,640,185
Rocky Mountain National Park	Colorado	2,955,821
Olympic National Park	Washington	2,844,563
Grand Teton National Park	Wyoming	2,669,374
Zion National Park	Utah	2,665,972
Acadia National Park	Maine	2,504,208
Cuyahoga Valley National Park	Ohio	2,492,670

Source: *National Park Service*

▲ *Grand Teton National Park, Jackson, WY*

If one of the parks in the list is selected at random, determine the probability the park

51. is located in California.

52. is located in Wyoming.

53. had more than 4 million visitors.

54. had fewer than 3 million visitors.

Dart Board In Exercises 55–58, a dart is thrown randomly and sticks on the circular dart board with 26 partitions, as shown.

Assuming the dart cannot land on the black area or on a border between colors, determine the probability that the dart lands on

55. the area marked 15.   **56.** an orange area.

57. an area marked with a number greater than or equal to 22.

58. an area marked with a number greater than 6 and less than or equal to 9.

Car Dealership In Exercises 59–64, refer to the following table, which shows the type and manufacturer of vehicles at a specific car dealership.

	General Motors	Toyota	Total
Car	55	30	85
SUV	28	17	45
Total	83	47	130

If one person selects a vehicle at random from the dealership, determine the probability that the person selects

59. a car.   **60.** an SUV.

61. a vehicle manufactured by General Motors.

62. a vehicle manufactured by Toyota.

63. a car manufactured by General Motors.

64. an SUV manufactured by General Motors.

Stocking Taco Sauce In Exercises 65–70, refer to the following table, which contains information about a shopping cart full of jars of taco sauce that must be stocked on a shelf. Assume all jars are the same size and shape.

Brand	Mild	Medium	Hot	Total
Taco Bell	5	8	4	17
Ortega	2	5	3	10
Old El Paso	3	6	2	11
Other	1	2	1	4
Total	11	21	10	42

If a stock clerk selects one jar at random to place on the shelf, determine the probability he selects a jar of

65. Ortega.   **66.** Old El Paso.

67. a mild taco sauce.   **68.** a hot taco sauce.

69. Taco Bell medium taco sauce.

70. Old El Paso hot taco sauce.

Bean Bag Toss *In Exercises 71–76, a bean bag is randomly thrown onto the square table top shown below and does not touch a line.*

Determine the probability that the bean bag lands on

71. a red area.　　　　**72.** a green area.

73. a yellow area.　　　**74.** a red or green area.

75. a yellow or green area.　**76.** a red or yellow area.

Challenge Problems/Group Activities

Before working Exercises 77 and 78, reread the material on genetics in Section 12.1.

77. *Genetics* Cystic fibrosis is an inherited disease that occurs in about 1 in every 2500 Caucasian births in North America and in about 1 in every 250,000 non-Caucasian births in North America. Let's denote the cystic fibrosis gene as c and a disease-free gene as C. Since the disease-free gene is dominant, only a person with cc genes will have the disease. A person who has Cc genes is a carrier of cystic fibrosis but does not actually have the disease. If one parent has CC genes and the other parent has cc genes, determine the probability that

a) an offspring will inherit cystic fibrosis, that is, cc genes.

b) an offspring will be a carrier of cystic fibrosis but not contract the disease.

78. *Genetics* Sickle-cell anemia is an inherited disease that occurs in about 1 in every 500 African-American births and about 1 in every 160,000 non–African-American births. Unlike cystic fibrosis, in which the cystic fibrosis gene is recessive, sickle-cell anemia is *codominant*. In other words, a person inheriting two sickle-cell genes will have sickle-cell anemia, whereas a person inheriting only one of the sickle-cell genes will have a mild version of sickle-cell anemia, called *sickle-cell trait*. Let's call the disease-free genes s_1 and the sickle cell gene s_2. If both parents have $s_1 s_2$ genes, determine the probability that

a) an offspring will have sickle-cell anemia.

b) an offspring will have the sickle-cell trait.

c) an offspring will have neither sickle-cell anemia nor the sickle-cell trait.

In Exercises 79 and 80, the solutions involve material that we will discuss in later sections of the chapter. Try to solve them before reading ahead.

79. *Marbles* A bottle contains two red and two green marbles, and a second bottle also contains two red and two green marbles. If you select one marble at random from each bottle, determine the probability (to be discussed in Section 12.6) that you obtain

a) two red marbles.　　　**b)** two green marbles.

c) a red marble from the first bottle and a green marble from the second bottle.

80. *Birds* Consider Table 12.3 on page 685. Suppose you are told that one bird's name was selected at random from the birds listed and the bird selected has a low attractiveness to peanut kernels. Determine the probability (to be discussed in Section 12.7) that

a) the bird is a sparrow.

b) the bird has a high attractiveness to cracked corn.

c) the bird has a high attractiveness to black-striped sunflower seeds.

Recreational Mathematics

81. *Dice* On a die, the sum of the dots on the opposite faces is seven. Two six-sided dice are placed together on top of one another, on a table, as shown in the figure below. The top and bottom faces of the bottom die and the bottom face of the top die cannot be seen. If you walk around the table, what is the sum of all the dots on all the visible faces of the dice?

Internet/Research Activity

82. On page 675, we briefly discuss Jacob Bernoulli. The Bernoulli family produced several prominent mathematicians, including Jacob I, Johann I, and Daniel. Write a paper on the Bernoulli family, indicating some of the accomplishments of each of the three Bernoullis named and their relationship to one another. Indicate which Bernoulli the Bernoulli numbers are named after, which Bernoulli the Bernoulli theorem in statistics is named after, and which Bernoulli the Bernoulli theorem of fluid dynamics is named after.

Odds

▲ *What are the odds against the San Francisco Giants winning the World Series this year?*

The odds against winning the Fabulous Fortune lottery are about 2.6 million to 1. The odds against being audited by the IRS this year are about 47 to 1. The odds against the San Francisco Giants winning the World Series this year may be 6 to 1. We see the word *odds* daily in newspapers and magazines and often use it ourselves. Yet there is widespread misunderstanding of its meaning. In this section, we will explain the meaning of odds. We will also discuss how to determine odds against an event and how to determine odds in favor of an event.

Why *This is Important* Many real-life applications involve odds, including sporting events and games of chance.

Did You Know?

Gambling in Ancient Times

Archaeologists have found evidence of gambling in all cultures, from the Stone Age Australian aborigines to the ancient Egyptians, and across cultures touched by the Roman Empire. There is an equally long history of moral and legal opposition to gambling.

Odds Against an Event

The odds given at horse races, at craps, and at all gambling games in Las Vegas and other casinos throughout the world are always *odds against* unless they are otherwise specified. The *odds against* an event is a ratio of the probability that the event will fail to occur (failure) to the probability that the event will occur (success). Thus, *to find odds you must first know or determine the probability of success and the probability of failure.*

Odds Against an Event

The following formula may be used to determine the odds against an event.

$$\text{Odds against event} = \frac{P(\text{event fails to occur})}{P(\text{event occurs})} = \frac{P(\text{failure})}{P(\text{success})}$$

Example 1 *Rolling a 4*

Determine the odds against rolling a 4 on one roll of a die.

Solution Before we can determine the odds, we must first determine the probability of rolling a 4 (success) and the probability of not rolling a 4 (failure). When a die is rolled there are six possible outcomes: 1, 2, 3, 4, 5, and 6.

$$P(\text{rolling a 4}) = \frac{1}{6} \qquad P(\text{failure to roll a 4}) = \frac{5}{6}$$

Now that we know the probabilities of success and failure, we can determine the odds against rolling a 4.

$$\text{Odds against rolling a 4} = \frac{P(\text{failure to roll a 4})}{P(\text{rolling a 4})}$$

$$= \frac{\frac{5}{6}}{\frac{1}{6}} = \frac{5}{\overset{1}{\cancel{6}}} \cdot \frac{\overset{1}{\cancel{6}}}{1} = \frac{5}{1}$$

The ratio $\frac{5}{1}$ is commonly written as 5:1 and is read "5 to 1." Thus, the odds against rolling a 4 are 5 to 1.

TIMELY TIP
The denominators of the probabilities in an odds problem will always divide out, as was shown in Example 1.

In Example 1, we considered the possible outcomes of the die: 1, 2, 3, 4, 5, 6. Over the long run, one of every six rolls will result in a 4, and five of every six rolls will result in a number other than 4. Therefore, if a person is gambling, for each dollar bet in favor of the rolling of a 4, $5 should be bet against the rolling of a 4 if the person is to break even. The person betting in favor of the rolling of a 4 will either lose $1 (if a number other than a 4 is rolled) or win $5 (if a 4 is rolled). The person betting against the rolling of a 4 will either win $1 (if a number other than a 4 is rolled) or lose $5 (if a 4 is rolled). If this game is played for a long enough period, each player theoretically will break even.

Example 2 involves a circle graph that contains percents; see Fig. 12.4. Before we discuss Example 2, let us briefly discuss percents. Recall that probabilities are numbers between 0 and 1, inclusive. We can change a percent between 0% and 100% to a probability by writing the percent as a fraction or a decimal number. In Fig. 12.4, we see 36% in one of the sectors (or areas) of the circle. To change 36% to a probability, we can write $\frac{36}{100}$ or 0.36. Note that both the fraction and the decimal number are numbers between 0 and 1, inclusive.

Example 2 *Occupations*

The circle graph in Fig. 12.4 shows the percent of U.S. workers employed in professional, service, sales, construction, and production occupations. If one U.S. worker is selected at random, use the graph to determine the odds against the person being employed in a sales occupation.

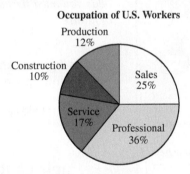

Occupation of U.S. Workers

Source: *Bureau of Labor Statistics*

Figure 12.4

Solution From the graph, we can determine that 25%, or $\frac{25}{100}$, of U.S. workers are employed in sales occupations. Therefore, the probability that a U.S. worker is employed in a sales occupation is $\frac{25}{100}$. The probability that a U.S. worker is *not* employed in a sales occupation is $1 - \frac{25}{100} = \frac{75}{100}$.

Odds against the person being employed in a sales occupation $= \dfrac{P(\text{person is not employed in a sales occupation})}{P(\text{person is employed in a sales occupation})}$

$$= \frac{\dfrac{75}{100}}{\dfrac{25}{100}} = \frac{75}{100} \cdot \frac{100}{25} = \frac{75}{25} = \frac{3}{1}, \text{ or } 3{:}1$$

Thus, the odds against the person being employed in a sales occupation are 3:1. ∎

Odds in Favor of an Event

Although odds are generally given against an event, at times they may be given in favor of an event. The *odds in favor of* an event are expressed as a ratio of the probability that the event will occur to the probability that the event will fail to occur.

Odds in Favor of an Event

The following formula may be used to determine the odds in favor of an event.

$$\text{Odds in favor of event} = \frac{P(\text{event occurs})}{P(\text{event fails to occur})} = \frac{P(\text{success})}{P(\text{failure})}$$

If the odds *against* an event are $a:b$, the odds *in favor of* the event are $b:a$.

Example 3 *Smartphones*

The circle graph in Fig. 12.5 shows the U.S. market share for the operating systems used in smartphones, as of December 2010. If an individual who owns a smartphone is selected at random, use the graph to determine

a) the odds against the individual owning a Google phone.

b) the odds in favor of the individual owning a Google phone.

U.S. Market Share of Operating Systems Used in Smartphones in 2010

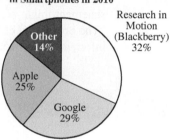

Source: ComScore

Figure 12.5

Solution

a) The graph shows that 29%, or $\frac{29}{100}$, of individuals who owned a smartphone owned a Google phone. Thus, the probability that an individual owned a Google phone is $\frac{29}{100}$. Therefore, the probability that an individual did not own a Google phone is $1 - \frac{29}{100} = \frac{71}{100}$

$$\begin{array}{l}\text{Odds against an individual} \\ \text{owning a Google phone}\end{array} = \frac{P(\text{an individual did not own a Google phone})}{P(\text{an individual owned a Google phone})}$$

$$= \frac{\dfrac{71}{100}}{\dfrac{29}{100}} = \frac{71}{\cancel{100}} \cdot \frac{\cancel{100}^{1}}{29} = \frac{71}{29} \quad \text{or} \quad 71:29$$

Thus, the odds against the individual owning a Google phone are $71:29$.

b) The odds in favor of the individual owning a Google phone are $29:71$. ∎

Finding Probabilities from Odds

When odds are given, either in favor of or against a particular event, it is possible to determine the probability that the event occurs and the probability that the event does not occur. The denominators of the probabilities are found by adding the numbers in the odds statement. The numerators of the probabilities are the numbers given in the odds statements.

Example **4** *Determining Probabilities from Odds*

The odds against Robin Murphy being admitted to the college of her choice are 9:2. Determine the probability that (a) Robin is admitted and (b) Robin is not admitted.

Solution

a) We have been given odds against and have been asked to find probabilities.

$$\text{Odds against being admitted} = \frac{P(\text{fails to be admitted})}{P(\text{is admitted})}$$

Since the odds statement is 9:2, the denominators of both the probability of success and the probability of failure must be $9 + 2$ or 11. To get the odds ratio of 9:2, the probabilities must be $\frac{9}{11}$ and $\frac{2}{11}$. Since odds against is a ratio of failure to success, the $\frac{9}{11}$ and $\frac{2}{11}$ represent the probabilities of failure and success, respectively. Thus, the probability that Robin is admitted (success) is $\frac{2}{11}$.

b) The probability that Robin is not admitted (failure) is $\frac{9}{11}$.   ∎

Odds and probability statements are sometimes stated incorrectly. For example, consider the statement, "The odds of being selected to represent the district are 1 in 5." Odds are given using the word *to*, not *in*. Thus, there is a mistake in this statement. The correct statement might be, "The odds of being selected to represent the district are 1 to 5" or "The probability of being selected to represent the district is 1 in 5." Without additional information, it is not possible to tell which statement is the correct interpretation.

SECTION 12.3   *Exercises*

Warm Up Exercises

In Exercises 1–8, fill in the blank with an appropriate word, phrase, or symbol(s).

1. The ratio of the probability that an event will fail to occur to the probability that the event will occur is called the odds _____ an event.

2. The ratio of the probability that the event will occur to the probability that the event will fail to occur is called the odds _____ an event.

3. If the odds in favor of *Just in Time* winning a horse race are $1:3$, then the odds against *Just in Time* winning the race are _____.

4. If the odds against winning at Monopoly are $4:1$, then the odds in favor of winning at Monopoly are _____.

5. If the probability that an event will occur is $\frac{2}{3}$ then the probability that the event will not occur is $\frac{1}{3}$, and the odds in favor of the event occurring are _____.

6. If the probability that an event will fail to occur is $\frac{1}{4}$ then the probability that the event will occur is $\frac{3}{4}$ and the odds against the event occurring are _____.

7. If the odds against an event are $1:3$, the probability that the event will fail to occur is _____.

8. If the odds against an event are a to b, then the probability that the event occurs is _____.

Practice the Skills/Problem Solving

9. *Dressing Up* Lila Jaquez is going to wear a blue dress and is trying to decide which pair of shoes she should wear with it. In her closet, she has 12 pairs of shoes, 5 of which go well with the dress. If Lila selects one pair of shoes at random, determine

   a) the probability that the shoes go well with the dress.

   b) the probability that the shoes do not go well with the dress.

   c) the odds against the shoes going well with the dress.

   d) the odds in favor of the shoes going well with the dress.

10. *Making a Donation* In her wallet, Anne Kelly has 12 bills. Six are $1 bills, two are $5 bills, three are $10 bills, and one is a $20 bill. She passes a volunteer seeking donations for the Salvation Army and decides to select one bill at random from her wallet and give it to the Salvation Army. Determine

    a) the probability that she selects a $5 bill.

    b) the probability that she does not select a $5 bill.

    c) the odds in favor of her selecting a $5 bill.

    d) the odds against her selecting a $5 bill.

Deal or No Deal *In Exercises 11 and 12, consider the TV show Deal or No Deal. (See the Mathematics Today on page 693.) In the game show, there are 26 numbered cases, each indicating a cash prize ranging from 1 cent to $1,000,000. Contestants on the show have a series of choices to make, and each time they can either accept the cash offer made by the banker or select a case from the remaining cases. Assume that one of the remaining cases contains a $1,000,000 cash prize. Determine the odds against and the odds in favor of selecting the case containing the $1,000,000 cash prize if there are*

11. seven cases remaining.

12. four cases remaining.

Toss a Die *In Exercises 13–16, a die is tossed. Determine the odds against rolling*

13. a 2.

14. an odd number.

15. a number less than 3.

16. a number greater than 4.

Deck of Cards *In Exercises 17–20, a card is picked from a standard deck of cards. Determine the odds against and the odds in favor of selecting*

17. a king.

18. a heart.

19. a picture card.

20. a card greater than 5 (ace is low).

Spin the Spinner *In Exercises 21–24, assume that the spinner cannot land on a line. Determine the odds against the spinner landing on the color red.*

21. **22.**

23. **24.**

25. *Students* One person is selected at random from a class of 16 men and 14 women. Determine the odds against selecting

a) a woman. b) a man.

26. *Lottery* One million tickets are sold for a lottery in which a single prize will be awarded.

a) If you purchase a ticket, determine your odds against winning.

b) If you purchase 10 tickets, determine your odds against winning.

Billiard Balls *In Exercises 27–32, use the rack of 15 billiard balls shown.*

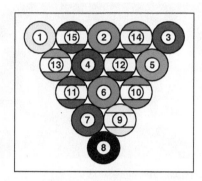

27. If one ball is selected at random, determine the odds against it containing a stripe. (Balls numbered 9 through 15 contain stripes.)

28. If one ball is selected at random, determine the odds in favor of it being a ball other than the 8 ball.

29. If one ball is selected at random, determine the odds in favor of it being an even-numbered ball.

30. If one ball is selected at random, determine the odds against it containing any red coloring (solid or striped).

31. If one ball is selected at random, determine the odds against it containing a number greater than or equal to 9.

32. If one ball is selected at random, determine the odds in favor of it containing two digits.

33. *LPGA Winnings* The chart below shows the winnings, in dollars, for the 10 golfers with the highest total LPGA winnings for the 2010 season.

Golfer	2010 Winnings
Na Yeon Choi	$1,871,166
Jiyai Shin	$1,783,127
Cristie Kerr	$1,601,552
Yani Tseng	$1,573,529
Suzann Pettersen	$1,557,175
Ai Miyazato	$1,457,384
In-Kyung Kim	$1,210,068
Song-Hee Kim	$1,208,698
Michelle Wie	$888,017
Paula Creamer	$883,870

Source: LPGA.com

If one of the golfers listed in the chart is selected at random, determine

a) the probability the golfer earned more than $1 million in 2010.

b) the odds against the golfer earning more than $1 million in 2010.

▲ *Paula Creamer*

34. *Rolling a Special Die* A special die used in a game contains one dot on one side, two dots on two sides, and three dots on three sides. If the die is rolled, determine

a) the probability of rolling two dots.

b) the odds against rolling two dots.

35. *Medical Tests* The results of a medical test show that of 85 people selected at random who were given the test, 80 tested negative and 5 tested positive. Determine the odds against a person selected at random testing negative on the test.

36. *A Red Marble* A box contains 9 red and 2 blue marbles. If you select one marble at random from the box, determine the odds against selecting a blue marble.

37. *Scholarship Award* The odds in favor of Wendy White winning a scholarship are $7:4$. Determine the probability that

a) Wendy wins.

b) Wendy does not win.

38. *Selling a Car* The odds in favor of Sam Riveria selling his car are $3:8$. Determine the probability that Sam will

a) sell his car.

b) not sell his car.

39. *College Acceptance* The odds against Jason Judd getting accepted into the college his choice are $4:11$. Determine the probability that Jason gets accepted into the college of his choice.

40. *Winning a Race* The odds against Paul Phillips winning the 100 yard dash are $7:2$. Determine the probability that

a) Paul wins.   **b)** Paul does not win.

Playing Bingo When playing bingo, 75 balls are placed in a bin and balls are selected at random. Each ball is marked with a letter and number as indicated in the following chart.

B	I	N	G	O
1–15	16–30	31–45	46–60	61–75

For example, there are balls marked B1, B2, up to B15; I16, I17, up to I30; and so on (see photo). In Exercises 41–46, assuming one bingo ball is selected at random, determine

41. the probability that it contains the letter *G*.

42. the probability that it does not contain the letter *G*.

43. the odds in favor of it containing the letter *G*.

44. the odds against it containing the letter *G*.

45. the odds against it being *B*9.

46. the odds in favor of it being *B*9.

Blood Types In Exercises 47–52, the following circle graph shows the percent of Americans with the various types of blood.

Blood Types of Americans

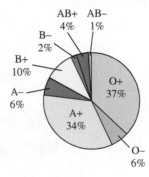

Source: *Red Cross*

If one American is selected at random, use the graph to determine

47. the probability that the person has A+ blood.

48. the probability that the person has B− blood.

49. the odds against the person having A+ blood.

50. the odds in favor of the person having B− blood.

51. the odds in favor of the person having either O+ or O− blood.

52. the odds against the person having either A+ or O+ blood.

53. *Fixing a Car* Suppose that the probability that a mechanic fixes a car correctly is 0.9. Determine the odds against the mechanic fixing a car correctly.

54. *Diabetes* According to the Centers for Disease Control, 8% of Americans have diabetes. If an American is selected at random, determine the odds in favor of this person having diabetes.

55. *Bookcase Assembly* Suppose that the probability that all the parts needed to assemble a bookcase are included in the carton is $\frac{7}{8}$. Determine the odds in favor of the carton including all the needed parts.

56. *Flight Delays* Of 899,000 flights in May 2010, five were delayed on the tarmac by more than three hours. If one of these 899,000 flights was selected at random, determine

a) the probability that the flight was delayed more than three hours.

b) the odds against the flight being delayed more than three hours.

57. *Birth Defects* Birth defects affect 1 in 33 babies born in the United States each year.

a) What is the probability that a baby born in the United States will have a birth defect?

b) What are the odds against a baby born in the United States having a birth defect?

Challenge Problems/Group Activities

58. *Odds Against* Determine the odds against an even number or a number greater than 3 being rolled on a die.

59. *Horse Racing* Racetracks quote the approximate odds against each horse winning on a large board called a *tote*

board. The odds quoted on a tote board for a race with five horses is as follows.

Horse Number	Odds
2	7 : 2
3	2 : 1
4	15 : 1
5	7 : 5
6	1 : 1

Determine the probability of each horse winning the race. (Do not be concerned that the sum of the probabilities is not 1.)

60. *Roulette* Turn to the roulette wheel illustrated on page 707. If the wheel is spun, determine

a) the probability that the ball lands on red.

b) the odds against the ball landing on red.

c) the probability that the ball lands on 0 or 00.

d) the odds in favor of the ball landing on 0 or 00.

Recreational Mathematics

61. *Multiple Births* Multiple births make up about 3% of births per year in the United States. The following illustrates the number and type of multiple births in 2008.

Source: *National Center for Health Services*

Using the above information, determine an estimate for the odds against a birth being a multiple birth in 2008.

Internet/Research Activities

62. *State Lottery* Determine whether your state has a lottery. If so, do research and write a paper indicating

a) the probability of winning the grand prize.

b) the odds against winning the grand prize.

c) Explain, using real objects such as pennies or table tennis balls, what these odds actually mean.

63. *Casino Advantages* There are many types of games of chance to choose from at casinos. The house has the advantage in each game, but the advantages differ according to the game.

a) List the games available at a typical casino.

b) List those for which the house has the smallest advantage of winning.

c) List those for which the house has the greatest advantage of winning.

SECTION 12.4   Expected Value (Expectation)

▲ *Expected value can be used to estimate the future profits of a new product.*

When a construction company estimates the number of days it will take to complete the resurfacing of a road, it will consider many things including the probability of rain, which can slow down the completion. In trying to decide whether to make a new product, such as a new cereal or new model car, a company will estimate its potential profit (or loss). When companies estimate how long it will take them to complete a task, or their expected profit, they often use expected value, or expectation, which we will discuss in this section.

Why *This is Important* Expectation is used to make important decisions in many areas, including insurance and business ventures, and in games of chance.

Expected value, also called *expectation*, is often used to determine the expected results of an experiment or business venture *over the long term*. People use expectation to make important decisions in many different areas. For example, expectation is used in business to predict future profits of a new product. In the insurance industry, expectation is used to determine how much each insurance policy should cost for the company to make an overall profit. Expectation is also used to predict the expected gain or loss in games of chance such as the lottery, roulette, craps, and slot machines.

Consider the following situation. Tim tells Barbara that he will give her $1 if she can roll an even number on a single die. If she fails to roll an even number, she must give Tim $1. Who would win money in the long run if this game were played many times? In this situation, we would expect in the long run that half the time Tim would win $1 and half the time he would lose $1; therefore, Tim would break even. Mathematically, we could find Tim's expected gain or loss by the following procedure:

$$\text{Tim's expected gain or loss} = P\left(\begin{array}{c}\text{Tim}\\\text{wins}\end{array}\right) \cdot \left(\begin{array}{c}\text{amount}\\\text{Tim wins}\end{array}\right) + P\left(\begin{array}{c}\text{Tim}\\\text{loses}\end{array}\right) \cdot \left(\begin{array}{c}\text{amount}\\\text{Tim loses}\end{array}\right)$$

$$= \frac{1}{2}(\$1) + \frac{1}{2}(-\$1) = \$0$$

Note that the loss is written as a negative number. This procedure indicates that Tim has an expected gain or loss (or expected value) of $0. The expected value of zero indicates that he would indeed break even, as we had anticipated. Thus, the game is a *fair game*. If Tim's expected value were positive, it would indicate a gain; if negative, a loss.

The expected value, E, is calculated by multiplying the probability of an event occurring by the *net* amount gained or lost if the event occurs. If there are a number of different events and amounts to be considered, we use the following formula.

Expected Value

$$E = P_1 \cdot A_1 + P_2 \cdot A_2 + P_3 \cdot A_3 + \ldots + P_n \cdot A_n$$

The symbol P_1 represents the probability that the first event will occur, and A_1 represents the net amount won or lost if the first event occurs. P_2 is the probability of the second event, and A_2 is the net amount won or lost if the second event occurs, and so on. The sum of these products of the probabilities and their respective amounts is the expected value. The expected value is the average (or mean) result that would be obtained if the experiment were performed a great many times.

Example 1 *A Building Contract*

The Rich Walker Construction Company has just received a building contract. From past experience, Rich estimates there is a 60% chance of making a $500,000 profit, a 10% chance of breaking even, and a 30% chance of losing $200,000, depending on weather conditions and other factors. What is the expected value of the company's contract?

Solution Three amounts are to be considered: a gain of $500,000, breaking even at $0, and a loss of $200,000. The probability of gaining $500,000 is 0.6, the probability of breaking even is 0.1, and the probability of losing $200,000 is 0.3.

$$\text{Rich's expectation} = P_1 A_1 + P_2 A_2 + P_3 A_3$$
$$= (0.6)(\$500,000) + (0.1)(\$0) + (0.3)(-\$200,000)$$
$$= \$240,000$$

Rich has an expectation, or expected average gain, of $240,000 for this contract. Thus, if the company receives similar contracts like this one, with these particular probabilities and amounts, in the long run the company would have an average gain of $240,000 per contract. However, you must remember that there is a 30% chance the company will lose $200,000 on this *particular* contract or any particular contract with these probabilities and amounts. ∎

Example 2 *Test-Taking Strategy*

Maria is taking a multiple-choice exam in which there are five possible answers for each question. The instructions indicate that she will be awarded 2 points for each correct response, that she will lose $\frac{1}{2}$ point for each incorrect response, and that no points will be added or subtracted for answers left blank.

a) If Maria does not know the correct answer to a question, is it to her advantage or disadvantage to guess at an answer?

b) If she can eliminate one of the possible choices, is it to her advantage or disadvantage to guess at the answer?

Solution

a) Let's determine the expected value if Maria guesses at an answer. Only one of five possible answers is correct.

$$P(\text{guesses correctly}) = \frac{1}{5} \qquad P(\text{guesses incorrectly}) = \frac{4}{5}$$

MATHEMATICS TODAY

Tough Decision

The concept of expected value can be used to help evaluate the consequences of many decisions. You use this concept when you consider whether to double-park your car for a few minutes. The probability of being caught may be low, but the penalty, a parking ticket, may be high. You weigh these factors when you decide whether to spend time looking for a legal parking spot.

Why This is Important Considering the expected value of an event helps us make decisions that benefit us in the long run.

$$\text{Maria's expectation} = \overset{\substack{\text{Guesses}\\\text{correctly}}}{\overbrace{P_1 \cdot A_1}} + \overset{\substack{\text{Guesses}\\\text{incorrectly}}}{\overbrace{P_2 \cdot A_2}}$$

$$= \frac{1}{5}(2) + \frac{4}{5}\left(-\frac{1}{2}\right)$$

$$= \frac{2}{5} - \frac{2}{5} = 0$$

Thus, Maria's expectation is zero when she guesses. Therefore, over the long run she will neither gain nor lose points by guessing.

b) If Maria can eliminate one possible choice, one of four answers will be correct.

$$P(\text{guesses correctly}) = \frac{1}{4} \qquad P(\text{guesses incorrectly}) = \frac{3}{4}$$

$$\text{Maria's expectation} = \overset{\substack{\text{Guesses}\\\text{correctly}}}{\overbrace{P_1 \cdot A_1}} + \overset{\substack{\text{Guesses}\\\text{incorrectly}}}{\overbrace{P_2 \cdot A_2}}$$

$$= \frac{1}{4}(2) + \frac{3}{4}\left(-\frac{1}{2}\right)$$

$$= \frac{2}{4} - \frac{3}{8} = \frac{4}{8} - \frac{3}{8} = \frac{1}{8}$$

Since the expectation is a positive $\frac{1}{8}$, Maria will, on average, gain $\frac{1}{8}$ point each time she guesses when she can eliminate one possible choice. ∎

Example 3 *Selling Hot Dogs*

An outdoor hot dog vendor sells an average of 50 hot dogs per day in dry weather and an average of 15 per day in wet weather. If the weather in this area is wet 20% of the time, determine the expected (average) number of hot dogs sold per day.

Solution The amounts in this example are the number of hot dogs sold. Since the weather is wet 20% of the time, it will be dry 100% − 20% = 80% of the time. When written as probabilities, 20% and 80% are 0.2 and 0.8, respectively.

$$E = P(\text{dry}) \cdot (\text{number sold}) + P(\text{wet}) \cdot (\text{number sold})$$

$$= 0.8(50) + 0.2(15)$$

$$= 40 + 3 = 43$$

Thus, the average, or expected, number of hot dogs sold per day is 43. ∎

When we gave the expectation formula, we indicated that the amounts were the **net amounts**, which are the actual amounts gained or lost. Examples 4 and 5 illustrate how net amounts are used in two applications of expected value.

Example 4 *Winning a Door Prize*

When Josh Rosenberg attends a charity event, he is given a free ticket for the $50 door prize. A total of 100 tickets will be given out. Determine his expectation of winning the door prize.

Solution The probability of winning the door prize is $\frac{1}{100}$ since Josh has 1 of 100 tickets. If he wins, his net or actual winnings will be $50 since he did not pay for the ticket. The probability that Josh loses is $\frac{99}{100}$. If Josh loses, the amount he loses is $0 because he did not pay for the ticket.

$$\text{Expectation} = P(\text{Josh wins}) \cdot (\text{amount won}) + P(\text{Josh loses}) \cdot (\text{amount lost})$$

$$= \frac{1}{100}(50) + \frac{99}{100}(0) = \frac{50}{100} = 0.50$$

Thus, Josh's expectation is $0.50, or 50 cents.   ∎

Now we will consider a problem similar to Example 4, but this time we will assume that Josh must purchase the ticket for the door prize.

Example 5   *Winning a Door Prize*

When Josh Rosenberg attends a charity event, he is given the opportunity to purchase a ticket for the $50 door prize. The cost of the ticket is $2, and 100 tickets will be sold. Determine Josh's expectation if he purchases one ticket.

Solution As in Example 4, Josh's probability of winning is $\frac{1}{100}$. However, if he does win, his actual or net winnings will be $48. The $48 is obtained by subtracting the cost of the ticket, $2, from the amount of the door prize, $50. There is also a probability of $\frac{99}{100}$ that Josh will not win the door prize. If he does not win the door prize, he has lost the $2 that he paid for the ticket. Therefore, we must consider two amounts when we determine Josh's expectation, winning $48 and losing $2.

$$\text{Expectation} = P(\text{Josh wins}) \cdot (\text{amount won}) + P(\text{Josh loses}) \cdot (\text{amount lost})$$

$$= \frac{1}{100}(48) + \frac{99}{100}(-2)$$

$$= \frac{48}{100} - \frac{198}{100} = -\frac{150}{100} = -1.50$$

Josh's expectation is $-1.50 when he purchases one ticket.   ∎

In Example 5, we determined that Josh's expectation was −$1.50 when he purchased one ticket. If he purchased two tickets, his expectation would be 2(−$1.50), or −$3.00. We could also compute Josh's expectation if he purchased two tickets as follows:

$$E = \frac{2}{100}(46) + \frac{98}{100}(-4) = -3.00$$

This answer, −$3.00, checks with the answer obtained by multiplying the expectation for a single ticket by 2.

Let's look at one more example in which a person must pay for a chance to win a prize. In the following example, there will be more than two amounts to consider.

Example 6   *Raffle Tickets*

One thousand raffle tickets are sold for $1 each. One grand prize of $500 and two consolation prizes of $100 will be awarded. The tickets are placed in a bin. The winning tickets will be selected from the bin. Assuming that the probability that any given ticket selected for the grand prize is $\frac{1}{1000}$ and the probability that any given ticket selected for a consolation prize is $\frac{2}{1000}$, determine

a) Irene Drew's expectation if she purchases one ticket.

b) Irene's expectation if she purchases five tickets.

Solution

a) Three amounts are to be considered: the net gain in winning the grand prize, the net gain in winning one of the consolation prizes, and the loss of the cost of the ticket. If Irene wins the grand prize, her net gain is $499 ($500 minus $1 spent for the ticket). If Irene wins one of the consolation prizes, her net gain is $99 ($100 minus $1). The probability that Irene wins the grand prize is $\frac{1}{1000}$ and the probability that she wins a consolation prize is $\frac{2}{1000}$. The probability that she does not win a prize is $1 - \frac{1}{1000} - \frac{2}{1000} = \frac{997}{1000}$.

$$E = P_1 \cdot A_1 + P_2 \cdot A_2 + P_3 \cdot A_3$$

$$= \frac{1}{1000}(\$499) + \frac{2}{1000}(\$99) + \frac{997}{1000}(-\$1)$$

$$= \frac{499}{1000} + \frac{198}{1000} - \frac{997}{1000} = -\frac{300}{1000} = -0.30$$

Thus, Irene's expectation is −$0.30 per ticket purchased.

b) On average, Irene loses 30 cents on each ticket purchased. On five tickets, her expectation is $(-\$0.30)(5)$, or −$1.50. ■

TIMELY TIP

In any expectation problem, the sum of the probabilities of all the events should always be 1. Note in Example 6 that the sum of the probabilities is

$$\frac{1}{1000} + \frac{2}{1000} + \frac{997}{1000} = \frac{1000}{1000} = 1.$$

Fair Price

In Example 5, we determined that Josh's expectation was −$1.50. Now let's determine how to find out how much should have been charged for a ticket so that his expectation would be $0. If Josh's expectation were to be $0, he could be expected to break even over the long run. Suppose that Josh paid 50 cents, or $0.50, for the ticket. His expectation, if paying $0.50 for the ticket, would be calculated as follows.

$$\text{Expectation} = P(\text{Josh wins}) \cdot (\text{amount won}) + P(\text{Josh loses}) \cdot (\text{amount lost})$$

$$= \frac{1}{100}(49.50) + \frac{99}{100}(-\$0.50)$$

$$= \frac{49.50}{100} - \frac{49.50}{100} = 0$$

Thus, if Josh paid 50 cents per ticket, his expectation would be $0. The 50 cents, in this case, is called the fair price of the ticket. The *fair price* is the amount to be paid that will result in an expected value of $0. The fair price may be found by adding the *cost to play* to the *expected value*.

Fair Price

To determine the fair price, use the following formula.

$$\textbf{Fair price} = \text{expected value} + \text{cost to play}$$

In Example 5, the cost to play was $2 and the expected value was determined to be −$1.50. The fair price for a ticket in Example 5 may be found as follows.

$$\text{Fair price} = \text{expected value} + \text{cost to play}$$

$$= -1.50 + 2.00 = 0.50$$

We obtained a fair price of $0.50. If the tickets were sold for the fair price of $0.50 each, Josh's expectation would be $0, as shown above. Can you now find the fair price that Irene should pay for a raffle ticket in Example 6? In Example 6, the cost of a ticket was $1 and we determined that the expected value was −$0.30.

$$\text{Fair price} = \text{expected value} + \text{cost to play}$$

$$= -\$0.30 + \$1.00 = \$0.70$$

Thus, the fair price for a ticket in Example 6 is $0.70, or 70 cents. Verify for yourself now that if the tickets were sold for $0.70, the expectation would be $0.00.

Example **7**   *Expectation and Fair Price*

At a game of chance, the expected value is found to be $-\$1.50$, and the cost to play the game is $4.00. Determine the fair price to play the game.

Solution   We use the formula

$$\text{Fair price} = \text{expected value} + \text{cost to play}$$
$$= -1.50 + 4.00$$
$$= 2.50$$

Thus, the fair price to play this game would be $2.50. If the cost to play was $2.50 instead of $4.00, the expected value would be $0. ∎

SECTION 12.4   *Exercises*

Warm Up Exercises

In Exercises 1–4, fill in the blank with an appropriate word, phrase, or symbol(s).

1. The expected gain or loss of an experiment over the long run is called the _____ value.

2. In an experiment, if an individual expects to have a loss in the long run, the expected value is _____.

3. In an experiment, if an individual expects to have a gain in the long run, the expected value is _____.

4. In an experiment, if an individual expects to break even in the long run, the expected value is _____.

Practice the Skills/Problem Solving

5. *Expected Attendance*   For an outdoor art and craft show, event organizers estimate that 60,000 people will attend if it is not raining. If it is raining, event organizers estimate that 21,000 people will attend. On the day of the show, meteorologists predict a 70% chance of rain. Determine the expected number of people who will attend this show.

6. *A New Business*   In a proposed business venture, Stephanie Morrison estimates that there is a 60% chance she will make $80,000 and a 40% chance she will lose $20,000. Determine Stephanie's expected value.

7. *Basketball*   Shenise Johnson is a star player for the University of Miami Hurricanes women's basketball team. She has injured her ankle, and it is doubtful that she will be able to play in an upcoming game. If Shenise can play, the coach estimates that the Hurricanes will score 78 points. If Shenise is not able to play, the coach estimates that they will score 62 points. The team doctor estimates that there is a 50% chance Shenise will play. Determine the number of points the team can expect to score.

▲ *Shenise Johnson (left)*

8. *Career Fair Attendance*   For a Nursing and Allied Health Care Career Fair, organizers estimate that 50 people will attend if it does not rain and 65 will attend if it rains. The weather forecast indicates that there is a 40% chance it will not rain and a 60% chance it will rain on the day of the career fair. Determine the expected number of people who will attend the fair.

9. *TV Shows*   The Fox television network is scheduling its fall lineup of shows. For the Tuesday night 8 P.M. slot, Fox has selected the show *Glee*. If its rival network CBS schedules the show *NCIS* during the same time slot, Fox estimates that *Glee* will get 1.2 million viewers. However, if CBS schedules the show *Survivor* during that time slot, Fox estimates that *Glee* will get 1.6 million viewers. Fox believes

that the probability that CBS will show *NCIS* is 0.4 and the probability that CBS will show *Survivor* is 0.6. Determine the expected number of viewers for the show *Glee*.

10. *Seattle Greenery* In July in Seattle, the grass grows $\frac{1}{2}$ in. a day on a sunny day and $\frac{1}{4}$ in. a day on a cloudy day. In Seattle in July, 75% of the days are sunny and 25% are cloudy.

a) Determine the expected amount of grass growth on a typical day in July in Seattle.

b) Determine the expected total grass growth in the month of July in Seattle.

11. *Investment Club* The Triple L investment club is considering purchasing a certain stock. After considerable research, the club members determine that there is a 70% chance of making $10,000, a 10% chance of breaking even, and a 20% chance of losing $7500. Determine the expectation of this purchase.

12. *Clothing Sale* At a special clothing sale at the Crescent Oaks Country Club, after the cashier rings up your purchase, you select a slip of paper from a box. The slip of paper indicates the dollar amount, either $5 or $10, that is deducted from your purchase price. The probability of selecting a slip indicating $5 is $\frac{7}{10}$, and the probability of selecting a slip indicating $10 is $\frac{3}{10}$. If your original purchase before you select the slip of paper is $200, determine

a) the expected dollar amount to be deducted from your purchase.

b) the expected dollar amount you will pay for your purchase.

13. *Fortune Cookies* At the Royal Dragon Chinese restaurant, a slip in the fortune cookies indicates a dollar amount that will be subtracted from your total bill. A bag of 10 fortune cookies is given to you from which you will select one. If seven fortune cookies contain "$1 off," two contain "$2 off," and one contains "$5 off," determine the expectation of a selection.

14. *Pick a Card* Mike and Dave play the following game. Mike picks a card from a deck of cards. If he selects a club, Dave gives him $4. If not, he gives Dave $2.

a) Determine Mike's expectation.

b) Determine Dave's expectation.

15. *Roll a Die* Alyssa and Gabriel play the following game. Alyssa rolls a die. If she rolls a 1, 2, or 3, Gabriel gives Alyssa $3. If Alyssa rolls a 4 or 5, Gabriel gives Alyssa $2. However, if Alyssa rolls a 6, she gives Gabriel $14.

a) Determine Alyssa's expectation.

b) Determine Gabriel's expectation.

16. *Blue Chips and Red Chips* A bag contains 4 blue chips and 6 red chips. Chi and Dolly play the following game. Chi selects one chip at random from the bag. If Chi selects

a blue chip, Dolly gives Chi $6. If Chi selects a red chip, Chi gives Dolly $5.

a) Determine Chi's expectation.

b) Determine Dolly's expectation.

17. *Multiple-Choice Test* A multiple-choice exam has five possible answers for each question. For each correct answer, you are awarded 5 points. For each incorrect answer, 1 point is subtracted from your score. For answers left blank, no points are added or subtracted.

a) If you do not know the correct answer to a particular question, is it to your advantage to guess? Explain.

b) If you do not know the correct answer but can eliminate one possible choice, is it to your advantage to guess? Explain.

18. *Multiple-Choice Test* A multiple-choice exam has four possible answers for each question. For each correct answer, you are awarded 5 points. For each incorrect answer, 2 points are subtracted from your score. For answers left blank, no points are added or subtracted.

a) If you do not know the correct answer to a particular question, is it to your advantage to guess? Explain.

b) If you do not know the correct answer but can eliminate one possible choice, is it to your advantage to guess? Explain.

19. *Fair Price* The expected value when you purchase a lottery ticket is −$2.00, and the cost of the ticket is $5.00. Determine the fair price of the lottery ticket.

20. *Fair Price* The expected value of a carnival game is −$6.50, and the cost to play the game is $10.00. Determine the fair price to play the game.

21. *Raffle Tickets* Five hundred raffle tickets are sold for $3 each. One prize of $500 is to be awarded. Raul Mondesi purchases one ticket.

a) Determine his expected value.

b) Determine the fair price of a ticket.

22. Raffle Tickets One thousand raffle tickets are sold for $1 each. One prize of $800 is to be awarded. Rena Condos purchases one ticket.

a) Determine her expected value.

b) Determine the fair price of a ticket.

23. Raffle Tickets Two thousand raffle tickets are sold for $3 each. Three prizes will be awarded: one for $1000 and two for $500. Assume that the probability that any given ticket is selected for the $1000 prize is $\frac{1}{2000}$ and the probability that any given ticket is selected for the $500 prize is $\frac{2}{2000}$. Jeremy Sharp purchases one of these tickets.

a) Determine his expected value.

b) Determine the fair price of a ticket.

24. Raffle Tickets Ten thousand raffle tickets are sold for $5 each. Four prizes will be awarded: one for $5000, one for $2500, and two for $1000. Assume that the probability that any given ticket is selected for the $5000 prize is $\frac{1}{10,000}$, the probability that any given ticket is selected for the $2500 prize is $\frac{1}{10,000}$, and the probability that any given ticket is selected for a $1000 prize is $\frac{2}{10,000}$. Sidhardt purchases one of these tickets.

a) Determine his expected value.

b) Determine the fair price of a ticket.

Spinners In Exercises 25 and 26, assume that a person spins the pointer and is awarded the amount indicated by the pointer. Determine the person's expectation.

25.   **26.**

Spinners In Exercises 27 and 28, assume that a person spins the pointer and is awarded the amount indicated if the pointer points to a positive number but must pay the amount indicated if the pointer points to a negative number. Determine the person's expectation if the person plays the game.

27.   **28.**

Selecting an Envelope In Exercises 29–32, a person randomly selects one of the six envelopes shown below. Each envelope contains a check that the person gets to keep. Determine the person's expectation if the checks in the envelopes are as follows.

29. Three envelopes contain a $500 check, and three envelopes contain a $1000 check.

30. Four envelopes contain a $1000 check, and two envelopes contain a $5000 check.

31. The six envelopes contain checks for $100, $200, $300, $400, $500, and $1000, respectively.

32. Two envelopes contain a check for $600, two envelopes contain a check for $2000, and two envelopes contain a check for $5000.

Spinners In Exercises 33–36, assume that a person spins the pointer and is awarded the amount indicated by the pointer. If it costs $2 to play the game, determine

a) the expectation of a person who plays the game.

b) the fair price to play the game.

33.   **34.**

35.   **36.**

Selecting an Envelope In Exercises 37–40 on page 706, a person randomly selects one of the four envelopes shown below. Each envelope contains a check that the person gets to keep. However, before the person can select an envelope, he or she must pay $15 to play. For the value of the checks indicated in the exercises, determine the expectation for a person who plays.

37. Two envelopes contain a $10 check, and two envelopes contain a $25 check.

38. Three envelopes contain a $20 check, and one envelope contains a $0 check.

39. The checks in the envelopes are for $0, $2, $5, and $20, respectively.

40. The checks in the envelopes are for $2, $2, $100, and $400, respectively.

41. *Reaching Base Safely* Based on his past baseball history, Jim Devias has a 17% chance of reaching first base safely, a 10% chance of hitting a double, a 2% chance of hitting a triple, an 8% chance of hitting a home run, and a 63% chance of making an out at his next at bat. Determine Jim's expected number of bases for his next at bat.

42. *Life Insurance* According to Bristol Mutual Life Insurance's mortality table, the probability that a 20-year-old woman will survive 1 year is 0.994 and the probability that she will die within 1 year is 0.006. If a 20-year-old woman buys a $10,000 1-year policy for $100, what is Bristol Mutual's expected gain or loss?

43. *Choosing a Colored Chip* In a box, there are a total of 10 chips. The chips are orange, green, and yellow, as shown below.

If you select an orange chip, you get 4 points, a green chip 3 points, and a yellow chip 1 point. If you select one chip at random, determine the expected number of points you will get.

44. *Choosing a Colored Chip* Repeat Exercise 43 but assume that an orange chip is worth 5 points, a green chip 2 points, and a yellow chip −3 points (3 points are taken away).

45. *Employee Hiring* The academic vice president at Brookdale Community College has requested that new academic programs be added to the college curriculum. If the college's Board of Trustees approves the new programs, the college will hire 75 new employees. If the new programs are not approved, the college will hire only 20 new employees. If the probability that the new programs will be approved is 0.65, what is the expected number of new employees to be hired by Brookdale Community College? Round your answer to the nearest whole number of employees.

46. *Completing a Project* A mechanical contractor is preparing for a construction project. He determines that if he completes the project on schedule, his net profit will be $450,000. If he completes the project between 0 and 3 months late, his net profit decreases to $120,000. If he completes the project more

than 3 months late, his net loss is $275,000. The probability that he completes the project on schedule is 0.6, the probability that he completes the project between 0 and 3 months late is 0.3, and the probability that he completes the project more than 3 months late is 0.1. Determine his expected gain or loss for this project.

47. *New Store* Dunkin' Donuts is opening a new store. The company estimates that there is a 75% chance the store will have a profit of $20,000, a 10% chance the store will break even, and a 15% chance the store will lose $3000. Determine the expected gain or loss for this store.

48. *China Cabinet* The owner of an antique store estimates that there is a 40% chance she will make $2000 when she sells an antique china cabinet, a 50% chance she will make $750 when she sells the cabinet, and a 10% chance she will break even when she sells the cabinet. Determine the expected amount she will make when she sells the cabinet.

49. *Rolling a Die* A die is rolled many times, and the points facing up are recorded. Determine the expected (average) number of points facing up over the long run.

50. *Lawsuit* Don Vello is considering bringing a lawsuit against the Dummote Chemical Company. His lawyer estimates that there is a 70% chance Don will make $60,000, a 10% chance Don will break even, and a 20% chance they will lose the case and Don will need to pay $30,000 in legal fees. Estimate Don's expected gain or loss if he proceeds with the lawsuit.

51. *Road Service* On a clear day in Boston, the Automobile Association of American (AAA) makes an average of 110 service calls for motorist assistance, on a rainy day it makes an average of 160 service calls, and on a snowy day it makes an average of 210 service calls. If the weather in Boston is clear 200 days of the year, rainy 100 days of the year, and snowy 65 days of the year, determine the expected number of service calls made by the AAA in a given day.

52. *Real Estate* The expenses for Jorge Estrada, a real estate agent, to list, advertise, and attempt to sell a house are $1400. If Jorge succeeds in selling the house, he will receive a commission of 6% of the sales price. If an agent with a different company sells the house, Jorge still receives 3% of the sales price. If the house is unsold after 3 months, Jorge loses the listing and receives nothing. Suppose that the probability that he sells a $150,000 house is 0.2, the probability that another agent sells the house is 0.5, and the probability that the house is unsold after 3 months is 0.3. Determine Jorge's expectation if he accepts this house for listing. Should Jorge list the house?

Dart Board *In Exercises 53 and 54, assume that you are blindfolded and throw a dart at the dart board shown below. Assume that your dart sticks in the dart board, and not on a line.*

a) *Determine the probabilities that the dart lands on $1, $10, $20, and $100, respectively.*

b) *If you win the amount of money indicated by the section of the board where the dart lands, determine your expectation when you throw the dart.*

53.

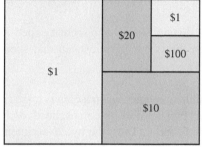

54.

Challenge Problems/Group Activities

55. *Term Life Insurance* An insurance company will pay the face value of a term life insurance policy if the insured person dies during the term of the policy. For how much should an insurance company sell a 10-year term policy with a face value of $40,000 to a 30-year-old man for the company to make a profit? The probability of a 30-year-old man living to age 40 is 0.97. Explain your answer. Remember that the customer pays for the insurance before the policy becomes effective.

56. *Lottery Ticket* Is it possible to determine your expectation when you purchase a lottery ticket? Explain.

Roulette *In Exercises 57 and 58, use the roulette wheel illustrated. A roulette wheel typically contains slots with numbers 1–36 and slots marked 0 and 00. A ball is spun on the wheel and comes to rest in one of the 38 slots. Eighteen numbers are colored red, and 18 numbers are colored black. The 0 and 00 are colored green. If you bet on one particular number and the ball lands on that number, the house pays off odds of 35 to 1. If you bet on a red number or black number and win, the house pays 1 to 1 (even money).*

57. Determine the expected value of betting $1 on a particular number.

58. Determine the expected value of betting $1 on red.

Recreational Mathematics

59. *Wheel of Fortune* The following is a miniature version of the Wheel of Fortune. When Dave Salem spins the wheel, he is awarded the amount on the wheel indicated by the pointer. If the wheel points to Bankrupt, he loses the total amount he has accumulated and also loses his turn. Assume that the wheel stops on a position at random and that each position is equally likely to occur.

a) Determine Mr. Salem's expectation when he spins the wheel at the start of the game (he has no money to lose if he lands on Bankrupt).

b) If Mr. Salem presently has a balance of $1800, determine his expectation when he spins the wheel.

SECTION 12.5   Tree Diagrams

▲ We can use a tree diagram to illustrate the possible lunch specials at a deli.

Suppose a deli offers a lunch special consisting of a sandwich, a beverage, and a dessert. The sandwich choices are roast beef, ham, or turkey. The beverage choices are soda, coffee, or tea. The dessert choices are a brownie or a chocolate chip cookie. If a customer purchases a lunch special and makes selections at random, what is the probability the customer selects a roast beef sandwich and a chocolate chip cookie? In this section, we will illustrate how the counting principle and tree diagrams can be used to determine the answers to questions like the one posed above. We will also illustrate how tree diagrams can be used to determine all the possible outcomes of an experiment.

Why *This is Important* Being able to determine the number of possible outcomes in an experiment is essential to solving many probability problems.

Now we will introduce the counting principle. The counting principle will be used again in Section 12.8.

Counting Principle
If a first experiment can be performed in M distinct ways and a second experiment can be performed in N distinct ways, then the two experiments in that specific order can be performed in $M \cdot N$ distinct ways.

If we wanted to find the number of possible outcomes when a coin is tossed and a die is rolled, we could reason that the coin has two possible outcomes, heads and tails. The die has six possible outcomes: 1, 2, 3, 4, 5, and 6. Thus, the two experiments together have $2 \cdot 6$, or 12, possible outcomes.

A list of all the possible outcomes of an experiment is called a *sample space*. Each individual outcome in the sample space is called a *sample point*. *Tree diagrams* are helpful in determining sample spaces.

A tree diagram illustrating all the possible outcomes when a coin is tossed and a die is rolled (see Fig. 12.6) has two initial branches, one for each possible outcome of the coin. Each of these branches will have six branches emerging from them, one for each possible outcome of the die. That will give a total of 12 branches, the same number of possible outcomes found by using the counting principle. We can obtain the sample space by listing all the possible combinations of branches. Note that this sample space consists of 12 sample points.

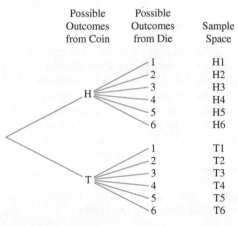

Figure 12.6

Example 1 uses the phrase "without replacement." This phrase tells us that once an item is selected, it cannot be selected again, making it impossible to select the same item twice.

Example 1 *Selecting Balls without Replacement*

Figure 12.7

Two balls are to be selected *without replacement* from a bag that contains one red, one blue, one green, and one orange ball (see Fig. 12.7).

a) Use the counting principle to determine the number of points in the sample space.

b) Construct a tree diagram and list the sample space.

c) Determine the probability that one orange ball is selected.

d) Determine the probability that a green ball followed by a red ball is selected.

Solution

a) The first selection may be any one of the four balls. Once the first ball is selected, only three balls remain for the second selection. Thus, there are 4 · 3, or 12, sample points in the sample space.

b) The first ball selected can be red, blue, green, or orange. Since this experiment is done without replacement, the same colored ball cannot be selected twice. For example, if the first ball selected is red, the second ball selected must be either blue, green, or orange. The tree diagram and sample space are shown in Fig. 12.8. The sample space contains 12 points. That result checks with the answer obtained in part (a) using the counting principle.

First Selection	Second Selection	Sample Space
R	B	RB
	G	RG
	O	RO
B	R	BR
	G	BG
	O	BO
G	R	GR
	B	GB
	O	GO
O	R	OR
	B	OB
	G	OG

Figure 12.8

c) If we know the sample space, we can compute probabilities using the formula

$$P(E) = \frac{\text{number of outcomes favorable to } E}{\text{total number of outcomes}}$$

The total number of outcomes will be the number of points in the sample space. From Fig. 12.8, we determine that there are 12 possible outcomes. Six outcomes have one orange ball: RO, BO, GO, OR, OB, and OG.

$$P(\text{one orange ball is selected}) = \frac{6}{12} = \frac{1}{2}$$

d) One possible outcome meets the criteria of a green ball followed by a red ball: GR.

$$P(\text{green followed by red}) = \frac{1}{12}$$

The counting principle can be extended to any number of experiments, as illustrated in Example 2.

Example 2 *Lunch Choices*

At Finlay's Restaurant, each lunch special consists of a sandwich, a salad, and a beverage. The sandwich choices are roast beef (R), ham (H), or turkey (T). The salad choices are macaroni (M) or potato (P). The beverage choices are coffee (C) or soda (S).

a) Use the counting principle to determine the number of different lunch specials offered by this restaurant.

b) Construct a tree diagram and list the sample space.

c) If a customer randomly selects one of the lunch specials, determine the probability that a roast beef sandwich and soda are selected.

d) If a customer randomly selects one of the lunch specials, determine the probability that neither macaroni salad nor coffee is selected.

Solution

a) There are 3 choices for a sandwich, 2 choices for a salad, and 2 choices for a beverage. Using the counting principle, we can determine that there are $3 \cdot 2 \cdot 2$, or 12, different lunch specials.

b) The tree diagram illustrating the 12 lunch specials is given in Fig. 12.9.

Sandwich	Salad	Beverage	Sample Space
	M	C	RMC
	M	S	RMS
R	P	C	RPC
	P	S	RPS
	M	C	HMC
	M	S	HMS
H	P	C	HPC
	P	S	HPS
	M	C	TMC
	M	S	TMS
T	P	C	TPC
	P	S	TPS

Figure 12.9

c) Of the 12 lunch specials, 2 contain both a roast beef sandwich and soda (RMS, RPS).

$$P(\text{roast beef sandwich and soda are selected}) = \frac{2}{12} = \frac{1}{6}$$

d) Of the 12 lunch specials, 3 contain neither macaroni salad nor coffee (RPS, HPS, TPS).

$$P(\text{neither macaroni salad nor coffee are selected}) = \frac{3}{12} = \frac{1}{4}$$

Example 3 *Selecting Ticket Winners*

A radio station has two tickets to give away to a Bon Jovi concert. It held a contest and narrowed the possible recipients down to four people: Christine (C), Mike Hammer (MH), Mike Levine (ML), and Phyllis (P). The names of two of these four people will be selected at random from a hat, and the two people selected will be awarded the tickets.

a) Use the counting principle to determine the number of points in the sample space.

b) Construct a tree diagram and list the sample space.

c) Determine the probability that Christine is selected.

d) Determine the probability that neither Mike Hammer nor Mike Levine is selected.

e) Determine the probability that at least one Mike is selected.

▲ *Bon Jovi*

RECREATIONAL MATH

Jumble

Many of you have seen the JUMBLE puzzles in newspapers and magazines. In these puzzles the letters of a word are scrambled, and your goal is to unscramble the letters to make a word. For each JUMBLE below,

a) Use the counting principle to determine the number of possible arrangements of letters given.

b) Determine the word that results when the letters are placed in their proper order (note that only one word is possible).

1. KANCS
2. CYMITS

The answers are listed upside down below. See Exercises 31 and 32 for more examples. We will expand upon this Recreational Math in Section 12.8

2. a) 720 b) MYSTIC
1. a) 120 b) SNACK

Solution

a) The first selection may be any one of the four people; see Fig. 12.10. Once the first person is selected, only three people remain for the second selection. Thus, there are $4 \cdot 3$, or 12, sample points in the sample space.

b)

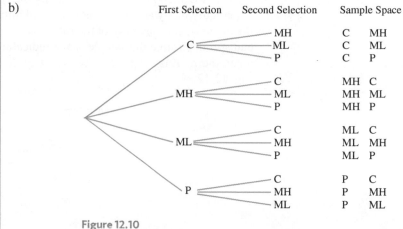

Figure 12.10

c) Of the 12 points in the sample space, 6 have Christine. They are C MH, C ML, C P, MH C, ML C, and P C.

$$P(\text{Christine is selected}) = \frac{6}{12} = \frac{1}{2}$$

d) Of the 12 points in the sample space, two have neither Mike. They are C P and P C.

$$P(\text{neither Mike selected}) = \frac{2}{12} = \frac{1}{6}$$

e) At least one Mike means that one or more Mikes are selected. There are 10 points in the sample space with at least one Mike (all those except C P and P C).

$$P(\text{at least one Mike is selected}) = \frac{10}{12} = \frac{5}{6}$$

 In Example 3, if you add the probability of no Mike being selected with the probability of at least one Mike being selected, you get $\frac{1}{6} + \frac{5}{6}$, or 1. In any probability problem, if E is a specific event, then either E happens at least one time or it does not happen at all. Thus, $P(E \text{ happening at least once}) + P(E \text{ does not happen}) = 1$, which leads to the following rule.

Probability of an Event Happening At Least Once

The probability of an event happening at least once can be determined by the following formula.

$$P(\text{event happening at least once}) = 1 - P(\text{event does not happen})$$

For example, suppose that the probability of not getting any red flowers from the seeds that are planted is $\frac{2}{7}$. Then the probability of getting at least one red flower from the seeds that are planted is $1 - \frac{2}{7} = \frac{5}{7}$. We will use this rule in later sections.

 In all the tree diagrams in this section, the outcomes were always equally likely; that is, each outcome had the same probability of occurrence. Consider a rock that has 4 faces such that each face has a different surface area and the rock is not

Figure 12.11

uniform in density (see Fig. 12.11). When the rock is dropped, the probability that the rock lands on face 1 will not be the same as the probability that the rock lands on face 2. In fact, the probabilities that the rock lands on face 1, face 2, face 3, and face 4 may all be different. Therefore, the outcomes of the rock landing on face 1, face 2, face 3, and face 4 are not equally likely outcomes. Because the outcomes are not equally likely and we are not given additional information, we cannot determine the theoretical probability of the rock landing on each individual face. However, we can still determine the sample space indicating the faces that the rock may land on when the rock is dropped twice. The tree diagram and sample space are shown in Fig. 12.12.

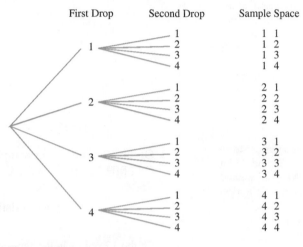

Figure 12.12

Since the outcomes are not equally likely, the probability of each of the 16 sample points in the sample space occurring cannot be determined. If the outcomes were equally likely, then each of the 16 points in the sample space would have a probability of $\frac{1}{16}$. See Exercises 27 and 28, which deal with outcomes that are not equally likely.

SECTION 12.5 *Exercises*

Warm Up Exercises

In Exercises 1–4, fill in the blank with an appropriate word, phrase, or symbol(s).

1. A list of all possible outcomes of an experiment is called a(n) _____ space.

2. Each individual outcome in a sample space is called a sample _____.

3. If a first experiment can be performed in two distinct ways and a second experiment can be performed in seven distinct ways, the two experiments together can be performed in _____ distinct ways.

4. A helpful method to determine a sample space is to construct a(n) _____ diagram.

Practice the Skills

5. **Selecting States** If two states are selected at random from the 50 U.S. states, use the counting principle to determine the number of possible outcomes if the states are selected

   a) with replacement.

   b) without replacement.

6. **Selecting Dates** If two dates are selected at random from the 365 days of the year, use the counting principle to determine the number of possible outcomes if the dates are selected

   a) with replacement.

   b) without replacement.

7. *Selecting Golfballs* A bag contains six golfballs, all the same size and equally likely to be selected. Each golfball is a different brand. If you select three golfballs at random, use the counting principle to determine how many points will be in the sample space if the golfballs are selected

   a) with replacement.

   b) without replacement.

8. *Remote Control* Your television remote control has buttons for digits 0–9. If you press two buttons, how many numbers are possible if

   a) the same button may be pressed twice.

   b) the same button may not be pressed twice.

Problem Solving

In Exercises 9–26, use the counting principle to determine the answer to part (a). Assume that each event is equally likely to occur.

9. *Coin Toss* Two coins are tossed.

   a) Determine the number of points in the sample space.

   b) Construct a tree diagram and list the sample space.

   Determine the probability that

   c) no heads are tossed.

   d) exactly one head is tossed.

   e) two heads are tossed.

10. *Boys and Girls* A couple plans to have two children.

   a) Determine the number of points in the sample space of the possible arrangements of boys and girls.

   b) Construct a tree diagram and list the sample space.

   Assuming that boys and girls are equally likely, determine the probability that the couple has

   c) two girls.

   d) at least one girl.

   e) a girl and then a boy.

11. *Cards* A box contains three cards. On one card there is a sun, on another card there is a question mark, and on the third card there is an apple.

Two cards are to be selected at random with replacement.

   a) Determine the number of points in the sample space.

   b) Construct a tree diagram and list the sample space.

Determine the probability that

   c) two apples are selected.

   d) a sun and then a question mark are selected.

   e) at least one apple is selected.

12. *Cards* Repeat Exercise 11 but assume that the cards are drawn without replacement.

13. *Marble Selection* A hat contains four marbles: 1 yellow, 1 red, 1 blue, and 1 green. Two marbles are to be selected at random without replacement from the hat.

   a) Determine the number of points in the sample space.

   b) Construct a tree diagram and list the sample space.

   Determine the probability of selecting

   c) exactly 1 red marble.

   d) at least 1 marble that is not red.

   e) no green marbles.

14. *Three Coins* Three coins are tossed.

   a) Determine the number of points in the sample space.

   b) Construct a tree diagram and list the sample space.

   Determine the probability that

   c) no heads are tossed.

   d) exactly one head is tossed.

   e) three heads are tossed.

15. *Paint Choices* The Flotterons plan to purchase paint for the walls and paint for the trim in their living room. They will select one color for the walls and one color for the trim from the following colors.

Walls	Trim
Sable	Alabaster
Java	White
Chocolate	Oyster

   a) Determine the number of points in the sample space.

   b) Construct a tree diagram and list the sample space.

   Determine the probability that they select

   c) Java.

   d) Java and Oyster.

e) paint other than Java.

16. *Pet Shop* A pet shop is selling a calico cat, a Siamese cat, a Persian cat, and a Himalayan cat. The Chens are going to select two cats to bring home as pets.

a) Determine the number of points in the sample space.

b) Construct a tree diagram and list the sample space.

Determine the probability that they select

c) the Persian cat.

d) the Persian cat and the calico cat.

e) cats other than the Persian cat.

17. *Rolling Dice* Two dice are rolled.

a) Determine the number of points in the sample space.

b) Construct a tree diagram and list the sample space.

Determine the probability that

c) a double (a 1, 1 or 2, 2, etc.) is rolled.

d) a sum of 8 is rolled.

e) a sum of 2 is rolled.

f) Are you as likely to roll a sum of 2 as you are of rolling a sum of 8?

18. *Voting* At a homeowners' association meeting, a board member can vote yes, vote no, or abstain on a motion. There are three motions on which a board member must vote.

a) Determine the number of points in the sample space.

b) Construct a tree diagram and determine the sample space.

Determine the probability that a board member votes

c) no, yes, no in that order.

d) yes on exactly two of the motions.

e) yes on at least one motion.

19. *Dinner Specials* At Brio Restaurant, each dinner special consists of an appetizer, a salad, and an entrée. The choices of appetizer, salad, and entrée are listed below.

Appetizer	Salad	Entrée
Bruschetta	Caesar	Ravioli
Antipasto	Greens	Salmon
		Lasagna

a) Determine the number of points in the sample space.

b) Construct a tree diagram and determine the sample space.

If a customer randomly selects one of the dinner specials, determine the probability the customer selects

c) bruschetta for the appetizer.

d) greens and lasagna.

e) an entrée other than ravioli.

20. *Gift Cards* Three different people are to be selected at random, and each will be given one gift card. There is one card from Home Depot, one from Best Buy, and one from Red Lobster. The first person selected gets to choose one of the cards. The second person selected gets to choose between the two remaining cards. The third person selected gets the third card.

a) Determine the number of points in the sample space.

b) Construct a tree diagram and determine the sample space.

Determine the probability that

c) the Best Buy card is selected first.

d) the Home Depot card is selected first and the Red Lobster card is selected last.

e) The cards are selected in this order: Best Buy, Red Lobster, Home Depot.

21. *Apartment Options* Don Cater plans to rent an apartment from Rustic Village Apartments. The following chart displays information regarding the possible number of bedrooms, bathrooms, and other features from which he can choose. For his apartment, Don will select the number of bedrooms, number of bathrooms, and one other feature.

Bedrooms	Bathrooms	Other Features
1	1	Fireplace
2	2	Hardwood floors
3		Balcony

a) Determine the number of points in the sample space.

b) Construct a tree diagram and determine the sample space.

Determine the probability that Don selects

c) a two-bedroom apartment.

d) a two-bedroom apartment with a fireplace.

e) an apartment without a balcony.

22. *A New Home Theater System* You visit Best Buy to purchase a new home theater system. You are going to purchase a Blu-ray player, a receiver, and a speaker system from among the following brands.

Blu-ray Player	Receiver	Speaker System
LG	Yamaha	Bose
Toshiba	Onkyo	JBL
Sony	Pioneer	
Insignia		

a) Determine the number of points in the sample space.

b) Construct a tree diagram and determine the sample space.

Determine the probability of selecting

c) a Sony Blu-ray player.

d) Bose speakers.

e) a Sony Blu-ray player and Bose speakers.

23. *Landscaping* Mr. and Mrs. Frank just moved into a new home and need to do some landscaping. They are going to purchase one tree, one shrub, and one lilac bush from the list below.

Trees	Shrubs	Lilac Bushes
Dogwood	Forsythia	Common
Maple	Holly	Sensation
Birch	Juniper	Primrose

a) Determine the number of points in the sample space.

b) Construct a tree diagram and determine the sample space.

Determine the probability that the Franks select

c) a maple tree.

d) a dogwood tree and a holly shrub.

e) a lilac bush other than Sensation.

▲ Lilacs

24. *Literature Choices* You decide to take a literature course. A requirement for the course is that you must read one classic book, one nonfiction book, and one science fiction book from the list below.

Classic	Nonfiction	Science Fiction
A Farewell to Arms (*F*)	*John Adams* (*J*)	*Dune* (*D*)
The Grapes of Wrath (*G*)	*Angela's Ashes* (*A*)	*Ender's Game* (*E*)
Tom Sawyer (*T*)		
Moby-Dick (*M*)		

a) Determine the number of points in the sample space.

b) Construct a tree diagram and determine the sample space.

Determine the probability that

c) *John Adams* is selected.

d) either *A Farewell to Arms* or *Tom Sawyer* is selected.

e) *Moby Dick* is not selected.

25. *Personal Characteristics* An individual can be classified as male or female with red, brown, black, or blond hair and with brown, blue, or green eyes.

a) How many different classifications are possible (for example, male, red-headed, blue-eyed)?

b) Construct a tree diagram to determine the sample space.

c) If each outcome is equally likely, determine the probability that the individual will be a male with black hair and blue eyes.

d) Determine the probability that the individual will be a female with blond hair.

26. *Mendel Revisited* A pea plant must have exactly one of each of the following pairs of traits: short (*s*) or tall (*t*); round (*r*) or wrinkled (*w*) seeds; yellow (*y*) or green (*g*) peas; and white (*wh*) or purple (*p*) flowers (for example, short, wrinkled, green pea with white flowers).

a) How many different classifications of pea plants are possible?

b) Use a tree diagram to determine all the classifications possible.

c) If each characteristic is equally likely, find the probability that the pea plant will have round peas.

d) Determine the probability that the pea plant will be short, have wrinkled seeds, have yellow seeds, and have purple flowers.

Challenge Problems/Group Activities

27. *Three Chips* Suppose that a bag contains one white chip and two red chips. Two chips are going to be selected at random from the bag *with replacement*.

a) What is the probability of selecting a white chip from the bag on the first selection?

b) What is the probability of selecting a red chip from the bag on the first selection?

c) Are the outcomes of selecting a white chip and selecting a red chip on the first selection equally likely? Explain.

d) The sample space when two chips are selected from the bag with replacement is ww, wr, rw, rr. Do you believe that the probability of selecting ww is greater than, equal to, or less than the probability of selecting rr? Explain.

28. *Thumbtacks* A thumbtack is dropped on a concrete floor. Assume that the thumbtack can land only point up (u) or point down (d), as shown in the figure below.

If two thumbtacks are dropped, one after the other, the tree diagram below can be used to show the possible outcomes.

First Thumbtack	Second Thumbtack	Sample Space
u	u	u u
	d	u d
d	u	d u
	d	d d

a) Do you believe that the outcomes of the thumbtack landing point up and the thumbtack landing point down are equally likely? Explain.

b) List the sample points in the sample space of this experiment.

c) Do you believe that the probability that both thumbtacks land point up (*uu*) is the same as the probability that both thumbtacks land point down (*dd*)? Explain.

d) Can you compute the theoretical probability of a thumbtack landing point up and the theoretical probability of a thumbtack landing point down? Explain.

e) Obtain a box of thumbtacks and drop the thumbtacks out of the box with care. Determine the empirical probability of a thumbtack landing point up when dropped and the empirical probability of a thumbtack landing point down when dropped.

Recreational Mathematics

29. *Ties* All my ties are red except two. All my ties are blue except two. All my ties are brown except two. How many ties do I have?

30. *Rock Faces* An experiment consists of 3 parts: flipping a coin, tossing a rock, and rolling a die. If the sample space consists of 60 sample points, determine the number of faces on the rock.

Jumble For Exercises 31–32, refer to the Recreational Math box on page 711. Determine

a) *the number of possible arrangements of the letters given.*

b) *the word when the letters are placed in the proper order.*

31. RAHIC

32. STEABK

OR and *AND* Problems

▲ *Selecting items from a restaurant menu often requires an understanding of the words* or *and* and.

Every day we see and interpret the words **or** and **and**. For example, in a court case a judge may sentence a person to five years in prison *and* payment of a $100,000 fine. Or a judge may sentence a person to either 1 night in jail *or* payment of a $100 fine. When you go into a restaurant, the menu may indicate that you should select soup *or* salad, *and* an entrée, *and* a dessert. In this section, we will learn to solve probability problems involving the words *or* and *and*.

Why *This is Important* Many real-life situations involve the words *or* and *and*. For example, what is the probability that a family planning to have 3 children has 3 boys (a boy *and* a boy *and* a boy)?

In Section 12.5, we showed how to work probability problems by constructing sample spaces. Often it is inconvenient or too time consuming to solve a problem by first constructing a sample space. For example, if an experiment consists of selecting two cards with replacement from a deck of 52 cards, there would be 52 · 52 or 2704 points in the sample space. Trying to list all these sample points could take hours. In this section, we learn how to solve *compound probability* problems that contain the words *and* or *or* without constructing a sample space.

Or Problems

The *or probability problem* requires obtaining a "successful" outcome for *at least one* of the given events. For example, suppose that we roll one die and we are interested in finding the probability of rolling an even number *or* a number greater than 4. For this situation, rolling either a 2, 4, or 6 (an even number) or a 5 or 6 (a number greater than 4) would be considered successful. Note that the number 6 satisfies both criteria. Since 4 of the 6 numbers meet the criteria (the 2, 4, 5, and 6), the probability of rolling an even number *or* a number greater than 4 is $\frac{4}{6}$ or $\frac{2}{3}$.

A formula for finding the probability of event A or event B, symbolized $P(A \text{ or } B)$, follows.

Probability of *A* or *B*

To determine the probability of A or B, use the following formula.

$$P(A \text{ or } B) = P(A) + P(B) - P(A \text{ and } B)$$

Since we add (and subtract) probabilities to find $P(A \text{ or } B)$, this formula is sometimes referred to as the *addition formula*. We explain the use of the *or* formula in Example 1.

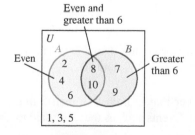

Even and greater than 6

Even

Greater than 6

1, 3, 5

Figure 12.13

Example 1 *Using the Addition Formula*

Each of the numbers 1, 2, 3, 4, 5, 6, 7, 8, 9, and 10 is written on a separate piece of paper. The 10 pieces of paper are then placed in a hat, and one piece is randomly selected. Determine the probability that the piece of paper selected contains an even number or a number greater than 6.

Solution We are asked to find the probability that the number selected is *even* or is *greater than 6*. Let's use set A to represent the statement "the number is even" and set B to represent the statement "the number is greater than 6." Figure 12.13 is a

Venn diagram, as introduced in Chapter 2, with sets *A* (even) and *B* (greater than 6). There are a total of 10 numbers, of which five are even (2, 4, 6, 8, and 10). Thus, the probability of selecting an even number is $\frac{5}{10}$. Four numbers are greater than 6: the 7, 8, 9, and 10. Thus, the probability of selecting a number greater than 6 is $\frac{4}{10}$. Two numbers are both even and greater than 6: the 8 and 10. Thus, the probability of selecting a number that is both even and greater than 6 is $\frac{2}{10}$.

If we substitute the appropriate statements for *A* and *B* in the formula, we obtain

$$P(A \text{ or } B) = P(A) + P(B) - P(A \text{ and } B)$$

$$P\left(\begin{array}{c}\text{even or}\\\text{greater than 6}\end{array}\right) = P(\text{even}) + P\left(\begin{array}{c}\text{greater}\\\text{than 6}\end{array}\right) - P\left(\begin{array}{c}\text{even and}\\\text{greater than 6}\end{array}\right)$$

$$= \frac{5}{10} + \frac{4}{10} - \frac{2}{10}$$

$$= \frac{7}{10}$$

Thus, the probability of selecting an even number or a number greater than 6 is $\frac{7}{10}$. The seven numbers that are even or greater than 6 are 2, 4, 6, 7, 8, 9, and 10. ■

Example 1 illustrates that when finding the probability of *A* or *B*, we add the probabilities of events *A* and *B* and then subtract the probability of both events occurring simultaneously.

Example 2 *Using the Addition Formula*

Consider the same sample space, the numbers 1 through 10, as in Example 1. If one piece of paper is selected, determine the probability that it contains a number less than 5 or a number greater than 8.

Solution Let *A* represent the statement "the number is less than 5" and *B* represent the statement "the number is greater than 8." A Venn diagram illustrating these statements is shown in Figure 12.14.

$$P(\text{number is less than 5}) = \frac{4}{10}$$

$$P(\text{number is greater than 8}) = \frac{2}{10}$$

Since there are no numbers that are *both* less than 5 and greater than 8, *P*(number is less than 5 and greater than 8) = 0. Therefore,

$$P\left(\begin{array}{c}\text{number is}\\\text{less than 5}\\\text{or greater}\\\text{than 8}\end{array}\right) = P\left(\begin{array}{c}\text{number is}\\\text{less than 5}\end{array}\right) + P\left(\begin{array}{c}\text{number is}\\\text{greater than 8}\end{array}\right) - P\left(\begin{array}{c}\text{number is}\\\text{less than 5}\\\text{and greater}\\\text{than 8}\end{array}\right)$$

$$= \frac{4}{10} + \frac{2}{10} - 0 = \frac{6}{10} = \frac{3}{5}$$

Thus, the probability of selecting a number less than 5 or greater than 8 is $\frac{3}{5}$. The six numbers that are less than 5 or greater than 8 are 1, 2, 3, 4, 9, and 10. ■

In Example 2, it is impossible to select a number that is both less than 5 *and* greater than 8 when only one number is to be selected. Events such as these are said to be *mutually exclusive*.

Figure 12.14

The ace of hearts is
both an ace and a heart.

Definition: **Mutually Exclusive**

Two events A and B are **mutually exclusive** if it is impossible for both events to occur simultaneously.

If events A and B are mutually exclusive, then $P(A \text{ and } B) = 0$ and the addition formula simplifies to $P(A \text{ or } B) = P(A) + P(B)$.

┌ Example **3**   *Probability of A or B*

One card is selected from a standard deck of playing cards. Determine whether the following pairs of events are mutually exclusive and determine $P(A \text{ or } B)$.

a) A = an ace, B = a 9

b) A = an ace, B = a heart

c) A = a red card, B = a black card

d) A = a picture card, B = a red card

Solution

a) There are four aces and four 9's in a standard deck of 52 cards. It is impossible to select both an ace and a 9 when only one card is selected. Therefore, these events are mutually exclusive.

$$P(\text{ace or } 9) = P(\text{ace}) + P(9) = \frac{4}{52} + \frac{4}{52} = \frac{8}{52} = \frac{2}{13}$$

b) There are 4 aces and 13 hearts in a standard deck of 52 cards. One card, the ace of hearts, is both an ace and a heart. Therefore, these events are not mutually exclusive.

$$P(\text{ace}) = \frac{4}{52} \qquad P(\text{heart}) = \frac{13}{52} \qquad P(\text{ace and heart}) = \frac{1}{52}$$

$$P(\text{ace or heart}) = P(\text{ace}) + P(\text{heart}) - P(\text{ace and heart})$$

$$= \frac{4}{52} + \frac{13}{52} - \frac{1}{52}$$

$$= \frac{16}{52} = \frac{4}{13}$$

c) There are 26 red cards and 26 black cards in a standard deck of 52 cards. It is impossible to select one card that is both a red card and a black card. Therefore, the events are mutually exclusive.

$$P(\text{red or black}) = P(\text{red}) + P(\text{black})$$

$$= \frac{26}{52} + \frac{26}{52} = \frac{52}{52} = 1$$

Since $P(\text{red or black}) = 1$, a red card or a black card must be selected.

d) There are 12 picture cards in a standard deck of 52 cards. Six of the 12 picture cards are red (the jacks, queens, and kings of hearts and diamonds). Thus, selecting a picture card and a red card are not mutually exclusive.

$$P\left(\begin{array}{c}\text{picture card}\\\text{or red card}\end{array}\right) = P\left(\begin{array}{c}\text{picture}\\\text{card}\end{array}\right) + P\left(\begin{array}{c}\text{red}\\\text{card}\end{array}\right) - P\left(\begin{array}{c}\text{picture card}\\\text{and red card}\end{array}\right)$$

$$= \frac{12}{52} + \frac{26}{52} - \frac{6}{52}$$

$$= \frac{32}{52} = \frac{8}{13}$$

And Problems

A second type of probability problem is the *and probability problem*, which requires obtaining a favorable outcome in *each* of the given events. For example, suppose that *two* cards are to be selected from a deck of cards and we are interested in the probability of selecting two aces (one ace *and* then a second ace). Only if *both* cards selected are aces would this experiment be considered successful. A formula for finding the probability of events A and B, symbolized $P(A \text{ and } B)$, follows.

Probability of *A* and *B*

To determine the probability of A and B, use the following formula.

$$P(A \text{ and } B) = P(A) \cdot P(B)$$

Since we multiply to find $P(A \text{ and } B)$, this formula is sometimes referred to as the *multiplication formula*. When using the multiplication formula, we **always assume that event A has occurred when calculating $P(B)$** because we are determining the probability of obtaining a favorable outcome in both of the given events.*

Unless we specify otherwise, $P(A \text{ and } B)$ indicates that we are determining the probability that event A occurs *and then* event B occurs (in that order). Consider a bag that contains three chips: 1 red chip, 1 blue chip, and 1 green chip. Suppose that two chips are selected from the bag with replacement. The tree diagram and sample space for the experiment are shown in Fig. 12.15. There are nine possible outcomes for the two selections, as indicated in the sample space.

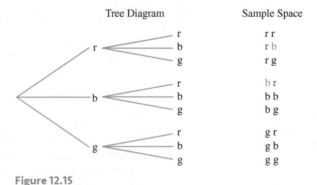

Figure 12.15

Note that the probability of selecting a red chip followed by a blue chip (rb), indicated by $P(\text{red and blue})$, is $\frac{1}{9}$. The probability of selecting a red chip and a blue chip, in any order (rb or br), is $\frac{2}{9}$. In this section, when we ask for $P(A \text{ and } B)$, it means the probability of event A occurring *and then* event B occurring, in that order.

Example 4 *An Experiment with Replacement*

Two cards are to be selected *with replacement* from a deck of cards. Determine the probability that two spades will be selected.

Solution Since the deck of 52 cards contains thirteen spades, the probability of selecting a spade on the first draw is $\frac{13}{52}$. The card selected is then returned to the deck. Therefore, the probability of selecting a spade on the second draw remains $\frac{13}{52}$.

---

*$P(B)$, assuming that event A has occurred, may be denoted $P(B|A)$, which is read "the probability of B, given A." We will discuss this type of probability (conditional probability) further in section 12.7

If we let A represent the selection of the first spade and B represent the selection of the second spade, the formula may be written as follows.

$$P(A \text{ and } B) = P(A) \cdot P(B)$$
$$P(2 \text{ spades}) = P(\text{spade 1 } and \text{ spade 2}) = P(\text{spade 1}) \cdot P(\text{spade 2})$$
$$= \frac{13}{52} \cdot \frac{13}{52}$$
$$= \frac{1}{4} \cdot \frac{1}{4} = \frac{1}{16}$$

Example 5 *An Experiment without Replacement*

Two cards are to be selected *without replacement* from a deck of cards. Determine the probability that two spades will be selected.

Solution This example is similar to Example 4. However, this time we are doing the experiment without replacing the first card selected to the deck before selecting the second card.

The probability of selecting a spade on the first draw is $\frac{13}{52}$. When calculating the probability of selecting the second spade, we must assume that the first spade has been selected. Once this first spade has been selected, only 51 cards, including 12 spades, remain in the deck. The probability of selecting a spade on the second draw becomes $\frac{12}{51}$. The probability of selecting two spades without replacement is

$$P(2 \text{ spades}) = P(\text{spade 1}) \cdot P(\text{spade 2})$$
$$= \frac{13}{52} \cdot \frac{12}{51}$$
$$= \frac{1}{4} \cdot \frac{4}{17} = \frac{1}{17}$$

Now we introduce *independent events*.

Definition: **Independent Events**

Event A and event B are **independent events** if the occurrence of either event in no way affects the probability of occurrence of the other event.

Rolling dice and tossing coins are examples of independent events. In Example 4, the events are independent since the first card was returned to the deck. The probability of selecting a spade on the second draw was not affected by the first selection. The events in Example 5 are not independent since the probability of the selection of the second spade was affected by removing the first spade selected from the deck. Such events are called *dependent events*. *Experiments done with replacement will result in independent events, and those done without replacement will result in dependent events.*

Example 6 *Independent or Dependent Events?*

One hundred people attended a charity benefit to raise money for cancer research. Three people in attendance will be selected at random without replacement, and each will be awarded one door prize. Are the events of selecting the three people who will be awarded the door prize independent or dependent events?

Solution   The events are dependent since each time one person is selected, it changes the probability of the next person being selected. In the first selection, the probability that a specific individual is selected is $\frac{1}{100}$. If that person is not selected first, the probability that the specific person is selected second changes to $\frac{1}{99}$. In general, in any experiment in which two or more items are selected *without replacement*, the events will be dependent.   ∎

The multiplication formula may be extended to more than two events, as illustrated in Example 7.

Example 7   *Drug Reaction*

A new medicine was given to a sample of 25 of Dr. Cleary's patients with flu symptoms. Of the total, 19 patients reacted favorably, 2 reacted unfavorably, and 4 were unaffected. Three of these patients are selected at random. Determine the probability of each of the following.

a) All three reacted favorably.

b) The first patient reacted favorably, the second patient reacted unfavorably, and the third patient was unaffected.

c) No patient reacted favorably.

d) At least one patient reacted favorably.

Solution   Each time a patient is selected, the number of patients remaining decreases by one.

a) The probability that the first patient reacted favorably is $\frac{19}{25}$. If the first patient reacted favorably, of the 24 remaining patients only 18 patients are left who reacted favorably. The probability of selecting a second patient who reacted favorably is $\frac{18}{24}$. If the second patient reacted favorably, only 17 patients are left who reacted favorably. The probability of selecting a third patient who reacted favorably is $\frac{17}{23}$.

$$P\begin{pmatrix}\text{three patients}\\\text{reacted}\\\text{favorably}\end{pmatrix} = P\begin{pmatrix}\text{first patient}\\\text{reacted}\\\text{favorably}\end{pmatrix} \cdot P\begin{pmatrix}\text{second patient}\\\text{reacted}\\\text{favorably}\end{pmatrix} \cdot P\begin{pmatrix}\text{third patient}\\\text{reacted}\\\text{favorably}\end{pmatrix}$$

$$= \frac{19}{25} \cdot \frac{18}{24} \cdot \frac{17}{23} = \frac{969}{2300}$$

b) The probability that the first patient reacted favorably is $\frac{19}{25}$. Once a patient is selected, there are only 24 patients remaining. Two of the remaining 24 patients reacted unfavorably. Thus, the probability that the second patient reacted unfavorably is $\frac{2}{24}$. After the second patient is selected, there are 23 remaining patients, of which 4 were unaffected. The probability that the third patient was unaffected is therefore $\frac{4}{23}$.

$$P\begin{pmatrix}\text{first patient reacted favorably, the}\\\text{second patient reacted unfavorably, and}\\\text{the third patient was unaffected}\end{pmatrix}$$

$$= P\begin{pmatrix}\text{first patient}\\\text{reacted}\\\text{favorably}\end{pmatrix} \cdot P\begin{pmatrix}\text{second patient}\\\text{reacted}\\\text{unfavorably}\end{pmatrix} \cdot P\begin{pmatrix}\text{third patient}\\\text{was}\\\text{unaffected}\end{pmatrix}$$

$$= \frac{19}{25} \cdot \frac{2}{24} \cdot \frac{4}{23} = \frac{19}{1725}$$

c) If none of the patients reacted favorably, the patients either reacted unfavorably or were unaffected. Six patients did not react favorably (2 reacted unfavorably and 4 were unaffected). The probability that the first patient selected did not react favorably is $\frac{6}{25}$. After the first patient is selected, 5 of the remaining 24 patients did not react favorably. After the second patient is selected, 4 of the remaining 23 patients did not react favorably.

$$P\left(\begin{array}{c}\text{none}\\\text{reacted}\\\text{favorably}\end{array}\right) = P\left(\begin{array}{c}\text{first patient}\\\text{did not react}\\\text{favorably}\end{array}\right) \cdot P\left(\begin{array}{c}\text{second patient}\\\text{did not react}\\\text{favorably}\end{array}\right) \cdot P\left(\begin{array}{c}\text{third patient}\\\text{did not react}\\\text{favorably}\end{array}\right)$$

$$= \frac{6}{25} \cdot \frac{5}{24} \cdot \frac{4}{23} = \frac{1}{115}$$

d) In Section 12.5, we learned that

$$P(\text{event happening at least once}) = 1 - P(\text{event does not happen})$$

In part (c), we found that the probability of selecting three patients none of whom reacted favorably was $\frac{1}{115}$. Therefore, the probability that at least one of the patients selected reacted favorably can be found as follows.

$$P\left(\begin{array}{c}\text{at least one of the three}\\\text{patients reacted favorably}\end{array}\right) = 1 - P\left(\begin{array}{c}\text{none of the three}\\\text{patients reacted favorably}\end{array}\right)$$

$$= 1 - \frac{1}{115} = \frac{115}{115} - \frac{1}{115} = \frac{114}{115}$$

SECTION 12.6 Exercises

Warm Up Exercises

In Exercises 1–10, fill in the blank with an appropriate word, phrase, or symbol(s).

1. Probability problems that contain the words *and* or *or* are considered _____ probability problems.

2. Probability problems that require obtaining a successful outcome for at least one of the given events are _____ probability problems.

3. Probability problems that require obtaining a favorable outcome in each of the given events are _____ probability problems.

4. If it is impossible for two events *A* and *B* to occur simultaneously, then the events are considered to be _____ exclusive.

5. For two events *A* and *B*, if the occurrence of either event in no way affects the probability of the occurrence of the other event, then the two events are considered to be _____ events.

6. For two events *A* and *B*, if the occurrence of either event has an effect on the probability of the occurrence of the other event, then the two events are considered to be _____ events.

7. Experiments done with replacement will result in _____ events.

8. Experiments done without replacement will result in _____ events.

9. The formula for finding the probability of event *A* or event *B* is $P(A \text{ or } B) = $ _____.

10. The formula for finding the probability of event *A* and event *B* is $P(A \text{ and } B) = $ _____.

Practice the Skills

In Exercises 11–14, determine the indicated probability.

11. If $P(A) = 0.8$, $P(B) = 0.4$, and $P(A \text{ and } B) = 0.5$, determine $P(A \text{ or } B)$.

12. If $P(A \text{ or } B) = 0.9$, $P(A) = 0.8$, and $P(B) = 0.3$, determine $P(A \text{ and } B)$.

13. If $P(A \text{ or } B) = 0.7$, $P(A) = 0.6$, and $P(A \text{ and } B) = 0.3$, determine $P(B)$.

14. If $P(A \text{ or } B) = 0.6$, $P(B) = 0.3$, and $P(A \text{ and } B) = 0.1$, determine $P(A)$.

15. *Exam Preparation* Professor Connell is in charge of a program to prepare students for a high school equivalency exam. Records show that the probability that a student in the program needs help in mathematics is 0.7, the probability that a student needs help in English is 0.6, and the probability that a student needs help in both mathematics and English is 0.55. Determine the probability that a student in the program needs help in mathematics or English.

16. *Car Repair* The manager at Arango Automotive has found that the probability that a car brought into the shop requires an oil change is 0.6, the probability that a car brought into the shop requires brake repair is 0.2, and the probability that a car requires both an oil change and brake repair is 0.1. For a car brought into the shop, determine the probability that the car will require an oil change or brake repair.

Roll a Die In Exercises 17–20, a single die is rolled one time. Determine the probability of rolling

17. a 2 or 6.

18. an odd number or a number greater than 4.

19. a number greater than 4 or less than 2.

20. a number greater than 3 or less than 5.

Select One Card In Exercises 21–26, one card is selected from a deck of playing cards. Determine the probability of selecting

21. an ace or a 4.

22. a jack or a club.

23. a picture card or a black card.

24. a club or a red card.

25. a card less than 6 or a club. (*Note:* The ace is considered a low card.)

26. a card greater than 9 or a black card.

Problem Solving

Select Two Cards In Exercises 27–34, a board game uses the deck of 20 cards shown.

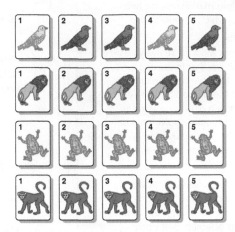

Two cards are selected at random from this deck. Determine the probability of the following

    a) *with replacement.*

    b) *without replacement.*

27. They both show lions.

28. They both show the number 3.

29. The first shows a monkey, and the second shows a bird.

30. The first shows a 2, and the second shows a 4.

31. The first shows a yellow bird, and the second shows a frog.

32. They both show even numbers.

33. Neither shows an even number.

34. The first shows a lion, and the second shows a red bird.

Select One Card In the deck of cards used in Exercises 27–34, if one card is drawn, determine the probability that the card shows

35. a monkey or an even number.

36. a yellow bird or a number greater than 3.

37. a lion or a 2.

38. a red bird or an even number.

Two Spins In Exercises 39–48, assume that the pointer cannot land on the line and that each spin is independent. If the pointer in Fig. 12.16 is spun twice, determine the probability that the pointer lands on

39. red on both spins.   **40.** red and then yellow.

Figure 12.16

Two Spins If the pointer in Fig. 12.17 is spun twice, determine the probability that the pointer lands on

41. green and then red.   **42.** red on both spins.

Figure 12.17

Two Spins If the pointer in Fig. 12.18 is spun twice, determine the probability that the pointer lands on

43. red on both spins.

44. a color other than green on both spins.

Figure 12.18

Two Spins In Exercises 45–48, assume that the pointer in Fig. 12.16 is spun and then the pointer in Fig. 12.17 is spun. Determine the probability of the pointers landing on

45. red on both spins.

46. yellow on the first spin and red on the second spin.

47. a color other than red on both spins.

48. yellow on the first spin and a color other than yellow on the second spin.

Selecting an Envelope In Exercises 49–56, consider the colored envelopes shown below.

If one of the envelopes is selected at random, determine the probability that

49. a yellow or a blue envelope is selected.

50. an envelope other than a red envelope is selected.

If two envelopes are selected at random, with replacement, determine the probability that

51. both are red envelopes.

52. the first is a blue envelope and the second is a yellow envelope.

If three envelopes are selected at random, without replacement, determine the probability that

53. they are all red envelopes.

54. none is a red envelope.

55. the first is a red envelope, the second is a blue envelope, and the third is a blue envelope.

56. the first is a red envelope, the second is a green envelope, and the third is a red envelope.

Having a Family In Exercises 57–60, a couple has three children. Assuming independence and that the probability of a boy is $\frac{1}{2}$, determine the probability that

57. all three children are girls.

58. all three children are boys.

59. the youngest child is a boy and the two older children are girls.

60. the youngest child is a girl, the middle child is a boy, and the oldest child is a girl.

61. a) *Five Children* The Martinos plan to have five children. Determine the probability that all their children will be boys. (Assume that $P(\text{boy}) = \frac{1}{2}$ and assume independence.)

  b) If their first four children are boys and Mrs. Martino is expecting another child, what is the probability that the fifth child will be a boy?

62. a) *The Probability of a Girl* The Bronsons plan to have eight children. Determine the probability that all their children will be girls. (Assume that $P(\text{girl}) = \frac{1}{2}$ and assume independence.)

  b) If their first seven children are girls and Mrs. Bronson is expecting another child, what is the probability that the eighth child will be a girl?

Books *Angel Sanchez has seven books on a shelf: 4 mysteries, 2 science fiction books, and 1 biography. In Exercises 63–66, two books will be selected at random. Determine the probability of selecting each of the following*

    a) *with replacement.*

    b) *without replacement.*

63. a mystery and then a biography

64. no science fiction books

65. at least one science fiction book

66. two biographies

Health Insurance *A sample of 75 people yielded the following information about their health insurance.*

Number of People	Type of Insurance
33	Managed care plan
27	Traditional insurance
15	No insurance

Two people who provided information for the table were selected at random, without replacement. Determine the probability that

67. neither had traditional insurance.

68. they both had a managed care plan.

69. at least one had traditional insurance.

70. the first had traditional insurance and the second had a managed care plan.

Hiring An Attorney *A sample of 40 people who recently hired an attorney yielded the following information about their attorneys.*

Number of People	Would You Recommend Your Attorney to a Friend
23	Yes
7	No
10	Not sure

Three people who provided information for the table were selected at random. Determine the probability that

71. they would all recommend their attorneys.

72. the first would not recommend the attorney, but the second and third would recommend their attorneys.

73. the first two would not recommend their attorneys, and the third is not sure if he or she would recommend the attorney.

74. the first would recommend the attorney, but the second and third would not recommend their attorneys.

A New Medicine *In Exercises 75–78, a new medicine was given to a sample of 100 hospital patients. Of the total, 70 patients reacted favorably, 10 reacted unfavorably, and 20 were unaffected by the drug. Assume that this sample is representative of the entire population. If this medicine is given to Mr. and Mrs. Rivera and their son Carlos, what is the probability of each of the following? (Assume independence.)*

75. Mrs. Rivera reacts favorably.

76. Mr. and Mrs. Rivera react favorably, and Carlos is unaffected.

77. All three react favorably.

78. No one reacts favorably.

Multiple-Choice Exam *In Exercises 79–84, each question of a five-question multiple-choice exam has four possible answers. Gurshawn Salk picks an answer at random for each question. Determine the probability that he selects the correct answer on*

79. any one question.

80. only the first question.

81. only the third and fourth questions.

82. all five questions.

83. none of the questions.

84. at least one of the questions.

A Slot Machine *In Exercises 85–88, consider a slot machine.*

Most people who play slot machines end up losing money because the machines are designed to favor the casino (the house). There are 22 positions on each reel. Assume that the following is a list of the number of symbols of each type on each of the three reels and each symbol has the same chance of occurring (which is not the case; see the Mathematics Today on page 722).

Pictures on Reels		Reels	
	1	**2**	**3**
Cherries 🍒	2	5	4
Oranges ⬤	5	4	5
Plums ◖	6	4	4
Bells ◁	3	4	4
Melons ⬤	3	2	3
Bars BAR	2	2	1
7s 7	1	1	1

For this slot machine, assuming that the wheels are independent, determine the probability of obtaining

85. an orange on the first reel.

86. bells on all three reels.

87. no bars.

88. three 7's.

Two Wheels *In Exercises 89–92, suppose that you spin the following double wheel.*

Assuming that the wheels are independent and each outcome is equally likely, determine the probability that you get

89. blue on both wheels.

90. red on the outer wheel and blue on the inner wheel.

91. red on neither wheel.

92. red on at least one wheel.

Hitting a Target *In Exercises 93–96, the probability that a heat-seeking torpedo will hit its target is 0.4. If the first torpedo hits its target, the probability that the second torpedo will hit the target increases to 0.9 because of the extra heat generated by the first explosion. If two heat-seeking torpedoes are fired at a target, determine the probability that*

93. neither hits the target.

94. the first hits the target and the second misses the target.

95. both hit the target.

96. the first misses the target and the second hits the target.

97. ***Polygenetic Afflictions*** Certain birth defects and syndromes are *polygenetic* in nature. Typically, the chance that an offspring will be born with a polygenetic affliction is small. However, once an offspring is born with the affliction, the probability that future offspring of the same parents will be born with the same affliction increases. Let's assume that the probability of a child being born with affliction *A* is 0.001. If a child is born with this affliction, the probability of a future child being born with the same affliction becomes 0.04.

   a) Are the events of the births of two children in the same family with affliction *A* independent?

   b) A couple plans to have one child. Determine the probability that the child will be born with this affliction.

A couple plans to have two children. Use the information provided to determine the probability that

   c) both children will be born with the affliction.

   d) the first will be born with the affliction and the second will not.

   e) the first will not be born with the affliction and the second will.

   f) neither will be born with the affliction.

98. ***Lottery Ticket*** In a bin are an equal number of balls marked with the digits 0, 1, 2, 3, . . . , 9. Three balls are to be selected from the bin, one after the other, at random with replacement to make the winning three-digit lottery number. Ms. Jones has a lottery ticket with a three-digit number in the range 000 to 999. Determine the probability that Ms. Jones's number is the winning number.

Chance of an Audit *In Exercises 99–102, assume that 36 in every 1000 people in the $34,000–$82,400 income bracket are audited yearly. Assuming that the returns to be audited are selected at random and each year's selections are independent of the previous year's selections, determine the probability that a person in this income bracket will be audited*

99. this year.

100. the next two years in succession.

101. this year but not next year.

102. neither this year nor next year.

Challenge Problems/Group Activities

103. *Picking Chips* A bag contains five red chips, three blue chips, and two yellow chips. Two chips are selected from the bag without replacement. Determine the probability that two chips of the same color are selected.

104. *Peso Coins* Ron has ten coins from Mexico: three 1-peso coins, one 2-peso coin, two 5-peso coins, one 10-peso coin, and three 20-peso coins. He selects two coins at random without replacement. Assuming that each coin is equally likely to be selected, determine the probability that Ron selects at least one 1-peso coin.

105. *A Fair Game?* Two playing cards are dealt to you from a well-shuffled standard deck of 52 cards. If either card is a diamond or if both are diamonds, you win; otherwise, you lose. Determine whether this game favors you, is fair, or favors the dealer. Explain your answer.

106. *Picture Card Probability* You have three cards: an ace, a king, and a queen. A friend shuffles the cards, selects two of them at random, and discards the third. You ask your friend to show you a picture card, and she turns over the king. What is the probability that she also has the queen?

Recreational Mathematics

A Different Die For exercises 107–110, consider a six-sided die that has 1 dot on one side, 2 dots on two sides, and 3 dots on three sides.

If the die is rolled twice, determine the probability of rolling

107. two 2's.   **108.** two 3's.

If the die is rolled only once, determine the probability of rolling

109. an even number or a number less than 3.

110. an odd number or a number greater than 1.

Internet/Research Activity

111. Girolamo Cardano (1501–1576) wrote *Liber de Ludo Aleae*, which is considered to be the first book on probability. Cardano had a number of different vocations. Do research and write a paper on the life and accomplishments of Girolamo Cardano.

SECTION 12.7 Conditional Probability

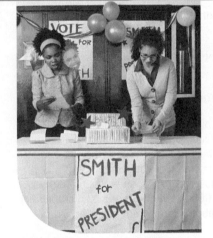

▲ *Conditional probability may play a role in a candidate's bid for re-election.*

Often the probability of an event occurring may depend on one or more other events that previously occurred. For example, the probability of a candidate being re-elected may depend on the candidate's voting record or the current state of the economy. Or the probability that a salesperson is successful in selling a particular item may depend on whether the customer is a male or female. Probability problems like these, where the outcome of a previous event affects the probability of a later event, are called conditional probability problems.

Why *This is Important* We consider and use conditional probabilities all the time without realizing it, as you will see from the examples in this section.

In Section 12.6, we learned when two events are *dependent*, the occurrence of the first event, A, affected the probability of the second event, B, occurring. When we calculated $P(A \text{ and } B)$, when we determined the probability of event B, we assumed that event A occurred. That is, we calculated the probability of event B, given event A. The probability of event B, given event A, is called a *conditional probability*. The definition of conditional probability follows.

Definition: Conditional Probability

In general, the probability of event E_2 occurring, given that an event E_1 has happened (or will happen; the time relationship does not matter), is called a **conditional probability** and is written $P(E_2 | E_1)$.

The symbol $P(E_2 | E_1)$, read "the probability of E_2, given E_1," represents the probability of E_2 occurring, assuming that E_1 has already occurred (or will occur).

Example 1 *Using Conditional Probability*

A single card is selected from a deck of cards. Determine the probability it is a club, given that it is black.

Solution We are told that the card is black. Thus, only 26 cards are possible, of which 13 are clubs. Therefore,

$$P(\text{club} | \text{black}) \text{ or } P(\text{C} | \text{B}) = \frac{13}{26} = \frac{1}{2}$$

Example 2 *Girls in a Family*

A family has two children. Assuming that boys and girls are equally likely, determine the probability that the family has

a) two girls.

b) two girls if you know that at least one of the children is a girl.

c) two girls given that the older child is a girl.

Solution

a) To determine the probability that the family has two girls, we can determine the sample space of a family with two children. Then, from the sample space we can determine the probability that both children are girls. The sample space of two children can be determined by a tree diagram (see Fig. 12.19).

```
        1st Child   2nd Child    Sample Space

                    ──── B         BB
              B ────
                    ──── G         BG

                    ──── B         GB
              G ────
                    ──── G         GG
```

Figure 12.19

There are four possible equally likely outcomes: BB, BG, GB, and GG. Only one of the outcomes has two girls, GG. Thus,

$$P(2 \text{ girls}) = \frac{1}{4}$$

b) We are given that at least one of the children is a girl. Therefore, for this example the sample space is BG, GB, GG. Since there are three possibilities, of which only one has two girls, GG,

$$P(\text{both girls} | \text{at least one is a girl}) = \frac{1}{3}$$

c) If the older child is a girl, the sample space reduces to GB, GG. Thus,

$$P(\text{both girls} | \text{older child is a girl}) = \frac{1}{2}$$

A number of formulas can be used to find conditional probabilities. The one we will use follows on page 730.

Conditional Probability

For any two events, E_1 and E_2, the conditional probability, $P(E_2|E_1)$, is determined as follows.

$$P(E_2|E_1) = \frac{n(E_1 \text{ and } E_2)}{n(E_1)}$$

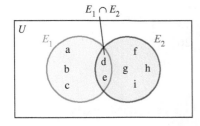

Figure 12.20

In the formula, $n(E_1 \text{ and } E_2)$ represents the number of sample points common to both event 1 and event 2, and $n(E_1)$ is the number of sample points in event E_1, the given event. Since the intersection of E_1 and E_2, symbolized $E_1 \cap E_2$, represents the sample points common to both E_1 and E_2, the formula can also be expressed as

$$P(E_2|E_1) = \frac{n(E_1 \cap E_2)}{n(E_1)}$$

Figure 12.20 is helpful in explaining conditional probability.

Here, the number of elements in E_1 is five, the number of elements in E_2 is six, and the number of elements in both E_1 and E_2, or $E_1 \cap E_2$, is two.

$$P(E_2|E_1) = \frac{n(E_1 \text{ and } E_2)}{n(E_1)} = \frac{2}{5}$$

Thus, for this situation, the probability of selecting an element from E_2, given that the element is in E_1, is $\frac{2}{5}$.

Example 3 Using the Conditional Probability Formula

Two hundred and fifty patients who had knee, hip, or heart surgery were asked whether they were satisfied, dissatisfied, or neutral regarding the results of their surgery. The responses are given in the table below.

Surgery	Satisfied	Dissatisfied	Total
Knee	70	25	95
Hip	90	15	105
Heart	45	5	50
Total	205	45	250

If one person from the 250 patients surveyed is selected at random, determine the probability that the person

a) was satisfied with the results of the surgery.

b) was satisfied with the results of the surgery, given that the person had knee surgery.

c) was dissatisfied with the results of the surgery, given that the person had hip surgery.

d) had heart surgery, given that the person was dissatisfied with the results of the surgery.

Solution

a) The total number of patients is 250, of which 205 were satisfied with the results of the surgery.

$$P(\text{satisfied with the results of the surgery}) = \frac{205}{250} = \frac{41}{50}$$

b) We are given that the person had knee surgery. Thus, we have a conditional probability problem. Let E_1 be the given information "the person had knee surgery." Let E_2 be "the person was satisfied with the results of the surgery." We are being asked to determine $P(E_2|E_1)$. The number of people who had knee surgery, $n(E_1)$, is 95. The number of people who had knee surgery and were satisfied with the results of the surgery, $n(E_1 \text{ and } E_2)$, is 70. Thus,

$$P(E_2|E_1) = \frac{n(E_1 \text{ and } E_2)}{n(E_1)} = \frac{70}{95} = \frac{14}{19}$$

c) We are given that the person had hip surgery. Thus, we have a conditional probability problem. Let E_1 be the given information "the person had hip surgery." Let E_2 be "the person was dissatisfied with the results of the surgery." We are asked to find $P(E_2|E_1)$. The number of people who had hip surgery, $n(E_1)$, is 105. The number of people who had hip surgery and were dissatisfied with the results of the surgery, $n(E_1 \text{ and } E_2)$, is 15. Thus,

$$P(E_2|E_1) = \frac{n(E_1 \text{ and } E_2)}{n(E_1)} = \frac{15}{105} = \frac{1}{7}$$

d) We are given that the person was dissatisfied with the results of the surgery. Thus, we have a conditional probability problem. Let E_1 be the given information "the person was dissatisfied with the results of the surgery." Let E_2 be "the person had heart surgery." We are asked to determine $P(E_2|E_1)$. The number of people who were dissatisfied with the results of the surgery, $n(E_1)$, is 45. The number of people who were dissatisfied with the results of the surgery and had heart surgery, $n(E_1 \text{ and } E_2)$, is 5. Thus,

$$P(E_2|E_1) = \frac{n(E_1 \text{ and } E_2)}{n(E_1)} = \frac{5}{45} = \frac{1}{9}$$

In many of the examples, we used the words *given that*. Other words may be used instead. For example, in Example 3(b), the question could have been worded "was satisfied with their surgery *if* the person had knee surgery."

SECTION 12.7 *Exercises*

Warm Up Exercises

In Exercises 1–4, fill in the blank with an appropriate word, phrase, or symbol(s).

1. The probability of event E_2 occurring, given that event E_1 has happened, is called a(n) _____ probability.

2. The notation for the probability of E_2, given E_1, is _____.

3. If $n(E_1 \text{ and } E_2) = 4$ and $n(E_1) = 12$, then $P(E_2|E_1) =$ _____.

4. If $n(E_1 \text{ and } E_2) = 5$ and $n(E_1) = 22$, then $P(E_2|E_1) =$ _____.

Practice the Skills

Select a Circle In Exercises 5–10, consider the circles shown.

Assume that one circle is selected at random and each circle is equally likely to be selected. Determine the probability of selecting

5. a 3, given that the circle is orange.

6. a 5, given that the circle is yellow.

7. an even number, given that the circle is not orange.

8. a number less than 2, given that the number is less than 5.

9. a red number, given that the circle is orange.

10. a number greater than 4, given that the circle is yellow.

Select a Number In Exercises 11–16, consider the following figures.

Assume that one number from 1 to 7 is equally likely to be selected at random. Each number corresponds to one of the seven figures shown. Determine the probability of selecting

11. a triangle, given that an even number is selected.

12. a triangle, given that a number greater than or equal to 5 is selected.

13. a red figure, given that an even number is selected.

14. a red or a blue figure, given that an even number is selected.

15. a circle or square, given that a number less than 4 is selected.

16. a triangle, given that an odd number is selected.

Spin the Wheel In Exercises 17–24, consider the following wheel.

If the wheel is spun and each section is equally likely to stop under the pointer, determine the probability that the pointer lands on

17. a two, given that the color is purple.

18. an odd number, given that the color is red.

19. purple, given that the number is odd.

20. a number greater than 6, given that the color is red.

21. a number greater than 4, given that the color is purple.

22. an even number, given that the color is red or purple.

23. gold, given that the number is greater than 5.

24. gold, given that the number is greater than 10.

Money from a Hat In Exercises 25–28, assume that a hat contains four bills: a $1 bill, a $5 bill, a $10 bill, and a $20 bill. Two bills are to be selected at random with replacement. Construct a sample space as was done in Example 2 and determine the probability that

25. both bills are $1 bills.

26. both bills are $1 bills if the first selected is a $1 bill.

27. both bills are $5 bills if at least one of the bills is a $5 bill.

28. both bills have a value greater than a $5 bill if the second bill is a $10 bill.

Two Dice In Exercises 29–34, two dice are rolled one after the other. Construct a sample space and determine the probability that the sum of the dots on the dice total

29. 7.

30. 7 if the first die is a 1.

31. 7 if the first die is a 3.

32. an even number if the second die is a 2.

33. a number greater than 7 if the second die is a 5.

34. a 7 or 11 if the first die is a 5.

Problem Solving

Costliest Hurricanes In Exercises 35–40, use the following information concerning the nine costliest hurricanes to strike the U.S. mainland as of January 1, 2010.

Hurricane	Category	Damage (billions of dollars)
Katrina (2005)	3	81.0
Andrew (1992)	5	35.0
Wilma (2005)	3	20.6
Ike (2008)	2	18.0
Charley (2004)	4	14.0
Ivan (2004)	3	13.0
Rita (2005)	3	10.0
Hugo (1989)	4	9.7
Frances (2004)	2	8.9

Source: *National Oceanic and Atmospheric Administration*

If one hurricane from the list is selected at random, determine the probability that it

35. was a category 4.

36. had damages of at least $16 billion.

37. had damages of at least $20 billion, given that it was a category 3.

38. had damages of at least $15 billion, given that it was a category 2.

39. was a category 5, given that it had damages of at least $25 billion.

40. was a category 3, given that it had damages of at least $10 billion.

E-Z Pass *In Exercises 41–46, use the following table, which shows the number of cars and trucks that used the Pennsylvania Turnpike on a particular day. The number of cars and trucks that used, and did not use, the E-Z Pass on that same day was also recorded.*

E-Z Pass	Cars	Trucks	Total
Used	527	316	843
Did not use	935	683	1618
Total	1462	999	2461

If one of these vehicles is selected at random, determine the probability (as a decimal number rounded to four decimal places) that the

41. vehicle was a car.

42. vehicle used the E-Z Pass.

43. vehicle used the E-Z Pass, given that the vehicle was a car.

44. vehicle used the E-Z Pass, given that the vehicle was a truck.

45. vehicle was a car, given that the vehicle used the E-Z Pass.

46. vehicle was a truck, given that the vehicle used the E-Z Pass.

▲ *A sign on the Pennsylvania Turnpike.*

Sales Effectiveness *In Exercises 47–52, use the following information. Sales representatives at a car dealership were split into two groups. One group used an aggressive approach to sell a customer a new automobile. The other group used a passive approach. The following table summarizes the records for 650 customers.*

Approach	Sale	No Sale	Total
Aggressive	100	250	350
Passive	220	80	300
Total	320	330	650

If one of these customers is selected at random, determine the probability

47. that the aggressive approach was used.

48. of a sale.

49. of no sale, given that the passive approach was used.

50. of a sale, given that the aggressive approach was used.

51. of a sale, given that the passive approach was used.

52. of no sale, given that the aggressive approach was used.

New Residence *For Exercises 53–58, use the following information, which shows the educational attainment and the location of their new residence for people who moved in 2008. The data are rounded to the nearest thousand people.*

Educational Attainment	Location of New Residence				Total
	Same County	Different County, Same State	Different State	Abroad	
Not a high school graduate	2247	470	254	98	3069
High school graduate	3842	1074	712	145	5773
Some college	3319	1020	707	112	5158
Bachelor's degree	2072	760	667	182	3681
Graduate degree	913	383	461	118	1875
Total	12,393	3707	2801	655	19,556

Source: *U.S. Census Bureau*

If one of these individuals is selected at random, determine the probability (as a decimal number rounded to four decimal places) that the individual

53. moved within the same county.

54. moved within the same county, given the individual has a bachelor's degree.

55. moved to a different state, given the individual has a graduate degree.

56. has a graduate degree, given the individual moved abroad.

57. is a high school graduate, given the individual moved within the same state but different county.

58. moved to a different state or abroad, given the individual has a bachelor's degree.

Quality Control In Exercises 59–64, Sally Horsefall, a quality control inspector, is checking a sample of lightbulbs for defects. The following table summarizes her findings.

Wattage	Good	Defective	Total
20	80	15	95
50	100	5	105
100	120	10	130
Total	300	30	330

If one of these lightbulbs is selected at random, determine the probability that the lightbulb is

59. good.

60. good, given that it is 50 watts.

61. defective, given that it is 20 watts.

62. good, given that it is 100 watts.

63. good, given that it is 50 or 100 watts.

64. defective, given that it is not 50 watts.

News Survey In Exercises 65–70, 270 individuals are asked which evening news they watch most often. The results are summarized as follows.

Viewers	ABC	NBC	CBS	Other	Total
Men	30	20	40	55	145
Women	50	10	20	45	125
Total	80	30	60	100	270

If one of these individuals is selected at random, determine the probability that the person watches

65. ABC or NBC.

66. ABC, given that the individual is a woman.

67. ABC or NBC, given that the individual is a man.

68. a station other than CBS, given that the individual is a woman.

69. a station other than ABC, NBC, or CBS, given that the individual is a man.

70. NBC or CBS, given that the individual is a woman.

▲ *Diane Sawyer*, ABC Evening News

Challenge Problems/Group Activities

Mutual Fund Holdings Use the following information in Exercises 71–74. Mutual funds often hold many stocks. Each stock may be classified as a value stock, a growth stock, or a blend of the two. The stock may also be categorized by how large the company is. It may be classified as a large company stock, medium company stock, or small company stock. A selected mutual fund contains 200 stocks as illustrated in the following chart.

	Value	Blend	Growth	
	28	23	42	Large
	19	15	18	Medium
	26	12	17	Small

Equity Investment Style

If one stock is selected at random from the mutual fund, determine the probability that it is

71. a large company stock.

72. a value stock.

73. a blend, given that it is a medium company stock.

74. a large company stock, given that it is a blend stock.

75. Consider the Venn diagram below. The numbers in the regions of the circle indicate the number of items that belong to that region. For example, 60 items are in set A but not in set B.

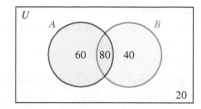

Determine   **a)** $n(A)$ **b)** $n(B)$ **c)** $P(A)$ **d)** $P(B)$

Use the formula on page 730 to determine

e) $P(A|B)$.   **f)** $P(B|A)$.

g) Explain why $P(A|B) \neq P(A) \cdot P(B)$.

76. A formula we gave for conditional probability is

$$P(E_2|E_1) = \frac{n(E_1 \text{ and } E_2)}{n(E_1)}$$

This formula may be derived from the formula

$$P(E_2|E_1) = \frac{P(E_1 \text{ and } E_2)}{P(E_1)}$$

Can you explain why? [*Hint:* Consider what happens to the denominators of $P(E_1 \text{ and } E_2)$ and $P(E_1,)$ when they are expressed as fractions and the fractions are divided out.]

77. Given that $P(A) = 0.3$, $P(B) = 0.5$, and $P(A \text{ and } B) = 0.15$, use the formula

$$P(E_2|E_1) = \frac{P(E_1 \text{ and } E_2)}{P(E_1)}$$

to determine

a) $P(A|B)$.   **b)** $P(B|A)$.

c) Are A and B independent? Explain.

Recreational Mathematics

In Exercises 78–83, suppose that each circle is equally likely to be selected. One circle is selected at random.

Determine the probability indicated.

78. $P(\text{green circle} \,|\, + \text{ obtained})$

79. $P(+| \text{ orange circle obtained})$

80. $P(\text{yellow circle} \,|\, - \text{ obtained})$

81. $P(\text{green } + \,|\, + \text{ obtained})$

82. $P(\text{green or orange circle} \,|\, \text{green } + \text{ obtained})$

83. $P(\text{orange circle with green } + \,|\, + \text{ obtained})$

The Counting Principle and Permutations

You are the manager of a movie theater and want to display a poster for each of the eight different movies showing at your theater. In how many different ways can you display the eight posters? In this section, we will learn how to determine the number of different ordered arrangements of a set of objects.

▲ *In how many different ways can movie posters be displayed?*

Why *This is Important* There are many real-life situations in which we need to determine the number of different ordered arrangements of a set of objects, such as the number of 5-digit zip codes or the number of 7-digit telephone numbers.

The Counting Principle

In Section 12.5, we introduced the counting principle, which is repeated here for your convenience.

Definition: Counting Principle

If a first experiment can be performed in M distinct ways and a second experiment can be performed in N distinct ways, then the two experiments in that specific order can be performed in $M \cdot N$ distinct ways.

Answer: For the NYSE there are
$26 + (26 \times 26) + (26 \times 26 \times 26) = 18,278$ different possible ticker symbols. For the NASDAQ there are $26 \times 26 \times 26 \times 26 = 456,976$ different possible ticker symbols.

The counting principle is illustrated in Examples 1 and 2.

Example 1   *Counting Principle: Passwords*

A password used to gain access to a computer account is to consist of two lowercase letters followed by four digits. Determine how many different passwords are possible if

a) repetition of letters and digits is permitted.

b) repetition of letters and digits is not permitted.

c) the first letter must be a vowel (*a, e, i, o, u*) and the first digit cannot be a 0, and repetition of letters and digits is not permitted.

Solution   There are 26 letters and 10 digits (0–9). We have six positions to fill, as indicated.

$$\overline{L}\ \overline{L}\ \overline{D}\ \overline{D}\ \overline{D}\ \overline{D}$$

a) Since repetition is permitted, there are 26 possible choices for both the first and second positions. There are 10 possible choices for the third, fourth, fifth, and sixth positions.

$$\frac{26}{L}\ \frac{26}{L}\ \frac{10}{D}\ \frac{10}{D}\ \frac{10}{D}\ \frac{10}{D}$$

Since $26 \cdot 26 \cdot 10 \cdot 10 \cdot 10 \cdot 10 = 6{,}760{,}000$, there are 6,760,000 different possible arrangements.

b) There are 26 possibilities for the first position. Since repetition of letters is not permitted, there are only 25 possibilities for the second position. The same reasoning is used when determining the number of digits for positions 3 through 6.

$$\frac{26}{L}\ \frac{25}{L}\ \frac{10}{D}\ \frac{9}{D}\ \frac{8}{D}\ \frac{7}{D}$$

Since $26 \cdot 25 \cdot 10 \cdot 9 \cdot 8 \cdot 7 = 3{,}276{,}000$, there are 3,276,000 different possible arrangements.

c) Since the first letter must be an *a, e, i, o,* or *u,* there are five possible choices for the first position. The second position can be filled by any of the letters except for the vowel selected for the first position. Therefore, there are 25 possibilities for the second position.

   Since the first digit cannot be a 0, there are nine possibilities for the third position. The fourth position can be filled by any digit except the one selected for the third position. Thus, there are nine possibilities for the fourth position. Since the fifth position cannot be filled by any of the two digits previously used, there are eight possibilities for the fifth position. The last position can be filled by any of the seven remaining digits.

$$\frac{5}{L}\ \frac{25}{L}\ \frac{9}{D}\ \frac{9}{D}\ \frac{8}{D}\ \frac{7}{D}$$

Since $5 \cdot 25 \cdot 9 \cdot 9 \cdot 8 \cdot 7 = 567{,}000$, there are 567,000 different arrangements that meet the conditions specified. ∎

Example 2   *Counting Principle: T-Shirt Colors*

At Old Navy, a supply of solid-colored T-shirts has just been received. The T-shirts come in the following colors: green, blue, white, yellow, and red. Billy Bragg, the floor manager, decides to display one of each color T-shirt in a row on a shelf.

a) In how many different ways can he display the five different color T-shirts on a shelf?

b) If he wants to place the blue T-shirt in the middle, in how many different ways can he arrange the T-shirts?

c) If Billy wants the white T-shirt to be the first T-shirt and the blue T-shirt to be the last T-shirt, in how many different ways can he arrange the T-shirts?

Solution

a) There are five positions to fill, using the five colors. In the first position, on the left, he can use any one of the five colors. In the second position, he can use any of the four remaining colors. In the third position, he can use any of the three remaining colors, and so on. The number of distinct possible arrangements is

$$\underline{5} \cdot \underline{4} \cdot \underline{3} \cdot \underline{2} \cdot \underline{1} = 120$$

b) We begin by satisfying the specified requirements stated. In this case, the blue T-shirt must be placed in the middle. Therefore, there is only one possibility for the middle position.

$$\underline{\ }\ \underline{\ }\ \underline{1}\ \underline{\ }\ \underline{\ }$$

For the first position, there are now four possibilities. For the second position, there will be three possibilities. For the fourth position, there will be two possibilities. Finally, in the last position, there is only one possibility.

$$\underline{4} \cdot \underline{3} \cdot \underline{1} \cdot \underline{2} \cdot \underline{1} = 24$$

Thus, under the condition stated, there are 24 different possible arrangements.

c) For the first T-shirt, there is only one possibility, the white T-shirt. For the last T-shirt, there is only one possibility, the blue T-shirt.

$$\underline{1}\ \underline{\ }\ \underline{\ }\ \underline{\ }\ \underline{1}$$

The second position can be filled by any of the three remaining T-shirts. The third position can be filled by any of the two remaining T-shirts. There is only one T-shirt left for the fourth position. Thus, the number of possible arrangements is

$$\underline{1} \cdot \underline{3} \cdot \underline{2} \cdot \underline{1} \cdot \underline{1} = 6$$

There are only six possible arrangements that satisfy the given conditions. ∎

Permutations

Now we introduce the definition of a permutation.

Definition: Permutations

A **permutation** is any *ordered arrangement* of a given set of objects.

"Larry, Shemp, Moe" and "Shemp, Moe, Larry" represent two different ordered arrangements or two different permutations of the same three names. In Example 2(a), there are 120 different ordered arrangements, or permutations, of the five colored T-shirts. In Example 2(b), there are 24 different ordered arrangements, or permutations possible, if the blue T-shirt must be displayed in the middle.

▲ *Shemp   Moe   Larry*

When determining the number of permutations possible, we assume that repetition of an item is not permitted. To help you understand and visualize permutations, we illustrate the various permutations possible when a triangle, rectangle, and circle are to be placed in a line; see Fig. 12.21.

Figure 12.21

For this set of three shapes, six different arrangements, or six permutations, are possible. We can obtain the number of permutations by using the counting principle. For the first position, there are three choices. There are then two choices for the second position, and only one choice is left for the third position.

$$\text{Number of permutations} = 3 \cdot 2 \cdot 1 = 6$$

The product $3 \cdot 2 \cdot 1$ is referred to as 3 factorial, and is written 3!. Thus,

$$3! = 3 \cdot 2 \cdot 1 = 6$$

Number of Permutations

The number of permutations of n distinct items is n factorial, symbolized $n!$, where

$$n! = n(n - 1)(n - 2) \cdots (3)(2)(1)$$

It is important to note that 0! is defined to be 1. Many calculators have the ability to determine factorials. Often to determine factorials you need to press the ⟨2nd⟩ or ⟨INV⟩ key. Read your calculator manual to determine how to find factorials on your calculator.

Example 3 *Cell Phones*

In how many different ways can six different cell phones be arranged on top of one another?

Solution Since there are six different cell phones, the number of permutations is 6!.

$$6! = 6 \cdot 5 \cdot 4 \cdot 3 \cdot 2 \cdot 1 = 720$$

The six cell phones can be arranged in 720 different ways.   ∎

Example 4 illustrates how to use the counting principle to determine the number of permutations possible when only a part of the total number of items is to be selected and arranged.

Example 4 *Permutations of Three Out of Five Letters*

Consider the five letters *a, b, c, d, e*. In how many distinct ways can three letters be selected and arranged if repetition is not allowed?

Solution We are asked to select and arrange only three of the five possible letters. Figure 12.22 shows some possibilities. Using the counting principle, we find that there are five possible letters for the first choice, four possible letters for the second choice, and three possible letters for the third choice:

$$5 \cdot 4 \cdot 3 = 60$$

Thus, there are 60 different possible ordered arrangements, or permutations. On the left, we show 5 of the 60 possible permutations.   ∎

Some of the many
permutations
of 3 of the 5 letters

b	a	d
d	a	b
e	c	a
c	d	e
a	b	c

Figure 12.22

In Example 4, we determined the number of different ways in which we could select and arrange three of the five items. We can indicate that result by using the notation $_5P_3$. The notation $_5P_3$ is read "the number of permutations of five items taken three at a time." The notation $_nP_r$ is read "the number of permutations of n items taken r at a time."

We use the counting principle below to evaluate $_8P_4$, $_9P_3$, and $_{10}P_5$. Note the relationship between the number preceding the P, the number following the P, and the last number in the product.

$$_8P_4 = 8 \cdot 7 \cdot 6 \cdot 5 \qquad \text{One more than } 8 - 4$$

$$_9P_3 = 9 \cdot 8 \cdot 7 \qquad \text{One more than } 9 - 3$$

$$_{10}P_5 = 10 \cdot 9 \cdot 8 \cdot 7 \cdot 6 \qquad \text{One more than } 10 - 5$$

To evaluate $_nP_r$, we begin with n and form a product of r consecutive descending factors. For example, to evaluate $_{10}P_5$, we start with 10 and form a product of five consecutive descending factors (see the preceding illustration).

In general, the number of permutations of n items taken r at a time, $_nP_r$, may be found by the formula

$$_nP_r = n(n-1)(n-2) \cdots \overbrace{(n-r+1)}^{\text{One more than } n-r}$$

Therefore, when evaluating $_{20}P_{15}$, we would find the product of consecutive decreasing integers from 20 to $(20 - 15 + 1)$ or 6, which is written as $20 \cdot 19 \cdot 18 \cdot 17 \cdots \cdot 6$.

Now let's develop an alternative formula that we can use to find the number of permutations possible when r objects are selected from n objects:

$$_nP_r = n(n-1)(n-2) \cdots (n-r+1)$$

Now multiply the expression on the right side of the equals sign by $\dfrac{(n-r)!}{(n-r)!}$, which is equivalent to multiplying the expression by 1.

$$_nP_r = n(n-1)(n-2) \cdots (n-r+1) \times \frac{(n-r)!}{(n-r)!}$$

For example,

$$_{10}P_5 = 10 \cdot 9 \cdot \cdots \cdot 6 \times \frac{5!}{5!}$$

or

$$_{10}P_5 = \frac{10 \cdot 9 \cdot \cdots \cdot 6 \times 5!}{5!}$$

Since $(n-r)!$ means $(n-r)(n-r-1) \cdots (3)(2)(1)$, the expression for $_nP_r$ can be rewritten as

$$_nP_r = \frac{n(n-1)(n-2) \cdots (n-r+1)\overbrace{(n-r)(n-r-1) \cdots (3)(2)(1)}^{(n-r)!}}{(n-r)!}$$

Since the numerator of this expression is $n!$, we can write

$$_nP_r = \frac{n!}{(n-r)!}$$

For example,

$$_{10}P_5 = \frac{10!}{(10-5)!}$$

Permutation Formula

The number of permutations possible when r objects are selected from n objects is found by the **permutation formula**

$$_nP_r = \frac{n!}{(n-r)!}$$

In Example 4, we found that when selecting three of five letters, there were 60 permutations. We can obtain the same result using the permutation formula:

$$_5P_3 = \frac{5!}{(5-3)!} = \frac{5!}{2!} = \frac{5 \cdot 4 \cdot 3 \cdot \cancel{2 \cdot 1}}{\cancel{2 \cdot 1}} = 60$$

Example 5 *Using the Permutation Formula*

You are among eight people forming a skiing club. Collectively, you decide to put each person's name in a hat and to randomly select a president, a vice president, and a secretary. How many different arrangements or permutations of officers are possible?

Solution There are eight people, $n = 8$, of which three are to be selected; thus, $r = 3$.

$$_8P_3 = \frac{8!}{(8-3)!} = \frac{8!}{5!} = \frac{8 \cdot 7 \cdot 6 \cdot \cancel{5 \cdot 4 \cdot 3 \cdot 2 \cdot 1}}{\cancel{5 \cdot 4 \cdot 3 \cdot 2 \cdot 1}} = 336$$

Thus, with eight people there can be 336 different arrangements for president, vice president, and secretary. ■

In Example 5, the fraction

$$\frac{8 \cdot 7 \cdot 6 \cdot \cancel{5 \cdot 4 \cdot 3 \cdot 2 \cdot 1}}{\cancel{5 \cdot 4 \cdot 3 \cdot 2 \cdot 1}} = 336$$

can be also expressed as

$$\frac{8 \cdot 7 \cdot 6 \cdot 5!}{5!} = 336$$

The solution to Example 5, like other permutation problems, can also be obtained using the counting principle.

EXAMPLE 6

The Prince George County bicycle club has 10 different routes members wish to travel exactly once, but they have only 6 specific dates for their trips. In how many ways can the different routes be assigned to the dates scheduled for their trips?

Many scientific calculators and all graphing calculators have the ability to evaluate permutations. Read your calculator's instruction manual to determine the procedure to follow to evaluate permutations.

To evaluate $_{10}P_6$ on a TI-83 Plus or a TI-84 Plus calculator, enter the number 10. Then press the MATH key. Use the right arrow key to scroll over to PRB, which stands for probability. Then scroll down to $_nP_r$. Press the ENTER key. You should now see 10 $_nP_r$ on your screen. Next press 6. Press the ENTER key again. The answer will be 151,200, which agrees with our answer in Example 6.

RECREATIONAL MATH

Jumble

Read the material on Permutations of Duplicate Items on this page and the next page before working this Jumble.

In the *Recreational Mathematics* box on page 711 we introduced the JUMBLE puzzles. Sometimes the puzzles contain one or more letters multiple times. For each Jumble below, use the knowledge you have learned in this section to determine

a) the number of possible arrangements of the letters given.

b) the word that results when the letters are placed in their proper order (note that only one word is possible).

1. NOOZE
2. ZBEERE
3. LOCGEEL

The answers are listed upside down below. See Exercises 53–56, 70, 71 for more examples.

Answers:
1. a) 60 b) OZONE
2. a) 120 b) BREEZE
3. a) 1260 b) COLLEGE

Solution There are 10 possible routes but only 6 specific dates scheduled for the trips. Since traveling route A on day 1 and traveling route B on day 2 is different than traveling route B on day 1 and traveling route A on day 2, we have a permutation problem. There are 10 possible routes; thus, $n = 10$. There are 6 routes that are going to be selected and assigned to different days; thus, $r = 6$. Now we calculate the number of different permutations of selecting and arranging the dates for 6 out of 10 possible routes.

$$_{10}P_6 = \frac{10!}{(10-6)!} = \frac{10!}{4!} = \frac{10 \cdot 9 \cdot 8 \cdot 7 \cdot 6 \cdot 5 \cdot \cancel{4!}}{\cancel{4!}} = 151{,}200$$

There are 151,200 different ways that 6 routes can be selected and scheduled from the 10 possible routes. ∎

Example 6 could also be worked using the counting principle because we are discussing an *ordered arrangement* (a permutation) that is done *without replacement*. For the first date scheduled, there are 10 possible outcomes. For the second date selected, there are 9 possible outcomes. By continuing this process we would determine that the number of possible outcomes for the 6 different trips is $10 \cdot 9 \cdot 8 \cdot 7 \cdot 6 \cdot 5 = 151{,}200$.

We have worked permutation problems (selecting and arranging, without replacement, r items out of n *distinct* items) by using the counting principle and using the permutation formula. When you are given a permutation problem, unless specified by your instructor, you may use either technique to determine its solution.

Permutations of Duplicate Items

So far, all the examples we have discussed in this section have involved arrangements with distinct items. Now we will consider permutation problems in which some of the items to be arranged are duplicates. For example, the name BOB contains three letters, of which the two Bs are duplicates. How many permutations of the letters in the name BOB are possible? If the two Bs were distinguishable (one red and the other blue), there would be six permutations.

BOB	BBO	OBB
BOB	BBO	OBB

However, if the Bs are not distinguishable (replacing all colored Bs with black print), we see that there are only three permutations.

BOB	BBO	OBB

The number of permutations of the letters in BOB can be computed as

$$\frac{3!}{2!} = \frac{3 \cdot \cancel{2 \cdot 1}}{\cancel{2 \cdot 1}} = 3$$

where 3! represents the number of permutations of three letters, assuming that none are duplicates, and 2! represents the number of ways the two items that are duplicates can be arranged (BB or BB). In general, we have the following rule.

Permutations of Duplicate Items

The number of distinct permutations of n objects where n_1 of the objects are identical, n_2 of the objects are identical, ..., n_r of the objects are identical is found by using

$$\frac{n!}{n_1! n_2! \cdots n_r!}$$

EXAMPLE 7   Duplicate Letters

In how many different ways can the letters of the word "TALLAHASSEE" be arranged?

Solution   Of the 11 letters, three are A's, two are S's, two are L's, and two are E's. The number of possible arrangements is

$$\frac{11!}{3!2!2!2!} = \frac{11 \cdot 10 \cdot 9 \cdot 8 \cdot 7 \cdot 6 \cdot 5 \cdot 4 \cdot 3 \cdot 2 \cdot 1}{3 \cdot 2 \cdot 1 \cdot 2 \cdot 1 \cdot 2 \cdot 1 \cdot 2 \cdot 1} = 11 \cdot 10 \cdot 9 \cdot 7 \cdot 6 \cdot 5 \cdot 4 = 831,600$$

There are 831,600 different possible arrangements of the letters in the word "TALLAHASSEE."

SECTION 12.8   Exercises

Warm Up Exercises

In Exercises 1–8, fill in the blank with an appropriate word, phrase, or symbol(s).

1. To determine the number of distinct ways two or more experiments can be performed, the _____ principle can be used.

2. Any ordered arrangement of a given set of objects is called a(n) _____.

3. The symbol for n factorial is _____.

4. The formula for the number of permutations of n distinct items is $n! =$ _____

5. The formula for the number of permutations when r objects are selected from n objects is $_nP_r =$ _____.

6. The number of permutations of n objects, where n_1 of the items are identical, n_2 of the items are identical, ..., n_r are identical, is found by _____.

7. The notation used to express the number of permutations of five items taken three at a time is _____.

8. The notation used to express the number of permutations of seven items taken two at a time is _____.

Practice the Skills

In Exercises 9–20, evaluate the expression.

9. $5!$ 10. $6!$ 11. $_4P_2$ 12. $_5P_2$

13. $0!$ 14. $_7P_3$ 15. $_8P_0$ 16. $_6P_0$

17. $_9P_5$ 18. $_3P_3$ 19. $_8P_3$ 20. $_{10}P_6$

Problem Solving

21. **ATM Codes** To use an automated teller machine, you generally must enter a four-digit code, using the digits 0–9. How many four-digit codes are possible if repetition of digits is permitted?

22. **Routes** There are three different routes that Cassidy Cole can walk from home to the post office and two different routes that she can walk from the post office to the bank. How many different routes can Cassidy walk from home to the post office and then to the bank?

23. **Outfits** Juan Rivera has three ties, four shirts, and two pairs of pants. How many different outfits can he wear if he chooses one tie, one shirt, and one pair of pants for each outfit?

24. **Passwords** Assume that a password to log onto a computer account is to consist of any four digits or letters (repetition is permitted). Determine the number of passwords possible if

   a) the letters are not case sensitive (that is, a lowercase letter is treated the same as an uppercase letter).

   b) the letters are case sensitive (that is, an uppercase letter is considered different than the same lowercase letter).

25. *Car Door Locks* Some doors on cars can be opened by pressing a correct sequence of buttons. A display of the five buttons by the door handle of a car follows.*

The correct sequence of five buttons must be pressed to unlock the door.

a) How many different sequences of five buttons are possible (repetition is permitted)?

b) If a sequence of five buttons is pressed at random, determine the probability that the sequence unlocks the door.

26. *Social Security Numbers* A social security number consists of nine digits. How many different social security numbers are possible if repetition of digits is permitted?

27. *License Plate* In Italy, most car and motorcycle license plates consist of 2 letters, followed by 3 digits, followed by 2 letters. (See photo.) Determine the number of license plates possible if

▲ *An Italian license plate*

a) repetition is permitted (as it is in Italy).

b) repetition is not permitted.

28. *Winning the Trifecta* The trifecta at most racetracks consists of selecting the first-, second-, and third-place finishers in a particular race in their proper order. If there are seven entries in the trifecta race, how many tickets must you purchase to guarantee a win?

29. *Choosing Classes* Kai Lu plans to enroll in four classes: sociology, chemistry, economics, and humanities. There are seven sociology classes, four chemistry classes, three economics classes, and four humanities classes that fit his schedule. How many different ways can he select his four classes?

30. *Geometric Shapes* Consider the five figures shown.

In how many different ways can the figures be arranged

a) from left to right?

b) from top to bottom if placed one under the other?

c) from left to right if the triangle is to be placed on the far right?

d) from left to right if the circle is to be placed on the far left and the triangle is to be placed on the far right?

31. *Arranging Pictures* The six pictures shown are to be placed side by side along a wall.

In how many ways can they be arranged from left to right if

a) they can be arranged in any order?

b) the bird must be on the far left?

c) the bird must be on the far left and the giraffe must be next to the bird?

d) a four-legged animal must be on the far right?

32. *Club Officers* If a club consists of 10 members, how many different arrangements of president, vice-president, and secretary are possible?

33. *Restaurant Positions* There are 10 candidates for three positions at Johnny Rockets. One position is for a cook. The second position is for a food server. The third position is for a cashier. If all 10 candidates are equally qualified for the three positions, in how many different ways can the three positions be filled?

34. *ISBN Codes* Each book registered in the Library of Congress must have an ISBN code number. For an ISBN number of the form D-DD-DDDDDD-D, where D represents a digit from 0–9, how many different ISBN numbers are possible if repetition of digits is allowed? (See research activity Exercise 72 on page 746.)

---

*On most cars, although each key lists two numbers, the key acts as a single number. Therefore, if your code is 1, 6, 8, 5, 3, the code 2, 5, 7, 6, 4 will also open the lock.

35. *Wedding Reception* At the reception line of a wedding, the bride, the groom, the best man, the maid of honor, the four ushers, and the four bridesmaids must line up to receive the guests.

    a) If these individuals can line up in any order, how many arrangements are possible?

    b) If the groom must be the last in line and the bride must be next to the groom, and the others can line up in any order, how many arrangements are possible?

    c) If the groom is to be last in line, the bride next to the groom, and males and females are to alternate, how many arrangements are possible?

36. *DJ* A disc jockey (DJ) has 9 songs to play. Five are slow songs, and 4 are fast songs. Each song is to be played only once. In how many ways can the DJ play the 9 songs if

    a) the songs can be played in any order?

    b) the first song must be a slow song and the last song must be a slow song?

    c) the first two songs must be fast songs?

Letter Codes In Exercises 37–40, an identification code is to consist of three letters followed by four digits. How many different codes are possible if

37. repetition is not permitted?

38. repetition is permitted?

39. repetition of letters is permitted, repetition of numbers is not permitted, and the first three entries must all be the same letter?

40. the first letter must be an *A, B, C,* or *D* and repetition is not permitted?

License Plates In Exercises 41–44, a license plate is to consist of three digits followed by two uppercase letters. Determine the number of different license plates possible if

41. repetition of numbers and letters is permitted.

42. repetition of numbers and letters is not permitted.

43. the first and second digits must be odd, and repetition is not permitted.

44. the first digit cannot be zero, and repetition is not permitted.

45. *Possible Phone Numbers* A telephone number consists of seven digits with the restriction that the first digit cannot be 0 or 1.

    a) How many distinct telephone numbers are possible?

    b) How many distinct telephone numbers are possible with three-digit area codes preceding the seven-digit number, where the first digit of the area code is not 0 or 1?

    c) With the increasing use of cell phones and paging systems, our society is beginning to run out of usable phone numbers. Various phone companies are developing phone numbers that use 8 digits instead of 7. How many distinct phone numbers can be made using a three digit area code followed by an eight digit phone number, where the first digit of the area code and the phone number cannot be 0 or 1?

46. *Fruit Juice Selection* Mrs. Hernandez and her three children go shopping at a local grocery store. Each of the children will be allowed to select one bottle of fruit juice. On the store's shelf there are 12 bottles of fruit juice, and each bottle contains a different type of juice. In how many ways can the selections be made?

47. *Skiing Event* A skiing event has 16 participants for the slalom. The 5 participants with the fastest speeds will be listed, in the order of their speed, on the leader board. How many different ways are there for the names to be listed?

48. *History Test* In one question on a history test, a student is asked to match 10 dates with 10 events; each date can only be matched with 1 event. In how many different ways can this question be answered?

49. *Color Permutations* Determine the number of permutations of the colors in the spectrum that follows.

50. *Drive-Through at a Bank* A bank has three drive-through stations. Assuming that each is equally likely to be selected by customers, in how many different ways can the next six drivers select a station?

51. *Computer Systems* At a computer store, a customer is considering 5 different computers, 4 different monitors, 7 different printers, and 2 different scanners. Assuming that each of the components is compatible with one another and that one of each is to be selected, determine the number of different computer systems possible.

52. *Selecting Furniture* The Johnsons just moved into their new home and are selecting furniture for the family room. They are considering 5 different sofas, 2 different chairs, and 6 different tables. They plan to select one item from each category. Determine the number of different ways they can select the furniture.

53. Determine the number of permutations of the letters of the word "EDUCATION."

54. Determine the number of permutations of the letters of the word "EFFECTIVE."

55. In how many ways can the letters in the word "TENNESSEE" be arranged?

56. In how many ways can the letters in the word "COMMUNICATION" be arranged?

57. In how many ways can the digits in the number 4,568,865 be arranged?

58. In how many ways can the digits of the number 2,142,332 be arranged?

59. *Flag Messages* Five different colored flags will be placed on a pole, one beneath another. The arrangement of the colors indicates the message. How many messages are possible if five flags are to be selected from nine different colored flags?

60. *Multiple-Choice Test* Keri Kershaw is taking a 12-question multiple-choice exam. Each question has three possible answers, (a), (b), and (c). In how many possible ways can Keri answer the questions?

61. *Batting Order* In how many ways can the manager of a National League baseball team arrange his batting order of nine players if

    a) the pitcher must bat last?

    b) there are no restrictions?

62. *Painting Exhibit* Five Monet paintings are to be displayed in a museum.

    a) In how many different ways can they be arranged if they must be next to one another?

    b) In how many different ways can they be displayed if a specific one is to be in the middle?

▲ The Water Lily Pond, Pink Harmony, *1900 by Claude Monet*

Challenge Problems/Group Activities

63. *Car Keys* Door keys for a certain automobile are made from a blank key on which five cuts are made. Each cut may be one of five different depths.

    a) How many different keys can be made?

    b) If 400,000 of these automobiles are made such that each of the keys determined in part (a) opens the same number of cars, determine how many cars can be opened by a specific key.

    c) If one of these cars is selected at random, what is the probability that the key selected at random will unlock the door?

64. *Voting* On a ballot, each committee member is asked to rank three of eight candidates for recommendation for promotion, giving first, second, and third choices (no ties). What is the minimum number of ballots that must be cast to guarantee that at least two ballots are the same?

65. *Scrabble* Nancy Lin, who is playing Scrabble with Dale Grey, has seven different letters. She decides to test each five-letter permutation before her next move. If each permutation takes 5 sec, how long will it take Nancy to check all the permutations?

66. *Scrabble* In Exercise 65, assume, of Nancy's seven letters, that three are identical and two are identical. How long will it take Nancy to try all different permutations of her seven letters?

67. Does $_nP_r = {}_nP_{(n-r)}$ for all whole numbers, where $n \geq r$?

Recreational Mathematics

68. *Stations* There are eight bus stations from town A to town B. How many different single tickets must be printed so that a passenger may purchase a ticket from any station to any other station?

A ○ ○ ○ ○ ○ ○ ○ ○ B

69. *Bus Loop* How many tickets with different points of origin and destination can be sold on a bus line that travels a loop with 25 stops?

Jumble *Many newspapers contain Jumble puzzles, where the letters of a word are given out of order. In Exercises 70 and 71, read the Recreational Math box on page 741 and determine*

  a) *the number of possible arrangements of the letters given.*

  b) *the word.*

70. HEICOC

71. ROSEGOC

Internet/Research Activity

72. When a book is published, it is assigned a 10-digit code number called the International Standard Book Number (ISBN). Do research and write a report on how this coding system works.

SECTION 12.9   Combinations

▲ *Combinations can be used to determine the number of different arrangements of toppings that can be placed on a hamburger.*

Zebb's Restaurant has 10 different toppings that can be added to a hamburger. Chase Weichman is going to select three of those toppings to add to his hamburger. How many different selections are possible? In this section, we will learn how to determine the number of selections when the order of selection of the items is not important to the final outcome.

Why *This is Important* There are many situations in which the order of the selections made is not important to the final outcome. For example, in determining the number of ways a committee can select 3 out of 8 candidates to receive a scholarship, the order in which the 3 are selected is not important.

When the order of the selection of the items is important to the final outcome, the problem is a permutation problem. When the order of the selection of the items is unimportant to the final outcome, the problem is a *combination* problem.

Recall from Section 12.8 that permutations are *ordered* arrangements. For example, *a, b, c* and *b, c, a* are two different permutations because the ordering of the three letters is different. The letters *a, b, c* and *b, c, a* represent the same combination of letters because the *same letters* are used in each set. However, the letters *a, b, c* and *a, b, d* represent two different combinations of letters because the letters contained in each set are different.

Definition: **Combination**

A **combination** is a distinct group (or set) of objects without regard to their arrangement.

┌ Example **1** *Permutation or Combination*

Determine whether the situation represents a permutation or combination problem.

a) A group of five friends, Arline, Inez, Judy, Dan, and Eunice, are forming a club. The group will elect a president and a treasurer. In how many different ways can the president and treasurer be selected?

b) Of the five individuals named, two will be attending a meeting together. In how many different ways can they do so?

Did You Know?

Powerball

On February 8, 2006, eight people won the largest Powerball in jackpot history, a $365 million prize.

As of this writing, Powerball is played in 42 U.S. jurisdictions, including Washington, DC and the U.S. Virgin Islands, as well as online. Winning the Powerball requires selecting 5 matching numbers between 1 and 55, as well as the Powerball number from 1 to 42. The probability of winning is about 1 in 146,107,962. Verify this probability yourself.

The largest lottery jackpot in U.S. history was a Mega Million jackpot of $390 million, which was won by two individuals in March 2007. Each person received $195 million. The largest lottery in the world is Spain's annual contest known as *El Gordo*, or "the Fat One." In 2010, *El Gordo* is expected to pay out 2.3 billion euros (about $3.22 billion U.S. dollars). Each year *El Gordo* has about 10,000 winning prizes ranging from $20 to $200,000 or more.

Solution

a) Since the president's position is different from the treasurer's position, we have a permutation problem. Judy as president with Dan as treasurer is different from Dan as president with Judy as treasurer. The order of the selection is important.

b) Since the order in which the two individuals selected to attend the meeting is not important, we have a combination problem. There is no difference if Judy is selected and then Dan is selected, or if Dan is selected and then Judy is selected. ∎

In Section 12.8, you learned that $_nP_r$ represents the number of permutations when r items are selected from n distinct items. *Similarly, $_nC_r$ represents the number of combinations when r items are selected from n distinct items.*

Consider the set of elements $\{a, b, c, d, e\}$. The number of permutations of two letters from the set is represented as $_5P_2$, and the number of combinations of two letters from the set is represented as $_5C_2$. Twenty permutations of two letters and 10 combinations of two letters are possible from these five letters. Thus, $_5P_2 = 20$ and $_5C_2 = 10$, as shown.

Permutations	Combinations
$\left. \begin{array}{l} ab, ba, ac, ca, ad, da, ae, ea, bc, cb, \\ bd, db, be, eb, cd, dc, ce, ec, de, ed \end{array} \right\} 20$	$\left. \begin{array}{l} ab, ac, ad, ae, bc, \\ bd, be, cd, ce, de \end{array} \right\} 10$

When discussing both combination and permutation problems, we always assume that the experiment is performed without replacement. That is why duplicate letters such as *aa* or *bb* are not included in the preceding example.

Note that from one combination of two letters, two permutations can be formed. For example, the combination *ab* gives the permutations *ab* and *ba*, or twice as many permutations as combinations. Thus, for this example we may write

$$_5P_2 = 2 \cdot (_5C_2)$$

Since $2 = 2!$, we may write

$$_5P_2 = 2!(_5C_2)$$

If we repeated this same process for comparing the number of permutations in $_nP_r$ with the number of combinations in $_nC_r$, we would find that

$$_nP_r = r!(_nC_r)$$

Dividing both sides of the equation by $r!$ gives

$$_nC_r = \frac{_nP_r}{r!}$$

Since $_nP_r = \dfrac{n!}{(n-r)!}$, the combination formula may be expressed as

$$_nC_r = \frac{n!/(n-r)!}{r!} = \frac{n!}{(n-r)!r!}$$

Combination Formula

The number of combinations possible when r objects are selected from n objects is found by the **combination formula**

$$_nC_r = \frac{n!}{(n-r)!\,r!}$$

Example 2 *Museum Selection*

While visiting New York City, the Friedmans are interested in visiting 8 museums but have time to visit only 3. In how many ways can the Friedmans select 3 of the 8 museums to visit?

Solution This problem is a combination problem because the order in which the three museums are selected does not matter.

$$_8C_3 = \frac{8!}{(8-3)!\,3!} = \frac{8!}{5!\,3!} = \frac{8 \cdot 7 \cdot 6 \cdot 5 \cdot 4 \cdot 3 \cdot 2 \cdot 1}{5 \cdot 4 \cdot 3 \cdot 2 \cdot 1 \cdot 3 \cdot 2 \cdot 1} = 56$$

There are 56 different ways that 3 of the 8 museums can be selected to visit. ■

Example 3 *Floral Arrangements*

Jan Funkhauser has 10 different cut flowers from which she will choose 6 to use in a floral arrangement. How many different ways can she do so?

Solution This problem is a combination problem because the order in which the 6 flowers are selected is unimportant. There are a total of 10 different flowers, so $n = 10$. Six flowers are to be selected, so $r = 6$.

$$_{10}C_6 = \frac{10!}{(10-6)!\,6!} = \frac{10!}{4!\,6!} = \frac{10 \cdot \overset{3}{9} \cdot 8 \cdot 7 \cdot 6 \cdot 5 \cdot 4 \cdot 3 \cdot 2 \cdot 1}{4 \cdot 3 \cdot 2 \cdot 1 \cdot 6 \cdot 5 \cdot 4 \cdot 3 \cdot 2 \cdot 1} = 210$$

Thus, there are 210 different ways Jan can choose 6 cut flowers from a group of 10 cut flowers. ■

Did You Know?

Poker versus Bridge

A nice bridge hand

In popular card games, there is such a variety of possible combinations of cards that a player rarely gets the same hand twice. The total number of different 5-card poker hands using a standard deck of 52 cards is 2,598,960, and for 13-card bridge hands this number increases to 635,013,559,600.

Example 4 *Dinner Combinations*

At the Royal Dynasty Chinese restaurant, dinner for eight people consists of 3 items from column A, 4 items from column B, and 3 items from column C. If columns A, B, and C have 5, 7, and 6 items, respectively, how many different dinner combinations are possible?

Solution For column A, 3 of 5 items must be selected, which can be represented as $_5C_3$. For column B, 4 of 7 items must be selected, which can be represented as $_7C_4$. For column C, 3 of 6 items must be selected, or $_6C_3$.

$$_5C_3 = 10 \quad _7C_4 = 35 \quad \text{and} \quad _6C_3 = 20$$

Using the counting principle, we can determine the total number of dinner combinations by multiplying the number of choices from columns A, B, and C:

$$\text{Total number of dinner choices} = {_5C_3} \cdot {_7C_4} \cdot {_6C_3}$$
$$= 10 \cdot 35 \cdot 20 = 7000$$

Therefore, 7000 different combinations are possible under these conditions. ■

We have presented various counting methods, including the counting principle, permutations, and combinations. You often need to decide which method to use to solve a problem. Table 12.4 may help you in selecting the procedure to use.

Table 12.4 Summary of Counting Methods

Counting Principle: If a first experiment can be performed in M distinct ways and a second experiment can be performed in N distinct ways, then the two experiments in that specific order can be performed in $M \cdot N$ distinct ways. The counting principle may be used with or without repetition of items. It is used when determining the number of different ways that two or more experiments can occur. It is also used when there are specific placement requirements, such as the first digit must be a 0 or 1.	Determining the Number of Ways of Selecting r Items from n Items (Repetition is not Permitted)	
	Permutations	**Combinations**
	Permutations are used when order is important. For example, *a, b, c* and *b, c, a* are two different permutations of the same three letters. $$_nP_r = \frac{n!}{(n-r)!}$$ Problems solved with the permutation formula may also be solved by using the counting principle.	Combinations are used when order is not important. For example, *a, b, c* and *b, c, a* are the same combination of three letters. But *a, b, c*, and *a, b, d* are two different combinations of three letters. $$_nC_r = \frac{n!}{(n-r)!\,r!}$$

SECTION 12.9 Exercises

Warm Up Exercises

In Exercises 1–6, fill in the blank with an appropriate word, phrase, or symbol(s).

1. A distinct group of objects without regard to their arrangement is called a(n) _____.

2. The symbol for the number of combinations when r items are selected from n distinct items is _____.

3. If we want to select r items from n items, and the order of the arrangement is important, then _____ are used.

4. If we want to select r items from n items, and the order of the arrangement is not important, then _____ are used.

5. The notation used to express the number of combinations of 3 items selected from 7 distinct items is _____.

6. The notation used to express the number of combinations of 4 items selected from 10 distinct items is _____.

Practice the Skills

In Exercises 7–20, evaluate the expression.

7. $_6C_2$

8. $_9C_3$

9. a) $_8C_4$ b) $_8P_4$

10. a) $_8C_2$ b) $_8P_2$

11. a) $_8C_0$ b) $_8P_0$

12. a) $_{12}C_8$ b) $_{12}P_8$

13. a) $_{10}C_3$ b) $_{10}P_3$

14. a) $_5C_5$ b) $_5P_5$

15. $\dfrac{_5C_3}{_5P_3}$

16. $\dfrac{_7C_2}{_7P_2}$

17. $\dfrac{_6C_4}{_6C_3}$

18. $\dfrac{_6C_6}{_8C_0}$

19. $\dfrac{_9P_4}{_{10}C_5}$

20. $\dfrac{_7P_0}{_7C_0}$

Problem Solving

21. *Hiring* There are 12 qualified applicants for 4 nursing positions at a hospital. In how many ways can the positions be filled?

22. *Banana Split* An ice-cream parlor has 20 different flavors. Cynthia orders a banana split and has to select 3 different flavors. How many different selections are possible?

23. *Test Essays* Tina Campbell must select and answer four of five essay questions on a test. In how many ways can she do so?

24. *Software Packages* During a special promotion at CompUSA, a customer purchasing a computer and a printer is given the choice of 2 free software packages. If there are 9 different software packages from which to select, how many different ways can the 2 packages be selected?

25. *Scholarships* A scholarship committee has received 8 applications for a $500 scholarship. The committee has decided to select 3 of the 8 candidates for further consideration. In how many ways can the committee do so?

26. *Attending Plays* While visiting New York City, the Nygens want to attend 3 plays out of 10 plays they would like to see. In how many ways can they do so?

▲ *Theater district, New York City*

27. *Taxi Ride* A group of 7 people wants to use taxis to go to a local restaurant. When the first taxi arrives, the group decides that 4 people should get into the taxi. In how many ways can that be done?

28. *Plants* Mary Robinson purchased a package of 24 different plants, but she only needed 20 plants for planting. In how many ways can she select the 20 plants from the package to be planted?

29. *Entertainers* Ruth Eckerd Hall must select 8 of 12 possible entertainers for its summer schedule. In how many ways can that be done?

30. *CD Selection* James Ruiz has 7 CDs and wants to select 4 to play in his car CD player. In how many ways can he select 4 of 7 CDs?

31. *Trophies* Matthew Abbott has 10 shirts in his closet and must select 4 to take with him on vacation. In how many ways can Matthew select the shirts?

32. *Quinella Bet* A quinella bet consists of selecting the first- and second-place winners, in any order, in a particular event. For example, suppose you select a 2–5 quinella. If 2 wins and 5 finishes second, or if 5 wins and 2 finishes second, you win. Mr. Smith goes to a jai alai match. In the match, 8 jai alai teams compete. How many quinella tickets must Mr. Smith purchase to guarantee a win?

33. *Cameras and Lenses* Rowe Photography has nine different digital cameras and six different long-range lenses in stock. The manager wants to place three of the nine cameras and

two of the six lenses on sale. In how many ways can the manager select the items to be listed as sale items?

34. *Test Question* On an English test, Tito Ramirez must write an essay for three of the five questions in Part 1 and four of the six questions in Part 2. How many different combinations of questions can he answer?

35. *Plasma and LCD TVs* A television/stereo store has 12 different plasma televisions and 8 different LCD televisions in stock. The store's manager wishes to place 3 plasma televisions and 2 LCD televisions on sale. In how many ways can that be done?

36. *Newsletter* An animal shelter has 15 cats and 12 dogs available for adoption. The shelter wants to select 6 cats and 4 dogs to feature in the adoption newsletter. In how many ways can this be done?

37. *Dinner Party* Sue Less is having a dinner party. She has 10 different bottles of red wine and 8 different bottles of white wine on her wine rack. She wants to select 4 bottles of red wine and 2 bottles of white wine to serve at her party. In how many ways can she do so?

38. *Forming a Committee* The Webster Town Board is forming a committee to explore ways to improve public safety in the town. The committee will consist of 4 representatives from the town board and 3 representatives from a citizens advisory board. If there are 7 town board members and 5 citizens advisory board members from which to choose, how many different ways can the committee be formed?

39. *Selecting Soda* Angel Ramirez is sent to the store to get 5 different bottles of regular soda and 3 different bottles of diet soda. If there are 10 different types of regular sodas and 7 different types of diet sodas to choose from, how many different choices does Angel have?

40. *Constructing a Test* A teacher is constructing a mathematics test consisting of 10 questions. She has a pool of 28 questions, which are classified by level of difficulty as follows: 6 difficult questions, 10 average questions, and 12 easy questions. How many different 10-question tests can she construct from the pool of 28 questions if her test is to have 3 difficult, 4 average, and 3 easy questions?

41. *Selecting Mutual Funds* Joe Chang recently graduated from college and now has a job that provides a retirement investment plan. Joe wants to diversify his investments, so he wants to invest in four stock mutual funds and two bond mutual funds. If he has a choice of eight stock mutual funds and five bond mutual funds, how many different selections of mutual funds does he have?

42. *Door Prize* As part of a door prize, Mary McCarty won three tickets to a baseball game and three tickets to a theater performance. She decided to give all the tickets to friends. For the baseball game she is considering six different friends, and for the theater she is considering eight different friends. In how many ways can she distribute the tickets?

43. *New Breakfast Cereals* General Mills is testing 4 oat cereals, 5 wheat cereals, and 6 rice cereals. If it plans to market 3 of the oat cereals, 2 of the wheat cereals, and 2 of the rice cereals, how many different combinations are possible?

44. *Catering Service* A catering service is making up trays of hors d'oeuvres. The hors d'oeuvres are categorized as inexpensive, average, and expensive. If the client must select three of the eight inexpensive, five of the nine average, and two of the four expensive hors d'oeuvres, how many different choices are possible?

Challenge Problems/Group Activities

45. *Test Answers* Consider a 10-question test in which each question can be answered either correctly or incorrectly.

a) How many different ways are there to answer the questions so that eight are correct and two are incorrect?

b) How many different ways are there to answer the questions so that at least eight are correct?

46. a) *A Dinner Toast* Four people at dinner make a toast. If each person is to tap glasses with each other person one at a time, how many taps will take place?

b) Repeat part (a) with five people.

c) How many taps will there be if there are n people at the dinner table?

47. *Pascal's Triangle* The notation $_nC_2$ may be written $\binom{n}{r}$.

a) Use this notation to evaluate each of the combinations in the following array. Form a triangle of the results,

similar to the one given, by placing the answer to each combination in the same relative position in the triangle.

$$\binom{0}{0}$$

$$\binom{1}{0} \quad \binom{1}{1}$$

$$\binom{2}{0} \quad \binom{2}{1} \quad \binom{2}{2}$$

$$\binom{3}{0} \quad \binom{3}{1} \quad \binom{3}{2} \quad \binom{3}{3}$$

$$\binom{4}{0} \quad \binom{4}{1} \quad \binom{4}{2} \quad \binom{4}{3} \quad \binom{4}{4}$$

b) Using the number pattern in part (a), find the next row of numbers of the triangle (known as *Pascal's triangle*).

48. *Lottery Combinations* Determine the number of combinations possible in a state lottery where you must select

a) 6 of 46 numbers.

b) 6 of 47 numbers.

c) 6 of 48 numbers.

d) 6 of 49 numbers.

e) Does the number of combinations increase by the same amount going from part (a) to part (b) as from part (b) to part (c)?

49. a) *Table Seating Arrangements* How many distinct ways can four people be seated in a row?

b) How many distinct ways can four people be seated at a circular table?

50. Show that $_nC_r = {_nC_{(n-r)}}$.

51. *Forming a Committee* A group of 15 people wants to form a committee consisting of a chair, vice chair, and three additional members. How many different committees can be formed?

Recreational Mathematics

52. a) *Combination Lock* To open a combination lock, you must know the lock's three-number sequence in its proper order. Repetition of numbers is permitted. Why is this lock more like a permutation lock than a combination lock? Why is it not a true permutation problem?

b) Assuming that a combination lock has 40 numbers, determine how many different three-number arrangements are possible if repetition of numbers is allowed.

c) Answer the question in part (b) if repetition is not allowed.

Internet/Research Activity

53. The area of mathematics called combinatorics is the science of counting. Do research and write a paper on combinatorics and its many applications.

SECTION 12.10	Solving Probability Problems by Using Combinations

▲ *What is the probability of selecting two picture cards from a standard deck of 52 cards when the two cards are selected without replacement?*

Suppose that we want to find the probability of selecting two picture cards (jacks, queens, or kings) when two cards are selected, without replacement, from a standard deck of cards. In Section 12.6, we used the *and* probability formula to solve this type of probability problem. In this section, we will learn another way to solve this type of probability problem by using combinations.

> **Why** **This is Important** Combinations can be used in a variety of real-world probability applications.

Using the *and* formula for determining the probability of selecting two picture cards from a dark of 52 cards, we could reason as follows:

$$P(2 \text{ picture cards}) = P(\text{first picture card}) \cdot P(\text{second picture card})$$

$$= \frac{12}{52} \cdot \frac{11}{51} = \frac{132}{2652} \quad \text{or} \quad \frac{11}{221}$$

Since the order of the two picture cards selected is not important to the final answer, this problem can be considered a combination probability problem.

We can also find the probability of selecting two picture cards, using combinations, by finding the number of possible successful outcomes (selecting two picture cards) and dividing that answer by the total number of possible outcomes (selecting any two cards).

The number of ways in which two picture cards can be selected from the 12 picture cards in a deck is $_{12}C_2$, or

$$_{12}C_2 = \frac{12!}{(12-2)!2!} = \frac{\overset{6}{\cancel{12}} \cdot 11 \cdot \cancel{10!}}{\cancel{10!} \cdot \cancel{2} \cdot 1} = 66$$

The number of ways in which two cards can be selected from a deck of 52 cards is $_{52}C_2$, or

$$_{52}C_2 = \frac{52!}{(52-2)!2!} = \frac{\overset{26}{\cancel{52}} \cdot 51 \cdot \cancel{50!}}{\cancel{50!} \cdot \cancel{2} \cdot 1} = 1326$$

Thus,

$$P(\text{selecting 2 picture cards}) = \frac{_{12}C_2}{_{52}C_2} = \frac{66}{1326} = \frac{11}{221}$$

Note that the same answer is obtained with either method. To give you more exposure to counting techniques, we will work the problems in this section using combinations.

Example 1 *Committee of Three Women*

A club consists of four men and five women. Three members are to be selected at random to form a committee. What is the probability that the committee will consist of three women?

Solution The order in which the three members are selected is not important. Therefore, we may work this problem using combinations.

$$P\left(\begin{array}{c}\text{committee consists}\\\text{of 3 women}\end{array}\right) = \frac{\text{number of possible committees with 3 women}}{\text{total number of possible 3-member committees}}$$

Since there is a total of 5 women, the number of possible committees with three women is $_5C_3 = 10$. Since there is a total of 9 people, the total number of possible three-member committees is $_9C_3 = 84$.

$$P(\text{committee consists of 3 women}) = \frac{10}{84} = \frac{5}{42}$$

The probability of randomly selecting a committee with three women is $\frac{5}{42}$. ∎

Example 2 *A Heart Flush*

A flush in the game of poker is five cards of the same suit (5 hearts, 5 diamonds, 5 clubs, or 5 spades). If you are dealt a five-card hand, determine the probability that you will be dealt a heart flush.

Solution The order in which the five hearts are dealt is not important. Therefore, we may work this problem using combinations.

$$P(\text{heart flush}) = \frac{\text{number of possible 5-card heart flushes}}{\text{total number of possible 5-card hands}}$$

Since there are 13 hearts in a deck of cards, the number of possible five-card heart flush hands is $_{13}C_5 = 1287$. The total number of possible five-card hands in a deck of 52 cards is $_{52}C_5 = 2{,}598{,}960$.

$$P(\text{heart flush}) = \frac{_{13}C_5}{_{52}C_5} = \frac{1287}{2{,}598{,}960} = \frac{33}{66{,}640}$$

The probability of being dealt a heart flush is $\frac{33}{66{,}640}$, or ≈ 0.000495. ∎

Example 3 *Employment Assignments*

A temporary employment agency has six men and five women who wish to be assigned for the day. One employer has requested four employees for security guard positions, and the second employer has requested three employees for moving furniture in an office building. If we assume that each of the potential employees has the same chance of being selected and being assigned at random and that only seven employees will be assigned, find the probability that

a) three men will be selected for moving furniture.

b) three men will be selected for moving furniture and four women will be selected for security guard positions.

Solution

a) $P\left(\begin{array}{c}\text{3 men selected}\\\text{for moving furniture}\end{array}\right) = \dfrac{\left(\begin{array}{c}\text{number of possible combinations}\\\text{of 3 men selected}\end{array}\right)}{\left(\begin{array}{c}\text{total number of possible combinations}\\\text{for selecting 3 people}\end{array}\right)}$

The number of possible combinations with 3 men is $_6C_3$. The total number of possible selections of 3 people is $_{11}C_3$.

$$P\left(\begin{array}{c}\text{3 men selected}\\\text{for moving furniture}\end{array}\right) = \frac{_6C_3}{_{11}C_3} = \frac{20}{165} = \frac{4}{33}$$

Thus, the probability that 3 men are selected is $\frac{4}{33}$.

b) The number of ways of selecting 3 men out of 6 is $_6C_3$, and the number of ways of selecting 4 women out of 5 is $_5C_4$. The total number of possible selections when 7 people are selected from 11 is $_{11}C_7$. Since both the 3 men *and* the 4 women must be selected, the probability is calculated as follows:

$$P\left(\begin{array}{c}\text{3 men and}\\\text{4 women selected}\end{array}\right) = \dfrac{\left(\begin{array}{c}\text{number of combinations}\\\text{of 3 men selected}\end{array}\right)\cdot\left(\begin{array}{c}\text{number of combinations}\\\text{of 4 women selected}\end{array}\right)}{\left(\begin{array}{c}\text{total number of possible combinations}\\\text{for selecting 7 people}\end{array}\right)}$$

$$= \frac{_6C_3 \cdot {_5C_4}}{_{11}C_7} = \frac{20 \cdot 5}{330} = \frac{100}{330} = \frac{10}{33}$$

Thus, the probability is $\frac{10}{33}$.   ∎

Example 4 *DVD Selection*

Jennifer Alfredo has 4 *Scooby Doo* DVDs, 5 *Magic School Bus* DVDs, and 3 *Bob the Builder* DVDs. If Jennifer randomly selects 4 DVDs for her children to take on a road trip, determine the probability that
a) no *Scooby Doo* DVDs are selected.
b) at least 1 *Scooby Doo* DVD is selected.
c) 2 *Scooby Doo* DVDs and 2 *Magic School Bus* DVDs are selected.

Solution

a) If no *Scooby Doo* DVDs are to be selected, then only *Magic School Bus* and *Bob the Builder* DVDs must be selected. Eight DVDs are either *Magic School Bus* or *Bob the Builder*. Thus, the number of ways that 4 *Magic School Bus* or *Bob the Builder* DVDs may be selected from the possible 8 *Magic School Bus* or *Bob the Builder* DVDs is $_8C_4$. The total number of possible selections is $_{12}C_4$.

$$P(\text{no } Scooby\ Doo \text{ DVDs}) = \frac{_8C_4}{_{12}C_4} = \frac{70}{495} = \frac{14}{99}$$

b) When 4 DVDs are selected, the choice must contain either no *Scooby Doo* DVDs or at least 1 *Scooby Doo* DVD. Since one of these outcomes must occur, the sum of the probabilities must be 1, or

$$P(\text{no } Scooby\ Doo \text{ DVDs}) + P(\text{at least 1 } Scooby\ Doo \text{ DVD}) = 1$$

Therefore,

$$P(\text{at least 1 } Scooby \ Doo \text{ DVD}) = 1 - P(\text{no } Scooby \ Doo \text{ DVDs})$$

$$= 1 - \frac{14}{99} = \frac{99}{99} - \frac{14}{99} = \frac{85}{99}$$

Note that the probability of selecting no *Scooby Doo* DVDs, $\frac{14}{99}$, was found in part (a).

c) The number of ways of selecting 2 *Scooby Doo* DVDs out of 4 *Scooby Doo* DVDs is $_4C_2$, which equals 6. The number of ways of selecting 2 *Magic School Bus* DVDs out of 5 *Magic School Bus* DVDs is $_5C_2$, which equals 10. The total number of possible selections when 4 DVDs are selected from the 12 choices is $_{12}C_4$, which equals 495. Since both the 2 *Scooby Doo* and 2 *Magic School Bus* DVDs must be selected, the probability is calculated as follows.

$$P(2 \ Scooby \ Doo \text{ and } 2 \ Magic \ School \ Bus) = \frac{_4C_2 \cdot {_5C_2}}{_{12}C_4} = \frac{6 \cdot 10}{495} = \frac{60}{495} = \frac{4}{33} \blacksquare$$

Example 5 *Rare Coins*

Conner Shanahan's rare coin collection is made up of 8 silver dollars, 7 quarters, and 5 dimes. Conner plans to sell 8 of his 20 coins to finance part of his college education. If he selects the coins at random, what is the probability that 3 silver dollars, 2 quarters, and 3 dimes are selected?

Solution   The number of ways that Conner can select 3 out of 8 silver dollars is $_8C_3$. The number of ways he can select 2 out of 7 quarters is $_7C_2$. The number of ways he can select 3 out of 5 dimes is $_5C_3$. He will select 8 coins from a total of 20 coins. The number of ways he can do so is $_{20}C_8$. The probability that Conner selects 3 silver dollars, 2 quarters, and 3 dimes is calculated as follows.

$$P(3 \text{ silver dollars, 2 quarters, and 3 dimes}) = \frac{_8C_3 \cdot {_7C_2} \cdot {_5C_3}}{_{20}C_8}$$

$$= \frac{56 \cdot 21 \cdot 10}{125{,}970} = \frac{11{,}760}{125{,}970} = \frac{392}{4199} \blacksquare$$

SECTION 12.10
Exercises

Practice the Skills

In Exercises 1–8, set up the problem as if it were to be solved, but do not solve. Assume that each problem is to be done without replacement.

1. Ten red balls and four blue balls are in a bag. If four balls from the bag are to be selected at random, determine the probability of selecting four red balls.

2. A class consists of 15 girls and 12 boys. If 8 of the students are to be selected at random, determine the probability that they are all girls.

3. Three letters are to be selected at random from the English alphabet of 26 letters. Determine the probability that 3 vowels (a, e, i, o, u) are selected.

4. Determine the probability of being dealt 3 aces from a standard deck of 52 cards when 3 cards are dealt.

5. A dog breeder has 15 puppies for sale, of which 8 are yellow Labrador retrievers. If 5 puppies are selected at random, determine the probability they are all yellow Labrador retrievers.

6. Of 80 people attending a dance, 28 have a college degree. If 4 people at the dance are selected at random, determine the probability that each of the 4 has a college degree.

7. Of 120 students attending a college orientation session, 23 are criminal justice majors. If 5 students at the orientation are selected at random, determine the probability that each of the 5 is a criminal justice major.

8. A class of 16 people contains 4 people whose birthday is in October. If 3 people from the class are selected at random, determine the probability that *none* of those selected has an October birthday.

Problem Solving

In Exercises 9–18, the problems are to be done without replacement. Use combinations to determine probabilities.

9. **Selecting Lightbulbs**   A box contains 3 defective and 7 good lightbulbs. If two lightbulbs are to be selected at random from the box, determine the probability that both lightbulbs are defective.

10. **Green and Red Balls**   A bag contains four red balls and five green balls. You plan to select three balls at random. Determine the probability of selecting three green balls.

11. **Flu Vaccine**   A doctor has five doses of flu protection vaccine left. He has six women and eight men who want the medication. If the names of five of these people are selected at random, determine the probability that five men's names are selected.

12. **Bills of Four Denominations**   Duc Tran's wallet contains 8 bills of the following denominations: four $5 bills, two $10 bills, one $20 bill, and one $50 bill. If Duc selects two bills at random, determine the probability that he selects two $5 bills.

13. **Selecting Digits**   Each of the digits 0–9 is written on a slip of paper, and the slips are placed in a hat. If three slips of paper are selected at random, determine the probability that the three numbers selected are greater than 5.

14. **Selecting Books**   Barnes & Noble has 20 different books listed on its clearance list. Twelve books are listed as mystery, and 8 are listed as romance. If 4 books are selected at random from the list, determine the probability that they are all mystery books.

15. **Gift Certificates**   The sales department at Atwell Studios consists of three people, the manufacturing department consists of six people, and the accounting department consists of two people. Three people will be selected at random from these people and will be given gift certificates to Sweet Tomatoes, a local restaurant. Determine the probability that two of those selected will be from the manufacturing department and one will be from the accounting department.

16. **Faculty-Student Committee**   A committee of four is to be randomly selected from a group of seven teachers and eight students. Determine the probability that the committee will consist of two teachers and two students.

17. **Winning the Grand Prize**   A lottery consists of 46 numbers. You select 6 numbers, and if they match the 6 numbers selected by the lottery commission, you win the grand prize. Determine the probability of winning the grand prize.

18. **Red Cards**   You are dealt 5 cards from a standard deck of 52 cards. Determine the probability that you are dealt 5 red cards.

TV Game Show   In Exercises 19–22, a television game show has five doors, of which the contestant must pick two. Behind two of the doors are expensive cars, and behind the other three doors are consolation prizes. The contestant gets to keep the items behind the two doors she selects. Determine the probability that the contestant wins

19. no cars.   20. both cars.

21. at least one car.   22. exactly one car.

Baseball   In Exercises 23–26, assume that a particular professional baseball team has 10 pitchers, 6 infielders, and 9 other players. If 3 players' names are selected at random, determine the probability that

23. all 3 are infielders.

24. none of the three is a pitcher.

25. 2 are pitchers and 1 is an infielder.

26. 1 is a pitcher and 2 are players other than pitchers and infielders.

Car Rental In Exercises 27–30, a car rental agency has 10 midsized and 15 compact cars on its lot, from which 6 will be selected. Assuming that each car is equally likely to be selected and the cars are selected at random, determine the probability (as a decimal number rounded to four decimal places) that the cars selected consist of

27. all midsized cars.

28. 2 midsized cars and 4 compact cars.

29. 3 midsized cars and 3 compact cars.

30. at least 1 compact car.

New Soup In Exercises 31–34, Campbell's is testing 12 new soups for possible production. They are testing 3 Chunky soups, 4 Healthy Request soups, and 5 Select Harvest soups. If we assume each of the 12 soups has the same chance of being selected and 4 new soups will be produced, determine the probability that the four new soups selected will be as follows

31. 2 are Healthy Request soups and 2 are Chunky soups.

32. 3 are Select Harvest soups and 1 is a Healthy Request soup.

33. 1 is a Healthy Request soup, 1 is a Select Harvest soup, and 2 are Chunky soups.

34. at least one is a Chunky soup.

Theater In Exercises 35–38, five men and six women are going to be assigned to a specific row of seats in a theater. If the 11 tickets for the numbered seats are given out at random, determine the probability that

35. five women are given the first five seats next to the center aisle.

36. at least one woman is in one of the first five seats.

37. exactly one woman is in one of the first five seats.

38. three women are seated in the first three seats and two men are seated in the next two seats.

39. *Working Overtime* Of 24 employees at Lowe's home improvement store, 10 work as cashiers and 14 stock shelves. If 3 of the 24 employees are selected at random to work overtime, determine the probability that all 3 are cashiers.

40. *Poker Probability* A full house in poker consists of three of one kind and two of another kind in a five-card hand. For example, if a hand contains three kings and two 5's, it is a full house. If 5 cards are dealt at random from a standard deck of 52 cards, without replacement,

determine the probability of getting three kings and two 5's.

41. *A Royal Flush* A royal flush consists of an ace, king, queen, jack, and 10 all in the same suit. If 7 cards are dealt at random from a standard deck of 52 cards, determine the probability of getting a

a) royal flush in spades.

b) royal flush in any suit.

42. *Restaurant Staff* The staff of a restaurant consists of 25 people, including 8 waiters, 12 waitresses, and 5 cooks. For Mother's Day, a total of 9 people will need to be selected to work. If the selections are made at random, determine the probability that 3 waiters, 4 waitresses, and 2 cooks will be selected.

43. *"Dead Man's Hand"* A pair of aces and a pair of 8's is often known as a "dead man's hand." (See the *Did You Know?* on page 753.)

a) Determine the probability of being dealt a dead man's hand (any two aces, any two 8's, and one other card that is not an ace or an 8) when 5 cards are dealt, without replacement, from a standard deck of 52 cards.

b) The actual cards "Wild Bill" Hickok was holding when he was shot were the aces of spades and clubs, the 8's of spades and clubs, and the 9 of diamonds. If you are dealt five cards without replacement, determine the probability of being dealt this exact hand.

Challenge Problems/Group Activities

44. *Alternate Seating* If three men and three women are to be assigned at random to six seats in a row at a theater, determine the probability that they will alternate by gender.

45. *Selecting Officers* A club consists of 15 people including Ali, Kendra, Ted, Alice, Marie, Dan, Linda, and Frank. From the 15 members, a president, vice president, and treasurer will be selected at random. An advisory committee of 5 other individuals will also be selected at random.

a) Determine the probability that Ali is selected president, Kendra is selected vice president, Ted is selected treasurer, and the other 5 individuals named form the advisory committee.

b) Determine the probability that 3 of the 8 individuals named are selected for the three officers' positions and the other 5 are selected for the advisory board.

46. *A Marked Deck* A number is written with a magic marker on each card of a deck of 52 cards. The number 1 is put on the first card, 2 on the second, and so on. The cards are then shuffled and cut. What is the probability that the top 4 cards will be in ascending order? (For example, the top card is 12, the second 22, the third 41, and the fourth 51.)

Recreational Mathematics

47. *Hair* When the Isle of Flume took its most recent census, the population was 100,002 people. Nobody on the isle has more than 100,001 hairs on his or her head. Determine the probability that at least two people have exactly the same number of hairs on their head.

SECTION 12.11   Binomial Probability Formula

▲ We can use the binomial formula to determine the probability that selected customers waited on will leave a tip.

Figure 12.23

Suppose that you are a waiter at a restaurant and have learned from past experience that 80% of your customers leave a tip. If you wait on 6 customers, what is the probability that all 6 customers will leave a tip? If you wait on 8 customers, what is the probability that at least 5 of them will leave you a tip? In this section, we will learn how to use the binomial probability formula to answer these and similar questions.

Why *This is Important* Binomial probabilities have many applications in business and industry, as well as in the sciences and the pharmacological industry.

Suppose that a basket contains three identical balls, except for their color. One is red, one is blue, and one is yellow (Fig. 12.23). Suppose further that we are going to select three balls *with replacement* from the basket. We can determine specific probabilities by examining the tree diagram shown in Fig. 12.24. Note that 27 different selections are possible, as indicated in the sample space.

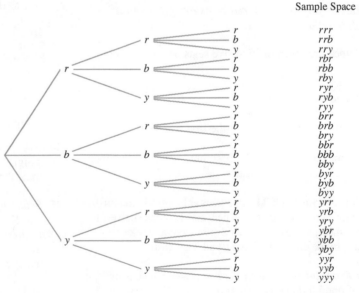

Figure 12.24

Our three selections may yield 0, 1, 2, or 3 red balls. We can determine the probability of selecting exactly 0, 1, 2, or 3 red balls by using the sample space. To determine the probability of selecting 0 red balls, we count those outcomes that do not contain a red ball. There are 8 of them (*bbb, bby, byb, byy, ybb, yby, yyb, yyy*). Thus, the probability of obtaining exactly 0 red balls is 8/27. We determine the probability of selecting exactly 1 red ball by counting the sample points that contain exactly 1 red ball. There are 12 of them. Thus, the probability is $\frac{12}{27}$, or $\frac{4}{9}$.

We can determine the probability of selecting exactly 2 red balls and exactly 3 red balls in a similar manner. The probabilities of selecting exactly 0, 1, 2, and 3 red balls are illustrated in Table 12.5.

Table 12.5 A Probability Distribution for Three Balls Selected with Replacement

Number of Red Balls Selected, (x)	Probability of Selecting the Number of Red Balls, $P(x)$
0	$\frac{8}{27}$
1	$\frac{12}{27}$
2	$\frac{6}{27}$
3	$\frac{1}{27}$
	Sum $= \frac{27}{27} = 1$

Note that the sum of the probabilities is 1. This table is an example of a *probability distribution*, which shows the probabilities associated with each specific outcome of an experiment. *In a probability distribution, every possible outcome must be listed and the sum of the probabilities must be 1.*

Let us specifically consider the probability of selecting 1 red ball in 3 selections. We see from Table 12.5 that this probability is $\frac{12}{27}$, or $\frac{4}{9}$. Can we determine this probability without developing a tree diagram? The answer is yes.

Suppose that we consider selecting a red ball success, S, and selecting a non–red ball failure, F. Furthermore, suppose that we let p represent the probability of success and q the probability of failure on any trial. Then $p = \frac{1}{3}$ and $q = \frac{2}{3}$. We can obtain 1 success in three selections in the following ways:

$$\text{SFF} \qquad \text{FSF} \qquad \text{FFS}$$

We can compute the probabilities of each of these outcomes using the multiplication formula because each of the selections is independent.

$$P(\text{SFF}) = P(\text{S}) \cdot P(\text{F}) \cdot P(\text{F}) = p \cdot q \cdot q = pq^2 = \frac{1}{3}\left(\frac{2}{3}\right)^2 = \frac{4}{27}$$

$$P(\text{FSF}) = P(\text{F}) \cdot P(\text{S}) \cdot P(\text{F}) = q \cdot p \cdot q = pq^2 = \frac{1}{3}\left(\frac{2}{3}\right)^2 = \frac{4}{27}$$

$$P(\text{FFS}) = P(\text{F}) \cdot P(\text{F}) \cdot P(\text{S}) = q \cdot q \cdot p = pq^2 = \frac{1}{3}\left(\frac{2}{3}\right)^2 = \frac{4}{27}$$

$$\text{Sum} = \frac{12}{27} = \frac{4}{9}$$

We obtained an answer of $\frac{4}{9}$, the same answer that was obtained using the tree diagram. Note that each of the 3 sets of outcomes above has 1 success and 2 failures

Rather than listing all the possibilities containing 1 success and 2 failures, we can use the combination formula to determine the number of possible combinations of 1 success in 3 trials. To do so, evaluate $_3C_1$.

$$\underset{\substack{\text{Number}\\\text{of trials}}}{\nearrow} {}_3C_1 \underset{\substack{\text{Number}\\\text{of successes}}}{\nwarrow} = \frac{3!}{(3-1)!1!} = \frac{3 \cdot 2 \cdot 1}{2 \cdot 1 \cdot 1} = 3$$

Thus, we see that there are 3 ways the 1 success could occur in 3 trials. To compute the probability of 1 success in 3 trials, we can multiply the probability of success in any one trial, $p \cdot q^2$, by the number of ways the 1 success can be arranged among the 3 trials, $_3C_1$. Thus, the probability of selecting 1 red ball, $P(1)$, in 3 trials may be found as follows.

$$P(1) = ({}_3C_1)p^1q^2 = 3\left(\frac{1}{3}\right)\left(\frac{2}{3}\right)^2 = \frac{12}{27} = \frac{4}{9}$$

The binomial probability formula, which we introduce shortly, explains how to obtain expressions like $P(1) = ({}_3C_1)p^1q^2$ and is very useful in finding certain types of probabilities.

To use the binomial probability formula, the following three conditions must hold.

To Use The Binomial Probability Formula
1. There are n repeated independent trials.
2. Each trial has two possible outcomes, *success* and *failure*.
3. For each trial, the probability of success (and failure) remains the same.

Before going further, let's discuss why we can use the binomial probability formula to find the probability of selecting a specific number of red balls when three balls are selected with replacement. First, since each trial is performed *with replacement*, the three trials are independent of each other. Second, we may consider selecting a red ball as success and selecting any ball of another color as failure. Third, for each selection, the probability of success (selecting a red ball) is $\frac{1}{3}$ and the probability of failure (selecting a ball of another color) is $\frac{2}{3}$. Now let's discuss the binomial probability formula.

Binomial Probability Formula
The probability of obtaining exactly x successes, $P(x)$, in n independent trials is given by the binomial probability formula

$$P(x) = ({}_nC_x)p^xq^{n-x}$$

where p is the probability of success on a single trial and q is the probability of failure on a single trial.

In the formula, p will be a number between 0 and 1, inclusive, and $q = 1 - p$. Therefore, if $p = 0.2$, then $q = 1 - 0.2 = 0.8$. If $p = \frac{3}{5}$, then $q = 1 - \frac{3}{5} = \frac{2}{5}$. Note that $p + q = 1$ and the values of p and q remain the same for each independent trial. The combination $_nC_x$ is called the *binomial coefficient*.

In Example 1, we use the binomial probability formula to solve the same problem we recently solved by using a tree diagram.

Example 1 Selecting Colored Balls with Replacement

A basket contains 3 balls: 1 red, 1 blue, and 1 yellow. Three balls are going to be selected with replacement from the basket. Find the probability that

a) no red balls are selected.

b) exactly 1 red ball is selected.

c) exactly 2 red balls are selected.

d) exactly 3 red balls are selected.

Solution

a) We will consider selecting a red ball a success and selecting a ball of any other color a failure. Since only 1 of the 3 balls is red, the probability of success on any single trial, p, is $\frac{1}{3}$. The probability of failure on any single trial, q, is $1 - \frac{1}{3} = \frac{2}{3}$. We are finding the probability of selecting 0 red balls, or 0 successes. Since x represents the number of successes, we let $x = 0$. There are 3 independent selections (or trials), so $n = 3$. In our calculations, we will need to evaluate $\left(\frac{1}{3}\right)^0$. Note that any nonzero number raised to a power of 0 is 1. Thus, $\left(\frac{1}{3}\right)^0 = 1$. We determine the probability of 0 successes, or $P(0)$, as follows.

$$P(x) = ({}_nC_x)p^xq^{n-x}$$
$$P(0) = ({}_3C_0)\left(\frac{1}{3}\right)^0\left(\frac{2}{3}\right)^{3-0}$$
$$= (1)(1)\left(\frac{2}{3}\right)^3$$
$$= \left(\frac{2}{3}\right)^3 = \frac{8}{27}$$

b) We are finding the probability of obtaining exactly 1 red ball or exactly 1 success in 3 independent selections. Thus, $x = 1$ and $n = 3$. We find the probability of exactly 1 success, or $P(1)$, as follows.

$$P(x) = ({}_nC_x)p^xq^{n-x}$$
$$P(1) = ({}_3C_1)\left(\frac{1}{3}\right)^1\left(\frac{2}{3}\right)^{3-1}$$
$$= 3\left(\frac{1}{3}\right)\left(\frac{2}{3}\right)^2$$
$$= 3\left(\frac{1}{3}\right)\left(\frac{4}{9}\right) = \frac{4}{9}$$

c) We are finding the probability of selecting exactly 2 red balls in 3 independent trials. Thus, $x = 2$ and $n = 3$. We find $P(2)$ as follows.

$$P(x) = ({}_nC_x)p^xq^{n-x}$$
$$P(2) = {}_3C_2\left(\frac{1}{3}\right)^2\left(\frac{2}{3}\right)^{3-2}$$
$$= 3\left(\frac{1}{3}\right)^2\left(\frac{2}{3}\right)^1$$
$$= 3\left(\frac{1}{9}\right)\left(\frac{2}{3}\right) = \frac{2}{9}$$

d) We are finding the probability of selecting exactly 3 red balls in 3 independent trials. Thus, $x = 3$ and $n = 3$. We find $P(3)$ as follows.

$$P(x) = (_nC_x)p^xq^{n-x}$$

$$P(3) = (_3C_3)\left(\frac{1}{3}\right)^3\left(\frac{2}{3}\right)^{3-3}$$

$$= 1\left(\frac{1}{3}\right)^3\left(\frac{2}{3}\right)^0$$

$$= 1\left(\frac{1}{27}\right)(1) = \frac{1}{27}$$

All the probabilities obtained in Example 1 agree with the answers obtained by using the tree diagram. Whenever you obtain a value for $P(x)$, you should obtain a value between 0 and 1, inclusive. If you obtain a value greater than 1, you have made a mistake.

Example 2   *Quality Control for Batteries*

A manufacturer of batteries knows that 0.4% of the batteries produced by the company are defective.

a) Write the binomial probability formula that would be used to determine the probability that exactly x out of n batteries produced are defective.

b) Write the binomial probability formula that would be used to find the probability that exactly 3 batteries of 75 produced will be defective. Do not evaluate.

Solution

a) We want to find the probability that exactly x batteries are defective where selecting a defective battery is considered success. The probability, p, that an individual battery is defective is 0.4%, or 0.004 in decimal form. The probability that a battery is not defective, q, is $1 - 0.004$, or 0.996. The general formula for finding the probability that exactly x out of n batteries produced are defective is

$$P(x) = (_nC_x)p^xq^{n-x}$$

Substituting 0.004 for p and 0.996 for q, we obtain the formula

$$P(x) = (_nC_x)(0.004)^x(0.996)^{n-x}$$

b) We want to determine the probability that exactly 3 batteries out of 75 produced are defective. Thus, $x = 3$ and $n = 75$. Substituting these values into the formula in part (a) gives

$$P(3) = (_{75}C_3)(0.004)^3(0.996)^{75-3}$$

$$= (_{75}C_3)(0.004)^3(0.996)^{72}$$

The answer may be obtained using a scientific calculator.

Example 3   *Spring Break*

According to a survey conducted by OnCampus Research, 20% of college students reported they will work during spring break. Determine the probability that

a) exactly 3 of 5 college students selected at random will work during spring break.

b) exactly 4 of 4 college students selected at random will work during spring break.

Solution

a) We want to determine the probability that exactly 3 of 5 college students selected at random will work during spring break. Therefore a college student working during spring break is considered a success. Thus, $x = 3$ and $n = 5$. The probability of success, p, is 20%, or 0.2. The probability of failure, q, is $1-0.2$, or 0.8. Substituting these values into the binomial formula yields

$$P(x) = (_nC_x)p^xq^{n-x}$$
$$P(3) = (_5C_3)(0.2)^3(0.8)^{5-3}$$
$$= 10(0.2)^3(0.8)^2$$
$$= 10(0.008)(0.64)$$
$$= 0.0512$$

Thus, the probability that exactly 3 of 5 randomly selected college students will work during spring break is 0.0512.

b) We want to find the probability that 4 of 4 college students selected at random will work during spring break. Thus, $x = 4$ and $n = 4$. We wish to find $P(4)$.

$$P(x) = (_nC_x)p^xq^{n-x}$$
$$P(4) = (_4C_4)(0.2)^4(0.8)^{4-4}$$
$$= 1(0.2)^4(0.8)^0$$
$$= 10(0.0016)(1)$$
$$= 0.016$$

Thus, the probability that exactly 4 of 4 randomly selected college students will work during spring break is 0.016. ∎

Example 4   *Planting Trees*

The probability that a tree planted by a landscaping company will survive is 0.8. Determine the probability that

a) none of four trees planted will survive.

b) at least one of four trees planted will survive.

Solution

a) Success is a tree survives. Thus, $p = 0.8$ and $q = 1 - p = 1 - 0.8 = 0.2$. We want to find the probability of 0 successes in 4 trials. Thus, $x = 0$ and $n = 4$. We find the probability of 0 successes, or $P(0)$, as follows.

$$P(x) = (_nC_x)p^xq^{n-x}$$
$$P(0) = (_4C_0)(0.8)^0(0.2)^{4-0}$$
$$= 1(1)(0.2)^4$$
$$= 1(1)(0.0016)$$
$$= 0.0016$$

Thus, the probability that none of the four trees planted will survive is 0.0016.

b) The probability that at least one tree of the four trees planted will survive can be found by subtracting from 1 the probability that none of the four trees survives. We worked problems of this type in earlier sections of the chapter, including Sections 12.6 and 12.10.

In part (a), we determined the probability that none of the four trees planted survives is 0.0016. Thus,

$$P(\text{at least one tree planted will survive}) = 1 - P\left(\begin{array}{c}\text{none of the four trees}\\\text{planted will survive}\end{array}\right)$$
$$= 1 - 0.0016$$
$$= 0.9984$$

SECTION 12.11   *Exercises*

Warm Up Exercises

In Exercises 1–4, fill in the blank with an appropriate word, phrase, or symbol(s).

1. A distribution that shows the probabilities associated with each specific outcome of an experiment is called a(n) _____ distribution.

2. In a probability distribution, the sum of all the probabilities must be _____.

3. In the binomial probability formula, p represents the probability of _____.

4. In the binomial probability formula, q represents the probability of _____.

Practice the Skills

In Exercises 5–10, assume that each of the n trials is independent and that p is the probability of success on a given trial. Use the binomial probability formula to find P(x).

5. $n = 4, x = 3, p = 0.1$

6. $n = 5, x = 2, p = 0.6$

7. $n = 5, x = 2, p = 0.4$

8. $n = 3, x = 3, p = 0.8$

9. $n = 6, x = 0, p = 0.5$

10. $n = 5, x = 3, p = 0.9$

Problem Solving

11. *A Dozen Eggs* An egg distributor determines that the probability that any individual egg has a crack is 0.14.

    a) Write the binomial probability formula to determine the probability that exactly x eggs of n eggs are cracked.

    b) Write the binomial probability formula to determine the probability that exactly 2 eggs in a one-dozen egg carton are cracked. Do not evaluate.

12. *Facebook* According to *Social Media Today,* as of April 2010, 41.6% of Americans had a Facebook account.

    a) Write the binomial formula to determine the probability that exactly x out of n randomly selected Americans had a Facebook account.

    b) Write the binomial formula to determine the probability that exactly 5 out of 20 randomly selected Americans had a Facebook account. Do not evaluate.

In Exercises 13–21, use the binomial probability formula to answer the question. Round answers to five decimal places.

13. *Auto Insurance* An insurance company reported that 60% of all automobile damage claims were made by people under the age of 25. If eight automobile damage claims were selected at random, determine the probability that exactly five of them were made by someone under the age of 25.

14. *Leaving a Tip* Thomas Zellner works as a waiter at Outback Steakhouse. He has learned from experience that 80% of customers who dine alone leave a tip. If Thomas waits on 6 customers dining alone, determine the probability that exactly 4 of them leave a tip.

15. *Staying Connected* According to a survey conducted by American Express, 77% of adults stated they want access to their cell phones and laptops while on vacation. If ten adults are selected at random, determine the probability that exactly six of them want access to their cell phones and laptops while on vacation.

16. *Bank Loans* Records from a specific bank show that 70% of car loan applications are approved. If eight car loan applications from this bank are selected at random, determine the probability that exactly five of the applications are approved.

17. *Dolphin Drug Care* When treated with the antibiotic resonocyllin, 92% of all dolphins are cured of a particular bacterial infection. If six dolphins with the particular bacterial infection are treated with resonocyllin, determine the probability that exactly four are cured.

18. *Manufacturing Lightbulbs* A quality control engineer at a GE lightbulb plant finds that 1% of its bulbs are defective. Determine the probability that exactly two of the next six bulbs made are defective.

19. *Water Heaters* The probability that a specific brand of water heater produces the water temperature it is set to produce is $\frac{4}{5}$. Determine the probability that if five of these water heaters are selected at random, exactly four of them will produce the water temperature they are set to produce.

20. *TV Purchases* At a Circuit City store, $\frac{1}{4}$ of those purchasing color televisions purchase a large-screen TV. Determine the probability that

a) none of the next four people who purchase a color television at Circuit City purchases a large-screen TV.

b) at least one of the next four people who purchase a color television at Circuit City purchases a large-screen TV.

21. *Multiple-Choice Quiz* Edward Dunn has to take a five-question multiple-choice quiz in his sociology class. Each question has four choices for answers, of which only one is correct. Assuming that Edward guesses on all five questions, what is the probability that he will answer

a) all five questions correctly.

b) exactly three questions correctly.

c) at least three questions correctly.

Challenge Problems/Group Activities

22. *Transportation to Work* In a random sample of 80 working mothers in Duluth, Minnesota, the following data indicating how they get to work were obtained.

Mode of Transportation	Number of Mothers
Car	40
Bus	20
Bike	16
Other	4

If this sample is representative of all working mothers in Duluth, determine the probability that exactly three of five working mothers selected at random

a) take a car to work.

b) take a bus to work.

23. *Selecting 6 Cards* Six cards are selected from a standard deck of playing cards with replacement. Determine the probability that

a) exactly three picture cards are obtained.

b) exactly two spades are obtained.

24. *Office Visit* The probability that a person visiting Dr. Guillermo Suarez's office is more than 60 years old is 0.7. Determine the probability that

a) exactly three of the next five people visiting the office are more than 60 years old.

b) at least three of the next five people visiting the office are more than 60 years old.

Recreational Mathematics

25. *Aruba* The island of Aruba is well known for its beaches and predictable warm, sunny weather. In fact, Aruba's weather is so predictable that the daily newspapers don't even bother to print a forecast. Strangely enough, however, on New Year's Eve, as the islanders were counting down the last 10 sec of 2011, it began to rain. What is the probability, from 0 to 1, that 72 hr later the sun will be shining?

CHAPTER 12) *Summary*

Important Facts And Concepts

Examples and Discussion

Section 12.1
Empirical Probability

$$P(E) = \frac{\text{number of times event } E \text{ has occurred}}{\left(\begin{array}{c}\text{total number of times the}\\\text{experiment has been performed}\end{array}\right)}$$

Examples 1–2, pages 676–677

The Law of Large Numbers

Probability statements apply in practice to a large number of trials, not to a single trial. It is the relative frequency over the long run that is accurately predictable, not individual events or precise totals.

Discussion, pages 678–679

Section 12.2
Theoretical Probability

$$P(E) = \frac{\text{number of outcomes favorable to } E}{\text{total number of possible outcomes}}$$

Examples 1–3, pages 684–687

Probability Facts	
The probability of an event that cannot occur is 0. The probability of an event that must occur is 1. Every probability must be a number between 0 and 1 inclusively; that is	Discussion, page 684
$$0 \le P(E) \le 1$$	
The sum of the probabilities of all possible outcomes of an event is 1.	Example 3, page 686
$$P(A) + P(\text{not } A) = 1$$	

Section 12.3

Odds Against an Event

$$\text{Odds against} = \frac{P(\text{event fails to occur})}{P(\text{event occurs})} = \frac{P(\text{failure})}{P(\text{success})}$$	Examples 1–3, pages 691–693

Odds in Favor of an Event

$$\text{Odds in favor} = \frac{P(\text{event occurs})}{P(\text{event fails to occur})} = \frac{P(\text{success})}{P(\text{failure})}$$	Example 3, page 693

Section 12.4

Expected Value

$$E = P_1 A_1 + P_2 A_2 + P_3 A_3 + \cdots + P_n A_n$$	Examples 1–6, pages 699–702

Section 12.5

Counting Principle

If a first experiment can be performed in M distinct ways and a second experiment can be performed in N distinct ways, then the two experiments in that specific order can be performed in $M \cdot N$ distinct ways.	Examples 1–3, pages 709–711

Section 12.6

OR and AND problems

$$P(A \text{ or } B) = P(A) + P(B) - P(A \text{ and } B)$$	Examples 1–3, pages 717–719
$$P(A \text{ and } B) = P(A) \cdot P(B)$$	Examples 4–7, pages 720–723

Section 12.7

Conditional Probability

$$P(E_2|E_1) = \frac{n(E_1 \text{ and } E_2)}{n(E_1)}$$	Examples 1–3, pages 729–731

Section 12.8

The **number of permutations** of n items is $n!$.	
$$n! = n(n-1)(n-2) \cdots (3)(2)(1)$$	Example 3, page 738

Permutation Formula

$$_nP_r = \frac{n!}{(n-r)!}$$	Examples 4–6, pages 738–741
The number of different permutations of n objects where $n_1, n_2, \ldots, n_r$ of the objects are identical is	
$$\frac{n!}{n_1! n_2! \cdots n_r!}$$	Example 7, page 742

Section 12.9, 12.10
Combination Formula

$$_nC_r = \frac{n!}{(n-r)!\,r!}$$

Examples 2–4, page 748
Examples 1–5, pages 753–755

Section 12.11
Binomial Probability Formula

$$P(x) = (_nC_x)p^x q^{n-x}$$

Examples 1–4, pages 761–763

CHAPTER 12   *Review Exercises*

12.1–12.11

1. In your own words, explain the law of large numbers.

2. Explain how empirical probability can be used to determine whether a dic is "loaded" (not a fair die).

3. *Cars* Of 45 people who purchase a vehicle at a car dealership, 9 purchased an SUV. Determine the empirical probability that the next person who purchases a vehicle from that car dealership purchases an SUV.

4. *Cards* Select a card from a deck of cards 40 times with replacement and compute the empirical probability of selecting a heart.

5. *Television News* In a small town, 250 people were asked whether they watched ABC, CBS, NBC, Fox, or MSNBC news. The results are indicated below.

Network	Number of People
ABC	80
CBS	35
NBC	60
Fox	35
MSNBC	40

Determine the empirical probability that the next person selected at random from the town watches ABC news.

Digits In Exercises 6–9, each of the digits 0, 1, 2, 3, 4, 5, 6, 7, 8, 9 is written on a piece of paper and all the pieces of paper are placed in a hat. One number is selected at random. Determine the probability that the number selected is

6. even.

7. odd or greater than 3.

8. greater than 2 or less than 6.

9. even and greater than 4.

Yogurt Preference In Exercises 10–13, a taste test is given to 50 customers at a supermarket. The customers are asked to taste 4 types of yogurt and to list their favorite. The results are summarized below.

Type	Number of People
Strawberry	18
Raspberry	14
Blueberry	11
Banana creme pie	7

If one person who participated in the taste test is selected at random, determine the probability that the person's favorite was

10. strawberry

11. blueberry

12. either strawberry or raspberry.

13. a yogurt other than banana creme pie.

14. *Obesity* According to the U.S. Centers for Disease Control and Prevention, 20% of children in the United States,

age 6–11, are obese. If a child age 6–11 was selected at random, determine the odds

a) against the child being obese.

b) in favor of the child being obese.

15. *Vegetable Mix-up* Nicholas Delaney, a mischievous little boy, has removed labels on the eight cans of vegetables in the cabinet. Nicholas's father knows that there are three cans of corn, three cans of beans, and two cans of carrots. If the father selects and opens one can at random, determine the odds against his selecting a can of corn.

16. *Horseracing* The odds against Buttermilk winning the Triple Crown in horse racing are 82 : 3. Determine the probability that Buttermilk wins the Triple Crown.

17. *Dry Cleaner Success* The probability that a new dry cleaner will succeed at a given location is 0.85. Determine the odds in favor of the dry cleaner succeeding.

18. *Raffle Tickets* One thousand raffle tickets are sold at $2 each. Three prizes of $200 and two prizes of $100 will be awarded. Assume that the probability that any given ticket is selected for a $200 prize is $\frac{3}{1000}$ and the probability that any given ticket is selected for a $100 prize is $\frac{2}{1000}$.

a) Determine the expectation of a person who purchases a ticket.

b) Determine the expectation of a person who purchases three tickets.

19. *Expectation of a Card* If Cameron selects a picture card from a standard deck of 52 cards, Lindsey will give him $9. If Cameron does not select a picture card, he must give Lindsey $3.

a) Determine Cameron's expectation.

b) Determine Lindsey's expectation.

c) If Cameron plays this game 100 times, how much can he expect to lose or gain?

20. *Expected Attendance* If the day is sunny, 1000 people will attend the baseball game. If the day is cloudy, only 500 people will attend. If it rains, only 100 people will attend. The local meteorologist states that the probability of a sunny day is 0.4, of a cloudy day is 0.5, and of a rainy day is 0.1. Determine the number of people that are expected to attend.

21. *Fair Price* At a game of chance, the expected value is found to be −$2.50, and the cost to play the game is $6.50. Determine the fair price to play the game.

22. *Fair Price* The expected value when you purchase a lottery ticket is −$1.50, and the cost to play the game is $5.00. Determine the fair price of the lottery ticket.

23. *Club Officers* Tina, Jake, Gina, and Carla form a club. They plan to select a president and a vice president.

a) Construct a tree diagram showing all the possible outcomes.

b) List the sample space.

c) Determine the probability that Gina is selected president and Jake is selected vice president.

24. *A Coin and a Number* A coin is flipped and then a number from 1 through 4 is selected at random from a bag.

a) Construct a tree diagram showing all the possible outcomes.

b) List the sample space.

c) Determine the probability that a head is flipped and an odd number is selected.

d) Determine the probability that a head is flipped or an odd number is selected.

Spinning Two Wheels In Exercises 25–30, the outer and inner wheels are spun.

Assuming that the wheels are independent and the outcomes are equally likely, determine the probability of obtaining

25. even numbers on both wheels.

26. numbers greater than 5 on both wheels.

27. an odd number on the outer wheel and a number less than 6 on the inner wheel.

28. an even number or a number less than 6 on the outer wheel.

29. an even number or a color other than green on the inner wheel.

30. gold on the outer wheel and a color other than gold on the inner wheel.

Sports Drink Selection *In Exercises 31–34, assume that Skip Bailey is going to purchase three bottles of sports drinks at a convenience store. The store has 12 different bottles of sports drinks, including 5 different bottles made by Gatorade, 4 different bottles made by Powerade, and 3 different bottles made by All Sport. If Skip selects 3 of these 12 bottles at random, determine the probability he selects*

31. 3 bottles of Gatorade.

32. no bottles of Powerade.

33. at least 1 bottle of Powerade.

34. a bottle of Gatorade, a bottle of Gatorade, and a bottle of All Sport, in that order.

Spinner Probabilities *In Exercises 35–38, assume that the spinner cannot land on a line.*

If spun once, determine

35. the probability that the spinner lands on yellow.

36. the odds against and the odds in favor of the spinner landing on yellow.

37. You are awarded $5 if the spinner lands on red, $10 if it lands on yellow, and $20 if it lands on green. Determine your expected value.

38. If the spinner is spun twice, determine the probability that it lands on red and then green (assume independence).

Spinner Probabilities *In Exercises 39–42, assume that the spinner cannot land on a line.*

If spun once, determine

39. the probability that the spinner does not land on green.

40. the odds in favor of and the odds against the spinner landing on green.

41. A person wins $10 if the spinner lands on green, wins $5 if the spinner lands on red, and loses $20 if the spinner lands on yellow. Find the expectation of a person who plays this game.

42. If the spinner is spun three times, determine the probability that at least one spin lands on red.

Restaurant Service *In Exercises 43–46, use the results of a survey regarding the service at the Lake View Diner, which is summarized as follows.*

Meal	Service Rated Good	Service Rated Poor	Total
Breakfast	85	10	95
Lunch	65	10	75
Total	150	20	170

If one person who completed the survey is selected at random, determine the probability that the person indicated that the

43. service was rated good.

44. service was rated good, given that the meal was breakfast.

45. service was rated poor, given that the meal was lunch.

46. meal was breakfast, given that the service was rated poor.

Neuroscience *In Exercises 47–50, assume that in a neuroscience course the students perform an experiment. Tests are given to determine if people are right brained, are left brained, or have no predominance. It is also recorded whether they are right handed or left handed. The following chart shows the results obtained.*

	Right Brained	Left Brained	No Predominance	Total
Right handed	40	130	60	230
Left handed	120	30	20	170
Total	160	160	80	400

If one person who completed the survey is selected at random, determine the probability the person selected is

47. right handed.

48. left brained, given that the person is left handed.

49. right handed, given that the person has no predominance.

50. right brained, given that the person is left handed.

51. ***Television Show*** Four contestants are on a television show. There are four different-colored rubber balls in a box, and each contestant gets to pick one from the box. Inside each ball is a slip of paper indicating the amount the contestant has won. The amounts are $10,000, $5000, $2000, and $1000.

   a) In how many different ways can the contestants select the balls?

   b) What is the expectation of a contestant?

52. *Spelling Bee* Five finalists remain in a high school spelling bee. Two will receive $50 each, two will receive $100 each, and one will receive $500. How many different arrangements of prizes are possible?

53. *Candy Selection* Mrs. Williams takes her 3 children shopping. Each of her children gets to select a different type of candy that only that child will eat. At the store, there are only 10 boxes of candy left and each is a different type. In how many ways can the 3 children select the candy?

54. *Astronaut Selection* Three of nine astronauts must be selected for a mission. One will be the captain, one will be the navigator, and one will perform scientific experiments. Assuming each of the nine astronauts can perform any of the tasks, in how many ways can a three-person crew be selected so that each person has a different assignment?

55. *Vaccine* Dr. Goldberg has three doses of vaccine for influenza type A. Six patients in the office require the vaccine. In how many different ways could Dr. Goldberg dispense the vaccine?

56. *Dogsled* Ten huskies are to be selected to pull a dogsled. How many different arrangements of the 10 huskies on a dogsled are possible?

57. *Mega Millions* To play the lottery game Mega Millions, you select 5 numbers from 1 through 56 and 1 Mega Ball number from 1 through 46. If you match all 6 numbers, you win the jackpot!

Select 5 numbers from 1–56

Mega Millions win

+

Select Mega Ball number from 1–46

a) What is the probability that you match the first 5 numbers?

b) What is the probability that you match the first 5 numbers and the Mega Ball?

58. *Parent-Teacher Committee* A committee of 7 is to be formed from 10 parents and 12 teachers. If the committee is to consist of 2 parents and 5 teachers, how many different committees are possible?

59. *Selecting Test Subjects* In a psychology research laboratory, one room contains eight men and another room contains five women. Three men and two women are to be selected at random to be given a psychological test. How many different combinations of these people are possible?

60. *Choosing Two Aces* Two cards are selected at random, without replacement, from a standard deck of 52 cards. Determine the probability that two aces are selected (use combinations).

Color Chips In Exercises 61–64, a bag contains five red chips, three white chips, and two blue chips. Three chips are to be selected at random, without replacement. Determine the probability that

61. all are red.

62. the first two are red and the third is blue.

63. the first is red, the second is white, and the third is blue.

64. at least one is red.

Magazines In Exercises 65–68, on a table in a doctor's office are five Newsweek *magazines, six* Parenting *magazines, and three* Sports Illustrated *magazines. If Ramona Cleary randomly selects three magazines, determine the probability that*

65. three *Newsweek* magazines were selected.

66. two *Parenting* magazines and one *Sports Illustrated* magazine were selected.

67. no *Parenting* magazine was selected.

68. at least one *Parenting* magazine was selected.

69. *New Homes* In the community of Spring Hill, 60% of the homes purchased cost more than $160,000.

a) Write the binomial probability formula to determine the probability that exactly x of the next n homes purchased in Spring Hill cost more than $160,000

b) Write the binomial probability formula to determine the probability that exactly 75 of the next 100 home purchases cost more than $160,000.

70. *Long-Stemmed Roses* At the Floyd's Flower Shop, $\frac{1}{5}$ of people ordering flowers select long-stemmed roses. Determine the probability that exactly 3 of the next 5 customers ordering flowers select long-stemmed roses.

71. *Taking a Math Course* During any semester at City College, 60% of the students are taking a mathematics course. Determine the probability that of five students selected at random,

a) none is taking a mathematics course this semester.

b) at least one is taking a mathematics course this semester.

CHAPTER 12) *TEST*

1. *Flowers* Of the last 50 people who purchased flowers at Whistlestop Florist, 14 purchased roses. Determine the empirical probability that the next person who purchases flowers at Whistlestop Florist purchases roses.

One Sheet of Paper *In Exercises 2–4, each of the numbers 1–9 is written on a sheet of paper and the nine sheets of paper are placed in a hat. If one sheet of paper is selected at random from the hat, determine the probability that the number selected is*

2. greater than 4.

3. even.

4. even or greater than 5.

Two Sheets of Paper *In Exercises 5–7, if two of the same nine sheets of paper mentioned above are selected, without replacement, from the hat, determine the probability that*

5. both numbers are greater than 5.

6. the first number is odd and the second number is even.

7. neither of the numbers is greater than 6.

8. One card is selected at random from a standard deck of 52 cards. Determine the probability that the card selected is a red card or a picture card.

One Chip and One Die *In Exercises 9–13, one colored chip–red, blue, or green–is selected at random and a die is rolled.*

9. Use the counting principle to determine the number of sample points in the sample space.

10. Construct a tree diagram illustrating all the possible outcomes and list the sample space.

In Exercises 11–13, by observing the sample space of the chips and die, determine the probability of obtaining

11. the color green and the number 2.

12. the color red or the number 1.

13. a color other than red or an even number.

14. *Passwords* A personal password for an Internet brokerage account is to consist of a letter, followed by two digits, followed by two letters. Determine the number of personal codes possible if the first digit cannot be zero and repetition is permitted.

15. *Puppies* A litter of collie puppies consists of four males and five females. If one of the puppies is selected at random, determine the odds

a) against the puppy being male.

b) in favor of the puppy being female.

16. *Pick a Card* You get to select one card at random from a standard deck of 52 cards. If you pick a club, you win $8. If you pick a heart, you win $4. If you pick any other suit, you lose $6. Determine your expectation for this game.

17. *Cars and SUVs* The number of cars and the number of SUVs going through the toll gates of two bridges is recorded. The results are shown below.

Bridge	Cars	SUVs	Total
George Washington	120	106	226
Golden Gate	94	136	230
Total	214	242	456

▲ *A toll booth at the Golden Gate Bridge*

If one of these vehicles going over the bridges is selected at random, determine the probability that

a) it is a car.

b) it is going over the George Washington Bridge.

c) it is an SUV, given that it is going over the George Washington Bridge.

d) it is going over the Golden Gate Bridge, given that it is a car.

18. *Awarding Prizes* Three of six people are to be selected and given small prizes. One will be given a book, one will be given a calculator, and one will be given an iTunes card. In how many different ways can these prizes be awarded?

19. *Quality Control* A bin contains a total of 20 batteries, of which 6 are defective. If you select 2 at random, without replacement, determine the probability that

a) none of the batteries is good.

b) at least one battery is good.

20. *University Admission* The probability that a person is accepted for admission to a specific university is 0.6. Determine the probability that exactly two of the next five people who apply to the university get accepted.

GROUP PROJECTS

The Probability Of An Exact Measured Value

1. Your car's speedometer indicates that you are traveling at 65 mph. What is the probability that you are traveling at *exactly* 65 mph? Explain your answer.

Taking An Exam

2. A 10-question multiple-choice exam is given, and each question has five possible answers. Pascal Gonyo takes this exam and guesses at every question. Use the binomial probability formula to determine the probability (to 5 decimal places) that

a) he gets exactly 2 questions correct.

b) he gets no questions correct.

c) he gets at least 1 question correct (use the information from part (b) to answer this part).

d) he gets at least 9 questions correct.

e) Without using the binomial probability formula, determine the probability that he gets exactly 2 questions correct.

f) Compare your answers to parts (a) and (e). If they are not the same, explain why.

Keyless Entry

3. Many cars have keyless entry. To open the lock, you may press a 5-digit code on a set of buttons like that illustrated. The code may include repeated digits like 11433 or 55512.

a) How many different 5-digit codes can be made using the 10 digits if repetition is permitted?

b) How many different ways are there of pressing 5 buttons if repetition is allowed?

c) A burglar is going to press 5 buttons at random, with repetition allowed. What is the probability that the burglar hits the sequence to open the door?

d) Suppose that each button had only one number associated with it as illustrated below. How many different 5-digit codes can be made with the 5 digits if repetition is permitted?

e) Using the buttons labeled 1–5, how many different ways are there to press 5 buttons if repetition is allowed?

f) A burglar is going to press 5 buttons of those labeled 1–5 at random with repetition allowed. Determine the probability that the burglar hits the sequence to open the door.

g) Is a burglar more likely, is he or she less likely, or does he or she have the same likelihood of pressing 5 buttons and opening the car door if the buttons are labeled as in the first illustration or as in the second illustration? Explain your answer.

h) Can you see any advantages in labeling the buttons as in the first illustration? Explain.*

---

*In actuality, in most cars that have key pads like that shown on the bottom left, each key acts as if it contains a single digit. For example, if your code is 7, 9, 5, 1, 3, the code 8, 0, 6, 2, 4 will unlock the door. The extra numbers, in effect, give the owner a false sense of security.

13

Statistics

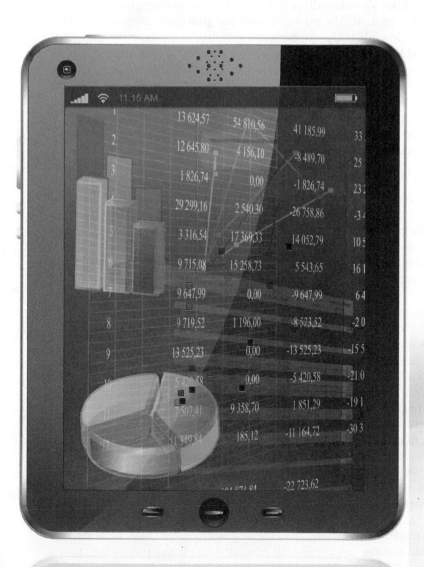

◀ *Numbers are the foundation of all statistical information.*

What You Will Learn

- Sampling techniques
- Misuses of statistics
- Frequency distributions
- Histograms, frequency polygons, stem-and-leaf displays
- Mode, median, mean, and midrange
- Percentiles and quartiles
- Range and standard deviation
- z-scores and the normal distribution
- Correlation and regression

Why This is Important

Benjamin Disraeli (1804–1881), once prime minister of the United Kingdom, said that there are three kinds of lies: lies, damned lies, and statistics. Do numbers lie? Numbers are the foundation of all statistical information. The "lie" occurs when, either intentionally or carelessly, a number is used in such a way that leads us to an unjustified or incorrect conclusion. Numbers may not lie, but they can be manipulated and misinterpreted. This chapter will provide information that can help you recognize when statistical information is being manipulated and misinterpreted. It will also help you see the many valuable uses of statistics.

SECTION 13.1   Sampling Techniques

▲ *Statisticians have several different techniques with which they can collect numerical information, such as how many Americans use an e-reader.*

According to Harris Interactive, 20% of Americans use an e-reader, an electronic reading device. It would be very expensive for Harris Interactive to ask every American if he or she uses an e-reader. Instead, to collect this information the polling company may ask a subset of Americans, called a *sample*. If it does not ask every American if he or she uses an e-reader, how do we know that Harris Interactive's results are accurate? In this section, we will discuss different techniques statisticians use to collect numerical information, and how they make accurate conclusions about an entire set of data from the sample collected.

Why *This is Important* Samples are used to determine a variety of information such as the percentage of college graduates in a city and the average credit card debt of an American family.

The study of statistics was originally used by governments to manage large amounts of numerical information. The use of statistics has grown significantly and today is applied in all walks of life. Governments use statistics to estimate the amount of unemployment and the cost of living. In psychology and education, the statistical theory of tests and measurements has been developed to compare achievements of individuals from diverse places and backgrounds. Newspapers and magazines carry the results of different polls on topics ranging from the president's popularity to the number of cans of soda consumed. Statistics is used in scores of other professions; in fact, it is difficult to find any profession that does not depend on some aspect of statistics.

Before we discuss different techniques used to collect numerical information, we will first introduce a few important definitions. *Statistics* is the art and science of gathering, analyzing, and making inferences (predictions) from numerical information obtained in an experiment. The numerical information so obtained is referred to as *data*. Statistics is divided into two main branches: descriptive and inferential. *Descriptive statistics* is concerned with the collection, organization, and analysis of data. *Inferential statistics* is concerned with making generalizations or predictions from the data collected.

Probability and statistics are closely related. Someone in the field of probability is interested in computing the chance of occurrence of a particular event when all the possible outcomes are known. A statistician's interest lies in drawing conclusions about possible outcomes through observations of only a few particular events.

If a probability expert and a statistician find identical boxes, the probability expert might open the box, observe the contents, replace the cover, and proceed to compute the probability of randomly selecting a specific object from the box. The statistician might select a few items from the box without looking at the contents and make a prediction as to the total contents of the box.

The entire contents of the box constitute the *population*. A population consists of all items or people of interest. The statistician often uses a subset of the population, called a *sample*, to make predictions concerning the population. It is important to understand the difference between a population and a sample. A population includes *all* items of interest. A sample includes *some* of the items in the population.

When a statistician draws a conclusion from a sample, there is always the possibility that the conclusion is incorrect. For example, suppose that a jar contains 90 blue marbles and 10 red marbles, as shown in Fig. 13.1 on page 775. If the statistician selects a random sample of five marbles from the jar and they are all blue, he or she may wrongly conclude that the jar contains all blue marbles. If the statistician takes a larger sample, say, 15 marbles, he or she is likely to select some red marbles. At that

Figure 13.1

Tune in Tomorrow

The A. C. Nielsen Company, which has been measuring the viewing population of TV shows for more than 50 years, uses a sample of about 9000 metered households in the United States to draw conclusions about more than 110 million American households that have a television. An electronic measurement system, called the People Meter, is placed on each TV in the sample household. Each household member is assigned a personal viewing button on the People Meter to keep track of which channels he or she watches and for how long. Nielsen then computes the rating of the show, using the data obtained from the sample.

You can learn more about the sampling techniques used by A. C. Nielsen at Nielsenmedia.com. A. C. Nielsen is involved in many other areas of statistical testing and measurement.

Why *This is Important* Television programs that have a large audience can charge more for commercial advertising. A. C. Nielsen is only one of a large number of companies that use a sample to make a prediction about an entire population.

point, the statistician may make a prediction about the contents of the jar based on the sample selected. Of course, the most accurate result would occur if every object in the jar, the entire population, were observed. However, in most statistical experiments, observing the entire population is not practical.

Statisticians use samples instead of the entire population for two reasons: (a) it is often impossible to obtain data on an entire population, and (b) sampling is less expensive because collecting the data takes less time and effort. For example, suppose that you wanted to determine the number of each species of all the fish in a lake. To do so would be almost impossible without using a sample. If you did try to obtain this information from the entire population, the cost would be astronomical. Or suppose that you wanted to test soup cans for spoilage. If every can produced by the company was opened and tested, the company wouldn't have any product left to sell. Instead of testing the entire population of soup cans, a sample is selected. The results obtained from the sample of soup cans selected are used to make conclusions about the entire population of soup cans.

Later in this chapter we will discuss statistical measures such as the *mean* and the *standard deviation*. When statisticians calculate the mean and the standard deviation of the entire population, they use different symbols and formulas than when they calculate the mean and standard deviation of a sample. The following chart shows the symbols used to represent the mean and standard deviation of a sample and of a population. Note that the mean and standard deviation of a population are symbolized by Greek letters.

Measure	Sample	Population
Mean	$\bar{x}$ (read "x bar")	μ (mu)
Standard deviation	s	σ (sigma)

Unless otherwise indicated, in this book we will always assume that we are working with a sample and so we will use $\bar{x}$ and s. If you take a course in statistics, you will use all four symbols and different formulas for a sample and for a population.

Consider the task of determining the political strength of a certain candidate running in a national election. It is not possible for pollsters to ask each of the approximately 213 million eligible voters his or her preference of a candidate. Thus, pollsters must select and use a sample of the population to obtain their information. How large a sample do you think they use to make predictions about an upcoming national election? You might be surprised to learn that pollsters use only about 1600 registered voters in their national sample. How can a pollster using such a small percentage of the population make an accurate prediction?

The answer is that when pollsters select a sample, they use sophisticated statistical techniques to obtain an unbiased sample. An *unbiased sample* is one that is a small replica of the entire population with regard to income, education, gender, race, religion, political affiliation, age, and so on. The procedures statisticians use to obtain unbiased samples are quite complex. The following sampling techniques will give you a brief idea of how statisticians obtain unbiased samples.

Random Sampling

If a sample is drawn in such a way that each time an item is selected each item in the population has an equal chance of being drawn, the sample is said to be a *random sample*. When using a random sample, one combination of a specified number of items has the same probability of being selected as any other combination. When all the items in the population are similar with regard to the specific characteristic we are interested in, a random sample can be expected to produce satisfactory results. For example, consider a large container holding 300 tennis balls that are identical except for color. One-third of the balls are yellow, one-third are white, and one-third are green. If the balls can be thoroughly mixed between each draw of a tennis ball so that each ball has an equally likely chance of being selected, randomness is not difficult to achieve. However, if the objects or items are not all the same size, shape, or texture, it might be impossible to obtain a random sample by reaching into a container and selecting an object.

The best procedure for selecting a random sample is to use a random number generator or a table of random numbers. A random number generator is a device, usually a calculator or computer program, that produces a list of random numbers. A random number table is a collection of random digits in which each digit has an equal chance of appearing. To select a random sample, first assign a number to each element in the population. Numbers are usually assigned in order. Then select the number of random numbers needed, which is determined by the sample size. Each numbered element from the population that corresponds to a selected random number becomes part of the sample.

Systematic Sampling

When a sample is obtained by drawing every *n*th item on a list or production line, the sample is a *systematic sample*. The first item should be determined by using a random number.

It is important that the list from which a systematic sample is chosen includes the entire population being studied. See the *Did You Know?* called "Don't Count Your Votes Until They're Cast" on page 777. Another problem that must be avoided when this method of sampling is used is the constantly recurring characteristic. For example, on an assembly line, every 10th item could be the work of robot X. If only every 10th item is checked for defects, the work of other robots doing the same job may not be checked and may be defective.

Cluster Sampling

A *cluster sample* is sometimes referred to as an *area sample* because it is frequently applied on a geographical basis. Essentially, the sampling consists of a random selection of groups of units. To select a cluster sample, we divide a geographic area into sections. Then we randomly select the sections or clusters. Either each member of the selected cluster is included in the sample or a random sample of the members of each cluster is used. For example, geographically we might randomly select city blocks to use as a sample unit. Then either every member of each selected city block would be used or a random sample from each selected city block would be used. Another example is to select x boxes of screws from a whole order, count the number of defective screws in the x boxes selected, and use this number to determine the expected number of defective screws in the whole order.

Stratified Sampling

When a population is divided into parts, called strata, for the purpose of drawing a sample, the procedure is known as *stratified sampling*. Stratified sampling involves dividing the population by characteristics called *stratifying factors* such as gender, race, religion, or income. When a population has varied characteristics, it is desirable to separate the population into classes with similar characteristics and then take a random sample from each stratum (or class). For example, we could separate the population of undergraduate college students into strata called freshmen, sophomores, juniors, and seniors.

The use of stratified sampling requires some knowledge of the population. For example, to obtain a cross section of voters in a city, we must know where various groups are located and the approximate number of voters in each location.

Convenience Sampling

A *convenience sample* uses data that are easily or readily obtained. Occasionally, data that are conveniently obtained may be all that is available. In some cases, some information is better than no information at all. Nevertheless, convenience sampling can be extremely biased. For example, suppose that a town wants to raise taxes to build a new elementary school. The local newspaper wants to obtain the opinion of some of the residents and sends a reporter to a senior citizens center. The first 10 people who exit the building are asked if they are in favor of raising taxes to build a new school. This sample could be biased against raising taxes for the new school. Most senior citizens would not have school-age children and may not be interested in paying increased taxes to build a new school. Although a convenience sample may be very easy to select, one must be very cautious when using the results obtained by this method.

Example 1   *Identifying Sampling Techniques*

Identify the sampling technique used to obtain a sample in the following. Explain your answer.

a) Every 20th soup can coming off an assembly line is checked for defects.

b) A $50 gift certificate is given away at the Annual Bankers Convention. Tickets are placed in a bin, and the tickets are mixed up. Then the winning ticket is selected by a blindfolded person.

c) Children in a large city are classified based on the neighborhood school they attend. A random sample of five schools is selected. All the children from each selected school are included in the sample.

d) The first 50 people entering a zoo are asked if they support an increase in taxes to support a zoo expansion.

e) Viewers of the *USA Network* are classified according to age. Random samples from each age group are selected.

Solution

a) Systematic sampling. The sample is obtained by drawing every nth item. In this example, every 20th item on an assembly line is selected.

b) Random sampling. Every ticket has an equal chance of being selected.

c) Cluster sampling. A random sample of geographic areas is selected.

d) Convenience sampling. The sample is selected by picking data that are easily obtained.

e) Stratified sampling. The viewers are divided into strata based on their age. Then random samples are selected from each strata.

Warm Up Exercises

In Exercises 1–12, fill in the blank with an appropriate word, phrase, or symbol(s).

1. The art and science of gathering, analyzing, and making inferences (predictions) from numerical information obtained in an experiment is called _____.

2. Making generalizations or predictions from the data collected is called _____ statistics.

3. The collection, organization, and analysis of data is called _____ statistics.

4. All items or people of interest in an experiment is called a(n) _____.

5. A subset of a population used by statisticians to make predictions about a population is called a(n) _____.

6. When a sample is obtained by drawing every *n*th item, the sample is called a(n) _____ sample.

7. If a sample is drawn in such a way that each time an item is selected, each item in the population has an equal chance of being drawn, the sample is called a(n) _____ sample.

8. When a population is divided into parts, called strata, for the purpose of drawing a sample, the procedure is known as _____ sampling.

9. A sample that consists of a random selection of groups or units is called a(n) _____ sample.

10. A sample that uses data that are easily or readily obtained is called a(n) _____ sample.

11. A sample that is a small replica of the entire population is called a(n) _____ sample.

12. An area sample is another name for a(n) _____ sample.

Practice the Skills

Sampling Techniques In Exercises 13–22, identify the sampling technique used to obtain a sample. Explain your answer.

13. All registered vehicles in the state of Georgia are classified according to type: subcompact, compact, mid-size, full-size, SUV, and truck. A random sample of vehicles from each category is selected.

14. Every 10th iPod coming off an assembly line is checked for defects.

▲ *See Exercise 14*

15. A state is divided into counties. A random sample of 12 counties is selected. A random sample from each of the 12 selected counties is selected.

16. A door prize is given away at a home improvement seminar. Tickets are placed in a bin, and the tickets are mixed up. Then a ticket is selected by a blindfolded person.

17. Every 17th person in line at a grocery store is asked his or her age.

18. The businesses in Iowa City are grouped according to type: medical, service, retail, manufacturing, financial, construction, restaurant, hotel, tourism, and other. A random sample of 10 businesses from each type is selected.

19. The first 25 adults leaving a grocery store are asked how much money they spend per week on entertainment.

20. The Food and Drug Administration randomly selects five stores from each of four randomly selected sections of a large city and checks food items for freshness. These stores are used as a representative sample of the entire city.

21. Bingo balls in a bin are shaken, and then balls are selected from the bin.

22. The Student Senate at the University of North Carolina is electing a new president. The first 25 people leaving the library are asked for whom they will vote.

Challenge Problems/Group Activities

23. a) *Random Sampling* Select and indicate a topic and population of interest to which a random sampling technique can be applied to obtain data.

    b) Explain how you or your group would obtain a random sample for your population of interest.

    c) Actually obtain the sample by the procedure stated in part (b).

24. *Data from Questionnaire* Some subscribers of *Consumer Reports* respond to an annual questionnaire regarding their satisfaction with new appliances, cars, and other items. The information obtained from these questionnaires is then used as a sample from which frequency of repairs and other ratings are made by the magazine. Are the data obtained from these returned questionnaires representative of the entire population, or are they biased?

Recreational Mathematics

25. Statistically speaking, what is the most dangerous job in the United States?

Internet/Research Activity

26. We have briefly introduced sampling techniques. Using statistics books and Internet Web sites as references, select one type of sampling technique (it may be one that we have not discussed in this section) and write a report on how statisticians obtain that type of sample. Also indicate when that type of sampling technique may be preferred. List two examples of when the sampling technique may be used.

SECTION 13.2   The Misuses of Statistics

▲ It is important to examine statistical statements about products before accepting the statements as fact.

Many of us may remember the advertisement stating, "Four out of five dentists recommend sugarless gum for their patients who chew gum." Seeing an advertisement like this one may cause some of us to be a bit skeptical. Should we believe that sugarless chewing gum will not harm our teeth? Or should we investigate a bit further before buying that next pack of chewing gum? In this section, we will learn how to examine statistical statements before accepting them as fact.

Why *This is Important* In order to be an educated consumer, it is important to be able to distinguish between misleading advertisements and actual facts.

Statistics, when used properly, is a valuable tool to society. However, many individuals, businesses, and advertising firms misuse statistics to their own advantage. You should examine statistical statements very carefully before accepting them as fact. You should ask yourself two questions: Was the sample used to gather the statistical data unbiased and of sufficient size? Is the statistical statement ambiguous; that is, can it be interpreted in more than one way?

Let's examine two advertisements. "Four out of five dentists recommend sugarless gum for their patients who chew gum." In this advertisement, we do not know the sample size and the number of times the experiment was performed to obtain the desired results. The advertisement does not mention that possibly only 1 out of 100 dentists recommended gum at all.

In a golf ball commercial, a "type A" ball is hit and a second ball is hit in the same manner. The type A ball travels farther. We are supposed to conclude that the type A is the better ball. The advertisement does not mention the number of times the experiment was previously performed or the results of the earlier experiments. Possible sources of bias include (1) wind speed and direction, (2) that no two swings are identical, and (3) that the ball may land on a rough or smooth surface.

Vague or ambiguous words also lead to statistical misuses or misinterpretations. The word *average* is one such culprit. There are at least four different "averages," some of which are discussed in Section 13.4. Each is calculated differently, and each may have a different value for the same sample. During contract negotiations, it is not uncommon for an employer to state publicly that the average salary of its employees is $45,000, whereas the employees' union states that the average is $40,000. Who is lying? Actually, both sides may be telling the truth. Each side will use the average that best suits its needs to present its case. Advertisers also use the average that most enhances their products. Consumers often misinterpret this average as the one with which they are most familiar.

Another vague word is *largest*. For example, ABC claims that it is the largest department store in the United States. Does that mean largest profit, largest sales, largest building, largest staff, largest acreage, or largest number of outlets?

Still another deceptive technique used in advertising is to state a claim from which the public may draw irrelevant conclusions. For example, a disinfectant manufacturer claims that its product killed 40,760 germs in a laboratory in 5 seconds. "To prevent colds, use disinfectant A." It may well be that the germs killed in the laboratory were not related to any type of cold germ. In another example, company C claims that its paper towels are heavier than its competition's towels. Therefore, they will hold more water. Is weight a measure of absorbency? A rock is heavier than a sponge, yet a sponge is more absorbent.

An insurance advertisement claims that in Duluth, Minnesota, 212 people switched to insurance company Z. One may conclude that this company is offering something special to attract these people. What may have been omitted from the advertisement is that 415 people in Duluth, Minnesota, dropped insurance company Z during the same period.

A foreign car manufacturer claims that 9 of every 10 of a popular-model car it sold in the United States during the previous 10 years were still on the road. From this statement, the public is to conclude that this foreign car is well manufactured and would last for many years. The commercial neglects to state that this model has been selling in the United States for only a few years. The manufacturer could just as well have stated that 9 of every 10 of these cars sold in the United States in the previous 100 years were still on the road.

Charts and graphs can also be misleading or deceptive. In Fig. 13.2, the two graphs show the performance of two stocks over a 6-month period. Based on the graphs, which stock would you purchase? Actually, the two graphs present identical information; the only difference is that the vertical scale of the graph for stock B has been exaggerated.

Figure 13.2

The two graphs in Fig. 13.3 show the same change. However, the graph in part (a) appears to show a greater increase than the graph in part (b), again because of a different scale.

Figure 13.3

Figure 13.4

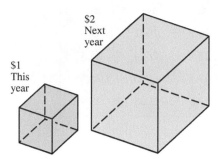

Figure 13.5

Consider a claim that if you invest $1, by next year you will have $2. This type of claim is sometimes misrepresented, as in Fig. 13.4. Actually, your investment has only doubled, but the area of the square on the right is four times that of the square on the left. By expressing the amounts as cubes (Fig. 13.5), you increase the volume eightfold.

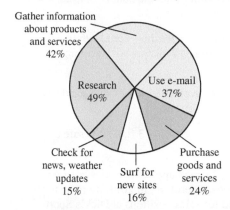

Figure 13.6

The graph in Fig. 13.6 is an example of a circle graph. We will discuss circle graphs in Section 13.3. In a circle graph, the total circle represents 100%. Therefore, the sum of the parts should add up to 100%. This graph is misleading since the sum of its parts is 183%. A graph other than a circle graph should have been used to display the top six reasons Americans say they use the Internet.

Despite the examples presented in this section, you should not be left with the impression that statistics is used solely for the purpose of misleading or cheating the consumer. As stated earlier, there are many important and necessary uses of statistics. Most statistical reports are accurate and useful. You should realize, however, the importance of being an aware consumer.

SECTION 13.2

Exercises

Practice the Skills

Misinterpretations of Statistics In Exercises 1–14, discuss the statement and tell what possible misuses or misinterpretations may exist.

1. *Cold Remedy* In a study of patients with cold symptoms, each patient was found to have improved symptoms after taking honey. Therefore, honey cures the common cold.

2. In 2011, Liberty Travel received more requests for travel brochures to Hawaii than to Las Vegas. Therefore, in 2012, Liberty Travel sold more travel packages to Hawaii than to Las Vegas.

3. There are more empty spaces in the parking lot of Mama Mia's Italian restaurant than at Shanghai Chinese restaurant. Therefore, more people prefer Chinese food than Italian food.

4. Healthy Snacks cookies are fat free. So eat as many as you like and you will not gain weight.

5. Most accidents occur on Saturday night. That means that people do not drive carefully on Saturday night.

6. Morgan's is the largest department store in New York. So shop at Morgan's and save money.

7. Eighty percent of all automobile accidents occur within 10 miles of the driver's home. Therefore, it is safer to take long trips.

8. Arizona has the highest death rate for asthma in the United States. Therefore, it is unsafe to go to Arizona if you have asthma.

▲ *Sedona, Arizona*

9. Thirty students said that they would recommend Professor Malone to a friend. Twenty students said that they would recommend Professor Wagner to a friend. Therefore, Professor Malone is a better teacher than Professor Wagner.

10. A steak is more expensive at Dino's Steak House than at Rick's Prime Rib House. Therefore, the quality of a steak at Dino's Steak House is better than the quality of a steak at Rick's Prime Rib House.

11. John Deere lawn tractors cost more than Toro lawn tractors. Therefore, John Deere lawn tractors will last longer than Toro lawn tractors.

12. More men than women are involved in automobile accidents. Therefore, women are better drivers.

13. The average depth of the pond is only 3 ft, so it is safe to go wading.

14. In 2011, more men than women applied for sales positions at Dick's Sporting Goods. Therefore, in 2011, more men than women were hired for sales positions at Dick's Sporting Goods.

15. *Population of Honolulu* The following table shows the population, in thousands, in Honolulu, Hawaii, for selected years.

Year	Population
1980	365.0
1990	365.2
2000	371.7
2010	371.7

Source: U.S Census Bureau

Draw a line graph that makes the increase in the population of Honolulu for the years shown appear to be

a) small.   **b)** large.

16. *Officers in the U.S. Marine Corps* The following table shows the number of officers, in thousands, on active duty in the U.S. Marine Corps for the years 2004–2009.

Year	Number of Officers
2004	19.1
2005	19.1
2006	19.2
2007	19.5
2008	20.1
2009	21.0

Draw a line graph that makes the increase in the number of officers on active duty for the U.S. Marine Corps appear to be

a) small.   **b)** large.

First Marriage In Exercises 17 and 18, use the following table.

Median Age at First Marriage

Male		Female	
Year	Age	Year	Age
2002	26.9	2002	25.3
2004	27.1	2004	25.3
2006	27.5	2006	25.5
2008	27.6	2008	25.9

Source: U.S. Census Bureau

17. a) Draw a bar graph that appears to show a small increase in the median age at first marriage for males.

   b) Draw a bar graph that appears to show a large increase in the median age at first marriage for males.

18. a) Draw a bar graph that appears to show a small increase in the median age at first marriage for females.

   b) Draw a bar graph that appears to show a large increase in the median age at first marriage for females.

19. *Price of a Movie Ticket* The following graph shows the average price of a movie ticket for the years 2009 and 2010.

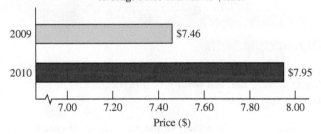

Average Price of a Movie Ticket

   a) Draw a bar graph that shows the entire scale from $0 to $8.00.

   b) Does the new graph give a different impression? Explain.

Concept/Writing Exercises

20. Find five advertisements or commercials that may be statistically misleading. Explain why each may be misleading.

21. The following circle graph shows the percentage of commuters who are frustrated by particular driving situations. Is the graph misleading? Explain.

**Driving Situations
Frustrating to Commuters**

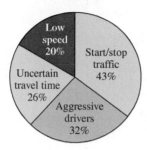

a) Compute the projected percent increase in population from 2000 to 2050 by using the formula given on page 603.

b) Measure the radius and then compute the area of the circle representing 2000. Use $A = \pi r^2$.

c) Repeat part (b) for the circle representing 2050.

d) Compute the percent increase in the size of the area of the circle from 2000 to 2050.

e) Are the circle graphs misleading?

Recreational Mathematics

23. What mathematical symbol can you place between 1 and 2 to obtain a number greater than 1 but less than 2?

Challenge Problem/Group Activity

22. Consider the following graph, which shows the U.S. population in 2000 and the projected U.S. population in 2050.

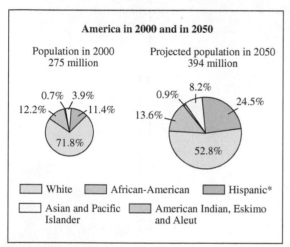

Source: U.S. Census Bureau

Internet/Research Activity

24. Read the book *How to Lie with Statistics* by Darrell Huff and write a book report on it. Select three illustrations from the book that show how people manipulate statistics.

| SECTION 13.3 | Frequency Distributions and Statistical Graphs |

Suppose you have a job as a waitress and decide to record the daily amount you make in tips. After keeping a list of your tips each day for several months, you realize that you have a large set of data and want to condense your data into a more manageable form. In this section we will learn a method to organize and summarize data. We will also introduce four types of graphs that can be used to display information in a meaningful way.

Why This is Important Organizing and summarizing data and using graphs to display information can make large sets of information more useful.

▲ *Organizing and summarizing data, such as a waitress's daily tips, can make large sets of information more useful.*

It is not uncommon for statisticians and others to have to analyze thousands of pieces of data. A *piece of data* is a single response to an experiment. When the amount of data is large, it is usually advantageous to construct a frequency distribution. A *frequency distribution* is a listing of the observed values and the corresponding frequency of occurrence of each value. Example 1 shows how we construct a frequency distribution.

Example 1 *Frequency Distribution*

The number of children per family is recorded for 64 families surveyed. Construct a frequency distribution of the following data:

$$
\begin{array}{cccccccc}
0 & 1 & 1 & 2 & 2 & 3 & 4 & 5 \\
0 & 1 & 1 & 2 & 2 & 3 & 4 & 5 \\
0 & 1 & 1 & 2 & 2 & 3 & 4 & 6 \\
0 & 1 & 2 & 2 & 2 & 3 & 4 & 6 \\
0 & 1 & 2 & 2 & 2 & 3 & 4 & 7 \\
0 & 1 & 2 & 2 & 3 & 3 & 4 & 8 \\
0 & 1 & 2 & 2 & 3 & 3 & 5 & 8 \\
0 & 1 & 2 & 2 & 3 & 3 & 5 & 9 \\
\end{array}
$$

Solution Listing the number of children (observed values) and the number of families (frequency) gives the following frequency distribution.

Number of Children (Observed Values)	Number of Families (Frequency)
0	8
1	11
2	18
3	11
4	6
5	4
6	2
7	1
8	2
9	$\dfrac{1}{64}$

Eight families had no children, 11 families had one child, 18 families had two children, and so on. Note that the sum of the frequencies is equal to the original number of pieces of data, 64. ∎

Often data are grouped in classes to provide information about the distribution that would be difficult to observe if the data were ungrouped. Graphs called *histograms* and *frequency polygons* can be made of grouped data, as will be explained later in this section. These graphs also provide a great deal of useful information.

When data are grouped in classes, certain rules should be followed.

PROCEDURE   RULES FOR DATA GROUPED BY CLASSES

1. The classes should be the same "width."
2. The classes should not overlap.
3. Each piece of data should belong to only one class.

In addition, it is often suggested that a frequency distribution should be constructed with 5 to 12 classes. If there are too few or too many classes, the distribution may become difficult to interpret. For example, if you use fewer than 5 classes, you risk losing too much information. If you use more than 12 classes, you may gain more detail

Can You Count the F's?

Statistical errors often result from careless observations. To see how such errors can occur, consider the statement below. How many F's do you count in the statement?

FINISHED FILES ARE THE RE-SULT OF YEARS OF SCIENTIF-IC STUDY COMBINED WITH THE EXPERIENCE OF YEARS.

Answer : There are 6 F's.

but you risk losing clarity. Let the spread of the data be a guide in deciding the number of classes to use.

To understand these rules, let's consider a set of observed values that go from a low of 0 to a high of 26. Let's assume that the first class is arbitrarily selected to go from 0 through 4. Thus, any of the data with values of 0, 1, 2, 3, 4 would belong in this class. We say that the *class width* is 5 since there are five integral values that belong to the class. This first class ended with 4, so the second class must start with 5. If this class is to have a width of 5, at what value must it end? The answer is 9 (5, 6, 7, 8, 9). The second class is 5–9. Continuing in the same manner, we obtain the following set of classes.

Classes

Lower class limits $\left\{ \begin{matrix} 0\text{–}4 \\ 5\text{–}9 \\ 10\text{–}14 \\ 15\text{–}19 \\ 20\text{–}24 \\ 25\text{–}29 \end{matrix} \right\}$ Upper class limits

We need not go beyond the 25–29 class because the largest value we are considering is 26. The classes meet our three criteria: They have the same width, there is no overlap among the classes, and each of the values from a low of 0 to a high of 26 belongs to one and only one class.

The choice of the first class, 0–4, was arbitrary. If we wanted to have more classes or fewer classes, we would make the class widths smaller or larger, respectively.

The numbers 0, 5, 10, 15, 20, 25 are called the *lower class limits*, and the numbers 4, 9, 14, 19, 24, 29 are called the *upper class limits*. Each class has a width of 5. Note that the class width, 5, can be obtained by subtracting the first lower class limit from the second lower class limit: $5 - 0 = 5$. The difference between any two consecutive lower class or upper class limits is also 5.

Example 2 *A Frequency Distribution of Consumer Magazines*

Table 13.1 on page 786 shows the 2008 circulation for the 46 leading U.S. consumer magazines (excluding *AARP Magazine* and *AARP Bulletin*, which are far ahead of the other magazines). The circulation is rounded to the nearest ten thousand. Construct a frequency distribution of the data, letting the first class be 173–237.

Solution Forty-six pieces of data are given in *descending order* from highest to lowest. We are given that the first class is 173–237. The second class must therefore start at 238. To find the class width, we subtract 173 (the lower class limit of the first class) from 238 (the lower class limit of the second class) to obtain a class width of 65. The upper class limit of the second class is found by adding the class width, 65, to the upper class limit of the first class, 237. Therefore, the upper class limit of the second class is $237 + 65 = 302$. Thus,

173–237   first class
238–302   second class

The other classes are found using a similar technique. They are 303–367, 368–432, 433–497, 498–562, 563–627, 628–692, 693–757, 758–822. Since the highest value in the data is 817, there is no need to go any further. Note that each two consecutive lower class limits differ by 65, as does each two consecutive upper class limits. There are 23 pieces of data in the 173–237 class. There are 8 pieces of data in the 238–302 class, 6 in the 303–367 class, 5 in the 368–432 class, 1 in the 433–497 class, 1 in the 498–562 class, 0 in the 563–627 class, 0 in the 628–692 class, 0 in the 693–757 class, and 2 in the 758–822 class. The complete frequency distribution of the 10 classes is given on page 786. The number of magazines totals 46, so we have included each piece of data.

Table 13.1

Magazine	Circulation (ten thousands)
Reader's Digest	817
Better Homes and Gardens	766
National Geographic	506
Good Housekeeping	468
Woman's Day	392
Family Circle	391
AAA Westways	384
Ladies' Home Journal	384
People	369
Game Informer	352
Time	336
Prevention	334
TV Guide	326
Sports Illustrated	322
Taste of Home	320
Cosmopolitan	293
Southern Living	283
AAA	281
Newsweek	270
Playboy	262
AAA Going Places	256
Maxim	252
American Legion Magazine	243
O, The Oprah Magazine	237
Glamour	229
Redbook	221
Guideposts	220
AAA World	213
Parenting	213
Parents	206
ESPN The Magazine	206
Seventeen	203
Martha Stewart Living	203
Smithsonian	203
Real Simple	198
Remedy/Remedy MD	196
Money	191
Us Weekly	190
Family Fun	188
Men's Health	186
Entertainment Weekly	180
Endless Vacation	179
Cooking Light	179
Every Day with Rachael Ray	178
InStyle	176
Country Living	173

Source: *Audit Bureau of Circulations*

Circulation	Number of Magazines (ten thousands)
173–237	23
238–302	8
303–367	6
368–432	5
433–497	1
498–562	1
563–627	0
628–692	0
693–757	0
758–822	2
	46

The *modal class* of a frequency distribution is the class with the greatest frequency. In Example 2, the modal class is 173–237. The *midpoint of a class*, also called the *class mark*, is found by adding the lower and upper class limits and dividing the sum by 2. The midpoint of the first class in Example 2 is

$$\frac{173 + 237}{2} = \frac{410}{2} = 205$$

Note that the difference between successive class marks is the class width. The class mark of the second class can therefore be obtained by adding the class width, 65, to the class mark of the first class, 205. The sum is 205 + 65 = 270. Note that $\frac{238 + 302}{2} = 270$, which checks with the class mark obtained by adding the class width to the first class mark.

Example 3   *A Frequency Distribution of Family Income*

The following set of data represents the family income (in thousands of dollars, rounded to the nearest hundred) of 15 randomly selected families.

46.5	31.8	45.8	44.7	40.9
65.2	52.4	44.6	53.7	48.8
35.5	40.3	39.8	56.3	50.7

Construct a frequency distribution with a first class of 31.5–37.6.

Solution First rearrange the data from lowest to highest so that the data will be easier to categorize.

31.8	40.3	44.7	48.8	53.7
35.5	40.9	45.8	50.7	56.3
39.8	44.6	46.5	52.4	65.2

The first class goes from 31.5 to 37.6. Since the data are in tenths, the class limits will also be given in tenths. The first class ends with 37.6; therefore, the second class must start with 37.7. The class width of the first class is 37.7 − 31.5, or 6.2. The upper class limit of the second class must therefore be 37.6 + 6.2, or 43.8. The frequency distribution is given on page 787.

Income ($1000)	Number of Families
31.5–37.6	2
37.7–43.8	3
43.9–50.0	5
50.1–56.2	3
56.3–62.4	1
62.5–68.6	$\frac{1}{15}$

Note in Example 3 that the class width is 6.2, the modal class is 43.9–50.0, and the class mark of the first class is $\frac{31.5 + 37.6}{2}$, or 34.55.

We have discussed how to organize and summarize data. Now we will introduce graphs that can be used to display information. We will consider four types of graphs: the histogram, the frequency polygon, the stem-and-leaf graph, and the circle graph.

Histograms and Frequency Polygons

Histograms and frequency polygons are statistical graphs used to illustrate frequency distributions. A *histogram* is a graph with observed values on its horizontal scale and frequencies on its vertical scale. A bar is constructed above each observed value (or class when classes are used), indicating the frequency of that value (or class). The horizontal scale need not start at zero, and the calibrations on the horizontal and vertical scales do not have to be the same. The vertical scale must start at zero. To accommodate large frequencies on the vertical scale, it may be necessary to break the scale. Because histograms and other bar graphs are easy to interpret visually, they are used a great deal in newspapers and magazines.

Example 4 *Construct a Histogram*

The frequency distribution developed in Example 1, on page 784, is repeated here. Construct a histogram of this frequency distribution.

Number of Children (Observed Values)	Number of Families (Frequency)
0	8
1	11
2	18
3	11
4	6
5	4
6	2
7	1
8	2
9	1

Solution The vertical scale must extend at least to the number 18 since that is the greatest recorded frequency. The horizontal scale must include the numbers 0–9, the number of children observed. Eight families have no children. We indicate that by constructing a bar above the number 0, centered at 0, on the horizontal scale

TIMELY TIP
When constructing a histogram or frequency polygon, be sure to label both scales of the graph.

extended up to 8 on the vertical scale (Fig. 13.7). Eleven families have one child, so we construct a bar extending to 11 above the number 1, centered at 1, on the horizontal scale. We continue this procedure for each observed value. Both the horizontal and vertical scales should be labeled, the bars should be the same width and centered at the observed value, and the histogram should have a title. In a histogram, the bars should always touch.

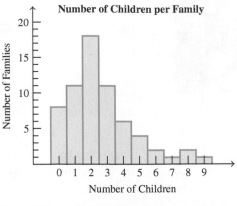

Figure 13.7

Frequency polygons are line graphs with scales the same as those of the histogram; that is, the horizontal scale indicates observed values and the vertical scale indicates frequency. To construct a frequency polygon, place a dot at the corresponding frequency above each of the observed values. Then connect the dots with straight-line segments. When constructing frequency polygons, always put in two additional class marks, one at the lower end and one at the upper end on the horizontal scale (values for these added class marks are not needed on the frequency polygon). Since the frequency at these added class marks is 0, the end points of the frequency polygon will always be on the horizontal scale.

Example 5   *Construct a Frequency Polygon*

Construct a frequency polygon of the frequency distribution in Example 1 on page 784.

Solution Since eight families have no children, place a mark above the 0 at 8 on the vertical scale, as shown in Fig. 13.8. Because there are 11 families with one child, place a mark above the 1 on the horizontal scale at the 11 on the vertical scale, and so on. Connect the dots with straight-line segments and bring the end points of the graph down to the horizontal scale, as shown.

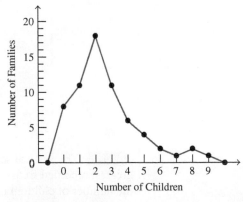

Figure 13.8

Table 13.2

Distance (miles)	Number of Workers
1–7	15
8–14	24
15–21	13
22–28	8
29–35	5
36–42	5

Example 6 *Commuting Distances*

The frequency distribution of the one-way commuting distances for 70 workers is listed in Table 13.2. Construct a histogram and then construct a frequency polygon.

Solution The histogram can be constructed with either class limits or class marks (class midpoints) on the horizontal scale. Frequency polygons are constructed with class marks on the horizontal scale. Since we will construct a frequency polygon on the histogram, we will use class marks. Recall that class marks are found by adding the lower class limit and upper class limit and dividing the sum by 2. For the first class, the class mark is $\dfrac{1+7}{2}$, or 4. Since the class widths are seven units, the class marks will also differ by seven units (see Fig. 13.9).

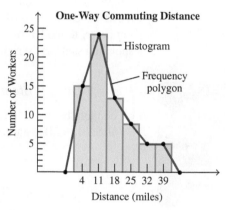

Figure 13.9

Example 7 *Carry-on Luggage Weights*

The histogram in Fig. 13.10 shows the weights of selected pieces of carry-on luggage at an airport. Construct the frequency distribution from the histogram in Fig. 13.10.

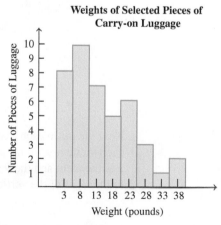

Figure 13.10

Table 13.3

Weight (pounds)	Number of Pieces of Luggage
1–5	8
6–10	10
11–15	7
16–20	5
21–25	6
26–30	3
31–35	1
36–40	2

Solution There are five units between class midpoints, so each class width must also be five units. Since three is the midpoint of the first class, there must be two units below and two units above it. The first class must be 1–5. The second class must therefore be 6–10. The frequency distribution is given in Table 13.3.

Stem-and-Leaf Displays

Frequency distributions and histograms provide very useful tools to organize and summarize data. However, if the data are grouped, we cannot identify specific data values in a frequency distribution and in a histogram. For example, in Example 7, we know that there are eight pieces of luggage in the class of 1 to 5 pounds, but we don't know the specific weights of those eight pieces of luggage.

A *stem-and-leaf display* is a tool that organizes and groups the data while allowing us to see the actual values that make up the data. To construct a stem-and-leaf display each value is represented with two different groups of digits. The left group of digits is called the *stem.* The remaining group of digits on the right is called the *leaf.* There is no rule for the number of digits to be included in the stem. Usually the units digit is the leaf and the remaining digits are the stem. For example, the number 53 would be broken up into 5 and 3. The 5 would be the stem and the 3 would be the leaf. The number 417 would be broken up into 41 and 7. The 41 would be the stem and the 7 would be the leaf. The number 6, which can be represented as 06, would be broken up into 0 and 6. The stem would be the 0 and the leaf would be the 6. With a stem-and-leaf display, the stems are listed, in ascending order, to the left of a vertical line. Then we place each leaf to the right of its corresponding stem, to the right of the vertical line.* Example 8 illustrates this procedure.

▲ *Captain Fairfield Inn Bed and Breakfast*

Example 8 *Stem-and-Leaf Display*

The table below indicates the ages of a sample of 20 guests who stayed at Captain Fairfield Inn Bed and Breakfast. Construct a stem-and-leaf display.

29	31	39	43	56
60	62	59	58	32
47	27	50	28	71
72	44	45	44	68

Solution By quickly glancing at the data, we can see the ages consist of two-digit numbers. Let's use the first digit, the tens digit, as our stem and the second digit, the units digit, as the leaf. For example, for an age of 62, the stem is 6 and the leaf is 2. Our values are numbers in the 20s, 30s, 40s, 50s, 60s, and 70s. Therefore, the stems will be 2, 3, 4, 5, 6, 7 as shown below.

$$
\begin{array}{c|}
2 & \\
3 & \\
4 & \\
5 & \\
6 & \\
7 & \\
\end{array}
$$

Next we place each leaf on its stem. We will do so by placing the second digit of each value next to its stem, to the right of the vertical line. Our first value is 29. The 2 is the stem and the 9 is the leaf. Therefore, we place a 9 next to the stem of 2 and to the right of the vertical line.

$$2 \,|\, 9$$

The next value is 31. We will place a leaf of 1 next to the stem of 3.

$$
\begin{array}{c|c}
2 & 9 \\
3 & 1 \\
\end{array}
$$

*In stem-and-leaf displays, the leaves are sometimes listed from lowest digit to greatest digit, but that is not necessary.

The next value is 39. Therefore, we will place a leaf of 9 after the leaf of 1 that is next to the stem of 3.

$$
\begin{array}{c|ccc}
2 & 9 \\
3 & 1 & 9
\end{array}
$$

We continue this process until we have listed all the leaves on the display. The diagram below shows the stem-and-leaf display for the ages of the guests. In our display, we will also include a legend to indicate the values represented by the stems and leaves. For example, 5|6 represents 56.

5| 6 represents 56

Stem Leaves

$$
\begin{array}{c|ccccc}
2 & 9 & 7 & 8 \\
3 & 1 & 9 & 2 \\
4 & 3 & 7 & 4 & 5 & 4 \\
5 & 6 & 9 & 8 & 0 \\
6 & 0 & 2 & 8 \\
7 & 1 & 2
\end{array}
$$

Every piece of the original data can be seen in a stem-and-leaf display. From the above diagram, we can see that five of the guests' ages were in the 40s. Only two guests were older than 70. Note that the stem-and-leaf display gives the same visual impression as a sideways histogram.

Circle Graphs

Circle graphs (also known as pie charts) are often used to compare parts of one or more components of the whole to the whole. The circle graph in Fig. 13.11 shows what moviegoers say is the most annoying distraction during a movie. Since the total circle represents 100%, the sum of the percents of the sectors should be 100%, and it is.

In the next example, we will discuss a circle graph.

Distractions at the Movies

Other 4%
People getting up and down 9%
Cell phones ringing 17%
Babies crying 26%
People talking 44%
Source: AMC Entertainment

Figure 13.11

Example 9 *Circus Performances*

Eight hundred people who attended a Ringling Bros. and Barnum & Bailey Circus were asked to indicate their favorite performance. The circle graph in Fig. 13.12 shows the percentage of respondents that answered tigers, elephants, acrobats, jugglers, and other. Determine the number of respondents for each category.

Favorite Performance at the Circus

Other 5%
Jugglers 14%
Acrobats 17%
Tigers 38%
Elephants 26%

Figure 13.12

Solution To determine the number of respondents in a category, we multiply the percentage for each category, written as a decimal number, by the total number of people, 800. The table on page 792 indicates the results.

Performance	Percent of Respondents	Percent Written as a Decimal Number	Number of People
Tigers	38%	0.38	$0.38 \times 800 = 304$
Elephants	26%	0.26	$0.26 \times 800 = 208$
Acrobats	17%	0.17	$0.17 \times 800 = 136$
Jugglers	14%	0.14	$0.14 \times 800 = 112$
Other	5%	0.05	$0.05 \times 800 = 40$
Total			800

As we can see from the table, 304 people indicated that the tigers were their favorite performance, 208 indicated elephants, 136 people indicated the acrobats, 112 people indicated the jugglers, and 40 people indicated some other performance. ■

SECTION 13.3 Exercises

Warm Up Exercises

In Exercises 1–8, fill in the blank with an appropriate word, phrase, or symbol(s).

1. A listing of observed values and the corresponding frequency of occurrence of each value is called a(n) _____ distribution.

2. In a frequency distribution, the class with the greatest frequency is called the _____ class.

3. In a frequency distribution, another name for the midpoint of a class is the class _____.

4. The class width of a frequency distribution with a first class of 9–16 and a second class of 17–24 is _____.

5. A bar graph with observed values on its horizontal scale and frequencies on its vertical scale is called a(n) _____.

6. A line graph with observed values on its horizontal scale and frequencies on its vertical scale is called a frequency _____.

7. In a stem-and-leaf display, the group of digits in the left-hand column is called the _____.

8. In a stem-and-leaf display, the group of digits in the right-hand column is called the _____.

Practice the Skills/Problem Solving

In Exercises 9 and 10, use the frequency distribution to determine

a) *the total number of observations.*

b) *the width of each class.*

c) *the midpoint of the second class.*

d) *the modal class (or classes).*

e) *the class limits of the next class if an additional class were to be added.*

9.

Class	Frequency
9–15	4
16–22	7
23–29	1
30–36	0
37–43	3
44–50	5

10.

Class	Frequency
40–49	7
50–59	5
60–69	3
70–79	2
80–89	7
90–99	1

11. *Visits to the Library* Johnson County Community College is planning to expand its library. Forty students were asked how many times they visited the library during the previous semester. Their responses are given below. Construct a frequency distribution, letting each class have a width of 1 (as in Example 1 on page 784).

0	1	1	3	4	5	7	8
0	1	2	3	5	5	7	8
0	1	2	3	5	5	7	9
1	1	2	3	5	6	8	10
1	1	3	4	5	6	8	10

12. *Hot Dog Sales* A hot dog vendor is interested in the number of hot dogs he sells each day at his hot dog cart. The number of hot dogs sold is indicated below for 32 consecutive days. Construct a frequency distribution, letting each class have a width of 1.

15	16	19	20	21	22	24	27
15	18	19	20	21	22	25	27
15	18	19	20	21	23	25	28
16	18	19	21	21	23	26	29

Note that there were no days in which the vendor sold 17 hot dogs. However, it is customary to include a missing value as an observed value and assign to it a frequency of 0.

▲ *See Exercise 12*

Magazine Circulation *In Exercises 13–16, use the data given in Table 13.1 on page 786 to construct a frequency distribution with a first class (in ten thousands) of*

13. 173–322.   **14.** 170–316.

15. 173–272.   **16.** 173–250.

City Population *In Exercises 17–20, use the following data, which represent the population of the 20 most populous cities in the world in 2010, in millions of people (rounded to the nearest 100,000).*

13.8	12.5	10.1	8.8	7.6
13.8	11.2	9.6	8.4	7.3
13.0	10.6	8.9	7.9	7.2
12.6	10.5	8.9	7.8	7.1

▲ *Shanghai, China, is the world's most populated city.*

Use these data to construct a frequency distribution with a first class of

17. 7.0–7.9.   **18.** 6.5–7.4.

19. 6.5–7.5.   **20.** 7.0–7.4.

Residents in Poverty *In Exercises 21–24, use the data in the table above to the right.*

Percent of U.S. Residents Living in Poverty in 2008, by State

State	Percent	State	Percent
AK	7.9	MT	12.9
AL	14.4	NC	14.7
AR	14.5	ND	10.5
AZ	16.1	NE	10.3
CA	13.6	NH	6.4
CO	10.4	NJ	9.0
CT	8.5	NM	16.6
DE	9.4	NV	10.3
FL	12.8	NY	14.3
GA	14.6	OH	13.2
HI	8.7	OK	13.5
IA	9.2	OR	11.7
ID	11.1	PA	10.7
IL	11.1	RI	11.1
IN	13.1	SC	14.0
KS	12.2	SD	11.2
KY	16.3	TN	14.9
LA	17.1	TX	16.2
MA	11.2	UT	8.6
MD	8.8	VA	9.5
ME	11.4	VT	9.4
MI	11.9	WA	10.3
MN	9.6	WI	10.4
MO	13.1	WV	14.6
MS	20.4	WY	10.5

Source: *Bureau of the Census*

Construct a frequency distribution with a first class of

21. 6.4–8.3.   **22.** 6.4–9.0.

23. 6.4–7.8.   **24.** 6.4–8.8.

25. Jogging Distances Twenty members of a health club who jog were asked how many miles they jog per week. The responses are as follows. Construct a stem-and-leaf display. For single digit data, use a stem of 0.

12	15	4	7	12	25	21
33	18	6	8	27	40	22
19	13	23	34	17	16	

26. College Credits Eighteen students in a geology class were asked how many college credits they had earned. The responses are as follows. Construct a stem-and-leaf display.

$$
\begin{array}{cccccc}
10 & 15 & 24 & 36 & 48 & 45 \\
42 & 53 & 60 & 17 & 24 & 30 \\
33 & 45 & 48 & 62 & 54 & 60
\end{array}
$$

27. Starting Salaries Starting salaries (in thousands of dollars) for social workers with a bachelor of science degree and no experience are shown for a random sample of 25 different social workers.

$$
\begin{array}{ccccc}
27 & 28 & 29 & 31 & 33 \\
28 & 28 & 29 & 31 & 33 \\
28 & 28 & 30 & 32 & 33 \\
28 & 29 & 30 & 32 & 34 \\
28 & 29 & 30 & 32 & 34
\end{array}
$$

a) Construct a frequency distribution. Let each class have a width of one.

b) Construct a histogram.

c) Construct a frequency polygon.

d) Construct a stem-and-leaf display.

28. Visiting a Symphony The ages of a random sample of 40 people attending a symphony are

$$
\begin{array}{cccccccc}
20 & 26 & 31 & 34 & 39 & 45 & 50 & 62 \\
20 & 29 & 31 & 35 & 40 & 47 & 51 & 63 \\
23 & 30 & 32 & 35 & 40 & 49 & 51 & 66 \\
23 & 30 & 33 & 37 & 40 & 49 & 54 & 69 \\
26 & 30 & 34 & 38 & 42 & 49 & 57 & 72
\end{array}
$$

a) Construct a frequency distribution with a first class of 20–30.

b) Construct a histogram.

c) Construct a frequency polygon.

d) Construct a stem-and-leaf display.

29. Concert Tours The following table shows the 25 top-grossing North American concert tours, in millions of dollars, for the years 1985–2008.

Artist	Total Gross ($ millions)
1. The Rolling Stones (2005)	162
2. U2 (2005)	139
3. The Rolling Stones (2006)	139
4. The Police (2007)	133
5. The Rolling Stones (1994)	121
6. Bruce Springsteen & the E Street Band (2003)	116
7. U2 (2001)	110
8. Madonna (2008)	105
9. Pink Floyd (1994)	104
10. Paul McCartney (2002)	103
11. The Rolling Stones (1989)	98
12. Celine Dion (2008)	94
13. Barbra Streisand (2006)	93
14. The Rolling Stones (1997)	89
15. Tim McGraw/Faith Hill (2006)	89
16. The Rolling Stones (2002)	88
17. Prince (2004)	87
18. 'N Sync (2001)	87
19. Madonna (2006)	86
20. Backstreet Boys (2001)	82
21. Cirque de Soleil: Delirium (2006)	82
22. Celine Dion (2005)	81
23. Celine Dion (2003)	81
24. Celine Dion (2004)	80
25. Tina Turner (2000)	80

Source: Pollstar

a) Construct a frequency distribution with a first class of 80–91.

b) Construct a histogram.

c) Construct a frequency polygon.

30. U.S. Presidents The ages of the 44 U.S. presidents at their first inauguration (as of 2011) are

$$
\begin{array}{ccccccccc}
57 & 57 & 49 & 52 & 50 & 42 & 54 & 55 & 64 \\
61 & 61 & 64 & 56 & 47 & 51 & 51 & 56 & 46 \\
57 & 54 & 50 & 46 & 55 & 56 & 60 & 61 & 54 \\
57 & 68 & 48 & 54 & 55 & 55 & 62 & 52 & 47 \\
58 & 51 & 65 & 49 & 54 & 51 & 43 & 69
\end{array}
$$

a) Construct a frequency distribution with a first class of 42–47.

b) Construct a histogram.

c) Construct a frequency polygon.

31. *Number of Televisions per Home* Use the histogram below to answer the following questions.

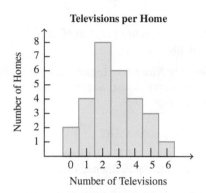

Televisions per Home

a) How many homes were included in the survey?

b) In how many homes were four televisions observed?

c) What is the modal class?

d) How many televisions were observed?

e) Construct a frequency distribution from this histogram.

32. *Car Insurance* Use the histogram below to answer the following questions.

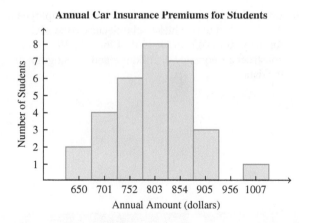

Annual Car Insurance Premiums for Students

a) How many students were surveyed?

b) What are the lower and upper class limits of the first and second classes?

c) How many students have an annual car insurance premium in the class with a class mark of $752?

d) What is the class mark of the modal class?

e) Construct a frequency distribution from this histogram. Use a first class of 625–675.

33. *E-mail Messages* Use the frequency polygon below to answer the following questions.

Number of E-mail Messages Sent per Day

a) How many people sent five e-mail messages?

b) How many people sent six or fewer e-mail messages?

c) How many people were included in the survey?

d) Construct a frequency distribution from the frequency polygon.

e) Construct a histogram from the frequency distribution in part (d).

34. *San Diego Zoo* Use the frequency polygon below to answer the following questions.

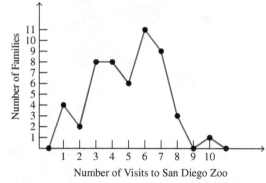

Number of Visits Selected Families Have Made to the San Diego Zoo

a) How many families visited the San Diego Zoo four times?

b) How many families visited the San Diego Zoo at least six times?

c) How many families were surveyed?

d) Construct a frequency distribution from the frequency polygon.

e) Construct a histogram from the frequency distribution in part (d).

35. *College Costs* The cost for Florida residents to attend the University of Florida for the 2010–2011 school year was $14,570. The circle graph on page 796 shows the

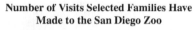

percentage of that cost for tuition/fees, room, board, and computer costs. Determine the cost, in dollars, for each category.

Cost to Attend the University of Florida for 2010–2011

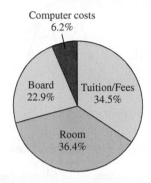

36. *Automobile Accessories* A sample of 600 people were asked which one automobile accessory they would most prefer to have on a family road trip. The following circle graph shows the percentage of respondents that answered GPS, DVD player, extra cup holders, roof rack, and other. Determine the number of respondents for each category.

Automobile Accessories for a Family Road Trip

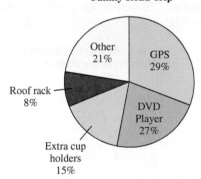

Challenge Problems/Group Activities

37. a) *Birthdays* What do you believe a histogram of the months in which the students in your class were born (January is month 1 and December is month 12) would look like? Explain.

b) By asking, determine the month in which the students in your class were born (include yourself).

c) Construct a frequency distribution containing 12 classes.

d) Construct a histogram from the frequency distribution in part (c).

e) Construct a frequency polygon of the frequency distribution in part (c).

38. *Social Security Numbers* Repeat Exercise 37 for the last digit of the students' Social Security numbers. Include classes for the digits 0–9.

Recreational Mathematics

39. a) Count the number of F's in the sentence at the bottom of the Recreational Mathematics box on page 785.

b) Can you explain why so many people count the number of F's incorrectly?

40. In what month do people take the least number of daily vitamins?

Internet/Research Activity

41. Over the years many changes have been made in the U.S. Social Security System.

a) Do research and determine the number of people receiving Social Security benefits for the years 1945, 1950, 1955, 1960, …, 2010. Then construct a frequency distribution and histogram of the data.

b) Determine the maximum amount that self-employed individuals had to pay into Social Security (the FICA tax) for the years 1945, 1950, 1955, 1960, …, 2010. Then construct a frequency distribution and a histogram of the data.

SECTION 13.4 Measures of Central Tendency

▲ *An average is used to describe the fuel efficiency of a car.*

Most people have an intuitive idea of what is meant by an "average." The term is used daily in many familiar ways. "This car averages 19 miles per gallon," "The average test grade was 82," and "The average height of adult males is 5 feet 9 inches" are three examples. In this section, we will introduce four different averages and discuss the circumstances in which each average is used.

Why *This is Important* An average is one of the most common ways to represent a set of data.

Measures of Central Tendency

An *average* is a number that is representative of a group of data. There are at least four different averages: the mean, the median, the mode, and the midrange. Each is calculated differently and may yield different results for the same set of data. Each will result in a number near the center of the data; for this reason, averages are commonly referred to as *measures of central tendency*.

The *arithmetic mean*, or simply the *mean*, is symbolized either by $\bar{x}$ (read "*x* bar") or by the Greek letter mu, μ. The symbol $\bar{x}$ is used when the mean of a *sample* of the population is calculated. The symbol μ is used when the mean of the *entire population* is calculated. Unless otherwise indicated, we will assume that the data featured in this book represent samples; therefore, we will use $\bar{x}$ for the mean.

The Greek letter sigma, Σ, is used to indicate "summation." The notation Σx, read "the sum of *x*," is used to indicate the sum of all the data. For example, if there are five pieces of data—4, 6, 1, 0, 5—then $\Sigma x = 4 + 6 + 1 + 0 + 5 = 16$.

Now we can discuss the procedure for determining the mean of a set of data.

Definition: Mean

The **mean, $\bar{x}$,** is the sum of the data divided by the number of pieces of data. The formula for calculating the mean is

$$\bar{x} = \frac{\Sigma x}{n}$$

where Σx represents the sum of all the data and n represents the number of pieces of data.

The most common use of the word *average* is the mean.

Example 1 *Determine the Mean*

Determine the mean age of a group of patients at a doctor's office if the ages of the individuals are 28, 19, 49, 35, and 49.

Solution

$$\bar{x} = \frac{\Sigma x}{n} = \frac{28 + 19 + 49 + 35 + 49}{5} = \frac{180}{5} = 36$$

Therefore, the mean, $\bar{x}$, is 36 years.

The mean represents "the balancing point" of a set of data. For example, if a seesaw were pivoted at the mean and uniform weights were placed at points corresponding to the ages in Example 1, the seesaw would balance. Figure. 13.13 shows the five ages given in Example 1 and the calculated mean.

Figure 13.13

A second average is the *median*. To find the median of a set of data, *rank the data* from smallest to largest, or largest to smallest, and determine the value in the middle of the set of *ranked data*. This value will be the median.

Definition: Median

The **median** is the value in the middle of a set of *ranked data*.

MATHEMATICS TODAY

Buying the American Dream

San Jose, California

One of the biggest dreams for most people is to own their own home. Yet depending on where you live, the American dream may be hard to achieve. In 2010, San Jose, California, had the highest median home price for major metropolitan housing markets, $630,000. Saginaw, Michigan, had the lowest median home price for major metropolitan housing markets, $59,700.

Saginaw, Michigan

Source: National Association of Realtors

Example 2 *Determine the Median*

Determine the median of the patients' ages in Example 1 on page 797.

Solution Ranking the data from smallest to largest gives 19, 28, 35, 49, and 49. Since 35 is the value in the middle of this set of ranked data (two pieces of data above it and two pieces below it), 35 years is the median. ∎

When there are an even number of pieces of data, the median is halfway between the two middle pieces. In this case, to find the median, add the two middle pieces and divide this sum by 2.

Example 3 *Determine the Median of an Even Number of Pieces of Data*

Determine the median of the following sets of data.

a) 9, 14, 16, 17, 11, 16, 11, 12   b) 7, 8, 8, 8, 9, 10

Solution

a) Ranking the data gives 9, 11, 11, 12, 14, 16, 16, 17. There are eight pieces of data. Therefore, the median will lie halfway between the two middle pieces, the 12 and the 14. The median is $\frac{12\ +\ 14}{2}$, or $\frac{26}{2}$, or 13.

b) There are six pieces of data, and they are already ranked. Therefore, the median lies halfway between the two middle pieces. Both middle pieces are 8's. The median is $\frac{8\ +\ 8}{2}$, or $\frac{16}{2}$, or 8. ∎

A third average is the *mode*.

Definition: Mode
The **mode** is the piece of data that occurs most frequently.

Example 4 *Determine the Mode*

Determine the mode of the patients' ages in Example 1 on page 797.

Solution The ages are 28, 19, 49, 35, and 49. The age 49 is the mode because it occurs twice and the other values occur only once. ∎

If each piece of data occurs only once, the set of data has no mode. For example, the set of data 1, 2, 3, 4, 5 has no mode. If two values in a set of data occur more often than all the other data, we consider both these values as modes and say that the data are **bimodal*** (which means two modes). For example, the set of data 1, 1, 2, 3, 3, 5 has two modes, 1 and 3.

The last average we will discuss is the midrange. The *midrange* is the value halfway between the lowest (L) and highest (H) values in a set of data. It is found by adding the lowest and highest values and dividing the sum by 2. A formula for finding the midrange follows.

Midrange
The **midrange** of a set of data can be calculated using the following formula.

$$\text{Midrange} = \frac{\text{lowest value}\ +\ \text{highest value}}{2}$$

---

*Some textbooks say that sets of data such as 1, 1, 2, 3, 3, 5 have no mode.

Example 5 *Determine the Midrange*

Determine the midrange of the patients' ages given in Example 1 on page 797.

Solution The ages of the patients are 28, 19, 49, 35, and 49. The lowest age is 19, and the highest age is 49.

$$\text{Midrange} = \frac{\text{lowest} + \text{highest}}{2} = \frac{19 + 49}{2} = \frac{68}{2} = 34 \text{ years}$$

The "average" of the ages 28, 19, 49, 35, 49 can be considered any one of the following values: 36 (mean), 35 (median), 49 (mode), or 34 (midrange). Which average do you feel is most representative of the ages? We will discuss this question later in this section.

Example 6 *Measures of Central Tendency*

The salaries of eight selected social workers rounded to the nearest thousand dollars are 40, 25, 28, 35, 42, 60, 60, and 73. For this set of data, determine the (a) mean, (b) median, (c) mode, and (d) midrange. Then (e) list the measures of central tendency from lowest to highest.

Solution

a) $\bar{x} = \dfrac{\Sigma x}{n} = \dfrac{40 + 25 + 28 + 35 + 42 + 60 + 60 + 73}{8} = \dfrac{363}{8} = 45.375$

b) Ranking the data from the smallest to largest gives

$$25, 28, 35, 40, 42, 60, 60, 73$$

Since there are an even number of pieces of data, the median is halfway between 40 and 42. The median $= \dfrac{40 + 42}{2} = \dfrac{82}{2} = 41$.

c) The mode is the piece of data that occurs most frequently. The mode is 60.

d) The midrange $= \dfrac{L + H}{2} = \dfrac{25 + 73}{2} = \dfrac{98}{2} = 49$.

e) The averages from lowest to highest are the median, mean, midrange, and mode. Their values are 41, 45.375, 49, and 60, respectively.

At this point, you should be able to calculate the four measures of central tendency: mean, median, mode, and midrange. Now let's examine the circumstances in which each is used.

The mean is used when each piece of data is to be considered and "weighed" equally. It is the most commonly used average. It is the only average that can be affected by *any* change in the set of data; for this reason, it is the most sensitive of all the measures of central tendency (see Exercise 23).

Occasionally, one or more pieces of data may be much greater or much smaller than the rest of the data. When this situation occurs, these "extreme" values have the effect of increasing or decreasing the mean significantly so that the mean will not be representative of the set of data. Under these circumstances, the median should be used instead of the mean. The median is often used in describing average family incomes because a relatively small number of families have extremely large incomes. These few incomes would inflate the mean income, making it nonrepresentative of the millions of families in the population.

Consider a set of exam scores from a mathematics class: 0, 16, 19, 65, 65, 65, 68, 69, 70, 72, 73, 73, 75, 78, 80, 85, 88, 92. Which average would best represent these grades? The mean is 64.06. The median is 71. Since only 3 of the 18 scores fall below the mean, the mean would not be considered a good representative score. The median of 71 probably would be the better average to use.

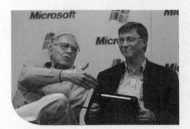
The mode is the piece of data, if any, that occurs most frequently. Builders planning houses are interested in the most common family size. Retailers ordering shirts are interested in the most common shirt size. An individual purchasing a thermometer might choose one, from those on display, whose temperature reading is the most common reading among those on display. These examples illustrate how the mode may be used.

The midrange is sometimes used as the average when the item being studied is constantly fluctuating. Average daily temperature, used to compare temperatures in different areas, is calculated by adding the lowest and highest temperatures for the day and dividing the sum by 2. The midrange is actually the mean of the high value and the low value of a set of data. Occasionally, the midrange is used to estimate the mean since it is much easier to calculate.

Sometimes an average itself is of little value, and care must be taken in interpreting its meaning. For example, Jim is told that the average depth of Willow Pond is only 3 feet. He is not a good swimmer but decides that it is safe to go out a short distance in this shallow pond. After he is rescued, he exclaims, "I thought this pond was only 3 feet deep." Jim didn't realize that an average does not indicate extreme values or the spread of the values. The spread of data is discussed in Section 13.5.

Measures of Position

Measures of position are used to describe the position of a piece of data in relation to the rest of the data. If you took the Scholastic Aptitude Test (SAT) before applying to college, your score was described as a measure of position rather than a measure of central tendency. *Measures of position* are often used to make comparisons, such as comparing the scores of individuals from different populations, and are generally used when the amount of data is large.

Two measures of position are *percentiles* and *quartiles*. There are 99 percentiles dividing a set of data into 100 equal parts; see Fig. 13.14. For example, suppose that you scored 520 on the math portion of the SAT, and the score of 520 was reported to be in the 78th percentile of high school students. This wording *does not* mean that 78% of your answers were correct; it *does* mean that you outperformed about 78% of all those taking the exam. In general, a score in the nth percentile means that you outperformed about n% of the population who took the test and that $(100 - n)$% of the people taking the test performed better than you did.

Figure 13.14

Example 7 *English Achievement Test*

Kara Hopkins took an English achievement test to obtain college credit by exam for freshman English. Her score was at the 81st percentile. Explain what that means.

Solution If a score is at the 81st percentile, it means that about 81% of the scores are below that score. Therefore, Kara scored better than about 81% of the students taking the exam. Also, about 19% of all students taking the exam scored higher than she did.

Quartiles are another measure of position. Quartiles divide data into four equal parts: The first quartile is the value that is higher than about $\frac{1}{4}$, or 25%, of the population. It is the same as the 25th percentile. The second quartile is the value that is higher than about $\frac{1}{2}$ the population and is the same as the 50th percentile, or the median. The third quartile is the value that is higher than about $\frac{3}{4}$ of the population and is the same as the 75th percentile; see Fig. 13.15.

Quartiles

Figure 13.15

PROCEDURE   **TO DETERMINE THE QUARTILES OF A SET OF DATA**

1. List the data from smallest to largest.

2. Determine the median, or the 2nd quartile, of the set of data. If there is an odd number of pieces of data, the median is the middle value. If there is an even number of pieces of data, the median will be halfway between the two middle pieces of data.

3. The first quartile, Q_1, is the median of the lower half of the data; that is, Q_1 is the median of the data less than Q_2.

4. The third quartile, Q_3, is the median of the upper half of the data; that is, Q_3 is the median of the data greater than Q_2.

Example 8 *Finding Quartiles*

Electronics World is concerned about the high turnover of its sales staff. A survey was done to determine how long (in months) the sales staff had been in their current positions. The responses of 27 sales staff follow. Determine Q_1, Q_2, and Q_3.

$$\begin{array}{ccccccccc} 25 & 3 & 7 & 15 & 31 & 36 & 17 & 21 & 2 \\ 11 & 42 & 16 & 23 & 19 & 21 & 9 & 20 & 5 \\ 8 & 12 & 27 & 14 & 39 & 24 & 18 & 6 & 10 \end{array}$$

Solution   First we list the data from smallest to largest.

$$\begin{array}{ccccccccc} 2 & 3 & 5 & 6 & 7 & 8 & 9 & 10 & 11 \\ 12 & 14 & 15 & 16 & 17 & 18 & 19 & 20 & 21 \\ 21 & 23 & 24 & 25 & 27 & 31 & 36 & 39 & 42 \end{array}$$

Next we determine the median. Since there are 27 pieces of data, an odd number, the median will be the middle value. The middle value is 17, with 13 pieces of data less than 17 and 13 pieces of data greater than 17. Therefore, the median, Q_2, is 17, shown in red.

To find Q_1, the median of the lower half of the data, we need to find the median of the 13 pieces of data that are less than Q_2. The middle value of the lower half of the data is 9. There are 6 pieces of data less than 9 and 6 pieces of data greater than 9. Therefore, Q_1 is 9, shown in blue.

To find Q_3, the median of the upper half of the data, we need to find the median of the 13 pieces of data that are greater than 17, or Q_2. The middle value of the upper half of the data is 24. There are 6 pieces of data greater than 17 but less than 24 and 6 pieces of data greater than 24. Therefore, Q_3 is 24, shown in blue. ∎

> **TECHNOLOGY TIP**
>
> Several computer software programs and calculators can be used to determine the mean of a set of data. These programs and calculators can also provide other types of statistical information that we will discuss in this chapter. In this *Technology Tip* we will provide the instructions for using a software program called Microsoft Excel as well as information on how to use Texas Instruments TI-83 Plus and TI-84 Plus graphing calculators. In the example, we will use the data from Example 1 on page 797, which represent the ages of patients in a doctor's office.
>
> **EXCEL**
> In our discussion, we will use the symbol > to indicate the next item to be selected from the list or menu of items.
>   Begin by entering the five pieces of data in column A. Press the Enter key after each piece of data is entered. Next select
>
> Insert > Function ... > Statistical > AVERAGE
>
> Then click the ☐ OK ☐ box at the bottom. The program will then generate a gray box, where you need to enter the data. In the area to the right of **Number1,** you need to enter the data for which you want to find the mean. Since you have already entered the data in column A, rows 1 to 5, if A1:A5 is not already listed, you can enter A1:A5 in the area to the right of **Number1.** Then, at the bottom of the gray box, *Formula Results* $= 36$ is displayed. The 36 is the mean of the set of data. If you then press the ☐ OK ☐ box, the mean will be displayed in the cell where the cursor was located. If you do not want the mean displayed in a cell, press ☐ CANCEL ☐. To find the median or mode you follow a similar procedure, except that instead of selecting AVERAGE you would select MEDIAN or MODE, respectively.
>
> **TI-83 PLUS AND TI-84 PLUS GRAPHING CALCULATORS**
> To enter the data, press ☐ STAT ☐. Then highlight **1: Edit** and press the ☐ ENTER ☐ key. If any data are currently listed in column **L1**, move the cursor to the **L1** and press ☐ CLEAR ☐ and then the ☐ ENTER ☐ key. This step will eliminate all data from column **L1**. Now enter the data in column **L1**. After you enter each piece of data, press the ☐ ENTER ☐ key. After all the data have been entered, press ☐ STAT ☐. Then highlight **CALC**. At this point, **1: 1–Var Stats** should be highlighted. Press the ☐ ENTER ☐ key twice. You will now see $\bar{x} = 36$. Thus, the mean is 36. Several other descriptive statistics that we will discuss shortly are also shown. If you scroll down, you will eventually see the values of Q_1, the median, and Q_3.

SECTION 13.4 *Exercises*

Warm Up Exercises

In Exercises 1–10, fill in the blank with an appropriate word, phrase, or symbol(s).

1. A number that is representative of a set of data is called a(n) _____.

2. Averages are referred to as measures of central _____.

3. The average that is found by summing the data and then dividing the sum by the number of pieces of data is called the _____.

4. The value in the middle of a set of ranked data is called the _____.

5. The piece of data that occurs most frequently is called the _____.

6. The value halfway between the lowest and highest values in a set of data is called the _____.

7. The measures of position that divide a set of data into four equal parts are called _____.

8. Data that are listed from the lowest value to the highest value or from the highest value to the lowest value are called _____ data.

9. a) The symbol for the sample mean is _____.

   b) The symbol for the population mean is _____.

10. a) Another name for the 25th percentile is the _____ quartile.

    b) Another name for the 50th percentile is the _____ quartile.

    c) Another name for the 75th percentile is the _____ quartile.

Practice the Skills

In Exercises 11–20, determine the mean, median, mode, and midrange of the set of data. Where appropriate, round your answer to the nearest tenth.

11. 8, 9, 9, 11, 13, 13, 13, 24, 26

12. 7, 9, 10, 10, 10, 12, 12

13. 76, 82, 94, 55, 100, 52, 96

14. 4, 6, 10, 12, 10, 9, 365, 40, 37, 8

15. 1, 3, 5, 7, 9, 11, 13, 15

16. 40, 50, 30, 60, 90, 100, 140

17. 1, 7, 11, 27, 36, 14, 12, 9, 1

18. 1, 1, 1, 1, 4, 4, 4, 4, 6, 8, 10, 12, 15, 21

19. 6, 8, 12, 13, 11, 13, 15, 17

20. 5, 15, 5, 15, 5, 15

21. *Cholesterol Level* The total cholesterol level of 10 patients of Dr. Novak are 176, 202, 285, 153, 200, 182, 248, 132, 214, and 195. Determine the

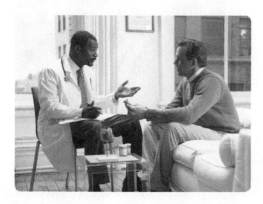

a) mean.   **b)** median.

c) mode.   **d)** midrange.

22. *Daily Commission* The amount of money Steve Kline collected in sales commission in each of seven days is $48, $67, $51, $25, $102, $61, $80. Determine the mean, median, mode, and midrange.

Problem Solving

23. *Change in the Data* The mean is the "most sensitive" average because it is affected by any change in the data.

a) Determine the mean, median, mode, and midrange for 1, 2, 3, 5, 5, 7, 11.

b) Change the 7 to a 10 in part (a). Determine the mean, median, mode, and midrange.

c) Which averages were affected by changing the 7 to a 10?

d) Which averages will be affected by changing the 11 to a 10 in part (a)?

24. *Life Expectancy* In 2010, the National Center for Health Statistics indicated a record "average life expectancy" of 78.2 years for the total U.S. population. The average life expectancy for men was 75.6 years, and for women it was 80.8 years. Which "average" do you think the National Center for Health is using?

25. *A Grade of B* To get a grade of B, a student must have a mean average of 80 or greater. Jim Condor has a mean average of 79 for 10 quizzes. He approaches his teacher and asks for a B, reasoning that he missed a B by only one point. What is wrong with Jim's reasoning?

26. *Employee Salaries* The salaries of 10 employees of a small company follow.

$29,000	$65,000
26,000	25,000
32,000	28,000
27,000	82,000
27,000	30,000

Determine the

a) mean.   **b)** median.

c) mode.   **d)** midrange.

e) If the employees wanted to demonstrate the need for a raise, which average would they use to show they are being underpaid: the mean or the median? Explain.

f) If the management did not want to give the employees a raise, which average would they use: the mean or the median? Explain.

27. *Ice Cream Consumption* The 10 countries with the highest per person consumption of ice cream in 2008 are listed below.

Country	Consumption (pints per person)
Australia	31.7
USA	26.0
Nauru	25.3
New Zealand	23.4
Canada	22.7
Norway	22.3
Finland	20.9
Sweden	20.4
Iceland	18.5
Italy	18.5

Source: *Euromonitor International*

Determine, to the nearest tenth, the

a) mean.   **b)** median.

c) mode.   **d)** midrange.

28. *Living Expenses* Bob Bennet's monthly living expenses for 1 year are as follows:

$1200	$1050	$1570	$1600
2000	1050	1550	1450
1800	1100	1310	1430

Where appropriate, round your answer to the nearest cent. Determine the

a) mean.   **b)** median.

c) mode.   **d)** midrange.

29. *Internet Retailers* The ten U.S. retailers with the highest Internet sales in 2008 are listed below.

Company	Sales ($ billion)
Amazon.com, Inc.	14.8
Staples, Inc.	5.6
Office Depot, Inc.	4.9
Dell, Inc.	4.2
HP Home & Home Office Store	3.4
OfficeMax, Inc.	3.2
Apple, Inc.	2.7
Sears Holding Corp.	2.6
CDW Corp.	2.4
Newegg.com	1.9

Source: *Internet Retailer*

Determine to the nearest tenth the

a) mean.   **b)** median.

c) mode.   **d)** midrange.

30. *Exam Average* Malcolm Sander's mean average on five exams is 86. Determine the sum of his scores.

31. *Exam Average* Jeremy Urban's mean average on six exams is 92. Determine the sum of his scores.

32. *Creating a Data Set* Construct a set of five pieces of data in which the mode has a lower value than the median and the median has a lower value than the mean.

33. *Creating a Data Set* Construct a set of six pieces of data with a mean, median, and midrange of 75 and where no two pieces of data are the same.

34. *Creating a Data Set* Construct a set of six pieces of data with a mean of 84 and where no two pieces of data are the same.

35. *Water Park* For the 2011 season, 27,000 people visited the Blue Lagoon Water Park. The park was open 120 days for water activities. The highest number of visitors on a single day was 500. The lowest number of visitors on a single day was 50. Determine whether it is possible to find the following with the given information.

a) the mean number of visitors per day

b) the median number of visitors per day

c) the mode number of visitors per day

d) the midrange number of visitors per day

36. *Determine a Necessary Grade* A mean average of 80 or greater for five exams is needed for a final grade of B in a course. Jorge Rivera's first four exam grades are 73, 69, 85, and 80. What grade does Jorge need on the fifth exam to get a B in the course?

37. *Grading Methods* A mean average of 60 on seven exams is needed to pass a course. On her first six exams, Sheryl Ward received grades of 51, 72, 80, 62, 57, and 69.

a) What grade must she receive on her last exam to pass the course?

b) An average of 70 is needed to get a C in the course. Is it possible for Sheryl to get a C? If so, what grade must she receive on the seventh exam?

c) If her lowest grade of the exams already taken is to be dropped, what grade must she receive on her last exam to pass the course?

d) If her lowest grade of the exams already taken is to be dropped, what grade must she receive on her last exam to get a C in the course?

38. Central Tendencies Which of the measures of central tendency *must* be an actual piece of data in the distribution?

39. Creating a Data Set Construct a set of six pieces of data such that if only one piece of data is changed, the mean, median, and mode will all change.

40. Changing One Piece of Data Consider the set of data 1, 1, 1, 2, 2, 2. If one 2 is changed to a 3, which of the following will change: mean, median, mode, midrange?

41. Changing One Piece of Data Is it possible to construct a set of six different pieces of data such that by changing only one piece of data you cause the mean, median, mode, and midrange to change? Explain.

42. Grocery Expenses The Taylors have recorded their weekly grocery expenses for the past 12 weeks and determined that the mean weekly expense was $85.20. Later Mrs. Taylor discovered that 1 week's expense of $74 was incorrectly recorded as $47. What is the correct mean?

43. Percentiles For any set of data, what must be done to the data before percentiles can be determined?

44. Percentiles Josie Waverly scored in the 73rd percentile on the verbal part of her College Board test. What does that mean?

45. Percentiles When a national sample of heights of kindergarten children was taken, Kevin Geis was told that he was in the 35th percentile. Explain what that means.

46. Percentiles A union leader is told that, when all workers' salaries are considered, the first quartile is $22,750. Explain what that means.

47. Quartiles The prices of a gallon of the 21 top-rated interior paints, as rated in the March 2010 issue of *Consumer Reports*, are as follows:

$18 $19 $19 $19 $20 $20 $21
$21 $22 $22 $23 $23 $25 $27
$30 $33 $35 $35 $35 $58 $61

Determine

a) Q_2.　　**b)** Q_1.　　**c)** Q_3.

48. Quartiles The prices of the 20 top-rated 16-inch laptops, as rated in the June 2010 issue of *Consumer Reports*, are as follows:

$450 $460 $500 $530 $550
$550 $650 $650 $680 $700
$720 $730 $800 $850 $900
$1000 $1200 $1350 $1700 $1900

Determine

a) Q_2.　　**b)** Q_1.　　**c)** Q_3.

49. The 50th Percentile Give the names of two other statistics that have the same value as the 50th percentile.

50. College Admissions Jonathan Burd took an admission test for the University of California and scored in the 85th percentile. The following year, Jonathan's sister Kendra took a similar admission test for the University of California and scored in the 90th percentile.

a) Is it possible to determine which of the two answered the higher percent of questions correctly on their respective exams?

b) Is it possible to determine which of the two was in a better relative position with regard to their respective populations? Explain.

51. Employee Salaries The following statistics represent weekly salaries at the Midtown Construction Company:

Mean	$600	First quartile	$560
Median	$590	Third quartile	$625
Mode	$580	83rd percentile	$665

a) What is the most common salary?

b) What salary did half the employees' salaries surpass?

c) About what percent of employees' salaries surpassed $625?

d) About what percent of employees' salaries were less than $560?

e) About what percent of employees' salaries surpassed $665?

f) If the company has 100 employees, what is the total weekly salary of all employees?

Challenge Problems/Group Activities

52. The Mean of the Means Consider the following five sets of values.

i) 5 6 7 7 8 9 14

ii) 3 6 8 9

iii) 1 1 1 2 5

iv) 6 8 9 12 15

v) 50 51 55 60 80 100

a) Compute the mean of each of the five sets of data.

b) Compute the mean of the five means in part (a).

c) Find the mean of the 27 pieces of data.

d) Compare your answer in part (b) to your answer in part (c). Are the values the same? Does your answer make sense?

53. *Ruth Versus Mantle* The tables below compare the batting performances for selected years for two well-known former baseball players, Babe Ruth and Mickey Mantle.

Babe Ruth
Boston Red Sox 1914–1919
New York Yankees 1920–1934

Year	At Bats	Hits	Pct.
1925	359	104	
1930	518	186	
1933	459	138	
1916	136	37	
1922	406	128	
Total	1878	593	

Mickey Mantle
New York Yankees 1951–1968

Year	At Bats	Hits	Pct.
1954	543	163	
1957	474	173	
1958	519	158	
1960	527	145	
1962	377	121	
Total	2440	760	

a) For each player, compute the batting average percent (pct.) for each year by dividing the number of hits by the number of at bats. Round to the nearest thousandth. Place the answers in the pct. column.

b) Going across each of the five horizontal lines (for example Ruth, 1925, vs. Mantle, 1954), compare the percents (pct.) and determine which is greater in each case.

c) For each player, compute the mean batting average percent for the 5 given years by dividing the total hits by the total at bats. Which is greater, Ruth's or Mantle's?

d) Based on your answer in part (b), does your answer in part (c) make sense? Explain.

e) Find the mean percent for each player by adding the five pcts. and dividing by 5. Which is greater, Ruth's or Mantle's?

f) Why do the answers obtained in parts (c) and (e) differ? Explain.

g) Who would you say has the better batting average percent for the 5 years selected? Explain.

54. *Employee Salaries* The following table gives the annual salary distribution for employees at Kulzer's Home Improvement.

Annual Salary	Number Receiving Salary
$100,000	1
85,000	2
24,000	6
21,000	4
18,000	5
17,000	7

Using the information provided in the table, determine the

a) mean annual salary.

b) median annual salary.

c) mode annual salary.

d) midrange annual salary.

e) Which is the best measure of central tendency for this set of data? Explain your answer.

Weighted Average Sometimes when we wish to find an average, we may wish to assign more importance, or weight, to some of the pieces of data. To calculate a weighted average, we use the formula: weighted average $= \dfrac{\Sigma xw}{\Sigma w}$, *where w is the weight of the piece of data, x; Σxw is the sum of the products of each piece of data multiplied by its weight; and Σw is the sum of the weights. For example, suppose that students in a class need to submit a report*

that counts for 20% of their grade, they need to take a midterm exam that counts for 30% of their grade, and they need to take a final exam that counts for 50% of their grade. Suppose that a student got a 72 on the report, an 85 on the midterm exam, and a 93 on the final exam. To determine this student's weighted average, first find Σxw:
$\Sigma xw = 72(0.20) + 85(0.30) + 93(0.50) = 86.4$. Next find Σw, the sum of the weights: $\Sigma w = 0.20 + 0.30 + 0.50 = 1.00$. Now determine the weighted average as follows.

$$\text{Weighted average} = \frac{\Sigma xw}{\Sigma w} = \frac{86.4}{1.00} = 86.4$$

Thus, the weighted average is 86.4. Note that Σw does not always have to be 1.00. In Exercises 55 and 56, use the weighted average formula.

55. **Course Average** Suppose that your final grade for a course is determined by a midterm exam and a final exam. The midterm exam is worth 40% of your grade, and the final exam is worth 60%. If your midterm exam grade is 84 and your final exam grade is 94, calculate your final average.

56. **Grade Point Average** In a four-point grade system, an A corresponds to 4.0 points, a B corresponds to 3.0 points, a C corresponds to 2.0 points, and a D corresponds to 1.0 points. No points are awarded for an F. Last semester, Tanya Reeves received a B in a four-credit hour course, an A in a three-credit hour course, a C in a three-credit hour course, and an A in another three-credit hour course. Grade point average (GPA) is calculated as a weighted average using the credit hours as weights and the number of points corresponding to the grade as pieces of data. Calculate Tanya's GPA for the previous semester. (Round your answer to the nearest hundredth.)

Recreational Mathematics

57. **Your Exam Average a)** Calculate the mean, median, mode, and midrange of your exam grades in your mathematics course.

   b) Which measure of central tendency best represents your average grade?

   c) Which measure of central tendency would you rather use as your average grade?

58. **Purchases** Matthew Riveria purchased some items at Staples each day for five days. The mode of the number of items Matthew purchased is higher than the median of the number of items he purchased. The median of the number of items Matthew purchased is higher than the mean of the number of items he purchased. He purchased at least two items but no more than seven items each day.

   a) How many items did Matthew purchase each day? (*Note:* There is more than one correct answer.)

   b) Determine the mean, median, and mode for your answer to part (a).

Internet/Research Activity

59. Two other measures of location that we did not mention in this section are *stanines* and *deciles*. Use statistics books, books on educational testing and measurements, and Internet Web sites to write a report on what stanines and deciles are and when percentiles, quartiles, stanines, and deciles are used.

SECTION 13.5   Measures of Dispersion

▲ *The average life span of a tablet PC battery may not be enough information to make a sound purchasing decision.*

Measures of central tendency by themselves do not always give sufficient information to analyze a situation and make decisions. For example, suppose Apple Computer is considering two companies to produce batteries for its iPads. Testing shows that Company A batteries have a mean life of 10 hours. Company B batteries have a mean life of 9.5 hours. If both manufacturers' batteries cost the same, which one should be purchased? The average battery life may not be the most important factor. If half of Company A batteries last only 5 hours, while half last 15 hours, there is a large variability in the life of the batteries. If all of Company B batteries last between 9.0 and 10.0 hours, the batteries are more consistent and reliable. This example illustrates the importance of knowing something about the *spread*, or *variability*, of the data. In this section we will discuss two measures of variability or dispersion.

Why *This is Important* Knowing the spread, or variability of a set of data helps us make accurate conclusions about the set of data.

easures of dispersion are used to measure the variability of the data, including the *spread of the data,* and how the data varies about the mean. The range and standard deviation* are the measures of dispersion that will be discussed in this section.

Range and Standard Deviation

The *range* is the difference between the highest and lowest values; it indicates the total spread of the data.

Range

The range of a set of data can be calculated using the following formula.

$$\textbf{Range} = \text{highest value} - \text{lowest value}$$

Example **1** *Determine the Range*

The amount of caffeine, in milligrams, of 10 different soft drinks is given below. Determine the range of these data.

$$38, 43, 26, 80, 55, 34, 40, 30, 35, 43$$

Solution   Range = highest value − lowest value = 80 − 26 = 54. The range of the amounts of caffeine is 54 milligrams.   ∎

The second measure of dispersion we discuss in this section, the *standard deviation,* measures how much the data *differ from the mean.* It is symbolized either by the letter s or by the Greek letter sigma, σ.[†] The s is used when the standard deviation of a *sample* is calculated. The σ is used when the standard deviation of the entire *population* is calculated. *Since we are assuming that all data presented in this section are for samples, we use s to represent the standard deviation* (note, however, that on the height and weight charts on page 814, σ is used).

The larger the variability of the data about the mean, the larger the standard deviation is. Consider the following two sets of data.

$$5, 8, 9, 10, 12, 13 \quad 8, 9, 9, 10, 10, 11$$

Figure 13.16

Both have a mean of 9.5. Which set of values on the whole do you believe differs less from the mean of 9.5? Figure 13.16 may make the answer more apparent. The scores in the second set of data are closer to the mean and therefore have a smaller standard deviation. You will soon be able to verify such relationships yourself.

Sometimes only a very small standard deviation is desirable or acceptable. Consider a cereal box that is to contain 8 oz of cereal. If the amount of cereal put into the boxes varies too much—sometimes underfilling, sometimes overfilling—the manufacturer will soon be in trouble with consumer groups and government agencies.

At other times, a larger spread of data is desirable or expected. For example, intelligence quotients (IQs) are expected to exhibit a considerable spread about the

---

Variance, another measure of dispersion, is the square of the standard deviation.
[†]Our alphabet uses both uppercase and lowercase letters, for example, *A* and *a*. The Greek alphabet also uses both uppercase and lowercase letters. The symbol Σ is the capital Greek letter sigma, and σ is the lowercase Greek letter sigma.

mean because everyone is different. The following procedure explains how we determine the standard deviation of a set of data.

PROCEDURE   TO DETERMINE THE STANDARD DEVIATION OF A SET OF DATA

1. Determine the mean of the set of data.
2. Make a chart having three columns:

   Data   Data − Mean   (Data − Mean)^2

3. List the data vertically under the column marked Data.
4. Subtract the mean from each piece of data and place the difference in the Data − Mean column.
5. Square the values obtained in the Data − Mean column and record these values in the (Data − Mean)^2 column.
6. Determine the sum of the values in the (Data − Mean)^2 column.
7. Divide the sum obtained in Step 6 by $n − 1$, where n is the number of pieces of data.[*]
8. Determine the square root of the number obtained in Step 7. This number is the standard deviation of the set of data.

Example 2 illustrates the procedure to follow to determine the standard deviation of a set of data.

Example 2   *Determine the Standard Deviation*

A veterinarian in an animal hospital recorded the following life spans of selected Labrador retrievers (to the nearest year):

$$7, 9, 11, 15, 18, 12$$

Determine the standard deviation of the life spans.

Solution   First determine the mean:

$$\bar{x} = \frac{\Sigma x}{n} = \frac{7 + 9 + 11 + 15 + 18 + 12}{6} = \frac{72}{6} = 12$$

Next construct a table with three columns, as illustrated in Table 13.4 on page 810, and list the data in the first column (it is often helpful to list the data in ascending or descending order). Complete the second column by subtracting the mean, 12 in this case, from each piece of data in the first column.

The sum of the values in the Data − Mean column should always be zero; if not, you have made an error. (If a rounded value of $\bar{x}$ is used, the sum of the values in the Data − Mean column will not always be exactly zero; however, the sum will be very close to zero.)

---

[*]To determine the standard deviation of a sample, divide the sum of (Data − Mean)^2 column by $n − 1$. To find the standard deviation of a population, divide the sum by n. In this book, we assume that the set of data represents a sample and divide by $n − 1$. The quotient obtained in Step 7 represents a measure of dispersion called the *variance*.

Table 13.4

Data	Data − Mean	(Data − Mean)^2
7	$7 - 12 = -5$	
9	$9 - 12 = -3$	
11	$11 - 12 = -1$	
12	$12 - 12 = 0$	
15	$15 - 12 = 3$	
18	$18 - 12 = 6$	
	0	

Next square the values in the second column and place the squares in the third column (Table 13.5).

Table 13.5

Data	Data − Mean	(Data − Mean)^2
7	−5	$(-5)^2 = (-5)(-5) = 25$
9	−3	$(-3)^2 = (-3)(-3) = 9$
11	−1	$(-1)^2 = (-1)(-1) = 1$
12	0	$(0)^2 = (0)(0) = 0$
15	3	$(3)^2 = (3)(3) = 9$
18	6	$(6)^2 = (6)(6) = 36$
	0	80

Add the squares in the third column. In this case, the sum is 80. Divide this sum by one less than the number of pieces of data ($n - 1$). In this case, the number of pieces of data is 6. Therefore, we divide by 5 and get

$$\frac{80}{5} = 16*$$

Finally, take the square root of this number. Since $\sqrt{16} = 4$, the standard deviation, symbolized s, is 4. ∎

Now we will develop a formula for determining the standard deviation of a set of data. If we call the individual data x and the mean $\bar{x}$, we could write the three column heads Data, Data − Mean, and (Data − Mean)^2 in Table 13.4 as

$$x \quad x - \bar{x} \quad (x - \bar{x})^2$$

Let's follow the procedure we used to obtain the standard deviation in Example 2. We found the sum of the (Data − Mean)^2 column, which is the same as the sum of the $(x - \bar{x})^2$ column. We can represent the sum of the $(x - \bar{x})^2$ column by using the summation notation, $\Sigma(x - \bar{x})^2$. Thus, in Table 13.5, $\Sigma(x - \bar{x})^2 = 80$. We then divided this number by 1 less than the number of pieces of data, $n - 1$. Thus, we have

$$\frac{\Sigma(x - \bar{x})^2}{n - 1}$$

---

*16 is the variance, symbolized s^2, of this set of data.

Finally, we took the square root of this value to obtain the standard deviation.

Standard Deviation
The standard deviation, *s*, of a set of data can be calculated using the following formula.

$$s = \sqrt{\frac{\Sigma (x - \bar{x})^2}{n - 1}}$$

Example 3 *Determine the Standard Deviation of Stock Prices*

The following are the prices of nine stocks on the New York Stock Exchange. Determine the standard deviation of the prices.

$$\$17, \$28, \$32, \$36, \$50, \$52, \$66, \$74, \$104$$

Solution The mean, $\bar{x}$, is

$$\bar{x} = \frac{\Sigma x}{n} = \frac{17 + 28 + 32 + 36 + 50 + 52 + 66 + 74 + 104}{9} = \frac{459}{9} = 51$$

The mean is $51.

Table 13.6

x	$x - \bar{x}$	$(x - \bar{x})^2$
17	−34	1156
28	−23	529
32	−19	361
36	−15	225
50	−1	1
52	1	1
66	15	225
74	23	529
104	53	2809
	0	5836

Table 13.6 shows us that $\Sigma(x - \bar{x})^2 = 5836$. Since there are nine pieces of data, $n - 1 = 9 - 1$, or 8.

$$s = \sqrt{\frac{\Sigma (x - \bar{x})^2}{n - 1}} = \sqrt{\frac{5836}{8}} = \sqrt{729.5} \approx 27.01$$

The standard deviation, to the nearest tenth, is $27.01.

Standard deviation will be used in Section 13.6 to find the percent of data between any two values in a normal curve. Standard deviations are also often used in determining norms for a population (see Exercise 29).

In this *Technology Tip*, we will explain how to find the standard deviation using Excel as well as with the TI-83 Plus and TI-84 Plus graphing calculators. In our illustration, we will use the data from Example 3 on page 811, which represent the prices of nine stocks on the New York Stock Exchange.

EXCEL
The instructions used to determine the standard deviation are very similar to those used to determine the mean in the *Technology Tip* on page 802 in Section 13.4. Please read that material now. Then enter the nine piece of data in columns A1–A9 and press the Enter key. Now select the following:

Insert > Function ... > Statistical > STDEV

Then click the OK box. The program will then generate a gray box where you need to enter the data. In the area to the right of **Number1** you need to enter the data for which you want to find the standard deviation. Since you have already entered the data in column A, rows 1 to 9, if A1:A9 is not already listed, you can enter A1:A9 in the area to the right of **Number1**. At the bottom of the gray box, *Formula Results* = 27.00925767, which is the standard deviation, is displayed. If you click OK, Excel will place the standard deviation in cell A10.

TI-83 PLUS AND TI-84 PLUS GRAPHING CALCULATORS
To find the standard deviation on Texas Instruments graphing calculators, follow the instructions for finding the mean in the *Technology Tip* on page 802 in Section 13.4. As explained there, press STAT > EDIT > ENTER. Remove existing data by highlighting **L1** and then pressing CLEAR > ENTER. Then enter the nine pieces of data, pressing the Enter key after each entry. Then press STAT > CALC > ENTER > ENTER. The fourth statistic down is S_x = 27.00925767. This value is the standard deviation.

SECTION 13.5 *Exercises*

Warm Up Exercises

In Exercises 1–6, fill in the blank with an appropriate word, phrase, or symbol(s).

1. Measures of dispersion are used to indicate the spread or _____ of the data.

2. The difference between the highest and lowest values in a set of data is called the _____.

3. The measure of dispersion that measures how much the data differ from the mean is called the _____.

4. The symbol, σ, is used to indicate the standard deviation of a(n) _____.

5. The symbol, s, is used to indicate the standard deviation of a(n) _____.

6. The standard deviation of a set of data in which all the data values are the same is _____.

Practice the Skills

In Exercises 7–14, determine the range and standard deviation of the set of data. When appropriate, round standard deviations to the nearest hundredth.

7. 11, 9, 6, 12, 17

8. 15, 15, 19, 21, 13, 13

9. 130, 131, 132, 133, 134, 135, 136

10. 3, 7, 8, 12, 0, 9, 11, 12, 6, 2

11. 4, 8, 9, 11, 13, 15

12. 9, 9, 9, 9, 9, 9, 9

13. 7, 9, 7, 9, 9, 10, 12

14. 60, 58, 62, 67, 48, 51, 72, 70

Problem Solving

15. *Digital Cameras* Determine the range and standard deviation of the following prices of selected digital cameras: $158, $95, $175, $180, $95, $129, $228, $300.

16. *Years Until Retirement* Seven employees at a large company were asked the number of additional years they planned to work before retirement. Their responses were 10, 23, 28, 4, 1, 6, 12. Determine the range and standard deviation of the number of years.

17. *Camping Tents* Determine the range and standard deviation of the following prices of selected camping tents: $109, $60, $80, $60, $210, $250, $60, $100, $115.

18. *Prescription Prices* The amount of money seven people spent on prescription medication in a year are as follows: $600, $100, $850, $350, $250, $140, $300. Determine the range and standard deviation of the amounts.

19. Can you think of any situations in which a large standard deviation may be desirable?

20. Can you think of any situations in which a small standard deviation may be desirable?

21. Without actually doing the calculations, decide which, if either, of the following two sets of data will have the greater standard deviation. Explain why.

10, 13, 14, 15, 17, 21   16, 17, 17, 18, 18, 19

22. Without actually doing the calculations, decide which, if either, of the following two sets of data will have the greater standard deviation. Explain why.

2, 4, 6, 8, 10   102, 104, 106, 108, 110

23. By studying the standard deviation formula, explain why the standard deviation of a set of data will always be greater than or equal to 0.

24. Patricia Wolff teaches two statistics classes, one in the morning and the other in the evening. On the midterm exam, the morning class had a mean of 75.2 and a standard deviation of 5.7. The evening class had a mean of 75.2 and a standard deviation of 12.5.

a) How do the means compare?

b) If we compare the set of scores from the first class with those in the second class, how will the distributions of the two sets of scores compare?

25. *Count Your Money* Six people were asked to determine the amount of money they were carrying, to the nearest dollar. The results were

$32, $60, $14, $25, $5, $68

a) Determine the range and standard deviation of the amounts.

b) Add $10 to each of the six amounts. How do you expect the range and standard deviation of the new set of data to change?

c) Determine the range and standard deviation of the new set of data. Do the results agree with your answer to part (b)? If not, explain why.

26. a) *Adding to or Subtracting from Each Number* Pick any five numbers. Compute the mean and the standard deviation of this distribution.

b) Add 20 to each of the numbers in your original distribution and compute the mean and the standard deviation of this new distribution.

c) Subtract 5 from each number in your original distribution and compute the mean and standard deviation of this new distribution.

d) What conclusions can you draw about changes in the mean and the standard deviation when the same number is added to or subtracted from each piece of data in a distribution?

e) How will the mean and standard deviation of the numbers 8, 9, 10, 11, 12, 13, 14 differ from the mean and standard deviation of the numbers 648, 649, 650, 651, 652, 653, 654? Determine the mean and standard deviation of both sets of numbers.

27. a) *Multiplying Each Number* Pick any five numbers. Compute the mean and standard deviation of this distribution.

b) Multiply each number in your distribution by 3 and compute the mean and the standard deviation of this new distribution.

c) Multiply each number in your original distribution by 9 and compute the mean and standard deviation of this new distribution.

d) What conclusions can you draw about changes in the mean and the standard deviation when each value in a distribution is multiplied by the same number?

e) The mean and standard deviation of the distribution 1, 3, 4, 4, 5, 7 are 4 and 2, respectively. Use the conclusion drawn in part (d) to determine the mean and standard deviation of the distribution

5, 15, 20, 20, 25, 35

28. *Waiting in Line* Consider the following illustrations of two bank-customer waiting systems.

a) How would you expect the mean waiting time in Bank A to compare with the mean waiting time in Bank B?

b) How would you expect the standard deviation of waiting times in Bank A to compare with the standard deviation of waiting times in Bank B?

29. *Height and Weight Distribution* The chart shown on the right uses the symbol σ to represent the standard deviation. Note that 2σ represents the value that is two standard deviations above the mean; -2σ represents the value that is two standard deviations below the mean. The unshaded areas, from two standard deviations below the mean to two standard deviations above the mean, are considered the normal range. For example, the average (mean) 8-year-old boy has a height of about 50 inches, but any heights between approximately 45 inches and 55 inches are considered normal for 8-year-old boys. Refer to the chart below to answer the following questions.

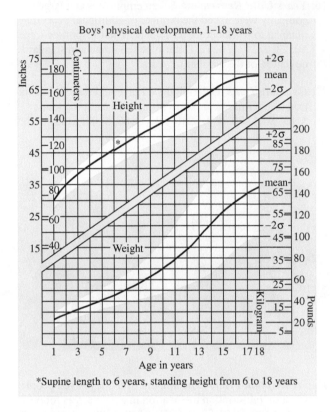

*Supine length to 6 years, standing height from 6 to 18 years

a) What happens to the standard deviation for weights of boys as the age of boys increases? What is the significance of this fact?

b) At age 16, what is the mean weight, in pounds, of boys?

c) What is the approximate standard deviation of boys' weights at age 16?

d) Determine the mean weight and normal range for boys at age 13.

e) Determine the mean height and normal range for boys at age 13.

f) Assuming that this chart was constructed so that approximately 95% of all boys are always in the normal range, determine what percentage of boys are not in the normal range.

Challenge Problems/Group Activities

30. *Athletes' Salaries* The tables on page 815 list the 10 highest-paid athletes in Major League Baseball and in the National Football League.

Major League Baseball (2010 Season)

Player	Salary (millions of dollars)
1. Alex Rodriguez	33.0
2. C. C. Sabathia	24.3
3. Derek Jeter	22.6
4. Mark Teixeira	20.6
5. Johan Santana	20.1
6. Miguel Cabrera	20.0
7. Carlos Beltran	19.4
8. Ryan Howard	19.0
9. Carlos Lee	19.0
10. Alfonso Soriano	19.0

Source: Major League Baseball Players Association

National Football League (2009–2010 season)

Player	Salary (millions of dollars)
1. Philip Rivers	25.6
2. Jay Cutler	22.0
3. Eli Manning	20.5
4. Kurt Warner	19.0
5. Kelvin Hayden	17.5
6. Matt Schaub	17.0
7. Julius Peppers	16.7
8. Chris Long	16.6
9. Greg Jennings	16.3
10. Antonio Smith	15.5

Source: National Football League Players Association

a) Without doing any calculations, which do you believe is greater, the mean salary of the 10 baseball players or the mean salary of the 10 football players?

b) Without doing any calculations, which do you believe is greater, the standard deviation of the salary of the 10 baseball players or the standard deviation of the salary of the 10 football players?

c) Compute the mean salary of the 10 baseball players and the mean salary of the 10 football players and determine whether your answer in part (a) was correct.

d) Compute the standard deviation of the salary of the 10 baseball players and the standard deviation of the salary of the 10 football players and determine whether your answer in part (b) is correct. Round each mean to the nearest tenth to determine the standard deviation.

31. *Oil Change* Jiffy Lube has franchises in two different parts of a city. The number of oil changes made daily, for 25 days, is given below.

East Store					West Store				
33	59	27	30	42	38	46	38	38	30
19	42	25	22	32	38	38	37	39	31
43	27	57	37	52	39	36	40	37	47
40	67	38	44	43	30	34	42	45	29
15	31	49	41	35	31	46	28	45	48

a) Construct a frequency distribution for each store with a first class of 15–20.

b) Draw a histogram for each store.

c) Using the histogram, determine which store appears to have a greater mean, or do the means appear about the same? Explain.

d) Using the histogram, determine which store appears to have the greater standard deviation. Explain.

e) Calculate the mean for each store and determine whether your answer in part (c) was correct.

f) Calculate the standard deviation for each store and determine whether your answer in part (d) was correct.

Recreational Mathematics

32. Calculate the range and standard deviation of your exam grades in this mathematics course. Round the mean to the nearest tenth to calculate the standard deviation.

33. Construct a set of five pieces of data with a mean, median, mode, and midrange of 6 and a standard deviation of 0.

Internet/Research Activity

34. Use a calculator with statistical function keys to find the mean and standard deviation of the salaries of the 10 Major League Baseball players and the 10 National Football League players in Exercise 30.

Suppose your mathematics teacher states that exam scores for the previous exam followed a bell-shaped distribution and that your score was 1.5 standard deviations above the mean. How does your exam grade compare with the exam grades of your classmates? What percentage of students in your class had exam grades below your exam grade? In this section, we will discuss sets of data that form bell-shaped distributions and learn how to determine the percentage of data that fall below a particular piece of data in the set of data.

▲ *Some sets of data, such as exam grades, may form a bell-shaped distribution.*

Why **This is Important** There are many real-life applications, such as IQ scores, heights and weights of males, heights and weights of females, and wearout mileage of automobile tires, that have a bell-shaped distribution.

When examining data using a histogram, we can refer to the overall appearance of the histogram as the *shape* of the distribution of the data. Certain shapes of distributions of data are more common than others. In this section, we will illustrate and discuss a few of the more common ones. In each case, the vertical scale is the frequency and the horizontal scale is the observed values.

In a *rectangular distribution* (Fig. 13.17), all the observed values occur with the same frequency. If a die is rolled many times, we would expect the numbers 1–6 to occur with about the same frequency. The distribution representing the outcomes of the die is rectangular.

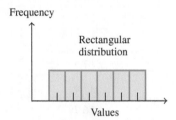

Figure 13.17

In *J-shaped distributions*, the frequency is either constantly increasing (Fig. 13.18(a)) or constantly decreasing (Fig. 13.18(b)). The number of hours studied per week by students may have a distribution like that in Fig. 13.18(b). The bars might represent (from left to right) 0–5 hours, 6–10 hours, 11–15 hours, and so on.

J-shaped Distributions

(a)   (b)

Figure 13.18

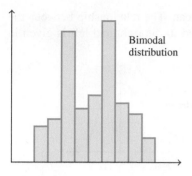

Figure 13.19

A *bimodal distribution* (Fig. 13.19) is one in which two nonadjacent values occur more frequently than any other values in a set of data. For example, if an equal number of men and women were weighed, the distribution of their weights would probably be bimodal, with one mode for the women's weights and the second for the men's weights. For a distribution to be considered bimodal, both modes need not have the same frequency but they must both have a frequency greater than the frequency of each of the other values in the distribution.

The life expectancy of lightbulbs has a bimodal distribution: a small peak very near 0 hours of life, resulting from the bulbs that burned out very quickly because of a manufacturing defect, and a much higher peak representing the nondefective bulbs. A bimodal frequency distribution generally means that you are dealing with two distinct populations, in this case, defective and nondefective lightbulbs.

Another distribution, called a *skewed distribution*, has more of a "tail" on one side than the other. A skewed distribution with a tail on the right (Fig. 13.20(a)) is said to be skewed to the right. If the tail is on the left (Fig. 13.20(b)), the distribution is referred to as skewed to the left.

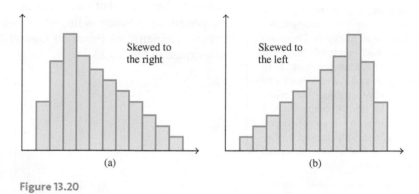

Figure 13.20

The number of children per family might be a distribution skewed to the right. Some families have no children, more families may have one child, the greatest percentage may have two children, fewer may have three children, still fewer may have four children, and so on.

Since few families have high incomes, distributions of family incomes might be skewed to the right.

Smoothing the histograms of the skewed distributions shown in Fig. 13.20 to form curves gives the curves illustrated in Fig. 13.21.

Figure 13.21

In Fig. 13.21(a), the greatest frequency appears on the left side of the curve and the frequency decreases from left to right. Since the mode is the value with the greatest frequency, the mode would appear on the left side of the curve.

Every value in the set of data is considered in determining the mean. The values on the far right side of the curve in Fig. 13.21(a) would tend to increase the value of the mean. Thus, the value of the mean would be farther to the right than the mode.

Did You Know?

What Conclusions Can You Draw?

City A   City B

0   200   400   600   800
Math scores

Based on the figure, which shows the distribution of scores on the mathematics part of the SAT test for two different cities, can we say that any given person selected at random from city B has outperformed any given person selected at random from city A? Both distributions appear normal, and the mean of city A is slightly smaller than the mean of city B. Consider, however, two randomly selected students who took this test: Sally from city A and Kendra from city B. The graph shows that many students in city A outperformed students from city B, so we cannot conclude that Sally scored higher than Kendra or that Kendra scored higher than Sally.

The median would be between the mode and the mean. The relationship between the mean, median, and mode for curves that are skewed to the right and left is given in Fig. 13.22.

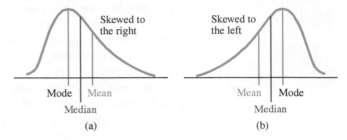

Figure 13.22

Normal Distributions

Each of these distributions is useful in describing sets of data. However, the most important distribution is the *normal* or *Gaussian distribution*, named for German mathematician Carl Friedrich Gauss. The histogram of a normal distribution is illustrated in Fig. 13.23.

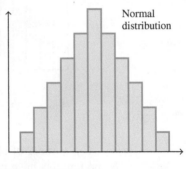

Figure 13.23

The normal distribution is important because many sets of data are normally distributed or closely resemble a normal distribution. Such distributions include intelligence quotients, heights and weights of males, heights and weights of females, lengths of full-grown boa constrictors, weights of watermelons, wearout mileage of automobile brakes, and life spans of refrigerators, to name just a few.

The normal distribution is symmetric about the mean. If you were to fold the histogram of a normal distribution down the middle, the left side would fit the right side exactly. **In a normal distribution, the mean, median, and mode all have the same value.**

When the histogram of a normal distribution is smoothed to form a curve, the curve is bell-shaped. The bell may be high and narrow or short and wide. Each of the three curves in Fig. 13.24 represents a normal curve. Curve 13.24(a) has the smallest standard deviation (spread from the mean); curve 13.24(c) has the largest.

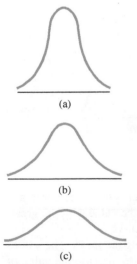

(a)

(b)

(c)

Figure 13.24

Properties of a Normal Distribution
- The graph of a normal distribution is called a normal curve.
- The normal curve is bell-shaped and symmetric about the mean.
- The mean, median, and mode of a normal distribution all have the same value and all occur at the center of the distribution.

Since the curve representing the normal distribution is symmetric, 50% of the data always falls above (to the right of) the mean and 50% of the data falls below (to the left of) the mean. In addition, every normal distribution has approximately 68% of the data between the value that is one standard deviation below the mean, and the value that is one standard deviation above the mean, see Fig. 13.25. Approximately 95% of the data falls between the value that is two standard deviations below the mean and the value that is two standard deviations above the mean. Approximately 99.7% of the data falls between the value that is three standard deviations below the mean, and the value that is three standard deviations above the mean. These three percentages, 68%, 95%, and 99.7%, are used in what is referred to as the *empirical rule*.

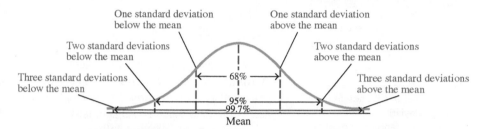

Figure 13.25

Thus, if a normal distribution has a mean of 100 and a standard deviation of 10, then approximately 68% of all the data falls between $100 - 10$ and $100 + 10$, or between 90 and 110. Approximately 95% of the data falls between $100 - 20$ and $100 + 20$, or between 80 and 120, and approximately 99.7% of the data falls between $100 - 30$, and $100 + 30$, or between 70 and 130.

The empirical rule is summarized as follows.

Empirical Rule

In any normal distribution.
- Approximately 68% of all the data lies within one standard deviation of the mean (in both directions).
- Approximately 95% of all the data lies within two standard deviations of the mean (in both directions).
- Approximately 99.7% of all the data lies within three standard deviations of the mean (in both directions).

Example 1 *Applying the Empirical Rule*

The cholesterol levels for females are normally distributed. In a random sample of 500 females, determine the approximate number of females in the sample who are expected to have a cholesterol level

a) within one standard deviation of the mean.

b) within two standard deviations of the mean.

Solution

a) By the empirical rule, about 68% of females have a cholesterol level within one standard deviation of the mean. Since there are 500 females in the sample, the number of females expected to have a cholesterol level within one standard deviation of the mean is

$$68\% \times 500 = 0.68 \times 500 = 340$$

Therefore, about 340 females are expected to have a cholesterol level within one standard deviation of the mean.

b) By the empirical rule, about 95% of females have a cholesterol level within two standard deviations the mean. Since there are 500 females in the sample, the number of females expected to have a cholesterol level within two standard deviations of the mean is

$$95\% \times 500 = 0.95 \times 500 = 475$$

Therefore, about 475 females are expected to have a cholesterol level within two standard deviations of the mean.   ■

z-Scores

Now we turn our attention to z-scores. We use *z-scores* (or *standard scores*) to determine how far, in terms of standard deviations, a given data value is from the mean of the distribution. For example, a data value that has a z-score of 1.5 indicates the data value is 1.5 standard deviations above the mean. The standard score or z-score is calculated as follows.

z-Scores or Standard Scores
The formula for finding **z-scores** or standard scores is

$$z = \frac{\text{value of the piece of data} - \text{mean}}{\text{standard deviation}}$$

In this book, the notation z_x represents the z-score, or standard score, of the value x. For example, if a normal distribution has a mean of 86 with a standard deviation of 12, a score of 110 has a standard score or z-score of

$$z_{110} = \frac{110 - 86}{12} = \frac{24}{12} = 2$$

Therefore, a value of 110 in this distribution has a z-score of 2 and is two standard deviations above the mean.

Data below the mean will always have negative z-scores; data above the mean will always have positive z-scores. The mean will always have a z-score of 0.

Example 2   Finding z-Scores

A normal distribution has a mean of 80 and a standard deviation of 10. Determine z-scores for the following values.

a) 90   b) 95   c) 80   d) 64

Solution

a)
$$z = \frac{\text{value} - \text{mean}}{\text{standard deviation}}$$

$$z_{90} = \frac{90 - 80}{10} = \frac{10}{10} = 1$$

A value of 90 has a z-score of 1. Therefore, a value of 90 is one standard deviation above the mean.

b)
$$z_{95} = \frac{95 - 80}{10} = \frac{15}{10} = 1.5$$

A value of 95 has a z-score of 1.5, and is 1.5 standard deviations above the mean.

c)
$$z_{80} = \frac{80 - 80}{10} = \frac{0}{10} = 0$$

The mean always has a z-score of 0.

d)
$$z_{64} = \frac{64 - 80}{10} = \frac{-16}{10} = -1.6$$

A value of 64 has a z-score of -1.6, and is 1.6 standard deviations below the mean. ∎

If we are given any normal distribution with a known mean and standard deviation, it is possible through the use of Table 13.7 on pages 822 and 823 (the z-table) to determine the percent of data between any two given values. The total area under any normal curve is 1.00. Table 13.7 will be used to determine the cumulative area under the normal curve that lies to the *left of a specified z-score*. We will use Table 13.7(a) when we wish to determine area to the left of a *negative z-score*, and we will use Table 13.7(b) when we wish to determine area to the left of a *positive z-score*.

Example 3 illustrates the procedure to follow when using Table 13.7 to determine the area under the normal curve. When you are determining the area under the normal curve, it is often helpful to draw a picture and shade the area to be determined.

Example 3 *Determining the Area Under the Normal Curve*

Determine the area under the normal curve
a) to the left of $z = -1.00$.
b) to the left of $z = 1.19$.
c) to the right of $z = 1.19$.
d) between $z = -1.62$ and $z = 2.57$.

Solution

a) To determine the area under the normal curve to the left of $z = -1.00$, as illustrated in Fig. 13.26, we use Table 13.7(a) since we are looking for an area to the left of a negative z-score. In the upper-left corner of the table, we see the letter z. The column under z gives the units and the tenths value for z. To locate the hundredths value of z, we use the column headings to the right of z. In this case, the hundredths value of $z = -1.00$ is 0, so we use the first column labeled .00. To determine the area to the left of $z = -1.00$, we use the row labeled -1.0 and move to the column labeled .00. The table entry, .1587, is circled in blue. Therefore, the total area to the left of $z = -1.00$ is 0.1587

b) To determine the area under the normal curve to the left of $z = 1.19$ (Fig. 13.27), we use Table 13.7(b) since we are looking for an area to the left of a positive z-score. We first look for 1.1 in the column under z. Since the hundredths value

Figure 13.26

Figure 13.27

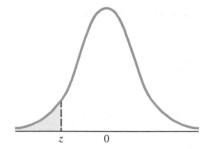

Table entry for z is the area to the left of z.

Table 13.7 Areas of a Standard Normal Distribution

(a) Table of Areas to the Left of z When z is Negative

z	.00	.01	.02	.03	.04	.05	.06	.07	.08	.09
−3.4	.0003	.0003	.0003	.0003	.0003	.0003	.0003	.0003	.0003	.0002
−3.3	.0005	.0005	.0005	.0004	.0004	.0004	.0004	.0004	.0004	.0003
−3.2	.0007	.0007	.0006	.0006	.0006	.0006	.0006	.0005	.0005	.0005
−3.1	.0010	.0009	.0009	.0009	.0008	.0008	.0008	.0008	.0007	.0007
−3.0	.0013	.0013	.0013	.0012	.0012	.0011	.0011	.0011	.0010	.0010
−2.9	.0019	.0018	.0018	.0017	.0016	.0016	.0015	.0015	.0014	.0014
−2.8	.0026	.0025	.0024	.0023	.0023	.0022	.0021	.0021	.0020	.0019
−2.7	.0035	.0034	.0033	.0032	.0031	.0030	.0029	.0028	.0027	.0026
−2.6	.0047	.0045	.0044	.0043	.0041	.0040	.0039	.0038	.0037	.0036
−2.5	.0062	.0060	.0059	.0057	.0055	.0054	.0052	.0051	.0049	.0048
−2.4	.0082	.0080	.0078	.0075	.0073	.0071	.0069	.0068	.0066	.0064
−2.3	.0107	.0104	.0102	.0099	.0096	.0094	.0091	.0089	.0087	.0084
−2.2	.0139	.0136	.0132	.0129	.0125	.0122	.0119	.0116	.0113	.0110
−2.1	.0179	.0174	.0170	.0166	.0162	.0158	.0154	.0150	.0146	.0143
−2.0	.0228	.0222	.0217	.0212	.0207	.0202	.0197	.0192	.0188	.0183
−1.9	.0287	.0281	.0274	.0268	.0262	.0256	.0250	.0244	.0239	.0233
−1.8	.0359	.0351	.0344	.0336	.0329	.0322	.0314	.0307	.0301	.0294
−1.7	.0446	.0436	.0427	.0418	.0409	.0401	.0392	.0384	.0375	.0367
−1.6	.0548	.0537	.0526	.0516	.0505	.0495	.0485	.0475	.0465	.0455
−1.5	.0668	.0655	.0643	.0630	.0618	.0606	.0594	.0582	.0571	.0559
−1.4	.0808	.0793	.0778	.0764	.0749	.0735	.0721	.0708	.0694	.0681
−1.3	.0968	.0951	.0934	.0918	.0901	.0885	.0869	.0853	.0838	.0823
−1.2	.1151	.1131	.1112	.1093	.1075	.1056	.1038	.1020	.1003	.0985
−1.1	.1357	.1335	.1314	.1292	.1271	.1251	.1230	.1210	.1190	(.1170)
−1.0	(.1587)	.1562	.1539	.1515	.1492	.1469	.1446	.1423	.1401	.1379
−0.9	.1841	.1814	.1788	.1762	.1736	.1711	.1685	.1660	.1635	.1611
−0.8	.2119	.2090	.2061	.2033	.2005	.1977	.1949	.1922	.1894	.1867
−0.7	.2420	.2389	.2358	.2327	.2296	.2266	.2236	.2206	.2177	.2148
−0.6	.2743	.2709	.2676	.2643	.2611	.2578	.2546	.2514	.2483	.2451
−0.5	.3085	.3050	.3015	.2981	.2947	.2912	.2877	.2843	.2810	.2776
−0.4	.3446	.3409	.3372	.3336	.3300	.3264	.3228	.3192	.3156	.3121
−0.3	.3821	.3783	.3745	.3707	.3669	.3632	.3594	.3557	.3520	.3483
−0.2	.4207	.4168	.4129	.4090	.4052	.4013	.3974	.3936	.3897	.3859
−0.1	.4602	.4562	.4522	.4483	.4443	.4404	.4364	.4325	.4286	.4247
−0.0	.5000	.4960	.4920	.4880	.4840	.4801	.4761	.4721	.4681	.4641

For z-scores less than −3.49, use 0.000 to approximate the area.

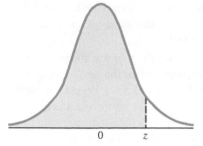

Table entry for *z* is the area to the left of *z*.

Table 13.7 Areas of a Standard Normal Distribution *(continued)*

(b) Table of Areas to the Left of *z* When *z* is Positive

z	.00	.01	.02	.03	.04	.05	.06	.07	.08	.09
0.0	.5000	.5040	.5080	.5120	.5160	.5199	.5239	.5279	.5319	.5359
0.1	.5398	.5438	.5478	.5517	.5557	.5596	.5636	.5675	.5714	.5753
0.2	.5793	.5832	.5871	.5910	.5948	.5987	.6026	.6064	.6103	.6141
0.3	.6179	.6217	.6255	.6293	.6331	.6368	.6406	.6443	.6480	.6517
0.4	.6554	.6591	.6628	.6664	.6700	.6736	.6772	.6808	.6844	.6879
0.5	.6915	.6950	.6985	.7019	.7054	.7088	.7123	.7157	.7190	.7224
0.6	.7257	.7291	.7324	.7357	.7389	.7422	.7454	.7486	.7517	.7549
0.7	.7580	.7611	.7642	.7673	.7704	.7734	.7764	.7794	.7823	.7852
0.8	.7881	.7910	.7939	.7967	.7995	.8023	.8051	.8078	.8106	.8133
0.9	.8159	.8186	.8212	.8238	.8264	.8289	.8315	.8340	.8365	.8389
1.0	.8413	.8438	.8461	.8485	.8508	.8531	.8554	.8577	.8599	.8621
1.1	.8643	.8665	.8686	.8708	.8729	.8749	.8770	.8790	.8810	(.8830)
1.2	.8849	.8869	.8888	.8907	.8925	.8944	.8962	.8980	.8997	.9015
1.3	.9032	.9049	.9066	.9082	.9099	.9115	.9131	.9147	.9162	.9177
1.4	.9192	.9207	.9222	.9236	.9251	.9265	.9279	.9292	.9306	.9319
1.5	.9332	.9345	.9357	.9370	.9382	.9394	.9406	.9418	.9429	.9441
1.6	.9452	.9463	.9474	.9484	.9495	.9505	.9515	.9525	.9535	.9545
1.7	.9554	.9564	.9573	.9582	.9591	.9599	.9608	.9616	.9625	.9633
1.8	.9641	.9649	.9656	.9664	.9671	.9678	.9686	.9693	.9699	.9706
1.9	.9713	.9719	.9726	.9732	.9738	.9744	.9750	.9756	.9761	.9767
2.0	.9772	.9778	.9783	.9788	.9793	.9798	.9803	.9808	.9812	.9817
2.1	.9821	.9826	.9830	.9834	.9838	.9842	.9846	.9850	.9854	.9857
2.2	.9861	.9864	.9868	.9871	.9875	.9878	.9881	.9884	.9887	.9890
2.3	.9893	.9896	.9898	.9901	.9904	.9906	.9909	.9911	.9913	.9916
2.4	.9918	.9920	.9922	.9925	.9927	.9929	.9931	.9932	.9934	.9936
2.5	.9938	.9940	.9941	.9943	.9945	.9946	.9948	.9949	.9951	.9952
2.6	.9953	.9955	.9956	.9957	.9959	.9960	.9961	.9962	.9963	.9964
2.7	.9965	.9966	.9967	.9968	.9969	.9970	.9971	.9972	.9973	.9974
2.8	.9974	.9975	.9976	.9977	.9977	.9978	.9979	.9979	.9980	.9981
2.9	.9981	.9982	.9982	.9983	.9984	.9984	.9985	.9985	.9986	.9986
3.0	.9987	.9987	.9987	.9988	.9988	.9989	.9989	.9989	.9990	.9990
3.1	.9990	.9991	.9991	.9991	.9992	.9992	.9992	.9992	.9993	.9993
3.2	.9993	.9993	.9994	.9994	.9994	.9994	.9994	.9995	.9995	.9995
3.3	.9995	.9995	.9995	.9996	.9996	.9996	.9996	.9996	.9996	.9997
3.4	.9997	.9997	.9997	.9997	.9997	.9997	.9997	.9997	.9997	.9998

For *z*-scores greater than 3.49, use 1.000 to approximate the area.

of $z = 1.19$ is 9, we move to the column labeled .09. Using the row labeled 1.1 and the column labeled 0.09, the table entry is .8830, circled in green. Therefore, the total area to the left of $z = 1.19$ is 0.8830.

c) To determine the area to the right of $z = 1.19$, we use the fact that the total area under the normal curve is 1. In part (b), we determined that the area to the left of $z = 1.19$ was 0.8830. To determine the area to the right of $z = 1.19$, we can subtract the area to the left of $z = 1.19$ from 1 (Fig. 13.28(a)). Therefore, the area to the right of $z = 1.19$ is $1 - 0.8830$, or 0.1170.

Figure 13.28

Another way to determine the area to the right of $z = 1.19$ is to use the fact that the normal curve is symmetric about the mean. Thus, the area to the left of a negative z-score is equal to the area to the right of a positive z-score. Therefore, the area to the left of $z = -1.19$ is equal to the area to the right of $z = 1.19$ (Fig. 13.28(b)). Using Table 13.7(a), we see that the area to the left of $z = -1.19$ is .1170. This value is circled in red in the table. Therefore, the area to the right of $z = 1.19$ is also .1170. This answer agrees with our answer obtained by subtracting the area to the left of $z = 1.19$ from 1.

d) To determine the area between two z-scores, we subtract the smaller area from the larger area (Fig. 13.29). Using Table 13.7(b), we see that the area to the left of $z = 2.57$ is .9949 (Fig. 13.29(a)). Using Table 13.7(a), we see that the area to the left of $z = -1.62$ is .0526 (Fig. 13.29(b)). Thus, the area between $z = -1.62$ and $z = 2.57$ is $0.9949 - 0.0526$, or 0.9423 (Fig. 13.29(c)).

Figure 13.29

To change the area under the normal curve to a percent, multiply the area by 100%. In Example 3(a), we determined the area to the left of $z = -1.00$ to be 0.1587. To change this area to a percent, multiply 0.1587 by 100%.

$$0.1587 = 0.1587 \times 100\% = 15.87\%$$

Therefore 15.87% of the normal curve is less than a score that is one standard deviation below the mean.

Below, we summarize the procedure to determine the percent of data for any interval under the normal curve.

PROCEDURE **TO DETERMINE THE PERCENT OF DATA BETWEEN ANY TWO VALUES IN A NORMAL DISTRIBUTION**

1. Draw a diagram of the normal curve, indicating the area or percent to be determined.

2. Use the formula $z = \dfrac{\text{value of the piece of data } - \text{ mean}}{\text{standard deviation}}$ to convert the given values to z-scores. Indicate these z-scores on the diagram.

3. Look up the areas that correspond to the specified z-scores in Table 13.7.
   a) When determining the area to the left of a negative z-score, use Table 13.7(a).

   b) When determining the area to the left of a positive z-score, use Table 13.7(b).

   c) When determining the area to the right of a z-score, subtract the percent of data to the left of the specified z-score from 100%.

| Area under entire curve = 1.0000 | Area to the left of z | Area to the right of z |

   Or, use the symmetry of a normal distribution.

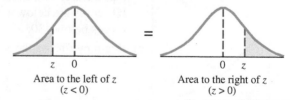

Area to the left of z Area to the right of z
$(z < 0)$ $(z > 0)$

   d) When determining the area between two z-scores, subtract the smaller area from the larger area.

   In the figure below, we let z_1 represent the smaller z-score and z_2 represent the larger z-score.

Area to the left of z_2 Area to the left of z_1 Area between z_1 and z_2

4. Change the areas you determined in Step 3 to percents as explained on page 824.

⌐ Example **4** *IQ Scores*

Intelligence quotients (IQ scores) are normally distributed with a mean of 100 and a standard deviation of 15. Determine the percent of individuals with IQ scores

a) below 115.   b) below 130.

c) below 70.   d) between 70 and 115.

e) between 115 and 130.   f) above 122.5.

Solution

a) We want to determine the area under the normal curve below the value of 115, as illustrated in Fig. 13.30(a). Converting 115 to a z-score yields a z-score of 1.00.

$$z_{115} = \frac{115 - 100}{15} = \frac{15}{15} = 1.00$$

Figure 13.30

The percent of individuals with IQ scores below 115 is the same as the percent of data below a z-score of 1.00 (Fig. 13.30(b)). Since our z-score is positive, we use Table 13.7(b). From Table 13.7(b), we determine that the area to the left of a z-score of 1.00 is .8413. Therefore, 84.13% of all the IQ scores are below a z-score of 1.00. Thus, 84.13% of individuals have IQ scores below 115.

b) Begin by finding the z-score for 130.

$$z_{130} = \frac{130 - 100}{15} = \frac{30}{15} = 2.00$$

The percent of data below a z-score of 130 is the same as the percent of data below a z-score of 2.00 (Fig. 13.31). Using Table 13.7(b), we determine that the area to the left of a z-score of 2.00 is .9772. Therefore, 97.72% of the IQ scores are below a z-score of 2.00. Thus, 97.72% of all individuals have IQ scores below 130.

c) Begin by finding the z-score for 70.

$$z_{70} = \frac{70 - 100}{15} = \frac{-30}{15} = -2.00$$

The percent of data below a score of 70 is the same as the percent of data below a z-score of −2.00 (Fig. 13.32). Since our z-score is negative, we use Table 13.7(a). Using the table, we determine that the area to the left of $z = -2.00$ is .0228. Therefore, 2.28% of the data is below a z-score of −2.00. Thus, 2.28% of all individuals have IQ scores below 70.

d) In part (a), we determined that $z_{115} = 1.00$, and in part (c), we determined that $z_{70} = -2.00$. The percent of data below a z-score of 1.00 is 84.13% (Fig. 13.33(a) on page 827). The percent of data below a z-score of −2.00 is 2.28% (Fig. 13.33(b)). Since we want to find the percent of data between two z-scores, we subtract the smaller percent from the larger percent: 84.13% − 2.28% = 81.85% (Fig. 13.33(c)). Thus, 81.85% of all individuals have IQ scores between 70 and 115.

97|72%

Original values   100   130
z-scores   0   2.00

Figure 13.31

2.28%

70   100   Original values
−2.00   0   z-scores

Figure 13.32

Figure 13.33

e) In part (a), we determined that $z_{115} = 1.00$, and in part (b), we determined $z_{130} = 2.00$. The percent of data below a z-score of 1.00 is 84.13%. The percent of data below a z-score of 2.00 is 97.72%. Since we want to find the percent of data between two z-scores, we subtract the smaller percent from the larger percent: 97.72% − 84.13% = 13.59% (Fig. 13.34). Thus, 13.59% of all individuals have IQ scores between 115 and 130.

Figure 13.34

f) Begin by determining a z-score for 122.5.

$$z_{122.5} = \frac{122.5 - 100}{15} = \frac{22.5}{15} = 1.50$$

The percent of IQ scores above 122.5 is the same as the percent of data above $z = 1.50$ (Fig. 13.35). To determine the percent of data above $z = 1.50$, we can determine the percent of data below $z = 1.50$ and subtract this percent from 100%. In Table 13.7(b), we see that the area to the left of $z = 1.50$ is .9332. Therefore, 93.32% of the IQ scores are below $z = 1.50$. The percent of IQ scores above $z = 1.50$ are 100% − 93.32%, or 6.68%. Thus, 6.68% of all IQ scores are greater than 122.5.

Figure 13.35   ∎

Example 5 *Horseback Rides*

Assume that the length of time for a horseback ride on the trail at Triple R Ranch is normally distributed with a mean of 3.2 hours and a standard deviation of 0.4 hour.

a) What percent of horseback rides last at least 3.2 hours?

b) What percent of horseback rides last less than 2.8 hours?

c) What percent of horseback rides are at least 3.7 hours?

d) What percent of horseback rides are between 2.8 hours and 4.0 hours?

e) In a random sample of 500 horseback rides at Triple R Ranch, how many are at least 3.7 hours?

Solution

a) In a normal distribution, half the data are always above the mean. Since 3.2 hours is the mean, half, or 50%, of the horseback rides last at least 3.2 hours.

b) Convert 2.8 hours to a z-score.

$$z_{2.8} = \frac{2.8 - 3.2}{0.4} = -1.00$$

Use Table 13.7(a) to find the area of the normal curve that lies below a z-score of −1.00. The area to the left of $z = -1.00$ is 0.1587. Therefore, the percent of horseback rides that last less than 2.8 hours is 15.87% (Fig. 13.36).

Figure 13.36

Figure 13.37

> **TIMELY TIP**
>
> Following is a summary of some important items presented in this section.
> - The normal curve is symmetric about the mean.
> - The area under the normal curve cannot be negative.
> - A negative z-score indicates that the corresponding value in the original distribution is less than the mean.
> - A positive z-score indicates that the corresponding value in the original distribution is greater than the mean.
> - A z-score of 0 indicates that the corresponding value in the original distribution is the mean.
> - Table 13.7 provides the area to the left of a specified z-score.
> - When using Table 13.7 to determine the area to the left of a specified z-score, locate the units value and tenths value of your specified z-score under the column labeled z. Then move to the column containing the hundredths value of your specified z-score to obtain the area.

c) At least 3.7 hours means greater than or equal to 3.7 hours. Therefore, we are seeking to find the percent of data to the right of 3.7 hours. Convert 3.7 hours to a z-score.

$$z_{3.7} = \frac{3.7 - 3.2}{0.4} = 1.25$$

From Table 13.7(b), we determine that the area to the left of $z = 1.25$ is .8944. Therefore, 89.44% of the data are below $z = 1.25$. The percent of data above $z = 1.25$ (or to the right of $z = 1.25$) is $100\% - 89.44\%$, or 10.56% (Fig. 13.37). Thus, 10.56% of horseback rides last at least 3.7 hours.

d) Convert 4.0 to a z-score.

$$z_{4.0} = \frac{4.0 - 3.2}{0.4} = 2.00$$

From Table 13.7(b), we determine that the area to the left of $z = 2.00$ is .9772 (Fig.13.38(a)). Therefore the percent of data below a z-score of 2.00 is 97.72%. From part (b), we determined that $z_{28} = -1.00$ and that the percent of data below a z-score of -1.00 is 15.87% (Fig. 13.38(b)). To find the percent of data between a z-score of -1.00 and a z-score of 2.00, we subtract the smaller percent from the larger percent. Thus, the percent of horseback rides that last between 2.8 hours and 4.0 hours is $97.72\% - 15.87\%$, or 81.85% (Fig. 13.38(c)).

Figure 13.38

e) In part (c), we determined that 10.56% of all horseback rides last at least 3.7 hours. We now multiply 0.1056 times the number in the random sample, 500, to determine the number of horseback rides that last at least 3.7 hours. There are $0.1056 \times 500 = 52.8$, or approximately 53, horseback rides that last at least 3.7 hours.

SECTION 13.6 *Exercises*

Warm Up Exercises

In Exercises 1–12, fill in the blank with an appropriate word, phrase, or symbol(s).

1. A distribution in which all the values have the same frequency is called a(n) _____ distribution.

2. A distribution in which the frequency is either constantly increasing or constantly decreasing is called a(n) _____ distribution.

3. A distribution that has a "tail" on its right is skewed to the _____.

4. A distribution that has a "tail" on its left is skewed to the _____.

5. A distribution in which two nonadjacent values occur more frequently than any other values in a set of data is called a(n) _____ distribution.

6. A normal distribution is a(n) _____ shaped distribution.

7. A measure of how far, in terms of standard deviations, a given data value is from the mean is called a z-score or a(n) _____ score.

8. The mean of a set of data will always have a z-score of _____.

9. A piece of data that has a negative z-score is _____ the mean.

10. A piece of data that has a positive z-score is _____ the mean.

11. According to the empirical rule, in a normal distribution,

  a) approximately _____ % of the data lie within plus or minus 1 standard deviation of the mean,

  b) approximately _____ % of the data lie within plus or minus 2 standard deviations of the mean, and

  c) approximately _____ % of the data lie within plus or minus 3 standard deviations of the mean.

12. In a normal distribution, the mean, median, and mode all have the same _____.

In Exercises 13–16, give an example of the type of distribution.

13. Rectangular   14. Skewed

15. J-shaped   16. Bimodal

For the distributions in Exercises 17–20, state whether you think the distribution would be normal, J-shaped, bimodal, rectangular, skewed left, or skewed right.

17. The wearout mileage of automobile tires

18. The numbers resulting from tossing a die many times

19. The number of people per household in the United States

20. The heights of a sample of high school seniors, where there are an equal number of males and females

Practice the Skills

In Exercises 21–32, use Table 13.7 on pages 822 and 823 to find the specified area.

21. Above the mean   22. Below the mean

23. Between two standard deviations below the mean and one standard deviation above the mean

24. Between 1.10 and 1.60 standard deviations above the mean

25. To the right of $z = 1.53$ 26. To the left of $z = 1.62$

27. To the left of $z = -1.78$ 28. To the right of $z = -1.78$

29. Between $z = -1.32$ and $z = -1.64$

30. To the left of $z = 1.84$

31. To the left of $z = -2.13$

32. To the left of $z = -0.92$

In Exercises 33–42, use Table 13.7 on pages 822 and 823 to determine the percent of data specified.

33. Less than $z = 0.71$ 34. Less than $z = -0.82$

35. Between $z = -1.34$ and $z = 2.24$

36. Between $z = -2.18$ and $z = -1.90$

37. Greater than $z = -1.90$

38. Greater than $z = 2.66$

39. Less than $z = 1.96$

40. Between $z = -1.53$ and $z = -1.82$

41. Between $z = 0.72$ and $z = 2.14$

42. Between $z = -2.15$ and $z = 3.31$

Problem Solving

Heights of Girls In Exercises 43 and 44, assume that the heights of 7-year-old girls are normally distributed. The heights of 8 girls are given in z-scores below.

Emily	0.9	Jenny	0.0	Heather	-1.3	Shenice	0.0
Sarah	1.7	Sadaf	-0.2	Carol	0.8	Kim	-1.2

43. a) Which of these girls are taller than the mean?

  b) Which of these girls are at the mean?

  c) Which of these girls are shorter than the mean?

44. a) Which girl is the tallest?

  b) Which girl is the shortest?

Police Officer's Salaries In Exercises 45–48, assume the annual salaries of police officers are normally distributed with a mean of $50,000 and a standard deviation of $7000.

45. Determine the percent of police officers with an annual salary of at least $50,000.

46. Determine the percent of police officers with an annual salary between $43,000 and $64,000.

47. Determine the percent of police officers with an annual salary of at least $58,750.

48. In a random sample of 500 police officers, how many have an annual salary of at least $58,750.

SAT Scores In Exercises 49–54, assume that the mathematics scores on the SAT are normally distributed with a mean of 500 and a standard deviation of 100.

49. What percent of students who took the test have a mathematics score below 550?

50. What percent of students who took the test have a mathematics score above 650?

51. What percent of students who took the test have a mathematics score between 550 and 650?

52. What percent of students who took the test have a mathematics score below 300?

53. What percent of students who took the test have a mathematics score between 400 and 525?

54. What percent of students who took the test have a mathematics score above 380?

Vending Machine In Exercises 55–58, a vending machine is designed to dispense a mean of 7.6 oz of coffee into an 8-oz cup. If the standard deviation of the amount of coffee dispensed is 0.4 oz and the amount is normally distributed, find the percent of times the machine will

55. dispense from 7.4 oz to 7.7 oz.

56. dispense less than 7.0 oz.

57. dispense less than 7.7 oz.

58. result in the cup overflowing (therefore dispense more than 8 oz).

▲ See Exercises 55–58

Automobile Speed In Exercises 59–64, assume that the speed of automobiles on an expressway during rush hour is normally distributed with a mean of 62 mph and a standard deviation of 5 mph.

59. What percent of cars are traveling faster than 62 mph?

60. What percent of cars are traveling between 58 mph and 66 mph?

61. What percent of cars are traveling slower than 56 mph?

62. What percent of cars are traveling faster than 70 mph?

63. If 200 cars are selected at random, how many will be traveling slower than 56 mph?

64. If 200 cars are selected at random, how many will be traveling faster than 70 mph?

Corn Flakes In Exercises 65–68, assume that the amount of corn flakes in a box is normally distributed with a mean of 16 oz and a standard deviation of 0.1 oz.

65. Determine the percent of boxes that will contain between 15.83 oz and 16.32 oz of corn flakes.

66. Determine the percent of boxes that will contain more than 16.16 oz of corn flakes.

67. If the manufacturer produces 300,000 boxes, how many of them will contain less than 15.83 oz of corn flakes?

68. If the manufacturer produces 300,000 boxes, how many of them will contain more than 16.16 oz of corn flakes?

Cost of Day Care In Exercises 69–74, assume the annual day care cost per child is normally distributed with a mean of $8000 and a standard deviation of $1500.

69. What percent of day care costs are more than $7250 annually?

70. What percent of day care costs are between $6500 and $8750 annually?

71. What percent of day care costs are more than $11,750 annually?

72. What percent of day care costs are less than $11,750 annually?

73. In a random sample of 120 families, how many pay more than $7250 annually for day care per child?

74. In a random sample of 120 families, how many pay between $6500 and $8750 annually for day care per child?

75. *Weight Loss* A weight-loss clinic guarantees that its new customers will lose at least 5 lb by the end of their first month of participation or their money will be refunded. If the weight loss of customers at the end of their first month is normally distributed, with a mean of 6.7 lb and a standard deviation of 0.81 lb, determine the percent of customers who will be able to claim a refund.

76. *Battery Warranty* The warranty on a car battery is 36 months. If the breakdown times of this battery are normally distributed with a mean of 46 months and a standard deviation of 8 months, determine the percent of batteries that can be expected to require repair or replacement under warranty.

77. *Coffee Machine* A vending machine that dispenses coffee does not appear to be working correctly. The machine rarely gives the proper amount of coffee. Some of the time the cup is underfilled, and some of the time the cup overflows. Does this variation indicate that the mean number of ounces dispensed has to be adjusted, or does it indicate that the standard deviation of the amount of coffee dispensed by the machine is too large?

78. *Grading on a Normal Curve* Mr. Sanderson marks his class on a normal curve. Those with z-scores above 1.8 will receive an A, those between 1.8 and 1.1 will receive a B, those between 1.1 and −1.2 will receive a C, those between −1.2 and −1.9 will receive a D, and those under −1.9 will receive an F. Determine the percent of grades that will be A, B, C, D, and F.

79. Consider the following normal curve, representing a normal distribution, with points *A*, *B*, and *C*. One of these points corresponds to the mean, one point corresponds to the mean plus one standard deviation and one point corresponds to the mean minus two standard deviations.

a) Which point corresponds to the mean?

b) Which point corresponds to the mean plus one standard deviation?

c) Which point corresponds to the mean minus two standard deviations?

80. Consider the following two normal curves.

a) Do these distributions have the same mean? If so, what is the mean?

b) One of these curves corresponds to a normal distribution with a standard deviation of 1. The other curve corresponds to a normal distribution with a standard deviation of 3. Which curve, A or B, has a standard deviation of 3?

Concept/Writing Exercises

81. In a distribution that is skewed to the right, which has the greatest value: the mean, median, or mode? Which has the smallest value? Explain.

82. In a distribution skewed to the left, which has the greatest value: the mean, median, or mode? Which has the smallest value? Explain.

83. List three populations other than those given in the text that may be normally distributed.

84. List three populations other than those given in the text that may not be normally distributed.

Challenge Problems/Group Activities

85. *Salesperson Promotion* The owner at Kim's Home Interiors is reviewing the sales records of two managers who are up for promotion, Katie and Stella, who work in different stores. At Katie's store, the mean sales have been $23,200 per month, with a standard deviation of $2170. At Stella's store, the mean sales have been $25,600 per month, with a standard deviation of $2300. Last month, Katie's store sales were $28,408 and Stella's store sales were $29,510. At both stores, the distribution of monthly sales is normal.

a) Convert last month's sales for Katie's store and for Stella's store to z-scores.

b) If one of the two were to be promoted based solely on the increase in sales last month, who should be promoted? Explain.

86. *Chebyshev's Theorem* How can you determine whether a distribution is approximately normal? A statistical theorem called *Chebyshev's theorem* states that the *minimum percent* of data between plus and minus K standard deviations from the mean $(K > 1)$ in *any distribution* can be found by the formula

$$\text{Minimum percent} = 1 - \frac{1}{K^2}$$

Thus, for example, between ± 2 standard deviations from the mean there will always be a minimum of 75% of data. This minimum percent applies to any distribution. For $K = 2$,

$$\text{Minimum percent} = 1 - \frac{1}{2^2}$$

$$= 1 - \frac{1}{4} = \frac{3}{4}, \quad \text{or} \quad 75\%$$

Likewise, between ± 3 standard deviations from the mean there will always be a minimum of 89% of the data. For $K = 3$,

$$\text{Minimum percent} = 1 - \frac{1}{3^2}$$

$$= 1 - \frac{1}{9} = \frac{8}{9}, \quad \text{or} \quad 89\%$$

The following table lists the minimum percent of data in *any distribution* and the actual percent of data in *the normal distribution* between ± 1.1, ± 1.5, ± 2.0, and ± 2.5 standard deviations from the mean. The minimum percents of data in any distribution were calculated by using Chebyshev's theorem. The actual percents of data for the normal distribution were calculated by using the area given in the standard normal, or z, table.

	$K = 1.1$	$K = 1.5$	$K = 2$	$K = 2.5$
Minimum (for any distribution)	17.4%	55.6%	75%	84%
Normal distribution	72.9%	86.6%	95.4%	98.8%
Given distribution				

The third row of the chart has been left blank for you to fill in the percents when you reach part (e).

Consider the following 30 pieces of data obtained from a quiz.

1, 1, 1, 1, 2, 2, 2, 2, 3, 3, 4, 4, 4, 5, 6,

6, 6, 7, 7, 7, 7, 8, 8, 8, 8, 9, 9, 9, 10, 10

a) Determine the mean of the set of scores.

b) Determine the standard deviation of the set of scores.

c) Determine the values that correspond to 1.1, 1.5, 2, and 2.5 standard deviations above the mean.
   Then determine the values that correspond to 1.1, 1.5, 2, and 2.5 standard deviations below the mean.

d) By observing the 30 pieces of data, determine the actual percent of quiz scores between

± 1.1 standard deviations from the mean.

± 1.5 standard deviations from the mean.

± 2 standard deviations from the mean.

± 2.5 standard deviations from the mean.

e) Place the percents found in part (d) in the third row of the chart.

f) Compare the percents in the third row of the chart with the minimum percents in the first row and the normal percents in the second row, and then make a judgment as to whether this set of 30 scores is approximately normally distributed.

87. *Test Scores* Obtain a set of test scores from your instructor.

a) Determine the mean, median, mode, and midrange of the test scores.

b) Determine the range and standard deviation of the set of scores. (You may round the mean to the nearest tenth when finding the standard deviation.)

c) Construct a frequency distribution of the set of scores. Select your first class so that there will be between 5 and 12 classes.

d) Construct a histogram and frequency polygon of the frequency distribution in part (c).

e) Does the histogram in part (d) appear to represent a normal distribution? Explain.

f) Use the procedure explained in Exercise 86 to determine whether the set of scores approximates a normal distribution. Explain.

88. Determine a value of z such that $z \geq 0$ and 47.5% of the standard normal curve lies between 0 and the z-value.

89. Determine a value of z such that $z \leq 0$ and 38.1% of the standard normal curve lies between 0 and the z-value.

Recreational Mathematics

90. Ask your instructor for the class mean and class standard deviation for one of the exams taken by your class. For that exam, calculate the *z*-score for your exam grade. How many standard deviations is your exam grade away from the mean?

91. If the mean score on a math quiz is 12.0 and 77% of the students in your class scored between 9.6 and 14.4, determine the standard deviation of the quiz scores.

Internet/Research Activity

92. In this project, you actually become the statistician.

a) Select a project of interest to you in which data must be collected.

b) Write a proposal and submit it to your instructor for approval. In the proposal, discuss the aims of your project and how you plan to gather the data to make your sample unbiased.

c) After your proposal has been approved, gather 50 pieces of data by the method you proposed.

d) Rank the data from smallest to largest.

e) Compute the mean, median, mode, and midrange.

f) Determine the range and standard deviation of the data. You may round the mean to the nearest tenth when computing the standard deviation.

g) Construct a frequency distribution, histogram, frequency polygon, and stem-and-leaf display of your data. Select your first class so that there will be between 5 and 12 classes. Be sure to label your histogram and frequency polygon.

h) Does your distribution appear to be normal? Explain your answer. Does it appear to be another type of distribution discussed? Explain.

i) Determine whether your distribution is approximately normal by using the technique discussed in Exercise 86.

SECTION 13.7 Linear Correlation and Regression

Do you believe that there is a relationship between the time a person studies for an exam and the exam grade the person receives? Is there a relationship between the age of a car and the value of the car? Can we predict the value of a car based on the age of the car? In this section, we will learn how to determine whether there is a relationship between two quantities and, if so, how strong that relationship is. We will also learn how to determine the equation of the line that best describes the relationship between two quantities.

▲ *You can predict the value of a car based on the age of the car.*

Why *This is Important* There are many real-life applications in which a relationship exists between two variables, such as the amount of time spent studying for an exam and the exam score.

In this section, we discuss two important statistical topics: correlation and regression. *Correlation* is used to determine whether there is a relationship between two quantities and, if so, how strong the relationship is. *Regression* is used to determine the equation that relates the two quantities. Although there are other types of correlation and regression, in this section we discuss only linear correlation and linear regression. We begin by discussing linear correlation.

Linear Correlation

The *linear correlation coefficient*, *r*, is a unitless measure that describes the strength of the linear relationship between two variables. A positive value of *r*, or a positive correlation, means that as one variable increases, the other variable also increases. A negative value of *r*, or a negative correlation, means that as one variable increases, the other variable decreases. The correlation coefficient, *r*, will always be a value between -1 and 1 inclusive. A value of 1 indicates the strongest possible positive correlation, a value of -1 indicates the strongest possible negative correlation, and a value of 0 indicates no correlation (Fig. 13.39).

Figure 13.39

A visual aid used with correlation is the *scatter diagram*, a plot of data points. To help understand how to construct a scatter diagram, consider the following data from Egan Electronics. During a 6-day period, Egan Electronics kept daily records of the number of assembly line workers absent and the number of defective parts produced. The information is provided in the following chart.

Day	1	2	3	4	5	6
Number of workers absent	3	5	0	1	2	6
Number of defective parts	15	22	7	12	20	30

For each of the 6 days, two pieces of data are provided: number of workers absent and number of defective parts. We call the set of data *bivariate data*. Often when we have a set of bivariate data, we can control one of the quantities. We generally denote the quantity that can be controlled, the *independent variable*, x. The other variable, the *dependent variable*, is denoted as y. In this problem, we will assume that the number of defective parts produced is affected by the number of workers absent. Therefore, we will call the number of workers absent x and the number of defective parts produced y. When we plot bivariate data, the independent variable is marked on the horizontal axis and the dependent variable is marked on the vertical axis. Therefore, for this problem, number of workers absent is marked on the horizontal axis and number of defective parts is marked on the vertical axis. If we plot the six pieces of bivariate data in the Cartesian coordinate system, we get a scatter diagram, as shown in Fig. 13.40.

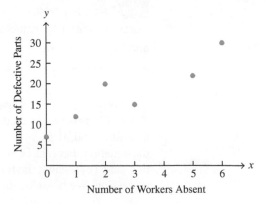

Figure 13.40

The figure shows that, generally, the more workers that are absent, the more defective parts are produced.

In Fig. 13.41, we show some scatter diagrams and indicate the corresponding strength of correlation between the quantities on the horizontal and vertical axes.

Earlier, we mentioned that r will always be a value between -1 and 1 inclusive. A value of $r = 1$ is obtained only when every point of the bivariate data on a scatter diagram lies in a straight line and the line is increasing from left to right (Fig. 13.41(a)). In other words, the line has a positive slope, as discussed in Section 6.7.

A value of $r = -1$ will be obtained only when every point of the bivariate data on a scatter diagram lies in a straight line and the line is decreasing from left to right. (Fig. 13.41(e)). In other words, the line has a negative slope.

The value of r is a measure of how far a set of points varies from a straight line. The greater the spread, the weaker the correlation and the closer the value of r is to 0. Figure 13.41 shows that the more the points diverge from a straight line, the weaker the correlation becomes.

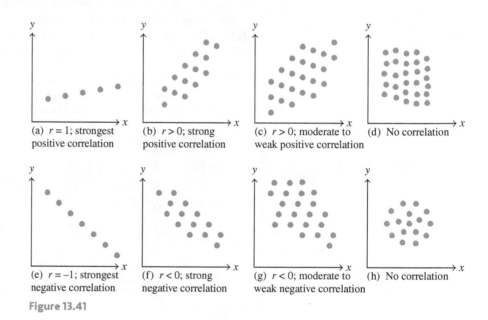

(a) $r = 1$; strongest positive correlation

(b) $r > 0$; strong positive correlation

(c) $r > 0$; moderate to weak positive correlation

(d) No correlation

(e) $r = -1$; strongest negative correlation

(f) $r < 0$; strong negative correlation

(g) $r < 0$; moderate to weak negative correlation

(h) No correlation

Figure 13.41

The following formula is used to calculate r.

Linear Correlation Coefficient
The formula to calculate the **correlation coefficient, r**, is as follows.

$$r = \frac{n(\Sigma xy) - (\Sigma x)(\Sigma y)}{\sqrt{n(\Sigma x^2) - (\Sigma x)^2}\ \sqrt{n(\Sigma y^2) - (\Sigma y)^2}}$$

To determine the correlation coefficient, r, and the equation of the line of best fit (to be discussed shortly), a statistical calculator may be used. On the statistical calculator, you enter the ordered pairs, (x, y) and press the appropriate keys. At the end of this section, we indicate the procedure to follow to use the computer software spreadsheet program, Microsoft Excel, and the TI-83 Plus or the TI-84 Plus calculators to determine the correlation coefficient.

In Example 1, we show how to determine r for a set of bivariate data without the use of a statistical calculator. We will use the same set of bivariate data given on page 834 that was used to make the scatter diagram in Fig. 13.40.

Example 1 *Number of Absences Versus Number of Defective Parts*

Egan Electronics provided the following daily records about the number of assembly line workers absent and the number of defective parts produced for 6 days. Determine the correlation coefficient between the number of workers absent and the number of defective parts produced.

Day	1	2	3	4	5	6
Number of workers absent	3	5	0	1	2	6
Number of defective parts	15	22	7	12	20	30

Solution   We plotted this set of data on the scatter diagram in Fig. 13.40 on page 834. We will call the number of workers absent x. We will call the number of defective parts produced y. We list the values of x and y and calculate the necessary sums: $\Sigma x, \Sigma y, \Sigma xy, \Sigma x^2, \Sigma y^2$. We determine the values in the column labeled x^2 by squaring the x's (multiplying the x's by themselves). We determine the values in the column labeled y^2 by squaring the y's. We determine the values in the column labeled xy by multiplying each x-value by its corresponding y-value.

Number of Workers Absent	Number of Defective Parts			
x	y	x^2	y^2	xy
3	15	9	225	45
5	22	25	484	110
0	7	0	49	0
1	12	1	144	12
2	20	4	400	40
6	30	36	900	180
17	106	75	2202	387

Thus, $\Sigma x = 17$, $\Sigma y = 106$, $\Sigma x^2 = 75$, $\Sigma y^2 = 2202$, and $\Sigma xy = 387$. In the formula for r, we use both $(\Sigma x)^2$ and Σx^2. Note that $(\Sigma x)^2 = (17)^2 = 289$ and that $\Sigma x^2 = 75$. Similarly, $(\Sigma y)^2 = (106)^2 = 11{,}236$ and $\Sigma y^2 = 2202$.

The n in the formula represents the number of pieces of bivariate data. Here $n = 6$. Now let's determine r.

$$r = \frac{n(\Sigma xy) - (\Sigma x)(\Sigma y)}{\sqrt{n(\Sigma x^2) - (\Sigma x)^2}\,\sqrt{n(\Sigma y^2) - (\Sigma y)^2}}$$

$$= \frac{6(387) - (17)(106)}{\sqrt{6(75) - (17)^2}\,\sqrt{6(2202) - (106)^2}}$$

$$= \frac{2322 - 1802}{\sqrt{6(75) - 289}\,\sqrt{6(2202) - 11{,}236}}$$

$$= \frac{520}{\sqrt{450 - 289}\,\sqrt{13{,}212 - 11{,}236}}$$

$$= \frac{520}{\sqrt{161}\,\sqrt{1976}} \approx 0.922$$

Since the maximum possible value for r is 1.00, a correlation coefficient of 0.922 is a strong, positive correlation. This result implies that, generally, the more assembly line workers absent, the more defective parts produced.   ■

In Example 1, had we found r to be a value greater than 1 or less than -1, it would have indicated that we had made an error. Also, from the scatter diagram, we should realize that r should be a positive value and not negative.

Table 13.8 Correlation Coefficient, r

n	$\alpha = 0.05$	$\alpha = 0.01$
4	0.950	0.990
5	0.878	0.959
6	0.811	0.917
7	0.754	0.875
8	0.707	0.834
9	0.666	0.798
10	0.632	0.765
11	0.602	0.735
12	0.576	0.708
13	0.553	0.684
14	0.532	0.661
15	0.514	0.641
16	0.497	0.623
17	0.482	0.606
18	0.468	0.590
19	0.456	0.575
20	0.444	0.561
22	0.423	0.537
27	0.381	0.487
32	0.349	0.449
37	0.325	0.418
42	0.304	0.393
47	0.288	0.372
52	0.273	0.354
62	0.250	0.325
72	0.232	0.302
82	0.217	0.283
92	0.205	0.267
102	0.195	0.254

The derivation of this table is beyond the scope of this text. It shows the critical values of the Pearson *correlation coefficient.*

In Example 1, there appears to be a cause–effect relationship. That is, the more assembly line workers who are absent, the more defective parts are produced. *However, a correlation does not necessarily indicate a cause–effect relationship.* For example, there is a positive correlation between police officers' salaries and the cost of medical insurance over the past 10 years (both have increased), but that does not mean that the increase in police officers' salaries caused the increase in the cost of medical insurance.

Suppose in Example 1 that r had been 0.53. Would this value have indicated a correlation? What is the minimum value of r needed to assume that a correlation exists between the variables? To answer this question, we introduce the term *level of significance*. The *level of significance*, denoted α (alpha), is used to identify the cutoff between results attributed to chance and results attributed to an actual relationship between the two variables. Table 13.8 gives *critical values** (or cutoff values) that are sometimes used for determining whether two variables are related. The table indicates two different levels of significance: $\alpha = 0.05$ and $\alpha = 0.01$. A level of significance of 5%, written $\alpha = 0.05$, means that there is a 5% chance that, when you say the variables are related, they actually are *not* related. Similarly, a level of significance of 1%, or $\alpha = 0.01$, means that there is a 1% chance that, when you say the variables are related, they actually are *not* related. More complete critical value tables are available in statistics books.

To explain the use of the table, we use *absolute value*, symbolized $|\ \ |$. The absolute value of a nonzero number is the positive value of the number, and the absolute value of 0 is 0. Therefore,

$$|3| = 3, \qquad |-3| = 3, \qquad |5| = 5, \qquad |-5| = 5, \qquad \text{and} \qquad |0| = 0$$

If the absolute value of r, written $|r|$, is *greater than* the value given in the table under the specified α and appropriate sample size n, we assume that a correlation does exist between the variables. If $|r|$ is less than the table value, we assume that no correlation exists.

Returning to Example 1, if we want to determine whether there is a correlation at a 5% level of significance, we find the critical value (or cutoff value) that corresponds to $n = 6$ (there are 6 pieces of bivariate data) and $\alpha = 0.05$. The value to the right of $n = 6$ and under the $\alpha = 0.05$ column is the critical value 0.811. From the formula, we had obtained $r = 0.922$. Since $|0.922| > 0.811$, or $0.922 > 0.811$, we assume that a correlation between the variables exists.

Note in Table 13.8 that the larger the sample size, the smaller is the value of r needed for a significant correlation.

Example 2 *Amount of Drug Remaining in the Bloodstream*

To test the length of time that an infection-fighting drug stays in a person's bloodstream, a doctor gives 300 milligrams of the drug to 10 patients, labeled 1–10 in the table below. Once each hour, for 10 hours, one of the 10 patients is selected at random and that person's blood is tested to determine the amount of the drug remaining in the bloodstream. The results are as follows.

Patient	1	2	3	4	5	6	7	8	9	10
Time (hr)	1	2	3	4	5	6	7	8	9	10
Drug remaining (mg)	250	230	200	210	140	120	210	100	90	85

---

*This table of values may be used only under certain conditions. If you take a statistics course, you will learn more about which critical values to use to determine whether a linear correlation exists.

Determine at a level of significance of 5% whether a correlation exists between the time elapsed and the amount of drug remaining.

Solution Let time be represented by x and the amount of drug remaining by y. We first draw a scatter diagram (Fig. 13.42).

Figure 13.42

The scatter diagram suggests that, if a correlation exists, it will be negative. We now construct a table of values and calculate r.

x	y	x^2	y^2	xy
1	250	1	62,500	250
2	230	4	52,900	460
3	200	9	40,000	600
4	210	16	44,100	840
5	140	25	19,600	700
6	120	36	14,400	720
7	210	49	44,100	1470
8	100	64	10,000	800
9	90	81	8100	810
10	85	100	7225	850
55	1635	385	302,925	7500

$$r = \frac{n(\Sigma xy) - (\Sigma x)(\Sigma y)}{\sqrt{n(\Sigma x^2) - (\Sigma x)^2}\sqrt{n(\Sigma y^2) - (\Sigma y)^2}}$$

$$= \frac{10(7500) - (55)(1635)}{\sqrt{10(385) - (55)^2}\sqrt{10(302,925) - (1635)^2}}$$

$$= \frac{-14,925}{\sqrt{825}\sqrt{356,025}} \approx \frac{-14,925}{17,138.28} \approx -0.871$$

From Table 13.8, for $n = 10$ and $\alpha = 0.05$, we get 0.632. Since $|-0.871| = 0.871$ and $0.871 > 0.632$, a correlation exists. The correlation is negative, which indicates that the longer the time period, the smaller is the amount of drug remaining. ∎

Figure 13.43

Linear Regression

Let's now turn to regression. *Linear regression* is the process of determining the linear relationship between two variables. Recall from Section 6.7 that the slope–intercept form of a straight line is $y = mx + b$, where m is the slope and b is the y-intercept.

Using the set of bivariate data, we will determine the equation of *the line of best fit*. The line of best fit is also called *the regression line*, or *the least squares line*. The *line of best fit* is the line such that the sum of the squares of the vertical distances from the line to the data points (on the scatter diagram) is a minimum, as shown in Fig. 13.43. In Fig. 13.43, the line of best fit minimizes the sum of d_1 through d_8. To determine the equation of the line of best fit, $y = mx + b,$* we must find m and then b. The formulas for finding m and b are as follows.*

The Line of Best Fit
The equation of the line of best fit is

$$y = mx + b,$$

$$\text{where } m = \frac{n(\Sigma xy) - (\Sigma x)(\Sigma y)}{n(\Sigma x^2) - (\Sigma x)^2} \quad \text{and} \quad b = \frac{\Sigma y - m(\Sigma x)}{n}$$

Note that the numerator of the fraction used to find m is identical to the numerator used to find r. Therefore, if you have previously found r, you do not need to repeat this calculation. Also, the denominator of the fraction used to find m is identical to the radicand of the first square root in the denominator of the fraction used to find r.

Example 3 *The Line of Best Fit*

a) Use the data in Example 1 on pages 835–836 to find the equation of the line of best fit that relates the number of workers absent on an assembly line and the number of defective parts produced.

b) Graph the equation of the line of best fit on a scatter diagram that illustrates the set of bivariate points.

Solution

a) In Example 1, we found $n(\Sigma xy) - (\Sigma x)(\Sigma y) = 520$ and $n(\Sigma x^2) - (\Sigma x)^2 = 161$. Thus,

$$m = \frac{n(\Sigma xy) - (\Sigma x)(\Sigma y)}{n(\Sigma x^2) - (\Sigma x)^2} = \frac{520}{161} \approx 3.23$$

Now we find the y-intercept, b. In Example 1, we found $n = 6$, $\Sigma x = 17$, and $\Sigma y = 106$.

$$b = \frac{\Sigma y - m(\Sigma x)}{n}$$

$$\approx \frac{106 - 3.23(17)}{6} \approx \frac{51.09}{6} \approx 8.52$$

---

*Some statistics books use $y = ax + b$, $y = b_0 + b_1 x$, or something similar, for the equation of the line of best fit. In any case, the letter next to the variable x represents the slope of the line of best fit, and the other letter represents the y-intercept of the graph.

Therefore, the equation of the line of best fit is

$$y = mx + b$$
$$y = 3.23x + 8.52$$

where x represents the number of workers absent and y represents the predicted number of defective parts produced.

b) To graph $y = 3.23x + 8.52$, we need to plot at least two points. We will plot three points and then draw the graph.

	$y = 3.23x + 8.52$	x	y
$x = 2$	$y = 3.23(2) + 8.52 = 14.98$	2	14.98
$x = 4$	$y = 3.23(4) + 8.52 = 21.44$	4	21.44
$x = 6$	$y = 3.23(6) + 8.52 = 27.90$	6	27.90

These three calculations indicate that if 2 assembly line workers are absent on the assembly line, the predicted number of defective parts produced is about 15. If 4 assembly line workers are absent, the predicted number of defective parts produced is about 21, and if 6 assembly line workers are absent, the predicted number of defective parts produced is about 28. Plot the three points (the three black points in Fig. 13.44) and then draw a straight line through the three points. The scatter diagram and graph of the equation of the line of best fit are plotted in Fig. 13.44.

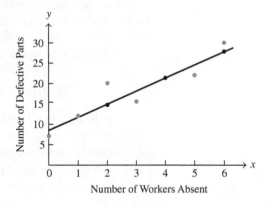

Figure 13.44

In Example 3, the line of best fit intersects the y-axis at 8.52, the value we determined for the y-intercept, b, in part (a).

Example 4 *Line of Best Fit for Example 2*

a) Determine the equation of the line of best fit between the time elapsed and the amount of drug remaining in a person's bloodstream in Example 2 on pages 837–838.

b) If the average person is given 300 mg of the drug, how much will remain in the person's bloodstream after 5 hr?

Solution

a) From the scatter diagram on page 838, we see that the slope of the line of best fit, m, will be negative. In Example 2, we found that $n(\Sigma xy) - (\Sigma x)(\Sigma y) = -14{,}925$ and that $n(\Sigma x^2) - (\Sigma x)^2 = 825$. Thus,

$$m = \frac{n(\Sigma xy) - (\Sigma x)(\Sigma y)}{n(\Sigma x^2) - (\Sigma x)^2}$$

$$= \frac{-14{,}925}{825}$$

$$\approx -18.09$$

From Example 2, $n = 10$, $\Sigma x = 55$, and $\Sigma y = 1635$.

$$b = \frac{\Sigma y - m\Sigma x}{n}$$

$$= \frac{1635 - (-18.09)(55)}{10}$$

$$\approx 263.00$$

Thus, the equation of the line of best fit is

$$y = mx + b$$
$$y = -18.09x + 263.00$$

where x is the elapsed time and y is the amount of drug remaining.

b) We evaluate $y = -18.09x + 263.00$ at $x = 5$.

$$y = -18.09x + 263.00$$
$$y = -18.09(5) + 263.00 = 172.55$$

Thus, after 5 hr, about 173 mg of the drug remains in the average person's bloodstream.

TECHNOLOGY TIP

We can use EXCEL and both the TI-83 Plus and the TI-84 Plus graphing calculators to determine the correlation coefficient, r, and the equation of the line of best fit. Below we use the data from Example 1 on page 835–836, where x represents the number of workers absent and y represents the number of defective parts for 6 selected days.

Excel

Begin by reading the *Technology Tip* on page 802. The instructions for determining the correlation coefficient and equation of the line of best fit are similar to the instructions given on page 802. In column A, rows 1 through 6, enter the 6 values representing the number of workers absent. In column B, rows 1 through 6, enter the 6 values that represent the number of defective parts. In general, the items listed on the horizontal axis in the scatter diagram (the independent variable if there is one) are placed in column A and the items listed on the vertical axis are placed in column B. Then select the following:

Insert > Function . . . > Statistical

Then to determine the value of the correlation coefficient, select **CORREL** and click OK. Excel will then generate a gray box and ask you for information about your data. In the box to the right of **Array1**, type in A1:A6, and in the box to the right of **Array2**, type in B1:B6. Then at the bottom of the box you will see *Formula results = .921927852*, which is the correlation coefficient. If you then wish to find the equation of the line of best fit, press CANCEL on the bottom of the gray box. Then select

Insert > Function . . . > Statistical > SLOPE > OK

Excel will then generate a gray box. In the box to the right of **Known_y's**, type in B1:B6. In the box to the right of **Known_x's**, type in A1:A6. At that point, at the bottom of the box you will see *Formula results = 3.229813665*, which is the slope of the equation of the line of best fit. To find the y-intercept, press cancel to remove the gray box. Then select

Insert > Function . . . > Statistical . . . > INTERCEPT > OK

Excel will then generate a gray box. In the box to the right of **Known_y's**, type in B1:B6. In the box to the right of **Known_x's**, type in A1:A6. At that point, at the bottom of the box you will see *Formula results* = *8.51552795*, which is the *y*-intercept of the equation of the line of best fit.

TI-83 Plus And TI-84 Plus Graphing Calculators

To determine the correlation coefficient and the equation of the line of best fit on a graphing calculator, press STAT. Then select Edit. If you have any data in **L1** or **L2**, delete the data by going to **L1** and pressing CLEAR and then ENTER. Follow a similar procedure to clear column **L2**. Now enter the 6 pieces of data representing the number of workers absent in column **L1** and enter the 6 pieces of data representing the number of defective parts in **L2**. Then press STAT and highlight **CALC**. At this point, **1: 1 − Var Stats** should be highlighted. Scroll down to highlight **4: LinReg (ax+b)**. Then press the Enter key twice. You will get *r* = .921927852, which represents the correlation coefficient. On the screen, you will also see values for *a* and *b*. Note that *a* represents the slope and *b* represents the *y*-intercept of the equation of the line of best fit. Thus, the slope is 3.229813665 and the *y*-intercept is 8.51552795.

SECTION 13.7
Exercises

Warm Up Exercises

In Exercises 1–10, fill in the blank with an appropriate word, phrase, or symbol(s).

1. A unitless measure that describes the strength of the linear relationship between two variables is called the linear correlation _____.

2. The process of determining the linear relationship between two variables is called linear _____.

3. The value of *r*, the linear correlation coefficient, that represents the strongest positive correlation is _____.

4. The value of *r*, the linear correlation coefficient, that represents the strongest negative correlation is _____.

5. The value of *r*, the linear correlation coefficient, that represents no correlation between two variables is _____.

6. If one quantity increases as the other quantity decreases, the two variables are said to have a(n) _____ correlation.

7. If one quantity increases as the other quantity increases, the two variables are said to have a(n) _____ correlation.

8. A plot of data points is called a(n) _____ diagram.

9. The line such that the sum of the squares of the vertical distances between the data points in the scatter diagram and the line is a minimum is called the line of best _____.

10. The cutoff between results attributed to chance and results attributed to an actual relationship between two variables is called the level of _____.

In Exercises 11–14, indicate if you believe that a correlation exists between the quantities on the horizontal and vertical axis. If so, indicate if you believe that the correlation is a strong positive correlation, a strong negative correla-tion, a weak positive correlation, a weak negative correla-tion, or no correlation. Explain your answer.

11.   **12.**

13.   **14.**

Practice the Skills

In Exercises 15–22, assume that a sample of bivariate data yields the correlation coefficient, r, indicated. Use Table 13.8 on page 837 for the specified sample size and level of signifi-cance to determine whether a linear correlation exists.

15. $r = 0.87$ when $n = 10$ at $\alpha = 0.01$

16. $r = 0.43$ when $n = 27$ at $\alpha = 0.01$

17. $r = -0.92$ when $n = 6$ at $\alpha = 0.05$

18. $r = -0.49$ when $n = 11$ at $\alpha = 0.05$

19. $r = -0.23$ when $n = 102$ at $\alpha = 0.01$

20. $r = -0.49$ when $n = 18$ at $\alpha = 0.01$

21. $r = 0.75$ when $n = 6$ at $\alpha = 0.01$

22. $r = 0.96$ when $n = 5$ at $\alpha = 0.01$

In Exercises 23–30, (a) draw a scatter diagram; (b) determine the value of r, rounded to the nearest thousandth;(c) determine whether a correlation exists at $\alpha = 0.05$; and (d) determine whether a correlation exists at $\alpha = 0.01$.

23.

x	y
5	8
6	10
7	12
8	12
11	16

24.

x	y
7	14
9	12
12	10
15	11
18	8

25.

x	y
23	29
35	37
31	26
43	20
49	39

26.

x	y
90	3
80	4
60	6
60	5
40	5
20	7

27.

x	y
5.3	10.3
4.7	9.6
8.4	12.5
12.7	16.2
4.9	9.8

28.

x	y
12	15
16	19
13	45
24	30
100	60
50	28

29.

x	y
100	2
80	3
60	5
60	6
40	6
20	8

30.

x	y
90	90
70	70
65	65
60	60
50	50
40	40
15	15

In Exercises 31–38, determine the equation of the line of best fit from the data in the exercise indicated. Round both the slope and the y-intercept to the nearest hundredth.

31. Exercise 23   **32.** Exercise 24

33. Exercise 25   **34.** Exercise 26

35. Exercise 27   **36.** Exercise 28

37. Exercise 29   **38.** Exercise 30

Problem Solving

In Exercises 39–49, round both the slope and y-intercept to the nearest hundredth.

39. *Fitness* Six students provided the following data about the number of sit-ups completed and the number of push-ups completed during a fitness test in their physical education class.

Sit-ups	50	53	60	35	43	62
Push-ups	40	42	45	25	34	45

a) Determine the correlation coefficient between the number of sit-ups completed and the number of push-ups completed.

b) Determine whether a correlation exists at $\alpha = 0.05$.

c) Determine the equation of the line of best fit for the number of sit-ups completed and the number of push-ups completed.

40. *Amount of Fat in Chicken Nuggets* The June 2010 issue of *Consumer Reports* provided the following information regarding the number of calories and the number of grams of fat per 3-ounce serving of chicken nuggets for the 6 top-rated chicken nuggets.

Calories	210	310	240	210	160	130
Fat (grams)	10	21	16	13	8	4

a) Determine the correlation coefficient between the number of calories and the number of grams of fat.

b) Determine whether a correlation exists at $\alpha = 0.05$.

c) Determine the equation of the line of best fit for the number of calories and the number of grams of fat.

41. *Time Spent Studying* Six students provided the following data on page 844 about the lengths of time they studied for a psychology exam and the grades they received on the exam.

Time studied (minutes)	20	40	50	60	80	100
Grade received (percent)	40	45	70	76	92	95

a) Determine the correlation coefficient between the length of time studied and the grade received.

b) Determine whether a correlation exists at $\alpha = 0.01$.

c) Find the equation of the line of best fit for the length of time studied and the grade received

42. *Price of a Home*   The following table shows the listing price and the selling price, in thousands of dollars, for eight houses listed and sold.

List price (thousands $)	139	165	210	287	189	115	125	95
Sale price (thousands $)	120	165	208	275	160	100	118	90

a) Determine the correlation coefficient between the listing price and the selling price of a house.

b) Determine whether a correlation exists at $\alpha = 0.01$.

c) Determine the equation of the line of best fit for the listing price and selling price of a house.

d) Use the equation in part (c) to estimate the selling price of a house listed for $130,000.

43. *Blood Pressure*   The following table shows the systolic blood pressure and diastolic blood pressure readings for six adults.

Systolic	110	153	120	143	100	112
Diastolic	70	110	80	98	70	75

a) Determine the correlation coefficient between the systolic blood pressure and the diastolic blood pressure readings.

b) Determine whether a correlation exists at $\alpha = 0.05$.

c) Determine the equation of the line of best fit for the systolic blood pressure and the diastolic blood pressure readings.

d) Use the equation in part (c) to estimate the diastolic blood pressure for an adult with a systolic blood pressure reading of 115.

44. *Selling Popcorn at the Movies*   The number of movie tickets sold and the number of units of popcorn sold at AMC Cinema for 8 days is shown below.

Ticket sales	89	110	125	92	100	95	108	97
Units of popcorn	22	28	30	26	22	21	28	25

a) Determine the correlation coefficient between ticket sales and units of popcorn sold.

b) Determine whether a correlation exists at $\alpha = 0.05$.

c) Determine the equation of the line of best fit for tickets sold and units of popcorn sold.

d) Use the equation in part (c) to estimate the units of popcorn sold if 115 tickets are sold.

45. *Fuel Efficiency of Cars*   The following table shows the weights, in hundreds of pounds, for six selected cars. Also shown is the corresponding fuel efficiency, in miles per gallon (mpg), for the car in city driving.

Weight (hundreds of pounds)	27	31	35	32	30	30
Fuel efficiency (mpg)	23	22	20	21	24	22

a) Determine the correlation coefficient between the weight of a car and the fuel efficiency.

b) Determine whether a correlation exists at $\alpha = 0.01$.

c) Determine the equation of the line of best fit for the weight of a car and the fuel efficiency of a car.

d) Use the equation in part (c) to estimate the fuel efficiency of a car that weighs 33 hundred pounds.

46. *City Muggings*   In a certain section of a city, muggings have been a problem. The number of police officers patrolling that section of the city has varied. The following chart shows the number of police officers and the number of muggings for 8 successive days.

Police officers	20	12	18	15	22	10	20	12
Muggings	8	10	12	9	6	15	7	18

a) Determine the correlation coefficient for number of police officers and number of muggings.

b) Determine whether a correlation exists at $\alpha = 0.05$.

c) Find the equation of the line of best fit for number of police officers and number of muggings.

d) Use the equation in part (c) to estimate the average number of muggings when 14 police officers are patrolling that section of the city.

47. *Chlorine in a Swimming Pool* A gallon of chlorine is put into a swimming pool. Each hour later for the following 6 hours the percent of chlorine that remains in the pool is measured. The following information is obtained.

Time	1	2	3	4	5	6
Chlorine remaining (percent)	80.0	76.2	68.7	50.1	30.2	20.8

a) Determine the correlation coefficient for time and percent of chlorine remaining.

b) Determine whether a correlation exists at $\alpha = 0.01$.

c) Determine the equation of the line of best fit for time and amount of chlorine remaining.

d) Use the equation in part (c) to estimate the average amount of chlorine remaining after 4.5 hr.

48. *Social Security Numbers* **a)** Match the first 9 digits of your phone number (including area code) with the 9 digits in your Social Security number. To do so, match the first digit in your phone number with the first digit in your Social Security number to get one ordered pair. Match the second digits to get a second ordered pair. Continue this process until you get a total of nine ordered pairs.

b) Do you believe that this set of bivariate data has a positive correlation, a negative correlation, or no correlation? Explain your answer.

c) Construct a scatter diagram for the nine ordered pairs.

d) Calculate the correlation coefficient, r.

e) Is there a correlation at $\alpha = 0.05$? Explain.

f) Calculate the equation of the line of best fit.

g) Use the equation in part (f) to estimate the digit in a social Security number that corresponds with a 7 in a telephone number.

49. *Hitting the Brakes* **a)** Examine the art below. Do you believe that there is a positive correlation, a negative correlation, or no correlation between speed of a car and stopping distance when the brakes are applied?

b) Do you believe that there is a stronger correlation between speed of a car and stopping distance on wet or dry roads?

c) Use the figure to construct two scatter diagrams, one for dry pavement and the other for wet pavement. Place the speed of the car on the horizontal axis.

d) Compute the correlation coefficient for speed of the car and stopping distance for dry pavement.

e) Repeat part (d) for wet pavement.

f) Were your answers to parts (a) and (b) correct? Explain.

g) Determine the equation of the line of best fit for dry pavement.

h) Repeat part (g) for wet pavement.

i) Use the equations in parts (g) and (h) to estimate the stopping distance of a car going 77 mph on both dry and wet pavements.

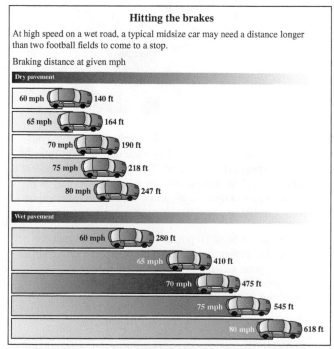

Source: *Car and Driver*, American Automobile Association

Challenge Problems/Group Activities

50. *Interchanging Variables* a) Assume that a set of bivariate data yields a specific correlation coefficient. If the *x*- and *y*-values are interchanged and the correlation coefficient is recalculated, will the correlation coefficient change?

b) Make up a table of five pieces of bivariate data and determine *r* using the data. Then switch the values of the *x*'s and *y*'s and recompute the correlation coefficient. Has the value of *r* changed?

51. *Height vs. Length* a) Do you believe that a correlation exists between a person's height and the length of a person's arm?

b) Select 10 people from your class and measure (in inches) their heights and the lengths of their arms.

c) Plot the 10 ordered pairs on a scatter diagram.

d) Calculate the correlation coefficient, *r*.

e) Determine the equation of the line of best fit.

f) Estimate the length of the arm of a person who is 58 in. tall.

52. *Calculating a Correlation Coefficient* a) Have your group select a category of bivariate data that it thinks has a strong positive correlation. Designate the independent variable and the dependent variable. Explain why your group believes that the bivariate data have a strong positive correlation.

b) Collect at least 10 pieces of bivariate data that can be used to determine the correlation coefficient. Explain how your group chose these data.

c) Plot a scatter diagram.

d) Calculate the correlation coefficient.

e) Does there appear to be a strong positive correlation? Explain your answer.

f) Calculate the equation of the line of best fit.

g) Explain how the equation in part (f) may be used.

53. *CPI* Use the following table. CPI represents consumer price index.

Year	2005	2006	2007	2008	2009	2010
CPI	195.3	201.6	207.3	215.3	214.5	218.1

a) Calculate *r*.

b) If 2005 is subtracted from each year, the table obtained becomes:

Year	0	1	2	3	4	5
CPI	195.3	201.6	207.3	215.3	214.5	218.1

If *r* is calculated from these values, how will it compare with the *r* determined in part (a)? Explain.

c) Calculate *r* from the values in part (b) and compare the results with the value of *r* found in part (a). Are they the same? If not, explain why.

54. a) There are equivalent formulas that can be used to find the correlation coefficient and the equation of the line of best fit. A formula used in some statistics books to find the correlation coefficient is

$$r = \frac{SS(xy)}{\sqrt{SS(x)SS(y)}}$$

where

$$SS(x) = \Sigma x^2 - \frac{(\Sigma x)^2}{n}$$

$$SS(y) = \Sigma y^2 - \frac{(\Sigma y)^2}{n}$$

$$SS(xy) = \Sigma xy - \frac{(\Sigma x)(\Sigma y)}{n}$$

Use this formula to find the correlation coefficient of the set of bivariate data given in Example 1 on page 835–836.

b) Compare your answer with the answer obtained in Example 1.

Internet/Research Activity

55. a) Obtain a set of bivariate data from a newspaper or magazine.

b) Plot the information on a scatter diagram.

c) Indicate whether you believe that the data show a positive correlation, a negative correlation, or no correlation. Explain your answer.

d) Calculate *r* and determine whether your answer to part (c) was correct.

e) Determine the equation of the line of best fit for the bivariate data.

56. Find a scatter diagram in a newspaper or magazine and write a paper on what the diagram indicates. Indicate whether you believe that the bivariate data show a positive correlation, a negative correlation, or no correlation and explain why.

CHAPTER 13 *Summary*

Important Facts and Concepts	Examples and Discussion
Section 13.1	
Sampling Techniques	
Random sampling	Example 1, page 777
Systematic sampling	
Cluster sampling	
Stratified sampling	
Convenience sampling	
Section 13.2	
Misuses of statistics	Discussion pages 779–781
Section 13.3	
Frequency Distribution	Examples 1–2, pages 784–786
Rules for Data Grouped by Classes	
1. The classes should be the same width.	Discussion, page 784; Examples 1–3, pages 784–787
2. The classes should not overlap.	
3. Each piece of data should belong to only one class.	
Statistical Graphs	
Histogram	Examples 4, 6, 7, pages 787–789
Frequency polygon	Examples 5–6, pages 788–789
Stem-and-leaf display	Examples 8, pages 790–791
Circle graph	Examples 9, pages 791–792
Section 13.4	
Measures of Central Tendency	
The **mean** is the sum of the data divided by the number of pieces of data: $\bar{x} = \frac{\Sigma x}{n}$.	Example 1, page 797
The **median** is the value in the middle of a set of ranked data.	Examples 2–3, 6, pages 798–799
The **mode** is the piece of data that occurs most frequently (if there is one).	Examples 4, 6, pages 798–799
The **midrange** is the value halfway between the lowest and highest values: midrange $= \frac{L+H}{2}$.	Examples 5, 6, page 799
Percentiles and **Quartiles** are measures of position.	Examples 7–8, pages 800–801

Section 13.5	
Measures of Dispersion	
The **range** is the difference between the highest value and lowest value in a set of data.	Discussion pages 808–812; Example 1, page 808
The **standard deviation,** s, is a measure of the spread of a set of data about the mean: $s = \sqrt{\dfrac{\Sigma(x - \bar{x})^2}{n - 1}}$.	Examples 2–3, pages 809–811
Section 13.6	
z–SCORES	
$z = \dfrac{\text{value of the piece of data } - \text{ mean}}{\text{standard deviation}}$	Discussion pages 820–828; Examples 2–5, pages 820–828
Section 13.7	
Linear Correlation And Regression	
Linear correlation coefficient, r, is	Discussion pages 833–835; Examples 1–2, pages 835–838
$r = \dfrac{n(\Sigma xy) - (\Sigma x)(\Sigma y)}{\sqrt{n(\Sigma x^2) - (\Sigma x)^2}\,\sqrt{n(\Sigma y^2) - (\Sigma y)^2}}$	
Equation of the Line of the Best Fit	
$y = mx + b$, where	Discussion pages 839–840; Examples 3–4, pages 839–841
$m = \dfrac{n(\Sigma xy) - (\Sigma x)(\Sigma y)}{n(\Sigma x^2) - (\Sigma x)^2}$	
$b = \dfrac{\Sigma y - m(\Sigma x)}{n}$	

CHAPTER 13) *Review Exercises*

13.1

1. a) What is a population?

 b) What is a sample?

2. What is a random sample?

13.2

In Exercises 3 and 4, tell what possible misuses or misinterpretations may exist in the statements.

3. The Stay Healthy Candy Bar indicates on its label that it has no cholesterol. Therefore, it is safe to eat as many of these candy bars as you want.

4. More copies of *Time* magazine are sold than are copies of *Money* magazine. Therefore, *Time* is a more profitable magazine than *Money*.

5. *U.S. Households with Cable Television* In 2008, 99.7 million households in the United States subscribed to cable

television. In 2009, 103.0 million households in the United States subscribed to cable television. Draw a graph that appears to show a

a) small increase in the number of households subscribing to cable television from 2008 to 2009.

b) large increase in the number of households subscribing to cable television from 2008 to 2009.

13.3

6. Consider the following set of data.

35	37	38	41	43
36	37	38	41	43
36	37	39	41	43
36	37	39	41	44
37	37	39	42	45

a) Construct a frequency distribution letting each class have a width of 1.

b) Construct a histogram.

c) Construct a frequency polygon.

7. *Average Monthly High Temperature* Consider the following average monthly high temperature in July for 40 selected U.S. cities.

$$
\begin{array}{cccccccc}
71 & 79 & 58 & 73 & 80 & 75 & 84 & 77 \\
82 & 72 & 80 & 70 & 75 & 66 & 73 & 72 \\
80 & 66 & 74 & 68 & 81 & 84 & 75 & 67 \\
91 & 76 & 82 & 79 & 63 & 69 & 68 & 79 \\
71 & 76 & 80 & 83 & 73 & 87 & 82 & 71 \\
\end{array}
$$

a) Construct a frequency distribution. Let the first class be 58–62.

b) Construct a histogram of the frequency distribution.

c) Construct a frequency polygon of the frequency distribution.

d) Construct a stem-and-leaf display.

13.4, 13.5

In Exercises 8–13, for the following test scores 67, 74, 79, 83, 84, 93, determine the

8. mean.

9. median.

10. mode.

11. midrange.

12. range.

13. standard deviation.

In Exercises 14–19, for the set of data 4, 5, 12, 14, 19, 7, 12, 23, 7, 17, 15, 21, determine the

14. mean.

15. median.

16. mode.

17. midrange.

18. range.

19. standard deviation.

13.6

Police Response Time In Exercises 20–24, assume that police response time to emergency calls is normally distributed with a mean of 9 minutes and a standard deviation of 2 minutes. Determine the percent of emergency calls with a police response time

20. between 7 and 11 minutes.   **21.** between 5 and 13 minutes.

22. less than 12.2 minutes.   **23.** more than 12.2 minutes.

24. more than 7.8 minutes.

Pizza Delivery In Exercises 25–28, assume that the amount of time to prepare and deliver a pizza from Pepe's Pizza

is normally distributed with a mean of 20 minutes and standard deviation of 5 minutes. Determine the percent of pizzas that were prepared and delivered

25. between 20 and 25 minutes.   **26.** in less than 18 minutes.

27. between 22 and 28 minutes.

28. If Pepe's Pizza advertises that the pizza is free if it takes more than 30 min to deliver, what percent of the pizza will be free?

13.7

29. *Hiking* The following table shows the number of hiking permits issued for a specific trail at Yellowstone National Park for selected years and the corresponding number of bears sighted by the hikers on that trail.

Hiking permits	765	926	1145	842	1485	1702
Bears	119	127	150	119	153	156

a) Construct a scatter diagram with hiking permits on the horizontal axis.

b) Use the scatter diagram in part (a) to determine whether you believe that a correlation exists between the number of hiking permits issued and the number of bears sighted by hikers. If so, is it a positive or negative correlation?

c) Calculate the correlation coefficient between the number of hiking permits issued and the number of bears sighted by hikers.

d) Determine whether a correlation exists at $\alpha = 0.05$.

e) Determine the equation of the line of best fit between the number of hiking permits issued and the number of bears sighted by hikers. Round both the slope and y-intercept to the nearest hundredth.

f) Assuming that this trend continues, use the equation of the line of best fit to estimate the number of bears sighted if 1500 hiking permits were issued.

30. *Daily Sales* Ace Hardware recorded the number of a particular item sold per week for 6 weeks and the corresponding weekly price, in dollars, of the item as shown in the table below.

Price ($)	0.75	1.00	1.25	1.50	1.75	2.00
Number sold	200	160	140	120	110	95

a) Construct a scatter diagram with price on the horizontal axis.

b) Use the scatter diagram in part (a) to determine whether you believe that a correlation exists between the price of the item and number sold. If so, it is a positive or a negative correlation?

c) Determine the correlation coefficient between the price and the number sold.

d) Determine whether a correlation exists at $\alpha = 0.05$.

e) Determine the equation of the line of best fit for the price and the number sold.

f) Use the equation in part (e) to estimate the number sold if the price is $1.60.

13.4–13.6

Men's Weight In Exercises 31–38, use the following data obtained from a study of the weights of adult men.

Mean	192 lb	First quartile	178 lb
Median	185 lb	Third quartile	232 lb
Mode	180 lb	86th percentile	239 lb
Standard deviation	23 lb		

31. What is the most common weight?

32. What weight did half of those surveyed exceed?

33. About what percent of those surveyed weighed more than 232 lb?

34. About what percent of those surveyed weighed less than 178 lb?

35. About what percent of those surveyed weighed more than 239 lb?

36. If 100 men were surveyed, what is the total weight of all men?

37. What weight represents two standard deviations above the mean?

38. What weight represents 1.8 standard deviations below the mean?

13.2–13.6

Presidential Children The following list shows the names of the 43 U.S. presidents and the number of children in their families.

Washington	0	B. Harrison	3
J. Adams	5	McKinley	2
Jefferson	6	T. Roosevelt	6
Madison	0	Taft	3
Monroe	2	Wilson	3
J. Q. Adams	4	Harding	0
Jackson	0	Coolidge	2
Van Buren	4	Hoover	2
W. H. Harrison	10	F. D. Roosevelt	6
Tyler	14	Truman	1
Polk	0	Eisenhower	2
Taylor	6	Kennedy	3
Fillmore	2	L. B. Johnson	2
Pierce	3	Nixon	2
Buchanan	0	Ford	4
Lincoln	4	Carter	4
A. Johnson	5	Reagan	4
Grant	4	G. Bush	6
Hayes	8	Clinton	1
Garfield	7	G. W. Bush	2
Arthur	3	Obama	2
Cleveland	5		

In Exercises 39–50, use the data to determine the following.

39. Mean

40. Mode

41. Median

42. Midrange

43. Range

44. Standard deviation (round the mean to the nearest tenth)

45. Construct a frequency distribution; let the first class be 0–1.

46. Construct a histogram of the frequency distribution.

47. Construct a frequency polygon of the frequency distribution.

48. Does this distribution appear to be normal? Explain.

49. Do you think the number of children per family in the United States is a normal distribution? Explain.

50. Is this set of data representative of the U.S. population? Explain.

CHAPTER 13) *Test*

In Exercises 1–6, for the set of data 27, 43, 43, 45, 52, determine the

1. mean.

2. median.

3. mode.

4. midrange.

5. range.

6. standard deviation.

In Exercises 7–9, use the set of data

26	28	35	46	49	56
26	30	36	46	49	58
26	32	40	47	50	58
26	32	44	47	52	62
27	35	46	47	54	66

to construct the following.

7. a frequency distribution; let the first class be 25–30

8. a histogram of the frequency distribution

9. a frequency polygon of the frequency distribution

Statistics on Salaries *In Exercises 10–16, use the following data on weekly salaries at Donovan's Construction Company.*

Mean	$740	First quartile	$690
Median	$710	Third quartile	$745
Mode	$735	79th percentile	$752
Standard deviation	$40		

10. What is the most common salary?

11. What salary did half the employees exceed?

12. About what percent of employees' salaries exceeded $690?

13. About what percent of employees' salaries was less than $752?

14. If the company has 100 employees, what is the total weekly salary of all employees?

15. What salary represents one standard deviation above the mean?

Anthropology *In Exercises 16–19, assume that anthropologists have determined that the akidolestes, a small primitive mammal believed to have lived with the dinosaurs, had a head circumference that was normally distributed with a mean of 42 cm and a standard deviation of 5 cm.*

16. What percent of head circumferences were between 36 and 53 cm?

17. What percent of head circumferences were greater than 35.75 cm?

18. What percent of head circumferences were greater than 48.25 cm?

19. What percent of head circumferences were less than 50 cm?

20. ***Minimum Wage*** The following table shows the hourly minimum wage in the U.S. for the years 2006–2010, where the column labeled Year refers to the number of years since 2006.

Year	Minimum Wage
0	$5.15
1	$5.85
2	$6.55
3	$7.25
4	$7.25

Source: *Bureau of Labor Statistics*

a) Construct a scatter diagram placing the year on the horizontal axis.

b) Use the scatter diagram in part (a) to determine whether you believe a correlation exists between the year and the minimum wage.

c) Determine the correlation coefficient between the year and the minimum wage.

d) Determine whether a correlation exists at $\alpha = 0.05$.

e) Determine the equation of the line of best fit between the year and the minimum wage. Round

both the slope and y-intercept to the nearest hundredth.

f) Use the equation in part (e) to predict the minimum wage in 2014.

GROUP PROJECTS

Watching TV

1. Do you think that men or women, aged 17–20, watch more hours of TV weekly, or do you think that they watch the same number of hours?

a) Write a procedure to use to determine the answer to that question. In your procedure, use a sample of 30 men and 30 women. State how you will obtain an unbiased sample.

b) Collect 30 pieces of data from men aged 17–20 and 30 pieces of data from women aged 17–20. Round answers to the nearest 0.5 hr. Follow the procedure developed in part (a) to obtain your unbiased sample.

c) Compute the mean for your two groups of data to the nearest tenth.

d) Using the means obtained in part (c), answer the question asked at the beginning of the problem.

e) Is it possible that your conclusion in part (d) is wrong? Explain.

f) Compute the standard deviation for each group to the nearest tenth. How do the standard deviations compare?

g) Do you believe that the distribution of data from either or both groups resembles a normal distribution? Explain.

h) Add the two groups of data to get one group of 60 pieces of data. If these 60 pieces of data are added and

divided by 60, will you obtain the same mean as when you add the two means from part (c) and divide the sum by 2? Explain.

i) Compute the mean of the 60 pieces of data by using both methods mentioned in part (h). Are they the same? If so, why? If not, why not?

j) Do you believe that this group of 60 pieces of data represents a normal distribution? Explain.

Bivariate Data Experiment

2. a) Have your group select a category of bivariate data that it thinks has a strong negative correlation. Indicate the variable that you will designate as the independent variable and the variable that you will designate as the dependent variable. Explain why your group believes that the bivariate data have a strong negative correlation.

b) Collect at least 10 pieces of bivariate data that can be used to determine the correlation coefficient. Explain how your group chose these data.

c) Plot a scatter diagram.

d) Calculate the correlation coefficient.

e) Is there a negative correlation at $\alpha = 0.05$? Explain your answer.

f) Calculate the equation of the line of best fit.

g) Explain how the equation in part (f) may be used.

Chapter 1

RECREATIONAL MATH. PAGE 24

The farmer crosses with the goat first. Then he can take the herbs across the river. But he must return the goat temporarily so that the goat doesn't eat the herbs. He then takes the wolf across the river. Then he returns for the goat. He will make seven crossings—four forward and three back.

The answer to the St. Ives riddle is 1.

SECTION 1.1, PAGE 5

1. Counting 3. Hypothesis 5. Inductive 7. Deductive
9. Inductive reasoning; a general conclusion is obtained from observation of specific cases.
11. $5 \times 5 = 25$ 13. 1 5 10 10 5 1 15. ⬡ 17. ⬡
19. 10, 12, 14 21. 3, −3, 3 23. $\frac{1}{5}, \frac{1}{6}, \frac{1}{7}$ 25. 36, 49, 64
27. 34, 55, 89 29. Y
31. a) 36, 49, 64 b) square 6, 7, 8, 9 and 10
    c) No, 72 is between 8^2 and 9^2, so it is not a square number.
33. Blue: 1, 5, 7, 10, 12; Purple: 2, 4, 6, 9, 11; Yellow: 3, 8
35. a) $\approx$ $200,000
    b) We are using specific cases to make a prediction.
37.
39. a) You should obtain the original number.
    b) You should obtain the original number.
    c) The result is the original number.
    d) $n, 4n, 4n + 12, \frac{4n + 12}{4} = n + 3, n + 3 - 3 = n$
41. a) 5
    b) You should obtain the number 5.
    c) The result is always the number 5.
    d) $n, n + 1, \frac{n + (n + 1) + 9}{2} = \frac{2n + 10}{2} = n + 5, n + 5 - n = 5$
43. $7 - 5 = 2$, which is not an odd number.
45. $(3 + 2)/2 = 5/2$, which is not an even number.
47. $1 - 2 = -1$, which is not a counting number.
49. a) The sum of the measures of the interior angles should be 180°.
    b) Yes, the sum of the measures of the interior angles should be 180°.
    c) The sum of the measures of the interior angles of a triangle is 180°.
51. 129, the numbers in positions are found as follows:
    $a \quad b$
    $c \quad a + b + c$
53. (c)

SECTION 1.2, PAGE 14

1. Estimation 3. 760 5. 600,000 7. 8000
9. 350,000,000 11. 320 13. $2 15. $1440 17. $3000

19. 400 lb 21. $3.90 23. $51 25. $120 27. $42
29. $\approx$ 60 mi 31. a) 210 b) 70 c) 175
33. a) 5 million b) 98 million c) 65 million d) 280 million
35. a) 85% b) 15% c) 59,500,000 acres
    d) No, since we are not given the area of each state
37. 20 39. $\approx$ 120 bananas 41. 150° 43. 10%
45. 9 square units 47. 150 feet 49. Answers will vary.
51. Answers will vary.
53. Answers will vary. 55. Answers will vary.
57. a) Answers will vary. b) Answers will vary.
    c) Answers will vary.
58. There are 118 ridges around the edge.
59. a) Answers will vary. b) 11.6 days

SECTION 1.3, PAGE 28

1. 69 mi 3. 48.4 ft 5. $8092
7. a) $117.25 b) $295.75
9. a) $308,920 b) $185,220 c) $1620
11. $70 13. $47,784.60 15. a) 10,000 b) 1 in 10,000
17. $\approx$ 18.7 mpg 19. $82.08 21. Snow 23. $84,010
25. a) 4106.25 gal b) $45.99
27. a) $\approx$ 35.61 gal b) $106.83 c) $\approx$ 4,985,400,000 gal
29. $897.76 31. $392
33. a) Water/milk: 3 cups; salt: $\frac{3}{8}$ tsp; Cream of Wheat: 9 tbsp (or $\frac{9}{16}$ cup)
    b) Water/milk: $2\frac{7}{8}$ cups; salt: $\frac{3}{8}$ tsp; Cream of Wheat: $\frac{5}{8}$ cup (or 10 tbsp)
    c) Water/milk: $2\frac{7}{4}$ cups; salt: $\frac{3}{8}$ tsp; Cream of Wheat: $\frac{9}{16}$ cup (or 9 tbsp)
    d) Differences exist in water/milk because the amount for 4 servings is not twice that for 2 servings. Differences also exist in Cream of Wheat because $\frac{1}{2}$ cup is not twice 3 tbsp.
35. a) 1 box of 20 and 1 box of 12 b) $420
37. 144 square inches
39. The area is 4 times as large.
41. The volume is 8 times as large. 43. 10¢ 45. 3
47. a) 30 b) 140
49.

| 4 |
| 3 2 |
| 5 1 6 |

51.
8	6	16
18	10	2
4	14	12

53. The sum of the four corners is 4 times the number in the center.
55. Multiply the center number by 9.
57. 6 ways
59.

7
3 1 4
5 8 6
2

61.
1	2	3	4	5
2	3	4	5	1
3	4	5	1	2
4	5	1	2	3
5	1	2	3	4

Other answers are possible, but 1 and 8 must appear in the center.

Other answers are possible.

63. Mary is the skier.   **65.** 714 square units

67. Thomas would have opened the box labeled grapes and cherries. Because all the boxes are labeled incorrectly, whichever fruit he pulls from the grapes and cherries box will be the only fruit in that box. If he pulls a grape from the box, the box must be labeled grapes; if he pulls a cherry from the box, the box must be labeled cherries. That leaves two boxes whose original labels were incorrect. Because all labels must be changed, there will be only one way for Thomas to assign the two remaining labels.

REVIEW EXERCISES, PAGE 35

1. 27, 32, 37   **2.** 26, 37, 50   **3.** −48, 96, −192

4. 25, 32, 40   **5.** 10, 4, −3   **6.** $\frac{3}{8}, \frac{3}{16}, \frac{3}{32}$

7. ◯ ▭ ◯   **8.** △ ◯ ▢   **9.** (c)

10. a) The final number is twice the original number.

   b) The final number is twice the original number.

   c) The final number is twice the original number.

   d) $n, 10n, 10n + 5, \dfrac{10n + 5}{5} = 2n + 1,$

   $2n + 1 - 1 = 2n$

11. This process will always result in an answer of 3.

12. $1^2 + 2^2 = 5$ **13.** 420,000,000   **14.** 2000   **15.** 200

16. Answers will vary.   **17.** $5000   **18.** $140   **19.** 3 mph

20. $14.00   **21.** 2 mi   **22.** 0.4 million   **23.** 1.0 million

24. 13 square units   **25.** Length $\approx$ 22 ft; height $\approx$ 8 ft

26. $30   **27.** $1.16   **28.** Taylor Rental is less expensive by $3

29. $4   **30. a)** 288 lb   **b)** 12,500 ft²   **31.** $661   **32.** 7.05 mg

33. $980   **34.** 6 hr 45 min   **35.** July 26, 11:00 A.M.

36. a) $\approx$ 1.47 ft/sec   **b)** $\approx$ 80.67 ft/sec   **37.** 201

38.

21	7	8	18
10	16	15	13
14	12	11	17
9	19	20	6

39.

23	25	15
13	21	29
27	17	19

40. 59 min 59 sec   **41.** 6   **42.**

| $ 25 Room |
| $ 3 Friends |
| $ 2 Clerk |
| $ 30 |

43. 140 lb

44. Yes; 3 quarters and 4 dimes, or 1 half dollar, 1 quarter and 4 dimes, or 1 quarter and 9 dimes. Other answers are possible.

45. 216 cm³

46. Place six coins in each pan with one coin off to the side. If it balances, the heavier coin is the one on the side. If the pan does not balance, take the six coins on the heavier side and split them into two groups of three. Select the three heavier coins and weigh two coins. If the pan balances, it is the third coin. If the pan does not balance, you can identify the heavier coin.

47. 125,250   **48.** 16 blue   **49.** 90

50. The fifth figure will be an octagon with sides of equal length. Inside the octagon will be a seven-sided figure with each side of equal length. The figure will have one antenna.

51. 61

52. Some possible answers are shown. Others are possible.

53. a) 2   **b)** 6   **c)** 24   **d)** 120

   e) $n(n-1)(n-2) \ldots 1$, (or $n!$), where $n =$ the number of people in the line

CHAPTER TEST, PAGE 38

1. 27, 33, 39   **2.** $\frac{1}{16}, \frac{1}{32}, \frac{1}{64}$

3. a) The result is the original number plus 1.
   b) The result is the original number plus 1.
   c) The result will always be the original number plus 1.
   d) $n, 5n, 5n + 10, \dfrac{5n + 10}{5} = n + 2,$
   $n + 2 - 1 = n + 1$

4. 16,000   **5.** 1,700,000   **6.** 9 square units

7. a) $\approx$ 23.03   **b)** He is in the at-risk range.

8. a) 3.5 million   **b)** 0.3 million

9. 65 min   **10.** 32 cans   **11.** $7\frac{1}{2}$ min

12. $\approx$ 39.5 in. by 29.6 in. (The actual dimensions are 100.5 cm by 76.5 cm.)   **13.** $49.00

14.

40	15	20
5	25	45
30	35	10

15. Less time if she had driven at 45 mph for the entire trip

16. $\frac{1}{2}$ tablespoon   **17.** 48 square meters   **18.** 243 jelly beans

19. a) $11.97   **b)** $11.81   **c)** Save 16 cents by using the 25% off coupon.   **20.** 24

Chapter 2

SECTION 2.1, PAGE 47

1. Set   **3.** Description, roster form, set-builder notation.

5. Infinite   **7.** Equivalent   **9.** Empty or null

11. Universal   **13.** Not well defined   **15.** Well defined

17. Well defined   **19.** Infinite   **21.** Infinite   **23.** Infinite

25. { Maine, Maryland, Massachusetts, Michigan, Minnesota, Mississippi, Missouri, Montana }

27. { 11, 12, 13, 14, …, 177 }   **29.** $B = \{ 2, 4, 6, 8, \ldots \}$

31. { } or $\varnothing$ **33.** $E = \{ 14, 15, 16, 17, \ldots, 84 \}$

35. { Louvre Museum, British Museum, National Gallery of Art, Tate Modern, Metropolitan Museum of Art }

37. { Musee d'Orsay, Musee d'Art Moderne Prado, Museum of Modern Art }

39. { 2007, 2008 }

41. { 2004, 2005, 2006, 2007 }

43. $B = \{ x \mid x \in N \text{ and } 6 < x < 15 \}$ or
$B = \{ x \mid x \in N \text{ and } 7 \le x \le 14 \}$

45. $C = \{ x \mid x \in N \text{ and } x \text{ is a multiple of } 3 \}$

47. $E = \{ x \mid x \in N \text{ and } x \text{ is odd} \}$

49. $C = \{ x \mid x \text{ is February} \}$

51. Set A is the set of natural numbers less than or equal to 7.

53. Set V is the set of vowels in the English alphabet.

55. Set T is the set of species of trees.

57. Set S is the set of seasons.

59. { China, India, United States }

61. { Russia, Brazil, Indonesia, Japan, Germany }

63. { 2008, 2009, 2010, 2011 }

65. { 2000, 2001, 2002, 2003, 2004, 2005, 2006, 2007 }

67. False; { e } is a set, and not an element of the set.

69. False; h is not an element of the set.

71. False; 3 is an element of the set.

73. True   75. 4   77. 0   79. Both

81. Neither   83. Equivalent

85. a) Set A is the set of natural numbers greater than 2. Set B is the set of all numbers greater than 2.

 b) Set A contains only natural numbers. Set B contains other types of numbers, including fractions and decimal numbers.

 c) $A = \{ 3, 4, 5, 6, \ldots \}$

 d) No; because there are an infinite number of elements between any two elements in set B, we cannot write set B in roster form.

87. Cardinal   89. Ordinal   91. Answers will vary.

93. Answers will vary.

SECTION 2.2, PAGE 55

1. Subset   3. 2^n 5. True

7. False; McIntosh is not in the second set.

9. True   11. False; no set is a proper subset of itself.

13. True   15. False; {swimming} is a set not an element

17. True   19. True

21. False; the set { $\varnothing$ } contains the element $\varnothing$.

23. False; the set { 0 } contains the element 0.

25. False; 0 is a numbner and { } is a set.

27. $B \subseteq A, B \subset A$ 29. $A \subseteq B, A \subset B$ 31. $B \subseteq A, B \subset A$

33. $A = B, A \subseteq B, B \subseteq A$ 35. { }

37. { }, {cow}, {horse}, {cow, horse}

39. a) { }, {a}, {b}, {c}, {d}, {a,b}, {a,c}, {a,d}, {b,c}, {b,d}, {c,d}, {a,b,c}, {a, b, d}, {a,c,d}, {b,c,d}, {a,b,c,d}

 b) {a, b, c, d}

41. False   43. True   45. True   47. True   49. True

51. True   53. 2^8 or 256   55. 2^7 or 128   57. $E = F$

59. a) Yes   b) No   c) Yes   61. 1   62. Yes   63. Yes

64. No

SECTION 2.3, PAGE 63

1. Complement   3. Intersection   5. Cartesian   7. Disjoint

9.

11.

13.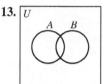

15. *And* is generally interpreted to mean *intersection*.

17.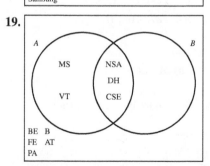

19.

21. The set of animals in U.S. zoos that are not in the San Diego Zoo

23. The set of farms in the United States that do not produce corn

25. The set of farms in the United States that produce corn or produce tomatoes

27. The set of farms in the United States that produce corn and do not produce tomatoes

29. The set of furniture stores that sell mattresses or leather furniture

31. The set of furniture stores that do not sell outdoor furniture and sell leather furniture

33. The set of furniture stores that sell mattresses or outdoor furniture or leather furniture

35. $\{b, c, t, w, a, h\}$ **37.** $\{a, h\}$

39. $\{c, w, b, t, a, h, f, r, d, g\}$ **41.** $\{p, m, z\}$

43. $\{L, \Delta, @, \$, *\}$ **45.** $\{L, \Delta, @, *, \$, R, \Box, \alpha, \infty, \Sigma, Z\}$

47. $\{R, \Box, \alpha, *, \$, \infty, Z, \Sigma\}$ **49.** $\{R, \Box, \alpha\}$

51. $\{1, 2, 3, 4, 5, 6, 7\}$ **53.** $\{1, 4, 7, 8\}$ **55.** $\{8\}$

57. $\{\ \}$ **59.** $\{8\}$ **61.** $\{a, e, h, i, j, k\}$ **63.** $\{a, f, i\}$

65. $\{b, c, d, e, g, h, j, k\}$ **67.** $\{a, c, d, e, f, g, h, i, j, k\}$

69. $\{a, b, c, d, e, f, g, h, i, j, k\}$, or U **71.** $\{2, 6, 9\}$

73. $\{1, 4\}$ **75.** $\{1, 3, 4, 5, 7, 8, 10\}$ **77.** $\{4, 9\}$

79. $\{(a, 1), (a, 2), (b, 1), (b, 2), (c, 1), (c, 2)\}$

81. No. The ordered pairs are not the same. For example, $(a, 1) \neq (1, a)$.

83. 6   **85.** $\{\ \}$ **87.** $\{2, 4, 6, 8\}$, or B **89.** $\{7, 9\}$

91. $\{1, 3, 5, 6, 7, 8, 9\}$ **93.** $\{6, 8\}$

95. $\{1, 2, 3, 4, 5, 6, 7, 8, 9\}$, or U

97. $\{1, 2, 3, 4, 5\}$, or C

99. A set and its complement will always be disjoint. For example, if $U = \{1, 2, 3\}$ and $A = \{1, 2\}$, then $A' = \{3\}$, and $A \cap A' = \{\ \}$.

101. 49

103. a) $8 = 4 + 6 - 2$

  b) Answers will vary.

  c) Answers will vary.

105. $\{1, 2, 3, 4, \ldots\}$, or A

107. $\{2, 4, 6, 8, \ldots\}$, or C

109. $\{2, 4, 6, 8, \ldots\}$, or C

111. $\{2, 6, 10, 14, 18, \ldots\}$

113. $\{2, 6, 10, 14, 18, \ldots\}$

115. $\{\ \}$ **117.** A **119.** U **121.** U **123.** $B \subseteq A$

125. A and B are disjoint sets.   **127.** $A \subseteq B$

SECTION 2.4, PAGE 72

1. 8   **3. a)** $A' \cap B'$ **b)** $A' \cup B'$ **5.** 8

7. a) Yes

  b) No, one specific case cannot be used as proof.

  c) No, not equal

9.

11.

13.

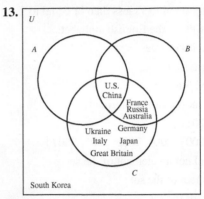

15. II   **17.** VIII   **19.** III   **21.** VI   **23.** III   **25.** III   **27.** V

29. II   **31.** VII   **33.** I   **35.** VIII   **37.** VI

39. $\{1, 2, 3, 4, 5, 7\}$ **41.** $\{3, 4, 5, 6, 8, 9, 12, 14\}$

43. $\{3, 4, 5\}$ **45.** $\{1, 2, 3, 7, 9, 10, 11, 12, 13, 14\}$

47. $\{1, 2, 3, 4, 5, 6, 7, 8, 9, 12, 14\}$ **49.** $\{9, 10, 12, 13, 14\}$

51. $\{6, 8, 9, 10, 11, 12, 13, 14\}$ **53.** Yes   **55.** No

57. No   **59.** Yes   **61.** No   **63.** Yes   **65.** Yes   **67.** Yes

69. No   **71.** $(A \cup B)'$ **73.** $(A \cup B) \cap C'$

75. a) Both equal $\{6, 7\}$.   **b)** Answers will vary.

  c) Both are represented by the regions IV, V, VI.

77.

79. a)

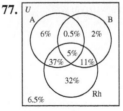

  b) V; $A \cap B \cap C$ **c)** VI; $A' \cap B \cap C$

  d) I; $A \cap B' \cap C'$

81. a)

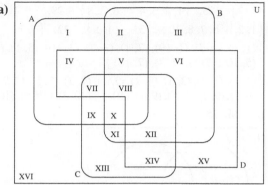

b)

Region	Set	Region	Set
I	$A \cap B' \cap C' \cap D'$	IX	$A \cap B' \cap C \cap D'$
II	$A \cap B \cap C' \cap D'$	X	$A \cap B \cap C \cap D'$
III	$A' \cap B \cap C' \cap D'$	XI	$A' \cap B \cap C \cap D'$
IV	$A \cap B' \cap C' \cap D$	XII	$A' \cap B \cap C \cap D$
V	$A \cap B \cap C' \cap D$	XIII	$A' \cap B' \cap C \cap D'$
VI	$A' \cap B \cap C' \cap D$	XIV	$A' \cap B' \cap C \cap D$
VII	$A \cap B' \cap C \cap D$	XV	$A' \cap B' \cap C' \cap D$
VIII	$A \cap B \cap C \cap D$	XVI	$A' \cap B' \cap C' \cap D'$

SECTION 2.5, PAGE 80

1.

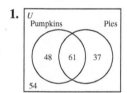

a) 48   **b)** 37   **c)** 54

3.

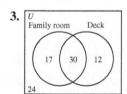

a) 17   **b)** 12   **c)** 59

5.

a) 3   **b)** 6   **c)** 22   **d)** 11   **e)** 12

7.

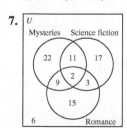

a) 22   **b)** 11   **c)** 64   **d)** 50   **e)** 23

9.

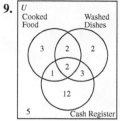

a) 3   **b)** 12   **c)** 3   **d)** 17   **e)** 8

11.

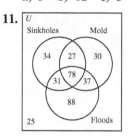

a) 67   **b)** 237   **c)** 37   **d)** 25

13. In a Venn diagram, regions II, IV, and V contain a total of 37 cars driven by women. This total is greater than the 35 cars driven by the women, as given in the exercise.

15.

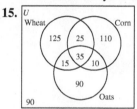

a) 410   **b)** 35   **c)** 90   **d)** 50

17. a) 10   **b)** 10   **c)** 6

SECTION 2.6, PAGE 86

1. Infinite

3. $\{3, 4, 5, 6, 7, \ldots, n+2, \ldots\}$
$\downarrow \downarrow \downarrow \downarrow \downarrow \qquad \downarrow$
$\{4, 5, 6, 7, 8, \ldots, n+3, \ldots\}$

5. $\{3, 5, 7, 9, 11, \ldots, 2n+1, \ldots\}$
$\downarrow \downarrow \downarrow \downarrow \downarrow \qquad \downarrow$
$\{5, 7, 9, 11, 13, \ldots, 2n+3, \ldots\}$

7. $\{5, 9, 13, 17, 21, \ldots, 4n+1, \ldots\}$
$\downarrow \downarrow \downarrow \downarrow \downarrow \qquad \downarrow$
$\{9, 13, 17, 21, 25, \ldots, 4n+5, \ldots\}$

9. $\left\{\frac{1}{2}, \frac{1}{4}, \frac{1}{6}, \frac{1}{8}, \frac{1}{10}, \ldots, \frac{1}{2n}, \ldots\right\}$
$\downarrow \downarrow \downarrow \downarrow \downarrow \qquad \downarrow$
$\left\{\frac{1}{4}, \frac{1}{6}, \frac{1}{8}, \frac{1}{10}, \frac{1}{12}, \ldots, \frac{1}{2n+2}, \ldots\right\}$

11. $\left\{\frac{4}{11}, \frac{5}{11}, \frac{6}{11}, \frac{7}{11}, \frac{8}{11}, \ldots, \frac{n+3}{11}, \ldots\right\}$
$\downarrow \downarrow \downarrow \downarrow \downarrow \qquad \downarrow$
$\left\{\frac{5}{11}, \frac{6}{11}, \frac{7}{11}, \frac{8}{11}, \frac{9}{11}, \ldots, \frac{n+4}{11}, \ldots\right\}$

13. $\{1, 2, 3, 4, 5, \ldots, n, \ldots\}$
$\downarrow \downarrow \downarrow \downarrow \downarrow \qquad \downarrow$
$\{3, 6, 9, 12, 15, \ldots, 3n, \ldots\}$

15. $\{1, 2, 3, 4, 5, \ldots, \quad n, \ldots\}$
$\downarrow \downarrow \downarrow \downarrow \downarrow \qquad \downarrow$
$\{4, 6, 8, 10, 12, \ldots, 2n + 2, \ldots\}$

17. $\{1, 2, 3, 4, 5, \ldots, \quad n, \ldots\}$
$\downarrow \downarrow \downarrow \downarrow \downarrow \qquad \downarrow$
$\{2, 5, 8, 11, 14, \ldots, 3n - 1, \ldots\}$

19. $\{1, 2, 3, 4, 5, \ldots, n, \ldots\}$
$\downarrow \downarrow \downarrow \downarrow \downarrow \qquad \downarrow$
$\left\{\dfrac{1}{3}, \dfrac{1}{6}, \dfrac{1}{9}, \dfrac{1}{12}, \dfrac{1}{15}, \ldots, \dfrac{1}{3n}, \ldots\right\}$

21. $\{1, 2, 3, 4, 5, \ldots, \quad n, \ldots\}$
$\downarrow \downarrow \downarrow \downarrow \downarrow \qquad \downarrow$
$\left\{\dfrac{1}{3}, \dfrac{1}{4}, \dfrac{1}{5}, \dfrac{1}{6}, \dfrac{1}{7}, \ldots, \dfrac{1}{n+2}, \ldots\right\}$

23. $\{1, 2, 3, 4, 5, \ldots, n, \ldots\}$
$\downarrow \downarrow \downarrow \downarrow \downarrow \qquad \downarrow$
$\{1, 4, 9, 16, 25, \ldots, n^2, \ldots\}$

25. $\{1, 2, 3, 4, 5, \ldots, n, \ldots\}$
$\downarrow \downarrow \downarrow \downarrow \downarrow \qquad \downarrow$
$\{3, 9, 27, 81, 243, \ldots, 3^n, \ldots\}$

27. = **29.** = **31.** =

REVIEW EXERCISES, PAGE 88

1. True

2. False; the word best makes the statement not well defined.

3. True **4.** False; no set is a proper subset of itself.

5. False; the elements 6, 12, 18, 24, … are members of both sets.

6. True

7. False; both sets do not contain exactly the same elements.

8. True **9.** True **10.** True **11.** True **12.** True

13. True **14.** True **15.** $A = \{7, 9, 11, 13, 15\}$

16. {Colorado, Nebraska, Missouri, Oklahoma}

17. $C = \{1, 2, 3, 4, \ldots, 161\}$

18. $D = \{9, 10, 11, 12, \ldots, 80\}$

19. $A = \{x \mid x \in N \text{ and } 50 < x < 150\}$

20. $B = \{x \mid x \in N \text{ and } x > 42\}$

21. $C = \{x \mid x \in N \text{ and } x < 7\}$

22. $D = \{x \mid x \in N \text{ and } 27 \le x \le 51\}$

23. A is the set of capital letters in the English alphabet from E through M, inclusive.

24. B is the set of U.S. coins with a value of less than a dollar.

25. C is the set of the first three lowercase letters in the English alphabet.

26. D is the set of numbers greater than or equal to 3 and less than 9

27. $\{3, 7\}$ **28.** $\{1, 2, 3, 4, 5, 6, 7, 8\}$ **29.** $\{9, 10\}$

30. $\{1, 2, 4, 6, 7, 8, 10\}$ **31.** $\{1, 5\}$ **32.** $\{1, 7\}$

33. $\{(1, 1), (1, 7), (1, 10), (3, 1), (3, 7), (3, 10), (5, 1), (5, 7),$
$(5, 10), (7, 1), (7, 7), (7, 10)\}$

34. $\{(3, 1), (3, 3), (3, 5), (3, 7), (7, 1), (7, 3), (7, 5), (7, 7),$
$(9, 1), (9, 3), (9, 5), (9, 7), (10, 1), (10, 3), (10, 5), (10, 7)\}$

35. 16 **36.** 15

37.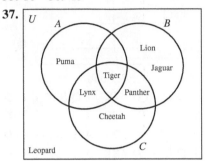

38. $\{a, c, d, f, g, i, k, l\}$ **39.** $\{i, k\}$

40. $\{a, b, c, d, f, g, h, i, k, l\}$ **41.** $\{f\}$

42. $\{a, f, i\}$ **43.** $\{a, b, d, f, h, i, l\}$ **44.** True

45. True **46.** II **47.** III **48.** I **49.** IV **50.** IV

51. II **52.** II **53.** $450

54.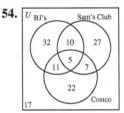

a) 131 **b)** 32 **c)** 10 **d)** 65

55.

a) 38 **b)** 298 **c)** 28 **d)** 236 **e)** 106

56. $\{2, 4, 6, 8, 10, \ldots, \quad 2n, \ldots\}$
$\downarrow \downarrow \downarrow \downarrow \downarrow \qquad \downarrow$
$\{4, 6, 8, 10, 12, \ldots, 2n + 2, \ldots\}$

57. $\{3, 5, 7, 9, 11, \ldots, 2n + 1, \ldots\}$
$\downarrow \downarrow \downarrow \downarrow \downarrow \qquad \downarrow$
$\{5, 7, 9, 11, 13, \ldots, 2n + 3, \ldots\}$

58. $\{1, 2, 3, 4, 5, \ldots, \quad n, \quad \ldots\}$
$\downarrow \downarrow \downarrow \downarrow \downarrow \qquad \downarrow$
$\{5, 8, 11, 14, 17, \ldots, 3n + 2, \ldots\}$

59. $\{1, 2, 3, 4, 5, \ldots, \quad n, \quad \ldots\}$
$\downarrow \downarrow \downarrow \downarrow \downarrow \qquad \downarrow$
$\{4, 9, 14, 19, 24, \ldots, 5n - 1, \ldots\}$

CHAPTER TEST, PAGE 91

1. True

2. False; the sets do not contain exactly the same elements.

3. True

4. False; the second set has no subset that contains the element 7.

5. False; the set has 2^4, or 16 subsets. 6. True

7. False; for any set A, $A \cup A' = U$, not $\{\ \}$.

8. True 9. $A = \{1, 2, 3, 4, 5, 6, 7, 8, 9\}$

10. Set A is the set of natural numbers less than 10.

11. $\{7, 9\}$ 12. $\{3, 5, 7, 9, 13\}$

13. $\{7, 9\}$ 14. 2 15. $\{3, 5\}$

16. $\{(3, 3), (3, 11), (3, 15), (5, 3), (5, 11), (5, 15), (7, 3),$
$(7, 11), (7, 15), (9, 3), (9, 11), (9, 15)\}$

17.   18. Equal

19.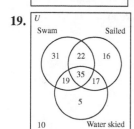

a) 52 b) 10 c) 93 d) 22 e) 69 f) 5

20. $\{7, 8, 9, 10, 11, \ldots, n + 6, \ldots\}$
$\downarrow \downarrow \downarrow \ \downarrow \ \downarrow \qquad\qquad \downarrow$
$\{8, 9, 10, 11, 12, \ldots, n + 7, \ldots\}$

Chapter 3

Answer to Recreational Math on page 97

7	1	9	4	8	2	5	6	3
5	4	6	7	3	9	8	1	2
2	3	8	6	5	1	4	9	7
8	2	4	3	9	5	1	7	6
6	7	5	1	2	4	3	8	9
1	9	3	8	6	7	2	4	5
9	6	1	5	4	3	7	2	8
3	8	7	2	1	6	9	5	4
4	5	2	9	7	8	6	3	1

SECTION 3.1, PAGE 101

1. Statement 3. Compound

5. a) Not b) And c) Or d) If-then e) If and only if

7. Some 9. Simple statement

11. Compound; biconditional, $\leftrightarrow$

13. Compound; conjunction, $\wedge$

15. Compound; conditional, $\rightarrow$

17. Compound; negation, $\sim$

19. Some butterflies are not insects.

21. All turtles have claws.

23. Some bicycles have three wheels.

25. No pedestrians are in the crosswalk.

27. Some Holsteins are Guernseys.

29. $\sim p$ 31. $\sim q \vee \sim p$

33. $\sim p \rightarrow \sim q$

35. $\sim p \wedge q$ 37. $\sim q \leftrightarrow p$

39. $\sim (p \vee q)$

41. Brie does not have a MacBook.

43. Joe has an iPad and Brie has a MacBook.

45. If Joe does not have an iPad then Brie has a MacBook.

47. Joe does not have an iPad or Brie does not have a MacBook.

49. It is false that Joe has an iPad and Brie has a MacBook.

51. $(p \wedge \sim q) \wedge r$ 53. $(p \wedge q) \vee r$

55. $p \rightarrow (q \vee \sim r)$ 57. $(r \leftrightarrow q) \wedge p$

59. $q \rightarrow (p \leftrightarrow r)$

61. The water is 70° or the sun is shining, and we do not go swimming.

63. The water is not 70°, and the sun is shining or we go swimming.

65. If we do not go swimming, then the sun is shining and the water is 70°.

67. If the sun is shining then we go swimming, and the water is 70°.

69. The sun is shining if and only if the water is 70°, and we go swimming.

71. Not permissible, you cannot have both soup and salad. The *or* used on menus is the *exclusive or*.

73. Not permissible, you cannot have both potatoes and pasta. The *or* used on menus is the *exclusive or*.

75. a) $w \wedge \sim p$ b) Conjunction

77. a) $\sim (b \rightarrow \sim p)$ b) Negation

79. a) $(f \vee v) \rightarrow h$ b) Conditional

81. a) $c \leftrightarrow (\sim f \vee p)$ b) Biconditional

83. a) $(c \leftrightarrow w) \vee s$ b) Disjunction

85. a) Answers will vary. b) Answers will vary.

86.

6	4	8	7	5	3	2	1	9
3	9	2	8	6	1	7	5	4
7	5	1	9	4	2	8	6	3
9	1	6	3	2	5	4	8	7
5	7	3	4	8	6	9	2	1
8	2	4	1	9	7	5	3	6
4	3	5	6	7	8	1	9	2
2	6	9	5	1	4	3	7	8
1	8	7	2	3	9	6	4	5

SECTION 3.2, PAGE 114

1. Opposite **3.** False

5. F **7.** T **9.** F **11.** T **13.** T
  F   F   T   F   F
          T   T   T
          T   T   T
                            F
                            F
                            T
                            T

15. T **17.** F **19.** $p \wedge q$
   F   F   T
   T   T   F
   T   F   F
   T   F   F
   F   F
   T   T
   F   T

21. $p \wedge \sim q$ **23.** $\sim(p \wedge q)$ **25.** $p \vee (q \vee r)$
   F   F   T
   T   T   T
   F   T   T
   F   T   T
                                      T
                                      T
                                      T
                                      F

27. a) False **b)** False **29. a)** False **b)** False
31. a) True **b)** False **33. a)** False **b)** True
35. a) True **b)** True **37.** True **39.** True
41. False **43.** False **45.** False **47.** True
49. True **51.** False

53. $p \wedge \sim q$ **55.** $p \vee \sim q$
   F   T
   T   T
   F   F
   F   T
   True in case 2   True in cases 1,
                             2, and 4.

57. $(r \vee q) \wedge p$ **59.** $q \vee (p \wedge \sim r)$
   T   T
   T   T
   T   F
   F   T
   F   T
   F   T
   F   F
   F   F
   True in cases   True in cases 1, 2,
   1, 2, and 3   4, 5, and 6.

61. a) Mr. Duncan and Mrs. Tuttle qualify.

   b) Mrs. Rusinek does not qualify, since their combined income is less than $46,000.

63. b) Gina Vela is returning on April 3. Kara Sharo is returning on a Monday. Christos Supernaw is not staying over on a Saturday. Alex Chang is returning on a Monday.

65. T **67.** Yes
   T
   T
   F
   T
   F
   T

SECTION 3.3, PAGE 124

1. False **3.** True **5.** Self-contradiction

7. T **9.** T **11.** F **13.** T **15.** F **17.** T
   T   F   T   T   T   T
   T   F   T   F   T   T
   F   F   F   T   T   T
                                             T
                                             F
                                             F
                                             F

19. F **21.** T **23.** T **25.** $p \rightarrow (q \wedge r)$
   F   T   T   T
   T   T   T   F
   F   T   F   F
   T   T   T   F
   T   F   T   T
   F   F   F   T
   T   F   T   T
                              T

27. $(p \leftrightarrow q) \vee r$ **29.** $(\sim p \rightarrow q) \vee r$
   T   T
   T   T
   T   T
   F   T
   T   T
   F   T
   T   T
   T   F

31. Neither **33.** Self-contradiction **35.** Tautology
37. Not an implication **39.** Implication **41.** Implication
43. True **45.** False **47.** False **49.** True **51.** True
53. True **55.** False **57.** True **59.** True **61.** True
63. False **65.** False **67.** True **69.** False **71.** True
73. No, the statement only states what will occur if your sister gets straight A's. If your sister does not get straight A's, your parents may still get her a computer.

75. F   **77.** It is a tautology. The statement may be
   T   expressed as $(p \rightarrow q) \vee (\sim p \rightarrow q)$, where
   T p: It is a head and q: I win. This statement is a
   T   tautology.
   T
   F
   F
   F

79. Allen was born in January. Booker was born in February. Chris was born in March. Dennis was born in April.

80.

Tiger	Boots	Sam	Sue
Blue	Yellow	Red	Green
Nine Lives	Whiskas	Friskies	Meow Mix

81. Katie was born last. Katie and Mary are saying the same thing.

SECTION 3.4, PAGE 136

Answer to Recreational Math on page 134

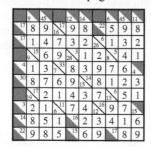

1. Equivalent   **3.** $\sim p \lor q$ **5.** $q \to p$ **7.** $\sim q \to \sim p$

9. Not equivalent   **11.** Equivalent   **13.** Not equivalent

15. Equivalent   **17.** Equivalent   **19.** Equivalent

21. Equivalent   **23.** Equivalent

25. Not equivalent   **27.** Equivalent

29. Oregon does not border the Atlantic Ocean or Delaware does not border the Pacific Ocean.

31. It is false that the dog was a bulldog or the dog was a boxer.

33. If Ashley Tabai takes the new job, then it is false that she will move and she will not buy a new house in town.

35. Janette Campbell does not buy a new car or she sells her old car.

37. If Bob the Tomato did not visit the nursing home then he did not visit the Cub Scout meeting.

39. If Chase is hiding, then the pitcher is broken.

41. We go to Chicago and we do not go to Navy Pier.

43. It is false that if I am cold then the heater is working.

45. Amazon has a sale and we will not buy $100 worth of books.

47. It is false that if John Deere will hire new workers then the city of Dubuque will not retrain the workers.

49. *Converse:* If she needs extra yarn, then Nanette Berry teaches macramé.

Inverse: If Nanette Berry does not teach macramé, then she does not need extra yarn.

Contrapositive: If she does not need extra yarn, then Nanette Berry does not teach macramé.

51. *Converse:* If I buy silver jewelry, then I go to Mexico.

Inverse: If I do not go to Mexico, then I do not buy silver jewelry.

Contrapositive: If I do not buy silver jewelry, then I do not go to Mexico.

53. *Converse:* If I scream, then that annoying paper clip shows up on my computer screen.

Inverse: If that annoying paper clip does not show up on my computer screen, then I will not scream.

Contrapositive: If I do not scream, then that annoying paper clip does not show up on my screen.

55. If a natural number is not divisible by 7, then the natural number is not divisible by 14. True.

57. If a natural number is not divisible by 6, then the natural number is not divisible by 3. False.

59. If two lines are not parallel, then the two lines intersect in at least one point. True.

61. b) and c) are equivalent.   **63.** a) and c) are equivalent.

65. b) and c) are equivalent.   **67.** b) and c) are equivalent.

69. None are equivalent.   **71.** None are equivalent.

73. a) and c) are equivalent.

75. True. If $p \to q$ is false, it must be of the form T → F.

Therefore, the converse must be of the form F → T, which is true.

77. False. A conditional statement and its contrapositive always have the same truth values.

79. Answers will vary.

81. Answers will vary.

83.

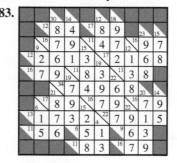

SECTION 3.5, PAGE 147

1. Valid   **3.** Fallacy   **5.** Valid   **7.** Inverse   **9.** Syllogism

11. Syllogism   **13.** Invalid   **15.** Valid   **17.** Valid

19. Invalid   **21.** Invalid   **23.** Valid   **25.** Valid

27. Invalid   **29.** Invalid   **31.** Valid

33. a) $\dfrac{\begin{array}{c} p \to q \\ \sim q \end{array}}{\therefore \sim p}$ b) Valid   **35.** a) $\dfrac{\begin{array}{c} p \to q \\ p \end{array}}{\therefore q}$ b) Valid

37. a) $\dfrac{\begin{array}{c} p \to q \\ \sim q \end{array}}{\therefore \sim p}$ b) Valid   **39.** a) $\dfrac{\begin{array}{c} p \to q \\ q \end{array}}{\therefore p}$ b) Invalid

41. a) $\dfrac{\begin{array}{c} p \lor q \\ \sim p \end{array}}{\therefore q}$ b) Valid   **43.** a) $\dfrac{\begin{array}{c} p \to q \\ q \to r \end{array}}{\therefore p \to r}$ b) Valid

45. a) $\dfrac{\begin{array}{c} p \land q \\ q \to r \end{array}}{\therefore r \to p}$ b) Valid   **47.** a) $\dfrac{\begin{array}{c} s \land g \\ g \to c \end{array}}{\therefore s \to c}$ b) Valid

49. a) $p \rightarrow q$ **b)** Valid   **51. a)** $p \lor q$ **b)** Valid

$$\frac{\sim q}{\therefore \sim p}$$ $$\frac{\sim p}{\therefore q}$$

53. a) $t \land g$ **b)** Valid   **55. a)** $c \land \sim h$ **b)** Invalid

$$\frac{\sim t \lor \sim g}{\therefore \sim t}$$ $$\frac{h \rightarrow c}{\therefore h}$$

57. a) $p \rightarrow q$ **b)** Invalid

$$\frac{q \rightarrow \sim r}{\therefore p \rightarrow r}$$

59. Therefore, you must rest for three days.

61. Therefore, I am stressed out.

63. Therefore, you did not close the deal.

65. Yes, if the conclusion does not necessarily follow from the premises, the argument is invalid, even if the conclusion is true.

67. Yes, if the conclusion does not necessarily follow from the premises, the argument is invalid, even if the premises are true.

69. Valid   **71. a)** $p \rightarrow q$ **b)** No   **c)** This argument is the fallacy of the inverse.

$$\frac{\sim p}{\therefore \sim q}$$

SECTION 3.6, PAGE 154

1. Euler   **3.** Invalid   **5.** No   **7.** Valid   **9.** Valid

11. Invalid   **13.** Valid   **15.** Invalid   **17.** Invalid

19. Invalid   **21.** Valid   **23.** Invalid

25. Invalid   **27.** Valid

29. Yes, if the conclusion necessarily follows from the premises, the argument is valid.

SECTION 3.7, PAGE 161

1. Series   **3.** Closed

5. a) $p \lor q$

  b) The lightbulb will be on when either p or q are closed.

7. a) $(p \lor q) \land \sim q$

  b) The lightbulb will be on when p is closed and q is open.

9. a) $(p \land q) \land [(p \land \sim q) \lor r]$

  b) The lightbulb will be on when p, q, and r are all closed.

11. a) $p \lor q \lor (r \land \sim p)$

  b) The lightbulb will be on in all cases except when p, q, and r are all open.

13.

15.

17.

19.

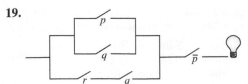

21. $p \lor \sim q; \overline{p} \land q$ not equivalent

23. $[(p \land q) \lor r] \land p; (q \lor r) \land p$; equivalent

25. $(p \lor \sim p) \land q \land r; p \land q \land r$; not equivalent

27. It is a series circuit; therefore, both switches must be closed for current to flow and the lightbulb to go on. When the p switch is closed, the $\overline{p}$ switch is open and no current will flow through the circuit. When the $\overline{p}$ switch is closed, the p switch is open and no current will flow through the circuit.

29. a)   **b)**

REVIEW EXERCISE, PAGE 164

1. Some Scions are not Toyotas.

2. Some pets are allowed in this park.

3. No women are presidents.   **4.** All pine trees are green.

5. The coffee is Maxwell House or the coffee is hot.

6. The coffee is not hot and the coffee is strong.

7. If the coffee is hot, then the coffee is strong and the coffee is not Maxwell House.

8. The coffee is Maxwell House if and only if the coffee is not strong.

9. The coffee is not Maxwell House, if and only if the coffee is strong and the coffee is not hot.

10. The coffee is Maxwell House or the coffee is not hot, and the coffee is not strong.

11. $p \lor r$ **12.** $r \rightarrow \sim p$ **13.** $(r \rightarrow q) \lor \sim p$

14. $(q \leftrightarrow p) \land \sim r$ **15.** $(r \land q) \lor \sim p$ **16.** $\sim (r \land q)$

17.	**18.**	**19.**	**20.**	**21.**	**22.**
F	T	T	T	F	F
F	F	T	F	T	T
T	F	T	T	F	T
F	F	T	T	F	T
	T	T	F	T	T
	F	F	F	T	T
	F	F	F	T	T
	T	T	F	T	T

23. False   **24.** True   **25.** False   **26.** True   **27.** True

28. True   **29.** False   **30.** False   **31.** Not equivalent

32. Equivalent   **33.** Equivalent   **34.** Not equivalent

35. It is false that if Lady Gaga sang "Poker Face", then Jay-Z sang "Beamer, Benz, or Bentley".

36. If Lynn Swann did not play for the Steelers, then Jack Tatum played for the Raiders.

37. Altec Lansing does not produce only speakers and Harman Kardon does not produce only stereo receivers.

38. It is false that Travis Tritt won an Academy Award or Randy Jackson does commercials for Milk Bone Dog Biscuits.

39. The temperature is above 32° or we will go ice fishing at O'Leary's Lake.

40. a) If you know Jay Stu, then you listen to Jim Rome.

   b) If you do not listen to Jim Rome, then you do not know Jay Stu.

   c) If you do not know Jay Stu, then you do not listen to Jim Rome.

41. a) If we will learn the table's value, then we take the table to *Antiques Roadshow*.

   b) If we do not take the table to *Antiques Roadshow*, then we will not learn the table's value.

   c) If we will not learn the table's value, then we do not take the table to *Antiques Roadshow*.

42. a) If you do not sell more doughnuts, then you do not advertise.

   b) If you advertise, then you sell more doughnuts.

   c) If you sell more doughnuts, then you advertise.

43. a) If we will not buy a desk at Miller's Furniture, then the desk is made by Winner's Only and the desk is in the Rose catalog.

   b) If the desk is not made by Winner's Only or the desk is not in the Rose catalog, then we will buy a desk at Miller's Furniture.

   c) If we will buy a desk at Miller's Furniture, then the desk is not made by Winner's Only or the desk is not in the Rose catalog.

44. a) If I let you attend the prom, then you will get straight A's on your report card.

   b) If you do not get straight A's on your report card, then I will not let you attend the prom.

   c) If I will not let you attend the prom, then you did not get straight A's on your report card.

45. a), b) and **c)** are equivalent.   **46.** None are equivalent.

47. a) and **c)** are equivalent.   **48.** None are equivalent.

49. Invalid   **50.** Valid   **51.** Valid   **52.** Invalid

53. Invalid   **54.** Valid   **55.** Invalid   **56.** Invalid

57. a) $p \land [(q \land r) \lor \sim p]$

   b) The lightbulb will be on when p, q, and r are all closed.

58.

59. Equivalent

CHAPTER TEST, PAGE 167

1. $(p \land r) \lor \sim q$ **2.** $(r \rightarrow q) \lor \sim p$ **3.** $\sim (r \leftrightarrow \sim q)$

4. Phobos is not a moon of Mars and Rosalind is a moon of Uranus, if and only if Callisto is not a moon of Jupiter.

5. If Phobos is a moon of Mars or Callisto is not a moon of Jupiter, then Rosalind is a moon of Uranus.

6. F   **7.** T
  T   T
  F   T
  F   T
  F   F
  F   T
  F   T
  F   F

8. True   **9.** True   **10.** True   **11.** True   **12.** Equivalent.

13. a) and **b)** are equivalent.   **14. a)** and **b)** are equivalent.

15. $s \rightarrow f$ **16.** Invalid   **17.** Some highways are not roads.
$\underline{f \rightarrow p}$
$\therefore s \rightarrow p$
Valid

18. Nick did not play football or Max did not play baseball.

19. *Converse:* If today is Saturday, then the garbage truck comes.

   Inverse: If the garbage truck does not come, then today is not Saturday.

   Contrapositive: If today is not Saturday, then the garbage truck does not come.

20.

Chapter 4

SECTION 4.1, PAGE 176

1. How many   **3.** Hindu–Arabic   **5.** Subtract

7. Multiplicative   **9.** 234   **11.** 2423   **13.** 334,214

15. ∩∩∩∩∥   **17.** ⌒⌒∩∩∩∩∥∥∥∥

19. ⌒⌜⌜⌜⌜⌜⌜⌜⌜99999999∩∩∩∥∥∥∥∥

21. 16   **23.** 194   **25.** 2642   **27.** 2946   **29.** 12,666

31. 9464   **33.** XXIV   **35.** DLV   **37.** MCMXIV

39. $\overline{\text{IV}}$DCCXCIII   **41.** $\overline{\text{IX}}$CMXCIX   **43.** $\overline{\text{XX}}$DCXLIV

45. 74   **47.** 4081   **49.** 8550   **51.** 4003

53. 五十三   **55.** 三百七十八   **57.** 四千二百六十   **59.** 七千零五十六

61. 81   **63.** 279   **65.** 2883   **67.** λγϛ   **69.** ψκ   **71.** ʹϵϵ

73. 1021, MXXI, 一千零二十一, ʹακα

75. 527, 99999∩∩∥∥∥∥∥, DXXVII, ϕκζ

77. A number is a quantity, and it answers the question "How many?" A numeral is a symbol used to represent the number.

79. $\overline{\text{CMXCIX}}$CMXCIX

81. Turn the book upside down.

83. 1888, MDCCCLXXXVIII

SECTION 4.2, PAGE 183

1. Positional **3.** Tens **5.** 10 **7.** Expanded

9. 60 **11.** Calendar **13.** $(5 \times 10) + (8 \times 1)$

15. $(7 \times 100) + (1 \times 10) + (2 \times 1)$

17. $(8 \times 100) + (9 \times 10) + (7 \times 1)$

19. $(4 \times 1000) + (3 \times 100) + (8 \times 10) + (7 \times 1)$

21. $(1 \times 10{,}000) + (6 \times 1000) + (4 \times 100) + (0 \times 10) + (2 \times 1)$

23. $(3 \times 100{,}000) + (4 \times 10{,}000) + (6 \times 1000) + (8 \times 100) + (6 \times 10) + (1 \times 1)$

25. 32 **27.** 784 **29.** 4868 **31.** (Babylonian numeral)

33. (Babylonian numerals) **35.** (Babylonian numerals)

37. 73 **39.** 4682 **41.** 4000

43. (Mayan numeral) **45.** (Mayan numeral) **47.** (Mayan numeral) **49.** 1944, (Babylonian numerals)

51. $\left(\triangle \times \bigcirc^{2}\right) + \left(\square \times \bigcirc\right) + \left(\bigcirc \times 1\right)$

53. The Mayan system has a different base and the numerals are written vertically.

55. a) (Mayan numeral) **b)** (Babylonian numerals)

57. (Babylonian numerals) **59.** (Mayan numeral)

SECTION 4.3, PAGE 190

1. Base **3.** 8 **5.** 1 **7.** 8 **9.** 161 **11.** 441

13. 1395 **15.** 53 **17.** 4012 **19.** 1549 **21.** 50,809

23. 1001_2 **25.** 212_3 **27.** 311_4 **29.** 402_5 **31.** 2112_8

33. 5264_{12} **35.** $24EF_{16}$ **37.** 2202120_3 **39.** 31023_5

41. 5604_7 **43.** $8E3_{15}$ **45.** 23 **47.** 78

49. (Mayan numerals)$_5$ **51.** (Mayan numerals)$_5$

53. 14 **55.** 36

57. (circles)$_4$ **59.** (circles)$_4$ **61. a)** 10213_5 **b)** 1373_8

63. a) 2 **b)** 8 **c)** 16 **d)** 32 **e)** b **65.** $b = 6$

67. a) $1_3, 2_3, 10_3, 11_3, 12_3, 20_3, 21_3, 22_3, 100_3, 101_3, 102_3, 110_3, 111_3, 112_3, 120_3, 121_3, 122_3, 200_3, 201_3, 202_3$
   b) 1000_3

69. a) Answers will vary. **b)** Answers will vary.

71. a) 876 **b)** (circles)$_4$

SECTION 4.4, PAGE 198

1. 12_5 **3.** 5 **5.** 22_5 **7.** 124_5 **9.** 1101_2

11. $9B5_{12}$ **13.** 2200_3 **15.** 24001_2 **17.** 10100_2

19. 3_5 **21.** 54_9 **23.** 110_2 **25.** 11_2 **27.** 3616_7

29. 1011_3 **31.** 134_5 **33.** 1201_3 **35.** 21020_6

37. 77676_{12} **39.** 100011_2 **41.** 6031_7 **43.** 110_2

45. $146_7 R2_7$ **47.** 123_4 **49.** $103_4 R1_4$ **51.** $41_5 R1_5$

53. $45_7 R2_7$ **55.** (Mayan numerals)$_5$ **57.** (Mayan numerals)$_5$ **59.** (circles)$_4$

61. (circles)$_4$ **63.** (circles)$_4$ **65.** (circles)$_4$ **67.** $3EAC_{16}$

69. a) 21252_8 **b)** 306 and 29 **c)** 8874 **d)** 8874 **e)** Yes

71. (circle) $= 0$, (circle) $= 1$, (circle) $= 2$, (circle) $= 3$

SECTION 4.5, PAGE 203

1. a) Divided **b)** Doubled **3.** Three; Two **5.** 308

7. 663 **9.** 8260 **11.** 8649 **13.** 753 **15.** 4172 **17.** 900

19. 204,728 **21.** 112 **23.** 410 **25.** 625 **27.** 60,678

29. a) 253×46 **b)** 11,638 **31. a)** 4×382 **b)** 1528

33. (Egyptian numerals) **35.** 1211_3

REVIEW EXERCISES, PAGE 205

1. 321 **2.** 42,053 **3.** 200,421 **4.** 1,214,330

5. (Egyptian numerals) **6.** (Mayan numeral)

7. (Egyptian numerals) **8.** (Egyptian numerals)

9. 24 **10.** 142 **11.** 2437 **12.** 5759 **13.** XXIX

14. DXLVII **15.** MCMLXIV **16.** $\overline{\text{VI}}$CDXCI

17. 32 **18.** 45 **19.** 267 **20.** 3429

21. (Chinese numerals) **22.** (Chinese numerals) **23.** (Chinese numerals) **24.** (Chinese numerals) **25.** 42 **26.** 789

27. 605 **28.** 3334 **29.** $o\eta$ **30.** $\phi\kappa\alpha$ **31.** $\omega\xi\zeta$

32. $'\delta\sigma\iota\theta$ **33.** 123 **34.** 189 **35.** 3673 **36.** 7388

37. (Babylonian numerals) **38.** (Babylonian numerals) **39.** (Babylonian numerals)

40. (Babylonian numerals) **41.** 63 **42.** 721 **43.** 1367 **44.** 15,923

45. (Mayan numeral) **46.** (Mayan numeral) **47.** (Mayan numeral) **48.** (Mayan numeral) **49.** 39 **50.** 5

51. 28 **52.** 1244 **53.** 1552 **54.** 186 **55.** 111001111_2

56. 1220011_3 **57.** 13033_4 **58.** 717_8 **59.** 327_{12} **60.** $1CF_{16}$

61. 140_7 **62.** 101111_2 **63.** 166_{12} **64.** $70F_{16}$ **65.** 12102_5

66. 12423_8 **67.** 3411_7 **68.** 100_2 **69.** $9A6_{12}$ **70.** 3324_5

71. 450_8 **72.** $CC1_{16}$ **73.** 110111_2 **74.** 21102_3 **75.** 1314_5

76. 13632_8 **77.** 5656_{12} **78.** $1D76_{16}$ **79.** $21_3 R1_3$

80. 130_4 **81.** $23_5 R1_5$ **82.** 433_6 **83.** $411_6 R1_6$

84. $664_8 R2_8$ **85.** 3408 **86.** 3408 **87.** 3408

CHAPTER TEST, PAGE 207

1. 2484   **2.** 1275   **3.** 8090   **4.** 969   **5.** 122,142

6. 2745   **7.** ⌁⌁⅁ꝯ∩∩ⅠⅠⅠⅠ   **8.** 'βυοϝ

9. ⋯   **10.** ⪡ⅠⅠⅠⅠⅠⅠⅠ ⪡⪡ⅠⅠⅠⅠⅠⅠⅠ   **11.** MMMDCCVI
⸱⸱
≡
⣀⣀

12. 103   **13.** 559   **14.** 100100_2 **15.** $B7A_{16}$ **16.** 11000_2

17. 2003_6 **18.** 220_5 **19.** 980   **20.** 8428

Chapter 5

SECTION 5.1, PAGE 217

1. Theory   **3.** Zero   **5.** Composite

7. Multiple   **9.** Conjecture   **11.** Fermat

13. The prime numbers between 1 and 100 are 2, 3, 5, 7, 11, 13, 17, 19, 23, 29, 31, 37, 41, 43, 47, 53, 59, 61, 67, 71, 73, 79, 83, 89, and 97.

15. True   **17.** False; 28 is a multiple of 7.

19. False; 56 is divisible by 8.   **21.** True

23. False; if a number is divisible by 3, then the sum of the digits of the number is divisible by 3.

25. True   **27.** 5390 is divisible by 2, 5, and 10.

29. 72,216 is divisible by 2, 3, 4, 6, 8, and 9.

31. 1,882,320 is divisible by 2, 3, 4, 5, 6, 8, and 10.

33. 60 (other answers are possible)   **35.** $36 = 2^2 \cdot 3^2$

37. $140 = 2^2 \cdot 5 \cdot 7$ **39.** $332 = 2^2 \cdot 83$

41. $513 = 3^3 \cdot 19$ **43.** $1336 = 2^3 \cdot 167$

45. $2001 = 3 \cdot 23 \cdot 29$ **47. a)** 2   **b)** 42   **49. a)** 5   **b)** 75

51. a) 20   **b)** 1800   **53. a)** 4   **b)** 5088   **55. a)** 8   **b)** 384

57. a) Yes   **b)** No   **c)** No   **d)** Yes   **59.** 17, 19, and 29, 31

61. 5, 17, and 257 are all prime.   **63.** 48 days

65. $2 \times 60, 3 \times 40, 4 \times 30, 5 \times 24, 6 \times 20, 8 \times 15,$ $10 \times 12, 12 \times 10, 15 \times 8, 20 \times 6, 24 \times 5, 30 \times 4,$ $40 \times 3, 60 \times 2$

67. 35 cars   **69.** 30 trees   **71.** 30 days

73. A number is divisible by 15 if both 3 and 5 divide the number.

75. 5   **77.** 35   **79.** 30   **81.** Yes   **83.** No

85. a) 12   **b)** 1, 2, 3, 4, 5, 6, 10, 12, 15, 20, 30, 60

87. For any three consecutive natural numbers, one of the numbers is divisible by 2 and another number is divisible by 3. Therefore, the product of the three numbers would be divisible by 6.

89. Yes

91. $8 = 2 + 3 + 3, 9 = 3 + 3 + 3, 10 = 2 + 3 + 5,$ $11 = 2 + 2 + 7, 12 = 2 + 5 + 5, 13 = 3 + 3 + 7,$ $14 = 2 + 5 + 7, 15 = 3 + 5 + 7, 16 = 2 + 7 + 7,$ $17 = 5 + 5 + 7, 18 = 2 + 5 + 11, 19 = 3 + 5 + 11,$ $20 = 2 + 7 + 11$

SECTION 5.2, PAGE 227

Answer to *Recreational Mathematics* box on page 225

$$0 = 4 + 4 - 4 - 4$$

$$1 = \frac{4 + 4}{4 + 4}$$

$$2 = \frac{4 \cdot 4}{4 + 4}$$

$$3 = \frac{4 + 4 + 4}{4}$$

$$4 = \frac{4 - 4}{4} + 4$$

$$5 = \frac{4 \cdot 4 + 4}{4}$$

$$6 = \frac{4 + 4}{4} + 4$$

$$7 = 4 + 4 - \frac{4}{4}$$

$$8 = 4 + 4 + 4 - 4$$

$$9 = 4 + 4 + \frac{4}{4}$$

Other answers are possible.

1. Whole   **3. a)** Positive   **b)** Negative

5. a) <   **b)** <   **c)** <   **d)** >   **7.** 2   **9.** −7

11. −5   **13.** 2   **15.** −21   **17.** −2   **19.** −8

21. −2   **23.** −6   **25.** −2   **27.** −56   **29.** 81

31. 96   **33.** −60   **35.** −720   **37.** 8   **39.** −1

41. −7   **43.** −15   **45.** −48   **47.** True

49. False; the difference of two negative integers may be a positive integer, a negative integer, or zero.

51. True   **53.** True

55. False; the sum of a positive integer and a negative integer may be a positive integer, a negative integer, or zero.

57. 3   **59.** 33   **61.** −12   **63.** −5   **65.** −6

67. −9, −6, −3, 0, 3, 6   **69.** −6, −5, −4, −3, −2, −1

71. 1100 feet under water   **73.** 14,777 ft

75. a) 9 hours   **b)** 2 hours

77. Division by zero is undefined because $\frac{a}{0} = x$ always leads to a false statement.   **79.** −1

81. $0 + 1 - 2 + 3 + 4 - 5 + 6 - 7 - 8 + 9 = 1$

82. a) $4\left(4 - \frac{4}{4}\right) = 12, 4 \cdot 4 - \frac{4}{4} = 15, \frac{4 \cdot 4 \cdot 4}{4} = 16,$ $4 \cdot 4 + \frac{4}{4} = 17, 4\left(4 + \frac{4}{4}\right) = 20$ **b)** $\frac{44 - 4}{4} = 10$

SECTION 5.3, PAGE 239

1. Integers   **3.** Denominator   **5.** Improper

7. Repeating   **9.** Hundredths   **11.** Least

13. $\frac{1}{2}$ **15.** $\frac{4}{9}$ **17.** $\frac{19}{25}$ **19.** $\frac{7}{11}$ **21.** $\frac{17}{7}$ **23.** $-\frac{31}{16}$

25. $-\dfrac{79}{16}$ **27.** $\dfrac{9}{8}$ **29.** $\dfrac{15}{8}$ **31.** $2\dfrac{2}{3}$ **33.** $-12\dfrac{1}{6}$

35. $-58\dfrac{8}{15}$ **37.** 0.3 **39.** $0.\overline{6}$ **41.** 0.375 **43.** $2.1\overline{6}$

45. $\dfrac{25}{100} = \dfrac{1}{4}$ **47.** $\dfrac{175}{1000} = \dfrac{7}{40}$ **49.** $\dfrac{2}{10} = \dfrac{1}{5}$

51. $\dfrac{131}{10,000}$ **53.** $\dfrac{2}{9}$ **55.** $\dfrac{1}{1} = 1$ **57.** $\dfrac{15}{11}$ **59.** $\dfrac{37}{18}$ **61.** $\dfrac{2}{7}$

63. $\dfrac{2}{5}$ **65.** $\dfrac{49}{64}$ **67.** $\dfrac{36}{35}$ **69.** $\dfrac{20}{21}$ **71.** $\dfrac{11}{15}$ **73.** $\dfrac{9}{22}$

75. $\dfrac{23}{54}$ **77.** $\dfrac{17}{144}$ **79.** $-\dfrac{109}{600}$ **81.** $\dfrac{23}{24}$ **83.** $-\dfrac{1}{24}$

85. $\dfrac{19}{24}$ **87.** $\dfrac{15}{28}$ **89.** $\dfrac{11}{10}$ **91.** $\dfrac{23}{42}$ **93.** $1\dfrac{3}{4}$ in.

95. $120\dfrac{3}{4}$ in. **97.** $9\dfrac{15}{16}$ in. **99.** $\dfrac{1}{10}$ **101.** $58\dfrac{7}{8}$ in.

103. a) $1\dfrac{49}{60}, 2\dfrac{48}{60}, 9\dfrac{6}{60}, 6\dfrac{3}{60}, 2\dfrac{9}{60}, \dfrac{22}{60}$

b) $22\dfrac{17}{60}$; 22 hours 17 minutes

105. $26\dfrac{5}{32}$ in. **107. a)** $29\dfrac{3}{16}$ in. **b)** 33 in. **c)** $32\dfrac{3}{4}$ in.

109. 0.215 **111.** -2.1755 **113.** 4.8725 **115.** $\dfrac{1}{2}$

117. $\dfrac{11}{200}$ **119.** $\dfrac{2}{33}$

121. a) $1\dfrac{3}{8}$ cup water (or milk) and $\dfrac{3}{4}$ cup oatmeal

b) $1\dfrac{1}{2}$ cup water (or milk) and $\dfrac{3}{4}$ cup oatmeal

123. a) $\dfrac{1}{8}$ **b)** $\dfrac{1}{2}$ **c)** $\dfrac{1}{8}$ **d)** $\dfrac{1}{16}$

SECTION 5.4, PAGE 249

1. Irrational **3.** Radicand **5.** Itself **7.** Rationalized

9. Rational **11.** Rational **13.** Irrational **15.** Rational

17. Irrational **19.** 0 **21.** 6 **23.** -13 **25.** -9

27. Rational number, integer

29. Rational number, integer, natural number

31. Rational number **33.** Rational number

35. Rational number **37.** $3\sqrt{2}$ **39.** $3\sqrt{5}$ **41.** $3\sqrt{7}$

43. $2\sqrt{21}$ **45.** $7\sqrt{3}$ **47.** 0 **49.** $-13\sqrt{3}$ **51.** $4\sqrt{3}$

53. 4 **55.** $2\sqrt{21}$ **57.** 2 **59.** 3 **61.** $\dfrac{\sqrt{2}}{2}$ **63.** $\dfrac{\sqrt{35}}{5}$

65. $\dfrac{2\sqrt{15}}{3}$ **67.** $\dfrac{\sqrt{15}}{3}$

69. Between 3 and 3.5; $\sqrt{11} \approx 3.32$.

71. Between 10 and 10.5; $\sqrt{107} \approx 10.34$.

73. Between 13 and 13.5; $\sqrt{170} \approx 13.04$.

75. False. $\sqrt{c}$ may be a rational number or an irrational number for a composite number c. (For example, $\sqrt{25}$ is a rational number; $\sqrt{8}$ is an irrational number.)

77. True

79. False. The product of a rational number and an irrational number may be a rational number or an irrational number.

81. $3\sqrt{2} + 5\sqrt{2} = 8\sqrt{2}$ **83.** $\sqrt{2} \cdot \sqrt{3} = \sqrt{6}$

85. 36.0 inches

87. a) 10 mph **b)** 20 mph **c)** 40 mph **d)** 80 mph

89. $\sqrt{2} \neq 1.414$ since $\sqrt{2}$ is irrational and 1.414 is rational.

91. No. π is irrational; therefore, it cannot equal $\dfrac{22}{7}$ or 3.14, both of which are rational.

93. $\sqrt{4 \cdot 9} = \sqrt{4} \cdot \sqrt{9}, \sqrt{36} = 2 \cdot 3, 6 = 6$

95. a) Rational. $\sqrt{0.04} = 0.2$, which is a rational number.

b) Irrational $\sqrt{0.7} = 0.8366600265\ldots$. Since the decimal number is not a terminating or a repeating decimal number, this number is an irrational number

97. a) $(44 \div \sqrt{4}) \div \sqrt{4} = 11$ **b)** $(44 \div 4) + \sqrt{4} = 13$

c) $4 + 4 + 4 + \sqrt{4} = 14$

d) $\sqrt{4}(4 + 4) + \sqrt{4} = 18$ Other answers are possible.

SECTION 5.5, PAGE 256

Answer to *Recreational Mathematics* box on page 254

8× 4	2	4+ 3	1
10+ 3	4	4× 1	2
1 1	3	2	11+ 4
3+ 2	1	4	3

1. Real **3.** Closed **5.** Commutative **7.** Associative

9. Yes **11.** No **13.** No **15.** Yes **17.** Yes **19.** No

21. No **23.** No **25.** Yes **27.** No

29. Commutative property of addition. The only difference between the expressions on both sides of the equal sign is the order of 5 and x.

31. $(-3) + (-4) = (-4) + (-3) = -7$

33. No. $4 - 3 \neq 3 - 4$.

35. $[(-2) + (-3)] + (-4) = (-2) + [(-3) + (-4)] = -9$

37. No. $(16 \div 8) \div 2 \neq 16 \div (8 \div 2)$.

39. No. $(81 \div 9) \div 3 \neq 81 \div (9 \div 3)$.

41. Distributive property

43. Associative property of multiplication

45. Associative property of addition

47. Commutative property of multiplication

49. Distributive property

51. Commutative property of addition

53. $4z + 4$ **55.** $-\frac{3}{4}x + 9$ **57.** $3x + 4$

59. $2x - 1$ **61.** 2 **63.** $5\sqrt{2} + 5\sqrt{3}$

65. a) Distributive property

b) Associative property of addition

67. a) Distributive property

b) Associative property of addition

c) Commutative property of addition

d) Associative property of addition

69. a) Distributive property

   b) Commutative property of addition

   c) Associative property of addition

   d) Commutative property of addition

71. Yes   **73.** No   **75.** No   **77.** Yes   **79.** Yes

81. Answers will vary.

83. No. $0 \div a = 0$ (when $a \neq 0$), but $a \div 0$ is undefined.

84.

^{2} 2	$^{2-}$ 3	$^{2+}$ 1	$^{24\times}$ 4
$^{3-}$ 4	1	2	3
1	$^{7+}$ 4	3	2
$^{1-}$ 3	2	$^{5+}$ 4	1

85. a) No   **b)** No   **c)** Answers will vary.

SECTION 5.6, PAGE 266

1. Exponent.   **3.** x^5 **5.** x^3 **7.** $\dfrac{1}{x^5}$ **9.** 2.013×10^3

11. 0.0000573   **13. a)** 9   **b)** 8   **15. a)** 25   **b)** -25

17. a) -16 **b)** 16   **19. a)** -64 **b)** -64

21. a) $-\dfrac{1}{4}$ **b)** $\dfrac{1}{4}$ **23. a)** 100   **b)** 1

25. a) 243   **b)** -243 **27. a)** 25   **b)** 25

29. a) 1   **b)** -1 **31. a)** 1   **b)** 6   **33. a)** $\dfrac{1}{27}$ **b)** $\dfrac{1}{49}$

35. a) $-\dfrac{1}{81}$ **b)** $\dfrac{1}{81}$ **37. a)** 64   **b)** 64   **39. a)** 4   **b)** $\dfrac{1}{16}$

41. 4.15×10^5 **43.** 2.75×10^{-3} **45.** 5.6×10^{-1}

47. 1.9×10^4 **49.** 1.86×10^{-4} **51.** 4.23×10^{-6}

53. 42,000   **55.** 0.0132   **57.** 0.0000862   **59.** 0.312

61. 9,000,000   **63.** 620,000   **65.** 0.0153   **67.** 250

69. 0.0021   **71.** 20   **73.** 2.3×10^{11} **75.** 4.5×10^{-7}

77. 7.0×10^1 **79.** 2.0×10^{-7} **81.** 3.0×10^8

83. 3.6×10^{-3}; 1.7; 9.8×10^2; 1.03×10^4

85. 8.3×10^{-5}; 0.00079; 4.1×10^3; 40,000

87. a) $28,026.76   **b)** $14,234.95

89. 0.045   **91.** About 2050 people per square km

93. $46,429   **95.** 11.95 hours   **97.** 1.25×10^9 hours

99. 8.64×10^9 ft^3 **101.** 2.9×10^8 cells

103. a) $720,000,000   **b)** $300,000,000

   c) $120,000,000   **d)** $60,000,000

105. 1000   **107.** 333,333 times

109. a) About 5.87×10^{12} (5.87 trillion) mi

   b) About 500 sec or 8 min 20 sec

SECTION 5.7, PAGE 275

1. Sequence   **3.** Arithmetic   **5.** Geometric   **7.** 3, 5, 7, 9, 11

9. 25, 20, 15, 10, 5   **11.** 5, 3, 1, -1, -3 **13.** $\dfrac{3}{4}, 1, \dfrac{5}{4}, \dfrac{3}{2}, \dfrac{7}{4}$

15. 6   **17.** 30   **19.** $-\dfrac{91}{5}$ **21.** -8 **23.** $a_n = n$

25. $a_n = 2n$ **27.** $a_n = 4n - 2$ **29.** $a_n = \frac{3}{2}n - \frac{9}{2}$

31. $s_{50} = 1275$ **33.** $s_{50} = 2500$ **35.** $s_{15} = 375$

37. $s_{24} = 60$ **39.** 1, 3, 9, 27, 81   **41.** 5, 10, 20, 40, 80

43. $-3, 3, -3, 3, -3$ **45.** 81, $-27, 9, -3, 1$ **47.** 112

49. $\frac{3}{4}$ **51.** -3645 **53.** $-39,366$ **55.** $a_n = 5^n$

57. $a_n = (-1)(-1)^{n-1}$ **59.** $a_n = 2 \cdot \left(\dfrac{1}{2}\right)^{n-1}$

61. $a_n = 9 \cdot \left(\dfrac{1}{3}\right)^{n-1}$ **63.** 189   **65.** -4095

67. $-620,011$ **69.** $-10,923$ **71.** 5050   **73.** 10,100

75. a) 63 in.   **b)** 954 in.   **77. a)** $44,800   **b)** $319,200

79. $\approx 15,992$ students   **81.** $\approx \$70,088$ **83.** $486,000

85. 161.4375   **87.** 267   **89.** 191.3568 ft

90. a) $32, $31   **b)** $320, $310

   c) $1024, $1023   **d)** $10,240; $10,230

   e) It is risky because it is likely that you won't have enough money to continue doubling your previous bet if you lose several times in a row. (Also, there may be a maximum amount you can bet in a game of chance.)

SECTION 5.8, PAGE 282

1. Fibonacci   **3.** Ratio   **5.** Divine

7. a) 1.618   **b)** 0.618   **c)** 1   **9.** Answers will vary.

11. Answers will vary.   **13.** Answers will vary.

15. Answers will vary.   **17.** No   **19.** Yes; 45, 73

21. Yes; 3, 5   **23.** Yes; 105, 170

25. a) Answers will vary.   **b)** Answers will vary.

27. The sums of the numbers along the diagonals (parallel to the one shown) are Fibonacci numbers.

29. The first and second terms are 1. Each term thereafter is the sum of the previous two terms.

31. a) Answers will vary.   **b)** Answers will vary.

33. $\frac{1}{1} = 1, \frac{2}{1} = 2, \frac{3}{2} = 1.5, \frac{5}{3} \approx 1.667, \frac{8}{5} = 1.6, \frac{13}{8} = 1.625,$ $\frac{21}{13} \approx 1.615, \frac{34}{21} \approx 1.619, \frac{55}{34} \approx 1.6176, \frac{89}{55} \approx 1.6182.$ The consecutive ratios alternate, increasing and decreasing about the golden ratio.

35. a) $-10, 4, -6, -2, -8, -10, -18, -28, -46, -74$

   b) $-10, 5, -5, 0, -5, -5, -10, -15, -25, -40$

   c) $-10, 6, -4, 2, -2, 0, -2, -2, -4, -6$

   d) $-10, 7, -3, 4, 1, 5, 6, 11, 17, 28$

   e) $-10, 8, -2, 6, 4, 10, 14, 24, 38, 62$

   f) Answers will vary.

37. Answers will vary.

39. a) Answers will vary.   **b)** Answers will vary.

   c) Answers will vary.

REVIEW EXERCISES, PAGE 286

1. 2, 3, 4, 5, 6, 10   **2.** 2, 3, 4, 6, 9   **3.** $2^2 \cdot 3 \cdot 7^2$

4. $2^3 \cdot 3 \cdot 5 \cdot 7$ **5.** $2^2 \cdot 3 \cdot 11^2$ **6.** 15; 210

7. 9; 756   **8.** 5; 2250   **9.** 30; 900   **10.** 45 days   **11.** -3

12. 3   **13.** -6 **14.** -4 **15.** -9 **16.** 3   **17.** -24

18. 24   **19.** 5   **20.** -2 **21.** 6   **22.** 0.85   **23.** 3.25
24. $0.\overline{857142}$ **25.** $0.58\overline{3}$ **26.** 0.375   **27.** 0.6875
28. $\frac{14}{10} = \frac{7}{5}$ **29.** $\frac{2}{3}$ **30.** $\frac{51}{99}$ **31.** $\frac{83}{1000}$ **32.** $\frac{19}{7}$
33. $-\frac{13}{4}$ **34.** $2\frac{1}{5}$ **35.** $-27\frac{1}{5}$ **36.** $\frac{1}{4}$ **37.** $\frac{17}{12}$ **38.** $\frac{1}{4}$
39. $\frac{35}{54}$ **40.** $\frac{53}{28}$ **41.** $\frac{1}{6}$ **42.** $2\frac{7}{32}$ tsp   **43.** $5\sqrt{3}$
44. $-3\sqrt{2}$ **45.** $8\sqrt{2}$ **46.** $-20\sqrt{3}$ **47.** $5\sqrt{7}$
48. $3\sqrt{2}$ **49.** $4\sqrt{3}$ **50.** 10   **51.** $\frac{4\sqrt{3}}{3}$ **52.** $\frac{\sqrt{35}}{5}$
53. $6 + 3\sqrt{7}$ **54.** $4\sqrt{3} + 3\sqrt{2}$
55. Commutative property of addition
56. Commutative property of multiplication
57. Associative property of addition   **58.** Distributive property
59. Associative property of multiplication
60. Commutative property of multiplication
61. Distributive property   **62.** No   **63.** Yes   **64.** No
65. Yes   **66.** No   **67.** 125   **68.** $\frac{1}{25}$ **69.** 81   **70.** 125
71. 1   **72.** 81   **73.** 8.2×10^9 **74.** 1.58×10^{-5}
75. 280,000   **76.** 0.000139   **77.** 6.0×10^{-5}
78. 3.0×10^0 **79.** 1,100,000,000,000   **80.** 120   **81.** 5
82. ≈ 388 times   **83.** $\approx$ \$5555.56   **84.** Arithmetic; 17, 21
85. Geometric; 8, 16   **86.** 10   **87.** 25   **88.** 48   **89.** -48
90. 3825   **91.** 57.5   **92.** 45   **93.** -21
94. Arithmetic; $a_n = 3n$ **95.** Arithmetic; $a_n = 3n - 2$
96. Geometric; $a_n = 2(-1)^{n-1}$
97. Geometric; $a_n = 5\left(\frac{1}{3}\right)^{n-1}$
98. No   **99.** Yes; $-8, -13$

CHAPTER TEST, PAGE 289

1. 5   **2.** $2 \cdot 3^2 \cdot 23$ **3.** 8   **4.** -175 **5.** $\frac{37}{8}$
6. 0.625   **7.** $\frac{129}{20}$ **8.** $\frac{1}{8}$ **9.** $9\sqrt{3}$ **10.** $\frac{\sqrt{14}}{7}$
11. Yes; the product of any two integers is an integer.
12. Associative property of addition
13. 64   **14.** 1024   **15.** $\frac{1}{81}$ **16.** 8.0×10^{11}
17. $a_n = -4n + 2$ **18.** -187 **19.** $a_n = 3(2)^{n-1}$
20. 1, 1, 2, 3, 5, 8, 13, 21, 34, 55

Chapter 6

SECTION 6.1, PAGE 295

1. Variable   **3.** Expression   **5.** 3   **7.** Evaluate   **9.** 36
11. -16 **13.** 686   **15.** -3 **17.** 13   **19.** 6
21. $-\frac{10}{9}$ **23.** 7   **25.** 16   **27.** 39   **29.** Yes   **31.** No

33. No   **35.** Yes   **37.** Yes   **39.** \$66
41. 115.4 million taxpayers
43. 88.72 min   **45.** 1.71 in.
47. The two expressions are not equal.
49. a) Answers will vary.   **b)** Answers will vary.

SECTION 6.2, PAGE 306

1. Terms   **3.** Coefficient   **5.** Simplify   **7.** Ratio
9. Identity   **11.** Isolate   **13.** $8x$ **15.** $-11x + 12$
17. $3x + 11y$ **19.** $-8x + 2$ **21.** $-5x + 3$
23. $13.3x - 8.3$ **25.** $\frac{5}{6}x - 5$ **27.** $13x - 12y + 2$
29. $8s - 17$ **31.** $1.4x - 2.8$ **33.** $\frac{3}{10}x + \frac{3}{5}$
35. $-\frac{5}{12}x + \frac{4}{5}$ **37.** 17   **39.** -6 **41.** $\frac{24}{7}$
43. $\frac{2}{3}$ **45.** 4   **47.** 3   **49.** $\frac{4}{27}$
51. 17   **53.** No solution   **55.** All real numbers
57. 3   **59.** -3 **61.** 13   **63.** \$71.28   **65.** 8 gallons
67. a) 24 oz   **b)** 12 servings
69. a) 1.6 kph   **b)** 56.25 mph
71. 0.375 cc   **73. a)** Answers will vary.   **b)** -1
75. a) $2:5$ **b)** $m:(m + n)$

SECTION 6.3, PAGE 312

1. Formula   **3.** 48   **5.** 56   **7.** 10   **9.** 251.2   **11.** 37.1
13. 2   **15.** 3000   **17.** 12   **19.** 25   **21.** 6   **23.** 200
25. 7.2   **27.** 14   **29.** 3240   **31.** 66.67   **33.** 18.75
35. $y = \frac{5x - 14}{4}$ or $y = \frac{5}{4}x - \frac{7}{2}$
37. $y = \frac{-8x + 21}{7}$ or $y = -\frac{8}{7}x + 3$
39. $y = \frac{2x + 6}{3}$ or $y = \frac{2}{3}x + 2$
41. $y = \frac{2x - z + 15}{3}$ or $y = \frac{2}{3}x - \frac{1}{3}z + 5$
43. $y = \frac{9x + 4z - 7}{8}$ or $y = \frac{9}{8}x + \frac{1}{2}z - \frac{7}{8}$
45. $w = \frac{A}{l}$ **47.** $a = p - b - c$ **49.** $B = \frac{3V}{h}$
51. $r = \frac{C}{2\pi}$ **53.** $b = y - mx$ **55.** $w = \frac{P - 2l}{2}$
57. $d = \frac{4L - c}{2}$ **59.** $m = \frac{c^2 r}{2g}$ **61.** $C = \frac{5}{9}(F - 32)$
63. $s = \frac{S - \pi r^2}{\pi r}$ **65.** 9 hr   **67.** 8%
69. a) ≈ 27.12 **b)** lose ≈ 8.27 1b

SECTION 6.4, PAGE 317

1. 5 more than x **3.** 2 times x, decreased by 3
5. $x - 5$ **7.** $4 + 3z$ **9.** $8w + 9$ **11.** $4x + 6$

13. $\frac{12-s}{4}$ **15.** $3(x+7)$ **17.** $x+7=15;\ 8$

19. $x-4=20;\ 24$ **21.** $4x-10=42;\ 13$

23. $4x+12=32;\ 5$ **25.** $x+6=2x-3;\ 9$

27. $x+10=2(x+3);\ 4$

29. $150+0.50x=255;\ 210$ miles

31. $x+0.05x=42;$ \$40 per half hour

33. $0.08x=250;\ 3125$ copies

35. $x+3x=1000;$ \$250 for business, \$750 for liberal arts

37. **a)** $x+(x+3x)=45{,}000;\ 9000\ \text{ft}^2,\ 9000\ \text{ft}^2,\ 27{,}000\ \text{ft}^2$
  b) Yes

39. $x+(4x+10)=85;\ 15$ species of threatened mammals, 70 species of endangered mammals

41. $x+(5x+7)=127;\ 20$ total hurricanes in November, 170 total hurricanes in September

43. $3w+2(2w)=140;$ width: 20 ft, length: 40 ft

45. $70x=760;\ \approx 11$ months

47. $\frac{r}{2}+0.07r=257;$ \$450.88

49. Deduct \$720 from Mr. McAdams's income and \$2920 from Mrs. McAdams's income.

51. $x+(x+1)+(x+2)=3(x+2)-3$
  $3x+3=3x+6-3$
  $3x+3=3x+3$

53. $-40°$

SECTION 6.5, PAGE 326

1. Inverse   **3.** Joint   **5.** Direct   **7.** Inverse
9. Direct   **11.** Inverse   **13.** Inverse   **15.** Inverse
17. Direct   **19.** Direct   **21.** Answers will vary.

23. a) $y=kx$ **b)** 140 **25. a)** $m=\frac{k}{n^2}$ **b)** 0.25

27. a) $A=\frac{kB}{C}$ **b)** 2.5 **29. a)** $F=kDE$ **b)** 210

31. a) $t=\frac{kd^2}{f}$ **b)** 200 **33. a)** $Z=kWY$ **b)** 100

35. a) $H=kL$ **b)** 3 **37. a)** $A=kB^2$ **b)** 720

39. a) $F=\frac{kq_1q_2}{d^2}$ **b)** 1200

41. a) $p=kn$ **b)** \$1125

43. a) $t=\frac{k}{T}$ **b)** 1.875 minutes

45. a) $l=\frac{k}{d^2}$ **b)** 80 dB

47. a) $R=\frac{kL}{A}$ **b)** 25 ohms

49. a) $W=kI^2R$ **b)** 9 watts

51. a) Directly **b)** 0.5

53. a) y will double. **b)** y will be half as large. **55.** $\frac{1}{9}$

SECTION 6.6, PAGE 333

1. Inequality   **3.** Compound   **5.** All   **7.** Open

9.

11.

13.

15.

17.

19.

21. No solution

23.

25.

27.

29.

31.

33.

35.

37.

39.

41.

43.

45.

47. a) 2005, 2006, 2007, 2010 **b)** 2004, 2008, 2009 **c)** 2010 **d)** 2004

49. 19 DVDs   **51.** 350 hours   **53.** 6 hours

55. $0.5 < t < 1.5$

57. $94 \le x \le 100$, assuming 100 is the highest grade possible

59. $6.875 \le x \le 11$

61. The student's answer is $x \le -12$, whereas the correct answer is $x \ge -12$. Yes, -12 is in both solution sets.

SECTION 6.7, PAGE 345

1. Graph   **3.** x

5. Plotting points, using intercepts, and using the slope and the y-intercept

7. m

For Exercises 9–15, see the following figure.

For Exercises 17–23, see the following figure.

25. $(0, 2)$ **27.** $(-2, 0)$ **29.** $(-5, -3)$

31. $(2, -3)$ **33.** $(2, 2)$ **35.** $(5, 2), (1, 3)$

37. $(8, 7), (\frac{10}{3}, 0)$ **39.** $(4, 3)$ **41.** $(8, 0), (0, 3)$

43.

45.

Slope: undefined   Slope is 0.

47.

49.

51.

53.

55.

57.

59.

61.

63.

65.

67. 2   **69.** $-\frac{5}{4}$ **71.** 0   **73.** Undefined   **75.** $-\frac{8}{11}$

77.

79.

81.

83.

85.

87. $y = -\dfrac{3}{4}x + 3$

89. $y = 3x + 2$

91. a) $D(4, 2)$ **b)** $A = 10$ square units

93. $(7, 2)$ or $(-1, 2)$ **95.** -3 **97.** 3

99. a)

b) \$130   **c)** 100 square feet

101. a)

b) \$40   **c)** \$60

103. a) 2   **b)** $y = 2x + 9$ **c)** 15 defects   **d)** 4 workers

105. a) 1.66   **b)** $y = 1.66x + 73.19$

   c) 76.51%   **d)** 4 years after 2004 or in 2008

107. a) Solve the equations for y to put them in slope-intercept form. Then compare the slopes and y-intercepts. If the slopes are equal but the y-intercepts are different, then the lines are parallel.

   b) The lines are parallel.

SECTION 6.8, PAGE 351

1. Half-plane

3. a) No   **b)** Yes   **c)** Yes   **d)** No

5.

7.

9.

11.

13.

15.

17.

19.

21.

23.

25.

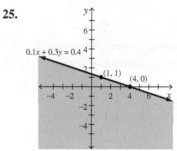

27. a) $x + y \leq 25$

   b)

29. a) No, you cannot have a negative number of shirts.

   b)

   c) Answers will vary.

SECTION 6.9, PAGE 360

1. Binomial   **3.** FOIL   **5.** Quadratic

7. $(x + 4)(x + 3)$ **9.** $(x + 2)(x - 1)$

11. $(x + 6)(x - 4)$ **13.** $(x + 1)(x - 3)$
15. $(x - 6)(x - 3)$ **17.** $(x - 4)(x + 4)$
19. $(x + 7)(x - 4)$ **21.** $(x + 9)(x - 7)$
23. $(2x + 1)(x - 3)$ **25.** $(5x + 1)(x + 3)$
27. $(5x + 2)(x + 2)$ **29.** $(4x + 3)(x + 2)$
31. $(4x - 3)(x - 2)$ **33.** $(4x - 3)(2x + 1)$
35. $7, -2$ **37.** $-\frac{4}{3}, \frac{1}{2}$ **39.** $-7, -3$ **41.** $8, 1$
43. $5, -3$ **45.** $3, 1$ **47.** $9, -9$ **49.** $-9, 4$
51. $\frac{2}{3}, -4$ **53.** $-\frac{1}{5}, -2$ **51.** $\frac{1}{3}, 1$ **57.** $\frac{1}{6}, 3$
59. $-4, 2$ **61.** $6, -3$ **63.** $9, -1$
65. No real solution   **67.** $2 \pm \sqrt{2}$ **69.** $\frac{4 \pm \sqrt{13}}{3}$
71. $\frac{3 \pm 2\sqrt{6}}{3}$ **73.** $-1, -\frac{5}{2}$ **75.** $\frac{9 \pm \sqrt{21}}{6}$
77. No real solution   **79.** Width $= 12$ m, length $= 22$ m
81. a) The zero-factor property cannot be used.   **b)** $\frac{11 \pm \sqrt{33}}{2}$
83. $x^2 - 2x - 3 = 0$, Other answers are possible

SECTION 6.10, PAGE 373

1. Relation   **3.** Domain   **5.** Upward   **7.** $x = -\frac{b}{2a}$
9. Not a function   **11.** Function, domain: $\mathbb{R}$; range: $\mathbb{R}$
13. Not a function   **15.** Function, domain: $\mathbb{R}$; range: $y \geq -4$
17. Not a function
19. Function, domain: $0 \leq x < 12$; range: $y = 1, 2, 3$
21. Not a function   **23.** Function, domain: $\mathbb{R}$; range: $y > 0$
25. Not a function   **27.** Yes   **29.** No   **31.** Yes   **33.** 9
35. 1   **37.** -6 **39.** 5   **41.** -23 **43.** 45   **45.** -17

47.

49.

51.

53. a) Upward   **b)** $x = 0$ **c)** $(0, -1)$ **d)** $(0, -1)$
e) $(1, 0), (-1, 0)$ **f)**

g) Domain: $\mathbb{R}$; range: $y \geq -1$

55. a) Downward   **b)** $x = 0$ **c)** $(0, 4)$ **d)** $(0, 4)$
e) $(-2, 0), (2, 0)$
f)

g) Domain: $\mathbb{R}$; range: $y \leq 4$

57. a) Downward   **b)** $x = 0$ **c)** $(0, -8)$ **d)** $(0, -8)$
e) No x-intercepts
f)

g) Domain: $\mathbb{R}$; range: $y \leq -8$

59. a) Upward   **b)** $x = 0$ **c)** $(0, -3)$ **d)** $(0, -3)$
e) $(-1.22, 0), (1.22, 0)$
f)
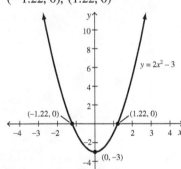

g) Domain: $\mathbb{R}$; range: $y \geq -3$

61. a) Upward   **b)** $x = -2$
c) $(-2, -8)$ **d)** $(0, -4)$
e) $(-4.83, 0), (0.83, 0)$
f)
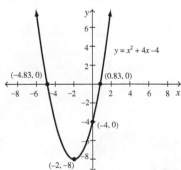

g) Domain: $\mathbb{R}$; range: $y \geq -8$

63. a) Upward   **b)** $x = -\frac{5}{2}$
c) $(-2.5, -0.25)$ **d)** $(0, 6)$ **e)** $(-3, 0), (-2, 0)$

f)

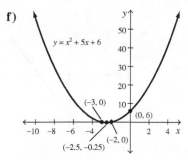

$y = x^2 + 5x + 6$

(−3, 0) (0, 6) (−2, 0) (−2.5, −0.25)

g) Domain: $\mathbb{R}$; range: $y \geq -0.25$

65. a) Downward   **b)** $x = 2$ **c)** $(2, -2)$ **d)** $(0, -6)$
e) No x-intercepts
f)

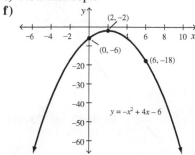

(2, −2) (0, −6) (6, −18) $y = -x^2 + 4x - 6$

g) Domain: $\mathbb{R}$; range: $y \leq -2$

67. a) Downward   **b)** $x = \frac{3}{4}$ **c)** $\left(\frac{3}{4}, -\frac{7}{8}\right)$ **d)** $(0, -2)$
e) No x-intercepts
f)

$\left(\frac{3}{4}, -\frac{7}{8}\right)$ (0, −2) (2, −4) (−1, −7) $y = -2x^2 + 3x - 2$

g) Domain: $\mathbb{R}$; range: $y \leq -\frac{7}{8}$

69. Domain: $\mathbb{R}$; range: $y > 0$

(2, 9) $y = 3^x$ (1, 3) $\left(-1, \frac{1}{3}\right)$ (0, 1)

71. Domain: $\mathbb{R}$; range: $y > 0$

(−2, 9) $y = \left(\frac{1}{3}\right)^x$ (−1, 3) $\left(1, \frac{1}{3}\right)$ (0, 1)

73. Domain: $\mathbb{R}$; range: $y > 1$

$y = 2^x + 1$ (2, 5) $\left(-1, \frac{3}{2}\right)$ (1, 3) (0, 2)

75. Domain: $\mathbb{R}$; range: $y > 1$

$y = 4^x + 1$ (1, 5) (0, 2)

77. Domain: $\mathbb{R}$; range: $y > 0$

(3, 9) $y = 3^{x-1}$ $\left(0, \frac{1}{3}\right)$ (2, 3) (1, 1)

79. Domain: $\mathbb{R}$; range: $y > 0$

$y = 4^{x+1}$ (0, 4) (−1, 1)

81. \$55,000   **83. a)** $\approx 13\%$ **b)** 1970   **c)** $x \approx 36$; $\approx 5\%$
85. 486,000 bacteria   **87. a)** 5200 people   **b)** $\approx 14,852$ people
89. 1.38 billion people   **91.** ≈ 6.52 grams
93. a) Yes   **b)** $\approx 270,000$ thousand subscribers
95. a) 23.2 cm   **b)** 55.2 cm   **c)** 69.5 cm
97. a) 170 beats per minute   **b)** ≈ 162 beats per minute
   c) ≈ 145 beats per minute   **d)** 136 beats per minute
   e) 120 years of age

REVIEW EXERCISES, PAGE 380

1. 21   **2.** −12   **3.** 17   **4.** −13   **5.** $5x + 7$ **6.** $12x - 6$

7. −14   **8.** −3   **9.** −13   **10.** −31   **11.** $\frac{1}{2}$ cup

12. 250 min, or 4 hr 10 min   **13.** 200   **14.** 84   **15.** 101.5

16. 25   **17.** $y = 2x - 8$

18. $y = \dfrac{-2x + 17}{9}$ or $y = -\dfrac{2}{9}x + \dfrac{17}{9}$

19. $w = \dfrac{A}{l}$ **20.** $w = \dfrac{P - 2l}{2}$

21. $l = \dfrac{L - 2wh}{2h}$ or $l = \dfrac{L}{2h} - w$ **22.** $d = \dfrac{a_n - a_1}{n - 1}$

23. $7 - 2x$ **24.** $3y + 4$ **25.** $10 + 3r$ **26.** $\dfrac{9}{q} - 15$

27. $2 + 8x = 18; x = 2$ **28.** $3x + 8 = x - 6; x = -7$

29. $5(x - 4) = 45; x = 13$

30. $10x + 14 = 8(x + 12); x = 41$

31. $x + 2x = 15,000$; bonds: \$5000, mutual funds: \$10,000

32. $9.50x + 15,000 = 95,000; \approx 8421$ chairs

33. $x + (5x + 4049) = 219,059$; Crater Lake National Park: 183,224 acres, Bryce Canyon National Park: 35,835 acres

34. $x + (x + 12,000) = 68,000$; \$28,000 for B and \$40,000 for A

35. 24   **36.** 4   **37.** 20   **38.** ≈ 426.7

39. a) 150 lb   **b)** 5 bags

40. \$3150   **41.** \$119.88   **42.** 1.75 in.

43.

44.

45.

46.

47.

48.

49.

50.

51.–54.

55. $D(-3,-1)$; area = 20 square units

56. $D(4,1)$; area = 21 square units

57.   **58.**

59.   **60.**

61. $\dfrac{4}{3}$ **62.** $-\dfrac{3}{2}$ **63.** $\dfrac{7}{3}$ **64.** Undefined

65.   **66.**

67. $y = 2x + 4$ **68.** $y = -x + 1$

69. a)   **b)** \$600   **c)** 70 cars

70. a)

b) \$110   **c)** 120 miles

71.   **72.**

73.   **74.**

75. $(x + 5)(x + 4)$ **76.** $(x + 4)(x - 3)$

77. $(x - 6)(x - 4)$ **78.** $(3x - 1)(2x + 3)$ **79.** $-1, -5$

80. $-5, 2$ **81.** $\frac{2}{3}, 5$ **82.** $-2, -\frac{1}{3}$ **83.** $-2, 8$ **84.** $-1, \frac{3}{2}$

85. No real solution   **86.** $\frac{3 \pm \sqrt{17}}{2}$

87. Function, domain: $x = -2, -1, 2, 3$; range: $y = -1, 0, 2$

88. Not a function   **89.** Not a function

90. Function domain: $\mathbb{R}$; range: $\mathbb{R}$ **91.** 18

92. 16   **93.** 39   **94.** -21

95. a) Downward   **b)** $x = -2$ **c)** $(-2, 25)$

    d) $(0, 21)$ **e)** $(-7, 0), (3, 0)$

    f)

    g) Domain: $\mathbb{R}$; range: $y \leq 25$

96. a) Upward   **b)** $x = -2$ **c)** $(-2, -2)$

    d) $(0, 6)$ **e)** $(-3, 0), (-1, 0)$

    f)

    g) Domain: $\mathbb{R}$; range: $y \geq -2$

97. Domain: $\mathbb{R}$; range: $y > 0$

98. Domain: $\mathbb{R}$; range: $y > 0$

99. 22.8 mpg   **100.** $\approx 68.7\%$

CHAPTER TEST, PAGE 383

1. -1 **2.** 10   **3.** 18   **4.** $3x + 5 = 17$; 4

5. $350 + 0.06x = 710$; $6000   **6.** 77

7. $y = \dfrac{-3x + 11}{5}$ or $y = -\dfrac{3}{5}x + \dfrac{11}{5}$ **8.** $3\frac{1}{3}$ **9.** 6.75 ft

10.   **11.** 2

12.   **13.**

14.

15. $(x + 9)(x + 2)$ **16.** $-1, -6$ **17.** $\frac{4}{3}, -2$

18. It is a function.   **19.** 15   **20. a)** Upward

    b) $x = 1$ **c)** $(1, 3)$ **d)** $(0, 4)$ **e)** No x-intercepts

    f)

    g) Domain: $\mathbb{R}$; range: $y \geq 3$

Chapter 7

SECTION 7.1, PAGE 393

1. System   **3.** Inconsistent   **5.** Dependent

7. One   **9.** Greater   **11.** $(2, 6)$

13.   **15.**

17.

19.

21.

23.

25.

27.

29.

31.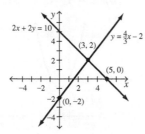

33. a) One unique solution; the lines intersect at one and only one point.
 b) No solution; the lines do not intersect.
 c) Infinitely many solutions; the lines coincide.

35. An infinite number of solutions

37. One solution   **39.** No solution

41. An infinite number of solutions   **43.** No solution

45. One solution   **47.** Not perpendicular   **49.** Perpendicular

51. a) Cost for U-Haul: $C = 0.79x + 30$
 Cost for Discount Rentals: $C = 0.85x + 24$
 b)   **c)** 100 miles

53. a) $C = 15x + 400$
 $R = 25x$
 b)   **c)** 40 backpacks

 d) $P = 10x - 400$ **e)** Loss of $100   **f)** 140 backpacks

55. a) $C = 115x + 3850, R = 150x$
 b)   **c)** 110 units

 d) $P = 35x - 3850$ **e)** Loss of $350   **f)** 135 units

57. a) Job 1: $s = 0.15x + 500$
 Job 2: $s = 650$
 b)   **c)** $1000

59. a) One   **b)** Three   **c)** Six   **d)** Ten
 e) To determine the number of points of intersection for n lines, add $n - 1$ to the number of points of intersection for $n - 1$ lines. For example, for 5 lines there were 10 points of intersection. Therefore, for 6 lines ($n = 6$) there are $10 + (6 - 1) = 15$ points of intersection.

60.

SECTION 7.2, PAGE 403

1. Infinite   **3.** $(1, 6)$ **5.** $(1, -1)$

7. No solution; inconsistent system   **9.** $\left(-2, \frac{8}{3}\right)$

11. An infinite number of solutions; dependent system

13. $(-3, -6)$ **15.** $(\frac{11}{5}, -\frac{13}{5})$ **17.** $(-\frac{1}{5}, -\frac{8}{5})$

19. No solution; inconsistent system

21. $(3, 1)$ **23.** $(7, 5)$ **25.** $(-2, 0)$ **27.** $(1, 2)$ **29.** $(3, 5)$

31. $(1, -2)$ **33.** No solution; inconsistent system

35. $(1, -\frac{1}{2})$

37. $s = 0.15p + 12{,}000$
$s = 0.05p + 27{,}000$
\$150,000 annual profit

39. $l + n = 55$
$34.08l + 41.90n = 2109$
25 shares of LG Electronics, 30 shares of Nintendo Company

41. $x + y = 15$
$0.40x + 0.10y = 0.25(15)$
$7.5l$ of 40%, $7.5l$ of 10%

43. $y = 0.02x + 18$
$y = 0.015x + 24$
1200 copies

45. $x + y = 20$
$3x + y = 30$
Mix 5 lb of nuts with 15 lb of pretzels.

47. $x + y = 4600$
$27x + 14y = 104{,}700$
3100 amphitheater tickets and 1500 lawn tickets

49. 3.5 years after 2007 or in 2010 **51.** $(\frac{1}{2}, \frac{1}{3})$

53. Answers will vary. **55.** Answers will vary.

57. Answers will vary.

SECTION 7.3, PAGE 412

1. Matrix **3.** 2 **5.** Dimensions **7.** Columns, rows

9. $\begin{bmatrix} 1 & 0 \\ 0 & 1 \end{bmatrix}$ **11.** $\begin{bmatrix} 5 & 3 \\ 7 & 5 \end{bmatrix}$ **13.** $\begin{bmatrix} 2 & 5 \\ -5 & 4 \\ 8 & 6 \end{bmatrix}$

15. $\begin{bmatrix} 10 & 1 \\ -5 & -3 \end{bmatrix}$ **17.** $\begin{bmatrix} 1 & 9 \\ 18 & 17 \\ -2 & 2 \end{bmatrix}$ **19.** $\begin{bmatrix} 6 & 4 \\ 10 & 0 \end{bmatrix}$

21. $\begin{bmatrix} 0 & 13 \\ 22 & 0 \end{bmatrix}$ **23.** $\begin{bmatrix} 13 & 0 \\ 7 & 0 \end{bmatrix}$ **25.** $\begin{bmatrix} 52 & 21 \\ 48 & 18 \end{bmatrix}$

27. $\begin{bmatrix} 15 \\ 22 \end{bmatrix}$ **29.** $\begin{bmatrix} 4 & 7 & 6 \\ -2 & 3 & 1 \\ 5 & 1 & 2 \end{bmatrix}$

31. $A + B = \begin{bmatrix} 8 & 1 & 3 \\ 4 & 3 & 0 \end{bmatrix}$; cannot be multiplied

33. Cannot be added; $A \times B = \begin{bmatrix} 24 & 34 \\ 24 & 34 \end{bmatrix}$

35. Cannot be added; $\begin{bmatrix} 1 \\ -1 \end{bmatrix}$

37. $A + B = B + A = \begin{bmatrix} 6 & 0 \\ 13 & 8 \end{bmatrix}$

39. $A + B = B + A = \begin{bmatrix} 8 & 0 \\ 6 & -8 \end{bmatrix}$

41. $(A + B) + C = A + (B + C) = \begin{bmatrix} 7 & 13 \\ 2 & 10 \end{bmatrix}$

43. $(A + B) + C = A + (B + C) = \begin{bmatrix} 5 & 5 \\ 7 & -37 \end{bmatrix}$

45. No **47.** No **49.** Yes

51. $(A \times B) \times C = A \times (B \times C) = \begin{bmatrix} 41 & 13 \\ 56 & 16 \end{bmatrix}$

53. $(A \times B) \times C = A \times (B \times C) = \begin{bmatrix} 16 & -10 \\ -24 & 2 \end{bmatrix}$

55. $(A \times B) \times C = A \times (B \times C) = \begin{bmatrix} 17 & 0 \\ -7 & 0 \end{bmatrix}$

57.

	Students	Adult	Senior citizen	
$\begin{bmatrix}$	158	280	95	$\end{bmatrix}$ Matinee
	215	362	94	Evening

59. Total cost
$\begin{bmatrix} 53 \\ 55 \end{bmatrix}$ Java's Coffee Shop
Spot Coffee Shop

61.

	Large	Small	
$\begin{bmatrix}$	38	50	$\end{bmatrix}$ Sugar
	56	72	Flour
	17	26	Milk
	10	14	Eggs

63. $[36.04 \quad 47.52]$ **65.** Answers will vary. **67.** Yes

69. False **71. a)** \$28.70 **b)** \$60.10 **c)** $\begin{bmatrix} 28.7 & 24.6 \\ 41.3 & 35.7 \\ 69.3 & 60.1 \end{bmatrix}$

73. Yes. Answer will vary. One example is
$$A = \begin{bmatrix} 2 & 7 & 6 \\ -3 & 0 & 8 \end{bmatrix}, \quad B = \begin{bmatrix} 1 & 2 \\ 3 & 4 \\ 5 & 6 \end{bmatrix}.$$

74. Answers will vary.

SECTION 7.4, PAGE 421

1. Augmented **3.** No **5.** $(3, 2)$ **7.** $(3, 2)$ **9.** $(2, 3)$

11. $(\frac{7}{2}, -1)$ **13.** $(1, 1)$ **15.** No solution; inconsistent system

17. $(3, 4)$ **19.** Xbox 360 systems: 6; Wii systems: 9

21. Truck driver: 8 hours; laborer: 10 hours

23. Basic systems: 150; premium systems: 50

SECTION 7.5, PAGE 425

1. Solution **3.** Solid

5.

7.

9. **11.**

$x - y < 4$
$x + y < 5$

$x + 2y \geq 4$
$3x - y \geq -6$

13. **15.**

$y \leq 3x$
$x \geq 3y$

$x \geq 1$
$y \leq 1$

17. 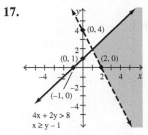 **19.**

$4x + 2y > 8$
$x \geq y - 1$

$3x \geq 2y + 6$
$x \leq y + 3$

21. a) $20x + 30y \leq 600, x \geq 2y, x \geq 10, y \geq 5$

b)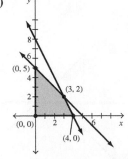
Small bowls

c) One example is 15 small bowls, 7 large bowls

23. $x \leq 0, y \geq 0$

25. Yes. One example is $x \geq 0, y \geq 0, x \leq 0, y \leq 0$ which has solution $(0, 0)$.

27. Answers will vary.

SECTION 7.6, PAGE 430

1. Constraints   **3.** Vertices   **5.** Objective

7. Maximum is 30 at $(5, 0)$, minimum is 0 at $(0, 0)$.

9. Maximum is 190 at $(50, 30)$, minimum is 70 at $(20, 10)$.

11. a)

b) Maximum is 18 at $(3, 2)$; minimum is 0 at $(0, 0)$.

13. a)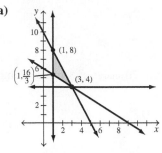

b) Maximum is 28 at $(4, 0)$; minimum is 0 at $(0, 0)$.

15. a)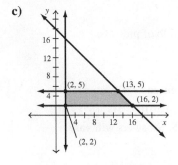

b) Maximum is 15.4 at $(1, 8)$; minimum is 11 at $\left(1, \frac{16}{3}\right)$.

17. a) $x + y \leq 18, y \leq 5, x \geq 2, y \geq 2$

b) $P = 20x + 25y$

c)

d) $(2, 5), (13, 5), (16, 2), (2, 2)$

e) 13 top load machines and 5 front load machines

f) $385

19. a) $3x + 4y \geq 60, 10x + 5y \geq 100, x \geq 0, y \geq 0$

b) $C = 28x + 33y$

c)

d) $(0, 20), (4, 12), (20, 0)$

e) 4 hours for Machine I and 12 hours for Machine II

f) $508

21. Three car seats and seven strollers, $320

1.

2.

3.

4.

5. An infinite number of solutions

6. No solution   **7.** One solution   **8.** One solution   **9.** (3, 1)

10. (−1, −5)   **11.** (−2, −8)   **12.** No solution; inconsistent

13. (−7, 16)   **14.** (4, −2)   **15.** (4, −2)

16. An infinite number of solutions; dependent   **17.** (2, −1)

18. (2, 0)   **19.** $\begin{bmatrix} 5 & -6 \\ 4 & 5 \end{bmatrix}$ **20.** $\begin{bmatrix} -3 & 0 \\ 0 & 3 \end{bmatrix}$

21. $\begin{bmatrix} 2 & -6 \\ 4 & 8 \end{bmatrix}$ **22.** $\begin{bmatrix} -10 & 3 \\ -2 & 5 \end{bmatrix}$ **23.** $\begin{bmatrix} -2 & -6 \\ 16 & -2 \end{bmatrix}$

24. $\begin{bmatrix} -2 & -24 \\ 4 & -2 \end{bmatrix}$ **25.** (2, 2)   **26.** (−2, 2)

27. (3, −3)   **28.** (1, 0)   **29.** $\left(\frac{12}{11}, \frac{7}{11}\right)$ **30.** (1, 2)

31. $250,000 at 3%, $150,000 at 6%

32. Mix $83\frac{1}{3}\ell$ of 80% acid solution with $16\frac{2}{3}\ell$ of 50% acid solution.

33. $245 per ton for topsoil, $183 per ton for mulch

34. a) 32.5 months   **b)** Model 6070B

35. a) 3 hr   **b)** All-Day parking lot

36.

37.

38.

39.

40. a)

b) Maximum is 21 at (3, 2); minimum is 0 at (0, 0).

1. If the lines do not intersect (are parallel), the system of equations is inconsistent. The system of equations is consistent if the lines intersect. If both equations represent the same line, the system of equations is dependent.

2.   **3.** One solution

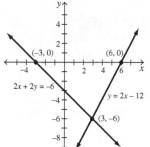

4. (2, −3)   **5.** (−2, −13)   **6.** No solution   **7.** (−2, −6)

8. (−1, 3)   **9.** (2, 0)   **10.** (−2, 2)   **11.** (2, 0)   **12.** (1, 1)

13. $\begin{bmatrix} 1 & -8 \\ 6 & 5 \end{bmatrix}$ **14.** $\begin{bmatrix} 4 & 1 \\ -9 & -1 \end{bmatrix}$

15. $\begin{bmatrix} 7 \\ -3 \end{bmatrix}$ **16.** $\begin{bmatrix} 26 & 2 \\ 48 & -6 \end{bmatrix}$

17.

18. Daily fee: $35; mileage charge: $0.18

19. a) 40 checks   **b)** Citrus Bank

20. a)

b) Maximum is 22.5 at (3.75, 0); minimum is 0 at (0, 0).

Chapter 8

SECTION 8.1, PAGE 442

1. Metric   **3. a)** Meter   **b)** Kilogram   **c)** Liter   **d)** Celsius
5. a) Deka   **b)** Deci   **7. a)** Kilo   **b)** Milli   **9.** 100
11. a) 0°C   **b)** 100°C   **c)** 37°C   **13. a)** Yard   **b)** Quart
15. 22   **17.** (d)   **19.** (c)   **21.** (f)
23. a) 0.001   **b)** 100   **c)** 1000   **d)** 0.01   **e)** 10   **f)** 0.1
25. mg; 0.001 g   **27.** dg; 0.1 g   **29.** hg; 100 g
31. 3 000 000 g   **33.** 7000   **35.** 0.0085   **37.** 0.018 62
39. 9200 mm   **41.** 895 000 mℓ **43.** 4.0302 daℓ **45.** 0.5 km
47. 5 hm   **49.** 80 000 000 mm/hr
51. 620 cm, 4.4 dam, 0.52 km   **53.** 1.4 kg, 1600 g, 16 300 dg
55. 105 000 mm, 2.6 km, 52.6 hm   **57.** Jim, 1 m > 1 yd
59. The pump that removes 1 daℓ per minute, 1 daℓ > 1dℓ
61. a) 346 cm   **b)** 3460 mm
63. a) $\approx 16.4\ \ell$ **b)** $\approx 12\ 210$ m/ℓ
65. a) 2160 mℓ **b)** 2.16 ℓ **c)** $1.13 per liter
67. a) 386 m   **b)** 0.386 km   **c)** 38 600 cm   **69.** 1000
71. $1 \times 10^{24} = 1\ 000\ 000\ 000\ 000\ 000\ 000\ 000\ 000$
73. 9 dam   **75.** 6 mg   **77.** 2 daℓ **79.** gram
80. decigram   **81.** liter   **82.** dekaliter
83. meter   **84.** milliliter   **85.** kilometer   **86.** centimeter
87. degrees celsius   **88.** hectogram

SECTION 8.2, PAGE 452

1. Volume   **3.** Area   **5.** Length   **7.** Volume   **9.** Volume
11. Volume   **13.** Centimeters   **15.** Centimeters or millimeters
17. Centimeters   **19.** Kilometers   **21.** Kilometers   **23.** (c)
25. (c)   **27.** (b)   **29.** (c)   **31.** Answers will vary.
33. Answers will vary.   **35.** Answers will vary.
37. Square meters   **39.** Square centimeters or square meters
41. Square centimeters or square millimeters
43. Square kilometers or hectares   **45.** (a)   **47.** (b)   **49.** (a)
51. (c)   **53.** Answers will vary.   **55.** Answers will vary.
57. Answers will vary.   **59.** Milliliters   **61.** Kiloliters
63. Cubic meters   **65.** Cubic meters   **67.** (c)   **69.** (c)
71. (c)   **73.** (b)   **75. a)** Answers will vary.   **b)** 10 580 cm^3
77. a) Answers will vary.   **b)** ≈ 0.20 m^3
79. A cubic decimeter   **81.** A cubic centimeter
83. Longer side $\approx$ 4 cm, shorter side $\approx$ 2.2 cm, area $\approx$ 8.8 cm^2
85. ≈ 706.86 m^2 **87. a)** 3869 m^2 **b)** 369 m^2
89. a) 1378 m^2 **b)** 0.1378 ha   **91.** $304
93. a) 56 000 cm^3 **b)** 56 000 mℓ **c)** 56 ℓ
95. 100 times larger   **97.** 1000 times larger
99. 100   **101.** 0.0001   **103.** 1 000 000   **105.** 419
107. 76   **109.** 60 kℓ **111.** 6700
113. a) 4,014,489,600 sq in.   **b)** Answers will vary.

114. a) Answers will vary. The average use is about 590 ℓ/day.
   b) Answers will vary. The average use is about 75 ℓ/day.

SECTION 8.3, PAGE 461

1. Kilogram   **3.** Mass   **5.** Celsius   **7.** 100   **9.** Kilograms
11. Grams   **13.** Grams   **15.** Kilograms
17. Kilograms or metric tonnes   **19.** (b)   **21.** (b)
23. (b)   **25.** Answers will vary.   **27.** Answers will vary.
29. (c)   **31.** (b)   **33.** (c)   **35.** (c)   **37.** (c)   **39.** 68°F
41. ≈ 33.3°C   **43.** ≈ -17.8°C   **45.** 98.6°F
47. ≈ -8.3°C   **49.** 32°F   **51.** ≈ -28.9°C
53. 71.6°F   **55.** 92.48°F   **57.** 64.04°F–74.30°F
59. a) 22.5 euros   **b)** $13.14   **c)** $\approx$ $5.97 per pound
61. 444 g   **63. a)** 2304 m^3 **b)** 2304 kℓ **c)** 2304 t
65. a) Yes; mass is a measure of the amount of matter in an object.   **b)** No; weight is a measure of gravitational force.
67. 0.0062   **69.** 17 400 000   **71. a)** 1200 g   **b)** 1200 cm^3
73. 1500 g   **74. a)** -79.8°F   **b)** 36.5°F   **c)** 134.1°F

SECTION 8.4, PAGE 471

1. Dimensional   **3.** $\dfrac{60\ \text{sec}}{1\ \text{min}}, \dfrac{1\ \text{min}}{60\ \text{sec}}$ **5.** $\dfrac{100\ \text{cm}}{1\ \text{m}}, \dfrac{1\ \text{m}}{100\ \text{cm}}$
7. a) $\dfrac{1\ \text{lb}}{0.45\ \text{kg}}$ **b)** $\dfrac{0.45\ \text{kg}}{1\ \text{lb}}$ **9. a)** $\dfrac{3.8\ \ell}{1\ \text{gal}}$ **b)** $\dfrac{1\ \text{gal}}{3.8\ \ell}$
11. 208.28 cm   **13.** 1.26 m   **15.** 360 lb   **17.** 62.4 km
19. 1687.5 acres   **21.** 43.19 pints   **23.** 1.46 mi^2 **25.** 54 kg
27. ≈ 561.11 yd   **29.** ≈ 1146.67 ft   **31.** 31.25 mph
33. 43.2 m^2 **35.** 50 mph   **37.** 0.21 oz   **39.** 36 678.4 ha
41. $0.495 per pound   **43.** ≈ 9078.95 gal   **45.** 6 qt
47. a) 0.55 km   **b)** ≈ 0.34 mi
49. a) 10.89 ft^2 **b)** 35.937 ft^3
51. 25.2 mg   **53.** 6840 mg, or 6.84 g
55. a) 25 mg   **b)** 900 mg
57. a) 0.75 mi   **b)** ≈ 2.63 mi^2 **c)** ≈ 1420 ft
59. a) ≈ 6.08 mi   **b)** ≈ 443.13 mph   **c)** ≈ 113.13 mph   **d)** -49°f
61. a) 70 € per kg   **b)** 31.5 € per pound   **c)** $44.10 per pound
63. a) $\dfrac{745\ \text{kph}}{402\ \text{knots}} \approx \dfrac{1.85\ \text{kph}}{1\ \text{knot}}$
   b) $\dfrac{402\ \text{knots}}{463\ \text{mph}} \approx \dfrac{0.87\ \text{knots}}{1\ \text{mph}}$ **c)** $\dfrac{463\ \text{mph}}{745\ \text{kph}} \approx \dfrac{0.62\ \text{mph}}{1\ \text{kph}}$
65. 1.0 cc, or b)   **67. a)** 3000 cc   **b)** ≈ 183.07 in.^{3}
68. 1 microscope   **69.** wonton   **70.** 1 pound cake
71. 1 kilohurtz   **72.** 2 megacycles   **73.** 1 megaphone
74. 1 dekacards   **75.** 2 kilomockingbird

REVIEW EXERCISES, PAGE 476

1. 1000 × base unit   **2.** $\dfrac{1}{100}$ of base unit
3. $\dfrac{1}{1000}$ of base unit   **4.** 100 × base unit

5. $10 \times$ base unit 6. $\frac{1}{10}$ of base unit 7. 0.082 g
8. 320 cℓ 9. 0.035 mm 10. 1 kg 11. 4620 ℓ
12. 19 260 dg 13. 3000 mℓ, 14 630 cℓ, 2.67 kℓ
14. 0.047 km, 47 000 cm, 4700 m
15. Meters 16. Degrees Celsius 17. Square meters
18. Milliliters or cubic centimeters 19. Millimeters
20. Kilograms or tonnes 21. Kilometers 22. Centimeters
23. a) Answers will vary. b) Answers will vary.
24. a) Answers will vary. b) Answers will vary.
25. (c) 26. (b) 27. (c) 28. (a) 29. (a) 30. (c)
31. 3.6 t 32. 4 300 000 g 33. 75.2°F 34. 20°C
35. ≈ -21.1°C 36. 102.2°F
37. $l = 4$ cm, $w = 1.6$ cm, $A = 6.4$ cm^2
38. $r = 1.5$ cm, $A \approx 7.07$ cm^2
39. a) ≈ 3.14 m^3 b) ≈ 3140 kg
40. a) 899.79 cm^2 b) 0.089 979 m^2
41. a) 96 000 cm^3 b) 0.096 m^3 c) 96 000 mℓ
    d) 0.096 kℓ
42. 10,000 times larger 43. ≈ 33.86
44. ≈ 233.33 45. 74.7 46. ≈ 111.11
47. 72 48. ≈ 44.21 49. 76 50. ≈ 78.95
51. ≈ 14.77 52. 3.8 53. 11.4
54. 99.2 55. 385.6 km 56. 429,322.37 yd^3
57. a) 1050 kg b) ≈ 2333.33 lb 58. 32.4 m^2
59. a) 190 kℓ b) 190 000 kg 60. a) 104 kph
    b) 104 000 meters per hour 61. a) 252 ℓ b) 252 kg
62. $1.58 per pound

CHAPTER TEST, PAGE 478

1. 0.759 daℓ 2. 2 730 000 cm 3. 100 times greater
4. 2.4 km 5. (b) 6. (a) 7. (c) 8. (b) 9. (b)
10. 10,000 times greater 11. 1,000,000 times greater
12. 6300 g 13. 564.3 ft 14. $\approx 20,508.1$ mi^2
15. ≈ -12.22°C 16. 68°F
17. a) 300 000 g b) ≈ 666.67 lb
18. a) 3200 m^3 b) 3 200 000 ℓ (or 3200 kℓ)
    c) 3 200 000 kg 19. $245
20. a) 6.27 euros per gallon b) $\approx$ $9.36 per gallon

Chapter 9

SECTION 9.1, PAGE 486

1. Parallel 3. Angle 5. Supplementary 7. Straight
9. Obtuse 11. Vertical 13. Ray, $\overrightarrow{AB}$
15. Half line, $\overset{\circ}{\overrightarrow{BA}}$ 17. Ray, $\overrightarrow{BA}$
19. Half open line segment, $\overset{\circ}{\overline{AB}}$
21. $\overline{AD}$ 23. $\overset{\circ}{\overline{BD}}$ 25. $\{B, F\}$ 27. $\{C\}$
29. $\angle CBF$ or $\angle FBC$ 31. $\overleftrightarrow{BC}$ 33. $\overleftrightarrow{DE}$ 35. $\overrightarrow{BC}$
37. $\angle ABE$ 39. $\overline{BF}$ 41. $\overset{\circ}{\overline{AC}}$ 43. $\overset{\circ}{\overline{BE}}$ 45. Right

47. Straight 49. Obtuse 51. None of these angles
53. 80° 55. $57\frac{1}{4}$° 57. 25.3° 59. 100° 61. 159.5°
63. $136\frac{2}{7}$° 65. (f) 67. (b) 69. (a)
71. $m\angle 1 = 75°$, $m\angle 2 = 15°$ 73. 134° and 46°
75. Angles 3, 4, and 7 each measure 125°; angles 1, 2, 5, and 6 each measure 55°.
77. Angles 1, 4, and 7 each measure 30°; angles 2, 3, 5, and 6 each measure 150°.
79. $m\angle 1 = 64°$, $m\angle 2 = 26°$
81. $m\angle 1 = 33°$, $m\angle 2 = 57°$
83. $m\angle 1 = 134°$, $m\angle 2 = 46°$
85. $m\angle 1 = 29°$, $m\angle 2 = 151°$
87. Plane ABG and plane JCD
89. $\overleftrightarrow{BG}$ and $\overleftrightarrow{DG}$
91. Plane $AGB \cap$ plane $ABC \cap$ plane $BCD = \{B\}$
93. $\overleftrightarrow{BC} \cap$ plane $ABG = \{B\}$
95. a) Undefined terms, definitions, postulates (axioms), and theorems
    b) First, Euclid introduced undefined terms. Second, he introduced certain definitions. Third, he stated primitive propositions called postulates about the undefined terms and definitions. Fourth, he proved, using deductive reasoning, other propositions called theorems.
97. a) An infinite number b) An infinite number
99. An infinite number
101. Always true. If any two lines are parallel to a third line, then they must be parallel to each other.
103. Sometimes true. Vertical angles are only complementary when each is equal to 45°.
105. Sometimes true. Alternate interior angles are only complementary when each is equal to 45°.
107. Answers will vary.
109. No. Line l and line n may be parallel or skew. 111. 360°

SECTION 9.2, PAGE 496

1. Polygon 3. Proportion 5. Congruent
7. a) Octagon b) Regular 9. a) Triangle b) Regular
11. a) Parallelogram b) Not regular
13. a) Heptagon b) Not regular
15. a) Isosceles b) Right 17. a) Isosceles b) Acute
19. a) Scalene b) Acute 21. a) Scalene b) Right
23. Trapezoid 25. Square 27. Rhombus
29. 96° 31. 150°
33. $m\angle 1 = 90°$, $m\angle 2 = 50°$, $m\angle 3 = 130°$, $m\angle 4 = 50°$, $m\angle 5 = 50°$, $m\angle 6 = 40°$, $m\angle 7 = 90°$, $m\angle 8 = 130°$, $m\angle 9 = 140°$, $m\angle 10 = 40°$, $m\angle 11 = 140°$, $m\angle 12 = 40°$
35. 540° 37. 1260° 39. 3240° 41. a) 60° b) 120°
43. a) 135° b) 45° 45. a) 144° b) 36°
47. $x = 2$, $y = 1.6$ 49. $x = 2\frac{2}{5}$, $y = 7\frac{1}{2}$
51. $x = 20$, $y = 21\frac{1}{4}$ 53. 3 55. $3\frac{1}{3}$ 57. 14 59. 15
61. 28° 63. 9 65. 10 67. 70° 69. 55° 71. 35°

73. 70 ft   **75. a)** ≈ 113.14 mi   **b)** ≈ 75.43 mi

77. The different types of triangles are acute, obtuse, right, isosceles, equilateral, and scalene. Descriptions will vary.

79. $D'E' = 4, E'F' = 5, D'F' = 3$

81. a) $m\angle HMF = m\angle TMB, m\angle HFM = m\angle TBM,$
$m\angle MHF = m\angle MTB$

   b) 44 ft

82. a) $m\angle CED = m\angle ABC, m\angle ACB = m\angle DCE,$
$m\angle BAC = m\angle CDE$

   b) ≈ 2141.49 ft

SECTION 9.3, PAGE 507

1. a) Perimeter   **b)** Area   **3.** Circle   **5.** $12\ cm^2$

7. $17.5\ cm^2$ **9. a)** $50\ ft^2$ **b)** 30 ft

11. a) $6000\ cm^2$ **b)** 654 cm

13. a) $288\ in^2$ **b)** 74 in.   **15. a)** $78.54\ m^2$ **b)** 31.42 m

17. a) $132.73\ ft^2$ **b)** 40.84 ft

19. a) 17 yd   **b)** 40 yd   **c)** $60\ yd^2$

21. a) 12 km   **b)** 30 km   **c)** $30\ km^2$

23. $7.73\ ft^2$ **25.** $8\ in^2$ **27.** $90\ yd^2$ **29.** $65.73\ in^2$

31. $56.55\ mm^2$ **33.** $8\ yd^2$ **35.** $132.3\ ft^2$ **37.** $50,000\ cm^2$

39. $0.8625\ m^2$ **41. a)** \$5494.50   **b)** \$6594.50

43. \$3056.60   **45.** \$3835.20   **47.** \$234.21

49. a) 288 ft   **b)** 4700 tiles   **51.** 21 ft   **53.** 312 ft

55. a) $A = s^2$ **b)** $A = 4s^2$ **c)** Four times larger

57. $24\ cm^2$ **59.** Answers will vary.

60. Answers will vary.

SECTION 9.4, PAGE 520

1. Volume   **3.** Platonic   **5.** Right   **7. a)** $64\ ft^3$ **b)** $112\ ft^2$

9. a) $8\ yd^3$ **b)** $24\ yd^2$ **11. a)** $150.80\ in^3$ **b)** $175.93\ in^2$

13. a) $131.95\ cm^3$ **b)** $163.22\ cm^2$

15. a) $381.70\ cm^3$ **b)** $254.47\ cm^2$ **17.** $750\ m^3$

19. $720\ cm^3$ **21.** $768\ ft^3$ **23.** $392\ ft^3$ **25.** $284.46\ cm^3$

27. $24\ ft^3$ **29.** $81\ ft^3$ **31.** $\approx 5.67\ yd^3$ **33.** $560,000\ cm^3$

35. $7.5\ m^3$ **37. a)** $225\ ft^3$ **b)** \$2475   **39.** $40,840\ mm^2$

41. ≈ 2.50 qt   **43. a)** $120,000\ cm^3$

   b) $120,000\ m\ell$ **c)** $120\ \ell$

45. $\approx 283.04\ in^3$ **47. a)** $\approx 323.98\ in^3$ **b)** $\approx 0.19\ ft^3$

49. $\approx 14.14\ in^3$ **51.** Ten edges   **53.** Six vertices

55. Seven faces

57. a) $\approx 5.11 \times 10^8\ km^2$ **b)** $\approx 3.79 \times 10^7\ km^2$

   c) ≈ 13 times larger   **d)** $\approx 1.09 \times 10^{12}\ km^3$

   e) $\approx 2.20 \times 10^{10}\ km^3$ **f)** ≈ 50 times larger

59. a) Answers will vary.   **b)** Answers will vary.

   c) Answers will vary.   **d)** Answers will vary.

   e) Answers will vary.

   f) If we double the length of each edge of a cube, the new volume will be eight times the original volume.

61. a) Answers will vary.

   b) $V_1 = a^3; V_2 = a^2b; V_3 = a^2b; V_4 = ab^2;$
$V_5 = a^2b; V_6 = ab^2; V_7 = b^3$

   c) ab^2

62. a) $330\ in^3$ **b)** $\approx 330.84\ in^3$

SECTION 9.5, PAGE 537

1. Rigid   **3.** Axis   **5.** Vector   **7.** Center   **9.** Glide

11. Reflective   **13.** Tessellation

This figure contains the answers for Exercises 15 and 16.

This figure contains the answers for Exercises 17 and 18.

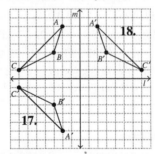

This figure contains the answers for Exercises 19 and 20.

This figure contains the answers for Exercises 21 and 22.

This figure contains the answers for Exercises 23 and 24.

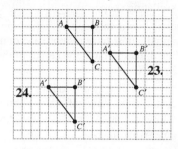

This figure contains the answers for Exercises 33 and 34.

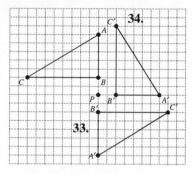

This figure contains the answers for Exercises 25 and 26.

This figure contains the answers for Exercises 35 and 36.

This figure contains the answers for Exercises 27 and 28.

This figure contains the answers for Exercises 37 and 38.

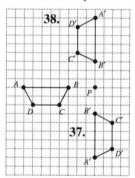

This figure contains the answers for Exercises 39 and 40.

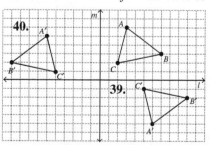

This figure contains the answers for Exercises 31 and 32.

This figure contains the answers for Exercises 41 and 42.

This figure contains the answers for Exercises 43 and 44.

This figure contains the answers for Exercises 45 and 46.

47. a) **b)** Yes **c)** Yes

49. a) **b)** No **c)** No

51. a) **b)** No **c)** No

d) **e)** Yes **f)** Yes

53. a)–c)

b) No. Any 90° rotation will result in the figure being in a different position than the starting position.

55. a)–b)

c) No

d) The order in which the translation and the reflection are performed is important. The figure obtained in part (a) is the glide reflection.

57. Answers will vary. **59.** A regular pentagon cannot be used as a tessellating shape.

60. Although answers will vary depending on the font, the following capital letters have reflective symmetry about a horizontal line drawn through the center of the letter: B, C, D, E, H, I, K, O, X.

61. Although answers will vary depending on the font, the following capital letters have reflective symmetry about a vertical line drawn through the center of the letter: A, H, I, M, O, T, U, V, W, X, Y.

62. Although answers will vary depending on the font, the following capital letters have 180° rotational symmetry about a point in the center of the letter: H, I, N, O, S, X, Z.

SECTION 9.6, PAGE 547

1. Rubber **3.** Klein **5.** Jordan **7.** One

9. Answers will vary. **11.** Answers will vary.

13. Answers will vary. **15.** Answers will vary.

17. Outside **19.** Outside **21.** Inside **23.** 1 **25.** 5

27. Larger than 5 **29.** 5 **31.** 0 **33.** Larger than 5

35. a) Answers will vary. **b)** Answers will vary.
  c) Answers will vary. **d)** Answers will vary.

37. One **39.** Two

41. a) No, it has an inside and an outside. **b)** Two
  c) Two **d)** Two strips, one inside the other

43. Answers will vary. **45.** Answers will vary.

SECTION 9.7, PAGE 556

1. Parallel **3.** Two **5.** Sphere **7.** Geodesic

9.

11.

13. a)

Start Step 1 Step 2

b) Infinite **c)** Finite

15. Each type of geometry can be used in its own frame of reference.

17. Coastlines, trees, mountains, galaxies, polymers, rivers, weather patterns, brains, lungs, blood supply

19. Answers will vary. **21.** Answers will vary.

23. Answers will vary.

REVIEW EXERCISES, PAGE 560

1. $\overrightarrow{BF}$ 2. $\overline{AD}$ 3. $\triangle BFC$ 4. $\overleftrightarrow{BH}$ 5. $\{F\}$

6. $\{\}$ 7. 54.6° 8. 79.5° 9. 10.2 in.

10. 2 in. 11. 58° 12. 92°

13. $m\angle 1 = 45°, m\angle 2 = 110°, m\angle 3 = 110°, m\angle 4 = 65°,$
    $m\angle 5 = 115°, m\angle 6 = 65°$

14. 1080° 15. a) 99 mi^2 b) 40 mi

16. a) 13 in^2 b) 19.4 in. 17. a) 84 in^2 b) 42 in.

18. a) 6 km^2 b) 12 km 19. a) 153.94 ft^2 b) 43.98 ft

20. 64.38 m^2 21. 79.73 yd^2 22. $1176

23. a) 120 cm^3 b) 164 cm^2

24. a) 254.47 ft^3 b) 226.19 ft^2

25. a) 603.19 mm^3 b) 435.20 mm^2

26. a) 1436.76 yd^3 b) 615.75 yd^2

27. 432 m^3 28. 28 ft^3 29. 75.40 cm^3 30. 458.15 in^3

31. a) ≈ 67.88 ft^3 b) 4610.7 lb; yes c) ≈ 510.3 gal

This figure contains the answers for Exercises 32 and 33.

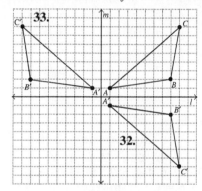

This figure contains the answers for Exercises 34 and 35.

This figure contains the answers for Exercises 36–38.

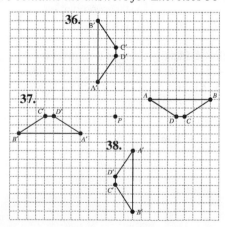

This figure contains the answers for Exercises 39 and 40.

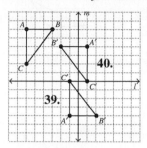

41. Yes 42. No 43. No 44. Yes

45. a) Answers will vary. b) Answers will vary.
    c) Answers will vary. d) Answers will vary.

46. Answers will vary. 47. Outside

48. Euclidean: Given a line and a point not on the line, one
    and only one line can be drawn parallel to the given line
    through the given point. Elliptical: Given a line and a
    point not on the line, no line can be drawn through the
    given point parallel to the given line. Hyperbolic: Given
    a line and a point not on the line, two or more lines can
    be drawn through the given point parallel to the given
    line.

49.

50.

CHAPTER TEST, PAGE 563

1. $\overrightarrow{EF}$ 2. $\triangle BCD$ 3. $\{D\}$ 4. $\overleftrightarrow{AC}$ 5. 15.1°

6. 169.6° 7. 65° 8. 540° 9. ≈ 2.69 cm

10. a) 5 in. b) 30 in. c) 30 in.^{2}

11. a) 1436.76 cm^3 b) 615.75 cm^2

12. 59.43 m^3 13. 112 ft^3

14.

15.

16.

17.

18. a) No   **b)** Yes

19. A surface with one side and one edge

20. a) Answers will vary.   **b)** Answers will vary.

Chapter 10

SECTION 10.1, PAGE 573

1. Binary   **3.** $b + a$ **5.** $a \cdot (b \cdot c)$ **7.** Closed

9. Identity   **11.** Inverse   **13.** Commutative

15. $a \cdot b = b \cdot a$ for any elements a and b; $2 \cdot 3 = 3 \cdot 2$

17. $(a + b) + c = a + (b + c)$ for any elements a, b, and c; $(3 + 4) + 5 = 3 + (4 + 5)$

19. $4 \div 2 \neq 2 \div 4$
   $2 \neq \frac{1}{2}$

21. $(6 - 4) - 1 \neq 6 - (4 - 1)$
   $2 - 1 \neq 6 - 3$
   $1 \neq 3$

23. Yes; it satisfies the five properties needed.

25. No; there is no identity element.

27. No; the system is not closed.

29. No; there is no identity element.

31. No; not all elements have inverses.

33. Yes; it satisfies the four properties needed.

35. No; the system is not closed. For example, $\frac{1}{0}$ is undefined.

37. Yes; it satisfies the four properties needed.

39. No; the system is not closed. For example, $\sqrt{2} + (-\sqrt{2}) = 0$, which is rational. There is also no identity element.

41. Answers will vary.

SECTION 10.2, PAGE 581

1. {1, 2, 3, 4, 5, 6, 7, 8, 9, 10, 11, 12}

3. Closed   **5.** Inverses   **7.** Associative

9. Commutative   **11.** Commutative   **13.** No

15. Yes; C is the identity element since the row next to C is identical to the top row, and the column under C is identical to the left-hand column.

---

17. a) The inverse of A is B since $A \oslash B = B \oslash A = C$.
   b) The inverse *of B is A since* $B \oslash A = A \oslash B = C$.
   c) The inverse of C is C since $C \oslash C = C$.

19. No; the elements are not symmetric about the main diagonal.

21. 9   **23.** 2   **25.** 4   **27.** 8   **29.** 6   **31.** 6

33. 10   **35.** 6   **37.** 8   **39.** 12

41.

+	1	2	3	4	5	6
1	2	3	4	5	6	1
2	3	4	5	6	1	2
3	4	5	6	1	2	3
4	5	6	1	2	3	4
5	6	1	2	3	4	5
6	1	2	3	4	5	6

43. 2   **45.** 3   **47.** 2   **49.** 4

51.

+	1	2	3	4	5	6	7
1	2	3	4	5	6	7	1
2	3	4	5	6	7	1	2
3	4	5	6	7	1	2	3
4	5	6	7	1	2	3	4
5	6	7	1	2	3	4	5
6	7	1	2	3	4	5	6
7	1	2	3	4	5	6	7

53. 2   **55.** 3   **57.** 4   **59.** 7

61. Yes; it satisfies the five required properties.

63. a) {0, 2, 4, 6}   **b)** £   **c)** Yes   **d)** Yes; 0
   e) Yes; 0–0, 2–6, 4–4, 6–2   **f)** $(2 £ 4) £ 6 = 2 £ (4 £ 6)$
   g) Yes; $2 £ 6 = 6 £ 2$ **h)** Yes

65. a) $\{*, 5, L\}$ **b)** \$ **c)** Yes   **d)** Yes, L
   e) Yes, $*-5, 5-*, L-L$ **f)** $(* \$ 5) \$ 5 = * \$ (5 \$ 5)$
   g) Yes, $L \$ * = * \$ L$ **h)** Yes

67. a) $\{f, r, o, m\}$ **b)** ~   **c)** Closed   **d)** m **e)** f **f)** f
   g) m **h)** r

69. Not closed   **71.** No inverse for $\odot$ or for *, not associative

73. No identity element, no inverses, not associative, not commutative

75. a)

+	E	O
E	E	O
O	O	E

   b) Yes, it is a commutative group; it satisfies the five properties.

77. a) Is closed; identity element is 6; inverses: 1–5, 2–2, 3–3, 4–4, 5–1, 6–6; is associative; for example,
   $$(2 \infty 5) \infty 3 = 2 \infty (5 \infty 3)$$
   $$3 \infty 3 = 2 \infty 2$$
   $$6 = 6$$

   b) $3 \infty 1 \neq 1 \infty 3$
      $2 \neq 4$

79. a)

*	R	S	T	U	V	I
R	V	T	U	S	I	R
S	U	I	V	R	T	S
T	S	R	I	V	U	T
U	T	V	R	I	S	U
V	I	U	S	T	R	V
I	R	S	T	U	V	I

b) Yes. It is closed; identity element is I; inverses R–V, S–S, T–T, U–U, V–R, I–I; and the associative property will hold.

c) No, it is not commutative. For example, $R*S \neq S*R$

81.

+	0	1	2	3	4
0	0	1	2	3	4
1	1	2	3	4	0
2	2	3	4	0	1
3	3	4	0	1	2
4	4	0	1	2	3

83. a) Yes **b)** Yes; 1 **c)** Yes; 1 **d)** Yes **e)** Yes **f)** Yes

SECTION 10.3, PAGE 592

1. $m - 1$ **3.** Remainder **5.** Congruent **7.** Monday
9. Sunday **11.** Friday **13.** Saturday **15.** Friday
17. May **19.** August **21.** September **23.** July
25. 2 **27.** 1 **29.** 3 **31.** 2 **33.** 1 **35.** 2 **37.** 2
39. 4 **41.** 5 **43.** 2 **45.** 6 **47.** 9 **49.** 5 **51.** 1
53. 3 **55.** 5 **57.** 5 **59.** { } **61.** 1 and 6 **63.** 5
65. 0 **67. a)** 2024, 2028, 2032, 2036, 2040 **b)** 3004
  c) 2552, 2556, 2560, 2564, 2568, 2572
69. a) Resting (for the second of two days)
  b) Resting (for the second of two days)
  c) Morning and afternoon lessons **d)** No
71. a) 5 **b)** No **c)** 54 weeks from this week
73. a) Evening **b)** Day **c)** Day
75. a)

+	0	1	2
0	0	1	2
1	1	2	0
2	2	0	1

b) Yes **c)** Yes, 0 **d)** Yes; 0–0, 1–2, 2–1
e) $(1 + 2) + 2 = 1 + (2 + 2)$
f) Yes; $2 + 1 = 1 + 2$ **g)** Yes **h)** Yes

77. a)

×	0	1	2	3
0	0	0	0	0
1	0	1	2	3
2	0	2	0	2
3	0	3	2	1

b) Yes **c)** Yes, 1
d) No; no inverse for 0 or for 2, inverse of 1 is 1, inverse of 3 is 3
e) $(1 \times 2) \times 3 = 1 \times (2 \times 3)$
f) Yes, $2 \times 3 = 3 \times 2$ **g)** No
79. 2 **81.** 1, 2, 3 **83.** 0 **85.** 2
87. a) Tuesday **b)** Wednesday
89. Knowledge is power **90.** 0

REVIEW EXERCISES, PAGE 595

1. A binary operation is an operation that can be performed on two and only two elements of a set. The result is a single element.
2. A mathematical system consists of a set of elements and at least one binary operation.
3. No; for example $2 \div 3 = \frac{2}{3}$ and $\frac{2}{3}$ is not a whole number.
4. Yes; the difference of any two real numbers is a real number.
5. 2 **6.** 7 **7.** 9 **8.** 8 **9.** 9 **10.** 11
11. Closure, identity element, inverses, and associative property
12. A commutative group **13.** Yes
14. No; no inverse for any integer except 1 and −1
15. No; no identity element
16. No; no inverse for 0
17. No identity element; no inverses
18. Not every element has an inverse; not associative. For example, $(P\,?\,P)\,?\,4 \neq P\,?\,(P\,?\,4)$.
19. Not associative. For example, $(!\,\square p)\,\square? \neq !\,\square(p\,\square?)$
20. a) $\{\odot,\ \bullet, \female, \delta\}$ **b)** $\cap$ **c)** Yes **d)** Yes; $\odot$
  e) Yes; $\odot$–$\odot$, $\bullet$–δ, $\female$–$\female$, δ–$\bullet$
  f) $(\bullet\ \cap\ \female)\ \cap\ \delta = \bullet\ \cap\ (\female\ \cap\ \delta)$
  g) Yes; $\bullet\ \cap\ \delta = \delta\ \cap\ \bullet$ **h)** Yes
21. 0 **22.** 1 **23.** 2 **24.** 4 **25.** 11 **26.** 2 **27.** 4
28. 12 **29.** 9 **30.** 11 **31.** 1 **32.** 6 **33.** 3 **34.** 7
35. 0, 2, 4, 6 **36.** 4 **37.** 5 **38.** 9
39. No solution **40.** 8

41.

+	0	1	2	3	4	5
0	0	1	2	3	4	5
1	1	2	3	4	5	0
2	2	3	4	5	0	1
3	3	4	5	0	1	2
4	4	5	0	1	2	3
5	5	0	1	2	3	4

Yes, it is a commutative group.

42.

×	0	1	2	3
0	0	0	0	0
1	0	1	2	3
2	0	2	0	2
3	0	3	2	1

No; no inverse for 0 or 2

43. a) Yes   **b)** Yes

CHAPTER TEST, PAGE 597

1. A set of elements and a binary operation.

2. Closure, identity element, inverses, associative property, commutative property

3. Yes   **4.** No; not closed

5.

+	1	2	3	4	5
1	2	3	4	5	1
2	3	4	5	1	2
3	4	5	1	2	3
4	5	1	2	3	4
5	1	2	3	4	5

6. Yes, it is a commutative group.

7. 2 **8.** 2 **9. a)** □   **b)** Yes **c)** Yes, T **d)** S **e)** S

10. No, not closed.   **11.** Yes, it is a commutative group.

12. Yes, it is a commutative group.   **13.** 3 **14.** 8 **15.** 4

16. 2 **17.** 5 **18.** 2 **19.** { }

20. a)

×	0	1	2	3	4
0	0	0	0	0	0
1	0	1	2	3	4
2	0	2	4	1	3
3	0	3	1	4	2
4	0	4	3	2	1

b) No; no inverse for 0.

Chapter 11

SECTION 11.1, PAGE 607

1. 100 **3.** 100 **5.** Previous **7.** 70% **9.** 55.0%

11. 0.8% **13.** 378.0% **15.** 0.07 **17.** 0.0515 **19.** 0.0025

21. 0.002 **23.** 0.01 **25.** 25% **27.** 4.7 grams

29. 471 comedy DVDs **31.** 192 horror DVDs

33. 21.46 mℓ of oxygen **35.** 9.7 mℓ of chlorine **37.** 47.0%

39. 14.0% **41.** 3.4% decrease

43. a) 6.9% increase **b)** 5.9% increase **c)** 11.6% increase
   d) 23.3% increase **e)** 10.2% increase

45. a) 22.7% decrease **b)** 29.3% increase
   c) 33.8% decrease **d)** 18.8% increase **e)** 11.0% increase

47. $6.75 **49.** 25% **51.** 300

53. a) $2.61 **b)** $46.11 **c)** $6.92 **d)** $53.03

55. 12 students **57.** $39,055 **59.** 5.3% decrease

61. 41.6% increase **63.** 18.6% decrease **65.** $3750

67. He will have a loss of $10. **69.** $21.95

SECTION 11.2, PAGE 618

1. Principal **3.** Interest **5.** Rate **7.** United States

9. $18.00 **11.** $24.06 **13.** $15.85 **15.** $80.06

17. $113.20 **19.** 5.6% **21.** $7000 **23.** 2 years

25. $25,750 **27. a)** $131.25 **b)** $3631.25

29. a) $182.50 **b)** $3467.50 **c)** ≈ 7.9%

31. $23,793.75 **33.** 239 days **35.** 272 days **37.** 264 days

39. July 24 **41.** March 24 **43.** $2017.03 **45.** $1459.33

47. $5278.99 **49.** $850.64 **51.** $6086.82 **53.** $2646.24

55. a) November 3, 2011 **b)** $999.24
   c) $0.76 **d)** 0.1504%

57. a) 409.01% **b)** 204.50% **c)** 102.25%

59. a) 6.663% **b)** ≈ 7.139 **c)** $6663 **d)** $6996.15

60. a) $6.42 **b)** $14.20 **c)** $22.47 **d)** Answers will vary.

SECTION 11.3, PAGE 627

1. Profit **3.** Variable **5.** Compound

7. $A = \$2622.86; i = \$122.86$

9. $A = \$2253.98; i = \$253.98$

11. $A = \$8252.64; i = \$1252.64$

13. $A = \$8666.26; i = \$666.26$ **15.** $30,695.66

17. $85,282.13 **19.** $54,142.84 **21.** $1653.36

23. $2341.82 **25. a)** $4195.14 **b)** $4214.36

27. $3106.62 **29.** $10,910.27 **31.** ≈ 3.53%

33. Yes, the APY should be 2.43%.

35. He will earn more interest in the account that pays the 5% simple interest.

37. a) $555,000 **b)** $58,907.61 **c)** $98.51

39. $212,687.10 **41.** $15,130.89

43. a) $1040.60, $40.60 **b)** $1082.43, $82.43
   c) $1169.86, $169.86 **d)** No

45. $2.33 **47. a)** 24 years **b)** 12 years **c)** 9 years
   d) 6 years **e)** 3.27%

49. The simple interest is $20,000. The compound interest is $22,138.58. The compound interest is greater by $2,138.58.

SECTION 11.4, PAGE 641

1. Installment **3.** Annual **5.** Installment **7.** $33.24

9. $345.44 **11. a)** $523.35 **b)** $104.65

13. a) $818.40 **b)** 8.5% **15. a)** $4465.20 **b)** 5.0%

17. a) 6.0% **b)** $726.00 **c)** $7858.00

19. a) $2818.20 **b)** $689.39 **c)** $347.90 **d)** $8614.17

21. a) $26.00 **b)** $46.01, which rounds up to $47

23. a) $21.14, which rounds up to $22
   b) $34.39, which rounds up to $35

25. a) $19.76 **b)** $743.41 **27. a)** $1.56 **b)** $133.11

29. a) $512.00 **b)** $6.66 **c)** $638.43

31. a) $121.78 **b)** $1.52 **c)** $133.07

   d) The interest charged using the average daily balance method is $0.04 less than the interest charged using the previous balance method.

33. a) $11.96 **b)** $886.96

35. a) $25 **b)** $35.60 **c)** 8.5% **d)** 6.5% **37.** $14,077.97

39. a) $6872.25 **b)** $610.37 **c)** $2637.42 **d)** $2501.05

SECTION 11.5, PAGE 654

1. Mortgage **3.** Points **5.** Adjusted **7.** $717.28

9. $1960.48 **11. a)** $26,250 **b)** $798.52

13. a) $262,500 **b)** $9583.98

15. a) $39,000 **b)** $156,000 **c)** $3120

17. a) $802.20 **b)** $1411.19 **c)** No

19. a) $187,714.80 **b)** $112,714.80 **c)** $38.62

21. a) $17,025 **b)** $2894.25 **c)** $1212.40 **d)** $931.00

   e) $1057.67 **f)** Yes **g)** $127.04 **23.** Bank B

25. a) $664,491.60 **b)** $927,379.20 **c)** $1,230,933.60

27. a) $804.62

   b)

Payment Number	Interest	Principal	Balance of Loan
1	$750.00	$54.62	$99,945.38
2	$749.59	$55.03	$99,890.35
3	$749.18	$55.44	$99,834.91

   c) 9.38%

   d)

Payment Number	Interest	Principal	Balance of Loan
4	$780.38	$24.24	$99,810.67
5	$780.19	$24.43	$99,786.24
6	$780.00	$24.62	$99,761.62

   e) 9.46%

29. a) The variable-rate mortgage **b)** $2149.80

SECTION 11.6, PAGE 664

1. Annuity **3.** Sinking **5.** Immediate **7.** 401k

9. $54,688.90 **11.** $299,929.32 **13.** $332.41

15. $175.48 **17.** $37,078.18 **19.** $56,559.36 **21.** $331.46

23. $5160.71 **25. a)** $23,003.87 **b)** $826,980.88

   c) $349,496.41 **d)** $12,000 **e)** $36,000 **f)** Alberto

REVIEW EXERCISES, PAGE 668

1. 80.0% **2.** 66.7% **3.** 62.5% **4.** 4.1%

5. 0.98% $\approx$ 1.0% **6.** 314.1% **7.** 0.05 **8.** 0.217

9. 1.23 **10.** 0.0025 **11.** 0.008$\overline{3}$ **12.** 0.0000045

13. $\approx$ 17.6% **14.** 3.0% **15.** 20.0% **16.** 80 **17.** 91.8

18. $6.42 **19.** 40 people **20.** 26.7% **21.** $112.50

22. 5.0% **23.** $450 **24.** 0.5 year **25.** $7875

26. a) $162 **b)** $3162

27. a) $1380 **b)** $4620 **c)** $\approx$ 14.9%

28. a) 7.5% **b)** $830 **c)** at least $941.18

29. a) $6691.13; $1691.13 **b)** $6719.58; $1719.58

   c) $6734.28; $1734.28 **d)** $6744.25; $1744.25

   e) $6749.13; $1749.13

30. $3503.48 **31.** 5.76% **32.** $13,415.00

33. a) 6.0% **b)** $253.16 **c)** $4150.34

34. a) 6.5% **b)** $64.32 **c)** $1962.51

35. a) 4.5% **b)** $32.06 **c)** $1420.43

36. a) $6.31 **b)** $847.61 **c)** $508.99 **d)** $6.62

   e) $847.92 **37. a)** $2.60 **b)** $546.92 **c)** $382.68

   d) $5.36 **e)** $549.68

38. a) $56,000 **b)** $84,000 **c)** $13,440 **d)** 6.0%

39. a) $10.44 **b)** 8.5%

40. a) $33,925 **b)** $1345.49 **c)** $855.78

   d) $1172.45 **e)** Yes

41. a) $13,485 **b)** $756.73 **c)** $24.42 **d)** $285,907.80

   e) $196,007.80

42. a) $550.63 **b)** 8.0% **c)** 7.75% **43.** $48,378.57

44. $3668.72

CHAPTER TEST, PAGE 671

1. a) $37.50 **b)** 3 years **2.** $166.50 **3.** $1366.50

4. $2523.20 **5.** $123.20 **6. a)** $7961.99, $461.99

   b) $3036.68, $536.68 **7.** $1997.50 **8.** $181.46

9. 8.5% **10. a)** 4.5% **b)** $64.02 **c)** $2836.28

11. a) $12.30 **b)** $1146.57 **c)** $765.67 **d)** $10.72

   e) $1144.99 **12.** $21,675 **13.** $2456.50

14. $1848.93 **15.** $1123.53 **16.** $1427.70 **17.** Yes

18. a) $428,602.30 **b)** $284,102.30 **19.** $25,858.69

20. $277.28

Chapter 12

SECTION 12.1, PAGE 679

1. Experiment **3.** Event **5.** Empirical

7. a) Answers will vary. **b)** Answers will vary.

   c) Answers will vary.

9. a) Answers will vary. **b)** Answers will vary.

   c) Answers will vary.

11. a) $\dfrac{7}{15}$ **b)** $\dfrac{1}{3}$ **c)** $\dfrac{1}{5}$ **13. a)** $\dfrac{3}{7}$ **b)** $\dfrac{8}{21}$ **c)** $\dfrac{1}{21}$

15. a) $\dfrac{13,674}{153,468}$, or $\approx$ 0.0891 **b)** $\dfrac{27,362}{153,468} \approx$ 0.1783

   c) $\dfrac{11,140}{153,468}$, or $\approx$ 0.0726

17. a) $\dfrac{16,600,000}{66,950,000} \approx 0.2479$ **b)** $\dfrac{8,870,000}{66,950,000} \approx 0.1325$

c) $\dfrac{18,880,000}{66,950,000}$, or ≈ 0.2820

19. a) $\dfrac{11}{40}$ **b)** $\dfrac{9}{40}$ **c)** $\dfrac{1}{4}$ **d)** $\dfrac{7}{40}$ **e)** $\dfrac{3}{40}$

21. a) $\dfrac{6}{20} = \dfrac{3}{10}$ **b)** $\dfrac{14}{20} = \dfrac{7}{10}$ **c)** $\dfrac{14}{20} = \dfrac{7}{10}$ **d)** $\dfrac{2}{20} = \dfrac{1}{10}$

23. a) 0   **b)** $\dfrac{50}{250} = 0.2$ **c)** 1

25. a) $\dfrac{224}{929} \approx 0.2411$ **b)** $\dfrac{705}{929} \approx 0.7589$

27. No, it means that if a coin was flipped many times, about $\frac{1}{2}$ of the tosses would land heads up.

29. a) Roll a die many times and then find the relative frequency of 5's to the total number of rolls.
b) Answers will vary.   **c)** Answers will vary.

31. a) Answers will vary.   **b)** Answers will vary.
c) Answers will vary.   **d)** Answers will vary.

32. a) Answers will vary.   **b)** Answers will vary.
c) Answers will vary.

SECTION 12.2, PAGE 687

1. Equally   **3.** 1   **5.** 1   **7.** $\dfrac{4}{7}$ **9.** 0.1   **11. a)** $\dfrac{1}{5}$ **b)** $\dfrac{1}{4}$

13. $\dfrac{1}{40}$ **15.** $\dfrac{1}{13}$ **17.** $\dfrac{12}{13}$ **19.** $\dfrac{1}{2}$ **21.** 1   **23.** $\dfrac{4}{13}$

25. a) $\dfrac{1}{4}$ **b)** $\dfrac{1}{2}$ **c)** $\dfrac{1}{4}$ **d)** 0

27. a) $\dfrac{1}{2}$ **b)** $\dfrac{1}{8}$ **c)** $\dfrac{1}{8}$ **d)** $\dfrac{1}{4}$

29. $\dfrac{1}{5}$ **31.** $\dfrac{9}{10}$ **33.** $\dfrac{1}{12}$ **35.** $\dfrac{1}{6}$ **37.** $\dfrac{1}{2}$ **39.** $\dfrac{2}{3}$ **41.** $\dfrac{11}{17}$

43. $\dfrac{12}{17}$ **45.** $\dfrac{2}{11}$ **47.** $\dfrac{6}{11}$ **49.** 0   **51.** $\dfrac{1}{10}$ **53.** $\dfrac{1}{5}$

55. $\dfrac{1}{26}$ **57.** $\dfrac{5}{26}$ **59.** $\dfrac{17}{26}$ **61.** $\dfrac{83}{130}$ **63.** $\dfrac{11}{26}$ **65.** $\dfrac{5}{21}$

67. $\dfrac{11}{42}$ **69.** $\dfrac{4}{21}$ **71.** $\dfrac{13}{36}$ **73.** $\dfrac{1}{3}$ **75.** $\dfrac{23}{36}$

77. a) 0   **b)** 1   **79. a)** $\dfrac{1}{4}$ **b)** $\dfrac{1}{4}$ **c)** $\dfrac{1}{4}$ **81.** 29 dots

SECTION 12.3, PAGE 694

1. Against   **3.** 3:1   **5.** 2:1   **7.** $\dfrac{1}{4}$

9. a) $\dfrac{5}{12}$ **b)** $\dfrac{7}{12}$ **c)** 7:5   **d)** 5:7

11. 6:1, 1:6   **13.** 5:1   **15.** 4:2 or 2:1   **17.** 12:1, 1:12
19. 10:3, 3:10   **21.** 1:1   **23.** 5:3   **25. a)** 8:7   **b)** 7:8

27. 8:7   **29.** 7:8   **31.** 8:7   **33. a)** $\dfrac{4}{5}$ **b)** 1:4   **35.** 1:16

37. a) $\dfrac{7}{11}$ **b)** $\dfrac{4}{11}$ **39.** $\dfrac{11}{15}$ **41.** $\dfrac{1}{5}$ **43.** 1:4   **45.** 74:1
47. 0.34   **49.** 33:17   **51.** 43:57   **53.** 1:9   **55.** 7:1

57. a) $\dfrac{1}{33}$ **b)** 32:1

59. Horse 2, $\dfrac{2}{9}$; Horse 3, $\dfrac{1}{3}$; Horse 4, $\dfrac{1}{16}$; Horse 5, $\dfrac{5}{12}$;

Horse 6, $\dfrac{1}{2}$ **61.** $\approx 97:3$

SECTION 12.4, PAGE 703

1. Expected   **3.** Positive   **5.** 32,700 people   **7.** 70 points
9. 1.44 million viewers   **11.** $5500   **13.** $1.60 off
15. a) $\approx -\$0.17$ **b)** $\approx \$0.17$

17. a) Yes, because you have a positive expectation of $\dfrac{1}{5}$

b) Yes, because you have a positive expectation of $\dfrac{1}{2}$

19. $3.00   **21. a)** $-\$2.00$ **b)** $1.00
23. a) $-\$2.00$ **b)** $1.00   **25.** $3.00   **27.** $-\$1.25$
29. $750   **31.** $416.67   **33. a)** $3.50   **b)** $5.50
35. a) $2.25   **b)** $4.25   **37.** $2.50   **39.** $-\$8.25$
41. 0.75 base   **43.** 2.9 points   **45.** 56 employees
47. $14,550   **49.** 3.5   **51.** ≈ 141.51 service calls

53. a) $\dfrac{9}{16}, \dfrac{1}{4}, \dfrac{1}{8}, \dfrac{1}{16}$ **b)** $11.81

55. An amount greater than $1200
57. $-\$0.053$ or $-5.3¢$ **59. a)** $458.33   **b)** $308.33

SECTION 12.5, PAGE 712

1. Sample   **3.** 14   **5. a)** 2500 **b)** 2450
7. a) 216   **b)** 120   **9. a)** 4

9. b)   Sample Space   **c)** $\dfrac{1}{4}$ **d)** $\dfrac{1}{2}$ **e)** $\dfrac{1}{4}$

11. a) 9   **b)**   Sample Space   **c)** $\dfrac{1}{9}$ **d)** $\dfrac{1}{9}$ **e)** $\dfrac{5}{9}$

13. a) 12   **b)**   Sample Space

c) $\frac{1}{2}$ d) 1 e) $\frac{1}{2}$

15. a) 9 **b)**   Sample Space   **c)** $\frac{1}{3}$ **d)** $\frac{1}{9}$ **e)** $\frac{2}{3}$

17. a) 36 **b)**   Sample Space

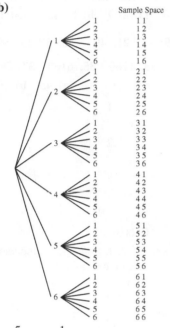

c) $\frac{1}{6}$ **d)** $\frac{5}{36}$ **e)** $\frac{1}{36}$ **f)** No

19. a) 12 **b)**   Sample Space

c) $\frac{1}{2}$ **d)** $\frac{1}{6}$ **e)** $\frac{2}{3}$

21. a) 18 **b)**   Sample Space

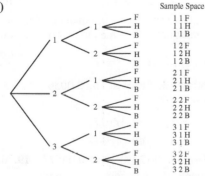

c) $\frac{1}{3}$ **d)** $\frac{1}{9}$ **e)** $\frac{2}{3}$

23. a) 27 **b)**   Sample Space

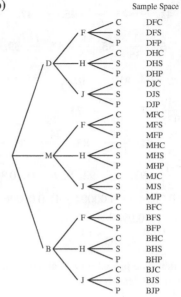

c) $\frac{1}{3}$ **d)** $\frac{1}{9}$ **e)** $\frac{2}{3}$

25. a) 24 **b)**   Sample Space

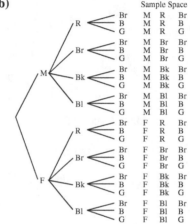

c) $\frac{1}{24}$ **d)** $\frac{1}{8}$

27. a) $\frac{1}{3}$ **b)** $\frac{2}{3}$

c) No, the probability of selecting a red chip is not the same as the probability of selecting a white chip.
d) Answers will vary.

29. 3; 1 red, 1 blue, and 1 brown   **30.** 5 faces

31. a) 120 **b)** CHAIR   **32. a)** 720 **b)** BASKET

SECTION 12.6, PAGE 723

1. Compound **3.** And **5.** Independent **7.** Independent
9. $P(A) + P(B) - P(A \text{ and } B)$ **11.** 0.7 **13.** 0.4
15. 0.75 **17.** $\frac{1}{3}$ **19.** $\frac{1}{2}$ **21.** $\frac{2}{13}$ **23.** $\frac{8}{13}$ **25.** $\frac{7}{13}$
27. a) $\frac{1}{16}$ **b)** $\frac{1}{19}$ **29. a)** $\frac{1}{16}$ **b)** $\frac{5}{76}$
31. a) $\frac{1}{40}$ **b)** $\frac{1}{38}$ **33. a)** $\frac{9}{25}$ **b)** $\frac{33}{95}$ **35.** $\frac{11}{20}$

37. $\dfrac{2}{5}$ **39.** $\dfrac{1}{4}$ **41.** $\dfrac{1}{8}$ **43.** $\dfrac{9}{64}$ **45.** $\dfrac{1}{8}$ **47.** $\dfrac{3}{8}$

49. $\dfrac{3}{7}$ **51.** $\dfrac{9}{49}$ **53.** $\dfrac{1}{35}$ **55.** $\dfrac{1}{35}$ **57.** $\dfrac{1}{8}$ **59.** $\dfrac{1}{8}$

61. a) $\dfrac{1}{32}$ **b)** $\dfrac{1}{2}$ **63. a)** $\dfrac{4}{49}$ **b)** $\dfrac{2}{21}$ **65. a)** $\dfrac{24}{49}$ **b)** $\dfrac{11}{21}$

67. $\dfrac{376}{925}$ **69.** $\dfrac{549}{925}$ **71.** $\dfrac{1771}{9880}$ **73.** $\dfrac{7}{988}$ **75.** $\dfrac{7}{10}$

77. $\dfrac{343}{1000}$ **79.** $\dfrac{1}{4}$ **81.** $\dfrac{27}{1024}$ **83.** $\dfrac{243}{1024}$ **85.** $\dfrac{5}{22}$

87. $\dfrac{1050}{1331}$ **89.** $\dfrac{1}{24}$ **91.** $\dfrac{5}{12}$ **93.** 0.36 **95.** 0.36

97. a) No **b)** 0.001 **c)** 0.00004 **d)** 0.00096
   e) 0.000999 **f)** 0.998001

99. $\dfrac{9}{250}$ **101.** $\dfrac{2169}{62,500}$ **103.** $\dfrac{14}{45}$

105. Favors dealer. The probability of at least one diamond is ≈ 0.44, which is less than 0.5.

107. $\dfrac{1}{9}$ **108.** $\dfrac{1}{4}$ **109.** $\dfrac{1}{2}$ **110.** 1

SECTION 12.7, PAGE 731

1. Conditional **3.** $\dfrac{1}{3}$ **5.** $\dfrac{1}{3}$ **7.** $\dfrac{2}{3}$ **9.** $\dfrac{2}{3}$ **11.** $\dfrac{2}{3}$

13. $\dfrac{2}{3}$ **15.** $\dfrac{2}{3}$ **17.** $\dfrac{1}{5}$ **19.** $\dfrac{1}{3}$ **21.** $\dfrac{3}{5}$ **23.** $\dfrac{1}{7}$

25. $\dfrac{1}{16}$ **27.** $\dfrac{1}{7}$ **29.** $\dfrac{1}{6}$ **31.** $\dfrac{1}{6}$ **33.** $\dfrac{2}{3}$ **35.** $\dfrac{2}{9}$ **37.** $\dfrac{1}{2}$

39. $\dfrac{1}{2}$ **41.** 0.5941 **43.** 0.3605 **45.** 0.6251 **47.** $\dfrac{7}{13}$

49. $\dfrac{4}{15}$ **51.** $\dfrac{11}{15}$ **53.** 0.6337 **55.** 0.2459

57. 0.2897 **59.** $\dfrac{10}{11}$ **61.** $\dfrac{3}{19}$ **63.** $\dfrac{44}{47}$ **65.** $\dfrac{11}{27}$

67. $\dfrac{10}{29}$ **69.** $\dfrac{11}{29}$ **71.** $\dfrac{93}{200}$ **73.** $\dfrac{15}{52}$

75. a) 140 **b)** 120 **c)** $\dfrac{7}{10}$ **d)** $\dfrac{3}{5}$ **e)** $\dfrac{2}{3}$ **f)** $\dfrac{4}{7}$
   g) Because A and B are not independent events

77. a) 0.3 **b)** 0.5 **c)** Yes; $P(A\,|\,B) = P(A) \cdot P(B)$

78. $\dfrac{1}{3}$ **79.** $\dfrac{1}{2}$ **80.** $\dfrac{1}{3}$ **81.** $\dfrac{1}{3}$ **82.** 1 **83.** $\dfrac{1}{3}$

SECTION 12.8, PAGE 742

1. Counting **3.** $n!$ **5.** $\dfrac{n!}{(n-r)!}$ **7.** $_5P_3$ **9.** 120

11. 12 **13.** 1 **15.** 1 **17.** 15,120 **19.** 336 **21.** 10,000

23. 24 **25. a)** $5^5 = 3125$ **b)** $\dfrac{1}{3125} = 0.00032$

27. a) 456,976,000 **b)** 258,336,000 **29.** 336

31. a) 720 **b)** 120 **c)** 24 **d)** 600 **33.** 720

35. a) 479,001,600 **b)** 3,628,800 **c)** 14,400

37. 78,624,000 **39.** 131,040 **41.** 676,000 **43.** 104,000

45. a) 8,000,000 **b)** 6,400,000,000 **c)** 64,000,000,000

47. 524,160 **49.** 5040 **51.** 280 **53.** 362,880 **55.** 3780

57. 630 **59.** 15,120 **61. a)** 40,320 **b)** 362,880

63. a) 3125 **b)** 128 **c)** 0.00032

65. 12,600 sec, or 3.5 hr **67.** No **68.** 56 **69.** 600

70. a) 360 **b)** CHOICE

71. a) 2520 **b)** SCROOGE

SECTION 12.9, PAGE 749

1. Combination **3.** Permutations **5.** $_7C_3$ **7.** 15

9. a) 70 **b)** 1680 **11. a)** 1 **b)** 1 **13.** a) 120 b) 720

15. $\dfrac{1}{6}$ **17.** $\dfrac{3}{4}$ **19.** 12 **21.** 495 **23.** 5 **25.** 56 **27.** 35

29. 495 **31.** 210 **33.** 1260 **35.** 6160 **37.** 5880

39. 8820 **41.** 700 **43.** 600 **45. a)** 45 **b)** 56

47. a)

$$
\begin{array}{ccccccccc}
 & & & & 1 & & & & \\
 & & & 1 & & 1 & & & \\
 & & 1 & & 2 & & 1 & & \\
 & 1 & & 3 & & 3 & & 1 & \\
1 & & 4 & & 6 & & 4 & & 1
\end{array}
$$

b) 1   5   10   10   5   1

49. a) 24 **b)** 24 **51.** 60,060

52. a) The order is important. Since the numbers may be repeated, it is not a true permutation lock.
   b) 64,000 **c)** 59,280

SECTION 12.10, PAGE 755

1. $\dfrac{_{10}C_4}{_{14}C_4}$ **3.** $\dfrac{_5C_3}{_{26}C_3}$ **5.** $\dfrac{_8C_5}{_{15}C_5}$ **7.** $\dfrac{_{23}C_5}{_{120}C_5}$ **9.** $\dfrac{1}{15}$

11. $\dfrac{4}{143}$ **13.** $\dfrac{1}{30}$ **15.** $\dfrac{2}{11}$ **17.** $\dfrac{1}{9,366,819}$ **19.** $\dfrac{3}{10}$

21. $\dfrac{7}{10}$ **23.** $\dfrac{1}{115}$ **25.** $\dfrac{27}{230}$ **27.** 0.0012 **29.** 0.3083

31. $\dfrac{2}{55}$ **33.** $\dfrac{4}{33}$ **35.** $\dfrac{1}{77}$ **37.** $\dfrac{5}{77}$ **39.** $\dfrac{15}{253}$

41. a) $\dfrac{1}{123,760}$ **b)** $\dfrac{1}{30,940}$

43. a) $\dfrac{33}{54,145}$ **b)** $\dfrac{1}{2,598,960}$ **45. a)** $\dfrac{1}{2,162,160}$ **b)** $\dfrac{1}{6435}$

47. 1; Since there are more hairs than people, two or more people must have the same number of hairs on their head.

SECTION 12.11, PAGE 764

1. Probability **3.** Success **5.** 0.0036 **7.** 0.3456

9. 0.015625

11. a) $P(x) = (_nC_x)(0.14)^x(0.86)^{n-x}$
   b) $P(2) = (_{12}C_2)(0.14)^2(0.86)^{10}$

13. 0.27869 **15.** 0.12248 **17.** 0.06877 **19.** 0.4096

21. a) 0.00098 **b)** 0.08789 **c)** 0.10352

23. a) ≈ 0.1119 **b)** ≈ 0.2966 **25.** 0; it will be midnight.

REVIEW EXERCISES, PAGE 767

1. Answers will vary.   **2.** Answers will vary.

3. $\dfrac{1}{5}$ **4.** Answers will vary.   **5.** $\dfrac{8}{25}$ **6.** $\dfrac{1}{2}$ **7.** $\dfrac{4}{5}$

8. 1   **9.** $\dfrac{1}{5}$ **10.** $\dfrac{9}{25}$ **11.** $\dfrac{11}{50}$ **12.** $\dfrac{16}{25}$ **13.** $\dfrac{43}{50}$

14. a) 4:1 **b)** 1:4   **15.** 5:3   **16.** $\dfrac{3}{85}$ **17.** 17:3

18. a) $-\$1.20$ **b)** $-\$3.60$ **19. a)** $-\$0.23$ **b)** $\$0.23$

 c) Lose $23.08   **20.** 660 people   **21.** $4.00   **22.** $3.50

23. a)

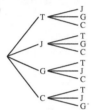

 b) Sample Space   **c)** $\dfrac{1}{12}$

   TJ
   TG
   TC
   JT
   JG
   JC
   GT
   GJ
   GC
   CT
   CJ
   CG

24. a)

 b) Sample Space   **c)** $\dfrac{1}{4}$ **d)** $\dfrac{3}{4}$
   H1
   H2
   H3
   H4
   T1
   T2
   T3
   T4

25. $\dfrac{1}{4}$ **26.** $\dfrac{9}{64}$ **27.** $\dfrac{5}{16}$ **28.** $\dfrac{7}{8}$ **29.** 1   **30.** $\dfrac{3}{16}$

31. $\dfrac{1}{22}$ **32.** $\dfrac{14}{55}$ **33.** $\dfrac{41}{55}$ **34.** $\dfrac{1}{22}$

35. $\dfrac{1}{4}$ **36.** Against, 3:1; in favor, 1:3   **37.** $13.75

38. $\dfrac{1}{8}$ **39.** $\dfrac{5}{8}$ **40.** In favor, 3:5; against, 5:3   **41.** $3.75

42. $\dfrac{7}{8}$ **43.** $\dfrac{15}{17}$ **44.** $\dfrac{17}{19}$ **45.** $\dfrac{2}{15}$ **46.** $\dfrac{1}{2}$ **47.** $\dfrac{23}{40}$

48. $\dfrac{3}{17}$ **49.** $\dfrac{3}{4}$ **50.** $\dfrac{12}{17}$ **51. a)** 24 **b)** $4500   **52.** 30

53. 720   **54.** 504   **55.** 20   **56.** 3,628,800

57. a) $\dfrac{1}{3,819,816}$ **b)** $\dfrac{1}{175,711,536}$ **58.** 35,640

59. 560   **60.** $\dfrac{1}{221}$ **61.** $\dfrac{1}{12}$ **62.** $\dfrac{1}{18}$ **63.** $\dfrac{1}{24}$ **64.** $\dfrac{11}{12}$

65. $\dfrac{5}{182}$ **66.** $\dfrac{45}{364}$ **67.** $\dfrac{2}{13}$ **68.** $\dfrac{11}{13}$

69. a) $P(x) = (_nC_x)(0.6)^x(0.4)^{n-x}$

 b) $P(75) = (_{100}C_{75})(0.6)^{75}(0.4)^{25}$

70. 0.0512   **71. a)** 0.01024 **b)** 0.98976

CHAPTER TEST, PAGE 771

1. $\dfrac{7}{25}$ **2.** $\dfrac{5}{9}$ **3.** $\dfrac{4}{9}$ **4.** $\dfrac{2}{3}$ **5.** $\dfrac{1}{6}$ **6.** $\dfrac{5}{18}$ **7.** $\dfrac{5}{12}$

8. $\dfrac{8}{13}$ **9.** 18   **10.**   Sample Space   **11.** $\dfrac{1}{18}$

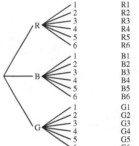

12. $\dfrac{4}{9}$ **13.** $\dfrac{5}{6}$ **14.** 1,581,840   **15. a)** 5:4 **b)** 5:4

16. $0   **17.** **a)** $\dfrac{107}{228}$ **b)** $\dfrac{113}{228}$ **c)** $\dfrac{53}{113}$ **d)** $\dfrac{47}{107}$

18. 120   **19. a)** $\dfrac{3}{38}$ **b)** $\dfrac{35}{38}$ **20.** 0.2304

Chapter 13

SECTION 13.1, PAGE 778

1. Statistics   **3.** Descriptive   **5.** Sample   **7.** Random

9. Cluster   **11.** Unbiased   **13.** Stratified sample

15. Cluster sample   **17.** Systematic sample

19. Convenience sample   **21.** Random sample

23. a) Answers will vary.   **b)** Answers will vary.

 c) Answers will vary.

25. President; four out of 44 U.S. presidents have been assassinated (Lincoln, Garfield, McKinley, Kennedy).

SECTION 13.2, PAGE 781

1. The patients may have improved on their own without taking honey.

3. Mama Mia's may have more empty spaces and more cars in the parking lot than Shanghi's due to a larger parking lot or because more people may walk to Mama Mia's than to Shanghi's.

5. More people drive on Saturday evening. Thus, one might expect more accidents.

7. Most driving is done close to home. Thus, one might expect more accidents close to home.

9. We don't know how many of each professor's students were surveyed. Perhaps more of Professor Malone's students than Professor Wagner's students were surveyed. Also, because more students prefer a teacher does not mean that he or she is a better teacher. For example, a particular teacher may be an easier grader and that may be why that teacher is preferred.

11. Just because they are more expensive does not mean that they will last longer.

13. There may be deep sections in the pond, so it may not be safe to go wading.

15. a)   **b)**

17. a)

b)

19. a)

b) Answers will vary.

21. Yes, the sum of its parts is 121%. The sum of the parts of a circle graph should be 100%. When the total percent of responses is more than 100%, a circle graph is not an appropriate graph to display the data. A bar graph is more appropriate in this situation.

23. A decimal point

1. Frequency   **3.** Mark   **5.** Histogram   **7.** Stem

9. a) 20   **b)** 7   **c)** 19   **d)** 16–22   **e)** 51–57

11.

Number of Visits	Number of Students
0	3
1	8
2	3
3	5
4	2
5	7
6	2
7	3
8	4
9	1
10	2

13.

Circulation (ten thousands)	Number of Magazines
173–322	33
323–472	10
473–622	1
623–772	1
773–922	1

15.

Circulation (ten thousands)	Number of Magazines
173–272	28
273–372	10
373–472	5
473–572	1
573–672	0
673–772	1
773–872	1

17.

Population (millions)	Number of Cities
7.0–7.9	6
8.0–8.9	4
9.0–9.9	1
10.0–10.9	3
11.0–11.9	1
12.0–12.9	2
13.0–13.9	3

19.

Population (millions)	Number of Cities
6.5–7.5	3
7.6–8.6	4
8.7–9.7	4
9.8–10.8	3
10.9–11.9	1
12.0–13.0	3
13.1–14.1	2

21.

Percent	Number of States
6.4–8.3	2
8.4–10.3	13
10.4–12.3	14
12.4–14.3	9
14.4–16.3	9
16.4–18.3	2
18.4–20.3	0
20.4–22.3	1

23.

Percent	Number of States
6.4–7.8	1
7.9–9.3	7
9.4–10.8	12
10.9–12.3	9
12.4–13.8	7
13.9–15.3	8
15.4–16.8	4
16.9–18.3	1
18.4–19.8	0
19.9–21.3	1

25. 1|2 represents 12

```
0|4  6  7  8
1|2  2  3  5  6  7  8  9
2|1  2  3  5  7
3|3  4
4|0
```

27. a)

Salaries (1000s of dollars)	Number of Social Workers
27	1
28	7
29	4
30	3
31	2
32	3
33	3
34	2

b) and c)

Starting Salaries for 25 Different Social Workers

d) 2|8 represents 28

```
2|7  8  8  8  8  8  8  8  9  9  9  9
3|0  0  0  1  1  2  2  2  3  3  3  4  4
```

29. a)

Total Gross (millions of dollars)	Number of Tours
80–91	12
92–103	4
104–115	3
116–127	2
128–139	3
140–151	0
152–163	1

b) and c)

Top 25 Grossing North American Concert Tours, 1985–2008

31. a) 28 **b)** 4 **c)** 2 **d)** 75

e)

Number of Televisions	Number of Homes
0	2
1	4
2	8
3	6
4	4
5	3
6	1

33. a) 7   **b)** 16   **c)** 36

d)

Number of Messages	Number of People	Number of Messages	Number of People
3	2	7	3
4	3	8	8
5	7	9	6
6	4	10	3

e)

Number of E-Mail Messages Sent

35.

Tution/Fees:	$5026.65
Room:	$5303.48
Board:	$3336.53
Computer costs:	$903.34

37. a) Answers will vary.   **b)** Answers will vary.

   c) Answers will vary.   **d)** Answers will vary.

   e) Answers will vary.

39. a) There are 6 F's.   **b)** Answers will vary.

40. February, since it has the fewest number of days

SECTION 13.4, PAGE 802

1. Average   **3.** Mean   **5.** Mode   **7.** Quartiles

9. a) $\bar{x}$ **b)** μ

11. 14, 13, 13, 17   **13.** 79.3, 82, none, 76

15. 8, 8, none, 8   **17.** 13.1, 11, 1, 18.5

19. 11.9, 12.5, 13, 11.5

21. a) 198.7   **b)** 197.5   **c)** None   **d)** 208.5

23. a) 4.9, 5, 5, 6   **b)** 5.3, 5, 5, 6   **c)** Only the mean

   d) The mean and the midrange

25. A 79 mean average on 10 quizzes gives a total of 790 points. An 80 mean average on 10 quizzes requires a total of 800 points. Thus, Jim missed a B by 10 points, not 1 point.

27. a) 23.0 pints   **b)** 22.5 pints   **c)** 18.5 pints   **d)** 25.1 pints

29. a) $4.6 billion   **b)** $3.3 billion

   c) None   **d)** $8.4 billion

31. 552

33. One example is 72, 73, 74, 76, 77, 78.

35. a) Yes   **b)** No   **c)** No   **d)** Yes

37. a) 29 or greater   **b)** Yes, 99 or greater

   c) 20 or greater   **d)** 80 or greater

39. One example: 1, 2, 3, 3, 4, 5 changed to 1, 2, 3, 4, 4, 5.

41. No. By changing only one piece of the 6 pieces of data, you cannot alter both the median and the midrange.

43. The data must be ranked.

45. He is taller than approximately 35 percent of all kindergarten children.

47. a) $23   **b)** $20   **c)** $34   **49.** Second quartile, median

51. a) $580   **b)** $590   **c)** 25%

   d) 25%   **e)** 17%   **f)** $60,000

53. a)

Ruth	Mantle
0.290	0.300
0.359	0.365
0.301	0.304
0.272	0.275
0.315	0.321

   b) Mantle's is greater in every case.

   c) Ruth: 0.316; Mantle: 0.311; Ruth's is greater.

   d) Answers will vary.

   e) Ruth: 0.307; Mantle: 0.313; Mantle's is greater.

   f) Answers will vary.

   g) Answers will vary.

55. 90   **57. a)** Answers will vary.   **b)** Answers will vary.

   c) Answers will vary.

58. a) Answers will vary. One example is 2, 3, 5, 7, 7.

   b) Answers will vary.

SECTION 13.5, PAGE 812

1. Variability   **3.** Standard deviation   **5.** Sample

7. 11, $\sqrt{16.5} \approx 4.06$ **9.** 6, $\sqrt{4.67} \approx 2.16$

11. 11, $\sqrt{15.2} \approx 3.90$ **13.** 5, $\sqrt{3} \approx 1.73$

15. $205, $\sqrt{4780.57} \approx 69.14

17. $190, $\sqrt{4725.25} \approx 68.74 **19.** Answers will vary.

21. The first set will have the greater standard deviation because the scores have a greater spread about the mean.

23. The sum of the values in the (Data $-$ Mean)^2 column will always be greater than or equal to 0.

25. a) $63, $\sqrt{631.6} \approx 25.13 **b)** Answers will vary.

   c) Answers remain the same, range: $63, standard deviation $\approx $25.13.

27. a) Answers will vary.   **b)** Answers will vary.

   c) Answers will vary.

   d) If each number in a distribution is multiplied by n, the mean and standard deviation of the new distribution will be n times that of the original distribution.

   e) 20, 10

29. a) The standard deviation increases. There is a greater spread from the mean as they get older.

   b) $\approx$ 133 lb   **c)** $\approx$ 21 lb

   d) Mean: $\approx$100 lb; normal range: $\approx$ 60 to 140 lb

   e) Mean: $\approx$ 62 in.; normal range: $\approx$ 53 to 68 in.   **f)** 5%

31. a)

East		West	
Number of Oil Changes Made	Number of Days	Number of Oil Changes Made	Number of Days
15–20	2	15–20	0
21–26	2	21–26	0
27–32	5	27–32	6
33–38	4	33–38	9
39–44	7	39–44	4
45–50	1	45–50	6
51–56	1	51–56	0
57–62	2	57–62	0
63–68	1	63–68	0

b)

Number of Oil Changes Made Daily at East Store

Number of Oil Changes Made Daily at West Store

c) They appear to have about the same mean since they are both centered around 38.

d) The distribution for East is more spread out. Therefore, East has a greater standard deviation.

e) East: 38, West: 38   **f)** East: ≈ 12.64, West: ≈ 5.98

32. Answers will vary.

33. 6, 6, 6, 6, 6

SECTION 13.6, PAGE 828

1. Rectangular   **3.** Right   **5.** Bimodal   **7.** Standard

9. Below   **11. a)** 68%   **b)** 95%   **c)** 99.7%

13. Answers will vary.   **15.** Answers will vary.

17. Normal   **19.** Skewed right   **21.** 0.5000   **23.** 0.8185

25. 0.0630   **27.** 0.0375   **29.** 0.0429   **31.** 0.0166

33. 76.11%   **35.** 89.74%   **37.** 97.13%   **39.** 97.50%

41. 21.96%   **43. a)** Emily, Sarah, Carol   **b)** Jenny, Shenice
c) Sadaf, Heather, Kim

45. 50%   **47.** 10.56%   **49.** 69.15%   **51.** 24.17%

53. 44.00%   **55.** 29.02%   **57.** 59.87%   **59.** 50.00%

61. 11.51%   **63.** ≈ 23 cars   **65.** 95.47%   **67.** 13,380 boxes

69. 69.15%   **71.** 0.62%   **73.** ≈ 83 families   **75.** 1.79%

77. The standard deviation is too large.

79. a) B **b)** C **c)** A

81. The mean is the greatest value. The median is lower than the mean. The mode is the lowest value.

83. Answers will vary.

85. a) Katie: $z = 2.4$; Stella: $z = 1.7$

b) Katie. Her z-score is higher than Stella's z-score, which means her sales are further above the mean than Stella's sales.

87. a) Answers will vary.   **b)** Answers will vary.

c) Answers will vary.   **d)** Answers will vary.

e) Answers will vary.   **f)** Answers will vary.

89. -1.18 **90.** Answers will vary.   **91.** 2

SECTION 13.7, PAGE 842

1. Coefficient   **3.** 1   **5.** 0   **7.** Positive   **9.** fit

11. No correlation   **13.** Strong positive correlation

15. Yes   **17.** Yes   **19.** No   **21.** No

23. a)

b) 0.981   **c)** Yes   **d)** Yes

25. a)

b) 0.228   **c)** No   **d)** No

27. a)

b) 0.999   **c)** Yes   **d)** Yes

29. a)   **b)** -0.968 **c)** Yes **d)** Yes

31. $y = 1.26x + 2.25$ **33.** $y = 0.18x + 23.82$

35. $y = 0.81x + 5.84$ **37.** $y = -0.08x + 9.50$

39. a) 0.974 **b)** Yes **c)** $y = 0.74x + 1.26$

41. a) 0.950 **b)** Yes **c)** $y = 0.77x + 24.86$

43. a) 0.984 **b)** Yes **c)** $y = 0.79x - 12.98$ **d)** 78

45. a) -0.804 **b)** No

  c) $y = -0.43x + 35.28$ **d)** 21.1 mpg

47. a) -0.977 **b)** Yes

  c) $y = -12.93x + 99.59$ **d)** 41.4%

49. a) Answers will vary. **b)** Answers will vary.

  c)

  d) 0.999 **e)** 0.990 **f)** Answers will vary.

  g) $y = 5.36x - 183.40$ **h)** $y = 16.22x - 669.80$

  i) Dry, 229.3 ft; wet, 579.1 ft

51. a) Answers will vary. **b)** Answers will vary.

  c) Answers will vary. **d)** Answers will vary.

  e) Answers will vary. **f)** Answers will vary.

53. a) 0.963 **b)** Should be the same.

  c) 0.963; the values are the same.

REVIEW EXERCISES, PAGE 848

1. a) A population consists of all items or people of interest.

  b) A sample is a subset of the population.

2. A random sample is one where every item in the population has the same chance of being selected.

3. The candy bars may have lots of calories, or fat, or sodium. Therefore, it may not be healthy to eat them.

4. Sales may not necessarily be a good indicator of profit. Expenses must also be considered.

5. a) **b)**

6. a)

Class	Frequency
35	1
36	3
37	6
38	2
39	3
40	0
41	4
42	1
43	3
44	1
45	1

b) and c)

7. a)

High Temperature	Number of Cities
58–62	1
63–67	4
68–72	9
73–77	10
78–82	11
83–87	4
88–92	1

b) and c)

Average Monthly High Temperature in July for Selected Cities

d) 5|8 represents 58

```
5|8
6|3 6 6 7 8 8 9
7|0 1 1 1 2 2 3 3 3 4 5 5 5 6 6 7 9 9 9
8|0 0 0 0 1 2 2 2 3 4 4 7
9|1
```

8. 80 **9.** 81 **10.** None **11.** 80 **12.** 26

13. $\sqrt{80} \approx 8.94$ **14.** 13 **15.** 13 **16.** 7 and 12

17. 13.5 **18.** 19 **19.** $\sqrt{40} \approx 6.32$ **20.** 68.26%

21. 95.44% **22.** 94.52% **23.** 5.48% **24.** 72.57%
25. 34.1% **26.** 34.5% **27.** 29.0% **28.** 2.3%

29. a)

Bear Sightings

b) Yes; positive **c)** 0.925 **d)** Yes
e) $y = 0.04x + 88.17$ **f)** ≈ 148 bears

30. a)

Daily Sales

b) Yes; negative **c)** -0.973 **d)** Yes
e) $y = -79.4x + 246.7$ **f)** ≈ 120 sold

31. 180 lb **32.** 185 lb **33.** 25% **34.** 25% **35.** 14%
36. 19,200 lb **37.** 238 lb **38.** 150.6 lb **39.** 3.53
40. 2 **41.** 3 **42.** 7 **43.** 14 **44.** $\sqrt{7.97} \approx 2.82$

45.

Number of Children	Number of Presidents
0–1	8
2–3	16
4–5	10
6–7	6
8–9	1
10–11	1
12–13	0
14–15	1

46. and **47.**

Number of Children of U.S. Presidents

48. No, it is skewed to the right. **49.** Answers will vary.
50. Answers will vary.

1. 42 **2.** 43 **3.** 43 **4.** 39.5 **5.** 25 **6.** $\sqrt{84} \approx 9.17$

7.

Class	Frequency
25–30	7
31–36	5
37–42	1
43–48	7
49–54	5
55–60	3
61–66	2

8.

9.

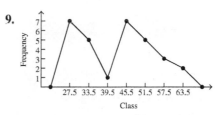

10. $735 **11.** $710 **12.** 75% **13.** 79% **14.** $74,000
15. $780 **16.** 87.10% **17.** 89.44% **18.** 10.56%
19. 94.52%

20. a) Hourly Minimum Wage in the U.S. **b)** Yes **c)** 0.970 **d)** Yes

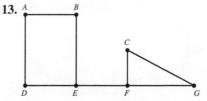

e) $y = 0.56x + 5.29$ **f)** $9.77

Chapter 14

1. Graph **3.** Edge **5.** Path **7.** Degree

9.   **11.**

13.

15. No. There is no edge connecting vertices *B* and *C*.

17. No **19.** Yes. One example is *C, A, B, D, F, E, C, D*

21.   **23.**

25.

27.   **29.**

31.

33. Disconnected **35.** Connected **37.** Edge *AC*

39. Edge *EF* **41.** Answers will vary.

43. a) Answers will vary. **b)** Answers will vary.
   c) Answers will vary.
   d) The sum of the degrees is equal to twice the number of edges, which is true since each edge must connect two vertices. Each edge then contributes two to the sum of the degrees.

45. a) Answers will vary. **b)** Answers will vary.

SECTION 14.2, PAGE 872

1. Euler **3.** No **5.** Odd **7.** *A, B, D, E, C, A, D, C*

9. No. This graph has exactly two odd vertices. Each Euler path must begin with an odd vertex. B is an even vertex.

11. *A, B, A, C, B, E, C, D, A, D, E*

13. No. A graph with exactly two odd vertices has no Euler circuits.

15. *A, B, C, D, E, F, B, D, F, A* **17.** *C, D, E, F, A, B, D, F, B, C*

19. *E, F, A, B, C, D, F, B, D, E*

21. a) Yes. There are no odd vertices.
   b) Yes. There are no odd vertices.

23. a) No. There are more than two odd vertices.
   b) No. There is at least one odd vertex.

25. a) Yes
   b) They could start on either island and finish at the other.

27. a)
   b) Yes; *WA, ID, MT, WY, ID, OR, WA*

29. a)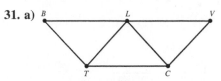
   b) Yes; *J, Q, T, N, A, P, N, Q* **c)** No

31. a)
   b) Yes; *T, B, L, V, C, L, T, C* **c)** No

33. a)
   b) Yes **c)** *O, A, B, C, D, F, C, E, O, A*

35. a)   **b)** No

37. a) Yes
   b) The residents would need to start at the intersection of Maple Cir., Walnut St., and Willow St. or at the intersection of Walnut St. and Oak St.

39. *B, A, C, E, D, B, C*

41. *H, I, F, C, B, D, G, H, E, D, A, B, E, F*

43. *A, B, C, D, I, H, G, B, E, H, C, E, G, F, A*

45. *A, C, D, G, H, F, C, F, E, B, A*

47. *A, B, C, E, B, D, E, F, I, E, H, D, G, H, I, J, F, C, A*

49. *UT, CO, NM, AZ, CA, NV, UT, AZ, NV*

51. *B, A, E, H, I, J, K, D, C, G, G, J, F, C, B, F, I, E, B*

53. *J, G, G, C, F, J, K, D, C, B, F, I, E, B, A, E, H, I, J*

55. a) No
   b) California, Nevada, and Louisiana (and others) have an odd number of states bordering them. Since a graph of the United States would have more than two odd vertices, no Euler path and no Euler circuit exist.

57. a)   **b)**   **c)**

SECTION 14.3, PAGE 884

1. Salesman **3.** Hamilton **5.** Euler **7.** Force

9. *A, B, C, E, F, G, D* and *G, D, F, E, C, A, B*

11. *A, B, C, D, G, F, E, H* and *E, H, F, G, D, C, A, B*

13. *A, B, C, E, D, F, G, H* and *F, G, H, E, D, A, B, C*

15. *A, B, D, G, E, H, F, C, A* and *E, H, F, C, A, B, D, G, E*

17. *A, B, C, F, I, E, H, G, D, A* and *A, E, B, C, F, I, H, G, D, A*

19.   **21.** 5! = 120 ways

23. 12! = 479,001,600 ways

25. a) 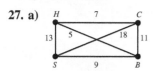   **b)** *C, G, S, O, C* or *C, G, O, S, C* or
C, S, O, G, C or *C, O, S, G, C*

c) 1030 miles

27. a)   **b)** *H, C, S, B, H* or *H, B, S, C, H*

c) 39 miles

29. a) 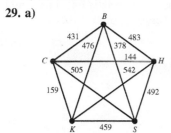   **b)** *S, B, C, H, K, S* for $1954

c) Answers will vary.

31. a)   **b)** *W, B, L, A, O, W* for $1210
c) Answers will vary.

33. a) Answers will vary.   **b)** Answers will vary.
c) Answers will vary.   **d)** Answers will vary.

35. *A, E, D, N, O, F, G, Q, P, T, M, L, C, B, J, K, S, R, I, H, A*

SECTION 14.4, PAGE 895

1. Tree   **3.** Circuits   **5.** Minimum-cost

7.

9.

11.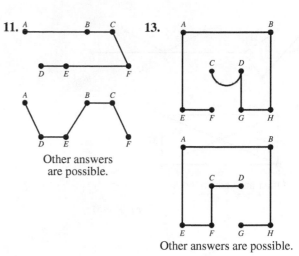
Other answers
are possible.

13.

Other answers are possible.

15.
Other answers are possible.

17.   **19.**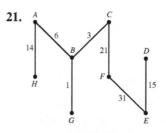

Other answers are possible.

21.

23.

25.

27. a)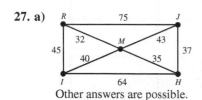

Other answers are possible.

b)   **c)** $3600

29. a)

b) $1,264,800

31. a)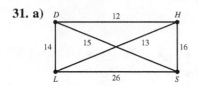

Other answers are possible.

b)

c) $140,000

33. a)

b) 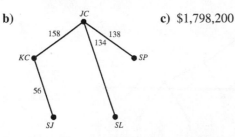   **c)** $1,798,200

35. Answers will vary.   **37.** Answers will vary.

1.

Other answers are possible.

2.

Other answers are possible.

3. *E, C, D, F, E, G, A, B, H, G*

4. No. A path that includes each edge exactly one time would start at vertex E and end at vertex *G*, or vice versa.

5.

6.

7. Connected   **8.** Disconnected   **9.** Edge *CD*

10. *D, A, B, C, E, H, G, F, D, B, E, G, D, E*; other answers are possible.

11. *E, D, B, E, G, D, A, B, C, E, H, G, F, D*; other answers are possible.

12. *A, B, E, G, F, D, C, A, D, E, A*

13. *E, D, C, A, E, B, A, D, F, G, E*

14. a)

b) Yes. *CO, NE, IA, MO, NE, KS, MO, OK, CO, KS, OK, TX*; other answers are possible.

c) No

15. a)

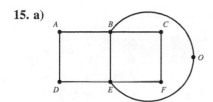

b) Yes

c) The person may start in any room or outside and will finish in the location from which he or she started.

16. a) Yes

b) The officer would have to start at either the intersection of Dayne St., Gibson Pl., and Alvarez Ave. or at the intersection of Chambers St., Fletcher Ct., and Alvarez Ave.

17. *A, B, F, E, H, G, D, C, A, D, E, B*; other answers are possible.

18. *A, B, D, E, I, J, O, N, L, K, G, H, L, M, I, H, D, C, G, F, A*; other answers are possible.

19. *A, C, B, F, E, D, G* and *A, C, D, G, F, B, E*; other answers are possible.

20. *A, B, E, F, J, I, L, K, H, G, C, D, A* and *I, J, F, E, B, A, D, C, G, H, K, L, I*; other answers are possible.

21.

22. 4! = 24 ways

23. a)

b) *P, D, M, C, P* or *P, C, M, D, P*

c) $2088

24. a)

b) *SJ, KC, C, SL, Sp, SJ* traveling a total of 745 miles

c) *Sp, C, SL, KC, SJ, Sp* traveling a total of 829 miles

25.

26.

Other answers are possible.

27.

28. a)

b)

c) $317.50

CHAPTER TEST, PAGE 904

1.

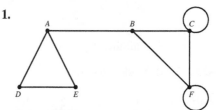

Other answers are possible.

2.

3.

4. One example:

5. *A, B, E, D, C, A, D, B*; other answers are possible.

6. *A, B, C, F, H, G, E, F, B, E, D, A*; other answers are possible.

7. Yes. The person may start in room *A* and end at room *B*, or vice versa.

8. *A, D, E, A, F, E, H, F, I, G, F, B, G, C, B, A*; other answers are possible.

9. *B, A, D, E, F, C, G*; other answers are possible.

10. *A, B, C, G, E, D, H, I, K, J, F, A*; other answers are possible.

11.   **12.** 4! = 24 ways   **13.**

14. *C, R, N, U, C* or *C, U, N, R, C* for $618

15. *C, R, U, N, C* for $639

16.

17.

Other answers are possible.

18.

19.

20. $183.75

Chapter 15

SECTION 15.1, PAGE 921

1. Majority **3.** $\dfrac{n(n-1)}{2}$ **5.** Plurality

7. Pairwise comparison **9. a)** Wade **b)** No

11.

Number of Votes	3	1	2	2	1
First	R	N	P	P	N
Second	N	R	R	N	P
Third	P	P	N	R	R

13. 21 **15.** Hydrant **17.** Fireman

19. Yellowstone National Park

21. Three-way tie, no winner **23.** Los Angeles

25. No winner, a tie between Honolulu and Los Angeles

27. A tie between Greenburg and Vazguez **29.** Vazquez

31. Greenburg **33.** Erie **35.** Erie

37. a) Becker **b)** Becker **c)** Becker **d)** Becker

39. a) Petunias **b)** Petunias **c)** Geraniums
  d) Tie between petunias and zinnias

41. Voters are able to provide more information, such as ranking choices, with the Borda count method.

43. a) If there were only two columns, only two of the candidates were the first choice of the voters. If each of the 15 voters cast a ballot, one of the voters must have received a majority of votes because 15 cannot be split evenly.
  b) An odd number cannot be divided evenly, so one of the two first-choice candidates must receive more than half of the votes.

45. a) Warriors, Rams and Tigers tied, Comets
  b) Rams, Tigers, Warriors, Comets

47. a) 150 **b)** 50 **c)** Yes

49. One possible answer is:

Number of Votes	5	5	2
First	A	B	C
Second	B	A	B
Third	C	C	A

SECTION 15.2, PAGE 934

1. Majority **3.** Monotonicity **5.** Borda count

7. Pairwise comparison

9. Boston wins with the Borda count method, but New Orleans has a majority of first-place votes.

11. No. Brown is the Borda count winner, but Alvarez has a majority of first-place votes.

13. No. Lounge areas wins by the Borda count method, but Parking is preferred to Security and to Lounge areas.

15. No. C wins by plurality with elimination, but A is preferred over each of the other candidates using head-to-head comparisons.

17. No. A wins the first election by plurality. If B drops out, C wins by plurality.

19. Yes. B wins by the Borda count method. If C drops out, B still wins.

21. No. C wins by plurality with elimination. If the voters change their preference, B wins by plurality with elimination.

23. No. D wins by pairwise comparison. If the voters change their preference, B wins by pairwise comparison.

25. No. B wins by pairwise comparison. If A, C, and E drop out, D wins by pairwise comparison.

27. No. B wins by the Borda count method, but A has a majority of first-place votes.

29. a) Washington, D.C. **b)** Washington, D.C.
  c) Washington, D.C. **d)** Washington, D.C.
  e) Washington, D.C. **f)** None of them

31. a) Albert Pujols **b)** Will Smith **c)** Yes

33. A candidate who holds a plurality only gains strength and holds an even larger lead if more favorable votes are added.

35. Answers will vary. **37.** Answers will vary.

SECTION 15.3, PAGE 952

1. Divisor **3.** Lower **5.** Quota **7.** Modified

9. a) Webster's **b)** Adams's **c)** Jefferson's

11. a) 50,000 **b)** 24.40, 54.60, 17.14, 53.86

13. a) 24.75, 55.38, 17.38, 54.62 **b)** 24, 55, 17, 54

15. a) 24.06, 53.85, 16.90, 53.11 **b)** 25, 54, 17, 54

17. 24, 55, 17, 54 **19. a)** 27 **b)** 11.33, 7.93, 5.74

21. a) 11.86, 8.29, 6.01 **b)** 11, 8, 6

23. a) 10.55, 7.38, 5.34 **b)** 11, 8, 6 **25.** 11, 8, 6

27. a) 12 **b)** 8.17, 9.50, 11.92, 20.42 **c)** 8, 10, 12, 20

29. 8, 10, 12, 20

31. a) 52 **b)** 33.58, 136.44, 40.98, 18.02, 20.98
  c) 34, 136, 41, 18, 21

33. 33, 137, 41, 18, 21

35. a) 90 **b)** 53.33, 40.09, 33.22, 23.36 **c)** 53, 40, 33, 24

37. 54, 40, 33, 23

39. a) 750   **b)** 12.09, 20.37, 17.08, 7.63, 33.67, 9.17
   c) 12, 20, 17, 8, 34, 9

41. 12, 20, 17, 8, 34, 9

43. a) 12   **b)** 62.58, 81.67, 41.92, 13.83   **c)** 62, 82, 42, 14

45. 63, 82, 42, 13

47. a) 7, 2, 2, 2, 8, 14, 4, 5, 10, 10, 13, 2, 6, 2, 18
   b) 7, 1, 2, 2, 8, 14, 4, 5, 10, 10, 13, 2, 6, 2, 19
   c) Benefited: Virginia; Disadvantage: Delaware

49. Answers will vary. One possible answer is A: 743, B: 367, C: 432, D:491, E: 519, F: 388

SECTION 15.4, PAGE 961

1. Population   **3.** Alabama   **5.** Small

7. No. The new apportionment is 14, 11, 11, 12, 13. No office suffers a loss, so the Alabama paradox doesn't occur.

9. a) 6, 8, 16
   b) Yes. When the number of seats increases, states B and C gain a seat and state A loses a seat.

11. a) 61, 40, 99   **b)** No

13. a) 7, 16, 9, 11, 11
   b) Yes. Division B loses an internship to division A even though the population of division B grew faster than the population of division A.

15. a) 8, 40
   b) Yes. The apportionment is now 9, 39, 7, and group B loses a manager.

17. a) 4, 15, 41
   b) Yes. The apportionment is now 4, 16, 40, 5, and state C loses a seat.

REVIEW EXERCISES, PAGE 964

1. a) Robert Rivera   **b)** No

2. a) Michelle MacDougal   **b)** Yes

3.

Number of Votes	3	2	1	1	3
First	B	A	D	D	C
Second	A	C	C	A	B
Third	C	D	A	B	A
Fourth	D	B	B	C	D

4.

Number of Votes	2	2	2	1
First	C	A	B	C
Second	A	C	A	B
Third	B	B	C	A

5. 24

6. A tie between the portable DVD player and the digital camera

7. iPod   **8.** Digital camera

9. Tie between iPod and digital camera   **10.** iPod

11. 110   **12.** Volleyball   **13.** Soccer   **14.** Volleyball

15. None, a three-way tie   **16.** Soccer

17. a) Yes, American Association of Retired Persons

b) American Association of Retired Persons
c) American Association of Retired Persons
d) American Association of Retired Persons
e) American Association of Retired Persons

18. a) No   **b)** Seattle   **c)** Las Vegas
   d) Las Vegas   **e)** Las Vegas

19. a) A tie between *Encyclopedia Britannica* and *World Book*
   b) *World Book*
   c) A tie between *Encyclopedia Britannica* and *World Book*

20. No. A has a majority, but B wins by the Borda count method.

21. No. B wins by the Borda count method, but A is preferred over each of the other candidates using head-to-head comparisons.

22. a) C wins the election by plurality with elimination.
   b) When the order is changed A wins. Therefore, the monotonicity criterion is not satisfied.
   c) No. If B drops out, A is the winner by plurality with elimination. Therefore, the irrelevant alternatives criterion is not satisfied.

23. a) Ball Park   **b)** Oscar Mayer
   c) Tie between Nathan's and Hebrew National
   d) Hebrew National   **e)** Ball Park
   f) Plurality method, Borda count method, and plurality with elimination method all violate the head-to-head criterion.

24. a) Fleetwood Mac   **b)** Boston   **c)** Fleetwood Mac
   d) REO Speedwagon   **e)** Fleetwood Mac
   f) The plurality method and the plurality with elimination method

25. The Borda count method

26. The plurality with elimination method

27. The pairwise comparison method and the Borda count method

28. 4, 3, 3   **29.** 5, 2, 3   **30.** 4, 3, 3   **31.** 5, 2, 3

32. Yes. The apportionment is 5, 2, 4. Region B loses one truck.

33. 13, 9, 7   **34.** 13, 9, 7   **35.** 12, 9, 8   **36.** 13, 9, 7

37. No. The apportionment with the additional population is still 13, 9, 7.

38. 4, 46   **39.** 4, 46   **40.** 5, 45   **41.** 4, 46

42. Yes. The new apportionment is 5, 45, 5. State B loses a seat.

CHAPTER TEST, PAGE 968

1. 24   **2.** No   **3.** Pizza   **4.** Pizza   **5.** Tacos   **6.** Tacos

7. 142   **8.** Salamander   **9.** Iguana   **10.** Hamster

11. Lemming

12. Plurality method, Borda count method, and plurality with elimination method

13. Yes, El Capitan has a majority of first-place votes but mule deer wins.

14. 6, 9, 15   **15.** 6, 9, 15   **16.** 6, 9, 15   **17.** 6, 9, 15

18. No. The apportionment is 6, 9, 16.

19. No. The apportionment is 6, 9, 15.

20. No. The apportionment is 6, 9, 15, 5.

Credits

PHOTO CREDITS

Page 01, David R. Frazier/Photolibrary/Alamy; Page 02, Flynavyjp/Dreamstime; Page 03, Michael Dwyer/Alamy; Page 04, Johnson Space Center/NASA; Page 08, OJO Images Ltd/Alamy; Page 09, Imagebroker/Alamy; Page 10, David Epperson/Photodisc/Getty Images; Page 11, Natali Glado/Shutterstock; Page 13, Courtesy of Allen Angel; Page 14, Courtesy of Allen Angel; Page 15, ex. 25, Stockbyte/Getty Images; Page 15, ex. 29, Evan Meyer/Shutterstock; Page 17, ex. 39, Courtesy of Allen Angel; Page 17, ex. 40, Michael C. Gray/Shutterstock; Page 18, ex. 47, Courtesy of Allen Angel; Page 18, ex. 48, Nick Stubbs/Shutterstock; Page 20, Anatoliy Kosolapov/Shutterstock; Page 22, box, AP Images; Page 22, margin, Christopher Eng-Wong Photography/Shutterstock; Page 23, Classic Image/Alamy; Page 25, ImageState/Alamy; Page 26, Norman Jung/Corbis; Page 31, Blend Images/Alamy; Page 37, Ron Buskirk/Alamy; Page 39, *Still Life: Vase With Twelve Sunflowers* (1888), Vincent Van Gogh. Oil on canvas. Neue Pinakothek, Munich, Germany/Bridgeman Art Library/SuperStock; Page 42, BananaStock/Thinkstock; Page 43, margin, Interfoto/Alamy; Page 43, box, Bill Bachmann/Alamy; Page 45, Jorge Salcedo/Shutterstock; Page 48, Johnson Space Center/NASA; Page 49, ex. 54, Pictorial Press, Ltd./Alamy; Page 49, ex. 58, Interfoto/Alamy; Page 51, ex. 87, Pete Whittle/Splash News/Newscom; Page 51, margin, Frank Tozier/Alamy; Page 53, BlueOrange Studio/Shutterstock; Page 54, Blend Images/Alamy; Page 55, George Doyle/Stockbyte/Thinkstock; Page 56, Courtesy of Allen Angel; Page 57, Jeff Greenberg/Alamy; Page 64, Courtesy of Allen Angel; Page 65, California California/Alamy; Page 67, ex. 102, Jeff Greenberg/Alamy; Page 67, Purestock/Getty Images; Page 68, Beth Anderson/Pearson; Page 73, Photos 12/Alamy; Page 75, Creatas/Thinkstock; Page 77, Vicki Beaver/Alamy; Page 79, Beth Anderson/Pearson; Page 80, Greg Probst/Danita Delimont/Alamy; Page 81, Stockbyte/Thinkstock; Page 82, ex. 12, JupiterImages/liquidlibrary/Thinkstock; Page 82, ex. 15, Melissa Brandes/Shutterstock; Page 83, Interfoto/Alamy; Page 85, AKG Images/Newscom; Page 89, Michael Wick/Shutterstock; Page 90, Jason DeCrow/AP Iimages; Page 91, Teekaygee/Shutterstock; Page 93, Goodluz/Shutterstock; Page 94, Daniel Hurst/Stock Connection Worldwide/Newscom; Page 95, Thinkstock; Page 96, Pictorial Press, Ltd./Alamy; Page 98, Library of Congress Prints and Photographs Division [LC-USZ62-61664]; Page 99, Andy Dean Photography/Shutterstock; Page 100, top, Beth Anderson/Pearson; Page 100, bottom, Gunter Marx/Alamy; Page 101, Lykovata/Shutterstock; Page 102, ex. 9, Exactostock/SuperStock; Page 102, ex. 13, Danylchenko Iaroslav/Shutterstock; Page 102, ex. 19, Specta/Shutterstock; Page 102, ex. 27, Joe Gough/Shutterstock; Page 103, Mlorenz/Shutterstock; Page 104, Tom Maelsa/AFP/Getty Images/Newscom; Page 105, British Retail Photography/Alamy; Page 108, Peter Nadolski/Shutterstock; Page 114, Violetkaipa/Shutterstock; Page 115, ex. 19, Lionel Hahn/Lionel Hahn/AbacaUsa/Newscom; Page 115, ex. 41, DFree/Shutterstock; Page 116, ex. 44, Jun Mu/Shutterstock; Page 116, ex. 48, EditorialByDarrellYoung/Alamy; Page 117, Digital Vision/Valueline/Thinkstock; Page 118, Cohen/Ostrow/Digital Vision/Getty Images; Page 121, Natalia Bratslavsky/Shutterstock; Page 125, ex. 28, Sonya Etchison/Shutterstock; Page 125, ex. 57, iStockphoto; Page 127, Dennis Runde; Page 130, box/top, Library of Congress Prints and Photographs Division [LC-USZ62-70064]; Page 130, box/bottom, Photos 12/Alamy; Page 131, top, Debby Wong/Shutterstock; Page 131, box, Mary Evans Picture Library/Alamy; Page 132, Ritu Manoj Jethani/Shutterstock; Page 133, Thefinalmiracle/Shutterstock; Page 135, Yuri Arcurs/Shutterstock; Page 137, ex. 41, Beth Anderson/Pearson; Page 137, ex. 54, Noel Powell, Schaumburg/Shutterstock; Page 138, ex. 62, Krivosheev Vitaly/Shutterstock; Page 138, ex. 66, Diane Macdonald/Stockbyte/Getty Images; Page 138, ex. 69, Charles T. Bennett/Shutterstock; Page 139, ex. 73, Beth Anderson/Pearson; Page 139, ex. 81, Paul Radenfeld/Digital Vision/Getty images; Page 140, Rob Hobson/UPI/Newscom; Page 142, margin/top, Bryan Busovicki/Shutterstock; Page 142, margin/bottom, Lane Ericcson-Photolink/Newscom; Page 144, James Steidl/Shutterstock; Page 146, Anthony Berenyi/Shutterstock; Page 148, ex. 33, Stockbyte/Getty Images; Page 148, ex. 43, FloridaStock/Shutterstock; Page 149, Shebeko/Shutterstock; Page 150, Helga Esteb/Shutterstock; Page 151, Interfoto/Alamy; Page 153, Pincasso/Shutterstock; Page 155, Olga_i/Shutterstock; Page 155, James Coleman/Shutterstock; Page 155, Wilfried Krecichwost/Getty Images; Page 156, Samson Yury/Shutterstock; Page 164, Motorlife/Alamy; Page 165, Steven Milne/Alamy; Page 166, NASA; Page 167, Jet Propulsion Laboratory/NASA; Page 169, Richard Hutchings/PhotoEdit, Inc.; Page 170, MCT/Newscom; Page 172, Sylvie Bouchard/Shutterstock; Page 173, Courtesy of Denise Schmandt-Besserat; Page 174, Courtesy of Allen Angel; Page 174, Courtesy of Allen Angel; Page 178, ex. 84, Digital Vision; Page 178, margin, Mark Davis/CBS/Newscom; Page 180, Andy Crawford/Dorling Kindersley, Ltd.; Page 181, Morgan Lane Photography/Shutterstock; Page 183, Olinchuk/Shutterstock; Page 185, David J. Green/Alamy; Page 186, Andersen Ross/Blend Images/Getty Images; Page 187, Darren Brode/Shutterstock; Page 188, James Hardy/PhotoAlto Agency RF Collections/Getty Images; Page 189, Khoroshunova Olga/Shutterstock; Page 192, margin, Michael Newman/PhotoEdit, Inc.; Page 192, ex. 70, GM/Wieck/Newscom; Page 195, BW Folsom/Shutterstock; Page 200, margin, JupiterImages/Thinkstock; Page 200, ex. 72, Ryan McVay/Photodisc/Getty Images; Page 201, PhotoDisc Vol. 41; Page 203, Interfoto/Alamy; Page 209, H. Mark Weidman Photography/Alamy; Page 210, Svetlana Mihailova/Shutterstock; Page 211, Interfoto/Alamy; Page 212, M. Favareille/Musée des Arts et Métiers.Cnam, Paris; Page 214, SPL/Photo Researchers, Inc.; Page 216, Nan728/Shutterstock; Page 219, ex. 65, Corbis Flirt/Alamy; Page 219, ex. 68, Aurora Photos/Alamy; Page 221, Bigchen/Shutterstock; Page 224, Dorling Kindersley, Ltd.; Page 228, ex. 71, General Dynamics Electric Boat/U.S. Navy; Page 228, ex. 75, Olinchuk/Shutterstock; Page 229, Elena Elisseeva/Shutterstock; Page 230, Jeff Greenberg/Alamy; Page 237, Mikhail/Shutterstock; Page 240, Ocean/Corbis; Page 241, 2399 2009/Shutterstock; Page 243, David Stluka/AP Images; Page 245, The Art Archive/Alamy; Page 251, ex. 85, Dyoma/Shutterstock; Page 251, ex. 86, Brad-calkins/Dreamstime; Page 252, margin, Digital Vision/Getty Images; Page 252, box, Robert D. Pinna/Shutterstock; Page 253, Colin McPherson/Corbis; Page 258, Gemenacom/Shutterstock; Page 259, Scott Camazine/Alamy; Page 262, Konstantin Mironov/Shutterstock; Page 263, box/left, Collections artistiques de l'Université de Liège; Page 263, box/right, Courtesy of MRA; Page 264, April Saul/Newscom; Page 265, Library of Congress Prints and Photographs Division [LC-USZC4-8886]; Page 268, ex. 95, Whitechild/Shutterstock; Page 268, ex. 98, Pablo Fonseca Q./La Nacion de Costa Rica/Newscom; Page 268, ex. 99, Aivolie/Shutterstock; Page 270, ex. 111, Carles O'Rear/Corbis; Page 270, margin, Deco Images II/Alamy; Page 271, Bilwissedition Ltd. & Co. KG/Alamy; Page 273, Christos Georghiou/Shutterstock; Page 274, Rob Marmion/Shutterstock; Page 276, ex. 78, Denise Kappa/Shutterstock; Page 276, ex. 79, Digital Vision/Thinkstock; Page 277, Bettmann/Corbis; Page 278, margin, lidiatt/Shutterstock; Page 278, box, David Lyons/Alamy; Page 279, Vasily Topko/Shutterstock; Page 280, margin/top, Sculpies/Shutterstock; Page 280, margin/bottom, Polartern/Shutterstock; Page 280, figure 5.14, Mircea Bezergheanu/Shutterstock; Page 281, *Fibonacci's Garden* (1995), Caryl Bryer Fallert. Hand-dyed and painted, machine pieced and quilted 100% cotton fabric; batting: 80% cotton, 20% polyester; 71 × 54 in.; Page 281, *Circus Sideshow* (1887–1888), Georges Seurat. Oil on canvas, 39 1/4 × 59 in. (99.7 × 149.9 cm). Metropolitan Museum of Art, Bequest of Stephen C. Clark, 1960. [61.101.17]/SuperStock; Page 286, Visions of America, LLC./Alamy; Page 287, Ryan McVay/Thinkstock; Page 288, Goddard Space Flight Center/NASA; Page 291, Blend Images/Shutterstock; Page 292, David R. Frazier/Photolibrary, Inc./Alamy; Page 293, Steve Stock/Alamy; Page 294, Alfonso Vicente/Alamy; Page 296, A. T. Willett/Alamy; Page 297, Gina Smith/Shutterstock; Page 298, Library of Congress Prints and Photographs Division [LC-USZ62-62123]; Page 305, Robert Harding Picture Library, Ltd./Alamy; Page 307, ex. 65, Orange Line Media/Shutterstock; Page 307, ex. 69, Courtesy of Allen Angel; Page 308, Exactostock/SuperStock; Page 310, World History Archive/Newscom; Page 311, The Art Gallery Collection/Alamy; Page 313, Iofoto/Shutterstock; Page 314, Iofoto/Shutterstock; Page 315, Monkey Business Images/Shutterstock; Page 317, Marnie Greenhut/Pearson; Page 318, ex. 31, Radius Images/Alamy; Page 318, ex. 38, Worachat Sodsri/Shutterstock; Page 319, Lindsey Stock/Dorling Kindersley, Ltd.; Page 319, Lichtmeister/Shutterstock; Page 320, Dueselder/Caro/Alamy; Page 322, Oleg Gerasymenko/Fotolia, LLC.; Page 324, Courtesy of Christine Abbott; Page 326, David P. Lewis/Shutterstock; Page 327, ex. 41, Liviu

FIGURE CREDITS